CATALOGUE
OF THE
McALPIN COLLECTION
OF
BRITISH HISTORY AND THEOLOGY
IN THE
Union Theological Seminary
New York
1501–1640

"New York. Union Theological Seminary. Library

The Union Theological Seminary
in the City of New York

CATALOGUE
OF THE
McALPIN COLLECTION
OF
BRITISH HISTORY AND THEOLOGY

COMPILED AND EDITED
BY
CHARLES RIPLEY GILLETT, D.D., L.H.D.
LIBRARIAN, 1883–1908

VOLUME I: 1500–1640

NEW YORK
1927

COMPOSITION, PRESSWORK AND BINDING BY
THE PLIMPTON PRESS · NORWOOD · MASS · U · S · A

Dedicated
TO THE MEMORY OF
DAVID HUNTER McALPIN
THROUGH WHOSE GENEROSITY THE FOLLOWING COLLECTION
WAS MADE POSSIBLE
AND OF
THE REVEREND EZRA HALL GILLETT, D.D.
BY WHOSE LABOR THE FIRST BEGINNINGS OF THE
COLLECTION WERE MADE
AND OF
THE REVEREND PROFESSOR CHARLES AUGUSTUS BRIGGS, D.D., D.LITT.
TO WHOM WAS DUE THE GREATER PART OF THE GROWTH
OF THE COLLECTION BY LABORS WHICH EXTENDED
THROUGH MANY YEARS

PREFACE

THE McAlpin Collection of British History and Theology is named for the late David Hunter McAlpin, Esq., of New York. Its inception and growth were due to the generosity of Mr. McAlpin and that of his children. The original endowment of the collection was made by the parent, and provision for the enlargement of the library and for the printing of the catalogue by the children. The further growth of the collection has been insured by the more recent provision for the McAlpin Foundation, which contains promise of much richer possibilities for the future.

Originally Mr. McAlpin agreed to meet the expenses incident to the purchase of books on English deism and kindred subjects, which were of particular interest to his pastor, the late Rev. Ezra Hall Gillett, D.D., who afterward became professor of Political Science in New York University. The only condition made by Mr. McAlpin was that the books so gathered should find their ultimate resting place in the library of the Union Theological Seminary. The collection thus made was very complete, and was pronounced by a specialist to be the most extensive anywhere in the United States.

After the death of Dr. Gillett in 1875, the same generosity was shown directly to the Seminary, and the further growth of the collection was due to the tireless labor of the late Rev. Professor Charles Augustus Briggs, D.D., D.Litt., who in the interval had become librarian. With Dr. Briggs the point of special interest shifted, and for years his efforts were directed to the gathering of the writings of the divines who constituted the Westminster Assembly, and such other works as bore upon the history of the periods before, during and immediately subsequent to the civil war and the commonwealth. The collection contains the volumes and tracts of which Dr. Briggs made such effective use in his various writings upon the history and teachings of the Westminster men. The constant and unremitting industry of Dr. Briggs resulted, after many years, in the increase of the library to a number of titles estimated at nearly twelve thousand. Obviously absolute completeness in the gathering of these volumes could not be attained, nor was it to be expected, but an exceedingly notable success crowned the efforts of nearly thirty years, so that since the death of Dr. Briggs in 1913, the number of strictly "Westminster" books which have been acquired has been comparatively small. Some gaps have been filled, to be sure, but the chances were distinctly slight, since the missing books which are known to have been written by these particular men are of great rarity, or have utterly disappeared. The collateral literature was very extensive, far more so than any except the initiated suppose.

Among the memoranda which Dr. Briggs left was a manuscript list of *desiderata*, extending to some two thousand titles. When this fact was disclosed to the children of Mr. McAlpin they most generously made provision whereby the compiler of this catalogue, son of the original collector of the "McAlpin books," was commissioned to visit England and Scotland in the endeavor to secure as many as possible of the desired volumes. Preparatory to undertaking this expedition the list of Dr. Briggs was extended to about nine thousand. In the course of a single summer vacation more than five hundred of these titles were secured, but in addition nearly three thousand books and tracts were purchased which were not on the list. From this statement some notion may be obtained of the mass of literature which poured from the press of the seventeenth century in particular. Among these books were many which lacked any indication of the place of publication or of the name of the printer, being mainly the productions of an unlicensed or secret press. In the collection there are more than one hundred books or tracts which fell under political or ecclesiastical censure, and were condemned to be burned, frequently by the common hangman, but occasionally otherwise in various public places.

Incorporated with the collection is a considerable number of volumes from the library of the late Walter William Law, merchant of New York, presented by his son, Henry Law, Esq.

At the time of the printing of this first volume no precise count has been made of the titles which will eventually be recorded in the collection, but it is estimated that the number will run to at least fifteen thousand. The year 1700 has been set arbitrarily as the date beyond which no listing will be made, though the McAlpin collection actually contains an immense number of books and tracts printed subsequently.

Scope of the Collection. The scope of the catalogue is even wider than the current conception of the collection as containing simply works on British history and theology printed prior to 1701. Many entries will be found which belong under such a description solely by an elastic definition. Only in the case of enactments of parliament has a restriction been practiced. Here the laws which had an obvious relevancy to the subject of religious history, have been included; while the majority of laws, manifestly important from other points of view, have been omitted. With the exception of the Acts, Orders, and Ordinances, etc., which dated from the period of the civil war and the commonwealth, the collections of statutes have been listed under the name and year of the reigning king or queen who assented to them. It is matter of regret that such collections are not more fully represented.

Supplied Matter. The usual practice has been followed of indicating any words which have been supplied from outside sources (except in the notes after the imprints), within square brackets; and any that have their source in the book itself, within round parentheses.

Among the earlier titles various abbreviations occurred for which the corresponding type-faces were not to be obtained in any of the fonts that were available in this country, except at a cost of time and money which seemed out of all proportion. In these cases the expedient was adopted of spelling out the words thus abbreviated, printing the supplied letters in italic, within square brackets.

Mutilated Books. In gathering so large a number of ancient books in the original bindings, in unbound condition, or in collected form, in which sometimes upward of a hundred thin pamphlets were bound inside the same cover, it has been inevitable that many have been found which had been mutilated more or less. When the end of a book is missing a note of the imperfection has been made, and its actual condition indicated. The absence of a title-page has been a more serious matter, and in some cases has presented insuperable difficulties. During the compiler's visit to England in 1914, he was able, by the courtesy of various librarians, to remedy a large number of such lacks. But in a few cases this was impossible because of his inability to find a copy of the particular book in question. Two cases in point may be mentioned. One was that of a Paul's Cross sermon (delivered by Thomas White, founder of Sion College, in 1578), from which the title-page had been lost. The date of delivery presented, apparently, a conflict with the calendar. A letter of inquiry, courteously printed by the editor of *Notes and Queries,* brought an answer from the other side of the American continent, from the librarian of the Huntington Library in California. The answer took the welcome form of a photostat copy of half a dozen pages, which corresponded with some of the pages in the McAlpin copy, and cleared up all questions of date and authorship. In the other case search has proved in vain.

The book in question was "Certaine fruitfull Instructions," written by John Frewen, a puritan rector, in 1587. The editor of *Notes and Queries* again most kindly published a letter of inquiry, but to date no reply has been received. It became necessary to reconstruct the title from such indications as could be found. This was done with the kind assistance of the custodian of the Rylands Library in Manchester. The statement of the Dictionary of National Biography that the book is "exceedingly rare" was thus abundantly verified.

Form of Entry. The separate entries contain several parts:

Author's Name. The name of the writer has been indicated if it is given on the title-page, at the end of the preface or dedication or even at the end of the entire book, or if it has been ascertained from sources outside of the book itself. In the foot-notes the particular fact has been stated. In the index also the general source of information is indicated by the use of round or square brackets. In those cases where only the initials of the author are given, a double entry has been made in the index, primarily under the initials, with a cross-reference from the title entry made in the usual way. If the initials have been identified as those of a given writer, the primary entry will be found under the full name, with cross-references from the initials and from the title entry, the author's name being given inside of square brackets.

Anonyms. Anonymous books, the authors of which remain unknown, are entered both in the catalogue and in the index under the first significant word of the title, not an article. Those which have been attributed to a definite person are entered in the catalogue and in the index under his name, and a title entry has been made in the usual fashion with a cross-reference in square brackets to the author. Such cross-references are very numerous, running into the hundreds if not thousands. Obviously the method of procedure with anonymous prints will be to consult the title entry in the index, and then turn to the year and name there indicated.

Titles. The title is given in full, with vertical marks to indicate where each type-line ends. The placing of these division marks has involved a large amount of detail and called for great care. But the method has been rewarding, since it has led to the discovery that certain prints which had titles identically worded, but with differently arranged line-lengths, really constituted second, third or even fourth printings of the same book in the same year. Some of these books were re-set by the same printer; some had been pirated by another. Obviously the present procedure renders identifications more accurate. Sometimes the difference between two impressions is found only in the imprints, which named different book-sellers, who apparently had shared the expense of printing, or who appealed each to a different clientele. There are also cases in which the only difference is in the variation in the border.

In making the entries the endeavor has been made to distinguish between the books which were actually printed in the indicated year, and subsequent re-issues as parts of a collection while retaining the date of the original edition. This has not been always either obvious or easy, since second-hand dealers and bookbinders have been known to obscure the fact in an endeavor to palm off, consciously or not, the later as though it were the earlier edition. The sins of these people are many, extending to the substitution of the title-page of a second part for a lost first title-page. It is quite possible that some of the entries in the following catalogue have served to perpetuate these errors, and that the compiler has fallen victim to the wiles of binder or dealer. Wherever such facts have been discovered they have been mentioned in the foot-notes, and occasionally a brief collation has been given to assist in identifying a given edition.

When a book appeared in two or more parts, each with separate pagination, each part has been entered, with indication of the actual fact. It thus receives the same treatment as an independent volume.

Omissions from Titles. Omissions from the title of books are indicated by a series of dots, thus . . . They occur uniformly in the case of Scripture quotations or mottoes taken from other writers. They occur also of necessity when part of the title-page has been torn away or otherwise damaged or made illegible. It must always be remembered that the ends of books, particularly those which never had the protection afforded by binding, may have suffered hard usage, and have lost one or more leaves. In the case of the omission of Biblical and other texts, the number of lines occupied by such quotations has been regularly indicated.

Capitals and Italics. No attempt has been made to reproduce either lower case italics, or capitals, whether large, small, or italic; but all initial capitals have been reproduced whether standing alone or at the beginning of words entirely printed in capitals. The omission of the italics and the failure to indicate differences in type are to be regretted since their absence serves to obscure certain facts which in the original printing are quite patent.

Spelling. The original spelling has been followed slavishly, even where the error was that of the type-setter, and the true reading abundantly apparent. The vagaries in the spelling by the writers and printers of the sixteenth and seventeenth century, have also been reproduced, and of course no attempt has been made to correct the author's grammar. A singular noun joined with a plural verb, or vice versa, will be found occasionally. It has not been thought necessary to call attention to such mistakes by the usual "sic."

Ornaments and Devices. These words, which in the catalogue frequently follow the title and precede the imprint, are intended to indicate different things. "Ornament" may stand for a single block impress, or a combination of two or more decorative designs. Frequently these blocks are identical with some of the ornaments used to form a border. "Device" is used where the decoration is more or less obviously a printer's mark or his particular decorative design. In some cases there is a reasonable question as to the accuracy in the use of the word, since some of the designs so indicated may be merely ornaments.

Imprint. The imprint, also in full, is divided like the title, with the date, if printed, or, if ascertained from an outside source, in square brackets. The date has been reproduced as it stands, unless it contains a palpable error in type setting. No attempt has been made to conform the dates to the current calendar of to-day, even in cases where this might have been done, as, for instance, with books between 1640 and 1660, by the aid of Thomason's lists. Hence a book issued between January 1 and March 24, will be found listed under the year preceding that of actual issue when counted in terms of the present calendar.

Border. This term describes a more or less ornate edging about the title, whether engraved or consisting of rows of printers' ornaments. Architectural designs are indicated, and occasionally the "pillar and vine" decoration. Line borders, whether consisting of a single or multiple series of rules, are thus specified.

Size. The measurements of the paper page (not of the type page) are given in centimetres as the most exact and generally available units, and also as avoiding the use of fractions of inches.

Pagination. Round brackets are used to indicate the number of prefatory pages which usually occur at the beginning of the volumes, and also for books wholly unpaged. In the latter case the numbers of the prefatory matter are separated from those which refer to the body of the book, by a comma. The counting begins with the first page on which printed matter occurs and is carried to include the page which precedes the book proper, unless that page happens to be blank. Intervening blank pages, however, are counted provided they consti-

PREFACE

tute an integral part of the signature in which they occur. If signature A1 is blank it has been so recorded only in exceptional cases. In the pagination of the main part of each volume the endeavor has been made to note irregularities or mistakes in numbering, and to give the actual pagination where it differs from that which is printed. Whenever the entire tract or book is unpaged, the count has been placed in round brackets, and the pages of a book containing two or more parts are given in series separated by a semi-colon.

Notes. In a great many cases notes are added after the imprint. Here items are given with regard to authorship, including the authority upon which attributions have been made, and other things that seem necessary for completeness.

Index. The index contains the names and brief descriptions of the authors, followed by the titles of the books which each has written. Supplementary thereto, introduced by the word " *see*," are references to other books whose title-pages contain references to such writer or to anonymous publications, books or tracts. Anonymous books are listed under the first significant word of the title, not an article, with the author's name, if known, in round or square brackets to indicate graphically the general source of the attribution. A book which appeared with only the writer's initials has been treated, like anonymous books, with a double entry.

Mistakes. The compiler does not pretend to suppose or to hope that errors will not be found in the catalogue. They are, of course, inevitable in an undertaking which involves as much of detail as the present. All that is claimed is that an endeavor has been made to render the catalogue reliable. It has been revised again and again, but inerrancy is not a human possibility. Doubtless with unlimited time at disposal, many mistakes and omissions might have been remedied, but they must be excused in the case of a compilation which has been prepared in intervals of time taken from other engrossing duties.

Authorities. The bibliographical apparatus available for the present undertaking has been none too ample. Some sources have been used constantly, others occasionally. Particular mention must be made of the persistent use that has been made of the Dictionary of National Biography. Authors' names and dates, and frequently the description given in the index, have been taken freely from this source without specific acknowledgment. The attributions of authorship have been fortified in a large number of cases by similar references, with citation of volume and page in the notes. Halkett and Laing's

Dictionary of Anonymous and Pseudonymous Literature has always been at hand and freely used. Dexter's list appended to his History of Congregationalism has been consulted, and much help has been derived from Smith's catalogues of quaker books and anti-quaker writings. Gillow's dictionary of the lives and writings of members of the Roman communion has given valuable aid. For the period from 1640 to 1660 the catalogue of the Thomason tracts has been consulted constantly, with the expenditure of much time on account of the unsatisfactory character of the index. Darling's pages have also been consulted, and other works too numerous for mention here. Library catalogues also have furnished much, particularly those of the British Museum, the Cambridge University, Madan's two volumes on Oxford books, the Williams Library, and many others.

Acknowledgments. The compiler takes great pleasure in expressing his indebtedness to the librarians and assistants connected with the libraries which he was privileged to visit, for many kindnesses and manifold courtesies. He has no doubt that his reception elsewhere would have been quite as cordial had the limited time at his disposal allowed of a more extended pilgrimage. He had the privilege of working in the Bodleian Library at Oxford, in the British Museum and the Williams Library in London, the Advocates' Library in Edinburgh, and the Rylands Library in Manchester. He expresses his thanks also for courteous replies to inquiries addressed to the institutions mentioned above, and particularly to the secretary of the Cambridge University Library. Acknowledgment must also be made to William Walker Rockwell, Ph.D., librarian of the Seminary, for useful suggestions which have added materially to the value of the catalogue. But the list of those to whom hearty thanks are due, would be gravely deficient if failure were made to acknowledge the valuable service rendered by Mr. Edward George Friehold of London, who generously and gratuitously supplied copies of a large number of title-pages, which, but for his aid, must have appeared in mutilated or incorrect shape.

ABBREVIATIONS

Abbreviations. Following is a list of the abbreviations used in the notes that follow the several entries. Other citations of authorities for the attribution of authorship are believed to be given with sufficient fullness, and are not included in the list below.

Advoc. Libr. Catalogue of the Printed Books in the Library of the Faculty of Advocates. 7 volumes. Edinburgh: 1863–1879.

Aldis. A List of Books printed in Scotland before 1700 including those printed furth of the Realm for Scottish Booksellers. With brief Notes on the Printers and Stationers. By Harry G. Aldis. Edinburgh: Bibliographical Society: MCMIV.

Almack. A Bibliography of the King's Book or Eikon Basilike. By Edward Almack. London: 1896.

Allibone. A Critical Dictionary of English Literature and British and American Authors Living or Deceased from the earliest Accounts to the latter half of the Nineteenth Century. . . . By S. Austin Allibone. 3 volumes. Philadelphia: 1872. With two supplemental volumes by John Foster Kirk. Philadelphia: 1892.

Arber. Transcript of the Registers of the Company of Stationers of London: 1554–1640. 5 volumes. London: 1875–1894.

Arber, TC. The Term Catalogues, 1668–1709 A. D. . . . A Contemporary Bibliography. . . . By Professor Edward Arber. 3 volumes. London, 1903– .

Bibl. Corn. Bibliotheca Cornubiensis. A Catalogue of the Writings, both Manuscript and Printed, of Cornishmen, and of Works relating to the County of Cornwall, with Biographical Memoranda and copious Literary References. By George Clement Boase and William Prideaux Courtney. 3 volumes. London: 1874–1882.

Black. A List of Works relating to Scotland. By George F. Black, The New York Public Library: 1916.

Bloom. English Tracts, Pamphlets and Printed Sheets. By J. Harvey Bloom. 1473–1640. Volumes I–II. London: 1922, 1923.

BMCat. British Museum Catalogue of Printed Books. London: 1885– .

Bodl. Bodleian Library, as quoted by Halkett and Laing.

Bowes. A Catalogue of Books printed at or relating to the University Town & County of Cambridge from 1521 to 1893. . . . By Robert Bowes. Cambridge: 1894.

Calamy-Palmer. The Nonconformist's Memorial. By Edmund Calamy, D.D. Edited by Samuel Palmer. 2 volumes. London: 1775.

Cambr. Univ. Cat. Early English Printed Books in the University Library, Cambridge (1475–1640). 4 volumes. Cambridge: 1900–1907.

Cat. Libr. Trin. Col., Dublin. Catalogus Librorum impressorum qui in Bibliotheca Collegii . . . Trinitatis . . . juxta Dublin adservantur. 9 volumes. Dublin: 1864–1887.

ABBREVIATIONS

Cath. Encyc. The Catholic Encyclopedia. New York: (1907–1914).

cm centimetres.

Cooper: Athen Cantab. Athenae Cantabrigienses. By Charles Henry Cooper and Thompson Cooper. 2 volumes. Cambridge: 1858–1861.

Darling. Encyclopedia Bibliographica. A Library Manual of Theological and General Literature. . . . By James Darling. 2 volumes. London: 1854.

Dexter. The Congregationalism of the last three hundred years, as seen in its Literature . . . With a Bibliographical Appendix. By Henry Martyn Dexter. New York: 1880.

DNB. Dictionary of National Biography. Edited by Leslie Stephens. 63 volumes, and 3 supplementary volumes. London: 1885–1912.

Duff. A Century of the English Book Trade. . . . By E. Gordon Duff. London: 1905.

Encyc. Brit. Encyclopaedia Britannica. 11th edition. 31 volumes. Cambridge and New York: 1910–1922.

fol folios.

Fore-title. Title preceding the true title page; frequently called "false title."

Gerould. Sources of English History of the Seventeenth Century, 1603–1689 in the University of Minnesota Library with a selection of secondary material. Compiled by James Thayer Gerould. Minneapolis: 1921.

Gillow. A Literary and Biographical History, Or Bibliographical Dictionary of the English Catholics. From the Breach with Rome in 1534, to the present time. By Joseph Gillow. 5 volumes. London and New York: (1885).

Grosart: Baxter. Annotated List of the Writings of Richard Baxter. . . . By the Rev. Alexander B. Grosart. (London): 1868.

H&L. A Dictionary of the Anonymous and Pseudonymous Literature of Great Britain. Including the Works of Foreigners written in, or translated into the English Language. By the late Samuel Halkett, . . . and the late Rev. John Laing, M.A. 4 volumes. Edinburgh: 1882–1888. New ed., Vol. I–II, 1926.

Harl Miscel. The Harleian Miscellany: A Collection of scarce, curious and entertaining Pamphlets and Tracts . . . from the Library of Edward Harley. 10 volumes. London: 1808–1813.

Herzog-Plitt. Realencyklopädie für protestantische Theologie und Kirche. . . . Albert Hauck. 24 volumes. 1896–1913. And the New Schaff-Herzog Encyclopedia of Religious Knowledge. 12 volumes. New York: 1908–1912.

Huntington Libr. Check-List or Brief Catalogue of the Library of Henry E. Huntington: English Literature to 1640. New York: 1919.

Lincoln's Inn. A Catalogue of Pamphlets, Tracts, Proclamations, Speeches, Sermons, Trials, Petitions, from 1506 to 1700 in the Library of the Honourable Society of Lincoln's Inn. London: 1908.

Lowndes. The Bibliographer's Manual of English Literature. . . . By William Thomas Lowndes. 11 volumes. London: 1857–1865.

McKerrow. A Dictionary of Printers and Booksellers in England, Scotland and Ireland, and of Foreign Printers of English Books, 1557–1640. London: 1910.

Madan: Early Oxford Press. The Early Oxford Press. A Bibliography of Printing and Publishing at Oxford, 1468–1640. By Falconer Madan, M.A. Oxford: 1895.

Madan II. Oxford Books. A Bibliography of Printed Works relating to the University and City of Oxford or printed or published there, with Appendices, Annals, and Illustrations. Volume 2. Oxford Literature, 1450–1640, and 1641–1650. By Falconer Madan, M.A., F.S.A. Oxford: 1912.

ABBREVIATIONS

Masson: Milton. The Life of John Milton. By David Masson. 6 volumes. London: 1875–1880.

New College Cat. As cited by Halkett and Laing.

Pierce. The Marprelate Tracts: 1588, 1589. Edited with Notes . . . by William Pierce. London: 1911.

Pierce, Introd. Historical Introduction to the Marprelate Tracts. By William Pierce. London: 1907.

Plomer. A Dictionary of the Booksellers and Printers who were at work in England, Scotland and Ireland from 1641 to 1667. By Henry R. Plomer. London: 1907.

Pollard. A Short-Title Catalogue of Books printed in England, Scotland, & Ireland, and of English Books printed abroad 1475–1640. Compiled by A. W. Pollard & G. R. Redgrave. London: 1926.

Reid: Memoirs. Memoirs of the Lives and Writings of those eminent Divines, who convened in the famous Assembly at Westminster. . . . By James Reid. 2 volumes. Paisley: 1811–1815.

Smith. A descriptive Catalogue of Friends Books. By Joseph Smith. 2 volumes. London: 1867.

Smith: Antiquaker. Bibliotheca Anti-Quakeriana; or a Catalogue of Books adverse to the Society of Friends. By Joseph Smith. London: 1873.

Sub. t.p. Subordinate title page.

Thomason. Catalogue of the Pamphlets, Books, Newspapers, and Manuscripts relating to the Civil War, the Commonwealth, and Restoration. Collected by George Thomason, 1640–1661. 2 volumes. London: 1908.

t.p. Title page.

Trin. Col. Camb. A Catalogue of the English Books printed before MDCI. Now in the Library of Trinity College, Cambridge. By Robert Sinker, B.D. Cambridge: 1885.

Warfield. The Printing of the Westminster Confession: Notes toward a Bibliography. By Professor Benjamin B. Warfield. The Presbyterian and Reformed Review: Philadelphia: 1901.

Watt. Bibliotheca Britannica; or a general Index to British and Foreign Literature. By Robert Watt. In two Parts: Authors and Subjects. Two volumes. Edinburgh: 1824.

Whitley. A Baptist Bibliography. . . . Compiled by W. T. Whitley. Vol. I: 1526–1776. London: 1916.

Williams Libr. Catalogue of the Library . . . founded pursuant to the Will of the Rev. Daniel Williams, D.D. 2 volumes and supplement. London, 1841 and 1870.

Wood: Athen Oxon. Athenae Oxonienses. An exact History of all the Writers and Bishops. . . . University of Oxford: 1500–1690. Editions of 1691–1692, 1721 and 1813–1820.

CATALOGUE
OF THE
McALPIN COLLECTION
OF
BRITISH HISTORY AND THEOLOGY
IN THE
Union Theological Seminary
New York

1501–1640

1501

LYNDWOOD, William. Prouinciale seu Constitu | tiones Anglie Cum summariis atq[ue] iustis an | notationibus: honestis characteribus: sum- | maq[ue] accuratione rursum impresse. |

Colophon: Explicitū est opus magistri wilhelmi lynde- | wode super cōstitutiones prouinciales Anglie summa diligen | tia & accuratione magīri Andree Bocard cū annotationibus et | castigationibus debitis. cūq[ue] summarijs suis locis ppositis In | inclyta parisiana academia. Anno salutis nostre Millesimo | quingentesimoprimo. Maij vero die .xxviij. | 33.6x23.3cm. Cxcii, (19)fol.
Cambr.Univ.Cat.7685.

1510

SPECULUM spiritualiū: in quo nō solum de vita acti- | ua et cōtemplatiua: verum etiā de viciis, quibus huma- | na mens inquinatur, ac virtutibus quibus in deū accē | ditur: p[er]pulchre tractatur. cū varijs exemplis ad vtrā- | q[ue] vitam conducentibus: oībus pie viuere cupientibus | vtile: religiosis tamen sūme necessariū. tū quia oīa ad | eor[um] officia pertinētia pa tēter declarat: tū etiam quia q[uae] | fugiēda ac p[er]sequēda sūt: potissimū demonstrat. Addi | tur insuper et opusculum Richardi hampole de emēda | tione vite: ac de regula bene viuendi. | (cuts, 5 panels).

Venale habetur in vico sancti Jacobi apud edē sacrā | sancti Benedicti ad signum sancti Georgij. | Colophon: Opera predicta in alma Parisior[um] acade | mia p[er] wolffgangū hopyliū sunt impressa: | sumptibus et expensis honesti viri Guilhel | mi brettoñ ciuis Londoñ. Anno dñi millesi | mo quingentesimo decimo. | 25.2x18.6cm. (7),208,(10)fol. Fols. 35, 42, 103, 126, 133–4, 136, 189, 191 and 199 are misnumbered; extra leaf at end with coat of arms on reverse.
Cambr.Univ.Cat.6151.

1516

BURGO, Joannes de. Pupilla oculi | De septem Sacramentorū admini | stratione: de decem Preceptis decalogi: ceterisq[ue] ecclesiasticor[um] | (que rite institutum sacerdotem haud quaq[ue] igno- | rare decet) officijs: Joannis de | Burgo, alme quondā | Cantabrigi- | ensis | Uniuersitat[is] Cancellarij: presbyteris | oīb[us], sacreq[ue] militie studiosis maiorē in modū necessaria. | Adiectis tabula Capitulor[um], atq[ue] Indice alphabetario omni- | um in hoc opusculo contentorum. | . . . (15 lines).

1516. | 21.2x15.3cm. clxx,(15)fol. Colophon: Tabule cum opusculo, Pupilla oculi | nūcupato, finis: sumptib[us] p[ro]uido | rū Joannis Knoblouchi, & | Pauli Götz ciuiū & biblio- | polar[um] Argeñ.p̄lo Joan- | nis Schotti vrbis in- | cole.sub Annū dni. | M.D.xvii.Kal | Martij. |

1522

LUTHER, Martin. Contra Henricvm | Regem Angliae | Martinvs Lv- | ther. |

VVittembergae. | 1522. | Engr.border. 20.4x15.1cm   (4,43)p
Dated from Wittemberg, 15 July, 1522.

1523

BUCER, Martin. Das ym selbs | niemāt, sonder | anderen leben | soll. vnd wie | der mensch da | hyn kumm- | en mög. | Martinus Butzer. | (woodcut border).

Without imprint. Vorred: Zu Straszburg. Anno M.D.xxiij. Mense Augusti. | 19.7x14.8cm. (16)fol.

NETTER, Thomas. Sacramentalia. F. Tho | mę VValden Theologię | & Carmelitani Sodalitii professoris celeberrimi: | sextū vidilicet volumen doctrinalis antiquitatū | fidei ecclesię catholicę cōtra VVitcleuistas & eo | rum asseclas Lutheranos, aliosq[ue] hæreticos. | (printer's mark: F. R.: Francovs Regnault).

Vęnundantur Francisco Reginaldo Bibliopo- | lę Academię Parisinę iurato. | Engraved border. 29.1x19.7cm. (8),344fol.
Colophon: . . . Impressum ac recognitum opera qui | dē Iodoci Badii Ascensii: impensis autem Francisci Reginaldi, pridie Natalis domi | nici. M.D.XXIII. Deo gratie. |

1524

BUCER, Martin. Grund vñ vrsach | ausz gotlicher schrifft d neū- | werungen, an dem nachtmal des herren, so man | die Mess nennet, Tauff, Feyrtagen, bildern | vñ gesang, in der gemein Christi, wañ die | zusamenkompt, durch vnnd auff das | wort gottes, zu Straszburg | fürgenomen. | Ein sendtbrieff an den durch- | leüchtigen hochgeboren fürsten vnd herrn, Frid- | reich Pfaltzgraue, auch in dem ein jede christlich | oberkeit ermanet würt, den genanten geistlichen | keins wegs gehellē, | einig leer oder predig, so man | sich vff die schrifft berüfft, vnuerhört, zu verdam | men, mitt ablenung irer losen nichtige einreden. | Martinus Butzer. |

Without imprint. Dedication signed: Geben zu Straszburg. xxvj. Decembris. | 1524. | 19.9x14.9cm. (8,52)fol.

1525

FISHER, John. Asserti- | onvm Martini Lvtheri | confutatio, per Reuerendum pa | trem D. Iohannem Roffensem | ep̄um, Cantabrigieñ. academiæ | cancellarium edita: Suntq[ue] singu | lis confutationibus singulæ Lu- | theri assertiones præfixæ, quo fa | cilius, utrius sententiæ subscribē | dum sit, cognoscatur. Accessit | præterea totius operis p[er] eundē, | præcipue tamen annotationum | additarum recognitio. |

Apud sanctam Vbiorum Agrippinam | Anno M.D.XXV. | Engr. border. Colophon: Colonie apud Eucharium Ceruicornum, | Impensa & ere M. Godefridi Hit- | torpij ciuis Colonieñ. Anno | M. ccccc xxv. mense | Januario. | 16.4x11cm. (12), 364fol.

FISHER, John. Convvlsio Calvm- | niarum Vlrichi Veleni Minhoni | ensis, quibus Petrum nunquam | Romæ fuisse cauillatur, per Io- | annem Roffensem Epi- | scopum, academiæ | Cantabrigien- | sis Cancel | lariū. | Petrvs Fuit Romae. |

Colophon: Parisijs, In ædibus Conradi Resch, | sub scuto Basiliensi. | [1525?]. 17.3x12.3cm. (52)fol. Engr. t. p.

FISHER, John. Defensio Regie | assertōis cōtra Ba- | bylonicam captiuitatē. per Reue- | rendū patrem et D.D. Ioannē Roffensem Episcopū. In qua | respōdet pro illustrissimo, eodēq[ue] doctissimo Anglor[um] Rege | Henrico .VIII. fidei defensore, ad maledicētissmū Martini | Lutheri libellū, in eūdē Regē scriptū plusquā impudētissime. |

Coloniæ. In officina honesti ciuis Petri Quentell | Anno. M.D.XXV. Mense Iunio. | Device. 19.4x13.5cm. (6),CIVfol.

FISHER, John. Defēsio Regie asser- | tionis cōtra Babylonicā captiuitatē, | per Reuerendum patrē & D.D. Johā- | nem Roffensem Episcopū. In qua re- | spondet pro illustrissimo, eodēq[ue] doctissimo Anglor[um] | Rege Henrico .viij. fidei defensore, ad maledicen- | tissimum Martini Lutheri libellū, in eundē Regē | scriptū plusq[uam] impudentissime. |

Colonie. In officina honesti ciuis Petri Quentel. | Anno M.D.XXV. Mense Iulio. | Device:royal arms. 15.4x10.3cm. (10),136fol.

FISHER, John. Sacri sacerdotij defensio | cōtra Lutherum, per Reuerendissimū Dominum, | dominum Johannem Roffeñ. Episcopum, virum | singulari eruditione omnifariam doctissimum, iam | primum, ab Archetypo euulgata. | Cum tabula et repertorio tractatorum. |

Colonie, impensis Petri Quentel. | Anno 1525. | Royal arms. 15.4x10.5cm. (9), (12),55fol. Some leaves, without numbers. Some misnumbered.

LAMBERT, François. De Fideli- | vm Vocatione In | regnum Christi, id est, Ecclesiam. | De Vocatione Ad Mi- | nisteria eius, maxime ad | Episcopatum. | Item | De Vocatione Matthiæ | per sortem, ac similibus. Et ibi | multa de sortibus. | Francisco Lamberto autore. | (device).

[Strasburg 1525?] 17.3x11cm. 23fol.

1526

BUCER, Martin. Apologia Martini Bvceri Qva | fidei suæ atque doctrinæ, circa Christi Cœ- | nam, quā, tum ipse, tū alij Ecclesiastæ Ar | gentoracenses profitentur, ratione sim | pliciter reddit, atq[ue]; citra dentem de- | pellit, quæ in ipsum Epistola quæ | dā Io. Brentij Ecclesiastæ Ha | lensis, inscio, ut creditur, | authore ædita, crimi- | na intendit. |

Anno, M.D.XXVI. | 15.4x10cm. 36 fol.

FISHER, John. Assertionis | Lvtheranae Confv- | tatio Ivxta Vervm Ac Ori- | ginalem archetypum, nunc ad vnguem diligen- | tissime recognita. Per reuerendum patrem | Ioannem Roffensem Episcopum, | academie Canthabrigien. | Cancellarium. | Additio vltima, variis annota- | tionibus in margine lo- | cupletata. | (device)

MD XX VI | Engr.border. Colophon: Venetiis in Aedibus Gregorii de Grego- | riis. Anno a Virginali partu | M.D.XXVI. Men- | se Augusto. | 30.4x20.9cm. (8), CCI fol.

1527

BUCER, Martin. Enar- | rationvm In Evan- | gelia Matthæi, Marci, & Lucæ, | libri duo. | Loci communes syncerioris Theologiæ | supra centum, ad simplicem scriptu- | rarum fidem, cura ullius insecta | tionem aut criminationem, | excussi, | Per M. Bvcervm. |

<small>Argentorati, Anno M.D.XXVII. | Woodcut border. 15.7x10.2cm. (8),256;(1), 48,(15)fol.</small>

BUCER, Martin. Epistola | D. Pavli Ad Ephesios, Qva | rationem Christianismi breuiter iuxta & | locuplete, ut nulla breuius simul & locu | pletius explicat, uersa paulò libe- | rius, ne peregrini idiotismi | rudiores scripturarum of- | fenderent, bona tamen fi- | de, sententijs Aposto- | li appensis. | In eandem Commentarius. | Per Martinvm Bvcervm. |

<small>Without imprint. Epistola dated: Argentorati pridie Calend. | Septemb. Anno Christi | M.D.XXVII. | 15.4x10.4cm. (1–8), 9–110,(2)fol.</small>

BUCER, Martin. Praefatio | M. Bvceri In Qvartvm To- | mum Postillæ Lutheranæ, continens sum- | mam doctrinæ Christi. | Eivsdem, | Epistola, explicans locum 1. Corinth. 10. An nescitis q[*uod*] | qui in stadio currant, usq;: sed plures illorum non approba | uerit Deus, cum Annotationibus in quædam pauculis Lu | theri. Epistola M. Lutheri ad Iohannem Heruagium supe- | riora criminans. | Responsio adhanc M. Buceri, Item ad Pomeranū satisfa | ctio, de uersione Psalterij. | . . . (2 lines).

<small>Anno M.D.XXVII. | (Dated: Arg. 25 Martij). 15x10cm. (2,45)fol.</small>

FISHER, John. De Verita- | te Corporis Et San- | gvinis Christi In Evcharistia, per | Reuerendum in Christo patrem, ac dominum. D. Iohannem | Roffensem Episcopum, aduersus Iohannem | Oecolampadium. | (coat of arms).

<small>Coloniæ, Anno domini M.D.XXVII. | Aeditio Prima. | 31.x20.8cm. (14),clxix,(1)fol.</small>

LUTHER, Martin. Auff des | königs zu En- | gelland lester | schrifft | titel, | Mart. Luthers. | Antwort. |

<small>M.D.XXVII. | Engr.border. 18.4x14.7cm (1,11)p. Signed from Wittenberg.</small>

1528

BUCER, Martin. Tzepha | niah, Qvem Sopho- | niam, uulgo uocāt, prophetarum | epitomographus, ad ebraicam | ueritatem uersus, & com- | mentario explanatus, | per M. Bucerum. |

<small>Argentorati Apvd | Ioannem Hervagi- | vm, Mense Sept. | Anno. M.D. | XXVIII. | Engr.border. 16x10cm. (16),96fol.</small>

BUCER, Martin. Vergleich- | ung D. Luthers, vnnd | seins gegentheyls, vom | Abentmal Christi. | Dialogus | Das ist, eyn freündtlich | gesprech. | Gar nahe alles so D. Lu | ther in seinē letsten buch |

Bekenntnüss genent, für- | bracht hat, würdt hierin | gehandelt, wie das zu er | kanntnüss der wahreyt vn | Christlichem frid dienet. |

<small>Without imprint. Woodcut border. Colophon: Gedruckt zu Straszburg bey Wolff | Köpphel, Anno M.D. | xxviij. | 14.6x9.7cm. (3,57)fol.
Prefatory note signed.</small>

1529

MORE, Thomas. The supplycacyon of soulys. | Made by syr Thomas More knyght councellour | to our souerayn lorde the Kynge and | chauncellour of hys Duchy | of Lancaster. | Agaynst the supply- cacyon of beggars. |

<small>No imprint. [1529?] 27.x19.cm. (1),xliiiifol.</small>

1530

BARNES, Robert. Sen- | tenciae Ex Doc- | toribvs Col- | lectae, Qvas | papistæ ualde im- | pudenter ho- | die dam- | nant. | Per Anto. Anglum. |

<small>VVitebergæ. | Border. Colophon: Impressum VVitebergæ apud Iosephum | Clug. Anno domini. | M.D.XXX. | 15.1x10.cm. 76 fol. Fol. 1b, 3b, 4, and 76b, blank.</small>

BARON, Stephen. Sermones Declamati coram | alma vniuersitate Cantibrigien | si, per venerandum patrem fra- | trem Stephanū baronis fratrū | minorum de obseruantia nuncu- | patorum, regni Anglie prouincia | lem vicarium, ac confessorem re- | giū. diligenter impressi in achade | mia parrhisiensi. Inquibus īpri | mendis ordo prioris impressionis | non sine consilio quibusdam in lo | cis mutatus extitit. |

<small>No impr. [1530?] 12.2x8.8cm. 70, (2); (23) fol.
Appended: Incipit tractatulus eiusdem ve | nerandi patris De regimine | principum ad serenissi- | mum regem an- | glie hēricū | octauū. |</small>

BUCER, Martin. Eyn kurtzer | ausszug, auss den | Bebstlichen rechten | der Decret vnd Decreta- | len, In den artickeln, die | vngeuerlich Gottes | wort vn Euāgelio | gemess sein, oder | zum wenigsten | nicht wider | streben. |

<small>1530. | Woodcut border. 20x15.1cm. (4,36)fol.
Dedication, signed.</small>

MORE, Thomas. A dyaloge of syr Thomas More | knyght: one of the | counsayll of our souerayne lorde the kyng and chaun | celloure of hys duchy of Lancaster. Wheryn he | treatyd dyuers maters, as of the veneracy- | on & worshyp of ymagys & relyques, | prayng to sayntis, & goynge on pyl | grymage. Wyth many other | thyngys touchyng the pes- | tylent secte of Luther | & Tyndale, by the | tone bygone in | Saxony, & | by the | tother laboryd | to be brought in to England.·. Newly ouersene by the sayd syr Thomas More | chauncellour of England.·. | 1530. | (device)

<small>Colophon: Cum priuilegio regali, | Anno Domini. M.D.C.XXX.mense Maii. | 27.1x19.2cm. (6), cliii fol. Fols. xv, xxi, xxvii and cix, misnumbered.</small>

1531

BARNES, Robert. Fürnemlich Artickel | der Christenlichenkirchē, wie die bey den alten im | brauch gewesen vnnd gehalten sind worden, | aber yetzt vnbillich von den Papisten, wider | die heilige geschrifft, ihr eigen Decret, Con | cilia, vnd schrifften der Lerer | verdampt werden. | Erstlich in latein durch D. An- | thonium auss Engelandt zusamen gebracht, | newlich, mit einer vorred Joan. Pomerani | pfarherr zu Wittenberg, verdeütscht. | 1531. |

Colophon: Vollendet erstlich im latein sampt der vorred Pome- | rani zu Wittenberg, und yetzt newlich durch | einen gelerten verteütscht vnd im druck ver- | fertigt zu Nürmberg im 1531.jar. | 18.6x14.2 cm. (4,85)p.

1533

BUCER, Martin. Furbereytung zum | Concilio, wie alle recht Gotszfortigen | von beden, yetz fürnemen theylen, so man alt vnd new gleu | bige, Bäpsttische, vn̄ Lutherische nen̄et, Zu einigkeit Christ | licher kirchen kom̄en, vnnd sich dariñ vnbewegt hal- | ten mögen, etliche freundtliche Gotsförchtige | gespräch, von fürnem̄enstucken Christ | licher lere, deren halb man yetz | im missuerstand ist. | Zu end des büchs findestu dise stuck noch | ordnung verzeychnet. |

Getruckt zu Strassburg durch Mathiam | Apiarium, Im jar | M.D.XXXIII. | 17.2x14cm. (4,54)fol.
B M Cat.

1534

BUCER, Martin. Defensio | Adversvs Axioma Catholi- | cum, id est criminationem R. P. Roberti | Episcopi Abrincēsis, in qua is impiæ | nouationis in cunctis Ecclesiæ cum do- | gmatis, tum ritibus, peculiarter aūt | circa Sacrosanctam Eucharistiam | importune accusat, quotquot | Christi doctrinam sectari | studēt, ab ijs hominum | cōmentis, quæ cum | illa pugnant, re | purgatam. | Hic videbis Christiane Le- | ctor, nos nihil prorsus uel in doctrinam, uel | ritus Ecclesiarū nostrarū admisisse, quod | non pulchre conueniat, & cum scri- | ptis orthodoxorum Patrum, & cum | obseruatione Ecclesiæ catholicæ. | Per Marti. Buce. | Catalogvs Eorvm | de quibus hic disputatur, est in | sequenti pagina. |

Colophon: Argentorati per mathiam | Apiarium. | Anno M D XXXIIII. | 15.8x10.2cm.(80)fol.

FOX, Edward. Opvs Exi- | mivm, | De Vera Differentia | Regiae Potestatis Et Ec- | clesiasticae, Et Qvae Sit | Ipsa Veritas Ac Vir- | tvs Vtrivs- | Qve. | (device)

Londini In AEdibvs Tho. | Bertheleti. M.D.XXXIIII. | Cvm Privilegio. | 19.5x13.8cm. 63 fol. Anon. Brit Mus. Cat. DNB. 20: 114 a. Cambr.Univ.Cat. 429.

1535

TYNDALE, William. The Obe- | dience of a Christen man, | and how Christen rulers ought to go- | uerne, where in also (yf thow marke di | ligently) thou shalt fynde eyes | to perceaue the cr- | afty con | uey- | aunce of all iugglers. | Newly Printed and diligently | corrected |

M.D.XXXV. | Colophon: At Marlborow in the lande of Hesse, | The. xxix. daye of October. Anno | MCCCCCXXXV. by | me Hans luft. | 13.2x8.7 cm. clx,(8) fol.
Anon. Cambr.Univ.Cat. No. 6100.

1536

A COPY of thacte made for thabrogacion of certayne | holy dayes, accordyng to the transumpte late sent by the | kyngs hyghnes to all bysshops with his graces strayght | commaundement, to signifie his farther pleasure to all Col- | leges, religious houses and Curates, within theyr diocesse | for the publicacion, and also effectuall & universall obser- | cion of the same. Anno 1536. |

No t.p. Colophon: Imprynted at London in Fletestrete, at the | sygne of the Sonne, by me John Byddell. | Cum priuilegio. Anno 1536. | 19.4x15.4cm. Pp. 225–226 of Sparrow's Collection: 1661. Reprint.

VON der Vorurteilung vnd Tode | ettwan des Grossen Cantzlers von En | geland, Hern Thome Mori, dorumb | das er dem Rathschlag vnd Newem Gesetz desselbig- | en Königreichs nicht hat zufallen oder anhang- | en wöllen. | Nicht vnwirdig, das vmb desselben Mannes besonder | tapferkeit vnd bestendikeit willen von jederman gelesen | werde. | Aus dem Welschen jns Deutsch gebracht. | (Cut of King). Heinrich König in Engeland. |

Zu Dressden hats gedruckt | Wolffgang Stöckel. 1536. | 19.4x15.2cm. (1),8p.

1537

FISHER, John. Assertio- | nis Lvtheranæ Con- | futatio iuxta verum ac originalem ar- | chetypum, nunc ad vnguem diligen- | tissime recognita, per reuerendum pa | trem Ioannem Roffensem | Episcopum, academiæ Canta- | brigieñ. Cancel- | larium. | Æditio ultima, uariis annotationibus | in margine locupletata. | Ezech. XIII. | . . . (4 lines).

Antverpiæ | Apud Ioan. Steelsium in scuto Burgundiæ, | Anno M.D.XXXVII. | 16x10.7 cm. 356,(4)fol.

FISHER, John. Sacri Sa- | cerdotii Defensio | contra Lutherum, per Reuerendissimum | D.D. Ioannem Roffen. Episcopum, | virum singulari eruditione omnifa- | riam doctissimum, iampri- | mum ab Archetypo | euulgata. | Psal. CXVII. | . . . (2 lines).

Antverpiæ | Apud Ioannem Steelsium in scuto Burgun- | dię. Anno à Christo nato | M.D.XXXVII. | 16x10.7 cm. 51,(1)fol.
Appended to his Assertio- | nis Lvtheranæ con- | futatio . . . 1537.

The INSTITV- | TION Of A | Christen | man, contey- | nynge the | expo- | sition or interpretation of | the cōmune Crede, of | the seuen sacra- | mentes, of the | x. cōmande- | mentes, & of the Pa- | ter noster, and the | Aue Maria, | Justifica- | tion and | purga- | torie. | 1534 |

[London: Berthelet] 1537? 14.6x9.9cm. (4),110fol. Lacks fol. 29, and last ten leaves.

The date 1534 is part of the engr.border. Cambr.Univ.Cat.439. Repr. in Formularies of Faith. Oxford, 1820. Pp. 21–211. Known as " The Bishops Book."

1538

BULLINGER, Henry. De Scriptv- | rae Sanctae Avthorita- | te, Certitvdine, Firmitate Et Absolvta | perfectione, deq́[ue] Episcoporum, qui uerbi dei mini- | stri sunt, institutione & functione, contra su- | perstitionis tyrannidisq́[ue] Romanæ anti | stites, ad Sereniss. Angliæ Regem | Heinrychvm VIII. | Heinrychi Bullin- | geri Libri | duo. | . . . (4 lines; device).

Tigvri In Officina Froschoviana | Mense Martio, Anno | M.D.XXXVIII. | 21.2x 13.8cm. (8), 180fol.

1539

CAMPEGGIO, Lorenzo. Refor- | matio Cleri | Germaniae Ad Corre- | ctionem vitæ & morum, ac ad remouendos ab- | usus, per Reuerendissimum in Christo patrem, | & dominum D. Laurentium, Tunc S. R. Eccle- | siæ. tr'. sanctæ Anastasiæ presbyterum, Nunc | Sabinen̄. ep̄m, Cardinalē, Ad nationem | Germanican, sedis apostolicæ | de latere Legatū Ratis- | ponę ædita. | Et Statvta Synodalia | Reuerendi in Christo patris & domini, | D. Valentini Episcopi Hilde- | semensis. | Necnon Formvla Vi- | uendi Canonicor[um], Vicariorum, & alio- | rum presbyterorum secula- | rium. ·. |

Coloniæ ex ædibus Quentelianis, | Anno M.D.XXXIX. | Mense Septembri. | Engraved border. 27.x18.6cm. (4),42fol. Fol. VII misnumbered. Colophon.

1540

BARNES, Robert. Bekanntnus dess Glaubens, | die Doctor Robertus Barus, der hailigen | Schrifft Doctor (in Teütschen Lannden | D. Antonius Anglus genannt) zu Lunden | in Engelland gethon hat, im jar M.D.XL. | am XXX dess Monats Julij, do Er zum | Feŭr, on Ortel vñ Recht, vnschuldig, | vnuerhörter Sach, gefürt, vnnd | verbrennt worden ist. | Auss der Englischen Sprach Verteütscht. |

No imprint. Colophon: Zu Augspurg Truckts Melcher Kriesstein. | [1540?] 17.9x12.6cm. (11)p.

1541

BUCER, Martin. Acta Collo | qvii In Comitiis Imperii Ra- | tisponae Habiti, Hoc Est Articvli | de religione conciliati, & non conciliati om- | nes, ut ab Imperatore Ordinibus Impe- | rij ad iudicandum, & deliberan- | dum propositi sunt. | Consulta & deliberata de his actis Imperatoris | singulorum Ordinum Imperij, & Le- | gati Romani. Et, quædam alia, quorum Catalogum ha- | bes sequenti pagina. | Per Martinum Bucerum. |

Argentorati Mense Sep- | tembri. M.D.XLI. | 17.2x13.6cm. (6),108fol. Fol. 87 and 90 omitted; 93–94, repeated.

BUCER, Martin. Alle Handlungen vnd | Schrifften, zu vergleichung der Re- | ligion, durch die Key. Mai., Churfürsten, Für- | sten, vnd Stände, allertheylen, Auch den Päbst. | Legaten, auff jüngst gehaltnem

Reichs- | tag zu Regenspurg, verhandlet, | vnd einbracht, Anno |
D.M.XLI. | Getrewes fleiss, beschriben, zusammen ge- | tragen, vnd
erkläret, durch | Martinum Bucerum. | Register alles jnhalts, zu ende
des Büchs. | . . . (2 lines).

<small>Without imprint. Colophon: Getruckt zu Straszburg, | bei Wendel Kihel. |
(1541) 17.3x13.9cm. (8),204fol.</small>

COVERDALE, Miles. A confutacion of that | treatise, which one
John Stan- | dish made agaynst the protestacion of | D. Barnes in
the yeare. | M.D.XL. | Wherin, the holy scriptures (peruerted and |
wrested in his sayd treatise) are restored to their | owne true vnderstonding
agayne | by Myles Couer- | dale. | . . . (3 lines).

<small>Without imprint [1541?]   14.6x9.5cm.   (103)fol.
Cf.Cambr.Univ.Cat.6281.</small>

PECKHAM, John. Colle- | ctanevm Bi- | bliorum quinq[ue] libris
sententias di- | uinæ scripturæ ad certos titulos, | seu locos communes
redigens, Au | tore Iohanne Pechano Cantua- | riensis ecclesiæ Archipræ-
| sule: Nunc à mendis | quibus scatebat re- | purgatum. | (device)

<small>Coloniae, ex officina Melchioris Noue- | siani, Anno a Christo nato, M.D.XLI. |
15.8x10.3cm.   (8,376)fol.</small>

1542

ALESIUS, Alexander. De Avtho | ritate Verbi Dei Liber | Alexandri
Alesij, contra Epi- | scopum Lun- | densem. | (device)

<small>An. M.D.XLII. | Colophon: Argentorati apud Cra | tonem Mylium An. |
M.D.XLII. | Mense Septembri. | 16x9.3 cm.   130p.</small>

BUCER, Martin. De Vera Ec- | clesiarvm In Doctri- | na,
Ceremoniis, Et Disci- | plina reconciliatione & | compositione. | Hic
Cognosces Veros | Ortvs Et Progressvs Dissi- | diorum in religione,
uerasq[ue] uias illa tol- | lendi, & Christianam consensio- | nem restituendi.
| Responsio Ad Calvmnias Alberti | Pighij Campensis, contra
Confessionem & Apologiam Prote- | stantium nuper uulgatas, & Refutatio
suggillationis | Eccianæ, contra Acta Ratisponensia. | Per Martinum
Bucerum. | Index rerum quæ tractantur hoc libro | post præfationem. |

<small>No imprint. [1542].   20.x14.4cm.   (5),(1–8),9–216 fol.</small>

1543

ACTE agaynst mummers. Cap. ix. |

<small>[1543]. Henry VIII. [Statutes]. Ann.3. fol. x.</small>

ACTE compellynge spirituall persons to kepe residence | vppon their
benefyces. Cap. xiii. |

<small>[1543?].   28.3x19.8cm.   Henry VIII.   [Statutes].   Ann.28.   fol. xxb–xxib</small>

ACTE concernynge outlandyshe peo- | ple, callynge them selfes
Egip- | tians. Cap. x. |

<small>[1543?].   28.3x19.8cm.   Henry VIII.   [Statutes].   Ann.22.   fol. xi</small>

ACTE concernynge the kynges generall pardon for | his spirtuall subiectes. Cap. xv. |
[1543?]. 28.3x19.8cm. Henry VIII. [Statutes]. Ann.22. fol. xixb–xxiii.

ACTE concernynge the kynges hyghnes to be supreme heed of the | churche of Englande, and to haue auctoritie to re- | fourme and redresse all errours, heresies, | and abuses in the same. Cap. i. |
[1543?]. 28.3x19.8cm. Henry VIII. [Statutes]. Ann. 26. fol. ii–iiia.

ACTE conteynynge an order for tythes through the realme. Cap. xx. |
[1543?] 28.3x19.8cm. Henry VIII. [Statutes]. Ann.27. fol. xxiib–xxiiib.

ACTE extyngyshyng the auctoritie of the bishop of Rome. Cap. x. |
[1543?]. 28.3x19.8cm. Henry VIII. [Statutes]. Ann.28. fol. xva–xviiia.

ACTE for the release of suche as haue obteyned pretended | lycences and dispensations from the see of | Rome. Cap. xvi. |
[1543?]. 28.3x19.8cm. Henry VIII. [Statutes]. Ann. 28. fol. xxiiiia–xxvb.

ACTE that appeles in suche cases as hath ben vsed to be pur- | sued to the See of Rome shall not be from hensforthe | had ne vsed but within this realme. Cap. xii. |
[1543?]. 28.3x19.8cm. Henry VIII. [Statutes]. Ann.24. fol. xiib–xva.

ACTE wherby the kynges maiestie shall haue power to no- | minate. xxxii. persons of his clergie and laye fee for ma- | kynge of ecclesiasticall lawes. Cap. xv. |
[1543?]. 28.3x19.8cm. Henry VIII. [Statutes]. Ann.27. fol. xix–xxa.

BEDE. Commenta | rii In Omnes Divi | Pavli Epistolas, Ex Lv- | cubrationibus. S. Augustini Catholicæ | Ecclesiæ probatissimi Doctoris, | Per Venerabilem Bedam | presbyterum selecti. | Addito Elencho Locorvm Prope | omnium, quorum in nouo testamento fit mentio, | aliarumque rerum, & vocum, quæ vsui esse | scripturarum studiosis possint. | (device)
Venetiis | Sub signo Sancti Bernardini, | M.D.XLIII. | 15.4x10.7cm. (19),639, (1)fol.

HENRY VIII: [Statutes and Ordinances: anno i]. Anno primo Hen- | rici octaui, | The kynge our souerayne lorde Henry the. viii. | after the conquest, by the grace of god kynge of Englāde and of | Fraunce, and lorde of Irelande, at his parliament holden at | westmynster the. xxi. day of January, in the fyrst yere of his | mooste noble reigne: to the honour of god and holye | church, and for the comon weale and profite of this | his realme, by the assent of the lordes spirituall | and temporall & the cōmons in this present | parliament assembled, & by auctoritie | of the same: hath do to be orday | ned, made, & enacted cer- | tayne statutes & ordi- | naūces in maner | and fourme | folow- | yng. | (device)

Colophon: Thomas Berthelet regius impressor | excudebat. Cum priuilegio. | [1543?] 28.3x19.8cm. 10fol.
Cambr.Univ.Cat. No. 515.

HENRY VIII: [Statutes and Ordinances: anno iii-vii]. Anno regni regis Hen- | rici, viii, Tertio, | The kynge our souerayne lorde Henry the. viii. | after the conquest, by the grace of god kynge of Englāde and of | Fraunce, and lorde of Irelande, at his parliament holden at | westmynster the. iiii. daye of February, in the. iii. yere of his | mooste noble reigne: to the honour of god and holye | churche, and for the comon weale and profite of this | his realme, by the assent of the lordes spirituall | and temporal, & the cōmons in this present | parliament assembled, & by auctoritie | of the same: hath do to be orday | ned, made, & enacted cer- | tayne statutes & ordi- | naūces in maner | and fourme | folow- | yng. |

Colophon: Londini in edibus Thome Bertheleti | regii impressoris excus. | [1543?] 28.3x19.8cm. 13 fol. Continuous register and folios through 7th year. 54fol.
Camb.Univ.Cat. No. 516.

HENRY VIII: [Statutes and Ordinances: Anno iv]. Anno regni regis Hen- | rici, viii, quarto, | The kynge our souerayne lorde Henry the. viii. | after the conquest, by the grace of god kynge of Englāde and of | Fraunce, and lorde of Irelande, at his parliament holden at | westmynster the. iiii. day of Nouembre in the. iiii. yere of his | moste noble reigne, after the prorogation to the honour | of god and holye churche, and for the comon weale | and profite of this his realme, by the assent of | the lordes spirituall and temporal, and the | commons in this present parliament | assembled, and by auctorytie of | the same: hath do to be orday- | ned, made, and enacted cer- | tayne statutes and ordi- | naūces in maner | and fourme | folow- | yng. | (leaf ornament).

Colophon: Thomas Berthelet regius impressor | excudebat. Cum priuilegio. | [1543?] 28.3x19.8cm. xv-xxiifol.

HENRY VIII: [Statutes and Ordinances, anno v]. Anno regni regis Hen- | rici, viii. quinto, | The kynge our souerayne lorde Henry the. viii. | after the conquest, by the grace of God kynge of Englāde and of | Fraunce, and lorde of Irelande, at his parliament holden at | westmister the. xxiii. day of January in the. v. yere of his most | noble reigne, after the laste prorogation to the honour | of god and holye churche, and for the comon weale | and profite of this his realm, by the assent of | the lordes spirituall and temporal, and the | commons in this present parliament | assembled, and by auctorytie of | the same: hath do to be orday- | ned, made, & enacted cer- | tayne statutes & ordi- | naūces in maner | and fourme | folow- | yng. | (leaf ornament).

Colophon: Thomas Berthelet regius impressor | excudebat. Cum priuilegio. | [1543?] 28.3x19.8cm. xxiii-xxviiifol.

HENRY VIII: [Statutes and Ordinances, anno vi]. Anno regni regis Hen- | rici, viii, sexto, | The kynge our souerayne lorde Henry the. viii. | after the conquest, by the grace of God kynge of Englāde and of | Fraunce, & lorde of Irelande, at his p[er]liament holden at westm̄ | the. v. day of February, in ye. vi. yere of his most noble reigne, | to the honour of god & holy churche, and for the comon | weale and p[ro]fite of this his realme, by the assent | of the lordes spirituall and temporall, and | the cōmons in this present parliament | assembled, and by auctorytie of | the same: hath do to be orday- | ned, made, & enacted cer- | tayne statutes & ordi- | naūces in maner | and fourme | folow- | yng. | (leaf ornament).

Colophon: Thomas Berthelet regius impressor | excudebat. Cum priuilegio. | [1543?] 28.3x19.8cm. xxix–xlvfol.

HENRY VIII: [Statutes and Ordinances, anno vii]. Anno Septimo Hen- | rici octaui, | The kynge our souerayne lorde Henry the. viii. | after the conquest, by the grace of God kynge of Englāde and of | Fraunce, & lorde of Irelande, at his p[er]liament holden at westm̄ | ye. xii. day of Nouēbre, in ye. vii. yere of his most noble reigne, | to the honour of god & holy churche, and for the comon | weale and p[ro]fite of this his realme, by the assent | of the lordes spirituall and temporall, and | the cōmons in this present parliament | assembled, and by auctorytie of | the same: hath do to be orday- | ned, made, & enacted cer- | tayne statutes & ordi- | nauces in maner | and fourme | folow- | yng. | (leaf ornament).

Colophon: Londini in edibus Thome Bertheleti | regii impressoris excus. | [1543?]. | 28.3x19.8cm. xlvi–liiifol.

HENRY VIII: [Statutes and Ordinances: anno xiv–xv]. Anno, xiiii, et anno, xv, | Henrici octaui. | The kynge our souerayne lorde Henry the. viii. | after the conquest, by the grace of god kynge of Englande and | of Fraunce, defender of the faythe, and lorde of Irelande, at his | parliament holden at London the. xv. day of Apryll, in the. xiiii. | yere of his mooste noble reigne: And from thens adiourned to | westmyster the last day of July, the. xv. yere of his sayde reigne, | and there holden to the honour of almyghty god and of holy | churche: and for the weale and profyte of this his | realme, and by the assent of the lordes spirituall | and temporall, & the cōmons in this present | parlyament assembled, & by auctoritie | of the same: hath do to be orday | ned, made, & enacted cer- | tayne statutes & ordi- | naūces in maner | and fourme | folow- | yng. | (ornament).

Colophon: Thomas Berthelet regius impressor | excudebat. Cum priuilegio. | [1543?] 28.3x19.8cm. 15fol.
Camb.Univ.Cat. No. 517.

HENRY VIII: [Statutes and Ordinances: anno xxii]. Anno Vicesimo Se- | cundo Henrici | Octavi. | Statvta Bonvm | Pvblicvm Concer- | nentia, edita in perliamento tento a- | pud vvestm̄. xvi. die Ianuarii, Anno | regni præpotentissimi et metuendis- | simi Anglie et Francie regis, fidei de- | fensoris, et domini Hibernie, Henri- | ci octaui. xxii.

post diuersas proroga- | tiones eiusdem perliamēti primo in- | choati apud Londinum. iii. die Nouembris, Anno. xxi. e- | iusdē regis: et inde adiurnati et prorogati usq; ad Vvest- | monasteriū, et ibidem continuati per. xliiii. dies, Vi- | delicet usq́; ad. xvii. diem Decembris: et ab | eodem die et loco usq;. xxvi. diem A- | prilis proxi. sequentis: et ab eo | die usq; ad. xxii. diem Iunii, | et ab illo die ad primū | diem Octobris, | et a primo | die | Octobris usq́; ad. xxii. diē eiusdē mensis, et ab illo | die usq;. xvi. diē Ianuarii secundū legesterre | rite prorogati, et ibidē cōtinnuati p. lxxv. | dies, uidelicet ad ultimū diem Martii | eodē Anno. xxii. et inde ulte- | rius prorogati usq; ad. xiiii. | diem Octobris pro- | xime sequentis. | (device).

Colophon: Tho. Berthelet regius impressor excudebat. | Cum Privilegio. | [1543?] 28.3x19.8cm. 24 fol. Cambr.Univ.Cat. No. 519

HENRY VIII: [Statutes and Ordinances: anno xxiii]. Anno XXIII.H.VIII. | The kynge our soueraigne lorde | Henry the eight by the grace of god | kynge of Englande and of Fraunce | defender of the faythe and lorde of | Irelande at the session of his highe | Courte of parliament after diuerse | prorogations, holden at westmister | the. xv. day of January, in the. xxiii. | yere of his moste noble reigne to the | honour of almyghtye god and holy | churche, and for the common weale | and profitte of this his realme, by | the assente of the lordes spiritualle | and temporall, and the commons in | this presente parliament assembled, | and by auctoritie of the same, hath | ordeigned establisshed and en- | acted certayne good statu- | tes lawes and ordi- | nāces in maner | and fourme | folow- | ing. | (border).

Colophon: Imprinted at London in Fletestrete by | Thomas Berthelet printer to | the kynges most noble | grace. Cum pri- | uilegio. | (device). [1543?] 28.3x 19.8cm. 28fol. Cambr.Univ.Cat. No. 520–521.

HENRY VIII: [Statutes and Ordinances: anno xxiv]. Anno XXIIII | Henrici | VIII. | Actis made | in the Session of this present parlya- | mente, holden vppon prorogation at | Westmynster, the. IIII. daye of Fe- | bruarie, in the. XXIIII. yere of the | reygne of our moste dradde souerayne | lorde kynge Henry the. VIII. and there con | tinued and kepte tyll the. VII. day of Aprill | than nexte ensuinge: to the honour of god | and holy Church, and for the com- | mon weale and pro- | fyte of this his | realme. | (device).

Londini In Ædibvs Tho- | mæ Bertheleti Re- | gii Impressoris. | Cvm Privilegio A Re- | ge Indvlto. | [1543?] 28.3x19.8cm. 18fol.

HENRY VIII: [Statutes and Ordinances: anno xxvi]. Anno XXVI. | Henrici | VIII. | Actes Made In The | session of this presente parly- | ament holden vpon prorogation at | Westm̄, the. III. daye of Nouēbre, | in the. XXVI. yere of the reygne | of our mooste drad soueraigne lorde | kynge Henry the VIII, and | there continued and kepte tyll | the, XVIII, day of Decē- | ber nexte insuynge. | To the honor | of god, | and | for the cōmon weale and | profite of this | realme. |

Tho. Berthelet | Excvdebat. | Cum Privilegio. | [1543?] Border. 28.3x19.8cm. 26fol. Cambr.Univ.Cat. No. 523.

HENRY VIII: [Statutes and Ordinances: anno xxvii]. Anno XXVII. | Henrici | VIII. | Actes Made In The | session of this present parly- | ament holden vpon prorogation at | Westm̄, the. IIII. day of February, | in the. XXVII. yere of the reygne | of our moste drad soueraygne lorde | kynge Henry the. VIII. and | there contynued and kepte tyll | the. XIIII. day of Apryll | next ensuynge. To | the honour of | God, and | for the | common-weale and | profyte of this | realme. |

Tho. Berthelet | Excvdebat. | Cvm Privilegio. | [1543?]   Border.   28.3x19.8cm. 46fol.

HENRY VIII: [Statutes and Ordinances: anno xxviii]. Anno XXVIII. | Henrici | VIII. | Actes Made In The | parlyament begōne and hol- | den at Westm̄, the .VIII. daye of | June, in the .XXVIII. yere of the | reygne of our most drad soueraigne | lorde kynge Henry the .VIII. & | there contynued and kepte tyll the | dissolution of the same parliament | the .XVIII. of July, to the | honour of God, | and for | the | common wele and | profyte of this | realme. |

Tho. Berthelet | Excvdebat. | Cvm Privilegio. | [1543?]   Border.   28.3x19.8cm. 26fol. Cambr. Univ.Cat. No. 524

A NECES- | **SARY** Doctrine and eru- | dition for any chrysten | man, set furth by the | kynges maiestye of | Englande. &c. | . . . (8 lines).

Colophon: Imprinted at London in | Fletestrete by Thomas Berthelet, | printer to the kynges hyghnes, | the .XXIX daye of Maye, | the yere of our lorde. | M.D.XLIII. | Cvm priuilegio ad impri- | mendum solum. | 12.8x8.7cm.   (156)fol. (Engraved border, with date 1534). Also repr. in Formularies of Faith. Oxford: 1825. Pp. 213–377.
Known as "The Kings Book."

TURNER, William. The Huntyng and Fyndyng out of the Romish Fox: whiche more than seven yeares hath bene hyd among the Byshoppes of England, after that the Kynges Hyghnes, Henry VIII. had commanded hym to be dryven out of hys Realme. Written by Wyllyam Turner, Doctour of Physicke, and formerly Fellow of Pembroke College in Cambridge. . . . (2 lines).

Basyl: Imprynted in the Yeare 1543.
Reprint: Amended and Curtailed: with a short account of the author prefixed, by Robert Potts, M.A., Trinity College Cambridge. Cambridge: Reprinted in the year 1851, xvi, 5–40p. 8vo.

ZWINGLI, Huldreich. The Rekening and de- | claratiō of the faith and beleif of Huldrik | Zwingly, bischoppe of Züryk the cheif | town of Heluetia, sent to Charles .v. that | nowe is Emprowr of Rome: holdinge a | Perlemente or Cownsaill at Aus- | brough with the cheif Lordis & | lerned men of Germanye. | The yere of owr Lorde | M.D. xxx. In the | monethe of | Julye. | . . . (5 lines).

Translated & Imprynted at | Züryk in Marche Anno | Do. M.D.XLIII. | Border.   14.2x9.4cm.   (34) fol.

1544

BALE, John. (The brefe chronycle, etc. Beginning with fol. 11.) The great processe of Thomas | Arundell the Archbysshop of Caunter | burye and of the Papisticall clergye w̄ | him, agaynst the most noble knyght syr | Johan Oldcastell the lorde Cobham | in the yeare of oure Lorde a. M. cccc. | and viii. wherein is cōtayned his | examinacyon, impresonmēt, | and excommu- | nycacyon. |

<small>Colophon, fol. 56a: Thus endeth the brefe chronycle | cōcernynge the Examynacyon & death | of ye blessed martyr of Christ syr Johan | Oldcastell the lorde Cobham, not ca- | nonysed of the Pope, but in the precyou- | se bloude of his Lorde Jesus Christ. | Collected by Johan Bale, and im- | prynted anno Domini. 1544. | & .vi. die Augusti. |
13.4x8.9cm. Fol.11–56. Lacks fol. 1–10, 16–17. fol. 33 supplica.</small>

1545

BUCER, Martin. De Concilio, | Et Legitime Ivdicandis | Controversiis Religionis, | Criminvm, Qvæ in Mart. | Bucerum Ioh Cochlæus ad Illustrissimos Prin- | cipes clarissimos Ordines S. Ro. Imperij | per Germaniam, & quæ Ioh. Groppe- | rus ad Maiest. Imperatoriam per- | scripsit, Confutatio. | Epistola Io. Cochlæi Ad | eosdem Ordines, in Mart. Bucerum | . . . (6 lines). Per Martinvm Bvcervm. |

<small>Anno M.D.XLV. | Colophon: Argentorati. Ex Officina Kno- | blochiana, Per Georgivm Ma- | chæropœvm, Mense Avgv- | sto, Anno M.D.XLV. | 17.5x13,8cm. (80)fol.</small>

BUCER, Martin. Von den einigen rech- | ten wegē vnd mitlen Deutsche nation | inn Christlicher Religion zu vergleichen, Vnd was | darfür, vnd darwider auff den tagen zu Hag | naw, Worms vnd Regenspurg, An- | no 40 vnd 41, vnd seither für | genomen vnd gehan | delt worden ist. | Mit | Warhaffter Verantwortung auff | das offenbar falsch erdichtes anklagen, des | sich an die Kei. Maie^r. D. Johan. | Gropper, wider Mart. Bucerū | angemasset hat. | Durch Martin. Bucerum. | . . . (5 lines).

<small>An. M.D.XLV. | Colophon: Getruckt zu Strassburg, bey | Wendel Riheln. | 17.6x14cm. 117,(1)p.</small>

BUCER, Martin. Wider vffrichtung der | Messen, anderer Sacramenten | vnd Ceremonien, Vnd | des Papstumbs. | Martin Bucer. | . . . (8 lines).

<small>Gedruckt zu Strassburg, durch | Georgen Messerschmidt. | 1545. | 18.9x14.6cm. (1,26)fol.</small>

BUCER, Martin. Wie leicht vnnd füg, | lich Christliche vergleichung der | Religion, vnd des gantzen kirchendiensts Refo- | mation, dey unss Teutschen zu finden, | vnd in das werck zu brin- | gen. Wellche die fürnemistenn hinder- | nüssen dises wercks, vnnd wie die Christlich | hinzulegen. | Mit erbiettung, alles gründtlich | zu erweisen, vor der Keiserl. vnd Königl. Maiesteten, Churfürstenn, | Fürstenn vnnd

Stenden des Reichs, gegen den | Cölnischen Sophisten vnd me- | niglich. | Durch Martinum Bucerum. |

Anno M.D.XLV. | . . . (2 lines) Colophon: Gedruckt zu Straszburg bey | Crafft Müller. | Anno M.D.XLV. | 19x14.6cm. (1),cxlviii,(1)p.

GARDINER, Stephen. Stephani | VVinton. Episcopi An | gli, ad Martinum Bucerum de im- | pudenti eiusdem Pseudolo- | gia Conquestio. | Nunc primum in lucem ædita. | (device).

Coloniæ ex officina Melchioris Nouesiani. | Anno M.D.XLIV. | 20.1x14.6cm. (1,40)fol.

HERE begyn- | neth a booke, called the faule of | the Romyshe churche, wyth all | the abhominations, wherby | euerye man maye knowe | and perceaue the dy- | uersite of it betwene | ye primatiue chur- | che, of the whi- | che our so- | uerayne | Lorde | and | kynge is the supreme | head, and the ma- | lignant chur- | che, a sun- | der. |

n.imp. [1545. ?] 13.8x9cm. (23).fol
With contemporary MS. at end "Whether Christian Faith maie be kept secret in the soul without confession thereof openlie to the worlde" signed " John Hoper". [1553].23p

1546

BUCER, Martin. Ein warhaffter berich | te vom Colloquio zu Regenspurg, | diss Jars angefangen, vnnd vonn dem abzug | der Auditoren vnd Colloquenten, die von | Fürsten vnd Stenden der Augspur | gischen Confession dahin | verordnet waren. . . . (7 lines). Martin Bucer. |

M.D.XLVI. | Without printer's name. 19.6x14.cm. (1,7) fol.

BUCER, Martin. Ein warhaffter berich | te vom Colloquio zu Regenspurg, | dis jars angefangen, vnd von dem abzug | der Auditoren vnd Colloquenten, die | von Fürsten vnd Stenden der | Augspurgischen Confes | sion dahin verord | netwaren. . . . (6 lines). Martin Bucer. |

Anno 1546. | Without printer's name. 18.1x14.1cm. (1,7) fol.

CALVIN, John. A Faythful | and moost Godlye treatyse concer- | nynge the most sacret Sacrament of the bles- | sed body and bloude of oure sauioure Christe, | cōpiled by John Caluyne, a man of no lesse ler | nyng and literature, then Godlye studye, | and example of liuynge. And translated | into Latyne by Lacius a man of lyke | excellencie. And nowe laste of all, | translated into Englyshe by a | faythfull brother, no lesse | desirous to profyt the | weake brothers | then to exer- | cise the ta- | lent of | the Lorde to this honoure and glorre. | In declaration whereof, he hath | set before this litle booke an | Epistle to the reader much | more effectuous then in | the fyrst edicion. | Wherunto the order that the | Churche and congregation of | Christ in Denmarke doth | vse at the receiuinge | of Baptisme, the | Supper of ye | Lorde, and Wedlocke: | is added. | Myles Couerdale. | . . . (2 lines)

No imprint. [1546?] 13.5x9.1. 48 fol.

GARDINER, Stephen. A Decla | ration Of Svche | true articles as George | Ioye hath gone | about to con- | fute as | false. |

1546. | Decorated title page. Colophon: Imprinted at London in Al- | dersgate strete by Johannes | Herforde, at the costes | and charges of Ro- | bert Toye, dwel- | lyng in Paules | church yarde | at the sygne of the Bell. | Anno dñi. | 1546. | 14.2x9.2 cm. 180 fol.
Cambr.Univ.Cat.No.759. Introductory note signed.

GARDINER, Stephen. A Detec | tion Of The | Deuils Sophistrie, wher- | with he robbeth the vn- | learned people, of the | true byleef, in the | most blessed Sa- | crament of the aulter . | . . (3 lines) 1546. |

1546. Col: Prynted at London in Aldersgate | strete, by Jhon Herforde, at the | costes & charges of Roberte | Toye, dwellynge in | Paules churche | yarde, at the | sygne of | the Bell. | 1546. | 15.3x9.8cm.   .cxxxiii, (1)fol. Between fol. 32 and 33 are 4 folios in Greek type. Portr. laid in.
Cambr.Univ.Cat.761.

GARDINER, Stephen. Stephani VVin- | ton. Episcopi Angli. | ad Martinum Bucerum Epistola, qua cessantem | hactenus & cunctantem, ac frustratoria responsio- | nis pollicitatione, orbis de se iudicia callide | sustinentē, urget ad respondendum de im- | pudentissima eiusdem pseudologia | iustissimæ cōquestioni ante | annum æditæ. |

Ingolstadii Apvd | Alexandrum Vueissenhorn. | M.D.XLVI. | 19.7x14.8cm. (24) fol.

JOYE, George. The refuta- | tion of the byshop of Win- | chesters derke declaratiō | of his false articles, | once before con- | futed by | George Ioye. | Heare novve the tother parte, | and iudge truely of the | trueth. | For the veritie vvyll haue the | victorye. | M.D.XLVI. |

M.D.XLVI. | Orn. border. 15 x9.5 cm. (8),192.fol.

LUPSET, Thomas. Tho.Lup- | sets | workes. | (device).

Londini. | Anno.M.D.XLVI. | (Architectural Border; 1534)   13.5x9.7cm. 212 fol. Colophon: Londini in ædibus Thomæ | Bertheleti typis impress. | Cum priuilegio ad imprimen- | dum solum. | Anno. M.D.XLVI. |

The PRIMER | Set Fvrth | By the kinges maiestie & his | Clergie, to be taught lerued, and | red: & none other to be vsed | thorowout all his | Dominions. |

Imprinted at London within | the precinct of the late dissoluted house of the | graye Friers by Richard Grafton Printer | to the Princes grace, the xvii. | day of August, the yeare of | our lorde M,D.XLVI. | Cum priuilegio ad imprimendum solum. | Reprinted without any Alteration. | Border. 1710? 17.3x10.8cm (168)p. Portr.frontisp. of Henry VIII.

RETUR- | NA breuium. |
An.M.D.XLVI. | Engraved border. 13.4x8.8cm. (12)fol.

SMITH, Richard. The As- | sertion And De- | fence of the sacramente | of the aulter. | Compyled and made by mayster Ri- | chard Smythe doctour of diuinitie, | and reader of the kynges ma- | iesties lesson in his graces | vniuersitie of Oxforde, | dedicate vnto his | hyghnes, | beynge the excellent | and moost worthy defen- | dour of Christes | faythe. | . . . (2 lines).

1546. | Engr border. Col: Printed at London in Aldersgate | strete by John Herforde, at the | costes and charges of Ro- | berte Toye, dwellynge | in Paules church | yarde at the | synge | of the Bell. | 1546. | 16.x10.2cm.   (4),2-260fol.   B.L.

1547

A BRIFE And Fayth | full declaration of the true | fayth of Christ, made by certeyne | men susspected of heresye | in these articles | folowyng. | . . . (13 lines).

Anno M.D.xlvii. | Per me I. B. | 12.8x7.9 cm.   (16)fol.

BUCER, Martin. Das sich niemand zu | verwunderen habe, Auch nit vrsach, | kleinmütig vnd zag zu werden, ab der schweren trieb- | sal diser zeit, Vnd wa mit man sich dage- | gen trösten vnd stercken solle. | Ein Sendbrieue Martini Bu- | ceri, An ein Christliche angefochtene | Gemeinde Christi. | . . . (5 lines).

Anno M.D.XLVII. | 19.5x14.6cm.   (1,15)fol.

CERTAYNE | Sermons, or Home- | lies, appoynted by the kyn- | ges Maiestie, to be decla- | red and redde, by all per- | sones, Vicars, or Cu- | rates, euery Son- | daye in their | churches, | where | they haue | Cure. |

Anno. 1547. | Colophon: Imprinted at London, | the laste daie of Iulii, in the firste yere | of the reigne of our souereigne | lorde kyng Edvvard the VI: | By Rychard Grafton | printer to his moste | royall Ma- | iestie. | In the yere of our Lorde. | M.D.XLVII. | Cum priuilegio ad impri- | mendum solum. | 19.4x13.9 cm.   (91)fol. (Also Sermons | Or | Homilies | Appointed to be Read in Churches | in the Time of | Queen Elizabeth | of Famous Memory. | The first American Edition, from the last Oxford Edition. New York: 1815).

COVERDALE, Miles. A christē ex- | hortacion vnto | customable swea- | rers. | What a righte & lawfull | othe is: whan, and before | whom, it ought to be. | Item. The maner of say- | ing grace, or geuyng thā- | kes vnto God. | Whosoeuer heareth God- | des worde, beleue it, and | do thereafter, shall | be saued. |

Engr. border, with printer's initials: N.H. Colophon: Imprinted at London by Nicholas | Hyll, for Richarde Kele. | [1547].   12.4x7.9cm.   35fol.
Anon. Cambr.Univ.Cat. 6706.

GILBY, Anthony. An ansvver | to the deuillish detection of Stephane Gar | diner, Bishoppe of Wynchester, pub- | lished to the intent that such as be de- | sirous of the truth should not be | seduced by hys errours, | nor the blind & obsti- | nate excused by | ignorance. | Compiled by A.G. | . . . (9 lines).

Anno.1547. the,24. | of January. | (2 lines).   14.1x9.5cm.   211,(6)fol.
Cambr.Univ.Cat.775

INIVNCCI- | ONS geuē by the moste ex- | cellent prince, Edward the | sixte, by the grace of God, | kyng of England, Fraūce | and Irelande: defendor of | the Faythe, and in earthe | vnder Christ, of the chur- | che of Englande and of | Ireland the supreme | hedde: To all and | singuler his lo- | uying subiec- | tes, aswell | of the | Clergie, as of the | Laietie. |

Engr. border. Colophon: Imprinted At London, The | Laste Daie Of Ivlii, In The | First Yere Of The Reigne | Of Ovr Sovereigne Lord | Kyng Edvvard The .VI. | By Richard Grafton | Printer To His | Moste Royall | Maiestie. | Anno. 1547. | Cum priuilegio ad impri- | mendum solum. | 17x13 cm. (14)fol.
Reprinted in Sparrow's Collection of Articles: 1661, 1675, and 1684.

The | ORDER | Of The | Communion. | (royal arms)

Imprinted at London by Richard | Grafton, 1547. | Border. 19.4x15.4cm. Pp. 13-24 of Sparrow's Collection, 1661.
Also in his Collection: 1675 and 1684.

The ORDER Of | The Communion. | With the Kings Majesties Proclamation. |

Imprinted at London, by Richard Grafton, | 1547. | 18.7x14.7 cm. 11,(1)p.
See INJUNCTION: 1547. (Reprinted in Sparrow's Collection of Articles: 1661, 1675, 1684.)

SMITH, Richard. A brief trea- | tyse settynge forth diuers | truthes necessary both to be be- | leued of chrysten people, & kepte | also, whiche are not expressed in | the scripture but left to ye church | by the apostles traditiō. Made | by Rychard Smyth doctour of | diuinitie, & reader of it ī Oxford. | . . . (10 lines)

Esaye viii. M.D.xlvii. | Cū priuilegio ad imprimendū folū. | Colophon: Imprinted at Lōdon in pau- | les churche yearde, at the sygne | of the maydēs hed, by Tho- | mas petit. M.D.XLvii. | 12.8x8.7 cm. (27 , 313)p.

1548

An ACTE against suche persons as shal vnre- | uerently speake against the Sacramente of the bodie | and bloude of Christe, cōmunely called ye Sacramēt of ye | Aulter: & for ye receiuing therof vnder both kindes. |

(1548) Edward VI [Statutes] An.i,fol.ii.

An ACTE for the election of Bishoppes, and what Seales and | stile they, and other Spiritual persōs exercising | iurisdiction Ecclesiastical that vse. | The ij. Chapiter. |

(1548) Edward VI. [Statutes] An.i,fol iib.

An ACTE for the vniformitie of Seruice, and ad- | mistration of the Sacramentes, | throughout the Realme. | (1548)

26.2x18.3cm. fol.2-4a. of Edward VI. [Statutes], Ann.2. Chapter I.

An ACTE wherby certeine Chaunteries, Colleges, free | Chappelles, and the possessions of the same, be | geuen to ye kinges Maiestie. | (1547).

(1548) Edward VI [Statutes] An.i,fol.xxv b.

The ANSWERE | that the Preachers of | the Gospel at Basile, made, for the | defence of the true administration, and vse | of the holy Supper of our Lord. Aga- | ynst the abhominatiō, of the Po- | pyshe Masse. Translated out | of Latin into Englyshe by | George Bancrafte. | 1548. |

Imprinted | at London by Jhon Day and | William Seres, dwellyng in Se- | pulchres Parish at the signe of | the Resurrectiō a little aboue | Holbourne Conduite. | Cum gratia & priuilegio | adimprimendum solum. | [1548] 13.7x8.7cm.(52)fol.

ARTI- | CLES | To Be | Inqvi- | red | Of. | 1548. |

Engraved border Colophon: Imprinted In London | the laste daie of August. M.D.xlviii. in | the second yere of the reigne of our | moste drad & souereigne lorde | Kyng Edvvarde the : VI: | By Richard Grafton | Printer to his | highnes: | Cum priuilegio ad imprimendum solum. | 19.3x13.1 cm. (16)p.
Reprinted in Sparrow's Collection of Articles: 1661, 1675 and 1684

BALE, John. A brefe Chronycle concerning | the examination and death of the Blessed | martir of Christ, Sir John Oldeca- | stell the Lord Cobham, collected | together by Johan | Bale. | (cut). . . . (4 lines).

(Back of t.p.): Imprinted | at London by Anthony Scoloker, | And Wyllyā Seres Dwel- | ling wythout Alders- | gate. | Cum Gratia et priuilegio ad Imprimendū | solum. | [1548?] 12.2x8.5cm. (10,46)fol. A1–G8 unp.

BARNES, Robert. The supplica- | tion of doctour Barnes | vnto the moost gracy- | ous kynge Henrye | the eyght with | the declara- | tion of his | articles | condē- | ned | for heresy by the | byshops. |

No imprint. [1548?] Border. Colophon: Imprinted at London in | Poules churchyard at | the signe of S. | Augustyne | by Hugh | Syngelton | Cum preuilegio, ad imprimen | dum solum | (Device) 13.2x9.1cm. (1,40,155)fol.
Not earlier than 1548.

BUCER, Martin. Gratvla- | tio Martini Bvceri Ad Ec- | clesiam Anglicanam, de Religionis | Christi restitutione: | Et, | Responsio Eivsdem | Ad Dvas Stephani Episcopi | Vintoniensis Angli cōuiciatrices Epistolas, | De cœlibatu sacerdotum & cœnobitarū: in | qua demonstratur, S. coniugij abstinentiam | contra Dei & Ecclesiæ leges exigi ab omni- | bus ad sacerdotium & admissis, | & admittendis. | . . . (4 lines).

1548. | 18.9x14.5cm. 84 p.

BULLINGER, Henry, and CALVIN, John. Two Epy- | stles, one of Henry bullynger, wyth the con- | sent of all the learned men of the Churche of | Tygury: another of Johan Caluyne, chefe | Preacher of the church of Geneue: whether | it be laufull for a chrysten man to com | municate or be partaker of the masse | of the papysts, without offendīg | God and hys neyghbour | or not. | . . . (4 lines)

Imprinted | At London by Robert Stoughton. | Dwellynge within Ludgate, | at the sygne of the Bis- | shoppes Mi- | ter. | Anno. 1548. | 12.3x8.3cm. (15)fol.

CRANMER, Thomas. A | Short Instruction | Into | Christian Religion, | Being | A Catechism | Set Forth By | Archbishop Cranmer |

in MDXLVIII: | Together With | The Same In Latin, | Translated from the German by | Justus Jonas | In MDXXXIX. |

Oxford, | At The University Press. | MDCCCXXIX. | 26.1x15.7cm. xxxv,214, (4); 182p.

Facsimile of t.p. of original: Catechismvs, | That is to say, | a shorte Instruction | into Christian Reli- | gion for the synguler | commoditie and profyte of | childrē and yong people.Set | forth by the mooste reuerende | father in God Thomas Arch | byshop of Canterbury,Pri- | mate of all England and | Metropolitane. |

Gualterus Lynne | excudebat. | 1548. | Engr.border.

EDWARD VI. [Statutes] Anno Primo Edvvar- | di Sexti. | Statvtes | made in the Parlamente be- | gon at Westminster the fowerthe daye | of Nouember, in the firste yeare of the | reigne of our most dreade Soueraine | lorde Edward the VI. By the Grace | of God, Kinge of Englande, Fraunce, | and Irelande, defendour of the faithe, | and of the Churche of Englande, and | also of Irelande in earthe the supreme | hed: and from thence continued to the | xxiiii daye of Decembre then next en- | suyng, that is to saye in the first | Session of the same Par- | lamente, as fo- | loweth. |

Colophon: Excusum Londini in ædibus Richardi Graftoni | Regii Impressoris. | Anno.M.D.xlviii. | Cum priuilegio ad imprimendum solum. | 26.2x18.3cm. 38fol. Fol. i supplied.

Camb Univ Cat. No. 610.

ERASMUS, Desiderius. The first tome or vo- | lume of the Paraphrase of | Erasmus vpon the newe | testamente. |

Enpriented at London in Flete- | strete at the signe of the sunne by | Edwarde Whitchurche the | last daie of Januarie, | Anno Domini. | 1548. | Engraved border. 27.2x19.2cm. (20),cvii; (8)xciiii;(14),lxxxix; xc–cxciiii; (8),cxiiii;(2)lxxxvii,(1) fol. (Bound in two volumes).

FRITH, John. A boke ma- | de by John Fryth prysoner in | the Tower of London, answerynge vnto | M. Mores letter, which he wrote agaynst | the fyrste lytle treatyse that John Fryth | made, concernynge the Sacramente of the | body and bloude of Christ: vnto which boke | are added in the ende the artycles of his exa- | mynacyon before the Byshoppes of Lon- | don, Wynchester and Lyncolne, in Paules | churche at London, for whych John Fryth | was condemned, and after brente in Smyth | felde wythout Newgate, the fourth | daye of July, Anno M.D. | xxxiij. |

Newly corrected and prynted after the | fyrst coppe, by Rychard Jugge, dwellynge | in Powles Church yarde, at the synge of the | Byble. | Deade men shall ryse agayne. |

Colophon: Jmprynted in the yare of oure | Lorde. M.D.XLviij. | 14.2x9cm. 108fol.

GEST, Edmund. A Treatise a- | gainste the preuee Masse | in the behalfe and furtheraunce | of the mooste hylye com- | munyon, made by | Edmund | Gest | Reade gentyll reader and | then iudge. | M.D.XLVIII | Cum Priuilegio ad Imprimendum | Solum. |

Imprinted | at Londō in saynt Andrewes Pa- | ryshe, In the Waredrop. By | Thomas Raynald: | 13.3x9.cm. (90) fol.

HERMAN V of Wied. A simple, and | Religious consultatiō of vs Her- | mā by the grace of God Archbishop of Co- | lone, and prince Electoure. &c. by what mea- | nes a Christian reformation, and founded in | Gods worde. Of doctrine, Administratiō of | deuine Sacramentes, Of Ceremonies, & the | whole cure of soules, and other ecclesiasticall | ministeries, may be begon among men com- | mitted to our pastorall charge, vntil the lord | graunte a better to be appoynted, either by a | free, and christian counsaile, generall or | national, or else by the states of the | Empire of the nation of Ger- | many, gathered together in | the holye Gost. Perused | by the translator ther- | of and amended in | many places. | 1548. |

Imprinted at London by Jhon Daye and | William Seres, dwellynge in Sepul- | chres paryshe at the singe of the | Resurrection, alytle aboue | Holbourne Conduit. | . . . (2 lines). 13.8x9.4cm. 292,(8)fol. Folioed to 288; cut on fol. 1b, and at end.

HOOPER, John. A Declaration | of the ten holy cōmaunde | mentes of allmygthye God, wrō- | ten Exo.20. Deu.5. Collectyd | out of the scripture Ca- | nonicall by Joan- | ne Hopper. | Cum, and se: Joan.1. |

Anno M.D.XLVIII. | 14.5x9.4cm. (20),234p.

HORTENSIUS, Lambertus. Tvmvltvvm | Anabaptistarvm Liber | Vnvs, Avtore. D. Lamberto | Hortensio Montfortio, Ludimode- | ratore Scholæ Nerdenæ. | Consulibus & inclito Senatui nobilissimi | Emporij Amstelredamensis. | . . . (2 lines).

Basileæ, | 1548. | 20.7x15.cm. 84,(2)p. Colophon: Basileæ, Per Ioan- | nem Oporinum, anno Salutis humanæ | MDXLVIII, Men- | se Septembri. |
Also in 1624, 1694, & French 1695 " Histoire des Anabaptistes."

LAMBERT, François. The | Minde and Judgement of maister | Frances Lambert of Auenna of the wyll of | Man declarynge and prouynge howe and af | ter what sorte it is captyue and bounde, and | not free. taken out of hys commentaries vpon | Osee the Prophete. Wherin vpō the .iiii. | Chapter of the said prophet, he most | Godly playnlye and learnedly | entreateth and writeth of | the same, as hereafter | euidētly shall | appere. | Newelie trāslated out of Englishe by N. L. | . . . (2 lines)

Anno Dom. MDXLVIII. | the xviij. day of Decēbre. | (Colophon.): Imprinted | at London, by John Day, | and William Seres, dwellynge | in Sepulchres parish, at the | signe of the Resurrecti- | on, a litle aboue Hol- | bourne conduite. | Cum gratia & priuelegio | ad imprimendum solum. | 13x9 cm. 74 fol.

NICHOLS, Philip. Here begyn | neth a god- | ly newe story of .xii. men that moy- | ses (by the Cōmaundement of god) | sent to spye owt the land of canaan: | of whiche .xii. onely Josua and Ca- | leb, wer found faythful messengers. | . . . (9 lines).

Colophon: Imprented At London | the Tenthe daye Of Maye: | Anno dominice incarua- | tionis M D XLViii. | By william hill remaynyng at the | Signe of the hill in Pau- | les Churche Yarde: and | be there by him | to be solde. | 13.3x8.8cm. (5,46)fol.
Epistle to the reader, signed Phillyp Nycolls. Camb.Univ.Cat:1029.

RHEGIUS, Urbanus. A declara- | ration of the twelue arti- | cles of the christen faythe with anno- | tations of the holy scripture, where | they be grounded in. And the righte | foundation and princip all comon pla- | ces of the hole godly scripture, a good | ly short declaration, to all Christians | profitable and necessarye for to come | to the right vnderstondynge of | holy Scripture compy- | led for the com- | modite of | al chil- | sten | people. By D. | Urbanum | Regi- | um. | (device)

No imprint. Colophon: Imprinted for Gwalter | Lynne, dwellyng vpon So- | mers kaye, by Byllinges | gate. In the yeare of oure | Lorde. M.D.XLVIII. | And they by to be solde at | Poules churche yarde | at the North doore, In | the signe of the By- | bell. By Richard | Jugge. | (device) . . . 3 lines. 13.5x9.1 cm. (6, 112) fol.

TYNDALE, William. A Briefe de- | claration of the sacraments, expressing | the fyrst oryginall how they came | up, ād were institute with the | true and mooste syncere | meaning and vnder- | standyng of the | same very | necessa- | rye | for all men, that | wyl not erre in the true | use and receauing therof. | Compyled by the godly | learned man Wyl- | lyam Tyndall. |

Imprinted | At London by Robert Stoughton. | Dwellynge within Ludgate, | at the sygne of the Bis- | shoppes Mi- | ter. | [1548?] 13.6x9.2 cm. (1,39)fol.

TYNDALE, William. The parable | Of the wycked mammon | taken out of the .xvi. Ca. | of Luke with an expo | sicyon thervpon la- | tely corrected & | prynted. | Luce .xvi | Facite vobis amicos de | mammon iniquitatis |

Engraved border. Colophon: Iprynted at London at the sygne | of the hill by Wyllyam hill | The .xv. day of september [1548]. 17.8x12cm (4),lii,(4)fol.
Anon. Cambr.Univ.Cat. 1033.

1549

ARTICLES to be enquired of, in the visitations to be had within the Dio- | cesse of Canterbury: in the second year of the Reign of our | Dread Soveraign Lord Edward the 6. by the grace of God, King | of England, France, and Ireland defender of the Faith, and in | earth of the Church of England and also of Ireland the supreme | head. |

Repr. in Sparrow's Collection: 1661: 19.4x15.4cm. Pp. 25–31. Also in his Collections, 1675 and 1684.

ERASMUS, Desiderius. The second tome | or volume of the Paraphrase of | Erasmus vpon the newe testament: contey- | nyng the Epistles of S.Paul, and other the | Apostles. Wherunto is added a Para- | phrase vpon the Reuelacion | of S.John. |

Imprinted at London in Flete- | strete at the signe of the Sunne by | Edwarde Whitchurche, the | xvi. daye of August. | Cum priuilegio ad imprimen- | dum solum. | Anno do. 1549. | Engraved border. 26.8x19.2cm. (16),xliiii; xliiii; xliii-lxiiii;xxi; (6),xv;x; x; xi;xxvi;xxxi,xxxi–xxxiii; xxvii;(2),xl,(1)fol.

PONET, John. A Defence | For Mariage Of | Priestes, by Scrip- | ture and aunciente | Wryters. | Made by Johñ Po- | net, Doctoure of | Diuinitie. | . . . (8 lines).

Imprinted at London, by Reynold Wolff. | Cum Sereniss.Regis priuilegio. | Architectural border. Colophon: Imprinted at London in the | house of Reynolde | Wolfe. | Anno Domini | M.D.XLIX. | 13.8x9.5cm   (1,45)fol.

VERMIGLI, Pietro Martire.   Tractatio | De Sacramento Ev- | charistiæ, habita in celeberrima vni- | uersitate Oxoniensi in Anglia, per | D.Petrvm Martyrem | Vermilivm Floren- | tinum, Regium ibidem | Theologiæ professorem, cum | iam absoluisset interpre- | tationem.II capi- | tis prioris | epistolæ D.Pauli Apostoli | ad Corinthios. | Ad Hec. | Disputatio de eodē | Evcharistiæ Sa- | cramento, in eadem Vniuersitate | habita per eundem D.P.Mar. | Anno Domini | M.D.XLIX. |

Londini, ad æneum serpentem. | (1549).   18.x13.7cm.   (10),67, (4),96 fol. Sub t.p.

1550

ARTICLES | to be enquired of | In The | Visitation | Of The | Dioces of London, | By the reverend Father in God, | Nicholas Bishop of London, | In the fourth year of our Soveraign Lord King Edward the 6. | by the Grace of God King of England France and Ireland | defender of the faith, and in earth, of the Church of En- | gland and also of Ireland, the supreme head, next and im- | mediately under our Saviour Christ. | (royal arms)

Imprinted at London by Reynold | Wolfe. M.DL. | Border. 19.5x15.2cm. Pp. 31-35 of Sparrow's Collection: 1661. Also in his reprints of 1675 and 1684.

BALE, John.   The Apology | of Johan Bale agaynste | a ranke Papyst, aunswering both | hym and hys doctours, that neyther their | vowes nor yet their priesthode are of the | Gospell, but of Antichrist. Anno. | Do. M.CCCCC.L. | A brefe exposycyon also vpō the .xxx | Chaptre of Numeri, which was the first occasion of thys | present varyaunce. | Cum Priuilegio ad imprimen- | dum solum. | . . .   10 lines

Colophon: Imprinted | at London by Ihon | Day, dwelling ouer Al- | dersgate. These bokes are | to be sold at his shop, by | the lytle Conduit | in Chepe | syde. | . . . 2 lines. (Last page: A dyspatche of vowes | and presthode, by the wurd | of God. Compyled by | Johan Bale. | 13.8x8.8 cm. fol, clvi, (3).

BALE, John.   The Image | Of both churches | after the moste wonderful and heauen- | ly Reuelacion of Sainct John the Euā- | gelist, contayning a very frutefull expo | sicion or paraphrase vpon the same, | Wherin it is conferred with the | other scripturs, and most auc | torised historyes. Compi- | led by John Bale an | exile also in this life | for the faythfull | testimonies of | Jesu. | (cut)

Colophon: Imprinted at | London by Jhon Daye, dwel- | linge at Aldersgate, and William Se- | res, dwellinge in Peter Colledge | These bokes are too be sold | at the new shop by the li- | tle Conduite in | Chepeside. | Three parts. [1550]. 13.5x9.2cm. (14,138;5,143; 3,133)fol.
Also another copy, lacking first t.p., and with same pagination, but different Colophon: Imprynted at London by | Richarde Jugge, dwelling | in Paules churche | yarde, at the sygne | of the Byble. | 13.5x8.6cm. (12,138;5,143;3,133) fol. Colophon at the end of each part.

CHAUNCY, Maurice. Historia | Aliqvot Nostri Saecv | li Martyrum cum pia, tum lectu iucunda, nun- | quám antehac typis excusa. | . . . (device; 7 lines; device).

Anno | M.D.L. | Colophon: Moguntiæ apud S.Victorem excudebat | Franciscus Behem. Anno | M.D.L. | 18.2x13.cm. (8),LXV,(3)fol.
Anon. Gillow,I:482.

CRANMER, Thomas. A Defence | Of The Trve And Ca- | tholike doctrine of the sacra- | ment of the body and bloud | of our sauiour Christ, with | a confutation of sundry errors | concernyng thesame, groun- | ded and stablished vpon God- | des holy woorde, & approued | by ye consent of the mosteaun- | cient doctors of the Churche. | Made by the moste Reuerende | father in God | Thomas Archebyshop | of Canterbury, Primate of all | Englande | and Metropolitane. |

Engr.border. Colophon: (Device) Imprinted at London in Poules | churcheyarde, at the signe of the Bra- | sen serpent, by Reynold Wolfe. | Cum priuilegio ad imprimen- | dum solum. | Anno Domini. M.D.L. | 19.1x13.5cm. (4),117,(3) fol.

CURIO, Cœlius Secundus. Pasquine in a Traunce | A Christian and learned Dia- | logue (contayning wonderfull and | most strange newes out of Heauen, | Purgatorie, and Hell) Wherein besydes | Christes truth playnely set forth, | ye shall also finde a numbre of | pleasaunt hystories, | discouering all the crafty conueyaunces | of Antechrist. | Whereunto are added certayne Questions | then put forth by Pasquine, to haue bene dis- | puted in the Councell of Trent. | Turned but lately out of the Italian | into this tongue, by | W.P. | Seene allowed according to the order appointed | in the Queenes Maiesties Iniunctions. | . . . (3 lines).

Imprinted at London by VVyl- | liam Seres dwelling at | the Weast ende of Paules | at the signe of the | Hedgehogge. | [1550?]. 17.7x13.3cm. (6),112 fol.
Anon.B.M.Cat.

HOOPER, John. A godly Con | fession and Protestacion | of the christian fayth, made and | set furth by Ihon Hooper, wher- | in is declared what a christiã | manne is bound to beleue of | God, hys King, his nei- | bour, and hymselfe. | . . . (4 lines).

No impr. Architectural border Colophon: Imprinted at London | by Ihon Daye dwellyng ouer | Aldersgate beneth saynt | Martyns, and are to | be solde at his shop | by the litle coun | duit in Chepe | syde. | Cum priuilegio ad imprimendum solum | Per septennium. | (1550). 18.6x13.7 cm. (7,52)p.
Dated on last page: The .xx. of Decembre | Anno M.D. and fiftie |

JOYE, George. The Exposycion | of Daniel the Prophete, gathe- | red out of Philip Melancthon, | Johan Ecolãpadius, Chonrade | Pellicane, & out of Johan Dra- | conite. &c. By George Joye. | A Prophecye diligentely | to be noted of al Em- | perours & Kinges, | in these laste | dayes. | . . . (12 lines).

No imps. Engr. border. Colophon: M.D.L. | Imprinted at London in Paules | Church yearde, at the signe of | the Starre, By Thomas | Raynalde. | 13.3x9.1cm. (244)fol.

SMITH, Richard. Defensio sacri Episcoporū | & sacerdotum Cœlibatus, contra impias & | indoctas Petri Martyris Vermelij nugas, & | calumnias, quas ille Oxoniæ in Anglia, duo- | bus retro annis in sacerdotaliū nuptiarum as- | serticnem temerè effutiuit. | Per Ricardum Smythœum Anglum, olim diu Oxoniæ in | Anglia, nunc verò Lutetiæ Parisiorum Theologiam | profitentem. | Eiusdem de votis monasticis cōtra eundem Martyrem, | ac eius furfuris alios, breuis libellus Vterque nūc denuo | prodit tersius & emaculatius, non sine haud pœnitēda ac- | cessione, & locupletatione, ac succincta libelli cuiusdā Io- | annis Poneti Angli refutatione. Quibus accessit index re | rum, quæ maximè visæ erant annotatione dignæ. |

Lvtetiae Parisiorvm. | Ex officina Reginaldi Calderij, | & Claudij eius filij. | 1550. | 14.1x9.1 cm. 80fol.

WYCLIFFE, John. The true copye | of a Prolog wrytten about two C. | yeres paste by John Wycklife (as maye | iustly be gatherid bi that, that John Bale | hath writtē of him in his boke entitlid the | Summarie of famouse writers of the Ile | of great Britā) the Originall whereof | is founde written in an olde English | Bible bitwixt the olde Testament | and the Newe. Whych Bible | remaynith now in ye Kyng | hys maiesties | Chamber. |

Imprinted at London by Ro- | bert Crowley dwellynge in Elie | rents in Dolburn. Anno Do. | M D L. | Cum priuilegio ad impri- | mendum solum. | 14.1x 9.2cm. (2,128)fol. Portr. on back of t.p. Only 2 leaves before Sig.B1.

ZWINGLI, Huldreich. The ymage | of bothe Pastoures, | sette forth by that mooste | famouse Clerck, Huldryck zwin- | glius, & now trāslated out of La- | tin into Englishe, By John Ve- | ron Sinonoys. A most fruite- | full & necessary Boke, to be | had & redde in all Chur- | ches, ther wyth to en- | arme all symple & | ignorant fole- | kes, agaynst | the raue- | ninge wolues and false | prophetes. |

M. D. L. | Cum Priuilegio ad Imprimendum | Solum. | Orn. border. 13.2x8.8cm. (23,172) p.

1551

BULLINGER, Henry. Absolv- | ta De Christi | Domini Et Catholicæ | eius Ecclesiæ Sacramentis, tracta- | tio, Autore Henrico | Bullengero. | Cui adiecta est eiusdem argumenti | Epistola, per Ioannem à Lasco, | Baronem Poloniæ ante quinquennium | scripta. | Accessit rerum ac uerborum copio- | sus index. | . . . (3 lines)

Londini Excvdebat | Stephanus Myerdmannus: | An. 1551. Men. Apri. | Cum Priuilegio ad imprimendum solum. | 13.8x8.4 cm. (12),123.fol.

CRANMER, Thomas. An Answer | Of The Most Reverend Fa- | ther in God Thomas Archebyshop Of | Canterburye, Primate of all Englande and | Metropolitane | Vnto | A crafty and sophisticall cauillation deuised by Ste- | phen Gardiner doctour of law, late byshop of Win- | chester, agaynst the trewe and godly doctrine of the moste | holy Sacrament of the body and bloud of our Sa- | uiour Iesv Christe. | Wherin is also, as occasion serueth, answered such places of the | booke of D. Rich. Smyth, as may seeme any | thyng woorthy the aunswer- yng. | Item | Ye shall fynde here also the true copye of the booke written, | and in open courte delyuered, by D. Stephen Gardiner, | not one woorde added or diminished, but fayth- | fully in all poyntes agree- yng with | the Oryginall. | . . . (device; 5 lines; device).

<small>Anno | M.D.LI. | Imprinted at London by Reynolde Wolfe, with the | Kyng his moste gracious priuilege. | And licenced according to the meaninge of | the late Proclamation. | Colophon: Imprinted at London in Paules churchyarde | at the signe of the brasen Serpent | by Reynolde Wolfe. | Cum priuilegio ad imprimen- dum | solum. | 25.9x18 cm. (8),459,(1)p.</small>

GARDINER, Stephen. An explicatiō | and assertion of the true Ca- | tholique fayth, touching the moost blessed | Sacrament of the aulter with confuta- | cion of a booke written agaynst the | same. Made by Steuen Byshop | of Wynchester, and exhibi- | ted by his owne hande | for his defence | to the Kynges maiesties Commis- | sioners at Lambeth. |

<small>Anno.1551. | 14.4x9.8cm. Fol.1–152. T.p. supplied; lacks errata and Preface.</small>

GILBY, Anthony. A Commen- | tarye vpon the | Prophet Mycha. | Wrytten by Anto- | ny Gilby. |

<small>Anno Domi. M. | D.LI. | Colophon: Imprinted at | London by Ihon Daye, dwel- | ling ouer Aldersgate | beneth Saint | Martins. | These bokes are to bee soulde | at hys shop in Schepesyde, | by the Litle Counduit | at the sygne of the | Resurreccion. | Cum priuilegio ad imprimendum | solum. Perseptēnium. | 13.x9.1 cm. (110)fol.</small>

1552

An ACT for the confirmacion of the | Subsidie of the Clergie. |
<small>(1552) Edward VI [Statutes] An.ii–iii,fol.xli b.</small>

An ACT for the qualifying of the | statute of Recusantes. |
<small>(1552) Edward VI. [Statutes] An.ii–iii, fol xxxii b.</small>

An ACT for the true payment of Tythes. |
<small>(1552). Edward VI. [Statutes]. An.ii–iii, fol xxi.</small>

An ACT to take away all positiue Lawes, made | against the mariage of Priestes. |
<small>(1552) Edward VI. [Statutes] An.ii–iii,fol xxxii b.</small>

An ACTE againste | Usurye. |
<small>(1552) Edward VI [Statutes] An.v–vi, fol.xxviii b.</small>

An ACTE, for the declaracion of a statute, made for the mari- | age of priestes, and for the legitimacion | of theyr children. |
<small>(1552) Edward VI [Statutes] An.v–vi, fol.xx.</small>

An ACTE for the declaration of a statute, made | in the .xxi. yere of Kyng Henry the eyght, | touching religious persons. |
<small>(1552) Edward VI [Statutes] An.v–vi. fol.xxi.</small>

An ACTE, for the keping of holy dayes, | and fasting daies. |
(1552) Edward VI [Statutes] An.v–vi. fol.iv b.

An ACTE for the vniformitie of | common praier, and administra- | tion of the Sacra- | mentes. |
(1552) Edward VI. [Statutes] An.v–vi, fol.ii.

An ACTE for the vniformitie of Seruice, and ad- | ministration of the Sacramentes, | throughout the Realme. |
(1552) Edward VI. [Statutes] An.ii–iii, fol.ii.

EDWARD VI. [Statutes] Anno ii–iii. Anno Secvndo | Et Tertio Edovardi | Sexti. | Actes | made in the Session of this | present Parlament, holden vppon pro- | rogation at Westminster, the fourthe | daye of Nouember, in the seconde yeare | of our moste dread souereigne Lorde, | Edwarde the .VI. by the grace of God, | Kynge of Englande, Fraunce, and Ire- | lande, defendoure of the faythe, and of | the Churche of Englande, and also of | Irelande, in earthe the supreme heade: | and there continued and kepte to | the xiiii. daye of Marche, in | the .III. yere of our said | souereigne Lorde, | as foloweth. |
With "King in council" compartment. Colophon: Richardvs Graftonvs | Typographus Regius excudebat. | Anno domini. 1552. | Cum priuilegio ad im-primen- | dum solum. | 26.3x18.5 cm. lxviiifol.

EDWARD VI. [Statutes] Anno v–vi. Anno Qvinto Et | Sexto Edvardi | Sexti. | Actes | made in the Session of this | presēt parlamente, holden vpon proro- | gacion at Westminster, the .xxiii. daye | of Januarye, in the fyueth yeare of the | reygne of our most dradde souereygne | Lorde, Edwarde the .VI. by the grace | of God, kynge of Englande, Fraunce, | and Irelande, defendour of the fayth, | and of the Churche of Englande and | Ireland, in earthe the supreme heade: | and there continued and kepte tyll | the .xv. daye of Apryll, in the | vi. yeare of the reygne of | our saied souereigne | Lorde, as fo- | loweth. |
With "King in council" compartment. Colophon: Richardvs Graftonvs | typographus Regius excudebat | Mense Iunii. | Anno. M.D.LII. | Cum priuilegio ad imprimendum solum. | 26.3x18.5 cm. xxxiiifol.

GARDINER, Stephen. Confvta- | tio Cavilla- | tionvm, Qvibvs Sa- | crosanctvm Evcharistiæ Sacra- | mentum, ab impiis Capernaitis, | impeti solet, Authore Mar- | co Antonio Constan- | tio, Theologo Lo- | uaniensi. |
Parisiis, | Apud Ioannem de Roigny, in via Iacobea sub insi- | gni quatuor elementorum. | 1552. | Cum priuilegio Regis. | 20.8 x 14.7 cm. (4),224,(2)fol.
BMCat DNB. 20:425 a

HAMILTON, John. The Catechisme, | That is to say, ane comōne and catholik | instructioun of the christin people in ma- | teris of our catholik faith and religioun, | quhilk na gud christin man or woman | suld misknaw: set furth be ye maist reue- | rend father in God Johne Archbischop | of sanct Androus Legatnait and primat | of ye kirk of

Scotland, in his prouincial | counsale haldin at Edinburgh the xxvi. |
day of Januarie, the zeir of our Lord | 1551, with the aduise and
counsale of | the bischoippis and vthir pralatis | with doctours of
Theologie and | Canon law of the said realme | of Scotland present
for | the tyme. | . . . (8 lines).

No imprint. Colophon: Prentit at sanct Androus be the command and | expensis of the maist reuerend father in God Johne | Archbischop of sanct Androus, and primat of ye | hail kirk of Scotland, the xxix. day of Au- | gust the zeir of our Lord m.d.lii. |
Reprint by Prof.Mitchell: Edinburgh,1882. Contains also " The Two-Penny Faith: 1559. 8vo. xxxiip,(13),ccv,(8)fol.

1553

An ACTE against fonde and Phantasti- | call Prophecies. |
(1553) Edward VI [Statutes] An.iii–iv, fol.xvii b.

An ACTE for the abolishing and putting awaie | of diuers bookes, and Images. |
(1553) Edward VI [Statutes] An.iii–iv, fol.xiii

An ACTE for the ordering of Eccle- | siasticall Ministers. | (1550)
(1553) Edward VI [Statutes] An.iii–iv. fol.xv.

An ACTE for the punishment of vnlawfull assemblies, | and rysing of the kinges subiectes. |
(1553). Edward VI. [Statutes] An.iii–iv, fol vi b

An ACTE that the kinges Maiestie maie nominate and. | appoincte .xxxii. persones, to peruse and | make Ecclesiasticall lawes, | (1550)
(1553) Edward VI. [Statutes] An.iii–iv, fol.xiiii.

ARTICLES | agreed on by the Bi- | shoppes, and other learned | menne in the Synode at London, | in the yere of our Lorde Godde, | M.D.LII. for the auoiding of | controuersie in opinions, and | the establishement of a god- | lie concorde, in certeine | matters of Reli- | gion. | Published by the kinges Maies- | ties commaundement, in | the Moneth of Maie. | Anno Domini. | 1553. |

Architec. border. Colophon: Richardus Craftonus typographus Re- | gius excudebat. | Londini, mense Iunij. | An. do. M.D.LIII. | Cum priuilegio ad impri- | mendum solum. | 17.4x13.6 cm. (12)fol
Repr. in Sparrow's Collection of Articles: 1661, 1675, 1684.

ARTICULI | de quibus in | Synodo Londinensi | Anno Dom. M.D.LII. | ad tollendam opinionum dissensionem & consensum | veræ religionis firmandum, | Inter | Episcopos | Et alios | Eruditos Viros convenerat, Regia autho- | ritate in lucem editi. | (royal arms)

Excusum Londini, apud Reginaldum Wolfi | um, Regiæ Majestatis in Latinis Typographum. | Anno Dom. M.D.LIII. | Border. 19.5x15.2cm. Pp. 50–60 of Sparrow's Collections: 1661. Also in his reprints of 1675 and 1684.

BARLOW, William. A dialoge | describing the originall | ground of these Luthe | ran faccions, and ma- | ny of their abuses. | Compyled by | syr William | Barlowe | chanon, | late byshop of Bathe. | Anno, 1553. |

Colophon:: Prynted at London in Paules | Churcheyard by John | Cawood. | Cum priuilegio ad imprimendum | solum. | 13.8x8.6cm. (88)fol.

BEZE, Théodore de. Epistola magistri | Benedicti Passavantii | Responsiua ad commissionem sibi | datam à venerabili D. Petro Ly- | seto, nuper Curiæ Parisiensis præ- | sidente: nunc verò Abbate sancti | Victoris, prope muros. |

1553. | 14.5x9.4 cm. (90)p.
BMCat. under Passavantius.

CRANMER, Thomas. Defensio | Verae Et Catholi- | cae Doctrinae De Sacra- | mento corporis & sanguinis Christi Ser- | uatoris nostri, & quorundam in hac causa er- | rorum confutatio, uerbo sanctissimo Domini | nixa atq; fundata, & consensu antiquissi- | morum Ecclesiæ scriptorum firmata, | à Reuerendiss. in Christo Patre ac | Domino D. Thoma Cran- | mero Archiepiscopo | Cantuariensi, Pri- | mate totius | Angliæ, & Metropolita- | no, scripta. | (device). . . . (4 lines).

M.D.LIII. | 15.1x10.1cm. (8),117,(1) fol.

EDWARD VI. [Statutes] Anno iii–iv. Anno. III & IIII. | Edvvardi Sexti. | Actes | made in the Session of this | present Parlament, holden vpon pro- | rogation at Westminster, the .iiii. daye | of Nouembre, in the thirde yere of the | reygne of our most dread Souereygne | Lorde Edward the .vi. by the grace of | God, kyng of Englande, Fraunce, and | Ireland, defendour of the fayth, and of | the Churche of Eng- lande, and also of | Irelande, in earth the supreme head: | and there continued, and kept to | the first daye of Februarye, in | the .iiii. yere of the reigne | of our sayed Soue- | reigne Lorde, as | foloweth. |

With "King in council" compartment. Colophon: Imprinted at London by Richard | Grafton, printer to the | Kynges Maiestie. | 1553. | Cum priuilegio ad impri- | mendum solum. | 26.3x18.5 cm. xxxiifol.

EDWARD VI. [Statutes] Anno vii. Anno Septimo | Edvvardi Sexti. | Actes | made in the Parlament hol- | den at Westminster, the first daie of | Marche, in the .VII. yere of the reigne | of our moste redoubted Souuereine | Lorde Edwarde the .VI. By the grace | of God, King of Englande, Fraunce, | and Irelande, defendour of the faith, | and of the Churche of Englande and | also of Irelande in earth the supreme | head: And there continued to the | dissolucion of the same being | the laste daie of the- | saied moneth of | Marche, as | foloweth. |

"King in council" compartment. Colophon: Londini in ædibus Richardi Graftoni | typographi Regii excusum. | Mense Aprilis. | Anno Domini M,D.LIII. | Cum priuilegio ad imprimendum solum. | 26.3x18.5 cm. xliiii fol. Last folio misnumbered.

GARDINER, Stephen. De Vera Obedientia. | An O- | ration made in Latine by thery- | ghte Reuerend father in God Ste- | phan B. of

VVinchestre, nowe lord | Chaŭcellour of england, With the | preface of Edmunde Boner, som- | time Archedeacō of Leicestre, and | the kinges maiesties embassadour | in Denmarke, & sithence B. of Lō- | don, touching true Obedience. | Printed at Hamburgh in La- | tine, In officina Francisci Rho- | di, Mense Ia. M.D.xxxvi. | And nowe translated into english | and printed bi Michael Wood: | With the Preface & con- | clusion of the traun- | slatour. |

From Roane .xxvi of | Octobre. M.D.liii. | In Readinge marke the Notes | in the margine. | . . . (2 lines). 13 x8.4 cm. (11),63fol
Cambr.Univ.Cat:6240.

HORNE, Robert. VVhether Chri- | stian faith maye be kepte secret in | the heart, without confession ther | of openly to the worlde as occasi- | on shal serue. Also what hurt | cōmeth by thē that hath receiued the Gospell, to | be presēt at Masse vn | to the simple and | vnlearned | . . . (15 lines).

From Roane. Anno.M.D.Liii. | the .iii. of October. | 13.4x8.6cm. (8)fol.
DNB.27:361b. Cf.Cambr.Univ.Cat:6242. Ms. copy with Here begynneth a booke: 1545.

PONET, John? Catechismus | Brevis, Christi- | anae Disciplinae | summam continens, omnibus | Ludimagistris authoritate | Regia | commendatus. | Hvic Catechismo Ad- | iuncti sunt Articuli, de quibus in vlti- | ma Synodo Londinensi, Anno Dom. | 1552. ad tollendam opinionum dissensionem, | & consensum uerae religionis firmandum, | inter Episcopos & alios eruditos at- | que pios uiros conuenerat: Regia | similiter authori- | tate promulgati. |

Londini, | Cum priuilegio Sereniss. Regis. | Anno Do. M.D.LIII. | Colophon: Excusum Londini apud Reginaldum | Wolfium, Regiae Maiestatis | in Latinis Typo- | graphum. Anno Domini.M.D.LIII. | 13.4x9.6cm. (3,65)fol.
Cambr.Univ.Cat. No.737.

1554

An ACTE agaynst offendours of preachers, and other | ministers in the churche. |

(1554) Mary, Queen. [Statutes] An.i,sessio ii, fol vii

An ACTE agaynst vnlawfull and rebellious assembles. | (1554).

(1554) Mary, Queen [Statutes] An.i, sessio ii, fol.xxvii

An ACTE declaryng the Quenes highnes to haue bene | borne in a most iuste and lawfull matrimonie, and also repea- | lyng, all actes of parliament, and sentences and diuours | had and made to the contrarye. |

(1554) Mary, Queen. [Statutes] An.i,fol.v.

An ACTE for the repeale of certayne Statutes, made in the | time of the rayne of king Edward the sixt. |

(1554) Mary, Queen [Statutes] An.ii, sessio ii, fol.vi.

GARDINER, Stephen. Confv- | tatio | Cavillationvm, | Quibus Sacrosanctũ Evcharistiæ | Sacramentum, ab impiis Caphar- | naitis impeti solet, | Authore | Stephano Winton. Episcop. | Angliæ Cancellario. | Editio Altera | Cui Index accesit lo- | cupletissimus. |

Lovanii, | Apud Petrum Colonæum Bibliop. Iura, | 1554. | Cum Priuilegio Cæ.Ma. | ad quadriennium. | 16x9.9cm. (15),799p.

An HUMBLE | supplicacion vnto God, for the | restoringe of hys holye woorde, vnto the | churche of Englande, mooste mete | to be sayde in these oure dayes, | euen with teares of euery | true & faythfull En- | glish harte. | . . . (6 lines).

Imprynted at Strasburgh | in Elsas, at the signe of the goldẽ Bi- | bell, In the moneth of Auguste. | the yeare of our Lord. | 1554. | 13.4x9.1 cm. (35)fol.
Attrib. to Thomas Becon: Pollard, Short-Title Catalogue.

LITVRGIA | Sacra, Sev Ritvs | Ministerij in Ecclesia peregrinorum | Francofordiæ ad Mœ- | num. | Addita est summa doctrinæ seu fidei pro- | fessio eiusdem Ecclesiæ. | . . . (5 lines).

Francofordiæ | 1554. | Colophon: Impressum Fran- | cofordiæ apud Petrum | Brubachium. | 1554. | 15.7x9.7 cm. 92,(2)p.

MARTYN, Thomas. A Traictise | declaryng and plain- | ly prouyng, that the preten- | sed marriage of Priestes, and pro- | fessed persones, is no mariage, but alto- | gether vnlawful, and in all ages, and | al countreies of Christendome, | bothe forbidden, and also | punyshed. | Herewith is comprised | in the later chapitres, a full | confutation of Doctour Poy- | nettes boke entitled a de- | fense for the marriage | of Priestes. | By Thomas Martin, Doctour | of the Ciuile Lavves. |

Excvsvm Londini in | ædibus Roberti Caly, Typographi: | Mense Maij Anno. 1554. | Cũ priuilegio. | Architec. border. 18x12.6 cm. (143)fol.

MARY, Queen [Statutes] Anno i. Anno Mariæ | Primo. | Actes | made in the Parlyamente be- | gonne and holden at Westminster | the seconde daye of Apryll, in the | firste yeare of the raygne of oure | moste gratious Soueraygne La- | dye, Marye by the grace of God, | Quene of England, Fraunce, and | Irelande, defender of the faythe, | and there continued and kepte to | the dissolution of the same, beynge | the v. daye of Maye then | next ensuing as fo- | loweth. | Cum priuilegio Reginæ | Mariæ. |

Wood-cut bordrs. Colophon: Excusum Londini in ædibus Iohannis | Cavvodi Typohraphi Regiæ | Maiestatis. | Anno. M.D.Liiij. | Mense Maio. | Cum priuilegio. Reginæ Mariae. | 26.3x18.5 cm. xxfol.

MARY, Queen [Statutes] Anno i. Anno Mariæ | Primo. | Actes | made in the Parliament be- | gonne and holden at Westmin- | ster the .v. daye of October, in the | first year of the reigne of our most | gratious Soueraigne Ladye, | Mary by ye grace of God, Quene | of England, Fraunce, & Ireland, | defender of the fayth, and of the | churche of Englande and of Ire- | lande, in earth the supreme head, | and there continued to the .xxi. | day of the same moneth, that | is to saye, in the fyrst session | of the same parliament, | as foloweth. | Cum priuilegio Regiæ | Maiestatis. |

Border. Colophon: Excusum | Londini in ædibus Iohannis Cawodi | Typographi Regiæ Maiestatis. | Anno. M.D.LIIII. | Cum priuilegio ad imprimendum solum. | 26.3x18.5 cm. xxvii,(1)fol.

Folio 3, blank. On folio 4, a second t.p.: Actes | Made in the Second and last Session of this | present parliament, holden vpon prorogation at | Westminster, the .xxiiii. daye of October, | in the first yeare of the reigne of oure | moost gratious soueraigne Lady | Marye by the grace of God, | Quene of Englande, | Fraunce, and | Irelande, | defendour of the fayth, and in earth supreme heade of | the Churche of Englande and of Irelande, and | there continued and kepte to the dissolu- | tion of the same, beyng the .vi. daye | of December then next ensuing, | as foloweth. |

PHILPOT, John. The trew re- | port of the dysputacyon | had & begōne in the con- | uocacyō hows at london | among the clargye there | assembled the xviij. da- | ye of October in the | yeare of our lord | M. D. LJJJJ. . . . (3 lines).

Roll border. Colophon: Imprinted at Basil by | Alexander Edmonds. | 12.6x 8.1cm. (8,66)p.

Anon. Cambr Univ. Cat. 6111.

WATSON, Thomas. Twoo notable | Sermons, made | the thirde and fyfte Fri- | dayes in Lent last past, be- | fore the Quenes highnes, | concerninge the reall pre- | sence of Christes body and | bloude in the blessed Sa- | crament: & also the Masse, | which is the sacrifice of | the Newe Testament. | By Thomas Wat- | son, Doctor of | Diuinitie. |

Engraved border. Colophon: Imprinted at London | in Paules churchyarde, | at the sygne of the holye | Ghost, by John Ca- | wood, Printer to | the Quenes | hyghnes. | The Tenth day of May. | Anno Domini.1554. | Cum priuilegio Re- | ginæ Mariæ. | 14.1x9.3cm. (91)fol.

1555

An ACT for the punishment of certayne persons callyng | themselues Egyptians. |

(1554) Philip and Mary [Statutes] An.i–ii, fol vi.

An ACTE for the reuiuing of three Estatutes made for the | punishment of heresie. |

(1555) Philip and Mary [Statutes] An.i–ii, fol.viii b

An ACTE repealyng all Statutes, articles, and prouisions made | agaynst the Sea Apostolike of Rome, synce the xx. yeare of | kyng Henry theyght, and also for the establishment of | al spiritual and ecclesiastical possessions and heredi | tamentes conueyed to the laytie. |

(1555) Philip and Mary [Statutes] An.i–ii, fol.xv b.

BARNES, Robert. Vitae | Romanorvm Ponti | ficum, quos Papas uocamus, summa | diligentia ac fide collectæ, per D. | Robertvm Barns, S. Theo- | logiæ Doctorem Anglum, Londini | Anno abhinc xv pro Chri- | sti nomine com- | bustum. | Eivsdem Sententiae, | siue præcipui Christianæ religionis articuli, | partim ex sacris literis, partim diuer- | sis doctorum patrum scri- | ptis asserti. | Accessit locuples rerum & uerborum memo- | rabilium Index. |

Basiliæ. | 15.4x9.5cm. (24),406,(24)p.

Epistola Nuncupatoria: dated Wittemberg, x Sept. Anno Domini, M.D.XXXV.

BONNER, Edmund. Home- | lies sette forthe by the | righte reuerende father in | God, Edmunde Byshop of | London, not onely promi- | sed before in his booke, inti- | tuled, A necessary doctrine, | but also nowe of late adioy- | ned, and added therevnto, | to be reade within his dio- | cesse of London, of all per- | sons, vycars, and curates, | vnto theyr parishioners, v- | pon sondayes, & holydayes. |

Anno. M.D.L.V. | Architectural border. Colophon: Imprinted at Lon | don in Poules churchyarde, at the sygne of | the holy Ghost, by Jhon Cawoode, Pryn- | ter to the Kyng and Queenes | Maiesties. | Cum priuilegio maiestatis. | 18.9x13.7 cm. 73,(1)fol.
Appended to his Profitable and necessarye doctrine: 1555.

BONNER, Edmund. A Profita | ble and necessarye doc- | trine, with certayne home- | lyes adioyned thervnto set | forth by the reuerend father | in God, Edmunde Byshop | of London, for the instruc- | tion and enformation of the | people being within his di- | ocesse of London, & | of hys cure and | charge. | . . . (2 lines). |

Colophon,fol.200: Excvsvm | Londini In Edibvs Io | hannis Cawodi, Typographi Regiæ | Maiestatis. | (1555). 18.9x13.7 cm. (4), (150 unpaged); 73, (1) fol. Sub t.p.
Cf.DNB.23:264b.

PHILIP and MARY [Statutes] Anno i–ii. Anno primo et secūdo Philippi | & Mariæ. | Actes | made at a Parliament begon | and holden at Westminster the .xj | day of Nouember in the firste and | secōd year of the reigne of our soue | raigne Lorde and Lady, Philippe | and Marye by the grace of God, | kinge and Quene of England, Fraunce | Naples, Jerusalem, and Ireland, defenders of the | faythe, Princes of Spayne, and Seicile, Arche- | dukes of Austria, Dukes of Millaine, Burgun- | dye and Brabant, counties of Haspurge, | Flaunders, and Tyroll. | And there contynued and kept, vntyll the dissoluti | on of the same, beynge the xvi. daye | of January then next ensu- | ing, were enacted | as foloweth. | Cum priuilegio Regiæ | Maiestatis. |

Wood-cut border. Colophon: Excusum Londini in ædibus Iohannis Cavvodi Tipographi | Regiæ Maiectatis Anno. M.D.L.V. | 26.3x18.5 cm. xxxiiiifol. Misnumberings.
Cambr Univ. Cat. No. 993.

PHILIP and MARY [Statutes] Anno ii–iii. Anno Secundo et Tertio Philippi | & Mariæ. | Actes | made at a Parlyamente begon | and holdē at Westminster the .xxj. | daye of October, in the seconde and | thyrd yeare of the reigne of our Soue | raygne Lorde and Ladye, Phylyppe | and Marye by the grace of God, | Kyng and Queene of Englande, Fraunce, | Naples Jerusalem, and Ireland, defendors | of the fayth, princes of Spayne, and Sicile, | Archdukes of Austria, Dukes of Millaine, | Burgondie and Brabante, counties of | Haspurge Flaunders, and Tyroll, | and there continued and | kepte vntyl the | dissolution | of the same, being the .ix. day | of December then next en- | suing, were enacted as | foloweth. | Cum priuilegio Regiæ | Maiestatis. |

Wood-cut border. Colophon: Excusum Londini in ædibus Iohannis Cavvodi | Tipographi Regiæ Maiestatis. | Anno. M.D.LV. | Cum priuilegio regiæ Maiestatis. | 26.3x18.5 cm. lviiifol.
Cambr.Univ.Cat.No.994

POLE, Reginald. Reginaldi | Poli Cardinalis Britanni | Pro Ecclesiasticæ Vnitatis Defensio- | ne, libri quatuor, in quibus conatus est maximo studio Ecclesiæ | Romanæ Primatum constabilire, nunc primum in Ger- | mania æditi, qui tamen antea in Italia fuerant ex- | cusi, sed latitarunt diu & ad paucurum | manus perueniebant. | Adiectvm Est Etiam Qvo- | rvndam Aliorvm Gravissimorvm Viro- | rum de Pontificis Romani Primatu | iudicium. | . . . (2 lines).

M. D. LV. | Colophon: Argentorati excudebat VVendelinus Rihelius, Anno | M.D.LV. | 29x18.7cm. (3),175,(1)fol.

RIDLEY, Nicholas. A brief declaracion | of the Lordes Supper, written by | the syngular learned man, and most | constaunt Martir of Jesus Christ, | Nicholas Ridley Bishop of Lon- | don prisoner in Oxforde, a litel | before he suffred deathe for | the true testimonie of | Christ. | . . . (9 lines).

No imprint. | Anno. 1555. | 14.1x9.2 cm. (1,38)fol.

1556

CALVIN, John. The Cate- | chisme Or Maner | to teache children the Christian religion, | wherin the Minister demandeth the que- | stion, and the childe maketh answere. | Made by the excellent Doctor and Pastor | in Christes Churche, Iohn Calvin. | . . . (cut; 3 lines).

By Iohn Crespin. | M.D.LVI. | Line border.
Reprinted in Bonar's Catechisms of the Scottish Reformation.London:1866. 12mo, Pp.1–111.

CRANMER, Thomas. The copy of certain | lettres sent to the Quene, and also to | doctour Martin and doctour Sto- | rye, by the most Reuerende father in | God, Thomas Cranmer Archebi- | shop of Cantorburye from prison in | Oxeforde: who (after long and most | greuous strayt emprisoning and cru- | ell handlyng) most constauntly | and willingly suffred Mar- | tirdome ther, for the true | testimonie of Christ, | in Marche. | 1556. | . . . (4 lines)

No imprint. 1556. | 14.3x9.2 cm. (16)fol. Cut of Cranmer laid in.

FISHER, John. Reveren | di Patris D. Ioan- | nis Fischerii, Qvondam E- | piscopi Roffensis Opuscu- | lum de fiducia & mi- | sericordia Dei. | Nunc primùm in lucem æditum. | (printer's device).

Coloniæ, | Apud hæredes Arnoldi Birckmanni. | 1556. | 15.x9.7cm. (2,96,2)fol.

FOX, John. Christus Tri- | vmphans, Comœ- | dia Apocalyptica: | Avtore Ioanne | Foxo Anglo. | Accessit, | In Christvm Trivm- | phantem, Autoris eiusdem Pa- | negyricon. | . . . (3 lines).

Basileæ, Per Ioan- | nem Oporinum. | Colophon: Basileæ, Ex Officina | Ioannis Oporini, Anno Salutis humanæ | M.D.LVI. Mense | Martio. | 16x10cm. (14),121, (2)(7)p.

LANGDALE, Alban. Catholica Confutatio | Impiae Cvivsdam Deter- | minationis D. Nicolai Ridlęi, eo tempore | sedem Episcopalem apud Roffam oc- | cupantis, post disputationem de | Eucharistia in

Academia | Cantabrigiēsi, habitæ, | in tres libros | diuisa. | Authore Albano Langdailo Archidiacono | Cicestriensi apud Anglos. | . . . (2 lines).

Lvtetiae, | Ex officina Michaëlis Vascosani, uia Iacobæa, | ad insigne Fontis. | M.D.LVI. | Cvm Privilegio Regis. | 20.7x14.8cm. 143fol.

LASKI, John. Epistolae | tres lectu dignis- | simæ, | De Recta Et Legi- | tima Ecclesiarvm Be- | nè instituendarum ratio- | ne ac modo: | Ad Potentiss. Regem | Poloniæ, Senatum, reliquosq; | Ordines: | D. Ioanne À Lasco Ba- | rone Poloniæ, &c. autore. |

Basileæ, Per Ioan- | nem Oporinum. | Colophon: Basileæ, Ex Officina Ioan- | nis Oporini, Anno salutis humanæ M.D.LVI. | Mense Martio. | 18x11.8 cm. 110p. Last page, numbered 100.

OCHINO, Bernardino. Bernar- | dini Ochini Senen- | sis uiri doctissimi, | De Purgatorio | dialogus. | Ad Lectorem. | Opus est lector, velut ex authoris præfatiuncula cogno- | sces, non tam vtile quàm iucundum lectu: ab ipso primum | authore Italica lingua scriptum, postea verò à quodam | eius studioso viro in Latinum translatum. Vale. | . . . (7 lines; ornaments).

Colophon: Tiguri apud Gess- | neros. | [1556] 14.4x8.9 cm. (6),115,(13)p. Epistola nuncupatoria, dated Dec.1555. BMCat.

PARKER, Matthew. A Defence | of priestes mariages, stablysshed | by the imperiall lawes of the | Realme of Englande, agaynst | a Ciuilian, namyng hym | selfe Thomas Mar- | tin doctour of | the Ciuile | lawes, | goyng about to disproue the saide mariages, lawfull | by the eternall worde of God, & by the hygh court | of parliament, only forbydden by forayne lawes | and canons of the Pope, coloured with the | visour of the Churche. Whiche lawes | & canons, were extynguyshed by the | sayde parliament, and so abro- | gated by the conuocation | in their Sinode by | their subscrip- | tions. | Herewith is expressed, what moderations and | dispensations haue ben vsed heretofore in | the same cause, & other like, the canons | of the Churche standyng in full | force. Whereby is proued, | these constitutions to be | but positiue lawes | of man tem- | porall. | . . . (3 lines).

Colophon: Imprinted at London by | Richarde Jugge, printer to the Queenes | Maiestie. | Cum priuilegio Regiæ Maiestatis. | [1556?]. 18.1x13.8 cm. (12)p. 22 fol, 23–359, (8)p. (Pp. 189–190 duplicate; 240–241 omitted.)

Anon. DNB.43:263b H&L. Doubtfully ascribed to John Ponet or Sir.Richard Morison. DNB.39:61b Cf. Cambridge Cat. No. 975. [1566?] Cancel pasted in at p.239.

PONET, John. A Shorte Trea- | tise of politike pouuer, and of the true Obe- | dience which subiectes owe to kynges and other | ciuile Gouernours, with an Exhortacion | to all true naturall Englishe | men, Compyled | by | D. I. P. B. R. VV. | 1556. | . . . (2 lines)

Without impr. or colophon. [1556]. 14.3x9.6 cm. (2,181) p. Cambr.Univ.Cat: 6731.

RATIO | Et Forma | Pvblice Orandi De- | vm, Atque Administran- | da Sacramenta, | Et Caet. | In Anglorvm Eccle- | siam, quæ Geneuæ colligitur, recepta: cum iu- | dicio & comprobatione D. Iohannis Caluini. | (device) . . . (3 lines).

Genevæ, | Apvd Ioannem Cristinvm, | M.D.LV I. | 14.8x9.4cm. 64p.

RIDLEY, Nicholas. Certein godly, lear- | ned, and comfortable conferences, be- | twene the two Reuerende Fathers, | and holy martyrs of Christe, D. Ni- | colas Rydley late Bisshoppe of | London, and M. Hughe La- | timer, sometyme Bisshop | of Worcester, during | the tyme of their | emprisonmen- | tes. | . . . (4 lines).

No imprint. 1556. | 14.1x9.2 cm. (4,40)fol.

WATSON, Robert. Aetiologi | a Roberti VVatsoni | Angli, in qua explicatur, quare depre- | hensus annum vnum & menses penè | quatuor, propter Euangeliū incarce- | ratus fuit: quęná inter ipsū & eius An- | tagonistas in carcere habita fuit disce- | ptatio, de Transubstantiatione & reali | Christi præsentia in Sacramento: & | quo pacto corpore incolumi & | illibata conscientia tandem | expediuit eum | Dominus. | . . . (12 lines).

Anno. M.D.LVI. | 14.9x9.5cm. (68)fol.

1557

BUCER, Martin. De Regno Chri- | sti Iesu seruatoris nostri, | Libri II. | Ad Edvardvm VI. Angliæ | Regem, Annis Abhinc Sex Scripti: | non solum Theologis atque Iurisperitis profutu- | ri, uerùm etiam cunctis Rempub. bene & feliciter | administraturis cognitu cumprimis | necessarij. | D. Martino Bvcero | Avtore. | Habes hîc, candide Lector, præter complura haud uulga- | ria, locum communem De Conivgio & Di- | vortio, tam solidè & plenè tractatum, quàm apud | scriptorem alium nostri seculi uix | inuenias. | Adiectus est singulorum totius operis | capitum Elenchus. | (device).

Basiliæ, Per Ioan- | nem Oporinum. | Preface dated; Argentorati, Calendis Septemb.Anno M.D.LVII. 31.7x20.2cm. 9,(3),249p.

1558

ACT for Uniformity. | Anno primo Reginæ Eliz.Cap.2. | There shall be Uniformity of Prayer, | and Administration of Sa- | craments. |

Without t.p. 19.5x15.2cm. Pp. 75-82 of Sparrow's Collection: 1661. Also in his reprints of 1675 and 1684.

ALEXIUS, Simon. De | Origine | Novi Dei Missati- | ci, Qvondam In Anglia | mortui, nunc denuò ab inferis excitati: | Dialogi VII. | In quibus, purissimi sacræ Scri- | pturæ fontes, ad impurissimas | Scholasticæ doctrinæ lacunas | collati, non tantum verum | Cœnæ Dominicæ vsum osten | dunt, sed etiam impium | Missæ Papisticæ abusum | patefaciunt. | Simone Alexio Avthore |

M.D.LVIII. | 15.x9.cm. (8),136p.

CRANMER, Thomas. A Confu- | tatiō of vnwrittē verities, both bi the | holye scriptures and moste auncient | autors, and also probable arguments, | and pithy reasons, with plaine auns- | wers to al (or at the least) to the moste | part and strongest argumentes, which | the aduersaries of gods truth, either | haue, or can bryng forth for the profe | and defence of the same vnwritten va | nities, verities as they woulde haue | them called: made by Thomas Cran- | mer, late Archebishop of Cantorbu | rie, Martyr of god, and burned | at Oxford for the defēce of the | trewe doctrine of our saui- | our Christ, translated | and set forth | by L. P. | The contents whereof, thou | shalte finde in the next side | folowinge. |

Without imprint. [1558?]. 13.6x9.3 cm. 26,85fol.

GOODMAN, Christopher. How Svperior | Powers Oght To | Be Obeyd Of Their | subiects: and Wherin they may law- | fully by Gods Worde be disobeyed | and resisted. | Wherin also is declared the cause of all this pre | sent miserie in England, and the onely way | to remedy the same. | By Christopher Goodman. | . . . (device; 3 lines).

Printed at Geneua by Iohn Crispin. | M.D.LVIII. | 13.6x8.3 cm. 230p.
Burned by order of the convocation at the University of Oxford, July 1683.

HOOPER, John. An ouersighte and de- | liberacion vppon the holy pro- | phet Jonas: made, and vttered be- | fore the kinges maiesty, and his | most honorable councell, | by Jhon Hoper in | lent last past. | Comprehended in seuen | Sermons. | Anno.M.D.L. | . . . (3 lines)

Imprinted at London by | Jhon Tisdale, dwelling in | Knight Riderstrete. | [1558?] 12.5x8.1cm. (18,364)p.

PHILIP and MARY [Statutes] Anno iv–v. Anno quarto et quinto Philippi | & Mariæ. | Actes | made at a Parliament begon | and holden at Westminster the .xx | day of January in the fourthe and | fifte yeare of the reigne of our soue- | raigne Lorde and Lady, Philippe | and Marye by the grace of God, | kinge and Quene of England, Spayne, | Fraunce, both the Sicilies, Jerusalem, and Ire- | land, defendours of the faythe, Archedukes of Au | stria, Dukes of Burgundy, Millaine; | & Brabant, counties of Haspurge, | Flaunders, and Tyroll. | And there contynued and kept, vntyll the .vii. | day of Marche then next folow- | ing and enacted | as foloweth. | Cum priuilegio Regiæ | Maiestatis. |

Wood-cut border. Colophon: Excusum Londini | In Ædibvs Iohannis. | Cavvodi. | Tipographi Regiæ Ma- | iestatis. | Anno. M.D.LVIII. | Cum priuilegio Regiæ Maie- | statis. | 26.3x18.5 cm. xli fol.
Cambr Univ Cat. No. 998.

WATSON, Thomas. Holsome | and Catholyke do- | ctryne concerninge the se- | uen Sacramentes of Chrystes | Church, expedient to be knowen | of all men, set forth in maner | of shorte Sermons to bee | made to the people, by | the reuerend father | in God.Thomas | byshop of Lin- | colne. | Anno. 1558. | Mense Februarij. |

Excusam Londini in ædibus Roberti | Caly, Typographi. | Cum priuilegio ad imprimen | dum solum. | Arch. Border. (Page 3): Imprynted at | London, by Robert Caly, within | the precinct of Christes Hospitall. | The .x. of February. | M.D.LVIII. | . . . (2 lines) 18.7x12.5 cm. (4),190 fol.

1559

An ACTE for the vnyformitie of Common Prayer, and | Seruice in the Churche, and the administration of the | Sacramentes. |

(1559) Elizabeth, Queen [Statutes] An.i,fol vii b.

An ACTE restoringe to | the Crowne the auncient Jurisdiction ouer the state | Ecclesiasticall and Spyrytuall, and abolyshynge all | forrayne power repugnaunt to the same. |

(1559) Elizabeth, Queen. [Statutes] An.i, fol.ii.

ARTICLES | to be enquired in the | visitation, in the first yere | of the raigne of our most | dread Soueraigne Lady | Elizabeth, by the | grace of God, of | England, | Fraunce, and Irelande, | Queene, defendour of | the Faith, &c. | Anno domini. | 1559. |

Colophon: Jmprinted At | London by Christopher Bar- | ker, Printer to the Queenes | Maiestie. | Cum priuilegio Regiæ Maiestatis. | Engraved border. 17.2x 12.6 cm. (1,6)fol.
Reprinted in Sparrow's Collection of Articles: 1661, 1675, and 1684.

AYLMER, John. An Harborovve | For Faith- | fvll And Trevve | Svbiectes, | agaynst the late blowne Blaste, concerninge the Go- | eurnmēt of VVemen, wherin be confuted all such | reasons as a straunger of late made in that | behalfe, with a breife exhortation to | Obedience. | Anno.M.D.lix. | . . . (8 lines)

At Strasborowe the | 26.of Aprill. | (device). 18.2x13.2cm. (4,61)fol.
Anon.Cambr.Univ.Cat.7117.

ELIZABETH, Queen [Statutes] Anno i. Anno Primo Regi- | næ Elizabethe. | At The | parliament be- | gonne at Westmynster, the | xxiij. of Januarye in the fyrste | yeare of the raygne of oure So- | ueraigne Ladye, Elizabeth by the | grace of God, of England, Fraunce | and Ireland, Quene, defen- | doure of the Fayth, &c. | And there proroged tyll the .xxv. of | the same moneth, and then and there holden, kepte, | and continued vntyll the dissolution of the | same, being the eyght day of May then | next ensuinge, were enacted as | foloweth. | Anno.1.5.5.9. | (device)

Evangelists border. Colophon: Imprinted at London | In Povvles Chvrchyarde, By | Richarde Iugge and Iohn Cawood, Printers to | the Quenes Maiestie. | Anno. M.D.LIX. | Cum priuilegio Regiæ Maiestatis. | 26.3x18.5 cm. xl, xvifol. Misnumbered.
Cambr. Univ Cat. No. 957.

FOX, John. Rervm | In Ecclesia Ge- | starum, quæ postremis & pericu- | losis his temporibus euenerunt, maxi- | marumq́; per Europam persecutionum, ac Sanctorum Dei | Martyrum, cæterarumq́; rerum si quæ insignioris | exempli sint, digesti per Regna & natio- | nes Commentarij. | (Mutilated) In qua primùm de rebus per Angliam & Scotiam gestis, atq[ue] in pri- | mis de horrenda, sub Maria nuper

Regina, per- | secutione, narratio continetur. | Autore Ioanne Foxo Anglo. | (device)

Basileæ, Per Nicolavm | Brylingervm, Et Ioan- | nem Oporinum. | Colophon: Basileæ, Per Nicolavm Brilingervm, | Et Ioannem Oporinvm, Anno | M.D.LIX. Mense | Avgvsto. | 31.5 x 20.2 cm. (14),732 p.

HUMPHREY, Laurence. De Religionis | conseruatione & | reformatione | uera: | Deq[ue] Primatu Regum & | magistratuum, & obedientia | illis ut summis in terra Chri- | sti uicarijs præstanda, | Liber: | Ad Nobilitatem, Clerum & po- | pulum Anglicanum. | Lavrentio Hym- | fredo autore. |

Basileæ, Per Ioan- | nem Oporinum. | Colophon: Basileæ, Per Ioannem | Oporinum, anno Salutis 1559. | Mense Septembri. | 16x10cm. 110p.

INIUNCTIONS giuen by | the Queenes Maiestie. | Anno domini. 1559. | The first yere of the | raigne of our soue- | raigne Lady Queene | Elizabeth. |

Cum priuilegio Regiæ | Maiestatis. | Engraved border. No imprint. [1559]. 17.2x12.6 cm. 16fol.

Repr. in Sparrow's Collection: 1661, 1675, and 1684.

1560

BALE, John. The first two | partes of the Actes or vn- | chaste examples of the Englyshe | Votaryes, gathered out of theyr | owne legendes and Chronycles | by Ihon Bale, and dedicated to | oure moste redoubted so- | ueraigne kyng Ed- | warde the | syxte. | . . . (9 lines).

Colophon: Imprinted at London | by Ihon Tisdale, dwelling | in Knight riders streate. | [1560]. 12.6x8.6 cm. (7),97;(10,153)fol. Part I: Folio numbers 10 and after 65, incorrect: Part II, unpaged.

CELEBRATIO | Coenæ Domini | In | Funebribus, | Si Amici & Vicini defuncti Com- | municare velint. &c. | Anno 2.Eliz.Regin,1560. | (royal arms)

Londini, | Apud Reginaldum Wolfium. 1560. | Border. 19.5x15.2cm. 6p.

Repr. in Sparrow's Collection: 1661, 1675 and 1684.

HUMPHREY, Laurence. Optimates, | Sive | De Nobilita- | te, Eivs'qve Antiqua | origine, natura, officijs, disciplina, | & recta ac Christiana institu- | tione Libri tres. | Lavrentio Hvm | fredo autore. | Adiunctus est propter utilitatem & | affinitatem argumenti, Philo Iudæus | de Nobilitate, Græcè & La- | tinè: Eodem inter- | prete. |

Basileæ, Per Ioan- | nem Oporinum. | (Pref.1559). Colophon: Basilaee, Ex Officina Ioannis Oporini, Anno Salutis hu- | manæ M.D.LX. Meñ- | se Martio. | 16x10 cm. 381 p.

HUTCHINSON, Roger. A Faithfvl | Declaration Of | Christes holy supper, compre- | hēded in thre Sermōs, | preached at Eaton | Colledge, by Ro- | ger Hutchin- | son. 1552. | Whose contentes are | in the other syde | of the lefe. |

Newly imprinted at London by | John Day, dwelling ouer | Aldersgate. | 1560. | Cum gratia & priuilegio Regiæ | maiestatis per sep- | tennium. | Engr.border. 12.7x8.5cm. (4,65)fol.

JEWEL, John. The Trve | Copies Of The Let- | ters betwene the reuerend fa- | ther in God Iohn Bisshop of Sa- | rum and D. Cole, vpon occasion | of a Sermon that the said Bishop | preached before the Quenes | Maiestie, and hyr most | honorable Coūsayle. | 1560. | Set forthe and allowed, ac- | cording to the order apointed | in the Quenes Maiesties | Iniunctions. | Cū gratia & priuilegio Regiæ | Maiestatis ad septemniū. | (Engraved border)

Colophon: Imprinted | at London, by John Day, | dwelling ouer Alders- | gate. beneath Saint | Martins. | . . . (2 lines). These bokes are to be solde | at his shop vnder the | Gate. | (ornament) 14.3x9cm. (196)fol. Fols. 132, and 195-196 blank. Fol. 133: The copie of | a Sermon pronounced by the | Byshop of Salisburie at Paules | Crosse the second Sondaye before E- | ster in the yere of our Lord.1560. | wher- | vpon D.Cole first sought occasion to | encounter, shortly setforthe as | nere as the authour could call it to | remembraunce, without any | alteration or addition. | . . . (12 lines).
CambUniv.Cat. 885.

KNOX, John. An Answer | To A Great Nomber | of blasphemous cauillations written by an | Anabaptist, and aduersarie to Gods eternal | Predestination. | And Confvted | By Iohn Knox, minister of Gods worde | in Scotland. | Wherein the Author so discouereth the craft and falsho- | de of that sect, that the godly knowing that error, | may be confirmed in the truethe by the euident Wor- | de of God. | . . . (device; 3 lines).

Printed by Iohn Crespin. | M.D.LX. | 14.9x9.4cm. 455p.

UTENHOVE, John. Simplex Et | fidelis narratio de | Institvta Ac Demvm Dis- | sipata Belgarum, aliorumq[ue] peregri- | norum in Anglia, Ecclesia: & potissi- | mum de susceptis postea illius nomine | itineribus, quæq[ue] eis in illis | euenerunt. | In qua multa de Cœnæ Dominicæ ne- | gocio, alijsq; rebus lectu dignis- | simis tractantur. | Per Ioannem Vten- | houium Gandauum. | . . . (3 lines)

1560. | Colophon: Basileæ, Ex Officina | Ioannis Oporini, Anno Salutis hu- | manæ M.D.LX. | Mense | Martio. | 15.7x9.8 cm. 282,(27)p.

VÉRON, John. A moste | necessary treatise of free | wil, not onlye against the Pa- | pistes, but also against the Anabap- | tistes, which in these our daies, go | about to renue the detestable here- | sies of Pelagius, and of the Luciferians, | whiche say and affirm, that we | be able by our own natural | strength to fulfil the law | and commaunde- | mentes of | God. | Made dialoge wyse by Ihon Ve- | ron, in a manner word by | woorde, as he did set it | forth in his lectures | at Paules. |

Without imprint. Engr. border. Colophon: Imprinted at Lon- | don by Ihon Tisdale, and | are to be sold at hys shop in | Lombard streate. | Cum priuilegio, ad imprimendum | solum. | [1560?] 13.2x9 cm. (8,80)fol.

1561

BALE, John. A declara- | tion of Edmonde Bon- | ners articles, concerning the | cleargye of Lōdon dyocese where- | by that excerable Antychriste, is in | his righte colours reue- | led in the yeare of our | Lord a.1554. | By John | Bale. | Newlye set fourth & allowed, ac- |

cording to the order appointed | in the Quenes Maiesties | Iniunctions. | . . . (7 lines).

Colophon: Imprynted | at London, by Jhon | Tysdall, for Frauncys Col- | docke, dwellinge in Lombard | strete, ouer agaynste the | Cardinalles hatte, and | are there to be sold | at his shoppe. | 1561. | 12.8x8.2cm.   (11),120,41–71 fol. Misnumbered throughout.

BUCER, Martin.   Nova Ve | tera Qvatvor Ev- | charistica Scripta Svm- | mi & acutissimi Theologi, Docto- | ris Martini Bvceri | Argentoratensis. | Ioannis Stvrmii Ve- | tvs, Renovatvs Do- | lor de hoc dissidio Eu- | charistico. | Ad D.Antonivm Cookvm | Equitem Anglum. |

Argentorati, | M.D.LXI. | Colophon: Argentinæ Ex Officina | Theobaldi Bergeri, Anno Sa- | lutis humanæ M.D.LXI. | Mense Martio. | 15.5x9.6cm.   (8),39fol.

CALVIN, John.   The Institvtion Of | Christian Religion, written in La- | tine by Maister Ihon Caluin, and transla- | ted into Englysh according to the | authors last edition. | Seen and allowed according to the order appointed in the | Quenes maiesties iniunctions. | (device).

Imprinted at London by | Reinolde Wolfe & Richarde Harison. | Anno. 1561. | Cum priuilegio ad imprimendum solum. | 28.6x18.7cm.   (8), 502, (2)fol.

FOX, John.   Historia | Von Thoma Cran- | mero, dem Ertzbischoff zu Cantu- | aria inn Engelland. | Wie er vmb der Warheit willen des heiligen | Euangelii gefenglich eingezogen, vnd folgends | zu Oxonien ist verbrand worden, vnd wie er | sich beide in seinem Gefengnus, vnd auch | in seiner Marter gehalten hat, | sehr nützlich zu | lesen. | Durch Johannem Foxum Engel- | lender beschrieben, Vnd itzt aus dem | Latein verdeutscht. |

Gedruckt zu Weissenfels, Durch | Georgium Dantzsch. | 1561. | Ornament.   19.3x 15.4cm.   (4,47)p.

ORDERS taken the | x. day of October, in the thirde yere | of the raigne of our Soueraigne Ladye, | Elizabeth Quene of Englande, Fraunce | and Irelande, defender of the fayth, &c. | By vertue of her Maiesties letters ad- | dressed to her hyghnesse Commissi- | oners for causes Ecclesiasti- | call as foloweth. | [An. 1561.] |

Colophon: Imprinted at London in Powles Church | yarde by Richarde Jugge, Printer | to the Quenes Maiestie. | Cum priuilegio Regiæ Maiestatis. | [1561] 18.3x13cm..   (2)fol.

TYNDALE, William.   The O | bedyence of a Chry- | sten man, and howe | christen rulers ought to | governe, wher in also (if | thou marke dilygently) | thou shalt finde eyes | to perceave ye craf | ty conveiaunce | of all jug- | glers |

Without imprint. Colophon: Imprinted at London by | Wyllyam Coplande | 1561. | Wood-cut border.   12.8x8.8cm.   iv-clxxi,(8)fol. Lacks fol i–v: t.p. supplied by Edward G. Friehold of London.

VÉRON, John.   The Hvn- | tynge of Purga- | torye to death, made | Dialoge wyse, by | Ihon Veron | Senonoys. | Newly setfoorth and alowed, ac | cordinge too the order appoynted | in the Quenes Maiesties | Jniunctions. | . . . (4 lines) (arch. border)

Colophon: Imprynted | at London, by Ihon | Tysdale, and are to be solde | at his shoppe in the vpper ende | of Lombard strete, in All- | hallowes churchyard, | nere vnto grace | churche. | 1561. | 14.1x9.4 cm.   (7),397,(15)fol.

VÉRON, John. The ouer | throw of the iustificati- | on of workes and of the vain | doctrin of the merits of men, with | the true assertion of the iustificati- | on of faith and of the good workes | that procead or come of the same, | and in what respect our good | workes are crouned or re- | warded of God sette | foorth dialoge wise | by Iohn Ve- | ron. | . . . (6 lines). Newlye set foorthe and alowed accor- | dynge to the order appoynted in the | Quenes maiesties iniunctions. | Ano. 1561. | (device)

Colophon: Imprynted | at London, by Ihon | Tysdale, and are to be solde | at his shoppe in the vpper ende | of Lombard strete, in All- | hallowes churchyard, | nere | vnto grace | churche. | 1561. | 13x8.6 cm.   (7),74,(6)fol.

1562

An ACT for Canturburie concerning the priuileges | of the same Cap. xviii. |
1562.   28.9x19.5cm.   Henry VIII. [Statutes] Anno 34–35.   fol.25b–26b.

An ACT for the new erected bisshops to pay their tenthes | in the courte of first fruites.   Cap. xvii. |
1562.   Henry VIII [Statutes], An.34–35.   fol.24b.

An ACTE for paymente of pencions and porcions, graunted | out of the late abbeyes,   Cap. xix. |
1562.   Henry VIII [Statutes] An.34–35.   fol.26b.

An ACTE for the aduauncement of true religion and for | the abolishment of the contrary.   Cap.i. |
1562.   Henry VIII [Statutes] An.34–35,fol.(2).

An ACTE touchinge the deane and chapiter of Welles, to be | one sole chapiter of it selfe.   cap.xv. |
1562.   Henry VIII. [Statutes] An.34–35, fol.(21b).

An APOLOGIE | of priuate Masse, spred a | broade in writing without name | of the authour: as it seemeth, a- | gainst the offer and protestacion | made in certayne Sermons by | the reuerent father Bisshop of | Salsburie: with an answer to | the same Apologie, set foorth | for the maintenance and | defence of the | trueth. | Perused and allowed, by the reuerent | father in God Edmonde Bisshop | of London, accordynge to the | order appointed in the | Queenes maiesties | Jniunctions. |
Londini. | Mens.Nouemb. | 1562. | Colophon: Imprynted at London in | Fleete- streete, by Thomas | Powell. | 14x9cm.   31;(5),123fol.
DNB.12:149b.   Camb.Univ.Cat.No.1246.

BECON, Thomas. The first part | of the bokes, whiche Tho- | mas Becon made and published | in ye name of Theodor Basille, dili- | gētly perused and corrected, and | now newely set forth in this | present yere of our Lorde, | 1560. | The names of the bokes | contayned in thys first parte. | 1. The Newes out of Heauen. . 2. The Christmas Banket. | 3. The Potacion for Lent. | 4. The Pathway vnto Prayer. | 5. The Nosegay. | 6. The Polecye of warre. | 7. Dauids Harpe. | 8. The Newe yeres gyfte. | 9. The Inuectiue against swearing | 10. The Gouernaunce of vertue. | 11. The Catechisme. | 12. The Boke of Matrimonie. |

No imprint. Arch. border. Colophon: Portrait I.D. dated 1562. Imprinted at London | by Iohn Day dwelling ouer Alders- | gate beneth saynt Martins. | Cum gratia & priuilegio Regiæ | magestatis. | These bookes are to be sold at his shop | vnder the gate. | 28.x18.9 cm. (20),1–96,(1),97–143,(1),144–169,(1),170–678,(1)fol. (Omitted: fols. 28,274–278,465–470,544,601,660,667; Repeated: fols. 263,285,286, 317,455–460,596; Misnumbered: fols. 5,77,84,121,223,301,315,317,331–2,349–352,465–470,498,514,526–527,530,532,543–544,554,562,566,592–593,595,620,629,641,646,654,662.

BUCER, Martin. Prælectiones Doctiss. | In Epistolam D. | P.ad Ephesios, eximij docto- | ris D. Martini Buceri, habitæ | Cantabrigiæ in Anglia, | Anno M D.L. & LI. | Ex ore prælegentis collectæ, & nunc primùm in lucem editæ, diligentia | Immanuelis Tremelij Theologiæ doctoris, & eiusdem profes- | soris in Academia Heydelbergensi. | Cvm Indice Copiosissimo. | (device).

Basileæ | Apvd Petrvm Pernam. | Colophon: Basileæ, | Apud Petrum Pernam, Anno dominicæ incarnationis | M.D.LXII. | 32.7x20.5cm. 190,(12)p.

CERTAYNE Ser- | mons appoynted by | the Queenes | Maiestie, | to be declared and read, by al | Persons, Vycars & Curates | euery Sundaye and holyday, | in their Churches: And bi her | Graces aduise perused and o- | uersene, for the better vn- | derstandynge of the | symple people. | Newely Imprinted in partes | according as is mentioned | in the boke of Com- | mon Prayers. |

M.D.LXIJ. | Wood-cut border. Colophon: Imprinted at London in Powles | Churchyarde, by Richarde Jugge, and | John Cawood Printers to the | Queenes Maiestyes. | Cum Privilegio Regiae Maiestatis. | (3,127)fol. Lacks 6 fol. at end. A–Rii in eights.
Items supplied by Mr. Edward G. Friehold, of London.
Second edition of Certayne Sermons, or Homelies: 1547.

COOPER, Thomas. An Answere in | defence of the truth. | Againste the | Apologie | of | priuate | Masse. |

Londini | Mens.Nouēb. | 1562. | Border. 14x9cm. (5),123fol.
Sub-title, Appended to the Apologie, to which it is the answer.
Anon. Cambr.Univ.Cat. 1245.

HENRY VIII [Statutes]. Anno XXXIIII. Et.V. | Henrici | Octavi. | Actes made in the session of this present | parliamente holden vpon prorogacion at | Westminster the .xxii. day of January in | the .xxxiiii. yere of the reigne of our moste | drad soueraigne lorde Henry the eyght by | the grace of god king of England Fraunce | and Ireland defendour of the faith and of | the church of England and also of Ireland | in earth the supreme head, and there conti- | nued and kepte tyll the .xii. day of May | in the .xxxv. yere of our sayde soue- | raigne lord, to the honour of god | and for the common weale | and profite of this | his realme. |

Execudebat Londoni, | 1562. | Border. 28.9x19.5cm. (47)fol.

JEWEL, John. An Apologie, | or aunswer in defence | of the Church of England, | conceringe the state of | Religion vsed in the same. | Newly set forth in Latine, and nowe translated | into Englishe. | (device) . . . (5 lines).

Londini, | Anno Domini M.D.LXII. | Colophon: Imprinted At London | by Reginalde Wolfe. | Anno 1562. | (device) 19.3x13.8 cm. 70fol. Misnumberings. Anon.Cambr.Univ.Cat. 744.

LATIMER, Hugh. Certayn Godly | Sermons, made vppon the lords | Prayer, preached by the right reuerende | Father, and constant martyr of Christ, Master | Hughe Latymer, before the ryght honora- | ble, and vertuous Lady Katherine, | Duches of Suffolke, in the | yeare of our Lorde. | 1553. | Whereunto are annexed certaine other ser- | mons, preached by the sayde reuerende Father, in | Lincolneshire, which were gathered, and collec- | ted by Augustine Bernher, a seruant of his, | though not so perfectly as they were vtte- | red: yet faythfully & truly, to the singu- | ler commoditie & profyt of the christē | reader, faythfully perused & alow- | ed according to thorder appoin- | ted in the Queenes Maie- | sties Iniunctions. | . . . (3 lines).

Imprinted at Lōdon by John | Day, dwelling ouer Albersgate. | Cumgratia & priuilegio Re- | gię Majestatis, per septen- | nium. | An.1562. | Engr.border. 17.7x 13.2cm. (6),148 fol.
Part of his 27 Sermons: 1562.

LATIMER, Hugh. 27 | Sermons Prea- | ched by the ryght Reuer- ende | Father in God and constant Matir of | Jesus Christe, Maister Hugh Latimer, as | well such as in tymes past haue bene printed, | as certayne other commyng to our handes of late, | whych were yet neuer set forth in print. | Faithfully perused & allowed accor- | dyng to the order appoynted in | the Quenes Maiesties | Iniunctions. | 1.Hys sermon Ad clerum. | 2.Hys fourth sermon vpon the plough. | 3.Hys 7.sermons before kyng Edward. | 4 Hys sermon at Stamforde. | 5.Hys last sermon before kyng Edward. | 6.Hys.7.sermons vpon the Lordes prayer. | 7.Hys other.9.sermons vpon certayne Gospels | and Epistles. |

Imprinted at London by John | Day, dwelling ouer Aldersgate. | Cum gratia & priuilegio Regię Maie- | statis, per septenium. | Anno. 1562. | Engr.border. 17.7x 13.2cm. 22;(3),23–83,91–130;(6),148fol. Folded cut: Latimer preaching before the king. Two sub t.p.

The | LAVVES and Statu- | tes of Geneua, as well concerning ecclesiastical | Discipline, as ciuill regiment, with certeine | Proclamations duly executed, whereby Gods | religion is most purelie mainteined, and their | common wealth quietli gouerned: Translated | out of Frenche into Englishe by | Robert Fills. | . . . (2 lines: device).

Printed At Lon- | don by Rouland Hall, dwellyng in Gutter | Lane, at the sygne of the halfe Egle | and the Keye. | 1562. | Colophon: Printed at London | by Rouland Hall | and Thomas Hac- | ket, the 16. of A- | prill, in the yere | of our lorde | 1562. | 13.2x8.7 cm. (8),87,(1)fol.

POLE, Reginald. De Concilio | Liber | Reginaldi Poli | Cardinalis. | (device).
Romae, M.D.LXII. | Apud Paulum Manutium Aldi F. | 17.8x13.8cm (7),64 fol.

POLE, Reginald. Reformatio Angliae, | Ex Decretis Reginaldi | Poli Cardinalis, | Sedis Apostolicae Legati, | Anno M.D.LVI. | (device)
Romae, M.D.LXII. | Apud Paulum Manutium Aldi F. | 17.8x13.8cm. 27,(1) fol.

POLE, Reginald. Reginaldi Poli | Card. Amplissimi | Liber, | De Concilio. | Eivsdem | De Baptismo Constantini | Magni Imperatoris. | Reformatio Angliæ. | Ex Decretis Eivsdem. | Accessit rerum, & uer- | borum me- | morabilium index. | (device)
Venetiis, | Ex Officina Iordani | Zileti, M.D.LXII. | Colophon: idem. 14,8x9.3 cm. 128,(7)fol.

VERMIGLI, Pietro Martir. Defensio | Doctrinæ veteris & Apos- | tolicæ | de sacrosancto Eucharistiæ Sacramento, D. | Petri Martyris Vermilii Florenti- | ni, diuinarum literarum in schola Tigurina pro- | fessoris, in quatuor distin- | cta partes, aduersus Stephani Gardineri, quondam Vuintoniensis Epi- | scopi, librum, sub nomine M.Antonij Constantij editum, &c. Cui de | nouo iam accesserunt, primùm quidem Tractatio, deinde ue- | rò Dispvtatio de eodem Eucharistiæ Sacramento, | eiusdem authoris, habita in celeberrima Vni- | uersitate Oxoniensi in Anglia. | . . . (4 lines; device) Accedvnt operi Indices duo, Rerum inquā, & Locorum cum Scripturæ | sanctæ, tum antiquorum Patrum, qui hoc in libro explicantur. | . . . (3 lines).
M.D.LXII. | 31.4x20.cm. (24),725p.

VERON, John. A stronge bat- | tery against the Ido- | latrous inuocation of the | dead Saintes, and against the | hauyng or setting vp of Ima- | ges in the house of prayer, or | in any other place where | there is any paril of | Idolatrye, made | dialoguewise | by John | Veron. | . . . (5 lines). Engraved border.
Colophon: Imprinted At | London by Henry Sutton for | Thomas Hacket. | The x. daye of Marche. | In the yere of our Lorde God | 1562. | 13.8x9.2cm. (15),108 fol.

1563

An ACTE against Coniurations, Enchaunt- | mentes, and Witch- craftes. |
1563. Elizabeth, Queen [Statutes] An.v, fol.53.

An ACTE against fonde and phantasti- | call Prophesies. |
1563. Elizabeth, Queen. [Statutes]. An.v, fol.52b

An ACTE for the due execution of the writ, | de excommunicato capiendo. |
1563. Elizabeth, Queen. [Statutes] An.v, fol 59.

An ACTE for the punishment of vagaboundes, | calling them selues Egiptians. |

1563   Elizabeth, Queen [Statutes] An.v, fol.55 b.

ELIZABETH, Queen. [Statutes] Anno v. Anno Qvinto Reginæ | Elizabethe. | At the Parliament holden at | Westminster the .xii. of Janu- | ary, in the fyfth yere of the | raigne of our Soueraigne | Lady Elizabeth, by the | grace of God, of Eng- | lande, Fraunce, | and Irelande | Queene, | defendour of the fayth, &c. To the | hygh pleasure of Almyghtie God, | and the weale publique of | this Realme, were | enacted as fo- | loweth. | 1563. |

Wood-cut border. Colophon: Imprinted at London in | Powles Churchyarde by Rycharde | Jugge and John Cawood, | Printers to the Queenes | Maiestie. | Cum priuilegio Regiæ Maiestatis. | 26.3x18.5 cm.   71,(19)fol.
Two parts: same colophon at the end of each. Cabr.Univ.Cat.No.962.
Chapters 26, 27, 28 and 30 are omitted, though included in table of contents.

FOX, John. Actes | and Monuments | of these latter and perillous dayes, | touching matters of the Church, wherein | ar comprehended and described the great persecu- | tions & horrible troubles, that have bene wrought | and practiced by the Romishe Prelates, special- | lye in this Realme of England and Scot- | lande, from the yeare of our Lorde a | thousande, vnto the tyme | nowe present. | Gathered and collected according to the | true copies & wrytinges certificatorie as wel | of the parties themselues that suffered, as | also out of the Bishops Registers, | which wer the doers therof, | by Iohn Foxe. |

Imprinted at London by Iohn Day, | dwellyng ouer Aldersgate. | Cum priuilegio Regię Maiestatis. | Engr.t.p.   29.4x20.5cm.   (24),1741,(1,40)p. Colophon: Imprinted at London | by Iohn Day dwelling ouer Alders- | gate beneth saynt Martins, Anno. | 1563. the .20 of March. | Cum gratia & priuilegio Regiae | Maiestatis. | These bookes are to be sold at his shop | vnder the gate. |

MUSCULUS, Wolfgang. Common | places | of Christian Religion, gathered by | Wolfgangus Musculus, for the vse of | suche as desire the knowledge of Godly | truthe. translated out of Latine | into Englishe. | Hereunto are added two other treatises made by the | same Author, one of Othes, and an | other of Vsurye. | With a most perfecte and plentifull Table. | (cut). |

Londini. | Anno Domini. M.D.LXIII. | Colophon: Imprinted at London by | Reginalde Wolfe. | Anno Domini.1563. | 27.9x19.cm   (6),587,(1,30)fol.

The SECONDE | Tome of Homelyes of | such matters as were pro- | mised and Jntituled in | the former part of Ho- | melyes, set out by | the aucthoritie of | the Quenes | Maiestie: | And to be read in euery | paryshe Churche | agreablye. |

1563 | Engraved border. Colophon, fol. 292b: Imprinted at Lon- | don in Powles Churcheyarde, | by Richard Jugge, and Jhon Ca- | wood, Prynters to the | Quenes Maie- | stie. | Cum priuilegio Regiæ Maiestatis. | At the end: An Homilie a- | gainst disobedience and wylfull | rebellion | (in six parts). Separate register 18.6x12.8 cm.   (2),292,(39)fol.

SMITH, Richard. De | Libero Ho- | minis Arbitrio Adversvs | Ioannem Caluinum, & quotquot impiè illud | auferunt, Lutherum

imitati. | Autore Richardo Smythæo VVigorniensi, Anglo, | S. Theo-
logiæ Professore in Academia Duacensi. | Omnium quæ hoc libro
tractabuntur, copiossissimum | in fine libri reperies Indicem. | (device).

Lovanii | Ex officina Ioannis Bogardi sub | Bibliis Aureis. An.1563. | Cvm
Gratia Et Privilegio. | 17x10.9cm. (3),69fol.

SMITH, Richard. Refvtatio | Locorum communium | Theologico-
rvm, Phi- | lippi Melanchthonis, Germani, M.Lu- | theri discipuli
primarij, dedicata Princi- | pum illustrissimo, ac catholicissimo Phi- |
lippo, Regi Hispaniarum, &c. | Autore, Ricardo Smythæo, Anglo,
eiusdem | Principis sacellano, ac Theologiæ, in illius | Achademia
Duacensi, Prælectore. | . . . (device: 1563).

Dvaci. | Prostant apud Nicolaum Lapidanum. | Cum gra. & Priuile.Regiæ
Maiestatis. | Colophon: Duaci, Typis Iacobi Bosschaert. | 16.x10.2 cm. (11),
112fol.

A SVM Or A Brief | collection of holy signes, sacrifices and | Sac-
raments, euen since the begin- | ning of the worlde. | And the true
originall of the sacrifice of the | Masse. Translated out of French
into | Englishe by N.Lynge. | . . . (4 lines; device).

Printed At London | by Rouland Hall, dwelling in gutter | Lane, at the signe
of the halfe | Egle and Key. | 1563. | 13.8x9.cm. (7,92)fol.
Title supplied by E.H.F.Mills, Cambridge University Library.

VERON, John. An Apolo- | gye or defence of the doc- | tryne of
Predestination, sette | foorth by the Quenes highnesse | hyr most
humble and obedy- | ente subiect Iohn Veron and | dedicated too hyr |
maiestye. |

Without t.p. Colophon: Imprynted | at London, by Jhon | Tysdale, and are
to be solde | at hys shoppe in the vpper ende | of Lombarde strete, in Alhal- |
lowes church yarde nere | vntoo Grace | churche. | 13x8.6cm. 43,(4)fol.
Part of his Frvtefvl treatise of predestination: 1563, with separate register and
pagination.

VERON, John. A Frvtefvl | treatise of predestination | and of the
diuine prouidence of god, | with an apology of the same, against | the
swynyshe gruntings of the | Epicures and Athey- | stes of oure | time. |
Whereunto are added, as de- | pending of it a very necessary boke
a | gainste the free wyll men, and an o- | ther of the true iustification
of faith, | and of the good workes procea- | dynge of the same, made |
Dialoge wyse by | Ihon Veron. |

Imprinted at London by | Iohn Tisdale, and are to be solde at | his shop in the
vpper end of Lom- | bard strete, in Alhallowes churchyard, nere vnto | grace
church. | [1563?] 13.x8.6cm. (12),115,(6);43,(4)fol. Colophon after each part,
with separate registers. Title supplied from Bodleian copy.

1564

ADUERTISMENTS | partly for due order in the publique | ad-
ministration of common prayers | and vsinge the holy Sacramentes, |
and partly for the apparrell of all persons ec- | clesiasticall, by vertue
of the Queenes maiesties | letters commaunding the same, the xxv. day

of | January, in the seuenth yeare of the raigne | of oure Soueraigne Lady Elyzabeth, by | the grace of God, of Englande, Fraunce | and Irelande Queene, defender | of the fayth, &c. | (device)

Londini. | Cum priuilegio ad imprimen- | dum solum. | Colophon: Imprinted at London by | Reginalde Wolfe. | [1564]. 17.3x13.4 cm. (8)fol.
Also Reprints in Sparrow's Collection of Articles: 1661, 1675 and 1684.

BALDWIN, William. A treatyce of | Moral philosophy contai- | ning the sayinges of the wise. Wher- | in you maye see the worthye and pithye | sayinges of ye Philosophers, Emperors, | kinges, and ora- tours, of their liues, their | aunswers, of what lignage they came | of, and of what coūtrey they were, whose | worthy and notable preseptes, counsailes | parables and semblables doth hereafter | folow: First gath- ered and englished by | Williā Baldwin, after that, twise aug- | mented by Thomas Paulfreyman, one | of the gentle men of the Queenes | maiesties chaple, & now once | againe enlarged by the | first aucthor |

Cum priuilegio. | 1564. | Colophon: Imprinted at London in Fleete | strete with- in Temple barre | at the signe of the hande | and Starre, by Ry- | charde Cortill. | The first day of Decembre. | Anno 1564. | Cum priuilegio ad impri- | mendum solum. | 13.7x9cm. (7),224fol. Fol. 173 omitted, and 184 repeated: lacks fol. 137-144.

BECON, Thomas. The | Worckes of | Thomas Becon, | whiche he hath hytherto made | and published, with diuerse other | newe Bookes added to the same, | heretofore neuer set forth in print | diuided into thre tomes or parts | diligently perused, corrected, | and amended: and now fini- | shed this present of our | Lord .1564. | Perused and allowed, accordyng to thorder ap | pointed in the Quenes maiesties iniunctions. | . . . (4 lines).

Imprinted at London, by John | Day, dwellyng ouer Aldersgate. | These Bookes are to be solde at his | shop vnder the gate. | Engraved border. 28.8 x 18.7 cm. I, (21),678 fol. (sub t.p. before fols.97,144,170,199,225. fol. 566 ommited) II, 299 fol. III, (7),513 fol. 123-128, misnumbered, 143-154 omitted.
Colophon Vol. III: Imprinted at London | by John Day, dwelling ouer Alders- gate, | beneath Saint Martins. | Cum gratia & priuilegio Regiæ Maiestatis. | The xxv, day of Nouember. 1563. |

CERTAIN most god- | ly, fruitful, and comfortable letters of | such true Saintes and holy Martyrs of | God, as in the late bloodye perse- cution here | within this Realme, gaue their lyues | for the defence of Christes holy | gospel: written in the tyme | of theyr affliction and | cruell impryson- | ment. | . . . (2 lines)

Jmprinted at London by Iohn Day, | dwelling ouer Aldersgate, be- | neath Saint Martines. 1564. | Cum gratia & priuilegio Regiæ Maiestatis. | Woodcut border Colophon. 17.5x12.8 cm. (8),682,(4)p.
Edited by Miles Coverdale.

DORMAN, Thomas. A Provfe Of Cer- | teyne Articles In Reli- | gion, Denied By M.Ivell, | sett furth in defence of the Catholyke be- | leef therein, by Thomas Dorman, | Bachiler of Diuinite | VVhere- vnto is added in the end, a conclusion, conteinyng .xij. | Causes, vvhereby the Author acknovvlegeth hym self to haue | byn stayd in hys olde Catholyke fayth that he vvas | baptized in, vvysshyng the same to be made | common to many for the lyke stay | in these perilouse tymes. | . . . (9 lines; device)

Imprinted at Antwerp by Iohn Latius, at the | signe of the Rape, with Priuilege. | Anno.1564. | 19.6x15 cm. (4),141 fol. Lacks fol. 142ff.

A GODLY and neces- | sarye admonition of the Decrees and Ca- | nons of the Counsel of Trent, celebrated vn- | der Pius the fourth, Byshop of Rome, in the | yeares of our Lord .M.D.LXJJ. | and M.D.-LXJJJ. | Wrytten for those godlye disposed persons | sakes, whych looke for amendement of Doctrine and | Ceremonies to bee made by generall | Counsels. Lately translated | out of Latine. | . . . (7 lines).

Imprinted at London by John Day, | dwellyng ouer Aldersgate beneath | Saint Martins. | Cum gratia et priuilegio Regiæ Maiestatis | per septennium. | The .xix. of February.1564. | These bookes are to be sold at hys shop | vnder the Gate. | 16.8x12.9 cm (10),125p. Colophon.
Ascribed to Archbishop Parker.

HARDING, Thomas. An Answere | To Maister Ivelles | Chalenge, By Doctor | Harding. | . . . (4 lines; device)

Imprinted in Louaine by Iohn Bogard at the | Golden Bible, with priuilege. | Anno.1564. | 16.2 x 13.4cm. (8),193,(5) fol.

VERMIGLI, Pietro Martir. Most fruit | full & learned Cōmenta- | ries of Doctor Peter Martir Ver- | mil Florentine, Professor of Deui- | nitie, in the Uniuersitye of Tygure, | with a very profitable tract of the | matter and places. | Herein is also added & contained | two most ample Tables, aswel of the | matter, as of the wordes: wyth | an Index of the places in | the holy scripture. | . . . (5 lines) Set forth & allowed, accordyng to thorder ap- | pointed in the Queens maiesties iniunctions. |

Imprinted at London by John | Day, dwellyng over Aldersgate. | These Bookes are to be solde at his | shop vnder the gate. | Engraved border. Colophon: Imprinted at London | by Iohn Day, dwellyng ouer Alders- | gate, beneath saynt Martyns. Anno | 1564. the 28. of September. | Cum gratia & priuilegio Regiæ | Maiestatis. | These bokes are to be sold at his shop | vnder the gate. | 28.6 x 19. cm. (5),288,(8) fol.

1565

ALLEN, William. A Defence | And Declaration | Of The Catholike | Chvrchies Doctrine, | touching Purgatory, and pra- | yers for the Soules departed. | by William Allen | Master of Arte and student | in Diuinitye. | . . . (2 lines; cut).

Imprinted at Antwerp by Iohn | Latius, with | Priuilege. | Anno. 1565. | 14.9x 9.5cm. 2–289,(6)fol. T.p. supplied: fols. 8 and 228 lacking.

ALLEY, William. Πτωχὸμυσεῖον. | The Poore mans | Librarie. | Rapsodiæ G.A. | Bishop of Exceter vpon the first Epistle | of saint Peter, red publiquely in the Cathedrall | Church of Saint Paule, within the Citye | of London .1560. | . . . (13 lines). Here are adjoyned at the end of euery special trea- | tie, certaine fruitful annotacions which may pro- | perly be called Miscellanea, because they do entreate | of diuerse and sundry matters, marked with the | nombre and figures of Augrime 2. | . . . (5 lines).

Imprinted at London by Iohn Day. | Colophon: Imprinted at London, by Iohn | Day, dwellyng ouer Aldersgate, beneath | Saint Martins. | Cum gratia & priuilegio Regiæ Maiestatis, | per Septennium. | These Bookes are to be solde, at hys shop | vnder the gate. | 1565. | 26.6x19.3cm. (3),2–292,140,14 fol. Lacks first three folios.
Camb Univ Cat. 806.

BÈZE, Théodore de. A briefe and pith- | thie some of the christian faith | made in forme of a confession, vvith a con- | futacion of all such superstitious | errours, as are contrary | therevnto. Made by | Theodore de Beza. | Translated out of Frenche by | R.F. | (device)

Printed at London | by Richard Serll, dwelling in Flete | lane, at the signe of the halfe | Egle an the Key. | [1565?] 13.3x9.3 cm. fol.(22)195.
See McKerrow's Dictionary of Printers . . . 1557–1640.
Dated 1563? by Herbert. DNB, 18:440a

BRES, Guy de. La Racine, | Sovrce Et | Fondement Des | Anabaptistes Ov | Rebaptisez De | Nostre Temps. | Avec Tresample Refv- | tation des arguments principaux, par lesquels | ils ont accoustumé de troubler l'Eglise de no- | stre Seigneur Iesus Christ, & seduire les sim- | ples. | Le tout reduict en trois liures, par | Gvy De Bres. | (device)

Chez Abel Clemence. | M.D.LXV. | 14x13.3 cm. (16),903,(1)p.

Ane | BREIF Gather- | ing Of The Halie Sig- | nes, Sacrifices And Sa- | cramentis Institvtit Of | God sen the Creation of the | warlde. And of the | trew originall of | the Sacrifice | of the | messe. | (Devices). Translatit out of Frenche into Scottis | be ane Faithful Brother. | . . . (3 lines).

Imprintit at Edinbvrgh | be Robert Lekprevik. | M.D.LXV. | 17.4x13.3cm. 46 fol. H&L, new edit. ascribes to W: Stewart.

COOPER, Thomas. Coopers Chronicle | Contenynge the vvhole discourse | of the histories as well of thys | realme, as all other countries. | with the succession of theyr | Kynges, the tyme of theyr | raign, and what notable | actes were do ne by thē | newely enlarged and | augmented, as well | in the first parte | wyth diuers | profitable | Histor- | ries. | as in the latter ende wyth the whole summe | of those thynges that Paulus Jouius | and Sleigdane hath written of late | yers that is now lately ouersene | and with great dilligence cor- | rected and augmented vn | to the .vii. yere of the | raigne of our most | gracious Quene | Elizabeth that | now is.

Anno.1565. the first day | of Auguste. | Device. 18.7x13.5cm. (30),376,(15)fol.
Camb. Univ Cat (6750) ascribes parts 1–2 to Thomas Languet.

HARDING, Thomas. A Confvtation | Of A Booke Intitvled | An Apologie Of The | Chvrch Of England, By | Thomas Harding Doctor | Of Divinitie. | . . . (8 lines; device).

Imprinted at Antwerpe, by Ihon Laet, | with Priuilege. 1565. | 19.9x14.7cm (12),351,(8)fol. 9–16 supplied in Ms.

HOSIUS, Stanislaus. A Most Excel- | lent Treatise Of The | begynnyng of heresyes in oure tyme, com- | pyled by the Reuerend Father in God | Stanislavs Hosivs Byshop | of Wormes in Prussia. | To the moste renomed Prynce Lorde Sigismund | myghtie Kyng of Poole, greate Duke of | Luten and Russia, Lorde and Heyre of | all Prussia, Masouia, Samogitia &c. | Translated out of Laten in to Englyshe by | Richard Shacklock M. of Arte, and student | of the Ciuil lawes, and intituled by hym: | The hatchet of heresies. | . . . (3 lines).

Imprinted at Antwerp by Æg Diest. | Anno. 1565. the .10. of August. | Cvm Privilegio. | 14.4x9.5 cm. (15),95,(1)fol.

JEWEL, John. A Replie | Vnto M.Hardinges | Ansvveare: | By perusinge whereof the discrete, and diligent Reader may | easily see, the weake, and vnstable groundes of | the Romaine Religion, whiche of late | hath beene accompted | Catholique. | By Iohn Iewel Bishoppe | of Sarisburie. | . . . (10 lines).

Imprinted at London in Fleetestreate, at | the signe of the Blacke Oliphante, | by Henry VVykes. | Decimoquinto Ianuarij. | Anno 1565. | VVith special Priuilege. | 27.x19.1cm. (49),641,(10)p.
Also another impression, lacking the month date. 27.6x19cm. (23),641,(10)p.

NOWELL, Alexander. A Reprovfe, | written by Alexander Nowell, of | a booke entituled, | A Provfe Of Cer- | tayne Articles in Reli- | gion denied by M.Iuell, set furth | by Thomas Dorman, Bachiler | of Diuinitie. | . . . (5 lines). Set foorth and allowed, according to the | Queenes Maiesties Iniunctions. |

Jmprinted at London in Fleete- | streete, by Henry Wykes. | Anno Domini 1565. | 30.die Maij. | 17.8x13.3cm. (8),124fol. Colophon.

STAPHYLUS, Fridericus. The Apologie | Of Fridericvs Staphy- | lvs Covnseller To | The Late Emperovr | Ferdinandvs, &c. | Intreating | Of the true and right vnderstanding of holy Scripture. | Of the translation of the Bible in to the vulgar tongue. | Of disagrement in doctrine amonge the protestants. | Translated out of Latin in to English by Thomas | Stapleton, Student in Diuinite. | Also a discourse of the Translatour vppon the doctrine of the | protestants vvhich he trieth by the three first founders | and fathers thereof, Martin Luther, Philip | Melanchthon, and especially | Iohn Caluin. | . . . (4 lines; device).

Imprinted at Antwerp by Iohn Latius, | at the signe of the Rape, with Pri- | uilege. Anno. 1565. | 19x13.2 cm. 254,(4)fol. 1 tab.

STAPLETON, Thomas. A Fortresse Of | The Faith | First planted amonge vs englishmen, and continued | hitherto in the vniuersall Church of Christ. | The faith of which time Protestants call, | Papistry. | By Thomas Stapleton | Student in Diuinite. | . . . (5 lines; device).

Imprinted at Antwerpe, by Ihon Laet, | with Priuilege. 1565. | 19.3x14.3cm. 162,(2)fol.

1566

An ACTE declaring the ma- | ner of making and consecrating of the Arch- | bishops and Bishops of this Realme, to be | good, lawfull, and perfect. |

1566. Elizabeth, Queen [Statutes] An.viii, fol.(2).

The ACTIS And Con, | stitutiounis of the Realme of Scotland maid in Parliamentis haldin | te the ryche excellent, hie and mychtie Princeis Kingis James the | First, Secund, thrid, Feird, Fyft, and in tyme of Marie now Quene | of Scottis, viseit, correctit, and extractit furth of the Registers be the | Lordis depute be hir Maiesteis speciall commissioun thairto. | Anno.Do .1566. | (arms.)

No imprint. Colophon: Imprentit at Edinburgh | be Robert Lekpreuik, the xxviij. day of Nouember, the zeir | of God ane thousand fyue hundreth thre scoir sax zeiris. | device. 27.4x19.1cm. (14),2–182fol

An ANSVVERE | For The | Tyme, To The Ex- | amination put in print, vvith out | the authours name, pretending to | mayntayne the apparrell prescribed | against the declaration of the myni- | sters of London. | . . . (4 lines).

M.D.LXVI. | 13.8x8.7 cm. 153,(1)p. folded leaf between A1 and 2.

BARTHLET, John. The Pedegrewe of Heretiques. | Wherein is truely and plainely | set out, the first roote of Heretiques be- | gon in the Church, since the time | and passage of the Gospell, together | with an example of the of- | spring of the same. | . . . (3 lines) | Perused and alowed according to the order appoynted in | the Queenes Maiesties Iniunctions. | (device).

Imprinted at London by Henry Denham, | for Lucas Harryson. Anno 1566. | Colophon. 17.2x13.3 cm. (4),89,(1)fol.
Epistle signed.

BUCER, Martin. The mynd and | exposition of that excellente | learned man Martyn Bu- | cer, uppon these wordes of | S.Mathew: Woo be to | the worlde bycause of | offences, Math .xviii. | Faythfully translated in to Englishe, | by a faythfull brother, with certayne | obiections & answeres to the same. | . . . (4 lines).

Printed at Emden. | 1566. | 12.5x8.9cm. (1,15)fol.

BULLINGER, Henry. The iudgement | of the Reuerend Father Ma- | ster Henry Bullinger, Pastor | of the church of Zurick, in certeyne | matters of religion, beinge in con- | trouersy in many countreys, | euen wher as the Gopel | is taught. | . . . (9 lines).

1566. | 14.5x8.8 cm. (12,35)p.

CROWLEY, Robert. An Apologie, | or Defence, of those | Englishe Writers & | Preachers which Cerberus | the three headed Dog | of Hell, chargeth wyth | false doctrine, vnder | the name of Prede- | stination. |

Written by Robert Crowley | Clerke, and Vicare of Sainct | Giles without Creple- | gate in London. |

Imprinted at Lon- | don, in Paternoster Rowe, at the | signe of the Starre, by | Henry Denham. | Anno. 1566. Octobris .14. | Lace border. 18.1x13.2 cm. (3),104 fol.

CROWLEY, Robert. A briefe discourse | against the outwarde apparell | and Ministring garmen- | tes of the popishe | church. | psalme.31. | I haue hated all those, that | holde of superstitious | vanities. | 1566. |

Without place or printer.. 14.3x8.9cm (24)fol.
Anon.Camb.Univ.Cat:Nos.6412-6413. B.M.Cat.

ELIZABETH, Queen [Statutes] Anno viii. Anno octauo Reginæ | Elizabethe. | At the Parliament | by prorogation holden at Westminster the last day of September, in the eyght | yere of the raigne of our Soueraigne | Lady Elizabeth, by the grace of God, | of England, Fraunce, and Irelande, | Queene, defendour of the faith. &c. | and there continued to the | end and dissolution of the | same: To the hygh | pleasure of al- | myghtie | God, | and the weale publique of this | Realme, amongst other | were enacted as | folow- | eth. | Anno Christi. 1566. |

Wood-cut border. Colophon: Imprinted at London | in Powles Churchyarde by | Rycharde Jugge, Prin- | ter to the Queenes | Maiestie. | Cum priuilegio Regiæ Maiestatis. | [1566] 26.3x18.5 cm. (28,22)fol. Fol. 18 of second part, blank.
Cambr.Univ.Cat. No.963.

GILBY, Anthony. To my louynge brethren | that is troublyd abowt the po- | pishe aparrell, two short and | comfortable Epistels. | Be ye constant: for the Lorde | shall fyght for yow, | yowrs in Christ. |

No imp. [1566?] 14.3x8.9 cm. (12)fol.
Anon.Cambr.Univ.Cat. 6413. Dexter:34

HARDING, Thomas. A Reioindre | To M.Jewels | Replie. | By perusing wherof the discrete and diligent Reader may | easily see, the Answer to parte of his insolent Chalenge iustified, | and his Obiections against the Masse, whereat the Priest some- | time receiueth the holy Mysteries without present com- | panie to receiue with him, for that cause by Lu- | thers Schoole called Priuate Masse, | clearly confuted. | By Thomas Harding Doctor of Diuinitie. | . . . (5 lines; device)

Antverpiæ. | Ex officina Ioannis Fouleri. | Anno.M.D.LXVI. | 19.1x14cm. (36), 315,(7)fol.

HESKYNS, Thomas. The | Parliament | Of Chryste Avov- | ching And Declaring The Enac- | ted and receaued trueth of the presence of his bodie and bloode in the | blessed Sacrament, and of other articles concerning the same, im- | pugned in a wicked sermon by M.Iuell, Collected and seth- | furth by Thomas Heskyns Doctour | of dyuinitie. | Wherin the reader shall fynde all the scripturs cōmonlie alleaged oute of the newe Testament, | touching the B.Sacrament, and some of the olde Testament, plainlie and truely expownded | by a nombre of holie learned Fathers and Doctours. | . . . (10 lines; device).

Imprinted in Antvverpe, | At the golden Angell, by VVilliam Silvius prynter to the Kynges | Maiestie. M. D. LXVI. | VVith Priuilege. | 28.8x19.2cm.(12), cccc, (7) fol.

HORNE, Robert. An | Ansvveare | Made by Rob. Bishoppe of VVyn- | chester, to a Booke | entituled, | The Declaration Of Svche | Scruples, and staies of Conscience, tou- | chinge the Othe of the Supremacy, as M. | Iohn Fekenham, by vvrytinge did deliuer | vnto the L. Bishop of VVinchester, vvith | his Resolutions made thereunto. | . . . (8 lines).

Imprinted at London in Fleetstreate, | at the signe of the Oliphante, | by Henry VVykes. | Anno 1566. | 18x13.8 cm. (2),130fol.

MORE, Thomas. Thomæ Mori | Angli, Viri Ervdi- | tionis Pariter Ac Vir- | tvtis Nomine Clarissi- | mi, Angliæqve Olim | Cancellarii, | Omnia, quæ hucusque ad manus nostras peruenerunt, Latina Opera: | quorum aliqua nunc primum in lucem prodeunt, reliqua | verò multo quàm antea casti- | gatiora. | Horvm Omnivm Elenchvm | Pagina duodecima commonstrabit. | (device)

Lovanii, | Apud Petrum Zangrium Tiletanum, | sub Fonte, Anno 1566. | 30.3x 19.8cm. (6),136fol. Frontisp.portr.mounted

NOWELL, Alexander. The | Reprovfe Of | M.Dorman his proufe of certaine | Articles in Religion &c. con- | tinued by Alexander | Nowell. | With a defense of the chiefe authoritie | and gouernment of Christian Princes | as well in causes Ecclesiasticall, as ci- | uill, within their owne dominions, by | M.Dorman malitiouslie oppugned. |

Imprinted at London in Fleetstreate, | at the signe of the Oliphante, | by Henry VVykes. | Anno.1566. | 18.3x12.9cm. (7),288fol.

RASTELL, John. The Third | Booke, Declaring By | Examples out of Auncient Coun- | cels, Fathers, and Later wri- | ters, that it is time to | Beware Of | M.Iewel. | By John Rastel Master of Art and | Student of Diuinitie. | . . . (4 lines. device)

Antverpiæ, | Ex officina Ioannis Fouleri. | M.D.LXVI. | 14.1 x 8.9 cm. (12), 239 fol. 118–120 wrongly numbered.

RASTELL, John. A Treatise | Intitled, Beware Of | M.Iewel. By Iohn Rastel | Master Of Arte And | Stvdent of Di- | vinitie. | . . . (4 lines; device).

Antverpiæ | Ex officina Ioannis Fouleri. | M.D.LXVI. | 14.8x9.6cm. (12),180 fol. Many folios misnumbered.

SANDERS, Nicholas. The supper of our Lord | Set Foorth Accor- | ding to the truth of the Gospell and Catholike faith. | By Nicolas Saunder, Doctor of Diuinitie. | with a confutation of such false doctrine as the Apologie of | the Churche of England, M.Nowels chalenge, or M.Iuels | Replie haue vttered, touching the reall presence | of

Christe in the Sacrament. | (Device: Man Hv? Device). What is this? | . . . (14 lines).

Lovanii. | Anno domini 1566. | 18.2x13.2cm. (3),424 fol.

STAPLETON, Thomas. A Retvrne Of Vn- | Trvthes Vpon M.- | Ievvel- | les Replie. | Partly of such, as he hath Slaunderously charged D. | Harding withal: Partly of such other, as he hath | committed about the triall thereof, in | the Text of the foure first Ar- | ticles of his Replie. | VVith a Reioyndre vpon the Principall Matters | of the Replie, treated in the Thirde | and Fourthe Articles. | By Thomas Stapleton student in Diuinite. | . . . (2 lines; device).

Printed in Antwerpe, by Iohn Latius, At the | signe of the Sower.1566. | With Speciall Grace | and Priuilege. | 19x13.9cm. (21),134;196 fol. Upper right corner, torn and restored. Modern portr. laid in.

VVHETHER it be mortall | sinne to transgresse ciuil lawes, | which be the commaun- | dementes of ciuill | Magistrates. | The iudgement of Philip Me- | lancton in his Epitome | of morall Philo- | sophie. | The resolution of. D. Hen. Bullin- | ger, and. D. Rod. Gualter, of. D. Mar- | tin Bucer, and. D. Peter Martyr, | concernyng thapparrel of | Ministers, and other | indifferent | thinges. |

Lace border. Colophon: Imprinted at London in | Powles Churchyarde by | Richarde Iugge Printer | to the Queenes | Maiestie. | Cum priuilegio Regiæ Maiestatis. | [1566]. 13.5x8.5 cm. 101,(1)p.
Camb.Univ.Cat.No.985,dates [1570–1?]

1567

ALESIUS, Alexander. Assertio Doctrinæ Ec- | clesiae Catholicae De Sancta Trinita- | te, cum confutatione erroris Valentini Gentilis, | Per Alexan- | drum Alesium, Academiæ Lipsicæ Theologum. |

Genevæ, | Ex officina Francisci Perrini. | M.D.LXVII. | 22x16.2cm. Pp.101–128 of Valentini Gentilis teter- | rimi Haeretici | impietatum . . . , breuis | explicatio, . . .

ALLEN, William. A Treatise | Made In Defence | of the lauful power and au- | thoritie of Priesthod to | remitte sinnes: Of | the peoples duetie for confession of their | sinnes to Gods ministers: And of | the Churches meaning concer- | ning Indulgences, com- | monlie called the | Popes Pardōs. | By William Allen M.of Arte, and | Student in Diuinitie. | . . . (4 lines; device).

Lovanii, | Apud Ioannem Foulerum, | Anno D. 1567. | 14.6x9.3cm. (24),412,(8)p.

BRADFORD, John. Godly | Meditations vppon the | ten Commaunde- | mentes, the Articles of | the fayth, and the | Lords prayer. | Whervnto is ioyned a trea- | tise against the feare of | death: Also a compari- | son beteweene the old | man and the new: | the lawe and | the gosple. | &c. | Made by Maister John | Bradford. | Seene and allowed according to the | Queenes Iniunctions. | 1567. |

Imprinted at London by | William Seres. | 13.3x8.6cm. Fol.(4),96. Wrongly printed as 66.

DERING, Edward. A Sparing | Restraint, of many lauishe | Vntruthes, which M. Doctor | Harding dothe chalenge, in the first | Article of my Lorde of | Sarisburies Replie. | By Edward Dering student | in Diuinitie. | With an answere vnto that long, and vncour- | teous Epistle, entituled to M. Iuel, and | set before M. Hardings | Reioinder. | ... (5 lines).

Imprinted at London, by | Henry Denham, for Humfrey Toy, | dwelling in Poules Church yarde, at | the signe of the Helmet. | Lace border. [1567]. 18.6x 14 cm. (20),114,216p.
B.M.Cat. [1568].

HARDING, Thomas. A Reioindre To M. | Iewels Replie Against | The Sacrifice Of The | Masse. | In which the doctrine of the Answere to the .xvij. Ar- | ticle of his Chalenge is defended, and further pro- | ued, and al that his Replie conteineth against | the Sacrifice, is clearely confuted, | and disproued. | By Thomas Harding Doctor of Diuinitie. | ... (6 lines; device).

Lovanii, | Apud Ioannem Foulerum, Anno.1567. | Cvm Privilegio. | 17.7x13.2cm. (10),1–10,9–35,34,48–50; 1–262,(6) fol. Misnumberings.

HENRY VII [Year Book, Anno i–xxi]. De Termino Michaelis Anno. | primo (–xxi) Henrici Septimi. |

Colophon: Imprinted at London in | Fleetestrete within Temple Barre at the signe | of the Hande and Starre, by Richard Tottill, | Anno.1567. | 29.2x20cm. xxxi;xix;xv; xviii;xl; xvi;xvi;xii;i–ii,vii–xxv;xxx;ii–xxviii;xxviii;xxviii;xxxii;xvii; xvii;xiii; xli fol. Sig.SS lacking.

HENRY VIII [Year Boox, anno xii–xiv]. De Termino Trinitatis Anno | regni Regis Henrici octaui, xii. | (–xiv).

Colophon: Imprinted at London in | Fleetestrete within Temple Barre at the signe | of the Hande and Starre, by Richard Tottill. | Anno.1567 | Cum priuilegio. | 29.2x20cm. xvi; xvi; xxxi fol.

HENRY VIII [Year Boox, anno xviii–xix]. De Termino Michaelis Anno | regni Regis Henrici octaui XVIII. | (–XIX.)

Colophon: Imprinted at London in | Fletestrete within Temple barre | at the signe of the Hand and starre, | By Richard Tottel,Anno. | 1567. | Cum priuilegio. | 29,2x20cm. xiv fol.

HENRY VIII [Year Book, anno xxvi]. De Termino Pasche Anno | XXVI. Regni Regis Henrici octaui. |

Colophon: Imprinted at London in | Fletestrete within Temple barre | at the signe of the Hand and starre, | By Richard Tottel,Anno. | 1567. | Cum priuilegio. | 29.2x20cm. x fol.

JEWEL, John. A Defence of the Apologie of | the Churche of Englande, | Conteininge an Answeare to a certaine | Booke lately set foorthe by M. | Hardinge, and Entituled, | A Confutation of &c. | By Iohn Iewel Bishop | of Sarisburie. | ... (3 lines; device).

Jmprinted at London in Fleetestreate, | at the signe of the Elephante, | by Henry VVyckes. | Anno 1567 .27. Octobris. | Cum Gratia & Priuilegio Regiæ | Maiestatis. | 27x19.2 cm. (24),742,(18)p.

NOWELL, Alexander. ¶ A Confutation, | as wel of M. Dor- | mans last Boke entituled | A Disproufe. &c. | as also of D. Sander his causes of | Transubstantiation, | by Alexander | Novvel. | Whereby our Cuntreymen (specially | the simple and vnlerned) may vnder- | stand, howe shamefully they are | abused by those and like | Bokes, pretended to be written | for their instruc- | tion. |

Imprinted at London, | by Henrie Bynneman. | Anno Do. 1567. | Cum priuilegio. | Lace border   18.3x13.6 cm.   (10),52fol.

OLIVER, John.   Preces | Horariae Ex | Sacris Literis | Et SS.Patrvm | Sententiis collectæ. | De Sacrosancta Trinitate. | De dulcissimo nomine Iesu. | De mysterio Sacrosanctæ Eu- | charistiæ. | Pro Statu Ecclesiæ Christianæ. | Ioanne Oliuero Vuigorniensi | Anglo Auctore. | . . . (6 lines; ornament).

Antverpiæ, | Apud Ioannem Bellerum, sub Aquila | Aurea, M.D.LXVII. | Cum priuilegio Regis. | 13.4x7.2cm.   203p.

PARKER, Matthew.   A Testimo- | nie of | Antiqvitie, | shewing the aunci- | ent fayth in the Church of | England touching the sacra- | ment of the body and bloude | of the Lord here publikely | preached, and also re- | ceaued in the Sax- | ons tyme, aboue | 600. yeares agoe. | . . . (7 lines).

Imprinted at London | by Iohn Day, dwelling | ouer Aldersgate beneath | S. Martyns. | Cum priuilegio Regiæ Maiestatis. | [1567?]   14x8.6 cm.   75,(14) fol.   49 omitted in numbering.
DNB.43:263b.   Camb.Univ.Cat:895.

STAPLETON, Thomas.   A Covnterblast To | M. Hornes Vayne | Blaste Against M. | Fekenham.   Wherein is set | forthe: | A ful Reply to M. Hornes Answer, and to euery part ther- | of made, against the Declaration of my L. Abbat of | Westminster, M. Fekenham, touching, The | Othe of the Supremacy. | By perusing vvhereof shall appeare, besides the holy Scriptures, as it vvere a | Chronicle of the Continual Practise of Christes Churche in al ages and | Countries, frõ the time of Constantin the Great, vntil our daies: | Prouing the Popes and Bishops Supremacy in Ecclesiasti- | cal causes: and Disprouing the Princes Supremacy | in the same Causes. | By Thomas Stapleton Student in Diuinitie. | . . .   (10 lines; device).

Lovanii, | Apud Joannem Foulerum. | An. 1567. Cum Priuil. | 19x13.9 cm.   (19),542,(6)fol.

VALENTINI Gentilis teter- | rimi Hæretici | impietatum ac triplicis perfidiæ & periurii, breuis | explicatio, ex actis publicis Senatus Geneuensis | optima fide descripta. | Earundem refutationes à doctissimis ætatis nostræ | Theologis scriptæ, quarum elenchum proxima | pagina continet. | Eiusdem Gentilis extremæ perfidiæ, & iusti supplicij de eo | sumpti, historia seorsim est excusa. | (device)

Genevæ, | Ex officina Francisci Perrini. | M.D.LXVII. | 22x16.2cm.   24,139,67p.

1568

CALVIN, John. The | Cathechisme, | or maner to teache | children the christen | Religion. | Made by the excellent doc- | tour and Pastour in Chri- | stes Churche Ihon Caluin. | Wherein the minister de- | maundeth the questi- | on, and the child | maketh aun- | swere. | . . . (5 lines) |

1568. | Engr.border. Colophon: Imprinted at London, by | Ihon Kingston. | Anno Domini. | 1568. | device. 12.7x8.8 cm. 78fol.

EDWARD V. [Year Book: Anno Primo]. De Termino Trinitatis Anno.I. | regni Regis Edwardi quinti. |

Colophon: Imprinted at London in | Fleetestrete within Temple Barre at the signe | of the Hande and Starre, by Richard Tottill, | Anno.1568 | Cum priuilegio ad imprimendum solum. | 29.2x20cm. viii fol.

JAMES VI. [Statutes]. The Actis Of Parliament | of the maist hie, maist excellent, and michtie Prince, and our Souerane Lord | James the sext, be the grace of God, King of Scottis, begun and haldin at Edinburgh, the xv. day | of Decemb. The zeir of God ane thousand, fyue hundretth lxvii. zeir. Be our said Souerane Lor- | dis derrest cousing & Uncle James Erle of Murray, Lord Abirnethie &c. Regēt to our Souerane | Lord, his Realme and Leigis. Togidder with the Prelatis, Erlis, Barrouis, Commissioneris of | Burrowis, specialie comperand in the said Parliament, as the thre estatis of this Realme. The | saidis actis being oppinlie rcd, concludit and votit in the said Parliament, to remane as perpe- | tuall lawis to the Subiectis of this Realme in all tymes cuming. | (coat of arms)

Without imprint. Colophon: Imprentit at Edinburgh | be Robert Lekpreuik, Prentar to the Kingis Majestie, the | vj. day of Aprill, the zeir of God ane thousand fyue hundreth | thre scoir aucht zeiris. | (Device). 27.4x19.1cm. fol. 23,(1).

RICHARD III [Year Book: Anno I]. De Termino Michaelis Anno | primo Richardi tertii. |

Colophon: Imprynted at Lon- | don in fletestrete within temple barre | at the signe of the Hand and starre, by | Rychard Tottel Anno. | 1568. | 29.2x20cm. iiii fol.

RICHARD III. [Year Book. Anno secundo]. De Termino Michaelis Anno | secūdo Richardi tertii. |

Colophon: Imprynted at Lon- | don in fletestrete within temple barre | at the signe of the Hand and starre, by | Rychard Tottel. Anno. | 1568. | 29.2x20cm. xxii fol.

1569

CAUSE, Bartholomew. The very True Shield, | and Buckler of Faith: | Wherein is intreated. 23. | Articles of Religion: written | Dialogue wise, firste in French, by | Bartholomew Cause: and nowe | Translated into English, | by T. S. | . . . (5 lines) Seene and allowed according to | the order appointed. |

Imprinted at London, by | Henry Wykes dwelling in Fleet streat, at | the signe of the blacke Elephant. | Anno. 1569. | Lace border. 18.2x13.3 cm. (4),166 fol.

CROWLEY, Robert. A setting open of the sub- | tyle Sophistrie of Tho- | mas VVatson Doctor of Di- | uinitie, which he vsed in hys two | Sermons made before Queene Mary, | in the thirde and fift Fridayes in Lent | Anno.1553. to prooue the reall presence of | Christis body and bloud in the sacra- | ment, and the Masse to be the sa- | crifice of the newe Testa- | ment, written by Ro- | bert Crowley | Clearke. | . . . (5 lines). Seene and allowed according to the Queenes | Maiesties Iniunctions.

Imprinted at London | by Henry Denham. | Lace border. Colophon: Imprinted at London by Henry | Denham, dwelling in Pater- | noster Rovve, at the | Signe of the | Starre. | (device). Anno Domini. | 1569. | Cum priuilegio. | 18.2x13.9cm. (15),209,188,(1)p.

HEMINGE, Nicholas. A Postill, or Ex- | position of the Gospels | that are vsually red in the chur- | ches of God, vpon the Sundayes | and Feast dayes of Sainctes, | Written by Nicholas | Heminge a Dane, a Preacher of | the Gospell, in the Vniuer- | sitie of Hafnie. | And translated into English by | Arthur Golding. | Before vvhich Postill is sette a vvarning of the | same Nicholas Heminge too the | Ministers of Gods vvorde, concerning the cō- | tinuall agreement of Chrystes Church in the | doctrine and true vvorshipping of God: least | anye beeing offended at the varietie of opi- | nions and multitude of sectes, might eyther | forsake their profession, or doo their duetie | more slouthfully. |

Imprinted at London by Henry | Bynneman, for Lucas Harrison | and George Byshop. | Lace border. Colophon: (device) Imprinted at London, | by Henry Bynneman, dwel- | ling in Knightrider streat, at the signe | of the Mermayde: for Lucas | Harrison, and George | Bishop. | Anno Domini. 1569. | Cvm Privilegio. | 18.3x13.7cm. (14),345,(6)fol.

HENRY VIII [Year Book, Anno XXVII]. De Termino Pasche Anno | XXVII, regni regis Henrici octaui. |

Colophon: Imprinted at London in | Fletestrete within Temple barre | at the signe of the Hand and starre, | By Richard Tottle. Anno. | 1569. | Cum priuilegio. | 29.2x20 cm. xxx fol.

POLE, Reginald. De Svmmo Pon- | tifice Christi In | Terris Vicario, Eivs- | que officio & potestate, Liber verè | singularis, & eruditionis, | & purisermonis | nomine, | In modum Dialogi cōscriptus olim, nunq[uam] verò | antehac editus, Authore Reginaldo | Polo Anglo S. R. E. Cardinali Reuerēdiss. | (device).

Lovanii, | Apud Ioannem Foulerum Anglum. | M.D.LXIX. | Cum Priuilegio. Subsign. Vander Aa[?]. | 14.8x9.3 cm. (8),151,(5) fol.

1570

MARLORAT, Augustine. A Catholike | And Ecclesiasti- | call exposition of the holy Gospell | after S.Mathewe, gathered out of | all the singuler and approued Deuines | (whiche the Lorde hath geuen to | his Churche) by Augustine | Marlorate. | And translated out of Latine into Englishe | by Thomas Tymme, | Mynister. | Sene and allowed according to | the order appointed, |

Imprinted at London in Fletestreate | neare vnto S.Dunstones churche, by | Thomas Marshe. | 1570. | Architec. t.p., 28.7x19.7cm. (12),759p. Portr.frontisp. mounted.

Gift of Clarence S. Brigham.

NOWELL, Alexander. A Catechisme, | or first Instruction and Lear- | ning of Christian | Religion. | Translated out of Latine into | Englishe. | (device).

At London. | Printed by Iohn Daye | dwelling ouer Aldersgate. | Cum Priuilegio Regiæ Maiestatis | per Decennium. | An.1570. | Lace border. 19.3x14.cm. (4),79,(4)fol. Colophon.

Anon. Cambr.Univ.Cat.818.

NOWELL, Alexander. Catechismvs, | siue prima Institutio, Disci- | plinæqve Pietatis | Christianæ, Latinè explicata. | . . . (4 lines).

Londini, | In Officina Reginaldi | Wolfij, Regiæ Maiest. in Latinis | Typographi. | Anno Dom. M.D.LXX. | xvi. Calend. Ivl. | 19.5x14.5 cm. (6),170p. Colophon.

Anon. Cambr.Univ.Cat.650.

REFORMATION of Disorders in the Mi- | nisters of the Church, &c. | Anno 13.Eliz.Cap.12. |

Without t.p. 19.5x15.2cm. Pp. 83–85 of Sparrow's Collection: 1661. Also in his reprints of 1675 and 1684.

SANDERS, Nicholas. Qvod Domi- | nus In Sexto Capite | Ioannis De Sacarmento | Eucharistiæ propriè sit locutus, | Tractatus vtilis. | Avctore Nicolao San- | dero Anglo S.Theologiæ professore. | . . .(5 lines; device.)

Antverpiæ, | Apud Viduam & haeredes Ionannis Stelsij. | Anno M. D. LXX. | Cvm Gratia Et Privilegio. | 13.9x8.9 cm. 167,(2)p.

1571

ARTICLES | to be enquired of in the visitation | of the Dioces of Londou, by the | Reuerende Father in God, Edwyn | Bishop of London. | (device). In the thirtenth yeare of the raigne of our Soueraigne | Ladie Elizabeth, by the grace of God Queene of | Englande, Fraunce and Irelande | defender of the fayth, &c. | 1571. |

Imprinted at London by | William Seres. | 17.8x13.1cm. (7)fol.

ARTICLES | Whereupon it was agreed | by the Archbishoppes and Bi- | shoppes of both prouinces and | the whole cleargie, in the Con- | uocation holden at London in | the yere of our Lorde God, | 1562. according to the compu- | tation of the Churche of En- | glande, for the auoiding of the | diuersities of opinions, and | for the stablishyng of | consent touching | true religion. | Put foorth by the Queenes | aucthoritie. |

Engraved border. Colophon: Imprinted at Lon- | don in Poules Churchyard, by | Richarde Iugge and Iohn Cawood, | Printers to the Queenes | Maiestie, in Anno | Domini. 1571. | Cum priuilegio Regiæ maiestatis. | 17.1x13.5cm. (1),25,(3)p.

ARTICULI | De quibus convenit inter | Archiepiscopos, | Et | Episcopos | Utriusque Provinciæ, | Et | Clerum Universum | In Synodo, Londini. | Anno 1562. secundum computationem Ecclesiæ Anglicanæ, | ad tollendam opinionum dissentionem, & consensum | in vera Religione firmandum. | Æditi authoritate serenissimæ Reginæ. | (ornaments)

Londini, | Apud Johannem Day, 1571. | 19.5x15.2cm. (1),14p.
Repr. in Sparrow's Collection: 1661, 1675 and 1684.

¶ A BOOKE | of certaine Canons, | concernyng some parte | of the discipline of | the Churche of | England. | In the yeare of our Lord. | 1571. |

At London | Printed by Iohn Daye, | dwellyng ouer Al- | dersgate. | Cum gratia & Priuilegio | Regiæ Maiestatis. | [1571]. Lace border. 17.2x12.6 cm. 30p.

BRIDGES, John. A Sermon, | preached at Paules Crosse on | the Monday in Whitson weeke | Anno Domini .1571. | Entreating on this Sentence | Sic Deus dilexit mundum, vt daret | vnigenitum filium suum, vt omnis | qui credit in eū non pereat, sed ha- | beat vitam æternam. | . . . (4 lines) Preached and augmented by Iohn Bridges. |

At London, | Printed by Henry Binneman | for Humfrey Toy. | [1571] Lace border. 18.4x12.7cm. (6),182p.

BULLINGER, Henry. Bvllæ Papisticæ | ante biennium contra | Sereniss. Angliæ, Franciæ | & Hyberniæ Reginam Eliza- | betham, & contra inclytum An- | gliæ regnum promulgatæ, refuta- | tio, Orthodoxæq; Reginæ, & | vniuersi Regni Angliæ de- | fensio, | Henrychi Bullingeri. | S. |

Londini, | apud Iohānem Dayum | Typographum. | An. Domini. | 1571. | Lace border 19.5x13.1 cm. 85,(1)fol.

FENTON, Geoffrey. Actes | of conference in | Religion, | Holden at Paris, betweene two | Papist Doctours of Sorbone, | and two godlie Ministers of | the Church. | Dravven out of French into English, | by Geffraie Fenton. | . . . (1 line).

Imprinted at Lon- | don by H.Bynneman, | for VVilliam Norton and | Humfrie Toye. | Lace border. 17.6x12.9cm. (6),120fol. Epistle dated:iiij July.1571.

FIELD, John and WILCOX, Thomas. An Admonition to the | Parliament. |

[1571] 14.4x9.6cm (56)p. A1–8–C8–D4.
Without t.p.; above title from p.3. A1 contains "To the godly Readers, grace, | and peace from God.&c." |
Anon. 4th ed:Bodl.Cat. Camb.Univ.Cat.No.5895, dates 1672.
Reprinted in 1617; also in 1641 in A Treatise | Exhibited | By | Diverse Reverend And | Godly | Divines, | To the High Court of Parliament, | . . . and in An Advertisement To The Parliament of England: 1644

FOX, John. Reformatio | Legvm Ecclesiasti- | carvm, Ex Avthorita- | te primum Regis Henrici.8. in- | choata: Deinde per Regem Edo- | uardum 6. prouecta, adauctaq́; | in hunc modum, atq; nunc ad | pleniorem ipsarum refor- | mationem in lucem | ædita. | (device).

Londini | Ex officina Johannis Daij Anno | salutis humanæ, 1571. | Mense Aprili. | Lace border.   18.8x13.2cm.   (9), 149,(3)fol
Attributed also to Thomas Cranmer.   DNB: 13:31a.   Cambr.Univ.Cat.825, Fox, editor.
Anon. DNB.20:146b.

LIBER | quorundam   Canonum | disciplinæ   ecclesiæ | Anglicanae. Anno | 1571. |

[1571].   18.6x14.3cm.   23,(1)p.
A part of Articuli de quibus convenit inter Archiepiscopos . . . 1571, Begins with sig.Ei–Giiij, with separate paging.
Also another copy, identical except that it begins with sig.Di–Fiiij.   18x13.5cm. 23,(1)p.
Attributed to Matthew Parker.   DNB.43:263b.

LIBER | Quorundam | Canonum | Disciplinæ | Ecclesiæ Anglicanæ. | Anno MDLXXI. | (*double column*) De Episcopis. | De Decanis Ecclesiarum. | De Archidiaconis. | De Cancellariis, &c. | De Ædituis Æclesiarum. || De Concionatoribus. | De Residentia. | De Pluralitatibus. | De Ludimagistris. | De Patronis, &c. |

Londini, | Apud Johannem Day. 1571. | Border, top and bottom. 19.5x15.2cm. Pp. 15–34, appended to Articuli: 1571. Repr. in Sparrow's Collection: 1661, 1675 and 1684.

NETTER, Thomas.   Thomae | VValdensis | Anglici Carmelitae, | Theologi Praestantissimi, | Doctrinale Antiqvitatvm Fidei | Ecclesiæ Catholicæ: | Opvs Sanè Divinvm, In Tres Tomos Digestvm; | In quorum primo de Deo Christo, Petro, Ecclesia, ac Religiosis; | In secundo de Sacramentis; In tertio verò de Sacramentalibus, | aduersus Vuitcleuistas, Hussitas, eorumq́; recentiores | asseclas exactissimè disseritur. | Nvnc Reverend.^{mi} P.Ioan.Baptistæ Rvbei, Ravennatis, | eiusdem familiæ Magistri Generalis, nutu, & fauore excusum. | In quo castigando ac restituendo, non modò id præstitum est, vt à mendis expurgaretur, marginalibusq[ue] | apostillis exornaretur, verumetiam vt Sanctorum Patrum sententiæ, quæ passim mutilæ | maleq́[ue] editæ fuerant, & nuper in libris accuratè impressis aliter leguntur, | & citantur, in integrum, inq́, sua loca restituerentur. | Accedvnt Denvò Svmmæ Capitvm, Simvlqve | Tripartitus Index. Insuper eiusdem Magistri Generalis ad complurium | locorum elucidationem, elimata scholia. | Tomus Primus. | Vin (device) cent |

Venetiis, Apud Vincentium Valgrisium.   M D LXXI. | 30.4x20.7cm.   (52),581, (1)p. (18),271; (22),299,(14)fol.   Two sub-titles for Parts II and III.

NORTHBROOKE, John.   Spiritus est Vicarius Christi | in terra. | A breefe and pithie | summe of the christian faith, | made in fourme of a confession, vvith | a confutation of the papistes obiections and | argumentes in sundry pointes of religion, | repugnaunt to the christian faith: made | by Iohn Northbrooke, Minister | and Preacher of the worde | of God. | . . . (5 lines). Seene and allowed, according to the order | appointed in the Queenes Iniunctions. |

At London. | Printed by Iohn Kingston for W. Williamson, | dwelling in Povvles Churchyarde, at the | signe of the vvhyte Horse. | Anno. 1571. | Lace border 19.2x14.6 cm.   (20),143,(5)fol.

NOWELL, Alexander.   Catechismvs, | siue prima Institutio, Disci- | plináqve Pietatis | Christianæ, Latinè explicata. | . . . (4 lines).

Londini, | in officina Reginaldi Wolfij, Regiæ Maiest. | in Latinis Typographi. | Anno Domini M.D.LXXI. | Cum Priuilegio Regiæ Maiestatis. | 19x13.9cm.   (6), 160,(8)p.
Cambr.Univ.Cat. 752

SANDERS, Nicholas.   De Visibili | Monarchia | Ecclesiæ, | Libri Octo. | In quibus diligens instituitur disputatio de certa & perpetua Ecclesiæ Dei tùm | Successione, tum Gubernatione Monarchica ab ipso mundi initio vsq[ue] ad finem. | Deinde etiam Ciuitatis Diaboli persæpè interrupta progressio proponitur, Se- | ctæq[ue] omnes & Hæreses confutantur, quæ vnq[uam] contra veram fidem emerserunt. | Deniqve de Antichristo ipso & membris eius: deq[ue] vera Dei & adulterina | Diaboli Ecclesia, copiosè tractatur. | Si quid præterea difficile & scopulosum vel in Pontificum Romanorum | Historia, vel in Conciliorum Generalium ratione accidit; id- | ipsum ex proposito discutitur & examinatur. | Cum Indice Rerum & Personarum locuplete. | Avctore Nicolao Sandero, | Sacræ Theologiæ Professore. | Singulorum Librorum Argumenta sequens Pagina indicabit. | (device) . . . (2 lines).

Lovanii, | Sub Capite Deaurato. | Ioannis Fouleri cura & impensa excudebat | Reynervs Velpivs Typ.Ivr. | M.D.LXXI. | Cvm Gratia Et Privilegio. | 33.7x22cm. (12),844,(15)p.

1572

BARNES, Robert.   The Workes | of Doctour Barnes. | His lyfe and Martyrdome. | 1 A supplication to K.Henry the viij. fol.183. | 2 His Articles condemned by Popishe By- | shops.   205. | 2.The disputation betweene the Byshoppes | and hym.   217. | 4.Fayth onely iustifieth before God.   226. | 5.What the Church is: and who bee thereof, | and whereby men may know her.   242. | 6 An other declaration of the Church, wher- | in hee aunswereth M.More.   252. | 7.What the keyes of the Church bee, and to | whom they were geeuen.   257. | 8. Freewill of man, after the fall of Adam | of his naturall strength, can bee nothyng | but sinne afore God.267. | 9.That it is lawfull for all maner of men to | read the Holy Scripture.   282. | 10. That mens constitutions, which are not | grounded in Scripture, bynde not the | cōscience of man vnder the payne of dead- | ly synne.292. | 11.That all mē are boūde to receiue the holy | Communion vnder both kyndes, vnder | the payne of deadly synne.   301. | 12. That by Gods woorde it is lawfull to | Priestes that hath not the gifte of chasti- | stie, to marry wiues.   309. | 13.That it is against the holy Scripture to | honor Images & to pray to Saintes.   339. | 14.Of the originall of the Masse.   356. | 15. A collection of Doctours testimonies.   358. |

Engr.t.p., without imprint. Colophon, At London | Printed by Iohn Daye, and are to bee sold | at hys shop vnder Aldersgate. | An 1572. | Cum gratia & Priuilegio Regiæ Maiestatis. | 27.6x19.5cm.   (8),183–376,(4)p. of The Whole workes of W.Tyndall: 1573.

CARTWRIGHT, Thomas. ?   Certaine | Articles, collected and | taken (as it is thought) by the Byshops | out of a litle boke entituled an Admo- | nition to the Parliament, wyth | an Answere to the same. | Containing a confirmation of the | sayde Booke in shorte | notes. | . . . (5 lines) The Prynter to the Reader. | Thys worke is fynished thankes be to God, | And he only wil keepe vs from the searchers rod. | And though master Day and Toy watch & warde, | We hope the liuing God is our sauegarde. | Let them seeke, loke, and doe what they can, | It is but inuentions, and pollicies of man. | But you wil maruel where it was fyninsed, (ended), | And you shal know (perchance) when domes day is. |

Imprinted we know where, and whan, | Judge you the place and you can. J.T.J.S. | 14.4x9.7cm. (20)p. A1–B4.

Dated at end: From my chamber in London, this 30. of September, in Anno.1572.

Dexter:47. Camb.Univ Cat.No.5898.

CARTWRIGHT, Thomas. A Second | Admonition to the | Parliament. |

Without t.p. [1572.] 14.4x9.6cm. (8),64p. *1–4–A1–4–H4. Two parts. Camb.Univ.Cat.No.5897.

An | EXHORTATION to the By- | shops to deale Brotherly with | theyr Brethren. |

Without t.p. 14.4x9.7cm (4,8,12)fol. *1–2,A1–4–C2.

Preceded by two leaves: Grace And | peace from God.&c. | ; dated at end, From my chamber in London, this 30. | of September, in Anno.1572. | Contains also, An Exhortation to | The Bishops and Their Cler- | gie to aunsvver a little booke that came forthe the | last Parliament, and to other Brethren to | iudge of it by Gods worde, vntill they | see it aunsweared, and not to be | caryed away with any | respect of men. |

FRITH, John. The Workes | of the excellent Martyr | of Christ, Iohn Frith. | His lyfe and Martyrdome. | 1.His booke of Purgatory. Fol.1. | 2.An aūswere to Rastals Dialogue.7. | 3.An aūswere to Syr Thomas More.32. | 4.Hys aunswere vnto Fisher Byshop | of Rochester. 51. | 5.A Bulwarke against Rastall.60. | 6.His iudgement vpon M.Tracyes will | and Testament.77. | 7.A letter written from the Tower to | Christes congregation.81. | 8. A mirrour or glasse to knowe thy | selfe. 83. | 9.A treatise vppon the Sacrament of | Baptisme.90. | 10.An antithesis betweene Christ and | the Pope.97. | 11.A booke of the Sacrament of the bo- | dy and bloud of Christ. 107. | 12.Articles for the which he dyed. 170. | A Table contayning the principall mat- | ters of all his workes. |

Engr.t.p.without imprint. Colophon, at end of Robert Barnes Works: At London | Printed by Iohn Daye, and are to bee sold | at hys shop vnder Aldersgate. | An.1572. | Cum gratia & Priuilegio Regiæ Maiestatis. | 27.6x19.5cm. (4),3–172,(3)p.

Part of The Whole workes of W.Tyndall: 1573.

FULKE, William. A Sermon | preached at Hamp- | ton Court, on Son- | day being the .12. day of No- | uember, in the yeare of | of our Lord .1570. | VVherin is playnly proued | Babylon to be Rome, both | by Scriptures and | Doctors. | Preached by VVilliam Fulke | Bacheler of Deuinity, and fel- | low of S.Johns Colledge | in Cambridge | . . . (6 lines).

Imprynted at Lon- | don by John Awdely, | Lace border. Colophon: Imprinted at | London by Iohn Awdely, | dwellyng in little Bryt- | tayne streete, without | Aldersgate. 1572. | 12.9x9.2 cm. (4),(56)p.

WHITGIFT, John. An ansvvere to a | certen Libel intituled, | An admonition to the | Parliament, | By Iohn VVhitgifte, | D.of Diuinitie. | . . . (12 lines).

Jmprinted at London, | by Henrie Bynneman, | for Humfrey Toy. | Anno. 1572. | Lace border. Colophon: Imprinted at London | by Henry Bynneman, for | Humfrey Toy, dvvelling in Paules | Church yard at the signe | of the Helmet. | Anno. 1572. | 19.4x14.5cm. (12),140,(5),146–246,(42)p.
Second copy: 19.4x13.7cm. Port.of Whitgift laid in.

1573

BRIDGES, John. The Supremacie of | Christian Princes, ouer all | persons throughout their domini- | ons, in all causes so wel Ecclesiasti- cal | as temporall, both | against the Counterblast of Thomas Staple- ton, | replying on the Reuerend father in Christe, | Robert Bishop of VVinchester: | and also | Against Nicolas Sanders his Visible | Mon- archie of the Romaine Church, touching | this controuersie of the Princes | Supremacie. | Ansvvered by Iohn Bridges. | . . . (10 lines).

Printed At London, | by Henrie Bynneman, for | Humfrey Toye. | 1573. | Lace border 18.6x14.1cm. (119),1114,(2)p.

CARTWRIGHT, Thomas. A | Replye To An | ansvvere made of M. | Doctor VVhitgifte. | Agaynste The Admonition | to the Parlia- ment. | By T.C. | . . . (11 lines).

No imprint. [1573?] 19.4x13.9cm. (12),3–174,(9)p. A1–4–Bb4.
Camb.Univ.Cat.No.5899. First edition
Also the second edition with similarly arrange title, except "Againste" in line 5.
No imprint [1573?] 17.8x14.4cm. (4),224p. A1–2,B1–4–GG4. Two blank leaves in front.
Cambr.Univ.Cat.No 5900. Second edition: see prefatory note by printer, J.S.

CLERKE, Bartholomew. Fidelis | Servi, Svbdito | Infideli Re- | sponsio, | vnà cum errorum & calumniarum | quarundam examine quæ continen- | tur in septimo libro de visibili | Ecclesiæ Monarchia a | Nicholæo Sandero | conscripta. |

Londini | Apud Johannem Dayum Typo- | graphum. An. 1573. | Lace border. 19.8x15.2cm. (1,150)p.
Anon. Cambr.Univ.Cat.835.

COOPER, Thomas. A briefe exposition | of such Chapters of the | olde testament as vsually are | redde in the Church at common praier on | the Sondayes, set forth for the better | helpe and instruction of the vn- | learned. By Thomas Coo- | per Bishop of Lin- | colne. | . . . (6 lines).

Imprinted at London by H.D. for Rafe | Newbery dwelling in Fleetestreete. | Colophon: Imprinted at London by Henrie | Denham for Rafe Newbery dwel- | ling in Fletestreete a little a- | boue the Con- | duite. | Anno. 1573. | 18.3x13.5cm. (6),1–181,201–392fol.

DULKEN, Vitus à, and SITTART, Gulielmus à. Illvstria | Ecclesiæ | Catholicæ | Trophoea, | Ex recentibus Anglicorum | martyrum, Scotiæ proditionis, Calli- | corumq́; furorum rebus gestis grauiss. | virorum fide notatis. | Charae Posteritati, | Vt nimirum ea de præsentium errorum | natura atq; ingenio integrè ac li- | berè tandem iudicet, | Erecta. |

Anno M.D.LXXIII. | device. Colophon: Monachii Excvdebat | Adamus Berg. Anno 1573. | 14.8x9 cm. (70,16,151,136)p.
Dedication (B1), signed.

ELIZABETH, Queen. By the Queen. | A Proclamation against the despisers or breakers of the | orders prescribed in the book of Common prayer. |

Without t.p. Colophon: Imprinted at London by Newgate Market, | next unto Christs Church, by Richard Jugge, | Printer to the Queens Majesty. | Cum privilegio Regiæ Majestatis. | Dated Oct. 20, 1573. 19.5x15.2cm. Pp. 227–228, of Sparrow's Collection: 1661. Also in his reprints of 1675 and 1684.

FULKE, William. Prælections vpon | the Sacred and holy | Reuelation of S.John, | written in latine by William | Fulke Doctor of Diuinitie, | and translated into English by | George Gyffard: | . . . (8 lines).

Imprinted at Lon- | don, by Thomas Purfoote, at | the signe of the Lucrece. | Anno. 1573. | Lace border. Colophon: (Device). Imprinted at London, in Paules | Churchyard: by Thomas | Purfoote, at the signe of the | Lucrece. Anno. 1573. | 18.2x13.8cm. (4),152fol.

HARPSFIELD, Nicholas. Dialogi Sex | Contra | Svmmi Pontificatvs, | Monasticae Vitae, Sanctorvm, | Sacrarvm Imaginvm Oppvgna- | tores, Et Psevdomartyres: | Ab Alano Copo Londinensi editi auctiores nonnullis | in locis & castigatiores. | In quibus præterquam quòd nonnulla, quæ alij hactenus vel atti- | gerunt liuiter, ver penitus omiserunt, paullò vberius & plenius | explicātur; Centurionū etiā Magdeburgensiū, auctorum Apo- | logiæ Anglicanæ, Pseudomartyrologorum nostri temporis, ma- | ximé verò Ioannis Foxi, & aliorum, qui adulterino Euangelio | nomina dederunt, variæ fraudes, putidæ calumniæ, & insignia in | historiis Ecclesiæ contaminandis mendacia deteguntur: | Cum triplici indice, primo auctorum, altero capitum, tertio | rerum & verborum. | . . . (4 lines, device)

Antverpiæ, | Ex officina Christophori Plantini, Prototypographi Regij. | M.D.LXXIII. | Cvm Privilegio. | 22.4x14.8cm. (24),741,(34)p. Colophon.
At end of text: A.H.L.N.H.E.V.E.A.C. signifying: Auctor hujus libri, Nicolaus Harpesfeldus.Eum vero edidit Alanus Copus. Gillow.I:561.

HUMPHREY, Laurence. Ioannis | Ivelli Angli, | Episcopi Sarisburiensis vita & | mors, eiusq́; veræ doctrinæ de- | fensio, cum refutatione quorun- | dam obiectorum, | Thomæ Hardingi, | Nicol.Sanderi, | Alani Copi, | Hieronymi Osorij Lusitani, | Pontaci Burdegalensis. | Laurentio Humfredo S.The- | ologiæ apud Oxonienses pro- | fessore Regio, Autore. | . . . (2 lines)

Londini | Apud Iohannem Dayum Typo- | graphum. An.1573. | Cum Gratia & Priuilegio Regiæ Maiestatis. | Lace border 19.1x13.5 cm. (34),269,(31)p.

TYNDALE, William, etc. The Whole | workes of W.Tyndall, Iohn | Frith, and Doct.Barnes, three | worthy Martyrs, and principall | teachers of this Churche of England, | collected and compiled in one Tome to- | gither, beyng before scattered, & now in | Print here exhibited to the Church. | To the prayse of God, and | profite of all good Chri- | stian Readers. | . . . (1 line).

At London | Printed by Iohn Daye, | and are to be sold at his shop | vnder Aldersgate. | An. 1573. | Cum gratia & Priuilegio | Regiæ Maiestatis. | Arch. border.   27.6x19.5cm.(14),478,(17);   (4), 3–172,(3);   (8), 183–376,(4)p.   Colophons: 1572. 2 Sub.t.p.

WHITGIFT, John. An answere to a | certen Libell intituled, | An admonition to the | Parliament, | By Iohn VVhitgifte, | D. of Diuinitie. | Newly augmented by the Authoure, as | by conference shall appeare. | . . . (12 lines)

Imprinted at London, | by Henrie Bynneman, | for Humfrey Toy. | Anno 1573. | Lace border.   Colophon: Imprinted at London | by Henry Bynneman, for | Humfrey Toy, dvvelling in Paules | Church yard at the signe | of the Helmet. | Anno 1573. | (Line and device)   18.6x13.3cm.   343,(1)p.
Camb.Univ.Cat. No.1476.   Ed.3.

1574

BRADFORD, John. Two no- | table Sermons, | Made by that wor- | thy Martyr of Christ Mai- | ster Iohn Bradford, the one | of Repentance, and the o- | ther of the Lordes sup- | per neuer before | imprinted. | (Device). Perused and allowed accor- | ding to the Quænes Ma- | iesties Iniunction. | (device).

1574 | Imprinted at London | by Iohn Awdeley, and | John Wyght. | Border. Colophon: Jmprinted at | London by Iohn Awde- | ley, and John Wyght. | The .xxx. of September. | Anno Domini. | 1574. | 13.5x8.8cm. (12,88) fol.

CALVIN, John. Sermons | of M.Iohn Cal- | uine vpon the Epistle | of Saincte Paule | to the Gala- | thians. |

Imprinted at Lon- | don, by Lucas Harison and | George Bishop. | 1574. | Arch border.   Colophon: Imprinted at London by Henrie | Bynneman, for Lucas Haryson | and George Byshop. | 19.3x14.2cm.   (20),329,(1)fol.

CALVIN, John. Sermons | of Master Iohn | Caluin, vpon the | Booke of | Iob. | Translated out of French | by Arthur Golding. | (device).

Imprinted | By Lvcas Harison and | George Byshop. | Colophon: Imprinted at London By | Henrie Binneman, for Lucas Harison | and George Bishop. Anno. 1574. | (Device).   (Pillar and vine border).   32.4x21.7 cm.   (34),752p.
Also another edition in the same year with identical title and colophon, except for an ornament after the colophon. Entirely reset. Arch. border. 29.6x19.8cm. (63),821,(1)p.

FENTON, Geoffrey. A forme of | Christian pollicie drawne | out of French by Gef- | fray Fenton. | A worke very necessary to al sorts | of people generally, as wherein is con- | tayned doctrine, both vniuersall, and spe- | cial touching the institution of al Christian pro | fession: and also conuenient perticularly for all | Magistrates and gouernours of common | weales, for their more happy Regi- | ment according | to God. | . . . (1 line).

Jmprinted at London by | H. Middelton for Rafe Newbery, | dwelling in Fleetestreat a little | aboue the Conduit. | Anno. 1574. | Lace border. 19.7x14.1 cm. (12),392 p. 182-191 folioed and pp. 187-192, 228-329, 377-392 incorrectly numbered.

HEMINGE, Nicholas. The Prea- | cher, or Methode of preaching, | vvrytten in Latine by Nicholas | Hemminge, and translated into En- | glishe by I.H. Very necessarie for al those | that by the true preaching of the word | of God, labour to pull downe the | Sinagoge of Sathan, and to | buylde up the Temple | of God. | . . . (4 lines). Seene and alowed according to the | Queenes Maiesties Jniunction. |

Imprinted at London by | Thomas Marshe. | Anno. 1574. | Cum Priuilegio. | Lace border. 13.5x8.8 cm. (8),68fol.

MARLORAT, Augustin. A Catholike | exposition vpon | the Reuelation of | Sainct Iohn. | Collected by M.Au- | gustine Marlorate out of diuers | notable Writers, whose na- | mes ye shal find in the | page following. |

Printed by H.Binneman, for | L.Harison, and G.Bishop. | Arch.border. Colophon: Imprinted at London by | Henrie Binneman, for Lucas | Harison, and George Byshop. | Anno. 1574. | 19.2x14.5cm. (22),318,(1)fol.

NICHOLAS, Henry. Annvn- | ciatio Pacis | Svper Terram, Tem- | porisque benigni, & Anni Domino accepti: | Quæ postremo hoc Tempore; ex Pace | Iesu Christi, eiusque sacro Charita- | tis Spiritu; per HN in Terra | annunciatur. | Qva Cvncti Homines Bellvm Præ- | liumve aduersum se mutuò gerentes, simul ac omnes Sapi- | entes & Literati, inter se contendentes ac disceptantes, ad | Pacem admonentur. Deque ingenti Miseria & Calamitate | præmonentur, quæ ijs omnibus; si sese ad Pacem non con- | uerterint; euenient. | Ex Germanico translata. | . . . (device; 6 lines).

No impr. [1574?] 14.5x10cm.8fol.

NICHOLAS, Henry. Dicta HN. | Documentall | Sentences: eauen-as | those-same were spoken-fourth by HN, | and writen-vp out of the Woordes | of his Mouth. | And are by Him pervsed, and more- | distinctlie declared. | Translated out of Base-almayne. | (device; 9 lines).

Without imprint [1574?] 13.8x9.5 cm 47fol.
Camb.Univ.Cat.No.6346. DNB.40:430a.

All of Nicholas' writings were denounced in a proclamation by Queen Elizabeth, issued Oct. 3, 1579, and ordered to be burned Oct. 13th.

NICHOLAS, Henry. Episto- | la Prima HN. | In Qva Cvnctæ Nati- | ones; ex mera Gratia; Voce sacri Spiritus Cha- | ritatis clamante, ad veram Peccatorum Cor- | rectionem ad probæ Vitæ christianæ Introi- | tum·& ad Charitatis Iesu Christi Do- | mum, per HN vocantur ac inuitantur. | Per eundem denuò recognita, & | apertiùs

explicata. | . . . (4 lines). Ex Germanico translata. | . . . (device: 9 lines).
  No imprint. [1574?] 14.5x10cm. 8 fol.
  Cf. B.M.Cat. DNB. 40:429b.

NICHOLAS, Henry. The Fift (and Sixt) Epistle. | A Stirring-vp | of the Heart to the Immi- | tation or Following of Christ, in | the Suffering of his Crosse: Written | and sent by HN in the tyme of his Suf- | fering and Affliction, vnto his Freende. | Wherwith he informeth him, with Vn- | derstanding and Woordes of Humilitee, | because that he shoulde not growe-offended | in any thing, but alwayes hope on the | Goodnes of the Lorde. | . . . (9 lines).
  No imprint. 14.3x9.9cm. 65–134p. (A fragment).

NICHOLAS, Henry. Prover- | bia HN. | Quæ; Diebvs Senectv- | tis suæ; tanquàm Similitudi- | nes abditasque Senten- | tias, in lucem e- | didit. | Ex Germanico translata. | . . . (device; 8 lines).
  No imprint. [1574?] 14.5x10cm. 38 fol.

RIDLEY, Nicholas. Certayne | Godly, learned, and com- | fortable conferences. | Betweene the two reuerende Fa- | thers and holy Martyrs of Christ | D.Nicolas Rydley late Bishop | of London, and M.Hugh La- | timer, sometyme Bishop | of Worcester, during | the tyme of their | imprison- | ments. | Whereunto is added a treatise | of the Lordes Supper, made by the | sayd reuerend Father D.Nico- | las Rydley, a little before he | suffered death. 1555. |
  Now newly againe | imprinted. | 1574. | Imprinted at London by | John Awdley. | Colophon: Imprinted | at London by Iohn Aw- | deley, dwelling in lyttle | Brittaine streete without Al- | dersgate.The.14. | day of October. | 1574. | 14.4x10 cm. (78) fol.

TRAVERS, Walter. Ecclesiasti- | cæ Disciplinæ, | Et Anglicanæ Ecclesiæ | Ab Illa Aberrationis, Ple- | na è verbo Dei, & dilucida | explicatio. | (device)
  Rvpellæ, | Excvdebat Adamvs | de Monte. | M.D.LXXIIII. | 15.8x10.1cm. (6), 147,(1) fol.
  Anon. B.M.Cat. DNB.57:163b

TRAVERS, Walter. A full and plaine de- | claration of Ecclesiasticall Discipli- | ne owt off the word off God, and off the | declininge off the churche | off England from | the same. | (device)
  Imprinted. | M.D.LXXIIII. | 19.6x13.8 cm.   (10),193,(1)p.
  Anon. Translated by Thomas Cartwright. Cambr.Univ.Cat. 6299.
  Burned by order of the convocation of the University of Oxford, July 1683.

WHITGIFT, John. The Defense | of the Aunsvvere to | the Admonition, against | the Replie of T. C. | By Iohn VVhitgift | Doctor of Diuinitie. | In the beginning are added these .4. Tables. | 1 Of dangerous doctrines in the Replie. | 2 Of Falsifications and Untruthes. | 3 Of matters handled at large. | 4 A table generall. | . . . (2 lines).
  Printed at London by Henry Binneman, | for Humfrey Toye. Anno. 1574. | Woodcut border. 27.7x18.7 cm. (23),812,(11) p. Colophon.

1574-75

WHITGIFT, John. A Defence | of the Ecclesiasticall | Regiment in Englande, | defaced by T.C. in his | Replie agaynst D. | VVhitgifte. | Seene and allowed according to the or- | der appoynted in the Queenes | Maiesties Iniun- | ctions. |

Imprinted at Lon- | don by Henry Bynneman, | for Humfrey Toy. | Anno. 1574. | Lace border. 13.4x9.cm. (2), 194p.
Anon. B.M.Cat. H&L, new edit, ascribes to H:Howard.

1575

ARTICLES, | wherupon it was agreed by | the most reuerend father in God the Arch- | bishop of Canterbury, & other the Bi- | shops & the whole Cleargie of the prouince | of Canterbury, in the conuocation or sy- | node holden at Westminster by Prorogati- | on, in the yeere of our Lorde God, after the | computation of the Church of Englande, | one thousande, fiue hundred, seuentie | fiue, touchyng thadmission of apt | and fytte persons to the Mini- | sterie, and thestablishing of | good orders in the | Churche. | Published by the Queenes | Maiesties aucthoritie. |

Colophon: Imprinted at Lon- | don, by Richard Iugge, Printer | to the Queenes | Maiestie. | Cum priuilegio Regiæ Maiestatis. | (device). 17.2x12.6 cm. (8)p.

CARTWRIGHT, Thomas. The second replie of | Thomas Cartwright: agaynst Mai- | ster Doctor Whitgiftes second answer, | touching the Churche Discipline. | . . . (4 lines; device) . . . (4 lines).

Imprinted. | M.D.LXXV. | [Zurich] 18.7x14.3 cm. (31),DCLXVI,(13)p.

CORRO, Antonio. A Theo- | logical Dia- | logve. | Wherin the Epistle of S.Paul the | Apostle to the Romanes is | expounded. | Gathered and set together | out of the Readings of Anto- | nie Corranus of Siuille, pro- | fessor of Diuinitie. | . . . (7 lines).

Imprinted at London | by Thomas Purfoote, dwelling | in Paules Churchyarde at the | signe of the Lucrece. | An.1575. | Border. 14.6x9.6cm. (27),155fol.

ELIZABETH, Queen [Statutes] Anno xviii. Anno. xviii. Reginæ Elizabethe. | At this present Sessi- | on of Parliament by prorogation holden | at VVestminster the .viii. day of Fe- | bruary, in the xviii. yeere of the raigne of our | most gratious soueraigne Lady Elizabeth, | by the grace of God, of Englande, | Fraunce, and Irelande, Queene, | defender of the fayth. &c. | and there continued | vntyl the .xv. day | of March fo- | lowyng. | To the high pleasure of almyghtie | God, and the weale publique | of this Realme, were | enacted as fo- | loweth. |

1575. | Ornam. border. 25.4x18.3 cm. (60)fol.

FENTON, Geoffrey. Golden Epistles, | Contayning | varietie of discourse both | Morall, Philosophicall, and | Diuine: gathered as well out of the | remaynder of Gueuaraes workes, | as other Authors, Latine, | French, and Italian. | By Geffray Fenton. | . . . (1 line)

Imprinted at London by | Henry Middleton, for Rafe New- | bery, dwelling in Fleetestreat a | litle aboue the Conduit. | 1575. | Engr.border. 19.6x14.2cm. (8),200fol. Colophon.

NICHOLAS, Henry. Introdvctio. | An Introduction to | the holy Understanding of the | Glasse of Righteousnes. | Wherin are vttered many notable Admonitions | and Exhortations to the Good-life. also sun- | dry discreet Warnings to beware of Destruc- | tion. and of wrong-conceiuing, and misun- | derstanding or censuring of any Sentences. | Sett-forth by HN, and by him perused a-new, and expressed more | playnly. | (device) . . . (7 lines).

<small>No imprint. 17.2x11.3 cm. 39,39,26,18,20 fol.
B.M.Cat.</small>

PATTEN, William. The Calender of Scripture. | VVhearin the Hebru, | Challdian, Arabian, | Phenician, Syrian, Per- | sian, Greek and Latin Names, of | Nations, Cuntreys, Men, | Weemen, Idols, Cities, Hils, Riuers, | & of oother places in the holly | Byble mentioned, by order of | letters ar set, and tur- | ned into oour Eng- | lish toong. | 1575. | . . . (5 lines). Ornam. border

<small>[Printed by Richard Jugge. 1575] 20.2x15.8cm. (3),193,(6)fol
Anon. Camb.Univ.Cat.No.968.</small>

TOBIAS. Mirabilia opera Dei: | Certaine wonderfull Works of | God which hapned to H. N. even from his | youth: and how the God of Heaven hath united | himself with him, and raised up his gracious | Word in him, and how he hath chosen | and sent him to be a Minister of | his gracious Word. | Published by Tobias a Fellow Elder with | H. N. in the Houshold of Love. | (device) Translated out of Base Almain. | . . . (7 lines).

<small>Without impr. [1575?] 16.1x12 cm. (11),137,(1)p. Engraved frontispiece.
Pages 11-14 supplied in manuscript.
BMCat. Niclas. col. 265.</small>

WHITTINGHAM, William. A Brieff discours | off the troubles begonne at Franck | ford in Germany Anno Domini 1554.Abowte | the Booke off off common prayer and Ceremonies, and conti- | nued by the Englishe men theyre, to thende off Q.Maries | Raigne, in the which discours, the gentle reader shall see | the very originall and beginninge off all the | contention that hathe byn, and what was | the cause off the same. | . . . (5 lines; device).

<small>[Zurich] M.D.LXXV. | 19.2x14.5 cm. (1),CCXV,(1)p.
Anon. Camb. Univ Cat. No 6301.
Also a reprint, London: John Petheram, 1846</small>

1576

ALLEN, William. Gvlielmi Alani Angli, | Regii Sacræ | Theologiæ Profes- | soris In Academia | Dvacensi. | Libri Tres. | Id est, | De Sacramentis in genere, Lib.I. | De Sacramento Eucharistiæ. Lib.I. | De Sacrificio Eucharistiae Lib.I. | Ex viuæ vocis diligenti & accurata tractatione, quam | idem his de rebus contra nostri temporis Hæreticos in | Schola Theologorum habuit. | . . . (5 lines; device).

<small>Antverpiæ, | Apud Iohannem Foulerum Anglum. | M.D.LXXVI. | Cvm Privilegio. | Colophon: Dvaci, | Excvdebat Lvdovicvs De VVinde, | Cura Et Impensa Iohannis | Fovleri. | An M.D.LXXVI. | 20.5x15.1cm. (28),657,(19)p.</small>

BULLINGER, Henry. A Most | excellent Sermon of the | Lordes Supper, wherein | briefely (and yet plainly ye- | nough) is liuely set foorth | the matter of the Supper of | the Lorde Iesus. | By Henry Bullinger. | Translated out of French | into English, by I.T. | . . . (3 lines; ornament).

Imprinted at London, nigh vnto | vnto the three Cranes in the | Vintree, for William Ponsonby. | [1576?] Colophon: Imprinted at London, | nigh vnto the three Cranes in | the Vintree, by Thomas Dawson | and Thomas Gardyner, for Willi- | am Ponsonby. | 13.9x9.5cm. (4, 28) fol.
BMCat[1570?]. Cf. Camb Univ. Cat. No. 1798.

CALVIN, John. Institvtionis | Christianæ Reli- | gionis, A Ioanne | Calvino Conscriptæ, | Compendivm Simvl, | Ac Methodi | Enarratio. | Per Edm. Bunnium Sacræ Theolo- | giæ Baccalaureum. | (device).

Londini, impensis Georgij Byshop, | & Thomæ Vautrollerij. | 1576. | 14.2x9.2 cm. (24),188p. 4 tab.

NOWELL, Alexander. A Catechisme, | or Institution of Christian Re- | ligion, to be learned of all youth | next after the little Catechisme: ap- | pointed in the booke of com- | mon Prayer | (cut)

At London. | Printed by Iohn Daye, and are to bee | solde at his shop vnder Aldersgate. | Cum priuilegio Regiæ Maiestatis | per Decennium. An.1576. | 14.4x 9.4cm. (3,129)p.
Anon. DNB. 41: 249a.

VERMIGLI, Pietro Martir. Petri Marty- | ris Vermilii, Floren- | tini Præstantissimi Nostra Ætate | Theologi, Loci Communes. | Ex varijs ipsius Aucthoris & libris in vnum volumen | collecti, & quatuor classes distributi. | . . . (2 lines; device; 2 lines).

Londini, | Ex Typographia Ioannis | Kyngstoni. | 1576. | 29.4x19.3cm. (24), 1–493, 487–1089,(1)p.

WOOLTON, John. The Christian | Manuell, or of the life | and maners of true | Christians. | A Treatise, wherein is plentifully | declared, how needefull it is for the | seruaunts of God to manifest and de- | clare to the world: their faith by their | deedes, their words by their works, | and their profession by their | conuersation. | VVritten by Ihon VVool- | ton Minister of the Gospel, | in the Cathedral church | of Excetor. |

Imprinted at London by I.C. | for Thomas Sturruppe dwel- | ling in Paules Church yarde, | at the singe of the George. | 1576. | Engr.border. 14x9.3cm. (8,95)fol.

1577

BROOKE, John. (Trans.) The Staffe | of Christian Faith, profi- | table to all Christians, for to arme them- | selues agaynst the enimies of the Gospell: | and also for to knowe the anti- | quitie of our holy fayth, | and of the true | Church. | Gathered out of the vvorks of the ancient Doctors | of the Church, and of the Councels, and many o- | ther Doctors, vvhose names you shall see here | follovving. Translated out of Frenche | into English, by Iohn Brooke | of Ashe next

Sand- | vviche. | With a Table to finde out all that which | is contayned in the booke. | . . . (4 lines).

Jmprinted at London | by Iohn Daye, dwelling ouer | Aldersgate. | Anno. 1577. | Cum Priuilegio. | 13.2x8.9 cm. (45),382,(9)p.

BUCER, Martin. Martini Bvceri | Scripta Anglicana | Ferè Omnia | Iis etiam, quæ hactenus vel nondum, vel sparsim, | vel peregrino saltem idiomate edi- | ta fuêre, adiunctis | À Con. Hvberto ad explicandas sedandasq́; religionis cùm | alias, tum præsertim Eucharisticas controuersias, | singulari fide collecta. | Quorum Catalogvm prima post Præfationes pa- | gina complectitur. | Adiuncta est Historia de Obitu Buceri: quæq́; illi & Paulo | Fagio post mortem & indigna & di- | gna contigêre. | . (device)

Basileæ | Ex Petri Pernæ Officina | M D LXXVII. | 31.8x20.6 cm. (23),959p.

BULLINGER, Henry. Fiftie Godlie And Lear- | ned Sermons, diuided into fiue Decades, con- | teyning the chiefe and principall pointes of Christian | Religion, written in three seuerall Tomes or Sections, by | Henrie Bullinger minister of the Churche of | Tigure in Swicer- | lande. | Wherevnto Is Adioyned A Triple | or three-folde Table verie fruitefull and | necessarie. | Translated out of Latine into English | by H. I. student in Diuinitie. | (device). . . . (3 lines).

Imprinted At London By Ralphe | Newberrie, dwelling in Fleete-streate a little | aboue the Conduite. | Anno. Gratiæ. | 1577. | 23.x17.6 cm. (48),1–781, 810–1142p.

CALVIN, John. A | Commen- | tarie vpon S.Paules | Epistles to the Co- | rinthians. | Written by M.Iohn Caluin: | and translated out of La- | tine into Englishe, by | Thomas Tymme | Minister. |

Imprinted at London, for | Iohn Harison and George | Byshop. | 1577. | Arch border. 19.3x14.1cm. (8),307,(3)fol.

CALVIN, John. The | Sermons | of M.Iohn Caluin, | vpon the Epistle of S. | Paule too the Ephe- | sians. | Translated out of French into | English by Arthur | Golding. |

Imprinted at London | for Lucas Harison, and | George Byshop. | 1577. | Arch border. 19.3x14.cm. (16),347fol.

CARTWRIGHT, Thomas. The rest of the second | replie of Thomas Cartvurihgt: | agaynst Master Doctor Vuhitgifts se- | cond ansvuer, touching the | Church discipline. | . . . (4 lines; device) . . . (4 lines).

Imprinted | M.D.LXXVII. | 17.8x14.2 cm. (7),265,(13)p.

FULKE, William. Tvvo Treatises | Written Against The | Papists, The One Being An | answere of the Christian Protestant to the | proud challenge of a Popish Catholicke: | The Other | A Confvtation | Of The Popish Chvrches | doctrine touching Purgatory & prayers | for the dead: by William Fulke | Doctor in diuinitie. | (device).

Imprinted at London by Thomas Vautrollier | dwelling in the Blackefriers. | 1577. | 16.2x10.7cm. (8),110; 461,(3)p.

GERARDUS, Andreas. The Practise | of preaching, | Otherwise Called The | Pathway to the Pulpet: | Conteyning an excellent Method how to | frame Diuine Sermons, & to interpret the | holy Scriptures according to the capacitie | of the vulgar people. First written in Latin | by the learned pastor of Christes Church, | D.Andreas Hyperius: and now lately (to | the profit of the same Church) Eng- | lished by Iohn Ludham, vicar | of Wethersfeld. | 1577. | Herevnto is added an Oration as concerning | the lyfe and death of the same Hyperius: | which may serue for a president to all the | learned men of his calling in our tyme. | (device)

Imprinted at London | by Thomas East. | 1577. | 18x13.2cm. (8),181,(18)fol. 1 sub.t.p.

NOWELL, Alexander. Χριστια- | νισμου Στοιχειω- | σις εἰς τὴν τῶν παίδων ὠφέλειαν | ἑλληνισὶ καὶ λατινισὶ ἐκ- | τεθεῖσα. | Christia- | næ pietatis prima in- | stitutio, ad vsum scho- | larum Græcè & Lati- | nè scripta. | (device).

Londini | Apud Ioannem Dayum. | An.1577. | Border. 13.1x8.8cm. (15,239)p. Latin dedication signed.

ROGERS, Thomas. Of the ende of | this world, and second com- | ming of Christ, a comforta- | ble and necessary Discourse, for | these miserable and daun- | gerous dayes. | . . . (7 lines; device).

Imprinted at London, nigh vnto | the three Cranes in the Vintree, for Andrew | Maunsell, dwelling in Paules Church- | yard, at the signe of the Paret. | Anno Domini. 1577. | Colophon: Imprinted . . . by Thomas Gardyner and Thomas Dawson. . . . 17.9x12.7cm. (7),48fol.
Epistle dedicatory signed.

SARCERIUS, Erasmus. Common | places of Scripture or- | derly & after a compen- | dious forme of teaching, set | forth with no litle labour, to | the great profit & help of all | such students in gods word | as haue not had long exer- | cise of the same, by the right | excellent clerke Erasmus | Sarcerius. | Translated into English | by Richard Ta- | uerner. |

At London | Printed by Thomas East. | 1577. | Border. 14.3x9.5 cm. 192 fol

1578

An ACT to reforme certaine | disorders touchyng Ministers of the Churche. | Chapter xii. |

1578. Elizabeth Q. [Statutes], Ann.13. Cap.12.

An ACT touchyng leasses of | benefices, and other Ecclesiastical lyuing with cure. | The xx. Chapter.

1578. Elizabeth, Q. [Statutes] Ann.13. Cap.20.

An ACTE agaynst the bryng- | ging in, and puttyng in execution of bulles, writynges, or in- | strumentes, and other superstitious thynges from the | sea of Rome. | The ij Chapter. |

1578. 27.8x19cm: Elizabeth, [Statutes] Ann. 13. Chapter 2.

An ACTE agaynst Vsurie. | Chapter viii. |
1578. Elizabeth, Q. [Statutes] Ann.13. Cap.8.

An ACTE for confyrmation of a subsidie graunted | by the Cleargie. | Chapter xxvi. |
1578. Elizabeth, Q. [Statutes]. Ann.13, Cap.26.

BÈZE, Théodore de. An euident Display of | Popish Practises, or patched | Pelagianisme. | Wherein is mightelie cleared the | soueraigne truth of Gods eternall | Predestination, the stayd groundworke | of oure most assured safe- | tie by Christ. | Written in Latin by that Reuerend Fa- | ther, Mayster Theodore Beza, and now lately | Englished by VV. H. Preacher | of the Gospell. | . . . (6 lines).
At London, | Imprinted by Ralph Newberie, and Henry | Bynnyman. Anno. 1578. | Lace border 17.5x13.6 cm. (7),275 p. Colophon.

CALVIN, John. A Commen- | tarie of M.Iohn Caluine, | vpon the Booke of Iosue, fini- | shed a little before his | death: | Translated out of Latine into | Englishe by W.F. | Wherevnto is added a table | of the principall | matters. | (device)
Imprinted at London, | for George Bishop, | 1578. | Border. Colophon: Imprinted at London, by Thomas | Dawson, for George Bishop. | Anno. 1578. | 18.3x 13.4cm. (4),104,(3)fol.

CROWLEY, Robert. A briefe discourse | against the outvvarde apparell | and Ministring garmen- | tes of the popishe | church. | psalme.31. | I haue hated all those, that | holde of superstititious vanities. | 1578. | I vvould that you so hattid them, that | you vsid them not, W.C. |
Without place or printer. 13.7x9.cm. (24)fol. [ed.2]
Anon.Camb.Univ.Cat. No.6764.

ELIZABETH, Queen [Statutes] Anno xiii. Anno xiii. Reginæ Elizabethe. | At the Parliament | begunne & holden at Westminster | the second of April, in the xiii. yere of the reigne of | our most gratious soueraigne Ladie Elizabeth, | by the grace of God, of England, Fraunce, and Ireland | Queene, defendour of the faith, &c. and there | continued vntil the dissolu- | tion of the same. | To the high pleasure of almightie God, and | the weale publique of this Realme, | were enacted as foloweth. |
Imprinted at London by Christo- | pher Barker, Printer to the | Queenes Maiestie. | Cum priuilegio ad imprimendum solum. | 1578. | Engr. border. 27.8x 19 cm. (70)fol.

HEMINGE, Nicholas. The Way of lyfe. | A Christian, and Catholique Insti- | tution comprehending principal poincts | of Christian Religion, which are necessary | to bee knowne of all men, to the atteyning | of Saluation. | First delyuered, in the Danish language | for the instruction of those people, by Doctor | Nicolas Hemmingius, Preacher of the Gospell, | and Professor of Diuinitie, for the Kynge | of Denmarcke, in his Uniuersitie | of Hafnia: | And about three yeares past, (for the commoditie | of others) translated into Latine, by Andrew | Seuerinus Velleius: | And now first, and newly Englished, for the com- | modity of English Readers: | By N.Denham, this yeare of our | Redemption. 1578. | (device).

Imprinted at London by Richard | Jones, and are to bee sould ouer | agaynst S.Sepulchers Churche. | 17.6x12.7cm. | (32),199p.

KELTRIDGE, John. The Exposition, and Rea- | dynges of Iohn Keltridge: | Mayster of the Artes: | Student of late in Trinitie Col- | ledge in Cambridge, Minister, Preacher, | and Pastor of the Church of Dedham, that | is in Essex: Upon the wordes of our | Sauiour Christe, that bee written | in the .xi. of Luke. | . . . (7 lines)

Imprinted at London, by | William How. for | Abraham Veale, 1578. | Lace border 19.2x14.2cm. (16),251p.

KNEWSTUB, John. The | Lectvres | of John Knewstub, | vpon the twentith Chap- | ter of Exodus, and cer- | teine other places | of Scripture. | Seene and allowed accor- | ding to the Queenes Ma- | iesties Iniunctions. |

Imprinted By | Lucas Harrison. | Anno. 1578. | Arch. border. 18.x12.cm. (17), 299p.

LATIMER, Hugh. Frvtefvll | Sermons Prea- | ched by the right reuerend father, and | constant Martyr of Iesus Christ M. Hugh | Latymer, newly Imprinted, with others | not heretofore set forth in print, to | the edifying of all which will dis- | pose them selues to the rea- | ding of the same | A Table on the third Page of this leafe, wherin | you shall finde the whole number of the Ser- | mons, and where to finde them by the folios. | Seene and allowed according to the | order appoynted in the Queenes Ma- | iesties Iniunctions. | 1578. |

At London. | Printed by Iohn Daye, dwelling | ouer Aldersgate. | Cum priuilegio Regiæ Maiestatis. | Engr. border. 19x14.4 cm. (7),265,150–215fol. 1 pl. Colophon after each part.

L'ESPINE, Jean de. An Excellent | Treatise Of Christian | Righteovsnes, Written First | in the French tongue by M. I.de l'Espine, & | translated into English by I. Feilde, for the | comfort of afflicted consciences, very neces- | sarie and profitable to be read of all Christi- | ans, as well for establishing them in the true | doctrine of Iustification, as also for ena- | bling them to confute the false doctrine of | all Papistes and Heretickes in that poinct. | (device)

Imprinted at London by Thomas Vau- | trollier dwelling in the Blackfriers. | 1578. | 13.7x9.5cm. (2),7–128p. Lacks Ai–ii.

RHEGIUS, Urbanus. The | Sermon, which Christ | made on the way to Emaus | to those two sorowfull dis- | ciples, set downe in a dialogue by | D.Vrbane Regius, wherein he | hath gathered and expounded | the chiefe prophecies of | the old Testament con- | cerning Christ. | (device).

At London, | Printed by Iohn Daye | dwelling ouer Aldersgate | and are to be sould at his long | shop at the west dore of | Paules. Anno. 1578. | Cum priuilegio

Regiæ Maiestatis. | Border. Colophon: At London. | Printed by Iohn Daye dwelling | ouer Aldersgate, and are to be sould | at his shop vnder the gate. | An.1578. | 17.9x12.3cm. (10),222,(4)fol. 136 repeated.

ROGERS, John. The Displaying | of an horrible secte of | grosse and wicked Heretiques, | naming themselues the Fa- | milie of Loue, with the liues | of their Authours, and what | doctrine they teach in | corners. | Newely set foorth by | I. R. 1578. | Wherevnto is annexed a confes- | sion of certain Articles, which was | made by two of the Familie of Loue, | being examined before a Justice of | peace, the 28. of May 1561. tou- | ching their errours taught a- | mongest them at their | assemblies. |

Imprinted at London | for George Bishop. | Lace border. 13.5x8.2 cm. (17, 132) p
Cambr.Univ.Cat. 1710.

WHITE, Thomas. A Ser- | mon Preached | at Pawles Crosse on | Sunday the ninth of | December.1576. | by T.W. |

Imprinted at Lon- | don by Francis Col- | dock. 1578. | Engr. border. 13.9x9.5 cm. (7),64p.
Title page (A:i), and "The faultes escaped" (A:v), supplied in photostat by George Watson Cole, librarian of the Henry E. Huntington Library, San Gabriel, Calif. The title at the head of the sermon, contains a misprint, 1577 for 1576. Ai-Av (Roman); Aj-Dviij (Gothic) in eights.

1579

An APOLOGY or defence for | the Christians of Fraūce which are | of the Euāgelicall or reformed religi- | on, for the satisfiiing of such as wil | not liue in peace and concord | with them. | Whereby the purenes of the same Religion in the | chiefe poyntes that are in variance, is eui- | dently shewed, not onely by the holy | scriptures, and by reason: But | also by the Popes owne | Canons. | Written to the king of Nauarre and | translated out of french into | English by Sir Iherom | Bowes Knight. |

At London | Printed by Iohn Day dwelling ouer | Aldersgate. And are to be sold | at his Shop under the gate. | 1579. | Cum Priuilegio Regiæ | Maiestatis. | 13.2x8.9cm. (11),132fol.

BÈZE, Théodore de. De Veris, Et | Visibilibvs | Ecclesiæ Cathol- icæ | notis, tractatio. | Theodore Beza | Vezelio auctore. | (device).
Genevæ, | Apvd Evstathivm Vignon. | M.D.LXXIX. | 16.6x10.4cm. 90p.

BULLINGER, Henry. A most godly | and learned Discourse of the | woorthynesse, authoritie, and suf- | ficiencie of the holy Scripture: Also | of the cleerenesse, and plain- | nesse of the same, and of the | true vse thereof. | Wherin is discussed this famous que- | stion: Whether the Canonical Scriptures haue | authoritie from the Church, or rather | the Church receiue authoritie from the Scriptures. | By occasion whereof are touched the dignities | and duties of the Church, touching tradi- | tions, with aunswere to all | obiections. | Translated out of Latine into English, | by Iohn Tomkys: and dedicated | to the right honorable Sir Ri- | charde Pipe, Knight, Lorde Ma- | ior of the Citie of London. | . . . (3 lines).

<small>Printed at London, for William | Ponnsonby. 1579. | Colophon: Imprinted at London, | at the three Cranes in the vine- | tree, by Thomas Dawson, for | William Pounsonby. | 1579. | 14x8.8cm. (10),119fol.</small>

CALVIN, John. Foure | Sermons Of | Maister Iohn Caluin, | Entreating of matters very | profitable for our time, as may | bee seene by the Pre- | face: | With a briefe exposition of the | LXXXVII. Psalme. | Translated out of Frenche into | Englishe by Iohn Fielde. | (device)

<small>Imprinted at London | for Thomas Man, dwelling | in Pater Noster Rowe, at the | Signe of the Talbot. | 1579. | Engraved border. Colophon: Imprinted at London at the | three Cranes in the Vinetree, by | Thomas Dawson, for | Thomas Man. | 1579. | 19.1x13.8cm. (6),59fol.</small>

CALVIN, John. Sermons | of M.John Caluin, | on the Epistles of S.Paule | to Timothie and | Titus. | Translated out of French | into English, by | L.T. |

<small>At London | Imprinted for G.Bishop | and T.Woodcoke. | 1579. | Arch. border. 22.4x16.8cm. (44),1248p.
Also another copy from the library of Walter W. Law. 20.9x15.2cm. T.p. supplied.</small>

CALVIN, John. Thirteene | Sermons Of | Maister Iohn Caluine, | Entreating of the Free Election | of God in Iacob, and of re- | probation in Esau. | A treatise wherein euery Christian | may see the excellent benefites of God to- | wardes his children, and his maruelous | iudgements towards the reprobate, firste | published in the French toung, & now | Translated into Englishe by | Iohn Fielde, For the | comfort of all | Christians. | . . . (4 lines)

<small>Imprinted at London for Thomas | Man and Tobie Cooke. | 1579. | Engraved border Colophon: Imprinted at London by Thomas | Dawson dwelling at the three Cranes in | the Vinetree, for Tobie Cooke, and | Thomas Man. | 1579. | 19.1x13.5cm. (7),176fol.</small>

DIGBY, Everard. Theoria | Analytica, | Viam ad Monarchiam Scienti- | arum demonstrans, totius Philoso- | phiæ & reliquarum Scientiarum, necnon | primorum postremorumq́; Philo- | sophorum mysteria arcanaq́; | dogmata enucleans. | In tres libros digesta: | Autore Everardo Dygbeio Anglo, | in Artibus Magistro, Socio Collegij Diui Io- | hannis Euangelistæ Cantabrigiensis. | (device).

<small>Londini, | Ex officina Henrici Bynneman. | Anno salutis humanæ. 1579. | Calend. Septemb. | Lace border. 19.1x12.8cm. (28), 404,(3)p.</small>

DYOS, John. A Sermon preached | at Paules Crosse the 19. | of Iuli 1579: setting forth the | excellencye of Gods heauenlye | worde: The exceeding mercye of | Christ our Sauiour: The state of this | world: A profe of the true Church: | A detection of the false Church: or | rather malignant rable: A con- | futation of sundry hæresies: | and other thinges necessary | to the vnskilfull to be | knowen. | By Iohn Dyos. | Seene and allowed. |

At London | Printed by Iohn Daye dwel- | ling ouer Aldersgate. | Anno. 1579. | Cum Priuilegio Regiæ Maiestatis. | Border 12.9x8.4cm. (8),79fol.

FULKE, William. D. Heskins, | D. Sanders, And | M. Rastel, accounted (among | their faction) three pillers and | Archpatriarches of the Popish Synagogue, | (vtter enemies to the truth of Christes Gospell, | and all that syncerely professe the same) | ouerthrowne, and detected of their | seuerall blasphemous | heresies. | By D. Fulke, Maister of Pembrooke | Hall in Cambridge. | Done and directed to the Church of England and | all those which loue the trueth. |

At London, | Printed by Henrie Middleton | for George Bishop. | Anno. 1579. | 15.5x10.1 cm. (6),803,(1)p.

FULKE, William. A Sermon preached | at Hampton Court, on | Sonday being the .12. day of | Nouember, in the yeare of | our Lord. 1570. | VVherein is plainly prooued | Babilon to be Rome, both by | Scriptures and | Doctors. | Preached by VVilliam Fulke, Doc- | tor of Diuinity lately fellow | of S.Johns Colledge | in Cambridge. | . . . (6 lines).

Imprinted at London | by Iohn Charlevvod. | 1579. | Border. Colophon: Imprinted at London by | Iohn Charlewood, dwelling in Bar- | bycan, at the signe of the | halfe Egle and Key. | 13.2x9.1cm. (2,30)fol.

GARTER, Bernard. A Newyeares Gifte, | dedicated to the Popes Holi- | nesse, and all Catholikes addicted to | the Sea of Rome: preferred the first day | of Ianuarie, in the yeare of our Lorde God, | after the course and computation of | the Romanistes, one thousand, fiue | hundreth, seauentie and nine, by | B.G Citizen of London: | In recompence of diuers singu- | lar and inestimable Reliques, of late | sent by the said Popes Holinesse into | England, the true figures and represen- | tations whereof, are heereafter | in their places di- | lated. | . . . (5 lines).

At London, | Printed by Henry Bynneman. | Anno Domini 1579. | Border. 17.1x12.5cm. (14,88)p.

DNB.21:30b. Erroneously attributed to Barnaby Googe. Camb.Univ.Cat. No.1503.

KNEWSTUB, John. An | Aunsvveare | vnto certaine assertions, | tending to maintaine the | Churche of Rome, | to bee the true and | Catholique | church. | By I.Knewstub. |

Imprinted in London at | the three Cranes on the Vine- | tree, by Thomas Dawson, for | Richard Sergier. | 1579. | Border. Colophon and printer's mark. 19.x13.7cm. (8),61,(1)fol.

First folio blank except for leaf device. Appended to his Confutation: 1579.

KNEWSTUB, John. A Confutation of mon- | strous and horrible here- | sies, taught by H.N. and embra- | ced of a number, who call them- | selues the Familie | of Loue. | by I.Knewstub. | . . . (7 lines). Seene and allowed, according to the Queenes | Maiesties Iniunctions. |

Imprinted in London at | the three Cranes in the Vine- | tree, by Thomas Dawson, for | Richard Sergier. | 1579. | Border. Colophon. 19.x13.7cm. (16),94, (28)fol.
Appended is A Sermon preached at Paules Crosse | the Fryday before Easter, commonly | called good Fryday, in the yeere of our | Lorde. 1576. By Iohn | Knewstub. | Sig.P–S4.

LANGUET, Hubert. Vindiciae, | Contra Ty- | rannos: | Sive, | De Principis In | Populum, Populíque in Princi- | pem, legitima potestate, | Stephano Ivnio | Bruto Celta, Auctore. |
Edimbvrgi, An- | no M.D.LXXIX. | 15x9.8cm. (14),236,(3)p.
Cf. H&L. English transl. 1689.
Appended is De Ivre Magistratvvm in Subditos, Et Officio subditorum erga Magistratus: . . . E Gallico in Latinum conuersus. . . . M.D.LXXX.
Burned by order of the convocation of the University of Oxford, July 1683.

MINISTRORVM | Qvi Verbvm Dei In Refor- | matis In Belgio Ecclesiis Con- | cionantvr, Ad Avthores Libri | Bergensis, qui etiam Concordiae dicitur, | Epistola. | Sectemini Pacem. | (device).
M.D.LXXIX. | 20x15cm. 40p.

MORNAY, Philippe de. A Notable | Treatise Of | The Chvrch, In | vvhich are handled all the | principall questions, that | haue bene moued in our | time concerning that | matter. | By Philip of Mornay, | Lord of Plessis Marlyn, Gentle- | man of Fraunce. | And translated out of French | into English by Io.Feilde. | . . . (6 lines).
Imprinted at London by | Christopher Barker, Printer | to the Queenes Maiestie. | Anno. Dom. | 1579. | Illust. border. 13.8x8.9 cm. (14,368)p.

RATIO | ineundæ Concordiæ | inter Ecclesias Reformatas. | Siue | Quibus modis occurri possit mirificis | artibus, quibus Pontificij per quosdam impruden- | tes Theologos vniuersas Christi ecclesias potissi- | mum autem & primum Germanicas pessundare | conantur. | Dissipa Domine consilium | Achitopelis. |
1579. | 20x15 cm. 32p.

ROGERS, John. The Dis- | playing of an horrible | secte of grosse and wicked | Heretiques, naming them- | selues the Family of Love, | with the liues of their Authours, | and what doctrine they teach | in corners. | Newly set foorth by I.R. | Wherevnto is added cer- | teine letters sent from the same | Family mainteyning their opi- | nions, which Letters are | aunswered by the same J.R. |
Imprinted At | London for George | Bishop. | 1579. | Colophon: Imprinted at London | By Henrie Middleton for | George Byshop. | 13.4x9.cm. (16,224)p. T.p. supplied.
Cambr.Univ.Cat.1628.

SHUTE, Christopher. A compendious | form and summe of Christian doct- | rine, called the Testimonie of a | true Faith, meete for well dispo- | sed families, for the more knowledge | of God, and better nourishing | vp, and confirming of all such, | as loue saluation in

Iesus | Christ. | Gathered, corrected, and newly | augmented, by Christopher Shutte, | Maister of Arte, | Seene and allowed. | . . . (4 lines).

Imprinted at London by | Thomas Dawson, dwelling at | the three Cranes in the Vinetree. | 1579. | Border. 14.2x9.2cm. (15,63)p. Colophon.

SMETON, Thomas. Ad | Virvlentvm | Archibaldi Hamiltonii | Apostatæ Dialogvm, De Con- | fusione Caluinianæ sectæ apud Scotos, impiè | conscriptum orthodoxa responsio. | Thoma Smetonio Scoto | Avctore. | In qua celebris illa quæstio de Ecclesia, de vniuersalitate, suc- | cessione, & Romani Episcopi primatu breuiter, dilu- | cidè, & accuratè tractatur. | Adiecta est vera historia extremæ vitæ & obitus | eximij viri Ioan.Knoxij Ecclesiæ Scoti- | canæ instauratoris fidelissimi. | I(device)R

Edinbvrgi, | Apud Iohannem Rosseum | Pro Henrico Charteris. Anno Do. 1579. | Cum Privilegio Regali. | 18.3x12.6 cm. (8),123,(1)p.

WILKINSON, William. A Confutation | Of Certaine Articles | deliuered vnto the Familye of Loue, with | the exposition of Theophilus, a suppo- | sed Elder in the sayd Familye vpon | the same Articles. | By William Wilkinson Maister of Artes and student | of Diuinitye. | Hereunto are prefixed | By the right reuerend Father in God I. Y. Byshop of Ro- | chester, certaine notes collected out of their Gospell, | and aunswered by the Fam. | By the Author, a description of the tyme, places, Authors, and | manner of spreading the same: of their liues, and wrestyng | of Scriptures: with Notes in the end how to know an He- | retique. | . . . (3 lines).

At London | Printed by Iohn Daye dwelling ouer | Aldersgate. An. 1579. | Cum Priuilegio Regiæ Maiestatis. | 19.3x13.9 cm. fol. (18),80 (erroneously printed 100).

1580

ARTICLES to be enqui- | red of, Within the Prouince of Canterbu- | rie, in the Metropoliticall visitation of | the most reuerende father in God, Edmond | Archbishop of Canterburie, Primate | of all England, and Me- | tropolitane. | In the xxii. yeere of the reigne of our most | gracious souereigne Ladie Elizabeth, by | the grace of God, Queene of England, | Fraunce and Ireland, defender of | the faith, &c. | (device)

Imprinted at London by Christo- | pher Barker, Printer to the Queenes | Maiestie. | 1580. | 17.9x12.9 cm. 10fol.

BARO, Peter. ¶ De Fide, | Ejusque Ortu, & Natura, plana | ac dilucida Explicatio. | (ceú) | P. Baronis Stempani sacræ Theologiæ in | Academia Cantab. Doctoris ac Pro- | fessoris, Prælectio, in Cap,3. ad | Rom. vers,28. | Adjecta sunt alia quędam ejusdem | Authoris, de eodem Argumento, quæ se- | quens Pagina indicabit. | (device).

Londini. | Apud Richardum Dayum, in | Occident. Cœmeterio D. Pauli | sub Arbore. 1580. | 13.3x8.6cm. (16),223,(1)p.

BICKNOLL, Edmond. A Swoorde against | swearyng, contey- | ning these principal | poyntes. | 1 That there is a lawful vse of an |

oth, contrary to the assertion of | the Manichees & Anabaptistes. | 2
Howe great a sinne it is to sweare | falsly, vaynely, rashly, or customa-
bly. | 3 That common or vsuall swearyng | leadeth vnto periurie. | 4
Examples of Gods iust and visible pu- | nishment upon blasphemers,
periurers, | and such as haue procured Gods wrath | by cursing and
banning, which we call | execration. |

<small>Imprinted at London for | William Towreolde, by the | assent of Richard | VVatkins. | [1580?]   Border   Colophon: Imprinted at London for | William Towreolde, by the | assent of Richard VVatkins, and | are to be solde at his shoppe | adioyning to the lytle Cun- | duite in Cheape. | 13.5x9.2 cm.   47,(1)fol
Trin.Col.Camb. No.681. Epistle dedicatorie signed.</small>

BRADFORD, John. The hurt of hea- | ryng Masse: | Sette forthe
by the faithfull | seruant of God, and constant | Martire of Christ
Ihon | Bradford, when he | was prisoner | in | the Tower of | London. |
. . . (6 lines).

<small>Imprinted at London for H. | Kirkham, & are to be sold at his Shop | at the little Northdore of Sainct | Paules churche, at the signe | of the blacke Boye. | 1580. | Border.   13.5x9.1cm.   (1,84)p.</small>

BUCHANAN, George. Paraphrasis | Psalmorvm | Davidis Poeti-
ca, | Mvlto Qvam Ante- | hac Castigatior; | Auctore Georgio Buchan-
ano, Scoto, poë- | tarum nostri seculi facilè principe. | Adnotata vbique
diligenter carminum genera. | Eivsdem Buchanani tragœdia quæ | in-
scribitur Iephthes. | (device).

<small>Londini, | Excudebat Thomas Vautrollerius, | Typographus. | 1580. | 11.3x7.9cm.
373p.</small>

CALVIN, John. The Lectures or daily | Sermons of that Reuerend
Di- | uine, M.Ihon Caluine, Pastor of the | Churche of God in Geneua,
vppon the | Prophet Ionas. Whereunto is annexed | an excellente ex-
position of the two last | Epistles of sainct Iohn, doen in Latine | by
that worthie Doctor August. | Marlorate, and Engli- | shed by N.B. |
And newly corrected | and amended. | . . . (4 lines).

<small>Imprinted at Londō by Edward White | dwellyng at the little Northdoore of | Paules, at the signe of the Gun. | 1580. | Engr. border.   19.7x13.8cm.   (6),70;(4), 16fol.</small>

CALVIN, John. Three Propositi- | ons or Speeches, which | that
excellent man M. Iohn | Caluin, one of the Pastors | of the Church of
God | in Geneua had | there. | To which also is added, | an exposition
vpon that parte of | the Catechisme, which is ap- | pointed for the three
and | fortieth Sunday in | number. | Translated into Englishe, by |
T. VV. |

<small>Imprinted at Lon- | don for George Bi- | shop. 1580. | Border, containing the initials, T.D. Colophon: Imprinted in London | at the three Cranes in | the Vin-
tree, by Thomas | Dawson, for George | Bishop, 1580. | 13.5x9.1 cm.   (15),82,(1)fol</small>

CALVIN, John. Two and twentie | Sermons of Maister | Iohn
Caluin. | In which Sermons is most religi- | ously handled, the hun-
dredth and nine- | teenth Psalme of Dauid, by eight | verses aparte

according to | the Hebrewe Al- | phabet. | Translated out of French into | Englishe by T.S. |

Imprinted at London | for Iohn Harison and | Thomas Man. | 1580. | Engraved border. Colophon: Imprinted at Lon- | don at the three Cranes in the Vin- | tree by Thomas Dawson, for Iohn | Harison and Thomas Man. | 1580. | 19.1x13.8cm. (4),190fol.

COOPER, Thomas. Certaine Sermons | vvherin is contained the | Defense of the Gospell nowe | preached, against such Cauils and false | accusations, as are obiected both a- | gainst the Doctrine it selfe, and | the Preachers and Professors | thereof, by the friendes | and fauourers of the | Church of Rome. | (stars) Preached of late, by Thomas by Gods suf- | ferance Byshop of Lincolne. |

Imprinted at Londō by Ralphe | Newbery dwelling in Fleet street. | Anno Domini | 1580. | Arch. border. 19.7x13.8cm. (4),240,(12)p.

ELIZABETH, Queen. By the Queen. | A Proclamation against the Sectaries of the Fa- | mily of love. |

Without t.p. Colophon: Imprinted at London by Christopher Barker, | Printer to the Queens most Excel- | lent Majesty. | [1580.] 19.5x15.2cm. Pp. 229–230, of Sparrow's Collection: 1661. Also in his reprints of 1675 and 1684.

An EPISTLE Of | The Persecvtion Of | Catholickes In En- | glande. | Translated ovvt of frenche into Englishe and | conferred vvith the Latyne copie. by. G.T. | To whiche there is added an epistle by | the translator to the right honorable | Lordes of her maiesties preeuie coun- | cell towchynge the same matter. | . . . (8 lines).

Imprynted at Douay in Artois. | [1580]. 13.3x8.8cm. 165,(17)p.

FULKE, William. A Godly | and learned Ser- | mon, preached before | an honourable audi- | torie the 26. day of | Februarie.1580. | (device)

Imprinted by | Henrie Mid- | dleton for Thomas | Man. | [1580]. Border. 12.6x9.cm.64p.
Anon.Cambr.Univ.Cat. 1658.

FULKE, William. A Retentive, | To Stay Good Chri- | stians, In Trve Faith | and religion, against the motiues of Ri- | chard Bristow. | Also | A Discoverie | Of The Davngerovs | Rocke Of The Popish | Church, commended by Nicholas Sander | D. of Diuinitie. | Done by VVilliam Fulke Doctor of diuinitie, | and Maister of Pembroke hall | in Cambridge. | (device).

Imprinted at London by Thomas Vautroullier | for George Bishop. | 1580. | 15.2x9.7 cm. (8),316,(1)p. Device and T.V. on last leaf.

HOOPER, John. Certeine | comfortable Expositions | of the constant Mar- | tyr of Christ, M. Iohn Hooper, | Bishop of Glocester and Worcester, | written in the time of his tribulation and | imprisonment, vpon the XXIII. LXII. | LXXIII. and LXXVII. Psalmes | of the Prophet Dauid. | Newly recognised, and neuer | before published. | . . . (3 lines).

At London, | Printed by Henrie Middleton. | Anno 1580. | Border. 17.1x11.8 cm. (4),9–129,(1)fol.

HUTCHINSON, Roger. The | Image Of God | or boke of a true Chri- | stian, wherin the right know- | ledge of God, of Christ, and of | the holy Ghost is disclosed, and | diuers reasons of heretiques | agaynst the Godhead are | dissolued. | Newly corrected, and fayth- | fully amended. |

At London | Printed by Iohn Daye dwel- | ling ouer Aldersgate. An. | 1580. | Cum priuilegio Regiæ | Maiestatis. | Border. 14.3x9.4cm. (15),184,(2)fol.

MORNAY, Phillippe de. A Notable | Treatise Of | The Chvrch, In | which are handled all the | principall questions, that | haue beene mooued in our | time concerning that | matter. | By Philip of Mornay, | Lorde of Plessis Marlyn, Gentle- | man of Fraunce. | Translated out of Frenche into | Englishe by I F[ielde] and againe | perused & corrected. | . . . (6 lines).

Imprinted at London | by Christopher Barker, | Printer to the Queenes | Maiestie. | Anno Dom. | 1580. | Engraved border. 14x9cm. 384p.

OCHINO, Bernardino. Certaine Godly | and very profitable Sermons, of Faith, | Hope, and Charitie. | First set foorthe by Master Bar- | nardine Occhine, of Siena in Italy, and now | lately collected, and translated out of the | Italian tongue, into the English, | by William Phiston of | London Student. | Published for the profit of such as | desire to vnderstand the | truth of the Gos- | pell. | (device).

Imprinted at London by | Thomas East, 1580. | Colophon: Imprinted At | London by Thomas East, | dwelling betweene Paules | Wharfe, and Baynards | Castle. 1580. | (device) 19.2x13.5 cm. (4),100 fol.

SAINT ALDEGONDE, Philips van Marnix. The Bee hiue | of the Romishe | Churche. | A worke of al good Catholikes | too bee read and most necessary | to bee vnderstood: | Wherin both the Catholike Religion is substan- | tially confirmed, and the Heretikes finely | fetcht ouer the coales. | Translated out of Dutch into English | by George Gilpin the Elder. | . . . (3 lines). Newly Imprinted with a table | thereunto annexed. |

1580. | These bookes are to be solde in Paules | Churchyarde, at the signe of the | Parret. | Colophon: Imprinted at | Lōdon, at the three Cranes | in the Vinetree, by Thomas | Dawson, for Iohn | Stell. | 1580. | Frontisp. 15.x9.3cm. (59),365 fol.

Anon. Camb.Univ.Cat.1810, under Marnix.

TRAVERS, Walter. A Fvl And Plaine | Declaration Of Ecclesiasti- | cal Discipline Ovt Of The VVord | of God, and of the declining of the Church | of England from the same. | (device).

At Geneva. | M.D.LXXX. | 15.9x10.3 cm. (7),202p. Pages 197–200 supplied in Ms.

Anon. Cambr.Univ.Cat.6330.

VOYON, Simon De. A Testimonie | Of The Trve | Church of God | Confjrmed | As Well By The Doctrine | As Lives Of Svndry Holy | Men, Both Patriarkes, And Pro- | phetes, And Also By The | Apostles And Their Trve | Svccessovrs. | Wherein Is Manifest- | ly Shewed How

That God | hath in all ages raysed vp some, yea euen | in most horrible darkenesse, which haue | beene faithfull Stewards, and true dis- | pencers of his will, with a Cata- | logue of their names. | Translated Ovt Of | French by William Phiston. |

At London | Printed by H.M. for Tho- | mas Charde at the signe of the | Helmet in Pauls Church | yarde. | Lace border. n.d. [1580?] 18.6x13.8cm. (3), 161,(11)p.
Anon. Cambr.Univ.Cat. No 1659.

1581

ALLEN, William. An Apologie | And Trve Decla- | ration Of The Insti- | tution and endeuours of the tvvo | English Colleges, the one in Rome, | the other novv resident in Rhemes: | against certaine sinister informa- | tions giuen vp against the same. | . . . (9 lines; device).

Printed at Mounts in Henault. | 1581. | 16.8x11.1 cm. 122,(1) fol.
Signed at end.

B., I. A Dialogue | betweene a ver- | tuous Gentleman | and a popish priest, verie | pleasaunt and profitable, | both for ministers and | gentlemen, men and | vvomen, old and | yong, made | by I.B. |

Imprinted at | London, by Robert Wal- | degraue, dwelling without | Temple-barre, neere vnto | Sommerset-House. | 1581. | Border. 12.7x8.6cm. (16,143)p.

BRADFORD, John. Two Notable | Sermons. | Made by that woorthie | Martyr of Christe, Maister Iohn | Bradford, the one of Repen- | taunce, and the other of the | Lords Supper, now new- | lie Imprinted. | Perused and allowed, according | to the Queenes Maiesties | Iniunctions. |

Imprinted at Lon- | don by Iohn Charlewood, and | Iohn VVight. 1581. | Border. 14x9.1cm. (20,122)p

BURNE, Nicol. The | Dispvtation | Concerning The | Controversit Headdis | of Religion, haldin in the Realme of | Scotland, the zeir of God ane thou- | sand, fyue hundreth fourscoir | zeiris. | Betuix. | The prætendit Ministeris of the deformed Kirk | in Scotland. | And, | Nicol Burne Professor of philosophie in S. | Leonardis college, in the Citie of Sanctan- | drois, brocht vp from his tender eage in the | peruersit sect of the Caluinistis, and nou be | ane special grace of God, ane membre of | the halie and Catholik kirk. | Dedicat | To his Souerane the kingis M. of Scotland, | King Iames the Saxt. | . . . (5 lines).

Imprented at Parise the first day of | October. | 1581. | Colophon. 15.3x9.6cm. (8),190,(5)fol.

CRAIG, John. A Shor te | Svmme Of The Who- | le Catechisme, Wherein | the Question is proponed and answered | in few wordes, for the greater ease | of the commoune peo- | ple and children. | Gathered by M.Iohne Craig, | Minister of Gods Worde, to | the Kings M. | . . . (4 lines).

Imprinted At Edin- | burgh, by Henrie Charteris. | Anno, M.D.LXXXI. | Cum Priuilegio Regali. | 17.2x11.cm. (9,100)p. Reprint in facsimile from the original edition of 1581, by Thomas Graves Law: Edinburgh: 1883. A reprint of the London, 1597, edition is contained in Bonar's Catechisms of the Scottish Reformation: 1866.

CROWLEY, Robert. An Aunswer to sixe Reasons, that | Thomas Pownde, Gentleman, and | Prisoner in the Marshalsey, at the commaunde- | ment of her Maiesties Commissioners for causes Ecclesiasti- | call: required to be aunswered. Because these Reasons | doo mooue him to think, that controuersies and doubts in | Religion may not be Judged by the Scriptures, | but that the Scriptures must be Judged | by the Catholicke Church. | 1.The First is:for that the Scriptures, are mute and dum. | 2.The second,for that they be full of hard, and deepe | mysteries. | 3.The third,for that S.Peter sayth.No Scripture is to | be taken after any priuate interpretation. | 4.The fourth,for that to appeale to the Scriptures, | dooth seems to denie all vnwritten verities. | 5.The fyft is,for that it were a great absurditie,not to | haue a certaine Iudge of absolute Authoritie in the | interpreting of Scriptures. &c. | 6.The sixt is,for that in refusing the Authoritie of the | Churches absolute Iudgement herein:we seeme to | denie the holy ghoste to be the spirit of trueth. |

Imprinted at London by Iohn | Charlewood. 1581. | Border. 16.9x11.9 cm. (6 , 50)p.
Anon.DNB.13:243a

CROWLEY, Robert. An Aunswer to sixe Reasons, that | Thomas vsuall notes, whereby | Christes Catholique Church is knowne:wher- | in it appeareth manifestly that the Romish Church | that now is, and that hath beene almoste a thou- | sand yeares last past: is not, neither hath | beene Catholique, but Schismaticall. | VVritten by Robert Crowley, Clerke. | Anno .1581. August .12. | Occasioned by a conference, had in | Newgate, with that obstinate and ranck Trai- | tor, Euerard Haunce, (alias) Ducket, beeing | condemned for [high] Treason. | (device).

Imprinted at London by | John Charlewood, dwelling in Bar- | bican, at the signe of the halfe Eagle | and the Key. 1581. | 17.3x13.6 cm. (6 , 26) p. Small defect in t.p.

FIELD, John. A Caveat | for Parsons Hovvlet, con- | cerning his vntimely flighte, and | scriching in the cleare day lighte | of the Gospell, necessarie for him | and all the rest of that darke broode, | and vncleane cage of papistes, vvho | vvith their vntimely bookes, seeke | the discredite of the trueth, and | the disquiet of this | Church of Eng- | land. | VVritten by Iohn Fielde, student | in Diuinitie. | . . . (5 lines).

Imprinted at London by Ro- | bert VValdegraue, for Thomas | Man, & Toby Smith. | Lace border. 12.9x9cm. (6,112)p

FULKE, William. A briefe Confutation, | of a Popish Discourse: | Lately set forth, and presumptuou- | sly dedicated to the Queenes most excel- | lent Maiestie:by Iohn Howlet, or some | other Birde of the night, vn- | der that name. | Contayning certaine Reasons, why | Papistes refuse to come to Church, vvhich | Reasons are here inserted and set downe | at large, with their seuerall | answeres. | By D.Fulke, Maister of Penbroke | Hall, in Cambridge. | Seene and allowed. |

At London printed | for George Byshop. | 1581. | Colophon: Imprinted at London by Thomas Daw- | son at the three Cranes in the Vinetree for | George Byshop. | 17.6x14.2 cm. (1),58fol.

GILBY, Anthony. A Pleasavnt | Dialogve, | Betweene a Souldior of Barwicke, | and an English Chaplaine, Wherein | are largely handled & laide open, | such reasons as are brought in | for maintenaunce of popishe | Traditions in our | Eng.Church. | Also is collected, as in a short table, | 120.particular corruptions yet | remaining in our saide Church, with | sundrie other matters, necessa- | rie to be knowen of | all persons. | Togither with a letter of the same | Author, placed before this booke, | in vvay of a Preface. | . . . (2 lines).

1581. | Lace border. 14.8x9.2cm. (17,182)p

HADDON, Walter, and FOX, John. Against | Ierome Osorivs | Byshopp of Siluane in Portingall and | against his slaunderous Inuectiues.An Aun- | swere Apologeticall: For the necessary de- | fence of the Euangelicall doctrine and veritie. | First taken in hand by M. Walter Haddon, then vnder- | taken and continued by M. Iohn Foxe, and now Eng- | lished by Iames Bell. | . . . (3 lines: device).

At London | Printed by Iohn Daye, dwellyng ouer Aldersgate. | Anno. 1581. | Colophon: At London | Printed by Iohn Daye dwel- | lyng ouer Aldersgate. | Cum Gratia & Priuilegio | Regiæ Maiestatis. | Anno. 1581. | 18.7x13.9 cm. (14),510,(4) fol.

HALL, Richard. Opvscvla | Qvædam His Temporibvs | Pernecessaria. | De Tribvs Primariis Cavsis | Tvmvltvvm Belgicorvm, Ad Illv- | strissimum D.D.Ludouicum à Barlaymont, Archiepi- | scopum & Ducem Cameracensem &c. Libelli tres. | Contra Coalitionem Mvl- | tarvm Religionvm, Qvam Libe- | ram religionem vocant, ad R. in Christo patrem, D.Ar- | noldum de le Cambe, dict Gantois Abbatem Marcia- | nensem, tractatus vnus. | Libellvs Exhortatorivs | Ad Pacem Qvibvsvis Conditioni- | bus cum Rege Catholico faciendam, ad R.D.D.Iacobum | Froye Abbatem Hasnoniensem. | Avctore Richardo Hall | Doctore Theologo. | . . . (3 lines; device).

Dvaci, | Ex officina Ioannis Bogardi, Typographi iurati, sub | Biblijs aureis. Anno 1581. | 15.5x10.5cm. (9),144 fol. 3 sub.t.p.

HAMILTON, Archibald. Calvinianæ | Confvsionis De- | monstratio, Contra | maledicam ministrorum Sco- | tiæ responsionem. | In Dvos Divisa Libros. | Quorum prior:proprietatum veræ Ecclesiæ euictionem: | Posterior earundem in hypothesi ad res subiectas appli- | catarum, contentionem continet. | Per Archibaldvm Hammiltonivm | in sancta Christi Ecclesia Presbyterum. | (device).

Parisiis, | Apud Nicolaum Chesneav, via Iacobæa | sub Quercu viridi. | M.D. LXXXI. | Cvm Privilegio Regis. | 17x10.4cm. (12),312,(6)fol.

HANMER, Meredith. The Iesuites Banner. | Displaying their original | and successe:their vow and othe: | their hypocrisie and superstiti- | on: their doctrine and po- | sitions: with | A Confutation of a late Pamphlet secret- | ly imprinted and entituled: A | Briefe Censure vpon two bookes | written in answeare to M. | Campions offer of dispu- | tation. &c. Com- | piled by | Meredith Hanmer M. of Arte, | and Student in Diuinity. |

Jmprinted at London | by Thomas Dawson and Ri- | chard Vernon, and are to be | solde in Paules Churchyard | at the Brazen Ser- | pent. 1581. | Border. 16.6x 12.3 cm. (12 , 80) p.

JEWEL, John. Apologia | Ecclesiæ | Anglicanæ. | Authore Iohanne Iuello, olim | episcopo Sarisburiensi. | . . . (5 lines; device).

Londini, | Excudebat Thomas Vautrollerius | Typographus. | 1581. | 11.8x6.1cm. (5),197p.

KELTRIDGE, John. Two Godlie And | learned Sermons, appointed, and | Preached, before the Jesuites, Se- | minaries, and other aduersaries to the | Gospell of Christ in the Tower | of London. | In which, were confuted to their | faces, the moste principall and cheefe | poincts of their Romish and VVhoarish religi- | on: And all such Articles as they defend, | contrarie to the woord of God, | were layed open and ripped vp | vnto them. In Maye .7. and | 21. Anno .1581. | By Iohn Keltridge, Preacher of the vvorde | of God, in London. | . . . (5 lines)

Jmprinted at London by Richard | Ihones, dwelling without Newgate, neere | vnto Holburne Bridge. | [1581]. Border. 18.7x14 cm. (10),28fol. + 60 p. Misnumberings.

LOQUE, Bertrande de. A Treatie of the | Churche, conteining a true | discourse, to knowe the true | Church by, and to discerne it from | the Romish Church, and all o- | ther false assemblies, or | counterfet congrega- | tions. | Written by M. Bertrande | de Loque of Dolphinee, and de- | dicated vnto my Lord the Vi- | count of Turenne. | And faithfully translated out of | French into English, by T.W. |

Imprinted at London, for | Richard Langton, dwelling in | Swythins Lane; and there | they are to be solde. | 1581. | Border. 14x8.9 cm. (32),384,(8) p.

LUTHER, Martin. A Commen- | tarie or Exposition vp- | pon the twoo Epistles gene- | rall of Sainct Peter, | and that of Sainct | Jvde. | First faithfullie gathered out of the | Lectures and Preachinges of that wor- | thie Instrumente in Goddes Churche, | Doctour Martine Luther. And now | out of Latine, for the singuler benefite | and comfort of the Godlie, fami- | liarlie translated into En- | glishe by Thomas | Newton. |

Imprinted at London for Abraham | Veale dwellyng in Paules Church- | yard at the signe of the Lābe. | 1581. | Wood-cut border. 18.4x13.5cm. (3),172fol.

T.p. supplied by Mr. Edward G. Friehold, of London.

LUTHER, Martin. Special And Cho- | sen Sermons Of D.Martin | Lvther, Collected Ovt Of His | writings and preachings for the necessary instruction and edification of | such, as hunger and seeke after the perfect knowledge and ine- | stimable glorie which is in Christ Iesu, to the comfort and | saluation of their soules. | Englished by VV.G. | . . . (7 lines; device).

Imprinted at London by Thomas Voutroullier dwelling | in the Blacke Friers by Ludgate. | Cvm Priuilegio. | 1581. | 18.6x13.5cm. (15),464p. Impf. after FF8.

NICHOLS, John. A declaration | of the recantation of Iohn Ni- | chols (for the space almost of two | yeeres the Popes Scholer in the | English Seminarie or Colledge at | Rome) which desireth to be recon- | ciled, | and receiued as a member into the | true Church of Christ in | England. | . . . (8 lines)

Imprinted at London | by Christopher Barker, Printer | to the Queenes most excellent | Maiestie. | Anno 1581. Fe- | bruarii. 14. | Border. 13.6x8.9 cm. (20 + 176)p.

NICHOLS, John. The Oration and Sermon | made at Rome, by commaun- | dement of the foure Cardinalles, | and the Dominican Jnquisitour, | vpon paine of death. By | Iohn Nichols, latelie the | Popes Scholler. | Which Sermon and Oration was presented before the | Pope and his Cardinalles in his Consistorie, the xxvij day | of Maie .1578. and remaineth there registred. Now by him | brought into the English tongue, for the great comfort | and commoditie of all faithfull Christians. | Heerin also is aunswered an infamous Libell, | maliciouslie written and cast abroad, | against the saide Iohn Nichols, with a | sufficient discharge of himselfe from | all the Papists lying reports, and | his owne life both largelie and | amplie discouered. | . . . (3 lines)

Imprinted at London by Iohn Charlewood, | and are to be sold at the little North dore | of S.Paules Church, at the signe of the | Gunne, by Edward VVhite. 1581. | 14.7x9.5 cm. (20,32,184) p.

OLEVIANUS, Kaspar. An Exposition | of the Symbole of the Apo- | stles, or rather of the Arti- | cles of Faith. In which the chiefe points | of the euerlasting and free couenant | betweene God and the faithfull | is briefly and plainly | handled. | Gathered Ovt Of The | catechising Sermons of Gasper | Olevian Trevir, | And now translated out of the Latine | tongue into the English for the | benefite of Christ his | Church. | By Iohn Fielde. |

At London, | Printed by H. Middleton | for Thomas Man, | and Tobie Smith. | Anno. 1581. | 14.2x9.3 cm. 253,(1)p.

WIBURN, Perceval. A | Checke or reproofe of M. | Howlets vntimely shreeching in | her Maiesties eares, with an answeare | to the reasons alleadged in a discourse | thereunto annexed, why Catholikes | (as they are called) refuse to goe | to Church: | Wherein (among other things) | the Papists traiterous and treacherous | doctrine and demeanour towardes | our Soueraigne and the State, is some- | what at large vpon occasion vnfolded: | their diuelish pretended conscience also | examined, and the foundation thereof vn- | dermined. And lastly shevved thatit is | the duety of all true Christians and | subiectes to haunt publike | Church assemblies. | . . . (3 lines).

Imprinted in London, at the three | Cranes in the Vintree, by Thomas | Dawson, for Toby Smyth, 1581. | Border. Colophon. 18.3x13.7cm. (1),175,(6)fol.
Appendix signed P.W. H&L.

1582

BUCHANAN, George. Rervm Scotica- | rvm Historia | Avctore | Georgio Buchanano | Scoto. | (device)

Edimbvrgi | Apud Alexandrum Arbuthnetum Typographum Regium | Anno M.D.LXXXII. | Cvm Privilegio Regali. | Lace border. 29.3x19.5cm. (4),249,(1) fol.

CARLILE, Christopher. A Discovrse, | concerning two diuine Positions. The first ef- | fectually concluding, that the soules of the | faithfull fathers, deceased before | Christ, went immediately | to heauen. | The second sufficientlye setting foorth vnto vs Christians, | what we are to conceiue, touching the descension | of our Sauiour Christ into Hell: | Publiquely disputed at a Commence- | ment in Cambridge, Anno | Domini 1552. | Purposely written at the first by way of a confutation, a- | gainst a Booke of Richard Smith of Oxford,D.of Di- | uinity, entituled a Refutation imprinted 1562. | & published against Iohn Caluin, & | C. Carlile: the title wherof | appeareth in ye 17. page. | And now first published by the said | Christopher Carlile, 1582. | . . . (2 lines).

Imprinted at London by Roger | Ward dwelling by Holborne con- | duit, at the signe of the Talbot | Anno 1582. | Colophon. 14.3x9.1 cm. (8),173,(3)fol.

CARLISLE, Christopher. A Discourse of Peters | Lyfe, Peregrination and | Death. | Wherein is plainly proued | by the order of time and place, | that Peter was neuer | at Rome. | VVith a confutation of such | coniectures as are alledged to | the contrary. | Fvrthermore, That | neither Peter nor the Pope is the | head of Christes Church. | Also an interpretation vpon the second Epistle | of S.Paule to the Thessalonians, the | second Chapter. | . . . (2 lines).

At London | Imprinted by Roger Ward. | Engr. border. Colophon: Imprynted At London | by Roger Ward Dwelling | by Holburne Conduit, at the signe | of the Talbot. Anno 1582. | 18.8x13.3cm. (4p),1–4fol.5–10p,11fol.12–104,(5)p. 47–48 repeated.
Dedication signed.

DURIE, John. Confvtatio | Responsionis | Gvlielmi VVhitakeri | in Academia Cantabrigen- | si Professoris regij, ad Rationes decem, | quibus fretus Edmvndvs Campianus | Anglus, Societatis Jesv Theologus cer- | tamen Anglicanę Ecclesię Ministris obtu- | lit in causa fidei. | Authore Ioanne Dvræo Scoto, | Societatis Iesv Presbytero. | (device).

Parisiis, | Apud Thomam Brumennium, in clauso | Brunello, sub signo Oliuæ. | M.D.LXXXII. | Cvm Privilegio Regis. | 16.8x10.3cm. (12),466,(4)fol.

GIFFORD, George. Foure Sermons | vpon the seuen chiefe ver | tues or principall effectes of | faith, and the doctrine of electi | on: wherein euerie man may | learne, whether he be Gods | childe or no. |

Preached at Malden in Essex | by Master George Gifford, pen- | ned from his mouth, and cor- | rected and giuen to the | Countesse of Sussex, for | a Newyeeres gift. | . . . (3 lines).

Jmprinted at Lon- | don for Tobie Cooke at | the Tigers head in Paules | Churchyard. 1582. | Border. Colophon: Imprinted at London at | the three Cranes in the | Vinetree by Thomas Daw- | son, for Tobie Cooke. | 1582. | 14.3x9.8cm. (55)fol.

Bound with his: Cathechisme . . . 1583.

GIFFORD, George. A | Godlye, zea- | lous, and profitable Ser- | mon, vpon the seconde | Chapter of S.Iames. | Preached at London, by | Maister George Gifford, and | published at the request of | sundry godly and well | disposed persons. | (device).

Imprinted at London, for | Tobie Cooke, dwelling at | the Tigers head in Paules | Churchyard. 1582. | Border. Colophon: Imprinted at Lon- | don by Iohn Wolfe, for Tobie | Cooke, dwelling at the Tigers | head in Paules Churchyard. | 1582. | 14.3x9.8 cm. (27)fol.

GIFFORD, George. A | Sermon on the Pa- | rable of the Sower, ta- | ken out of the 13. of | Mathew. | Preached at London by | M.G. Gifford, & published | at the request of sundrie | godly and well disposed | persons. | (device).

Imprinted at London for | Tobie Cooke, dwelling at | the Tigres head in Paules | Churchyard. | 1582. | Border. 14.3x9.8cm. 20fol.

HUMPHREY, Laurence. Iesvitismi | Pars Prima: | Sive | De Praxi Romanæ Cvriæ | contra Resp.& Principes:Et De noua le- | gatione Iesuitarū in Angliam, προθεράπεια | & præmunitio ad Anglos. | Cvi Adivncta Est Concio | eiusdem Argumenti, Laur.Humfredo | S.Theologiæ in Academia Oxoni- | ensi professore Regio, Autore. | . . . (5 lines; device).

Londini, | Excudebat Henricus Middletonus | impensis G.B. | 1582. | 16.3x10.7 cm (63),17–159;(1),163–186,(1)p.

JEWEL, John. A Viewe | Of A Seditiovs | Bul sent into Englande, from Pius | Quintus Bishop of Rome, Anno.1569. | Taken by the reuerende Father in | God, Iohn Iewel, late | Bishop of Salisbvrie. | Wherevnto is added | A short Treatise of the holie Scriptures. Both which | hee deliuered in diuers Sermons in his Cathe- | dral Church of Salisburie,Anno.1570. | (device).

At London: | Printed by R.Newberie, & H.Bynneman. | Anno.1582. | Cum gratia & Priuilegio. | 16.5x10.8cm. (8),175p. 1–2 blank.

LOQUE, Bertrande de. An excellent and | plaine Discourse of | the Chvrch, where- | by the Godlie may knowe and | discerne the true Church, from the | Romish Church, and all other | false and counterfet Chur- | ches, as well for matters | of doctrine, as Dis- | cipline, &c. | Written in Frenche by M. | Bartrand de Loque, a godlie | Minister of Dolphenine. | And faithfully translated into | English, by M.T.W. | Seene and allowed. |

Imprinted at Lon- | don, for Thomas Man. | 1582. | Border. Colophon: Imprinted at London at the three | Cranes in the Vintree, by Thomas Dawson | for Thomas Man. 1582. | 14.5x9.4 cm. (23),384, (8)p.

LUPTON, Thomas.   The | Christian against the Iesuite. | Wherein
the secrete or | namelesse writer of a pernitious | booke, intituled A
Discouerie of I. | Nicols Minister &c. priuily prin- | ted, couertly cast
abrod, and | secretely solde, is not only | iustly reprooued: | But also
a booke, dedicated to the | Queenes Maiestie, called A persuasion |
from papistrie, threin derided and fal- | sified, is defended by Thomas
Lupton | the authour thereof. | Reade with aduisement, and judge vp- |
rightly: and be affectioned only to | truth. | . . . (3 lines). Seene and
allowed. |

Imprinted at London for Thomas | Woodcocke dwelling in Paules Church |
yard, at the signe of the blacke Beare. | 1582. | Border. Colophon: Imprinted at
Lon- | don at the three Cranes in the Vin- | tree by Thomas Dawson, for Thomas |
Woodcocke, dwelling in Paules Church-yard | at the signe of the blacke Beare. |
1582. | 18.3x13.2cm.   (10),99,(1)fol.

MARTIN, Gregory.   A Discoverie | Of The Manifold | Corrvptions
Of The | Holy Scriptvres By The | Heretikes of our daies, specially
the | English Sectaries, and of their foule | dealing herein, by partial
& false trans- | lations to the aduantage of their here- | sies, in their
English Bibles vsed and | authorised since the time of Schisme. | By
Gregory Martin one of the readers | of Diuinitie in the English Col-
lege | Of Rhemes. | . . . (8 lines).

Printed at Rhemes, | By Iohn Fogny. | 1582. | 15.8x10.cm.   (28),322,(5)p.

PARSONS, Robert.   A Defence | Of The Censvre, | Gyven Vpon
Tvvo Bookes | of william Charke and Meredith Han- | mer mynys-
ters , whiche they wrote a- | gainst M. Edmond Campian preest, of |
the Societie of Iesus, and against his | offer of disputation. | Taken in
hand since the deathe of the sayd | M. Campian, and broken of agayne
be- | fore it could be ended, vpon the | causes sett downe in an epi- |
stle to M. Charke in the | begynninge. | . . . (6 lines).

An. 1582. | Cum priuilegio. | Border.   16.1x10.6 cm.   37,(1),173,(3) p.
Anon. Gillow. V:277.

A PARTICULAR declara- | tion or testimony, of the vndutifull
and | traiterous affection borne against her | Maiestie by Edmond
Campion Jesuite, and | other condemned Priestes, witnessed by | their
owne confessions: in reproofe of those slaun- | derous bookes & libels
deliuered out to | the contrary by such as are malitiously af- | fected
towards her Maiestie | and the state. | Published by authoritie. |

Imprinted at Lon- | don by Christopher Barker, | Printer to the Queenes most |
excellent Maiestie. | An.Do.1582. | 17.9x12.5cm.   (3,11,1) fol. Colophon.

STAPLETON, Thomas.   Vniversa | Ivstificationis | Doctrina
Hodie | Controversa. | Libris Duodecim tradita. | In quibus Christi
gratia, & hoc ipsum quo Christiani sumus (Iustitia nostra | coram
Deo) contra varias & pestilentes horum temporum | hæreses solidè
defenditur, & ordini explicatur. | . . . (5 lines).   Librorum Argumenta
& Capita proxima pòst Præfationes pagina indicabit. | Authore Thoma
Stapletono Anglo S.Theolog.Doctore,& in Academia | Duacena Con-

trouersiarum Professore Regio & Ordinario. | Huic operi triplex adiectus est index. | . . . (device).

Parisiis, | Apvd Michaelem Sonnivm, Via | Iacobæa, Svb Scvto Basiliensi. | M.D.LXXXII. | Cvm Privilegio Regis.   34.9x22.6cm.   (36),409,(26)p.

WESTFALING, Herbert. A | Treatise of reformation | in religion, diuided into seuen | Sermons preached in | Oxeford, | By Harbart Westfaling, Doctor | of diuinitie. | Hereunto are added two sermons | touching the supper of the | Lorde. | . . . (11 lines). Seene and allowed.

Londini impen,Geor.Byshop. | 1582. | Border. Colophon: Imprinted at London at the three Cranes in the vine- | tree, by Thomas Dawson, for George | Byshop, dwelling in Paules Church- | yarde at the signe of | the Bell. | 1582. | 17.9x13.8 cm.   111,(1) fol.   Portrait frontisp.

WHITAKER, William. Edmvndi | Campiani Iesvitæ | Rationes Decem, | quibus fretus certamen Anglicanæ | Ecclesiæ Ministris obtulit | in causa fidei: | & ad eas | Gvlielmi Whitaker | Theologiæ in Academia | Cantabrigiensi professoris Regij | Responsio. | . . . (2 lines; device).

Antverpiæ, | Excudebat Ægidius Radæus. | M.D.XXCII. | 15.9x10.2 cm.   (20), 333,(3)p.

1583

ALLEN, William. Dvo Edicta | Elizabe- | thæ Reginæ An- | gliæ Contra Sacerdo- | tes Societatis Iesu, & alumnos seminariorum, quæ à | Gregorio xiii. Pont.Max.Romæ & Remis pro Anglis | sunt instituta; quibus non solùm illi vt perduelles pro- | scribuntur, sed Angli omnes, qui in iisdem Collegiis | viuunt reuocantur: Vna cum Apologia doctissimi viri | D.Gulielmi Alani pro iisdem sacerdotibus societatis | Iesu, & aliis seminariorum Alumnis; in qua expli- | cantur causæ institutionis prædictorum se- | minariorum, & cur sacerdotes | Catholici in Angliam | mittantur. | Additur eiusdem Gulielmi Alani pijssima admonitio & con- | solatio verè Christiana ad afflictos Catholicos Angliæ. | (device).

Avgvstæ Trevirorvm | Apud Emondum Hatotum, An. M.D.Lxxxiii. | Cum gratia & priuilegio. | 14.6x9.3cm.   175p.

ANDREWES, Bartimæus. Certaine Ve- | rie worthie, godly and profi- | table Sermons, vpon the | fifth Chapter of the Songs | of Solomon: | Preached by Bartimevs Andreas, Minister of | the word of God; Published at the earnest | and long request of sundrie well | minded Christians. | . . . (10 lines).

At London; | Printed by Robert Walde- | graue, for Thomas man. | 1583. | 14.6x9.6cm.   (16),264p.

An | ANSWEARE for the time, vnto that foule, | and wicked Defence of the Censure, | that was giuen vpon M.Charkes Booke, and | Meredith Hanmers. | Contayning a maintenance of the credite | and persons, of all those woorthie men: namely, of M. | Luther,Caluin, Bucer, Beza, and the rest of those Godlie ministers | of Gods worde, whom he, with a shamelesse penne most slande- | rously hath sought to deface: finished sometime | sithence: | And now published for the stay of the Christian Rea- | der till Maister Charkes Booke come | foorth. | . . . (5 lines; device).

Imprinted at London by Thomas | Dawson and Tobie Smith. | 1583. | Colophon.: Imprinted at London at the three | Cranes in the Vintree, by Thomas | Dawson, and Toby Smith. | 1583. | 17.6x13.4cm. (1),107 fol.

BAKER, John. Lectures of I. B. | vpon the xii. Articles of | our Christian faith, briefely | set forth for the comfort of the | godly, and the better instruc- | tion of the simple and | ignorant. | Also hereunto is annexed a | briefe and cleare Confession of | the Christian faith, conteining an hun- | dreth articles, according to the or- | der of the Creede of the Apostles, | Written by that learned & godly | martyr I. H. sometime Bishop | of Glocester in his | life time. | . . . (5 lines).

Imprinted at London | by C. Barker. | Engr. border. Colophon: Jmprinted at London, by | Christopher Barker, Printer to | the Queenes most ex- | cellent Maiestie. | Anno 1583. | 13.9x9 cm. (12,472)p.
"Confession" has a separate title-page. Dedication signed.

BROWN, Robert. An ansvvere to Ma- | ster Cartvvright His | Letter For Ioyning | with the English Churches:where- | vnto the true copie of his | sayde letter is an- | nexed. | . . . (9 lines)

Imprinted at London. | [1583] 17.7x13.4cm (4),96p.
Anon. Dexter:96. Attributed also to Robert Harrison, DNB.25:38b.

CALVIN, John. The | Sermons | Of M. Iohn Calvin | Vpon The Fifth Booke Of | Moses called Deuteronomie: | Faithfully gathered word for word as he preached | them in open Pulpet; | Together with a preface of the Ministers of the Church of | Geneua, and an admonishment made by the Deacons there. | Also there are annexed two profitable Tables, the one containing | the chiefe matters; the other the places of Scripture herein alledged. | Translated out of French by Arthvr Golding. | (cut).

At London, | Printed by Henry Middleton | for Thomas Woodcocke. | Anno Domini 1583. | 27.9x19.3cm. (11),1247,(144) p.

CECIL, William. The Execution of | Iustice in England for maintenaunce | of publique and Christian peace, | against certeine stirrers of sedition, and adhe- | rents to the traytors and enemies of the | Realme, without any persecution of them | for questions of Religion, as is falsely | reported and published by the | fautors and fosterers of | their treasons. | xvii.Decemb. | 1583. | (device)

Imprinted at | London. 1583. | 18.2x12.4 cm. (2, 38)p
Anon.Cambr.Univ.Cat:7291.
(Also reprinted in part in A Collection of Several Treatises:1688).

A COLLECTION in English, of the | Statutes nowe in force, continued from the beginning of Magna | Charta, made in the 9.yeere of the reigne of King H.3. vntill | the ende of the Session of Parliament holden in the 23. yeere of the reigne of our gra- | tious Queene Elizabethe, vnder Titles placed by order of Alphabet: wherein is per- |

formed (touching the Statutes wherewith Iustices of the peace haue to deale) | so much as was promised in the booke of their office lately published. For which purpose | also the Statutes concerning those Iustices haue this marke ☞ at the be- | ginning, and this marke * at the ende of them, noted in the | margent ouer against the same. | Hereunto is added two Tables: the one at the beginning of the | booke, declaring vnder titles by order of Alphabet the substance of such referments | as stoode at the end of eche Title in the first Collection of Statutes, set forth by Master | Iustice Rastall. And in this Table, the Title of Iustices of the peace is specially | perused and amended, for their more easie finding of matters | in this booke, concerning their authoritie. | In the other Table (being at the ende of this booke) are set downe | by order of the Kings reignes, the seuerall times of their Parliaments, together | with the sundry chapters and intitulings of the particular Statutes | in euery of the same: whereby the Reader may easily finde vnder what Title, | and in what leafe of this booke, any of these Statutes be placed: and | may also (by helpe of certaine hands prefixed to diuers of | them) readily see, what, & how many Statutes in eche Kings reigne, doe concerne the Iustices of | peace, and in what leafe of this booke | to finde them. | . . . (ornament).

Imprinted at London by | Christopher Barker, Printer to the | Queenes most excellent Maiestie. | [1583]. Colophon. 27x20.1cm. (33), 559, (20) fol. Imprint torn.
Cambr.Univ.Cat.1677.

A DECLARATION | of the fauorable dealing of her | Maiesties Commissioners | appointed for the Examinati- | on of certaine Trai- tours, and of | tortures vniustly reported to | be done vpon them for | matters of re- | ligion. | 1583. | (ornament).

No imprint. 18.2x12.4 cm. Pp. (2 , 6).
Appended to W:Cecil, lord Burghley, Execution of Iustice in England:1583, with separate register.

FENNER, Dudley. An | Ansvvere vn- | to The Confvtation Of | Iohn Nichols his Recantation, in | all pointes of any weight con- | teyned in the same: | Especially in the matters of Doctrine, | of Pur- gatorie, Images, the Popes ho- | nor, and the question of | the Church. | By Dudley Fenner, Minister of Gods word . | (device: ubique floret).

London | Imprinted by Iohn wolfe, for Iohn | Harrison, and Thomas Manne, dwel- | ling in Pater noster rowe, and | are there to be solde. | 1583. | 18.5x13.6cm. (4),100fol.

FOX, John. De Christo gratis | iustificante . | Contra Osorianam iustitiam, cæ- | terosque eiusdem inhærentis iusti- | tię patronos, Stan. Hosiũ. Andrad. | Canisiũ. Vegam, Tiletanũ, Lori- | chium, contra vni- uersã denique | Turbam Tridentinam & | Iesuiticam. | Amica & modes- ta defensio | Ioan.Foxij. | (device)

Londini, | Excudebat Thomas Purfutius | impensis Geor.Byshop. | 1583. | 16x10 cm. (8),436,47p.

Contains also: Liber Quartus, | In Quo Subse- | quitur Gravis Et Erudita | Concio Eximii Doct.D. | Guliel.Fulsii, De Duobus | Abrahæ filiis, ex D.Paulo, | Galat.4. | De lingua populari, in Latinum sermonem | reddita per Ioan.Foxium. | 47p

FULKE, William. A Defense | of the sincere and true Tran- | slations of the holie Scriptures into | the English tong, against the manifolde cauils, | friuolous quarels, and impudent slaunders of Gre- | gorie Martin, one of the readers of Po- | pish diuinitie in the trayterous Semi- | narie of Rhemes. | By William Fvlke D. in Diuinitie, | and M. of Pembroke haule in Cambridge. | Wherevnto is added a briefe confutation of all such | quarrels & cauils, as haue bene of late vttered by diuerse | Papistes in their English Pamphlets, against the writings | of the saide William Fvlke. | (device).

At London: | Imprinted by Henrie Bynneman. | Anno. 1583. | Cum gratia & Priuilegio. | Colophon: Imprinted at London by | George Bishop, and | Henrie Binneman. | 1583. | 16.2x10.8 cm. (6),3-95,(1),532,(4),71p.

GIFFORD, George. A | Briefe discourse of | certaine pointes of the reli- | gion, which is among the commō | sort of Christians, which | may bee termed the Coun- | trie Diuinitie. | With a manifest confutation of the same, after the | order of a Dialogue. | Compiled by George | Gifforde. |

Imprinted at Lon- | don for Toby Cook, dwel- | linge at the Tigers head in | Paules churchyard & | are there to besolde. | 1583. | Border. 14.3x9.8cm. (4),84fol.

GIFFORD, George. A Cathechisme | conteining the summe | of Christian Religion, gi- | uing a most excellent light to all | those that seek to enter the | path-way to salua- | tion: | Newlie set foorth by G.G. | Preacher of Gods word at | Malden in Essex. | . . . (5 lines).

Imprinted at London at | the three Cranes in the | Vintree by Thomas | Dawson. | 1583. | Border. Colophon. 14.3x9.8cm. 86fol.
B.M.Cat.

GIFFORD, George. A Dialogue be- | tweene a Papist and | a Protestant, applied to | the capacitie of the | vnlearned. | Made by G.Gifford,Prea- | cher in the Towne of Mal- | don. | Seene and allowed accor- | ding to the order ap- | poynted. |

Imprinted at | London for Tobie | Cooke. 1583. | Border. Colophon: Imprinted at London | at the three Cranes in the | Vintree, by Thomas Daw- | son, for Tobie Cooke. | 1583. | 14.3x9.8cm. (4),115,(1)fol.

HARRISON, Robert. A Little | Treatise | vppon the firste | Verse of the 122.Psalm. | Stirring vp vnto carefull | desiring & dutifull labou- | ring for true church | Gouernement. | . . . (4 lines). R.H. |
1583. | Border. 13.8x8.5cm. (6;126)p
Dexter:87.

HOWARD, Henry. A defensatiue against | the poyson of supposed | Prophesies: | Not hitherto confuted by the penne | of any man, which being grounded, eyther vppon the | warrant and authority of olde paynted bookes, expositions | of Dreames, Oracles, Reuelations, Inuocations of damned | spirites, Judicialles of Astrologie, or any other kinde of pretended | knowledge whatsoeuer, De futuris contingentibus: haue beene causes of | great disorder in the common wealth, and cheefely among the sim- | ple and vnlearned people: very needefull to be published | at this time, considering the late offence which grew | by most palpable and grosse errours | in Astrology. | . . . (5 lines).

At London | Printed by Iohn Charlewood, Printer | to the right Honourable Earle | of Arundell. | 1583. | 18.7x13.6cm. (20,312)p.
Anon, Camb.Univ.Cat.No.1356

JEWEL, John. An Exposition | vpon the two Epistles of | the Apostle Sainct Paule to | the Thessalonians, | By the reuerende Father Iohn Iewel | late Byshop of Sarisbvrie. | (device)

At London: | Printed by R. Newberie, and H.Bynneman. | Anno Salvtis | 1583. | 15.7x10.cm. (6),424p. (1-2) blank. Lacks A4.

NOWELL, Alexander and DAY, William. A true report of the | Disputation or rather priuate Confe- | rence had in the Tower of London, with | Ed.Campion Iesuite, the last of August,1581. | Set downe by the Reuerend learned men | them selues that dealt | therein. | Whereunto is ioyned also a true report | of the other three dayes conferences had there | with the same Iesuite. Which nowe are thought | meete to be published in print | by authoritie. | (royal arms)

Imprinted At London | by Christopher Barker, Printer to the | Queenes most excellent Maiestie. | Ianuarij.1.1583. | 17.7x12.7cm. 4 parts. (2,19,26,38,28)fol. Royal arms on G iii. b. and on Ggii.a, followed by colophon.
Also another edition, with variant signature marks, but same catchwords, except on Gg i. Lacks royal arms, but has device on Cciv and Gg i. 18.8x13.6cm. (2,19,26,38,27)fol.
To the Reader, signed; the various conferences were further signed by William Fulke and Roger Goade, and the fourth day's conference by John Walker and William Charke.

RAINOLDS, William. A Refvtation Of | Svndry Reprehen- | sions, Cavils, And False | Sleightes, by which M. Whitaker la- | boureth to deface the late English | translation, and Catholike annota- | tions of the new Testament, | and the booke of Dis- | couery of hereti- | cal corrup- | tions. | By William Rainolds, Student of Diui- | nitie in the English Colledge at Rhemes. | . . . (8 lines).

Printed at Paris, | the yere 1583. | 15.4x9.7 cm. 92,(3),561,(26)p.

TRAVERS, Walter. An Answere | To A Svpplica- | torie Epistle, of G. T. for | the pretended Catholiques: | written to the right Honorable | Lords of her Maiesties priuy | Councell. | By VVater Travers, Minister of the | worde of God. | . . . (14 lines).

At London; | Printed for Tobie Smith, dwelling in Paules | Church-yard at the signe of | the Crane. | [1583]. 13.4x9.3 cm. (1),400, (6)p.

The VNLAWFVLL Prac- | tises Of Prelates A- | gainst Godly Mini- | sters, The Maintainers | Of The Discipline Of | God. |

n.p.n.d. [1583]. 14.5x9.5 cm. (2, 51)p.

VERMIGLI, Pietro Martire. The | Common Places | of the most famous and | renowmed Diuine Doctor | Peter Martyr, diuided | into foure principall parts: with | a large addition of manie theo- | logicall and necessarie dis- | courses, some neuer | extant before. | Translated and partlie gathered by | Anthonie Marten, one of the | Sewers of hir Maiesties | most Honourable | Chamber. | Meliora spero. | In the end of the booke are annexed two tables of | all the notable matters therein conteined. | . . . (4 lines)

No imprint. Arch. border. Colophon: Imprinted at London in Pater noster Rovve, | at the costs and charges of Henrie Denham, | Thomas Chard, VVilliam Broome, and | Andrew Maunsell. | 1583. | Allowed according to hir Maiestie Iniunctions. | 30.9x21.3 cm (29),640,398,331; (sub-title) (4),101–252, 165,(101)p.

WHITAKER, William. Responsionis ad | Decem illas Rationes, quibus | fretus Edmundus Campianus cer- | tamen Ecclesiæ Anglicanæ ministris | obtulit in causa fidei, Defensio contra | Confutationem Ioannis Duræi Scoti, | Presbyteri, Iesuitæ: | Authore Guilielmo Whitakero Theologiæ | in Academia Cantabrigiensi | professore Regio. | In hoc libro controuersiæ pleræque omnes, quæ inter | nostras & pontificias Ecclesias intercedunt, bre- | uiter ac dilucidè pertractantur. | (ornament)

Londini | Excudebat Henricus Midletonus | impensis Thomæ Chardi. | Anno 1583. | 17.3x10.8 cm. (14),887,(15)p.

1584

An | ABSTRACT, Of Cer- | taine Acts Of Parle- | ment: of certaine her Maiesties | Iniunctions: of certaine Canons, | Constitutions, and Synodals prouinciall, | established & in force, for the peaceable gouernment | of the Church, within her Maiesties Dominions and | Countries, for the most part heretofore vnknowen and | vnpractized. | . . . (9 lines; device).

N.d.n.p. [1584] 17.7x14.1 cm. (4,75+42)p.

Printed in connection with Richard Cosin's Answer:1584. Contains: A learned Ministerie commanded by the Lawe; and Dispensations For Many Benefices vnlavvfull.

ADUERTISEMENTS | partely for due order in the publique ad- | ministration of Common | prayers, and vsing the holy | Sacramentes: | And partely for the apparel of all persons | Ecclesiastical, by vertue of the Queenes Maiesties | letters, commaunding the same, the xv. | day of Ianuary, in the seauenth yeere of the | reigne of our Souereigne Lady Eliza- | beth, by the grace of God, of | England, Fraunce, and Ire- | land Queene, defender | of the faith, &c. | (device)

Imprinted at London at the | three Cranes in the Vine- | tree, by Thomas Dawson | 1584. | 17.2x12.6 cm. (2,6)fol.

ALLEN, William. De Iustitia | Britannica, | Sive | Anglica, | Qvae Contra Chri- | sti Martyres Conti- | nenter exercetur. | (device).

Ingolstadii, | Ex Officina Typographica | Davidis Sartorii. | Anno | M.D.XXCIV. | 15.9x10.4cm. (16),92,(1).
Anon. Gillow: I:22.

ARTICULI | Per | Archiepiscopum, Episcopos & reliquum | Clerum Cantuariensis Provinciæ in Synodo incho- | ata Londini vicesimo quarto die Mensis Novem- | bris, Anno Domini 1584. Regnique Serenissimæ | in Christo Principis Dominæ Elizabethæ, Dei | gratia Angliæ, Franciæ & Hyberniæ Reginæ, fidei | Defensoris, &c. vicesimo septimo stabiliti, & Re- | gia auctoritate approbati & confirmati. | (royal arms)

Londini, in aedibus C.B. | [1584.] Border. 19.5x15.2cm. Pp. 241-247 of Sparrow's Collection:1661. Also in his reprints of 1675 and 1684.

BRENZ, Johannes. A Right Godly and | learned discourse vpon | the booke of Ester. | Most necessary for this time and age, to en- | struct all noble men, and such as God hath | aduanced vnto high places about princes, | that God looketh for this as an especiall | duety at their handes, principally to ende- | uour themselues to procure the wealth of | God his people, and the benefite and good | of his church, and withall to teach the ser- | uants of the Lord that are in daunger and | misery, with pacience and prayer to attend | vpon the Lord vntill hee send them deliue- | rance. | Written in latin by Iohn Brentius a German, and | newly turned into English for the comfort | of God his children, by Iohn Stock- | wood Schoolemaster of | Tunbridge. | . . . (6 lines).

London | Imprinted by Iohn Wolfe for Iohn | Harrison the yonger, dwelling at | the signe of the golden Anker | in Pater noster row. | 1584. | Orn. border. 14x9.3cm (44), 180p. Mispagings.

BUCHANAN, George. Rervm Scoticarvm Historia, | libris XX. descripta, | Qvi Regionvm | Sitvs, Qvod Soli Cæ- | liqve Sit Ingenivm, Qvæ Vetv- | sta Gentis Nomina, Mores, Leges, Et In- | stituta, quiq; primi cultores fuerint insularum, quæ veteribus | Britanniæ vocantur, à primordio repetens: | Item | Regnum à Fergusio, primo Scotorum regni conditore, in præsens vsque deductam | recensionem, singulorum verò vitas, mores, res bello paceq[ue] gestas, vitæq[ue] exitus, | obseruata temporum serie, tum perpetuis familiarum in imperio | successionibus adnotatis, complectens. | Avctore | Georgio Bvchanano Scoto. | Accessit De Ivre Regni apud Scotos Dialogus, | eodem auctore. | Cum Indice rerum & verborum locupletissimo. | (device)

Francofvrti | Excudebat Ioan.Wechelus, impensis Sigis.Feyerabendij. | Colophon: Impressvm Franco- | fvrti Ad Moenvm, Apvd | Ioannem Wechelvm, Im- | pensis Sigismundi Feyer- | abendij. | (device). Anno M.D.LXXXIIII. | 16.4x10.2 cm. (8),723,(100)p.

BUNNY, Edmund. The | Scepter Of | Ivdah: | Or, what maner of Government it | was, that unto the Common-wealth | or Church of Israel was | by the Law of God | appointed. | By Edm.Bunny. | . . . (6 lines).

Imprinted at London by N.New- | ton, and A. Hatfield, for | Iohn Wight. | 1584. | (Ornam. border). 15.1x9.8cm. (9),160,(61)p.

CALVIN, John. A Commentarie | of M.Iohn Caluine | vppon the Epistle to the Phi- | lippians, wherein is set out the neces- | sitie and profite of affliction vnto the faith- | full, the benefite of God his word, the fruits, | of vnitie and humilitie, free iustification by | faith in Iesus Christ without our owne merites, | the assurance, ioy, and contented

mindes of | the godlie, and their perseueraunce in god- | linesse vnto the end. With many other | comfortable and profitable | pointes of Religion. | (device) Translated out of Latine by W(illiam) B(ecket). |
 Imprinted at London for | Nicolas Lyng, and are to be | sold at the West dore of | S. Paules Church. | Anno. 1584. | Lace border. 18.6x13.6cm. (4),95p.

CALVIN, John. Sermons | of Maister Iohn | Caluin, vpon the | Booke of | Iob, | Translated out of French by | Arthur Golding. | (device).
 Londini | Impensis Georgij | Bishop. | 1584. | Engr. border. Colophon: Imprinted in London at the | three Cranes in the Vintree, by Thomas Dawson, | for George Byshop and Thomas | VVoodcocke. | Anno 1584. | 31.9x21.6cm. (32),752p.

CALVIN, John. Two godly and learned | Sermons, made by that fa- | mous and woorthy instrument in | Gods church, M. Iohn Caluin. Which | Sermons were long since translated out of | Latine into English, by H. Robert Horne | late Byshop of Winchester, at what time | he suffered exile from his Country, for the te- | stimony of a good conscience, as his A- | pology in the beginning of the | booke will witnes. | And because these Sermons haue | long lyen hidden in silence, and many | godly and religious persons, haue beene | very desirous of them: at theyr ear- | nest request they are nowe | published by | A. M. |
 At London | Printed for Henry Car, | and are to be solde ouer against | the signe of the blasing | Starre. | [1584]. 13.6x8.8 cm. (46 , 99) p.

CHADERTON, Laurence. A fruitfull Ser- | mon, vpon the 3.4.5. 6.7.& 8. | verses of the 12. Chapiter of the Epistle | of S. Paule to the Romanes: | Very necessarie for these times to be read of all | men, for their further instruction and edification, | in things concerning their fayth and obedience | to Saluation. | (device).
 At London; | Printed by Robert Walde-graue. 1584. | 13.5x9.2 cm. (8),80.p.
 Anon. Camb.Univ.Cat. No.1897. Attribution doubtful. H&L, new ed. names Edward Waring.

COSIN, Richard. An Answer | To the two first and principall Treatises | of a certeine factious libell, put foorth latelie, | without name of Author or Printer, and | without approbation by authoritie, | vnder the title of | An Abstract of certeine Acts of Par- | lement: of certeine hir Maiesties | Iniunctions: of certeine | Canons, &c. | . . . (7 lines) Published by authoritie. | (device).
 Printed at London by Henrie Denham | for Thomas Chard. | 1584. | 17.7x14.1 cm. (12), 350p. lacks p. 337–338
 Anon. Dexter:99. Cambr.Univ.Cat.1428–1429.

CURIO, Cœlius Secundus. Pasquine in a Traunce. | A Christian and learned Dialogue | (containing wonderfulll and most straunge newes, | out of Heauen, Purgatorie and Hell). Wherein | besides Christes truth plainly set foorth, | shall also finde a number of plea- | sant hystories, discouering all | the craftie conueyances of |

Antichrist. | VVherevnto are added certaine Que- | stions then put foorth by Pasquine, to haue bene | disputed in the Councell of Trent. | Turned but lately out of the Italian in- | to this tongue, by | W.P. | Seene and allowed according to the order appointed in | the Queenes Maiesties Iniunctions. | . . . (3 lines; device).

 Imprinted at London, by | Thomas Este. | 1584. | Colophon. Imprinted at London, by | Thomas East. | 1584. | 17.3x12.1 cm. (4),88fol.
 Anon. B.M.Cat.

A DIALOGVE, | Concerning | the strife of our Churche: | Wherein are aunswered diuers of those | vniust accusations, wherewith the godly | preachers and professors of the Gospell, are falsly | charged; with a briefe declaration of some such | monstrous abuses, as our Byshops haue | not bene ashamed to foster. | (device).

 At London; | Printed by Robert Walde-graue, 1584. | 12.9x8.6 cm. (14),136p. First leaf missing.
 Ms. attribution to George Gifford.

FENNER, Dudley. (Device). A Covnter-Poyson, | Modestly writ- | ten for the time, to make | aunswere to the obiections and repro- | ches, wherewith the aunswerer to the | Abstract, would disgrace the holy | Discipline of Christ. | . . . (3 lines).

 At London; | Printed by Robert Walde- | graue. | [1584]. 13.4x9.3cm. (16), 195p. 81–89 omitted.
 Anon Reprinted also in Parte of a register: 1593. Pp. 412–421.
 Ascribed also to Henry Jacob. Dexter, 103. Cambr.Univ.Cat:1903.

HUMPHREY, Laurence. Iesvitismi | Pars Secunda: | Pvritanopapismi, | seu doctrinæ Iesuiticæ aliquot Rationi- | bus ab Ed.Campiano comprehensæ, | & à Ioan.Dvræo defensæ, | Confvtatio: | Et ex ijsdem Fundamentis Reformatæ | nostræ Religionis | Assertio: | Autore Lavrentio Hvmfredo | S.Theologiæ in Acad.Oxoniensi | Professore Regio. | . . . (6 lines)

 Londini | Excudebat Henricus Midletonus | impensis Georg.Byshop, | Anno 1584. | 15.7x11.1 cm. (36),(23),667,(16)p.

MARLORAT, Augustin. A Catholike | and ecclesiasticall expo- | sition vppon the epistle of S.Iude | the Apostle: | Collected And Gathered out of the workes of the best | writers by Augustine Marlorat, | that most notable and excellent | Diuine: | Translated Ovt Of | Latin into Englishe, for the behoofe of the | vnlearned in the same tongue: both for | the better increase of their knowledge | and fayth in the true worship & ser- | uice of God, as also for the better | framing of their liues & con- | uersation according to | the same; | by I.D.Mynister. | . . . (4 lines).

 At London By | Gerard Dewes, and Hen- | ry Marshe. | 1584. | 13.3x8.8cm. (4), 38fol.

MUNDAY, Anthony. A VVatch-vvoord | to Englande | To beware of traytours and | tretcherous practises, which haue | beene the ouerthrowe of many | famous Kingdomes and | common weales. | Written by a faithfull affected | freend to his Country: who desireth God long | to blesse it from Traytours, and their | secret conspiracyes. | Seene and allowed, according to the order ap- | pointed in the Queenes Iniunctions. | . . . (5 lines).

London | Printed for Thomas Hacket, and | are to be solde at his shop in Lumberd streete, | vnder the signe of the Popes | head. 1584. | Lace border. 18.7x13.3 cm. (7),47fol. Lacks fol. 17 and 40.
B.M.Cat. DNB. 39:296 a. Dedicatory epistles signed A.M.

TRAVERS, Walter. A Briefe | and plaine declaration, con- | cerning the desires of all those faithfull | Ministers, that haue and do seeke for the | Discipline and reformation of the Church | of Englande: | Which may serue for a iust Apologie, against | the false accusations and slaunders | of their aduersaries. | (device).

At London; | Printed by Robert Walde-graue, | 1584. | 13.5x8.8 cm. (8),148p.
Anon. Attributed by Brook to William Fulke. DNB.18:318b, and 20:307b.
Running head: A learned Discourse of Ecclesiasticall Gouernment.

1585

An ACT against Iesuites, | Seminarie Priestes, and such other | like disobedient persons. | Chapter ii. |

1585. Elizabeth, Q. [Statutes]. Ann.27. Cap.2.

ADAMSON, Patrick. A | Declaratioun | Of The | Kings Majesties | Intentioun And Meaning Toward | The Lait Actis Of | Parliament. | (arms).

Imprinted at Edinburgh, by Thomas | Vautroullier. | 1585. | 16.6x12.4 cm. (1), 13–22p. Impf & clipped at edge and foot.
Anon. DNB.1:113a.

BILSON, Thomas. The Trve Diffe- | rence Betweene Chri- | stian Svbiection And | Vnchristian Rebellion: | Wherein The Princes Lawfvll | power to commaund for trueth, and indepriuable | right to beare the sword are defended against the | Popes censures and the Iesuits sophismes vt- | tered in their Apologie and De- | fence Of English | Catholikes: | With a demonstration that the thinges refourmed in the Church of England by the | Lawes of this Realme are truely Catholike, notwithstanding the vaine shew | made to the contrary in their late Rhemish Testament: by | Thomas Bilson Warden of Winchester. | Perused and allowed by publike authoritie. | (device) . . . (5 lines)

At Oxford, | Printed by Ioseph Barnes Printer to the | Vniuersitie, M.D.XXCV. | 21.3x15.6 cm. .(22),820,(9)p.

BISSE, James. Two Sermons | preached, | The One At | Paules Crosse the eight of | Ianuarie, 1580.the other | at Christes Church in London, | the same day in the af- | ter-noone; | By Iames Bisse, Maister | of Arte, and Fellowe of Magdalene | Colledge in Oxenford. |

At London; | Printed by Robert wal- | degraue, for Thomas Woodcoke, dwel- | ling in Paules Church-yard, at the | signe of the Beare. 1585. | 13x9cm. (4,136)p.

BUNNY, Edmund. A Treatise Ten- | ding to Pacification: By laboring | those that are our aduersaries in | the cause of Religion, to receiue the | Gospel, and to ioyne with vs | in profession thereof. | By Edmund Bunny. | (device) . . . (7 lines).

(1585) 15.7x10 cm. (4),96p
Appended to R.Parsons: A Booke of Christian exercise. 1585. Aa1–Gg2 in eights.

CALVIN, John. The | Commentaries | of M.Iohn Calvin | vpon the Actes of the | Apostles, | Faithfully translated out of | Latine into English for the | great profite of our coun- | trie-men, | By Christopher Fetherstone | student in Diuinitie. | (device)

Londini, | Impensis G.Bishop. | 1585. | Lace border. Colophon: Imprinted At Lon- | don by Thomas Dawson for | George Bishop. | 1585. | 19.6x14.cm. (16), 598,(29) p.

CHUB, William. The | True trauaile of all | faithfull Christians, howe to | escape the daungers of this | vvicked vvorld. | VVhereunto is added a Christi- | an' exercise for priuate | housholders. | . . .(9 lines)

Printed at London, by Iohn | Charlewood. 1585. | Border. 13.1x8.7cm. (12,131)p. Dedication signed.

CRVDELITATIS | Calvinianæ Ex- | empla Dvo Recen- | tissima Ex | Anglia. | Quorum primum, continet barbarum ac sæuum | Caluinianorum edictum recenter editum con- | tra Catholicos: alterum verò, exhibet indignis- | simam mortem IIlustrissimi viri comitis Nor- | thumbriæ in castro Londinensi occisi mense Iu- | lio huius Anni. 1585. | Præmissa est præfatio ad Principes populosque Catho- | licos de cladibus quas hæresis infert Rebuspub. | cum congratulatione de pace recen- | ter facta in Gallia. | Adiectum est in fine exemplar quarundam | literarum ex Anglia. | . . . (2 lines; device).

[Cologne?] Anno Domini 1585. | 15.6x9.9cm. (20,39)p.

DUAREN, François. De Sacris Ecclesiæ | Ministeriis Ac Bene- | ficiis Libri VIII. | In quibus quicquid ad plenam Iuris Pontificij cognitio- | nem necessarium est, breuiter ac dilucidè ex- | plicatum continetur. | Item, | Pro Libertate Ecclesiæ Galli- | cæ aduersus Romanam aulam Defensio Parisiensis cu- | riæ, Ludouico XI. Gallorum Regi | quondam oblata. | Authore Francisco Duareno Iureconsulto, & or- | dinario Iuris ciuilis Doctore in ci- | uitate Biturig. | Opus ab authore denuo auctum ac emen- | datum. | His Insvper Petri Re- | bvffi Ivris Vtrisqve | doctoris tractatum de de- | cimis visum est an- | nectare. | (device).

Londini. | Impensis G.Bishop. | 1585. | 15.6x10.2cm. (12),113;(1),68fol.

DURIE, John. Confvtatio | Responsionis | Gvlielmi VVhitakeri | In Academia Cantabrigensi | Professoris Regii, Ad Rationes De- | cem, quibus fretus Edmvndvs Campianvs | Anglus, Societatis Iesv Theologus, certa- | men Anglicanæ Ecclesiæ Ministris | obtulit in caussa fidei. | Liber antehac in Germania nunquam excusus. | Avctore | Joanne Dvræo Scoto, | Societatis Iesv Presbytero. | Habes hîc, amice Lector, dogmatum præcipuo- | rum, nostro seculo controuersorum eruditam, | elegantem & dilucidam explicationem. | (ornament.)

Ingolstadii, | Ex Typographia Davidis Sartorii. | Anno Domini, | M.D.LXXXV. | 16.2 x 10.3 cm. (36),856,(43) p.

ELIZABETH, Queen [Statutes] Anno xxvii. Anno xxvii. Reginæ Elizabethæ. | At the Parliament | begunne and holden at Westminster, | the xxiij. day of Nouember, in the | xxvii. yeere of the reigne of our most | gracious Soueraigne Lady Elizabeth, by the | grace of God, of England, France, and Ire- | land Queene, defender of the Faith, &c. | and there continued, vntill the | xxix. of March following: | To the high pleasure of Almightie God, | and the weale publike of this | Realme, were enacted | as followeth. |

Imprinted at London by Christopher | Barker, Printer to the Queenes most ex- | cellent Maiestie. | 1585. | Engraved border 26.9x18.cm. (1,42) fol.

KETT, Francis. The Glori- | ous and beautifull | Garland of Mans | Glorification. | Containing the Godlye | Misterie of heauenly Iervsalem, | the helmet of our Saluation. The | comming of Christ in the fleshe | for our glorie, and his glo- | rious cōming in the end | of the world, to crowne | men with crownes | of eternall | glorie. | Beeing an heauenly Adamant to | drawe thee to Christ | and a spirituall Rod to | mortifie thy Life. | Made and set foorth by | Fravncis Kett. | Doctor of Phisick. | . . . (3 lines)

At London | printed by Roger Ward. | 1585. | Lace border. 19.3x14 cm. (6,120)p. Frontispiece: Vivat Elizabetha | Regina | (Coat of arms and device.)

A LAMENTABLE | Complaint Of The | Commonalty, By Way Of | Svpplication To The | High Covrt Of Parlia- | ment, For A Learned Mi- | nistery. |

In Anno. 1585. | 14.8x10.3 cm. (2,81)p.
(Also Reprinted in The Humble Petition: 1588).
Dexter, 106. Camb.Univ.Cat. No 1898.

PARSONS, Robert. A | Booke of Christian ex- | ercise appertaining to Reso- | lution, that is, shewing how | that vve should resolue our | selues to become Christi- | ans indeede: by | R. P. | Perused, and accompanied | now with a Treatise ten- | ding to Pacification: | By | Edmvnd Bvnny. | . . . (3 lines).

Imprinted 1585. | Lace border. 15.8x10 cm. (24),342,(4),96 p.
Cambr.Univ.Cat.7306.

PARSONS, Robert. A Christian | Directorie | Gviding Men To | Their Salvation. | Devided Into Three Bookes. | The first vvherof apperteining to Resolu- | tion, is only conteined in this volume, deui- | ded into tvvo partes, and set forth novv | againe vvith many corrections, and ad- | ditions by th' Authour him self, vvith re- | profe of the corrupt and falsified edition | of the same booke lately published by M. | Edm.Buny. | Ther is added also a methode for the vse | of al; with two tables, and a prefa- | ce to the Reader, which is ne- | cessarie to be reade. | . . . (6 lines).

    Anno. 1585. Avgvsti.30. | 14.2x8cm. (3),4–23fol;883,(21)p.
    Anon. Madan: Early Oxford Press: 1585 (5), note.

ROGERS, Thomas. The | English Creede, | Consenting VVith | The Trve Avncient Catho- | lique, and apostolique Church in al the points, | and articles of Religion which euerie Chri- | stian is to knowe and beleeue that would be saued. | The First Parte, | In Most Loyal Maner To The | Glorie Of God, Credit Of Ovr | Church, and displaieng of al hærisies, and er- | rors, both olde and newe, contrarie to | the faith, subscribed vnto by | Thomas Rogers. | Allowed by auctoritie. | . . . (3 lines; device).

    At London | Imprinted By Iohn VVin- | det for Andrew Maunsel at the brasen Serpent | in Pauls church yard. 1585. | 27.x18.8cm. (8),1–64,49–63; 1–74,76–91, (1)p. p.75 omitted.

SANDERS, Nicholas. Doctissimi | Viri Nicolai Sanderi, | De Origine Ac Pro- | gressu Schismatis Anglicani, | Liber. | Continens historiam maximè Ecclesiasticam, annorum cir- | citer sexaginta, lectu dignissimam: nimirum, ab anno | 21. regni Henrici 8, quo primum cogitare cœpit | de repudianda legitima vxore serenissima Cathe- | rina, vsque ad hunc vigesimum septimum Eli- | zabethæ, quæ vltima est eiusdem Henrici | soboles. | Editus & auctus per Edouardum Rishtonum. | Præcipua capita totius operis post præfatio- | nem authoris continentur. |

    Coloniæ Agrippinæ, Anno Domini | 1585. | 16.6x10.3 cm. .(6),207,(5)fol.
    Translation by David Lewis. London:1877.

SANDYS, Edwin. Sermons | Made by the most reue- | rende Father in God,Edwin,Arch- | bishop of Yorke, Primate of England | and Metropolitane. | . . . (3 lines; device).

    At London, | Printed by Henrie Midleton, | for Thomas Charde. | 1585. | Lace border. 21.x15.5cm. (8),384p.

1586

BILSON, Thomas. The | Trve Difference | Betweene Christian | Svbiection And Vn- | christian Rebel- | lion: | Wherein The Princes Law- | ful power to command for truth, and indepriue- | able right to beare the sword, are defended against the | Popes censures and the Iesuits sophismes, vtte- | red in their Apologie and De- | fence Of English | Catholikes: | With a demonstration that the things reformed in the | Church of England by the lawes of this Realme are tru- | ly Catholike, notwithstanding the vaine shew made | to the contrarie in their late Rhemish | Testament: by Thomas | Bilson Warden of | Winchester. | Perused and allowed by publike authoritie. | . . . (7 lines)

    Imprinted at London by Iohn Iack- | son and Edmund Bollifant. | Anno 1586. | 15.7x10.3cm (21),430,686,(10)p.

The | BRVTISH Thvn- | derbolt: | or rather | Feeble Fier-Flash | of Pope Sixtvs the fift, against | Henrie the most excellent King of | Nauarre, and the most noble Hen- | rie Borbon, Prince of | Condie. | Togither with a declaration of the ma- | nifold insufficiencie of | the same. | Translated out of Latin into English by Chri- | stopher Fetherstone Mini- | ster of Gods word. | . . . (5 lines).

Imprinted at London, by Arnold | Hatfield, for G.B. and R. | Newbery. | 1586 | 14x9cm. (14),321,(13)p.
H&L, new ed., attributes to Franciscus Hotomanus.

FULKE, William. A comfortable Ser- | mon of Fayth, in temptations | and afflication. | Preached at Saint Botulphes with- | out Aldersgate in London, the xv. of | February .1573. By Master | William Fulke. Doctor of | Diuinitie. | . . . (5 lines).

Imprinted at Lon- | don by John Charlewood, | dwelling in Barbican, at the | signe of the halfe Eagle | and the Key. 1586, | Border. 13.2x9.cm. (28)fol.

FULKE, William. A Confvta- | tion Of A Trea- | tise Made By William | Allen In Defence Of | the vsurped power of Popish | Priesthood to remit sinnes, | of the necessity of Shrift, | and of the Popes | Pardons. | By William Fvlke. | (device).

Imprinted by Thomas Thomas, Printer to the | Vniuersitie of Cambridge. | [1586] 15.7x10.cm. 531;(1),54p.
Sub-title: An Apologie | Of The Profes- | sors Of The Gospel | In Fravnce Against The | Railing Declamation Of Pe- | ter Frarine a Louanian turned into En- | glish by Iohn Fowler. | Written by William Fulke. | (device).
Part 2-3 of William Charke's Treatise: 1586

ORLEANS, Louis d'. Advertissement, | Des Catho- | liqves Anglois Aux | François Catholiques, du danger | où ils sont de perdre leur Religiõ, | & d'experimenter, comme en An- | gleterre, la cruauté des Ministres | s'ils reçoiuent à la Couronne vn | Roy qui soit Heretique. | . . . (6 lines).

1586. | 15.7x10 cm. 133,(1)p.
Anon. B.M.Cat.

PARSONS, Robert. A | Book Of | Christian exercise, | appertaining to Reso- | lvtion, that is, she- | wing how that wee shoulde | resolue our selues to be- | come Christians in- | deed. By R.P. | Perused and accompanied | now with a tretise tending | to pacification. By Edm. | Bvnny. | . . . (device; 4 lines).

Imprinted At | London; 1586. | Lace border. 12.1x7.1cm. (26),381;(1),108p.
Folded leaf. One sub.t.p.
Madan: Early Oxford Press: 1585 (5), note.

SALNAR, ——. An Harmony | Of The Confessions | Of The Faith Of The Chri- | stian And Reformed Chvrches, | which purelie professe the holy doctrine | of the Gospell in all the chiefe Kingdomes, Na- | tions, and Prouinces of Europe: the Cato- | logue and order whereof the Pages | following will declare. | There are added in the ende verie shorte notes: in | which both the obscure thinges are made plaine, & those | thinges which maie in shew seeme to be contrarie each | to other, are plainelie and verie modestlie reconciled, | and if anie points doe as yet hang in doubt, they are sin- | cerelie pointed at. | All which things, in the name of the Churches of Fraunce and Belgia, are | submitted to the free and discrete iudgement of all other Churches. | Newlie translated out of Latine into English. | Also in the end is added the Confession of the Church of | Scotland. | Alowed by publique authoritie. |

Imprinted by Thomas Thomas, Printer to the | Vniuersitie of Cambridge. | 1586. | 16.2x10.5 cm. (36), 608 ,(41),26,(2)p.
Anon. H & L.

SANDERS, Nicholas. Nicolai | Sanderi | De Origine Ac Progressv | Schismatis Anglicani | Libri Tres. | Quibus historia continetur maximè Ecclesiastica, anno- | rum circiter sexaginta, lectu dignissima; nimirum, ab | anno 21. regni Henrici octaui, quo primum co | gitare cœpit de repudianda legitima vxore serenissi- | ma Catharina, vsque ad hunc vigesimum | octauum Elizabethæ, quæ vltima est eius- | dem Henrici soboles. | Aucti per Edouardum Rishtonum, & impressi pri- | mùm in Germania, nunc iterum locuple- | tiùs & castigatius editi. | Cuiusq, libri argumenta, pagella versa monstrabit. | Cum Priuilegio, & Licentia Superiorum. | (device).

Romæ, | Typis Bartholomæi Bonfadini, In via Pellegrini. | M D LXXXVI. | 15.7x10.5cm. (8),500,(35)p. Colophon and device.

1587

ANWICK, John. Anwick his | Meditations | vpon Gods Monarchie, | and the Deuill his | Kingdome. | And | Of the knowledge that Man | in this life may obtaine of the | almightie, eternal, and most | glorious Godhed: | With | |other thinges not only worth the reading | but also the marking and the | retayning. | . . . (5 lines).

Imprinted At London by | Gerred Dewes, dwelling in Powles | Churchard, at the signe | of the Swan. | 1587. | Lace border. 18x13.3cm. (13),117p.

BÉZE, Théodore de. Master Bezaes Ser- | mons Vpon The Three | First Chapters Of The | Canticle Of Canticles: | Wherein Are Handled The | Chiefest Points Of Religion | Controversed And Debated Be- | tweene Vs And The Adversa- | rie At This Day, Especially Tov- | ching The Trve Iesus Christ and | The Trve Chvrch, And The Certaine & Infallible Marks | Both Of The One And | Of The Other. | Translated Ovt Of French Into | English By Iohn Harmar, Her Highnes | Professor In The Greeke Tovng | In The Universitie Of Oxford, | And Felowe Of The Newe | College There. | (device).

At Oxford, | Printed By Ioseph Barnes, And Are | To Be Sovld In Pauls Chvrch- | yard At The Tygers Head, 1587. | 18.2x12.5cm. (12),435p.

BRIDGES, John. A | Defence Of The | Government Established | In The Chvrch Of Englande | For Ecclesiasticall Matters. | Contayning an aunswere vnto a Treatise called, | The Learned Discourse of Eccl. Gouernment, | otherwise intituled, | A briefe and plaine declaration concerning the desires of all the | faithfull Ministers that haue, and do seeke for the discipline and | reformation of the Church of Englande. | Comprehending likewise an aunswere to the arguments in a Treatise named | The iudgement of a most Reuerend and Learned | man from beyond the Seas, &c. | Aunsvvering also to the argumentes of Caluine, Beza, and Da- | næus, with other our Reuerend learned Brethren, besides Cænalis and Bo- | dinus, both for the regiment of women, and in defence of her Maiestie, and | of all other Christian Princes supreme Gouernment | in Ecclesiastical causes, | Against | The Tetrarchie that our Brethren would erect in euery particular congre- | gation, of Doctors, Pastors, Gouernors and Deacons, with their seu- erall | and ioynt authoritie in Elections, Excommunications, Synodall | Constitutions and other Ecclesiasticall matters. | Aunsvvered by Iohn Bridges Deane of Sarum. | . . . (2 lines).

At London, | Printed by Iohn VVindet, for Thomas Chard. | 1587. | 20.9x15.5cm. (10),1417,(1)p. Omitted: 395–400, 1087–1104, 1223–1232; frequent misnumberings, but particularly 1377–1417, marked as 1361–1401.

FENNER, Dudley. A Defence | Of the godlie Ministers, against the | slaunders of D. Bridges, contayned in | his ansvvere to the Pref- ace before | the Discourse of Ecclesiasticall gouerne- | ment, with a Declaration of the | Bishops proceeding a- | gainst them. | Wherein chieflie, | 1 The lawfull authoritie of her Maiestie is defended by the | Scriptures, her lawes, and authorised interpretation of them, to | be the same which we haue affirmed, against his cauilles and | slaunders to the contrarie. | 2 The lawfull refusinge also of the Ministers to subscribe, is | maintayned by euident groundes of Gods worde, and her Maie- | sties lawes, against his euident wresting of both. | 3 Lastlie, the forme of Church-gouernement, which we pro- | pounde, is accord- ing to his demaunde Sillogisticallie proued to | be ordinarie, perpetuall, and the best. | . . . (5 lines).

1587. | 17.9x12.6 cm. (4),150,(1)p. Paging begins with 49.
Anon. Camb. Univ. Cat. No. 6787.

FENNER, Dudley. The Song | Of Songs, | that is, the most ex- cellent song | which was Solomons, translated | out of the Hebrue into English | meeter, vvith as little libertie in | departing from the wordes, | as any plaine translation in prose | can vse: and interpreted | by a short com- | mentarie. | . . . (5 lines).

Middlebvrgh, | Imprinted by Richard Schil- | ders, Printer to the States of | Zealande. | Cum priuilegio. | 1587. | 13.7x8.9 cm. (15,68)p.
Anon. Camb Univ. Cat. No. 6747.

FOX, John. Eicasmi | Sev Meditationes, | In Sacram Apo- | calyp- sin. | Authore Io.Foxo | Anglo. | (device)

Londini | Impensis Geor. | Byshop. | 1587. | Engraved border. 27.2 x 19. cm. (8),396,(26) p. Last sig. Nn 2.

FREWEN, John. Certaine fruitfull Instructions and necessary doctrines meete to edify in the feare of God: faithfully gathered to- gether by Iohn Frewen.

London: Printed for Thomas Chard, dwelling at the Helmet in Pauls Churchyard. 1587. 12.3x7.3cm. 384p.

Lacks t.p. and dedication. Title from DNB, and imprint from Maunsell's First Part of the Catalogue of English Printed Books. London, 1695, p. 52a. and Arber's Register, V.

HOLINSHED, Raphael, HARRISON, William, etc. The | First and second | volumes of Chronicles, | comprising | 1 The description and historie of England, | 2 The description and historie of Ireland, | 3 The description and historie of Scotland: | First collected and published by Raphaell | Holinshed, William Harrison, | and others: | Now newlie augmented and continued | (with manifold matters of singular | note and worthie memorie) | to the yeare 1586. by | Iohn Hooker alias Vowell Gent. | and others. | With conuenient tables at | the end of these | volumes. | . . . (1 line).

Without imprint. Column and vine border. Colophon: Finished in Ianuarie 1587, and the 29 of the Queenes | Maiesties reigne, with the full continuation of the | former yeares, at the expenses of Iohn Hari- | son, George Bishop, Rafe Newberie, | Henrie Denham, and Tho- | mas Woodcocke. | (device). At London | Printed in Aldersgate street at the signe | of the Starre. | Cum priuilegio. |
Bound in 4 vols. 38.2x23.8cm. Vol.I: (8),250;(3),202;60;(12),183; Vol.II: 464,(52); Vol.III: (8),789; Vol.IV: 799-1592,(58)p.

HOLINSHED, Raphael. The | Third volume of Chronicles, be- | ginning at duke William the Norman, | commonlie called the Conqueror: and | descending by degrees of yeeres to all the | kings and queenes of England in their | orderlie successions: | First compiled by Raphaell Holinshed, | and by him extended to the | yeare 1577. | Now newlie recognised, augmented, and | continued (with occurrences and | accidents of fresh memorie) | to the yeare 1586. | wherein also are conteined manie matters | of singular discourse and rare obser- | uation, fruitfull to such as be | studious in antiquities or | take pleasure in the | grounds of anci- | ent histories. | With a third table (peculiarlie seruing | this third volume) both of | names and matters | memorable. | . . . (1 line).

Without imprint. Vignette border. Colophon: Finished in Ianuarie 1587, and the 29 of the Queenes | Maiesties reigne, with the full continuation of the | former yeares, at the expenses of Iohn Hari- | son, George Bishop, Rafe Newberie, | Henrie Denham, and Tho- | mas Woodcocke. | (device). At London | Printed in Aldersgate street at the signe | of the Starre. | Cum priuilegio. | Bound in 2 vols. 38.2x23.8cm. (8),1592,(58)p.

MORNAY, Philippe de. A | Woorke | concerning the trew- | nesse of the Christian | Religion, written | in French: | Against Atheists, Epicures, Paynims, Iewes, | Mahumetists, and other Infidels. | By Philip of Mornay Lord of | Plessie Marlie. | Begunne to be translated into English by Sir | Philip Sidney Knight, and at his request | finished by Arthur Golding. |

Imprinted at London for Thomas | Cadman. 1587. | Engraved border. Colophon: Imprinted at London | by George Robinson for Thomas | Cadman, dwelling at the great North- | doore of S.Paules Church at the signe | of the Byble. 1587. | 20.5x14.7cm. (28),641,(1)p.

PFLACHER, Moses. Analysis | Typica | Omnium cum veteris tum noui | Testamenti Librorum Historicorum: | ad intelligendam rerum seriem, | & memoriam iuuandam, | accommodata. | Avtore | Mose Pflachero, Sa- | cræ Theologiæ Doctore. | Subiecta est Methodvs resoluendi | quoscunque Autores. | Cvm | Indicibvs duobus: altero exegetico ter- | minorum Græcorum: altero Rerum | & Verborum accurato. | Editio secunda. |

Londini | Excvdebat Edm.Bolli- | fantvs Impensis G.B. | M D XXCVII. | Lace border. 19.2x14.5cm. (14),576,(25)p.

SANDERS, Nicholas. Nicolai | Sanderi, | De Origine Ac Progressv | Schismatis Anglicani, | Libri Tres: | Quibvs Historia Continetvr | maximè Ecclesiastica, annorum circiter sexaginta, lectu di- | gnissima; nimirum, ab anno 21. regni Henrici octaui, | quo primùm cogitare coepit de repudianda legitima vxore | serenissima Catharina, vsque ad hunc vigesi- | mum octauum Elisabethæ, quæ | vltima est eiusdem Henrici | soboles: | Aucti per Edovardvm Rishtonvm, Romæq́; impressi; | nunc verò in Germania iterum locupletiùs & | castigatiùs editi. | Cuiusq[ue] libri argumenta, pagella versa monstrabit. | (device)

1587. | Cum gratia & priuilegio Cæsareæ Maiestatis. | Ingolstadii, Ex officina Typographica | VVolfgangi Ederi. | Line border. 15.8x10.3cm (16),373,(26)p.

WILCOX, Thomas. A | Christian And | Learned Exposition, | vpon certaine verses of that eight chapter | of the Epistle of that blessed Apostle Pavle to the | Romanes, and namely, vpon verse, | 18.19.20. 21.22.23. | VVritten Long Agoe, By T.W.For | a most deare frend of his in Christ, and now lately pub- | lished in printe, for the benefite and good of Gods peo- | ple wheresoeuer. | . . . (device, God Is My | Helper. |).

At London, | Printed by Robert Walde-graue, for | Thomas Man. 1587. | 13x9.2 cm (5),147p.
D N B. 61: 220 a.

1588

BABINGTON, Gervase. A profitable | Exposition of the Lords | Prayer, by way of Questions and | Answers for most playnnes: | Together with many fruitfull appli- | cations to the life and Soule, aswell for | the terror of the dull and dead, | as for the sweet comfort of | the tender harted. | By Geruase Babington. | With a Table of the principall matters | conteyned in this Booke. | . . . (3 lines).

At London, | Printed by Thomas Orwin for | Thomas Charde. | 1588. | 14.9x9.9 cm (16),582,(7)p. Mispagings.

BANCROFT, Richard. A | Sermon Prea- | ched At Paules | Crosse the 9. of Februarie, | being the first Sunday in the | Parleament, Anno .1588. by Ri- | chard Bancroft D. of Divinitie, and | Chaplaine to the right Honora- | ble Sir Christopher Hatton | Knight L. Chancelor | of England. | Wherein some things are now added, | which then were omitted, either | through want of time, or default in | memorie. | . . . (4 lines).

Imprinted at London, by | E.B. for Gregorie Seton, | and are to be sold at | his shop under Al- | dersgate. | 1588. | Lace border. 15.3x9.2cm. (1),106,(1)p.

BARO, Peter. Fower Sermons | and two Que- | stions. | As they were vt- | tered and disputed ad Cle- | rum in S. Maries Church | and Schools in | Cambridge. | By that learned Frenche- | man P.B.D. of Diui- | nitye. | And Englished by I.L. |

Imprinted at London by Iohn | Woolfe. | [1588?] Lace border 13.7x9.1 cm. Pp. (4),375–541 (of his Special Treatise of God's Providence. [1588?]

BARO, Peter. A speciall Trea- | tise of Gods Prouidence, | and of comforts against all | kinde of crosses & calami- | ties to be fetched from | the same. | With an exposition of the | 107. Psalme. | Heerunto is added | an appendix of certaine | Sermons & Questions, (contei | ning sweet & comfortable doc- | trine) as they were vttered | and disputed ad Cle- | rum in Cam- | bridge. | By P. Baro. D. in Diui. | Englished by I. L. Vicar | of Wethers-fielde. |

Imprinted by Iohn Wolfe. | [1588?]. Lace border. 13.7x9.1 cm. .(4),541, p. Paging begins on p.225; 290–313 irregular. Between 374 and 375, 4 pages containing a secondary title: Fower Sermons | and two Que- | stions. | . . . By . . . P.B. . . . N.d.
Camb.Univ.Cat.No.1952.

BREDWELL, Stephen. The Rasing | Of The Fovndations | of Brovvnisme. | Wherein Against All The Wri- | tings of the principall Masters of that sect, those chiefe con- | clusions in the next page, are, (amongst sundry other | matters, worthie the Readers knowledge) pur- | posely handled, and soundly prooued. | Also Their Contrarie Argvments And Obiec- | tions deliberately examined, and clearly refelled by the word of God. | . . . (2 lines; device).

Imprinted at London by Iohn Windet, dvvelling at | Pawles wharfe at the signe of the Crosse keyes, and | are to be sold at the Rose in Powles churchyard, 1588. | Colophon. 17.5x13.4 cm. (16),145,(1).
Dedication signed S.B. H&L. Camb.Univ.Cat. No.2124.

BRIDGEWATER, John. Concertatio | Ecclesiae Ca- | tholicæ In Anglia Adver- | svs Calvinopapistas Et Pvritanos | sub Elizabetha Regina quorundam hominum | doctrina & sanctitate illustrium | renouata. | Ac Nvnc Denvo Centvm | Et Eo Amplivs Martyrvm, Sexcentorvmqve | insignium virorum rebus gestis variisq[ue] certaminibus, lapsorum Palinodijs, nouis per- | secutorum edictis, ac doctissimis Catholicorum de Anglicano seu muliebri Pon- | tificatu, ac Romani Pontificis in Principes Christianos auctoritate; | disputationibus & defensionibus aucta, & | in tres partes diuisa. | . . . (5 lines; device).

Avgvstae Trevirorvm | Excudebat Henricus Bock. Anno 1588. | Cvm Gratia Et Privilegio. | 20x14.5cm. (6),426fol. 414–426 unfolioed.
Preface signed Ioannes Aquepontanus Anglus.

BROUGHTON, Hugh. A Con- | cent Of | Scripture | by | H:-Broughton |

[1588?] Pillar and vine border. 21.8x16cm. (6, 32) fol.
Engraved t.p., without name of printer. Has map of the earth, but lacks engravings. T.p. and map without signature marks. Sig Ai–Biv, Bi–Hiv.
Camb.Univ.Cat.No.2192. Huntington Libr. dates 1591? For date, see Samuel Clark, Lives of sundry Eminent Persons: 1683, p. 2.

BULKELEY, Edward. An | Answere To Ten | friuolous and foolish reasons, | set downe by the Rhemish Iesuits | and Papists in their Preface before the | new Testament by them lately translated in- | to English, which haue moued them to forsake the | originall fountaine of the Greeke, wherein the Spirit | of God did indite the Gospell, and the holie A- | postles did write it, to follow the streame | of the Latin translation, transla- | ted we know not when | nor by whom. | With a discouerie of many great Corrup- | tions and faults in the said English | Translation set out at Rhemes. | By E.B. | . . . (10 lines).
Londini, | Impensis Georg.Bishop. | 1588. | Lace border. 18.4x12.9 cm (7),103p Epistle dedicatorie signed.

CARPENTER, John. Remember | Lots wife. | Two godly and fruitfull | Sermons verie conuenient | for this our time: lately preached | on a Sunday in the Cathedral Church | of S.Peters in Excester: the one, | in the forenoone: the o- | ther, in the afternoone | the same day. | By Iohn C. | . . . (3 lines).
At London, | Printed by Thomas Orwin, | and are to be solde by Edward | White at the litle North-doore | of S.Paules, at the signe | of the Gunne. | 1588. | Lace border. 13.3x9.2ch. (8,116)p.
Epistle dedicatorie signed.

ELIZABETH, Queen. By the Queen. | A Proclamation against certain seditious and schisma- | tical Books and Libels &c. |
Without t.p. Colophon: Imprinted at London by the Deputies of | Christopher Barker, Printer to the Queens most | excellent Majestie 1588. | 19.5x15.2cm. Pp. 231–232, of Sparrow's Collection: 1661. Also in his reprints of 1675 and 1684.

FEGUERNEKIUS, Isaacus L. Enchiridion | Locorvm Commvnivm | Theologicorvm, | Rerum, Exemplorum, atque Phra- | seon sacrarum; | Ex Avgvstini Marlorati Thesauro, | & Christ. Obenhinii | Promptuario | ab | Isaaco L.Fegvernekino Vngaro, | conflatum, recognitum, | actum. | . . . (7 lines; device).
Londini, | Impensis Georg.Bishop. | M D XXCVIII. | 16.4x10.cm. (16),381, (50)p.

HARVEY, John. A | Discovrsive Pro- | bleme concer- | ning Prophesies, | How far they are to be valued, or credi- | ted, according to the surest rules, and | directions in Diuinitie, Philoso- | phie, Astrologie, and other | learning: | Deuised especially in abatement of | the terrible threatenings, and menaces, | peremptorily denounced against the king- | doms, and states of the world, this present | famous yeere .1588. supposed the | Greatwoonderfull, and Fatall | yeere of our Age. | By I. H. Physition. |
Printed at London, by Iohn | Iackson. for Richard | Watkins. | 1588. | Lace border 17.9x12.5 cm. (8),133p.
Cambr.Univ.Cat:2100.

An HUMBLE petition of the | Communaltie to their nost re- | nowned and gracious Soueraigne, the Lady | Elizabeth, by the grace of God, Queene of Eng- | land, France and Ireland, defender of the faith, &c. | Also the lamentable complaint of | the communaltie, by way of Supplication to | the high court of Parliament, for a learned mi- | nisterie, renued and augmented. | A petition made to the Con- uocation | house, 1586. by the godly ministers tending | to reconcilia- tion, and translated into English. | . . . (15 lines).
   1588.| 13x8.2 cm.   (2,233)p.

JUNIUS, Franciscus.   Sacrorvm | Parallelorvm | Libri Tres: | Jd Est, | Comparatio locorum Scripturæ | sacræ, qui ex Testamento vetere in | Novo adducuntur: summam utri- | usque in verbis convenientiam, in | rebus consensum, in mutationibus | fidem veritatémq; breviter & per- | spicuè ex fontibus Scripturæ S.ge- | nuinâque linguarum Hebrææ & | Grȩcæ conformatione monstrans: | & contra Atheos, Arianos, Iudæos, | Mahumedistas, aliósque afferens | simplicitatem Euangelis- tarum & | Apostolorum Christi. | Primo libro continentur loci, qui in Eu- | angeliis & Actis Apostolorum exstant: | Secvndo, qui in tredecim Pauli Epi- | stolis: | Tertio, Epistolæ ad Hebræos justus & | methodicus Commentarius. His postre- | mò accedit Appendix, ex scriptis | reli- quis canonicis. | Francisci Iunii Biturigis. | Editio secunda. |
   Londini, | Impensis G.Bishop. | [1588?]   Engraved border.   15.8x10.2cm.   (16), 374p.
   Cambr. Univ. Cat. No. 1715.

MARTIN MARPRELATE. Oh read ouer D.John Bridges, for it is worthy worke: | Or an epitome of the | fyrste Booke, of that right worshipfull vo- | lume, written against the Puritanes, in the defence of | the noble cleargie, by as worshipfull a prieste, John Bridges, | Presbyter, Priest or elder, doctor of Diuillitie, and Deane of | Sarum. Wherein the arguments of the puritans are | wisely prevented, that when they come to an- | swere M.Doctor, they must needes | say some thing that hath | bene spoken. | Compiled for the behoofe and over- throw of | the vnpreaching Parsons, Fyckers, and Currats, | that haue lernt their Catechismes, and are past grace: | By the reverend and worthie Martin Marprelat | gentleman, and dedicated by a second Epistle | to the Terrible Priests. | In this Epitome, the foresaide Fickers, &c. are very in- | sufficiently furnished, with notable inabilitie of most vin- | cible reasons, to answere the cauill | of the puritanes. | And lest M.Doctor should thinke that no man can write with- | out sence but his selfe, the senceles titles of the seueral pages, | and the handling of the matter throughout the Epitome, | shewe plainely, that beetleheaded ignoraunce, must not liue | and die with him alone. |
   Printed on the other hand of some of the Priests. | [1588].   17.2x13cm.   (4,42)p. A2,B4–G2.
   Pierce, Tracts, p.115.

MARTIN MARPRELATE. Oh read ouer D.John Bridges, for it is a worthy worke: | Or an epitome of the | fyrste Booke, of that right worshipfull vo- | lume, written against the Puritanes, in the defence of | the noble cleargie, by as worshipfull a prieste, John Bridges, | Presbyter, Priest or elder, doctor of Diuillitie, and Deane of | Sarum. Wherein the arguments of the puritans are | wisely prevented, that when they come to an- | swere M.Doctor, they must needes | say something that hath | bene spoken. | Compiled for the behoofe and overthrow of | the Parsons, Fyckers, and Currats, that have lernt | their Catechismes, and are past grace: By the reverend | and worthie Martin Marprelate gentleman, and | dedicated to the Confocation-house. | The Epitome is not yet published, but it shall be when | the Bishops are at conuenient leysure to view the same. | In the meane time, let them be content with | this learned Epistle. |

Printed oversea, in Europe, within two fur- | longs of a Bounsing Priest, at the cost and charges | of M.Marprelate, gentleman. | [1588]   17.7x13.8cm.   (1),54p.
Pierce: Tracts, p. 13ff.

PENRY, John. A defence of that which hath bin | written in the questions of the ig- | norant ministerie, and the communicating | with them. By Iohn Penri. |

N.d.n.p. [1588?]   13.5x9.2 cm.   63p.   Imperfect, lacking Sig.A.

RIBADENEIRA, Pedro de. Historia | Ecclesiastica | Del Scisma Del Reyno | De Inglaterra. | Recogida de diuersos y graues Auto- | res, por el Padre Pedro de Ribade- | neyra, de la Compañia de Iesus. | . . (2 lines: royal arms).

En Emberes, | En casa de Christoual Plantino, | Imprimidor del Rey. | 1588. | 16x9.9cm.   (16),386,(11)p

SANDERS, Nicholas. De Clave David | Sev | Regno Christi | Libri Sex | Contra Calvmnias Acleri | pro visibili Ecclesiæ Monarchia. | Avctore Nicolao Sandero | Anglo, sacræ Theologiæ professore. | (device).

Romæ, In Aedibus Populi Romani, | Apud Georgium Ferrarium, M D LXXXVIII. | Svperiorvm Permissv. | 24.2x17,5cm.   (16), 396p. Colophon.

SOME, Robert. A | Godly Treatise | containing and deciding cer- taine | questions, mooued of late in London and | other places, touching the Ministerie, | Sacraments, and Church. | Whereunto one Proposition more is added. | After the ende of this Booke you shall | finde a defence of such points as M. Penry | hath dealt against: And a confuta- ti- | on of many grosse errours broched | in M. Penries last | Treatise. | Written by Robert Some Doctor | of Diuinitie. | . . . (3 lines; device).

Imprinted at London by G. B. Deputie to Chri- | stopher Barker, Printer to the Queenes most ex- | cellent Maiestie. 1588. | 20.4x14,5cm.   (4),36,(12),53–200p. Sub. t.p. after p. 36.

STAPLETON, Thomas. Tres Thomae. | Sev | De S.Thomæ Apos- toli rebus gestis. | De S. Thoma Archiepiscopo Can- | tuariensi & Martyre. | D. Thomæ Mori Angliæ quon- | dam Cancellarij Vita. | His adiecta est Oratio Fvnebris | in laudem R.P. Arnoldi de Ganthois |

Abbatis Marchennensis. | Avthore | Thoma Stapletono Anglo | S.Theolog. Doctore. | . . . (2 lines; device).

Dvaci, | Ex officina Ioannis Bogardi | M.D.LXXXVIII. | 16.2x10.2cm. (16), 375,(20)p.

TEDDER, William and TYRRELL, Anthony. The | Recantations as they were seue- | rallie pronounced by VVylliam Tedder and | Anthony Tyrrell: (sometime two Seminarie Priests | of the English Colledge in Rome, and nowe by the | great mercie of almightie God conuerted, vnto the profession | of the Gospell of Iesus Christ) at Paules Crosse, the day | and yeere as is mentioned in their seuerall | Tytles of theyr Recan- | tations. | VVith an Epistle dedicatorie vnto her Maiestie, | and their seuerall Præfaces vnto the Reader, contay- | ning the causes that mooued them | to the same. | (device)

At London, | Printed by Iohn Charlewood and VVilli- | am Brome. Anno Domini. | M.D.LXXXVIII. | 17.2x11.8cm. (2),47p. Two sub-t.ps.

TRAVERS, Walter. A Defence Of The | Ecclesiastical | Discipline ordayned of God to | be vsed in his Church. | Against a Replie of Maister Bridges, to a briefe and plain | Declaration of it, which was printed An. 1584. | Which replie he termeth, A Defence | of the gouernement established in | the Church of Englande, | for Ecclesiasticall | matters. | . . . (16 lines)

1588. | 16.9x12.1 cm. 228p 200 misnumbered; 201–220 are omitted in numbering: complete.

H&L, new edition.

UDALL, John. A Demonstration Of | the trueth of that Discipline which | Christe hath prescribed in his worde for the | gouernement of his Church, in all times | and places, vntill the ende of the worlde. | Wherein are gathered into a plaine | forme of reasoning, the proofes thereof; out of | the scriptures, the euidence of it by the | light of reason rightly ruled, and the testimonies | that haue beene giuen therevnto, by the course | of the Churche certaine hundreths of yeares af- | ter the Apostles time; and the generall con- | sent of the Churches rightly reformed in | these latter times: according as they | are alleaged and maintained, in | those seuerall bookes that | haue bin written con- | cerning the | same. | . . . (6 lines).

No imprint. [1588]. 14x9.5 cm. (24),102,(1)p. 1 tab.

Also Repr. in Parte of a register: 1593. Dexter 161. Cambr.Cat.1913. Pierce, Introd. p 313.

Burned by order of Star Chamber.

WITHER, George. A | View Of The Mar- | ginal Notes Of The | Popish Testament, translated | into English by the English fu- | gitiue Papists resiant at | Rhemes in | France. | By George Wither. | . . . (18 lines)

Printed at London by Edm. Bollifant | for Thomas Woodcocke. | [1588] Lace border 19.1x14.3 cm. (8),316 p.

Camb.Univ.Cat.No.2047.

1589

BASTINGIUS, Jeremias. An | Exposition | Or Commentarie | vpon the Catechisme of Chri- | stian religion which is taught in | the Scholes and Churches | both of the Lowe Countries, | & of the dominions of | the Countie Pa- | latine. | By Ieremias Bastingivs | Minister of the word of God. | Translated out of Latine into English. | With three Tables. |

Cambrjdge. | Printed By Iohn | Legatt. | And are to be sold at the | signe of the Sunne in | Paules Churchyard | in London. | [1589] Engraved title. Colophon. 15.2x9.7 cm. (6),275,(11)fol.
Camb.Univ.Cat.No.5541.

BRIDGEWATER, John. Concertatio | Ecclesiae Ca- | tholicæ In Anglia Adver- | svs Calvinopapistas Et Pvritanos | sub Elizabetha Regina quorundam hominum | doctrina & sanctitate illustrium | renouata. | Ac Nvnc Denvo Centvm | Et Eo Amplivs Martyrvm, Sexcentorvmque | insignium virorum rebus gestis varijsq̇ certaminibus, lapsorum Palinodijs, nouis per- | secutorum edictis, ac doctissimis Catholicorum de Anglicano seu muliebri Pon- | tificatu, ac Romani Pontificis in Principes Christianos auctoritate; | disputationibus & defensionibus aucta, & | in tres partes diuisa. | . . . (5 lines: device)

Avgvstae Trevirorvm | Excudebat Henricus Bock. Anno 1589. | Cvm Gratia Et Privilegio. | 19.7 x 14.4 cm. (6),212,(22),215–413,(12) fol. (215, 217 misnumbered)

CARTWRIGHT, Thomas. Two very | Godly and comfor- | table Letters, written ouer | into England. | The One To A God- | ly and zealous Lady: wherin the | Annabaptists errour is confuted: and | the sinne against the Holye Ghoste | plainly declared. | The Other An | answer to a Godly Merchants | Letter: written for his comfort, | being greeued with the heauye bur- | den of sinne: wherin is declared the | true confession of sinne. | Written by T. C. |

At London | Printed by Edward Allde for | Edward White. | 1589. | Colophon: At London. | Printed by Ed- | ward Allde for | Edward White, and | are to be solde at the | little North doore of S. | Paules Church at the | signe of the | Gun. | (lace ornament) 12.9x7 cm. (1,112)p.

Perfect: 5 sigs. in 12s. with first and last two leaves blank. Dated: From Copyn Hauen in | Denmarke the 3. of | Februarye. | If you write againe to me | write to Geneua, for thi- | therwards by Gods grace, | I intend to goe shortly. | Yours in the | Lord. T.C. |
"Unique":C.A.Briggs. Cf.DNB.9:229b.

COOPER, Thomas. An | Admonition | To The People Of | England: | VVherein Are An- | svvered Not Onely The | slaunderous vntruethes, reprochfully vt- | tered by Martin the Libeller, but also many other | Crimes by some of his broode, obiected gene- | rally against all Bishops, and the chiefe of the | Clergie, purposely to deface and | discredite the present state of | the Church. | . . . (2 lines). | Seene and allowed by authoritie. |

Imprinted at London by the Deputies | of Christopher Barker, Printer to the | Queenes most excellent Maiestie. | 1589. | Colophon. 17x12 cm. (8),245p.
Anon. H&L. Trin.Col,Camb. No.522.

A DIALOGVE. | VVherin Is | Plainly Laide Open, | the tyrannicall dealing of L. Bishopps a- | gainst Gods children: vvith certaine points | of doctrine, vvherein they approoue themselues | (according to D. Bridges his judgement) | to be truely the Bishops of | the Diuell. | . . . (9 lines).

No imprint. [1589?] 13.3x8.7 cm. (1,30)p.
Attributed to Martin Marprelate. Cambr.Cat.7054. Cf. ed. of 1640. Dexter, 156. Trin.Col.Camb.No.1058. Pierce,Introd.p.242,320.

ELIZABETH, Queen [Statutes] Anno xxxi. Anno xxxj. Reginæ | Elizabethae. | At a Session of Par- | liament holden at Westminster the | fourth day of Februarie, in the one and | thirtieth yeere of the Reigne of our most gra- | tious Soueraigne Lady Elizabeth by the grace | of God of England, Fraunce and Ireland | Queene, defender of the faith, &c. | And there continued vntill the | dissolution thereof, being | the xxix. of March. | To the high pleasure of Almightie God, | and the weale publique of this | Realme, were enacted | as followeth. |

Imprinted at London by the De- | puties of Christopher Barker, Printer | to the Queenes most excellent Maiestie. | 1589. | Engraved border 27.1x18.7 cm. (1,51) fol.

ERASTUS, Thomas. Explicatio | Grauissimae Quaestionis | vtrùm Excommunicatio, quatenùs Religio- | nem intelligentes & amplexantes, à Sacra- | mentorum vsu, propter admissum faci- | nus arcet; mandato nitatur Diuino, | an excogitata sit ab ho- | minibus. | Autore Clariss. viro Thoma Erasto D. Medico. | Opus nunc recèns ex ipsius Autoris authographo | erutum, & in lucem, prout moriens | iusserat, editum. | Ad Operis Calcem Adiectae | sunt clarissimorum aliquot Theologorum Episto- | lae, partim ad ipsum Autorem scriptae, partim ad | alios, quibus suum rogati, de hac re iudicium | ac sententiam proferunt. | Cvm Indice Copiosissimo. |

Pesclavii | Apud Baocium Sultaceterum Anno Salutis. | M.D.LXXXIX. 22.9x 15.6 cm. (15),390,(10)p.

FENNER, Dudley. Sacra | Theologia, | Sive | Veritas quæ est secundum | pietatem, | Ad vnicæ & veræ methodi leges descripta, & | in decem libros per Dvdleivm | Fennervm digesta. | Altera editio, priore emendatior. | (device)

Apvd Evstathivm Vignon. | M.D.LXXXIX. | 16x10.1cm. (8),176fol.

FREGEVILLE, Jean de. The Reformed | Politicke. | That is, | An Apologie For The Ge- | nerall cause of Reformation, written against the | sclaunders of the Pope and the League. | VVith most profitable aduises for the appeasing of schisme, | by abolishing superstition, and preseruing the | state of the Clergie. | Whereto is adioyned a discourse vpon the death of the Duke | of Guise, prosecuting the argument of | the booke. | Dedicated to the King by Iohn Fregeuille of Gaut. | (device).

Imprinted at London by Richard Field, dwelling | in the Blacke Friers. | 1589. | 17.4x12.7cm. (7),90p.

L., A. Antimartinvs, | Sive | Monitio cuiusdam Londinensis ad | Adolescentes vtriúsque Academiæ, con- | tra personatum Quendam rabu- | lam, qui se Anglicè | Martin Marprelat, | Hoc est, | Martinum Μαστιγάρχον, ἢ μισάρχον vocat. . . . (3 lines; device)

> Londini, | Excudebant Georgius Bishop, | & Radulphus Newbery. | Anno Domini, | 1589. | 17.3x13.2cm. (1),60p.
> Camb.Univ.Cat.No.1717. Pierce,Introd.p.326. Signed A.L. at end.

LYLY, John? Pappe with an hatchet. | Alias, | A figge for my God sonne. | Or | Cracke me this nut. | Or | A Countrie cuffe, that is, a sound boxe of the | eare, for the idiot Martin to hold his peace, | seeing the patch will take no | warning. | VVritten by one that dares call a dog, a dog, | and made to preuent Martins dog daies. | Imprinted by Iohn Anoke, and Iohn Astile, for the | Bayliue of Withernam, cum priuilegio perennita- | tis, and are to bee sold at the signe of the | crab tree cudgell in thwack- | coate lane. | A sentence. | Martin hangs fit for my mowing. |

> Without place or date [1589.] 18.2x12.9cm. (1),4,(2,30)p.
> Anon. Pierce,Introd.p.328.

MAR-MARTINE, | I know not why a trueth in rime set out | Maie not as wel mar Martine and his mates, | As shamelesse lies in prose-books cast about | Marpriests, & prelates, and subvert whole states. | For where truth builds, and lying overthroes, | One truth in rime, is worth ten lies in prose. |

> Without imprint. [1589] 21.4x12.1cm. (4)fol.
> Pierce, Introd. p.326.

MARRE Mar-Martin: | Or | Marre-Martins medling, in a | manner misliked. | Martins vaine prose, Marr-Martin doth mislike, | Reason (forsooth) for Martin seekes debate: | Marre-Martin will not so; yet doth his patience strike: | Last verse, first prose, conclude in one selfe hate: | Both maintaine strife, vnfitting Englands state. | Martin, Marre-Martin, Barrow ioyned with Browne | Shew zeale: yet striue to pull Religion downe . | (device)

> Printed with authoritie. | [1589] 18x13.2cm (1,3)p.
> Pierce, Introd. p.328.

MARTIN JUNIOR. Theses Martinianae: | That is, | Certaine Demonstrative | Conclusions, sette downe and collected (as it | should seeme) by that famous and renowmed | Clarke, the reuerend Martin Marprelate the | great: seruing as a manifest and sufficient con- | futation of al that euer the Colledge of Cater- | caps with their whole band of Clergie-priests, | haue, or canbring for the defence of their am- | bitious and Antichristian Prelacie. | Pvblished And Set Foorth | as an after-birth of the noble Gentleman himselfe, by a | prety stripling of his, Martin Ivnior, and | dedicated by him to his good name and nuncka, Mai- | ster Iohn Kankerbury: Hovv the youngman came by | them, the Reader shall vnderstande sufficiently in the | Epilogue. In the meane time, vvhosoeuer can bring | mee acquainted vvith my father, Jle bee bounde hee | shall not loose his labour. |

Printed by the assignes of | Martin Iunior, without any pri- | uiledge of the Cater- | caps. | [1589]   14x8.8 cm.   (2,29)p.
Pierce, Introd, p. 285

MARTIN MARPRELATE. Hay any worke for Cooper: | Or a briefe Pistle directed by waye of an | hublication to the reuerende Byshopps, counselling | them, if they will needs be barrelled vp, for feare of smelling | in the nostrels of her Maiestie & the State, that they would | vse the aduise of reuerend Martin, for the prouiding of their | Cooper. Because the reuerend T.C. (by which misticall | letters, is vnderstood, eyther the bounsing Par- | son of Eastmeane, or Tom Coakes his | Chaplaine) to bee an vnskil- | full and a deceytfull | tub-trimmer. | Wherein worthy Martin quits himselfe like a man | I warrant you, in the modest defence of his selfe and his | learned Pistles, and makes the Coopers hoopes | to flye off, and the Bishops Tubs to | leake out of all crye. | Penned and compiled by Martin the Metropolitane. |

Printed in Europe, not farre from some | of the Bounsing Priestes. | [1589] 17.7x13.8cm.   (10),48p.   Pp. 47–48 supplied.
Pierce, Tracts, p.211. Reprinted in 1641 as Reformation No Enemie.
All of the Martinist tracts were denounced, and probably burned, in consequence of a proclamation of Queen Elizabeth, issued Feb. 12, 1589–90.

MARTIN MARPRELATE. The Protestatyon | Of Martin Marprelat | Wherin not with standing the sur- | prizing of the printer, he maketh it | known vnto the world that he fear | eth, neither proud priest, Antichri | stian p ope, tiranous prellate, nor | godlesse catercap: but defiethe all | the race of them by these presents | and offereth conditionally, as is | farthere expressed herein by open | disputation to appear in the defence | of his caus aginst them and | theirs | Which chaleng if they dare not | maintaine aginst him: then doth he al- | soe publishe that he never meaneth by | the assistaunce of god to leaue the assayl- | ing of them and theire generation vn- | till they be vterly extinguished | out of our church | Published | by the worthie gentleman D martin mar | prelat D. in all the faculties primat and | metropolitan |

Without imprint.   [1589]   13.4x8.9cm.   32p.
Pierce, Introd. p.383

MARTIN SENIOR. The iust censure and reproofe | of Martin Iunior. | Wherein the rash and vndiscreete hea- | dines of the foolish youth, is sharp- | ly mette with, and the boy hath his | lesson taught him, I warrant you, by | his reuerend and elder brother, Mar- | tin Senior, sonne and heire vnto the | renowmed Martin Mar-prelate the | Great. | Where also, least the springall shold | be vtterly discouraged in his good | meaning, you shall finde, that hee | is not bereaued of his due | commendations. |

No imprint.   [1589]   13.8x9.1cm.   (1),30p.

NASH, Thomas ? A | Countercuffe giuen to | Martin Iunior: by the venturous, | hardie, and renowned Pasquill of Eng- | lande, Caualiero. | Not of olde Martins making, which newlie knighted | the Saints in Heauen, with rise vppe Sir Peter and Sir Paule; | But latelie dubd for his seruice at home in the defence of his | Countrey, and for the cleane breaking of his | staffe vpon Martins face. | (ornament)

Printed between the skye and the | grounde, wythin a myle of an Oake, and not manie | Fieldes off, from the vnpriuiledged Presse of | the Ass-ignes of Martin | Junior. | [1589]. 16.8x12.2cm. (4)fol.
Anon. Pierce, Introd. p.327.

RYTHMES | against Martin | Marre-Prelate. | (device) Ordo Sacerdotum fatuo turbatur ab omni, | Labitur & passim Religionis honos. |

Without imprint. [1589] 16.6x12.4cm. (1),3–7p.
From the same type as A Whip for an Ape: or Martin displaied. Pierce, Introd p.327.

SOME, Robert. A | Godly Trea- | tise, Wherein Are | Examined And Confv- | ted many execrable fancies, giuen out and | holden, partly by Henry Barrow and Iohn | Greenewood: partly, by other of the | Anabaptistical order. | Written by Robert Some Doctour | of Diuinitie. | . . . (4 lines ; device).

Imprinted At London | by G.B. Deputie to Christopher Barker, Prin- | ter to the Queenes most excellent Maiestie. | 1589. | 18.3x13.2cm. (8),40p.

THROKMORTON, Job. M. Some laid open in his coulers: | VVherein The Indiffe- | rent reader may easily see, hovve vvretchedly and loosely he hath handeled | the cause against M. Penri. | Done by an Oxford man, to his | friend in Cambridge. | . . . (7 lines).

N.p.n.d. [1589?] 14.3x9.8 cm. (4),124p.
Anon. Pierce, Introd., p.235. Signed I.G. at end.

UDALL, John. The Combate | betweene Christ, and | the Deuill. | Foure Sermons vpon the temptati- | ons of Christ in the wildernes by Sa- | than: wherein are to be seene the subtile | sleights that the tempter vseth against the | children of God, and the meanes that | God hath appointed to resist him, | sanctified by our vse, in the | example of our Sauiour | Iesus Christ. | By Iohn Vdall, Preacher of the word of | God, at Kyngston vpon | Thames. | . . . (6 lines).

At London, | printed by Thomas Orwin, for Thomas | Man, and Thomas Gubbin. | 1589. | 13.8x9.cm. (10,140)p.

WRIGHT, Leonard. The Hunting of | Antichrist. | VVith a caueat to the contentious. | By Leonard Wright. | . . . (10 lines: device).

London | Imprinted by John Wolfe. | 1589. | 17.2x13.6 cm. (8),28p. Paging confused.

WRIGHT, Leonard. A Summons for | Sleepers. | Wherein most grieuous and notorious | offenders are cited to bring forth true frutes | of repentance, before the day of the Lord | now at hand. | Hereunto is annexed, A Patterne for Pastors, | deciphering briefly the dueties pertaining to | that function, by Leonard Wright. | Newly reprinted, corrected and amended. | . . . (6 lines ; device).

1589. | 17.6x13.1cm.   (4),56p.   Title mounted.

1590

BABINGTON, Gervase. A | Verie fruitefull | Exposition of the Com- | mandements by way of Que- | stions and Answers for | greator plainnesse: | Together with an application of | euery one to the soule and conscience of | man, profitable for all, and especially for them | that (being not otherwise furnished) are yet | desirous both to see themselues, and to | deliuer to others some larger speech | of euerie point that is but | briefely named in the | shorter Cate- | chismes. | By Geruase Babington. | Whereunto is newlie annexed a Table; con- | teyning the principall matters in this Booke. | . . . (4 lines).

Imprinted at London, by Thomas Orwin for | Thomas Charde. 1590. | 14.4x9.7 cm.   (39),457,(7)p.

BARROW, Henry and GREENWOOD, John. A Collection | Of certain Let- | ters And Conferences | Lately Passed Betvvixt Cer- | taine Preachers & Tvvo | Prisoners In The | Fleet. |

1590. | 17.6x12.5 cm.   (4),70 p.
Cf To the Reader.

BARROW, Henry and GREENWOOD, John. A Collection Of | Certaine Sclavnderovs | Articles gyuen out by the Bishops | against such faithfull Christians as they now vniustly | deteyne in their Prisons togeather with the an- | sweare of the saide Prisoners | therunto. | Also The Some Of Certaine | Conferences Had In The Fleete | according to the Bisshops bloudie Mandate | with two Prisoners there. |

1590. | 17.1x12.9cm.   (1,51,1)p.
Anon. Cambr.Univ.Cat:6506.

BARROW, Henry. A petition directed to her most excellent | Maiestie, wherein is deliuered | 1 A meane howe to compound the ciuill dis- | sention in the church of England. | 2.A proofe that they who write for Reformati- | on, do not offend against the stat.of 23. Eliz. | c.2.and therefore till matters be compoun- | ded, deserue more fauour. | . . . (5 lines). Herevnto is annexed: | Some opinions of such as sue for Reformation: By vvhich it maie appeare hovve vniustlie | they are slaundered by the Bishops,&c.pag,53.Togither vvith the Authours | Epistle to the Reader.Pag.58. | Also: | Certayne Articles vvherein is discouered the negligence of the Bishoppes, their Officialls, | Fauourers and Follovvers, in performance of sundrie Ecclesiasticall Statutes Lawes | and Ordinances Royall and Episcopall, published for the gouernement of the Church | of England, pag.60. | Lastlie: | Certayne Questions or Jnterrogatories dravven by a fauourer of Reformation, vvherein | he desireth to be resolued by the Prelates,pag.74. |

Without place or date.   [1590].   17.7x13.8cm.   83p.
Anon.Dexter:187.

BEZE, Théodore de. Tractatvs | Pivs Et Moderatvs | de vera Ex-communicatione, & | christiano Presbyterio, | iampridem pacis con-ciliandę causa, Cl. V. Th. Erasti | D. Medici centum manuscriptis thesibus | oppositus, & nunc primum, | cogente necessitate, | editus. | Theodoro Beza | Vezelio auctore. | (device)

Genevæ | Apud Ioannem le Preux. | M.D.XC. | 22.9x15.8 cm. (23),126p.

A BRIEFE Dis- | covery Of The | Vntrvthes And Slan- | ders (Against The Trve Go- | uernement of the Church of Christ) contained in a | Sermon, preached the 8. of Februarie 1588. by | D. Bancroft, and since that time, set forth in | Print, with additions by the said | Authour. | This Short Ansvver May | Serve For The Clearing Of | the truth, vntill a larger confutation of the | Sermon be published. | . . . (8 lines; device).

Without place or date. [1590] 17.8x13.5 cm. (5),56 p.
Usually ascribed to John Penry. Trin.Col.Camb. No.926. Pierce,Introd.p.176.

COTTON, Roger. A | Direction to the wa- | ters of lyfe. | Come and beholde, | How Christ shineth before the | Law, in the Law, and in the Pro- | phetes: and withall the iudgements | of God vpon all Nations for the | neglect of his holy worde, where- | in they myght haue seene the | same: Both which are | layde before your | eyes in this litle | discourse, by | Roger Cotton | Draper. |

Imprinted at London, for | Gabriell Simson and William White, | and are to be solde at their | house in Fleete lane. | 1590. | (Ornam. border) 17.5x12.7cm. (3),51fol.

DAVIDSON, John. D. Bancrofts Rashnes | In Rayling | Against The Chvrch | Of Scotland, Noted In | An Answere To A Letter | of a worthy person of England, and | some reasons rendred, why the | an-swere thereunto hath | not hitherto come | foorth. | By I. D. a brother of the sayd | Church of Scotland. | Ex Mvltis Pavca. | (device).

At Edinburgh | Printed By Robert VVal- | de-Grave. Anno. 1590. | 13.5x9.cm. (1,30)p
Cambr.Univ.Cat:5924. Suppressed by order of James VI. DNB. 14: 126b.

DERING, Edward. XXVII. | Lectvres, | or readings, vpon | part of the Epistle | written to the | Hebrues. | Made by Maister Edward | Deering, Bachelour of | Diuinitie. |

At London, | Printed for Thomas | Woodcocke. | Anno. 1590. | Arch. border. 18.x12.7cm. (8,416)p
Included in his Workes:1597.

DIGBY, Everard. Everard Digbie | his Disuasiue. | From taking away the lyuings | and goods of the Church. | Wherein all men may plainely behold | the great blessings which the Lord | hath powred on all those who | liberally haue bestowed on his ho- | ly Temple: And the strange | punishments that haue be- | fallen them vvhich haue | done the contrarie. | Hereunto is annexed Celsus of Verona, | his Disuasiue translated into English. | . . . (1 line).

Printed by Robert Robinson, | and Thomas Nevvman. | [1590?] Arch. border. 18.3x12.8cm.(12), 242p.

GIFFORD, George. A | Plaine Declaration | that our Brownists be full Dona- | tists, by comparing them together | from point to point out of the wri- | tings of Augustine. | Also a replie to Master Greenwood touching | read prayer, wherein his grosse ignorance is de- | tected, which labouring to purge himselfe | from former absurdities, doth plunge | himselfe deeper into the mire. | By George Gyffard Minister of Gods word | in Maldon. | (device).

At London, | Printed for Toby Cooke, dwelling at the Tygers head | in Paules Churchyard. 1590. | 18.2x12.6cm. (16),126p.

GIFFORD, George. A | Short Treatise | against the Donatists of England, | whome we call Brownists. | Wherein, by the Answeres vnto certayne Writings | of theyrs, diuers of their heresies are noted, | with sundry fantasticall | opinions. | By George Giffard, Minister of Gods holy Word | in Maldon. | (device)

At London | Printed for Toby Cooke, dwelling at the Tygers head | in Paules Churchyard. 1590. | 18.2x13.6 cm. (11),110p. Colophon: Printed by Iohn VVindet, etc.

GREENWOOD, John. An Avnsvver To | George Giffords | Pretended Defence | Of Read Prayers And Devi- | sed Leitourgies with the vngodly cauils and | vvicked sclanders comprised in the first | part of his book entituled, A Short | Treatise against the Donatists | of England. | By Iohn Greenwood | Christs Poore Afflicted | prisoner in the Fleete at London, for | the trueth of the gospel. | (device).

[Dort.] 1590. | 18.1x13.5 cm. (1),8,3–66p.

JAMES, William. A Sermon | Preached At Pavles | Crosse The IX. Of | November, | 1589. | By | William Iames D. of Diuini- | tie, and Deane of Christes-church | in Oxford. | . . . (14 lines).

Imprinted At London | by George Bishop and Ralph | Newberie. | 1590. | 18.4x 13.9cm. (7,51)p.

L'ALOUETTE, Edmond de. A Catholicke | Apologie A- | gainst The Libels, De- | clarations, Advices, And | Consvltations Made, Written, | and published by those of the League, perturbers | of the quiet Estate of the Realme of France. | Who are risen since the decease of the late | Monsier, the Kings onely brother. | By E. D. L. I. C. | . . . (2 lines: device).

Imprinted at London for Edward Aggas. | [1590]. 14.4x9.5 cm. (7),149fol. Fol. 90–99 repeated; making 149 altogether.
Camb.Univ.Cat:1846. ascribes to Pierre de Belloy.

MARTIN, Anthony. A | Reconcili- | ation Of All | the Pastors and Cleargy | of this Church of | England. | By Anthony Marten, Sewer of her Maiesties | most honorable Chamber. | . . . (3 lines).

Printed at London by John Windet. 1590. | 18.2x12.4 cm. (7),108fol.
Title page torn and imprint supplied.

MORICE, James. A briefe treatise of Oathes exacted | by Ordinaries and Ecclesiasticall Iudges, | to answere generallie to all such

Articles | or Interrogatories, as pleaseth them to | propound. And of
their forced and con- | strained Oathes ex officio, wherein is proued
that | the same are vnlawfull. |
   Without imprint. [1590?] 18.5x13.6cm 58p.
   Anon. H&L. Camb.Univ.Cat.6796.

PENRY, John. An | Hvmble Mo- | tion VVith Svb- | mission Vnto
The Right | Honorable LL. Of Hir Ma- | iesties Privie Covnsell. |
VVherein Is Laid Open To | be considered, how necessarie it were |
for the good of this Lande, and the Queenes Ma- | jesties safety, that
Ecclesiasticall discipline were | reformed after the worde of God:
And | how easily there might be pro- | vision for a learned | Minis-
tery. | . . . (8 lines; device).
   Anno 1590. | 18.3x13.7 cm. 111p.
   Anon. Trin.Col.Camb. No.925.

PENRY, John. A Treatise | Wherein Is Ma- | nifestlie Proved,
That | Reformation And Those | that sincerely fauor the same, | are
vnjustly charged to be enemies, | vnto hir Maiestie, and | the state. |
Written Both For The | clearing of those that stande in that | cause:
and the stopping of the sclaunde- | rous mouthes of all the ene- | mies
thereof. | Zephaniah 3. (3 stars) . . . (10 lines).
   1590. | Lace border. 17.3x13.1 cm. (12,60)p.
   Anon. Trin.Col.Camb. No.924.

RAINOLDS, William. De Ivsta | Reipvb. Christianæ | In Rrges
Impios Et Hae- | reticos authoritate: | Iustissimáque Catholicorum ad
Henricum | Nauarræum & quemcunque hæreticum | à regno Galliæ
repellendum | confœderatione, | Liber. | Cuius particularia capita vide |
post præfationem. | (device).
   Parisiis, | Apud Guilielmum Bichonium, via | Iacobæa sub signo Hinnulei. |
M.D.LXXXX. | Cvm Privilegio Regis. | 17.2x10.7cm. (12),532,(14)fol.
   Anon. Gillow,V:410. B.M.Cat. sub Rossaeus, G. Guilelmus.

A REMONSTRANCE: | Or | Plaine Detection | Of Some Of The
Favlts | And Hideovs Sores Of Svch | Sillie Syllogismes And Imper- |
tinent Allegations, As Ovt Of | sundrie factious Pamphlets and
Rhapsodies, are | cobled vp together in a Booke, | Entituled, | A
Demonstration Of Discipline: | Wherein also, | The true state of the
Controuersie of most | of the points in variance, is (by the | way)
declared. | . . . (12 lines).
   Imprinted at London by George | Bishop and Rafe Newberie. | An. Domini
1590. | 17.3x13.3 cm. (12),210,(1)p.
   Camb.Univ.Cat. No. 1725

ROGERS, Thomas. A Sermon | vpon the 6.7. and 8. Verses of | the
12. Chapter of S. Pauls Epistle | vnto the Romanes; | Made to the
Confutation of so much of an- | other Sermon, entituled, A Frutful
Sermon &c. | as concerneth both the depriuation of | the præsent
gouerment, and the perpetual, | and vniforme regiment of | our
Church | By certaine their described Officers to | be in euerie par-

ticular Parish | through-out al her Ma- | iesties Dominions; | More fullie penned, than could by | mouth be expressed, the tyme | limitted to the speaker being | verie short. | Published at the request of certaine frendes by | Thomas Rogers. | Allowed by Auctoritie. | . . . (3 lines).

Printed by Iohn Windet, | 13. April. 1590. | 19.2x13.9 cm. (4),62p.

S., C. A | Briefe resolution of a | right Religion. | Tovching The Con- | trouersies, that are nowe in | England. | Written by C. S. | (device).

London. | Printed by Roger Ward, for Iohn Proctor, | and are to be sold at his shop vpon | Holborne Bridge. | 1590. | Lace border 17.1x12.7 cm. (8),32p.
Possibly by Christopher Shute: DNB.52.

SARAVIA, Hadrian. De | Diversis Ministro- | rvm Evangelii Gra- | dibvs, Sicvt A Domino | fuerunt instituti, & traditi ab Aposto- | lis, ac perpetuo omnium Ecclesiarum | vsu confirmati, liber vnus: | Cvi | Duo alij additi, alter de Honore qui debe- | tur Ecclesiarum Pastoribus, alter de | Sacrilegijs & Sacrilegorum | pœnis. | Authore Hadriano Saravia | Belga. | . . . (7 lines).

Londini | Excudebant Georgivs Bishop | & Rodolphvs Newberie. | An. Domini. | 1590. | 19.3x13 cm. (20),(4) 5–170p.

SUTCLIFFE, Matthew. A Treatise Of | Ecclesiasticall | Discipline: | Wherein that confused forme of gouernment, | which certaine vnder false pretence, and title of | reformation, and true discipline, do striue | to bring into the Church of England, | is examined and confuted. | By Matth.Svtcliffe. | . . . (10 lines).

At London | Printed by George Bishop and | Ralph Newberie. | Anno 1590. | Colophon: Imprinted at London by George | Bishop, and Ralph Newberie. | 1591. | 19.3x13.9cm. (13),231p. Impf to p 2. and after p. 226. T.p. supplied.

The | TREASVRE | of the Soule. | Wherein wee are taught how | in dying to Sinne, we may attaine | to the perfect loue of God, | and our Neighbour, and conse- | quently vnto true blessed- | nes and saluation. | Many yeares since written in the | Spanish tongue, and now newly | translated into English. | By A(drian) P(oyntz) | I. Timot. 1 . . . (7 lines).

London | Printed by John Wolfe. | 1590. | Colophon: At London | Printed by Ed- | ward Allde for | Edward White, and | are to be solde at the | little North doore of S. | Paules Church at the | signe of the | Gun. | 12.9x7 cm. (6),179p.

WHITAKER, William. Dispvtatio | De Sacra | Scriptvra; | Contra Hvivs Tem- | poris Papistas, Inprimis | Robertvm Bellarminvm Iesuitam, Pontificium | in Collegio Romano, & Thomam Stapletonvm, | Regium in Schola Duacena Controuer- | siarum Professorem: | Sex Qvaestionibus Proposita | & tractata à Gvilielmo Whitakero Theologiæ | Doctore ac Professore Regio, & Collegij D. | Ioannis in Cantabrigiensi Academia | Magistro. | . . . (4 lines; device)

Herbornæ | Typis Christophori Coruini. | M D XC. | 16.9x10.8cm. (26),811, (23)p. Colophon; device.

WILLET, Andrew. De | Vniversali | Et Novissima Iv- | dæorvm Voca- | tione, Secvndvm A- | pertissimam Divi Pauli propheti- | am, in vltimis hisce diebus | præstanda Liber vnus. | Vbi demonstratur, tum quem in modum | illius gentis conversio expectanda sit, tum quid eam | maximè adhuc impediat & remoretur, & | alia explicantur quæ ad huius | rei cognitionem necessaria | videri possint. | . . . (4 lines; device).

Ex officina Johannis Legati Canta- | brigiensis Typographi. 1590. | 18.1x14.cm. (4),(1–8),12–37fol. Misnumberings.
Epistola dedicatoria, signed.

1591

ARTICLES To | be enquired in the visi- | tation, in the first yeare of | the raigne of our moste | dread Soueraigne Ladie | Elizabeth, by the grace | of God, of Eng- | land, | Fraunce, and Irelande, | Queene, defender of | the faith, &c. |

Anno domini. 1591. | Colophon: Imprinted At London | by the Deputies of Christopher | Barker, printer to the Queenes | Maiestie. | Cum priuilegio Regiæ Maiestatis. | 18x14.1 cm. (13)p.

BARNE, Thomas. A | Sermon Prea- | ched At Pavls Crosse | The Thirteenth Of Ivne, the Se- | cond sunday in Trinitie tearme 1591. by | Thomas Barne student in Diuinity. | . . . (8 lines; device).

Printed at Oxford by Joseph Barnes, Printer to the | Vniuersitie. 1591. | 17.7x 13.7cm. (6,1–26)p. In fours, A–D4. Impf. at end.
Cf. Madan: Oxford Press: 1591(1).

BÈZE, Théodore de. Propositions | And Principles | of Diuinitie, propounded and | disputed in the vniuersitie of | Geneua, by certaine students of Di- | uinitie there, vnder M. Theod. | Beza, and M. An- | thonie | Faivs, professors of | Diuinitie. | Wherein Is Con- | tained a Methodicall sum- | marie, or Epitome of the common | places of Diuinitie. | Translated Ovt Of | Latine into English, to the end that | the causes, both of the present dangers | of that Church, and also of the trou- | bles of those that are hardlie dealt | vvith els-vvhere, may appeare in the | English tongue. |

At Edinbvrgh | Printed by Robert Walde- | graue, printer to the Kings | Maiestie. | Anno Dom. 1591. | Cum Priuilegio Regali. | 18.3x13.6 cm. (12),274, (2)p. Paging at end, incorrect.

BROUGHTON, Hugh. Textes | of Scripture, | Chayning the holy | Chronicle vntyll the | Sunne lost his lyght, | and the Sonne brake | the Serpentes head: | dying, rising, and | ascending. | (device, 3 lines).

Imprinted at London, | for Gabriell Simson and W.White: | and are to be solde at their | house in Fleete lane. | 1591. | Engr. border. 18.x14.cm. (6,14)p.
Cf.Cambr.Univ.Cat.2319. To the Christian Reader, signed H.B.

GIFFORD, George. A short Reply vn- | to the last printed books | of Henry Barrow and Iohn | Greenwood, the chiefe ring- | leaders of our Donatists | in England: | VVherein is layd open their grosse |

ignorance, and foule errors: | vpon which their whole buil- | ding is founded. | By George Gyfford, Minister of Gods holy | worde, in Maldon. |

<small>Imprinted at London by | Thomas Orwin, for Tobie | Cooke: and are to be solde | at the Tygers head, in | Pauls Churchyard. | 1591. | Ornam. border. 18.3x 13cm. (6),98p.</small>

JEWEL, John. Apologia | Ecclesiæ | Anglicanæ. | Authore Iohanne Iuello, olim | episcopo Sarisburiensi. | . . . (5 lines; device).

<small>Londini, | Impensis Thomæ | Chardi. 1591. | 11.9x6.3 cm (5),197;107,(5)p.
Appended is: Vincentii | Lirinensis | Galli Pro Catho- | licæ Fidei Antiqvi- | tate & veritate, aduersus prophanas | omnium hæreseon nouationes, | Libellus verè aureus: Nunc | primum per Capita | distinctus. | (device). Excusum. 1591. |</small>

PERKINS, William. A Golden Chaine, | Or | The Descripti- | on of Theologie, containing the | order of the causes of Saluation and | Damnation, according to Gods | woord. A view of the order wherof, | is to be seene in the Table | annexed. | Written in Latin by William Perkins, and | Translated by an other. | Hereunto is adioyned the Order | which M. Theodore Beza vsed in | comforting troubled con- | sciences.

<small>At London | Printed by Edward Alde, and | are to sold by Edward White, at | the little North doore of S. Paules | Church at the signe of the | Gunne. 1591. | 15.3x9.5 cm. (4 , 329) p.</small>

RHEGIUS, Urbanus. The | Solace of Sion, and Ioy of | Jervsalem: | Or consolation of Gods Church in the | latter age, redeemed: by the preaching of the | Gospell vniuersallie. | Beeing a Godly and learned exposition of the | Lxxxvij. Psalme of the Princelie Prophet | Dauid: VVritten in Latine by the reuerend | Doctor Vrbanus Regius, Pastor of | Christes Church at Zella in | Saxonie. 1536. | Translated into English by Richard | Robinson Cittizen of | London. | 1587. | . . . (6 lines).

<small>At London, | Printed by Richard Iones. | 1591. | 14.2x8.7 cm. (8 , 72)p.</small>

SPARK, Thomas. An Answere To Ma- | ster Iohn De Albines, | Notable Discovrse Against | heresies (as his frendes call his booke) | compiled by Thomas Spark pastor | of Blechley in the County of Buck. | . . . (6 lines; coat of arms).

<small>Printed at Oxforde by Ioseph Barnes, Printer | to the Vniversitie. 1591. | 19x14.3cm. (76),426,(5)p.</small>

URSINUS, Zacharias. The Svmme | Of Christian | Religion: | De- livered by Zacharias Vrsinvs in | his Lectures vpon the Catechisme, authori- | sed by the noble Prince Fredericke | throughout his Do- minions. | Wherein are debated and resolved the Questions | of what- soever points of moment, which haue beene | or are controversed in Divinity. | Translated into English, by Henry Parry, out of the last and | best Latine Editions, together with some supplie of | wants out of his Discourses of Divinity, and with correction | of sundry faults

& imperfections, which are | as yet remaining in the best | corrected Latine. | (device).

At Oxford, | Printed by Ioseph Barnes, and are to bee solde in | Paules-Church- yeard at the signe of the Ty- | greshead. 1591. | 16.9x10.7cm. (15),966,(9)p.

1592

BABINGTON, Gervase. Certaine Plaine, | briefe, and comfortable | Notes vpon euerie Chapter | of Genesis. | Gathered And Laid Downe | for the good of them that are not able to vse better | helpes, and yet carefull to reade the worde, | and right heartilie desirous to taste | the sweete of it. | By the Reuerend Father Geruase | Babington, Bishop of | Landaph. | . . . (6 lines; device).

London | Printed for Thomas Charde, 1592, | 18.8x13.9cm. (4),192fol.

BROUGHTON, Hugh. An | Apologie | In Briefe Asser- | tions Defending That | our Lord died in the time proper- | ly foretold to Daniel. | For satisfaction of some studentes in | both Vniuersities. | H.Brovghton. | (ornament).

London, | Imprinted by VVilliam Kearney | dwelling within Creeple-gate. | 1592. | 18.6x13.8cm. (6,78)p.

COSIN, Richard. Conspiracie, | for Pretended Reformation: | viz. | Presbyteriall Discipline. | A Treatise discouering the late designments and courses | held for aduancement thereof, by William Hacket Yeo- | man, Edmund Coppinger, and Henry Arthington | Gent. out of others depositions and their | owne letters, writings & confes- | sions vpon examination: | Together | With some part of the life and conditions, and the two | Inditements, Arraignment, and Executi- | on of the sayd Hacket: | Also | An answere to the calumniations of such as affirme they | were mad men: and a resemblance of this acti- | on vnto the like, happened here- | tofore in Germanie. | Vltimo Septembris 1591. | . . . (6 lines). Published now by authoritie. |

Imprinted at London by the Deputies of | Cristopher Barker, Printer to | the Queenes most excellent Maiestie. | Anno Domini. | 1592. | 17.1x12 cm. (12),102p. Page 36 repeated in numbering.

Anon. Cambr. Univ. Cat. 1693

COTTON, Roger. A | Direction to the Wa- | ters of lyfe. | Come and beholde, | How Christ shineth before the Law, | in the Law, and in the Prophetes: | and withall the iudgementes of God | vpon all Nations for the neglect of | his holy worde, wherein they might | haue seene the same: Both which | are layde before your | eyes in this litle dis- | course, by | R.C. |

Imprinted at London, for | Gabriell Simson and William White: | and are to be solde by William | Barley, dwelling at the vp- | per ende of Gratious | streete. 1592. | Border. 18.3x13.6 cm. (3),51fol. Colophon.

Dedication to Hugh Broughton, signed.

HILL, Adam. The | Defence Of | the Article: | Christ descended into Hell. | With Arguments obiected against | the truth of the same doctrine: of one | Alexander Humes. | All which reasons are confuted, and the same doctrine | cleerely defended. | By Adam Hyll, D. of Diuinity. | . . . (1 line; device).

At London | Printed for William Ponsonbie. 1592. | 18.6x13.9 cm. (3),66fol. Incorrectly numbered 70:fol.53–56, omitted; several folios misnumbered.

JUNIUS, Franciscus. Apocalypsis. | A Briefe And | Learned Commentarie | Vpon The Revelation Of Saint | Iohn the Apostle and Euangelist, applyed vnto the history | of the Catholicke and Christian Church. | Written in Latine by M. Francis Ivnivs Doctor of Diuinitie, | and professor in the Vniuersitie of Heidelberge: | And translated into English for the benefit of those that | vnderstand not the Latine. | . . . (4 lines: device).

Imprinted at London by Richard Field for Robert Dexter, dwel- | ling in Paules Church yard at the signe of the | brasen serpent. 1592. | 14.4x9.5 cm. (18),88 p.

L'ESPINE, Jean de. A Very Excel- | lent And Lear- | ned Discovrse, | touching the Tranquilitie and Con- | tentation of the minde: | Conteining | Svndry Notable In- | strvctions, And Firme | Consolations, most necessarie for all sortes | of afflicted persons in these | latter dayes. | Distinguished in seven Bookes, | 1.Against Covetousnes. | 2.Against Ambition. | 3.Against Anger. | 4.Against Envie. 5. Against Pleasure. | 6.Against Curiositie. | 7.Against Feare. | Written in French By The Fa- | mous and learned M.I. Del'Espine, and new- | ly translated into English by Ed.Smyth. |

Printed by John Legate, Printer to the | Vniuersitie of Cambridge. 1592. | And are to be solde at the signe of the Sunne in Paules | Church-yarde in London. | 19.8x14.3cm. (11),1–199,101–106fol.

PARSONS, Robert. The | Second part of the Booke | of Christian exercise, apper- | tayning to Reso- | lution. | Or | A Christian directory, guiding | all men vnto theyr sal- | uation. | VVritten by the former Au- | thour. R. P. | . . . (6 lines).

At London, | Printed by Iohn Charle- | wood for Simon Waterson, in | S.Paules Church-yarde, at | Cheape-gate. | 1592. | 12.5x7cm. (32),527p.
Gillow.V:278.

SARAVIA, Hadrian. D. | Saravia. | I. | Of the diuerse degrees of the Ministers of the | Gospell. | 2. | Of the honor vvhich is due vnto the Priestes | and Prelates of the Church. | 3. | Of Sacrilege, and the punishment thereof. | The particular Contents of the aforesaide Treatises | to be seene in the next Pages. | . . . (5 lines; device).

London. | Printed by Iohn VVolfe, and are to be | sold by Iohn Perin at the signe of the Angell | in Paules Church-yard. | 1592. | 18.5x14.4cm. (39),240p.

STAPLETON, Thomas. Apologia | Pro Rege Catholico Philippo II. | Hispaniæ, & cæt. Rege. | Contra varias & falsas accusationes | Elisabethæ Angliæ Reginæ. | Per Edictum suum 18. Octobris Richemondiæ | datum, & 20. Nouembris Londini procla- | matum, publicatas & excusas. | In qua omnium turbarum & bellorum quibus- | cum his annis 30. Christiana Respub. con- | flictatur, fontes aperiuntur, & remedia de- | monstrantur. | Avthore Didymo Veridico | Henfildano. | (device).

Constantiæ, | Apud Theodorum Samium. | [1592]. 15.5x9.7cm. (16),275,(13)p. Anon. Gillow,V:528.

STAPLETON, Thomas. Avthori- | tatis Ecclesia- | sticæ Circa S.Scriptv- | rarvm Approbationem, | Adeoqve In Vniversvm, Lv- | culenta & accurata Defensio Li- | bris III, digesta. | Contra Dispvtationem De | Scriptura Sacra Guilielmi VVhitakeri Anglocaluinistæ | in Academia Cantabrig. Professoris Regij. | Authore D.Thoma Stapletono Anglo S. | Theologiæ Doctore & in Academia Louaniensi | S. Script. Professore Regio. | . . . (5 lines; device)

Antverpiæ | Apud Ioannem Keerbergium. | Anno M. D. XCII. | Cum Priuilegio Senatus Brabantiæ ad sexennium. | 16.6x10.3 cm. 812,(21)p.

SUTCLIFFE, Matthew. An | Answere To | A Certaine Libel | Svpplicatorie, Or Rather | Diffamatory, and also to certaine Calumnious | Articles, and Interrogatories, both printed and scattered | in secret corners, to the slaunder of the Ecclesiasticall | state, and put forth vnder the name | and title of a Petition di- | rected to her | Maiestie: | Wherein not onely the friuolous dis- | course of the Petitioner is refuted, but also the | accusation against the Disciplinarians his clyents | iustified, and the slaunderous cauils at the present | gouernement disciphred by | Mathew Sutcliffe. | . . (6 lines).

Imprinted at London by the Depvties | of Christopher Barker, Printer | to the Qveenes most ex- | cellent Maiestie. 1592 | 18.3x13.3cm. (18),208,(5)p.

VERSTEGEN, Richard. Theatrvm | Crudelitatum Hæreticorum | Nostri Temporis. |

Antverpiæ. | Apud Adrianum Huberti, | Anno M.D.XCII. | Cum Priuilegio. | 20.9x16.cm. 95p. Engraved t.p.
Contains a section entitled: Inqvisitionis | Anglicanæ | Et | Facinorvm Crvdelivm | Machiavellanorvm In An- | glia Et Hibernia A Calvini- | stis Protestantibvs, Svb Eli- | zabetha etiamnum regnante peracto- | rum, Descriptiones. |
Dedication signed.

ZANCHI, Hieronymus. An Excel- | lent And Lear- | ned Treatise, of the spirituall | mariage betvveene Christ | and the Church, and every | faithfull man. | Written In Latine | by that famous and worthie mem- | ber of Christ his Church | H. Zanchivs: | and translated into English. | Cant. 8. 6. | . . . (2 lines)

Printed By Iohn Legate, | Printer to the Vniversitie of Cambridge. | 1592 | (Border). 14.6x9.6 cm. (1),147p.

1593

An ACTE for the restrei- | ning of Popish Recusants to some cer- | taine places of aboade. | The ij Chapter. |

1593. Elizabeth, Q. [Statutes] Ann.35, fol.3-5.

BANCROFT, Richard. Davngerovs Po- | sitions And Procee- | dings, published and practised within this Iland | of Brytaine, vnder pretence of Reformation, and | for the Presbiteriall Discipline. | . . . (5 lines; device).

London | Imprinted by Iohn Wolfe. | 1593. | 17.9x13.6 cm.   (8),183p.
Anon. Cambr.Univ.Cat:1967.

BANCROFT, Richard. A Svrvay | Of The Pretended | Holy Discipline. | Contayning the beginninges, successe, parts, proceedings, | authority, and doctrine of it: with some of the ma- | nifold, and materiall repugnances, varie- | ties and vncertaineties, in that | behalfe. | Faithfully gathered, by way of historicall narration, out of the | bookes and writings, of principall fauourers of that platforme | Anno 1593. | . . . (4 lines; device).

Imprinted at London by Iohn Wolfe. 1593. | 18.8x13.4 cm.   (8),464,(1)p.
Anon.Cambr.Univ.Cat:1968.

BARROW, Henry. A petition directed to her most excellent | Maiestie, wherein is deliuered | 1 A meane howe to compound the ciuill dissention in | the church of Englande. | 2 A proofe that they who write for Reformation, doe | not offende against the stat. of 23. Eliz. c. and there- | fore till matters bee compounded, deserue more | fauour. | . . . (5 lines). | Herevnto is annexed | Some opinions of such as sue for Reformation: By vvhich it may appear hovve vniustlie | they are slaundered by the Bishops, &c. pag. 53. Togither vvith the Authours | Epistle to the Reader. pag. 58. | Also: | Certayne Articles vvherein is discouered the negligence of the Bishops, their Officials, | Fauourers and Follovvers, in performance of sundrie Ecclesiasticall Statutes, Lawes, | and Ordinances Royall and Episcopall, published for the gouuernement of the Church | of Englande, pag. 60. | Lastlie: | Certayne Questions or Interrogatories dravven by a fauourer of Reformation, vvherein | he desireth to be resolued by the Prelates, pag. 74. |

Without place or date. [1593].   17.2x13.9 cm.   83p.
No imprint.
Anon. D N B. 3: 298 a.   Cf.Cambr.Univ.Libr:7916.

BELL, Thomas. Thomas | Bels Motives: | Concerning | Romish Faith | And Religion. | . . . (1 line; device).

Printed by Iohn Legate, printer to the | Vniversitie of Cambridge. 1593. | And are to be sold at the signe of the Sunne in Paules | Churchyard in London. | 20.3x15.5cm.   (16),157,(2)p.

BILSON, Thomas. The Perpetval | Governement Of | Christes Chvrch. | Wherein are handled; | The fatherly superioritie which God first established in the Pa- | triarkes for the guiding of his Church, and after con- | tinued in the Tribe of Leui and the Prophetes; | and lastlie confirmed in the New Testa- | ment to the Apostles and their | successours: | As also the points in question at this day; | Touching the Iewish Synedrion: the true kingdome of Christ: the Apostles |

commission: the Laie Presbyterie: the Distinction of Bishops from Pres- | byters, and their succcssion from the Apostles times and hands: | the calling and moderating of Prouinciall Synodes by Pri- | mates and Metropolitanes: the allotting of Diœ- | ceses, and the Popular electing of such as | must feed and watch the flocke: | And diuers other points concerning the Pastorall regiment | of the house of God: By | Tho. Bilson Warden of Winche- | ster Colledge. | Perused and allowed by publike authoritie. | . . . (6 lines).

Imprinted at London by the Deputies | of Christopher Barker, Printer to | the Queenes most excellent Maiestie. | An.Dom.1593. | 19x13.6cm. (28),414,(1)p.

A BRIEFE aunswere to the principall pointes | in the Archbishops Articles. Also certayne reasons against | subscription to the booke of common prayers, and the | booke of articles, as followeth: Written about an̄. 1583. |

[1593]. Without t.p., pagination or register. 18.6x13.3cm. (6)p.
Appended to A parte of a register: 1593.

COSIN, Richard. An Apologie | For Svndrie | Proceedings | by Iurisdiction Ecclesiasticall, of late | times by some chalenged, and al- | so diuersly by them impugned. | By which Apologie (in their seuerall due places) all the Reasons and Allegations set | downe as well in a Treatise, as in certaine Notes (that goe from hand | to hand) both against proceeding ex Officio, and against Oaths | ministred to parties in causes criminall; are also | examined and answered: | Vpon that occasion lately reuiewed, and much enlarged aboue the first priuate proiect, | and now published, being diuided into three partes: the first part whereof chief- | lie sheweth what matters be incident to Ecclesiasticall conisance; and so | allowed by Statutes and Common law: the second treateth (for the | most part) of the two wayes of proceeding in causes Cri- | minal, viz. by way of Accusation, & ex officio Iudicis: | the third concerneth Oaths in generall, but | more specially the lawfulnesse of such as | be ministred touching supposed of- | fenses, either of themselues | that sweare, or of their | brethren: | Respectiuelie submitted to the graue iudgements of the reuerend Iudges and | other Sages of the Common lawe: of Iudicious Professors of the | Ciuill lawe: and of the right reuerend Prelates and other | grounded Diuines in this Realme. | Whereunto (for the learneds sake, and for similitude of Argument and Iudgement) | I haue presumed to adioine that right excellent and sound determina- | tion (concerning Oaths) which was made by M. Lance- | lot Androvves Doctor in Diuinitie, in | the common Diuinitie Schoole of the Vni- | uersitie of Cambridge in Iulie, | An.1591. | . . . (1 line).

Imprinted at London by the Depu- | ties of Christopher Bar- | ker, Printer to the Queenes most | excellent Maiestie. | 1593. | 18.8x13.6cm. (30),130,(10),140,(4),255,(1)p.

The Second and Third Parts have separate title-pages, without date; pagination distinct; register continuous in pts 1-2, but distinct in pt. 3.
Anon. Cambr.Univ.Libr:1696.

COVERDALE, Miles. Fruitfull Lessons, | Vpon The | Passion, Bv- | riall, Resvrrection, | Ascension, and of the sending of | the holy

Ghost. | Gathered Ovt Of The Fovre | Euangelists: with a plaine exposition | of the same. | By Miles Coverdall. | . . . (3 lines; device).

London | Printed by Thomas Scarlet. | 1593. | 16.8x12.6cm. (13,302)p. Top trimmed

ELISABETHEN | Der Königin inn En- | gellandt, vnd Irrlandt, &c. | Edict, | Den neun vnd zweyntzigisten Nouembris | dess fünfftzehenhundert ein vnd neuntzigsten | Jars zu Londra öffentlich publiciert. | Mit einer Erleutterung Andreæ Philopatri, darinnen | von jetzigem Verlauff vnd Zustandt der Cron Engel- | landt, Franckreich vnd Schotten, allerley | zufinden, sehr nutzlich vnd lu- | stig zulesen. | (device).

Getruckt im 1593. Jar. | 18.4x14.4 cm. (4),271p.

ELIZABETH, Queen [Statutes] Anno xxxv. Anno xxxv. Reginæ | Elizabethæ. | At the Parliament | begun and holden at Westminster | the xix. day of Februarie, in the | fiue and thirtieth yeere of the Reigne of | our most gracious Soueraigne Ladie | Elizabeth, by the grace of God of | England, France and Ireland Queene, | defender of the faith, &c. And there | continued vntill the dissoluti- | on thereof, being the | x. of Aprill, | To the high pleasure of Almightie God, | and the weale publique of this | Realme, were enacted | as followeth. |

Imprinted at London by the Deputies of | Christopher Barker, Prin- | ter to the Queenes most excel- | lent Maiestie. | 1593. | Engraved border. 27.x18.cm. (1,23) fol.

FRÉGEVILLE. Palma | Christiana, | Sev, | Speculum veri status Ecclesiastici, sub lege Naturæ, & lege Mo- | sis, & institutione Christi, & traditione Apostolorum, & | virorum Apostolicorum, | & consuetudine Primitiuæ Eccle- | siæ ab Apostolis ad Patres Nicenos, & inde apud Aphrica- | nos respuentes iugum Antichristi tempore Aureli Cartha- | ginensis, & Augustini Hipponensis. | Demonstrata iuxta septem canones; Apodicticum, analogicum, | harmonicum, æquitatis, spiritualem, iuris primæui, & iuris vni- | uersalis. Vnde verus typus Reformationis desumi potest, ex | antiquorum veritate potius depromendus, quam ex nouo- | rum authorum vanitate. | Ad serenissimam Reginam Angliæ. | Authore Frigeuillæo Gautio. | (device).

Londini, | Excudebat Iohannes Wolfius.1593. | 19.4x14.6cm. (15),151,(1)p. Mispaged.

L., A. Antjsandervs | Dvos Continens | Dialogos Non Ita Pri- | dem Jnter Vjros | quosdam doctos Venetijs ha- | bitos: | Jn quibus variæ Nicholaj Sanderi, | aliorumque Romanensium calumniæ in hæc | Anglorum ab excusso Pontifice tem- | pora vaferrimè confictæ, licèt | obitèr & fortuitò, verè ta- | men candidèque re- | felluntur. | . . . (3 lines; device).

Excusvm Cantabrigiæ | cum consensu Primariorum hominum quo- | rum authoritas chartâ Regiâ | ad hoc requiritur. | M.D.XCIII. | 18.8x13.6cm. (8),200p. Attributed to Dr.Court? and also to John Cowell. Dedication signed A.L.

PARSONS, Robert. Elizabethæ, | Angliæ Reginæ | Hæresin Calvinianam | Propvgnantis, Sævissimvm | in Catholicos sui regni Edictum, quod | in alios quóque Reipublicæ Chri- | stianæ Principes, contume- | lias continet indi- | gnissimas. | Promulgatum Londini 29. Nouembris. 1591. | Cum responsione ad singula capita, qua non tantùm sæuitia | & impietas tam iniqui Edicti, sed mendacia quóque, | & fraudes, & imposturæ deteguntur, | & confutantur. | Per D. Andream Philopatrum presbyterum, ac Theologum | Romanum, ex Anglis olim oriundum. | . . . (3 lines)

Lvgdvni, | Apvd Ioannem Didier. | M.D.X CIII. | 16.1x10.5 cm. (16),278,(14)p.
Anon. Gillow:V:279.

PARSONS, Robert. Elizabethae | Reginae | Angliae | Edictvm | Promulgatum Londini 29. Nouemb. | Anni M.D.XCI. | Andreae Philopatri | Ad Idem Edictvm | Responsio. | (device).

Excvsvm. M.D.XCIII. | 15 x9.6 cm. 361,(9)p.
Anon. Gillow:V:279.

PARSONS, Robert. Responce | A L'Inivste Et | Sangvinaire Edict | D'Elizabeth Royne | D'Angleterre. | Contre les Catholiques de son Royaume. | Publié à Londres le 29. Nouembre 1591. | En laquelle sont descouuertes & refutees les ca- | lomnies & impostures dont se seruent | les Heretiques contre les Princes | Protecteurs de la Religion | Catholique. | Traduicte du Latin d'André Philopatre | Prestre Theologien à Rome. | . . . (3 lines; device).

A Lyon | par Iean Pilehotte. | M.D.XCIII. | Auec permission. | 16.5x10.1 cm. (8),157,(5)fol.
Anon. Cf.Gillow:V:279.

A PARTE of a register, contayninge | sundrie memorable matters, written by | diuers godly and learned in our time, which stande | for, and desire the reformation of our Church, in | Discipline and Ceremonies, accordinge to | the pure worde of God, and | the Lawe of our | Lande. | . . . (8 lines). See the contentes of this Booke on the | next leafe. | (device).

No imprint. [1593] 18.6x13.3cm. (4),548;(6);86p. 2 leaves, A–Zzz1, in fours, with 1+4 leaves; A–L4 in fours, last leaf blank
Dexter, 188, dates [1590]

Contents: The Table. | A Comfortable epistle written by Mai.D.W.Do- | ctor of Diuinitie, fol. 1. | A godly and zealous letter written by Mai.Antony | Gilby, about anno 1570. fol. 12. | A Letter written by Mai.D.Pilkenton, about anno | 1570. fol. 19. | An examination of certayne Londonners before the | Commissioners, about anno 1567. fol. 23. | Certayne questions answered, touching the defence of | popishe ceremonies, anno 1570. fol. 37 | A viewe of Antichrist his lawes and ceremonies in | our Church vnreformed fol. 55 | Articles answered by Mai.Edm. Dering, anno | 1573 fol. 73 | Mai.Greneham, Minister of Drayton, his aun- | swere to the Bish. of Eley, fol. 86 | The Bishops proceedings against Maist.Robart | Johnson Preacher, who dyed in the gate 1573. fol. 94 | The exceptions of Mai. Nicolas Crane, Preacher: | against subscription, who died in Newgate, | anno 1588. fol. 119 | A letter sent from the Ministers of Scotlande, to | the Bishops of Englande, anno 1566 fol. 125 | A complaint presented to the right Hon. the Lords | of her Ma. priuie Counsell by the godly Min. fol. 128. | The answere to the complaint against the ill dispo- | sed whatsoeuer fol. 131 | A letter written to a Londoner, contayning an an- | swere to the Arch. articles at large, an. 1583 fol. 132 | A brief answere to the principall pointes of the | same articles, written an. 1583 fol. 201 | Certayne reasons against subscription to the booke | of common prayer | The complaint of the communaltie of Eng. 1586 fol. 201 | The vnlawfull practice of Prelates against the | godly Ministers fol. 280 | The humble petition of the communaltie to her | gracious Maiestie fol. 304 | A petition to the conuocation house, anno 1583. fol. 323 | The state of the Church of England laide open in | a conference fol. 333 | A pythie letter to the Bish. of Nor. 1576. by R.T. fo. 365 | A friendlie caueat to the Bishops, anno 1567 fol. 371 | The conference betweene some of the high Cōmis- | sioners, and Mai.Marbury, onno 1578 fol. 381 | The defence of the godly Ministers against D. | Bridges slaunders, by Ma.Dudley Fenner, fol. 387 | The troubles of Ma.Gawton Preacher in Norw. fol. 393 | The iudgement of certayne godly brethren vppon a | question propounded fol. 401 | Certayne reasons against the crosse in baptisme fol. 409 | Reasons against kneeling at Communion fol. 410 | The Counterpoyson fol. 412 | The certayne forme of ecclesiasticall gouernement, | prescribed by the worde of God, And perpe- | tuall fol. 421 | Election with consent of the people fol. 428 | Euery Minister ought to preach fol. 442 | Ministers falling to Jdolatrie, ought not to bee | receyued to the Ministrie fol. 455 | The authoritie of the Ministers fol. 461 | The office of the Doctor is ordinarie, perpetuall & | distinct from the Pastor fol. 470 | Of Elders and the Eldership fol. 474 | A reply to the variable collections, against Disci. fol. 480 | That part of D.Copquot his sermon which concer- | ned Discipline fol. 507 | Tho defence of the reasons of the Counterpoyson fol. 509 | A confession of the faith fol. 528 | A prayer for the faithfull fol. 547. |

Appended are A briefe aunswere to the principall pointes, p(6); and [J:Udall], A demonstration of the trueth of that Dis- | cipline: 86p.

Burned by the bishop of London, July 1593.

RHEGIUS, Urbanus. An | Homely or Sermon | of Good and Euill Angels: | preached by the Reuerend D, | Vrbanus Rhegius, Pastor and Su- | perintendent of Christes | Church, at Zella in | Saxony. Anno | 1537. | Translated into English by Ri: Ro- | binson, and then first Printd 1583. | Secondly printed 1590. And | lastly printed 1593. | . . . (6 lines). Seene, perused, and allowed. |

At London, | Printed by the VViddowe | Charlwood. 1593. | Lace border. 13.6x 8.6cm. (4),38,(2)fol.

SARAVIA, Hadrian. De | Imperandi | Avthoritate, | Et Christiana | Obedientia, | Libri Quatuor. | Authore Hadriano | Saravia. | . . . (3 lines ; device).

Londini | Excudebant Reg.Typog. | Anno salutis humanæ | M D XCIII. | 19x 14.6cm. (15),256p.

STAPLETON, Thomas. Promptvarivm | Morale | Svper Evangelia | Dominicalia | Totivs Anni: | Ad } Instructionem Concionatorum. | Reformationem Peccatorum. | Consolationem Piorum. | Ex Sacris Scripturis SS. Patribus, & optimis | quibusq[ue] authoribus studiosè collectum: | Authore Thoma Stapletono, Anglo; | S.Theol. Doctore, & Regio Professore Louanij. | Editio altera, ab ipso authore aucta & recognita. | Pars Hyemalis. | (et Æstivalis) . . . (2 lines; device)

Antverpiæ, | In Officina Plantiniana, | Apud Viduam, & Ioannem Moretum. | M.D.XCIII. | Cum gratia & priuilegio. | 17.5 x 11 cm. (39),750,(26) ;(16),640, (15) p. 2 pts

UDALL, John. A demonstration of the trueth of that Dis- | cipline which Christ hath prescribed in his worde for the | gouernment of his

Church, in all times and places, vntill | the end of the world. | Wherein are gathered into a plain forme of reasoning, the proofs | thereof out of the Scriptures, the euidence of it by the light of reason | rightlie ruled, and the testimonies that haue been giuen thereunto, by | the course of the Church certaine hundredths of yeares after the A- | postles time: and the generall consent of the Churches rightly re- | formed in these latter times: according as they are alleadged and | maintained, in those seuerall bookes that haue been vvritten concer- | ning the same. | . . . (6 lines)

Without t.p. [1593]. 18.6x13.3cm. 86p.
Appended to Parte of a register, [1593]
Anon. Cambr. Univ. Cat. 6807.

WILLET, Andrew. Tetrastylon | Papisticvm, | That is, | The Fovre Principal Pillers | of Papistrie, the first conteyning their raylings, slanders, | forgeries, vntruthes: the second their blasphemies, flat con- | tradictions to scripture, heresies, absurdities: the third their loose | arguments, weake solutions, subtill distinctions: the fourth | and last the repugnant opinions of New | Papistes | With the old; of the new one with an other; of the same writers | with themselues: yea of Popish religion with | and in it selfe. | Compiled as a necessarie supplement or fit appertinance to the | Authors former worke, intituled Synopsis Papismi: To the glorie of | God for the dissuading of lightminded men from trusting to the | sandie foundation of poperie, and to exhort good Christians | stedfastlie to hold the rockie foundation of | faith in the Gospell. | . . . (6 lines; device)

Printed by Robert Robinson for Thomas Man dwelling in | Pater noster row at the signe of the Talbot.1593. | 19.3x14.7 cm. (16),170p.
Epistle dedicatorie, signed,

1594

CLERKE, William. The Triall of Bastardie: | That Part Of The | second part of Policie, or maner of Gouerne- | ment of the Realme of England: so termed, Spiri- | tuall, or Ecclesiasticall. | Annexed at the end of this Treatise, touching | the prohibition of marriage, a Table of the Leuitical, | English, and Positiue Canon Catalogues, their | concordance and difference. | By William Clerke. | . . . (2 lines; device).

London, | Printed by Adam Jslip. | 1594. | 17.3x13.8 cm. (16),82,(22)p. 2 folded plates. Sub-title.

DANEAU, Lambert. A Frvitfvll Com- | mentarie vpon the twelue Small Prophets, | Briefe, Plaine, And Easie, Going | Over The Same Verse By Verse, And Shew- | ing euery where the Method, points of doctrine, and figures | of Rhetoricke, to the no small profit of all godly and well di- | sposed Readers, with very necessarie fore-notes for | the vnderstanding both of these, and also | all other the Prophets. | The text of these Prophets together with that of the quotations o- | mitted by the Author, faithfully supplied by the Translatour, and | purged of faults in the Latine coppie almost innumerable, with | a table of all the chiefe matters herein handled, and marginall | notes very plentifull and profitable; so that it may in manner be | counted a new Booke in regard of these additions. | VVritten in Latin by Lambertus Danæus, | and newly turned into English by Iohn Stockwood Mini- | ster and Preacher at Tunbridge. | . . . (3 lines; device).

Printed by Iohn Legate, Printer to | the Vniversitie of Cambridge. 1594. | And are to be sold at the signe of the Sunne in Paules Church- | yard in London. | 19.4x14.7cm. (13),1136,(8)p.

ELIZABETH, Queen. Advertisements | Partly for the due Order in the | Publick Administration | Of The | Holy Sacraments, | And partly for the | Apparel of all Persons Ecclesiastical, | By virtue of the Queens Majesties Letters com- | manding the same, the Twenty fifth day of | January, in the seventh year of the Reign of | our Soveraign Lady Elizabeth, by | the Grace of God, of England, France, and | Ireland Queen, Defender of the Faith, &c. | (device).

Londini, | Cum privilegio ad imprimendum solum. Anno Dom.1594. | Anno 7.Eliz.R. | Border. 22.6x16.5cm. Pp. 121–128 of Sparrow's Collections: 1675.

HOOKER, Richard. Of | The Lavves | of Ecclesiasticall | Politie. | Eyght Bookes. | By Richard Hooker. | (device).

Printed at London by Iohn Windet, dwelling at the signe of the | Crosse keyes neere Powles Wharffe, and are there | to be soulde. | [1594] 26. x17.9 cm. 209,(1)p.

Entered, Jan. 29, 1593 Contains also the Fifth Book: 1597.

LIBER | Precvm Pvb- | licarvm, Sev | Ministerii Ec- | clesiasticæ administra- | tionis Sacramen- | torum, | Aliorumque Rituum, & | Cæremoniarum, in | Ecclesia An- | glicana. |

Excusum Londini, per | assignationem Fran- | cisci Floræ. | Cvm Privilegio | Regiæ Maiestatis. | 1594. | Lace border Colophon: Londini | Excudebat Ioan. Iacksonus. | 1594 | 15.1x9.9 cm. (28),299fol.

MOREL, John. De | Ecclesia | Ab Antichristo | Liberanda, Ea- | que ex Dei promissioni- | bus reparanda: | Cui addita est ad calcem verissima, certis- | simaque ratio conciliandi dissidii de | Cœna Domini. | Avctore | Ioanne Morelio. | Ad Sereniss. potentiss. Angliæ, Franciæ, | Hiberniæ, &c. Reginam. | (device; frame only).

Londini | Apud Georgium Bischop. | M D X CIIII. | 15.8x9.9cm. (36),104p.

NAPEIR, John. A Plaine | Discoverie Of | The Whole Revelation Of | Saint Iohn: Set Down in Two | Treatises: The one searching and proving | the true interpretation thereof. The other | applying the same Paraphrastically | and Historicallie to the text. | Set Forth By John Napeir | L. of Marchistovn younger. | Wherevnto are Annexed Cer- | taine Oracles of Sibylla, agreeing | with the Revelation and other | places of Scripture. | Newlie Imprinted and corrected. | . . . (device).

Printed For John Norton Dwel- | ling in Paules Church-yarde, neere vnto | Paules Schoole. | 1594. | 18.8x13.7cm.(14),269,(11)p.

PISCATOR, Johann. Analysis Logica | Evangelii | Secundum Mat- | thæum. | Una Cum Scholiis Et Obser- | vationibus locorum doctrinæ. | Inserta est etiam passim Refutatio sophismatum Ro- | berti Bellarmini Iesuitæ, quibus dicta quæ- | dam corrumpere & ad stabiliendum dogmata Pa- | pistica detorquere conatur. | Authore M.Johan.Piscatore, sacrarum literarum in | illustri schola Herbornensi Professore. | (device).

Londini | Excudebat R.F. impensis B.Nortoni. | 1594. | 14.6x9.5cm.   (10),475p. Folded leaf.

POLLINI, Girolamo. L' Historia | Ecclesiastica | Della Rivolvzion | D'Inghilterra | Divisa In Libri Qvattro | Ne' Qvali Si Tratta Di Qvello Ch'e Avvenvto | in quell'Isola, da chè Arrigo Ottauo cominciò à pensare di ripudiar | Caterina sua legittima moglie, infino à quest' vltimi | anni di Lisabetta, vltima sua figliuola. | Racolta Da Gravissimi Scrittori Non Meno | di quella Nazione, chè dell' altre, da F. Girolamo Pollini dell' Ordine | de' Predicatori, della Prouincia di Toscana. | Con Privilegio. | (device).

In Roma, Presso Guglielmo Facciotti. M.D.XCIV. | Con Licenza De' Svperiori. | . . . (1 line).   21.4x15.5cm.   (24),766,(48)p Colophon.

SARAVIA, Hadrian. Defensio | Tractationis | De Diversis Ministrorvm Evan- | gelij gradibus, ab Hadriano | Saravia editæ | Contra | Responsionem Clarissimi viri D. | Theodori Bezæ, | Eodem | Hadriano Saravia | authore. | (device).

Londini | Excudebant Reg.Typog. | Anno salutis humanæ. | M D XCIIII. | 18.6x13.3cm.   (12),598,(1)p.

STAPLETON, Thomas. Thomæ | Stapletoni, | Angli, S. Theo- | logiæ Doctoris, Et | Professoris Regii | Lovanii, | Promptvarivm | Catholicvm | Ad instructionem Concionatorum con- | tra nostri temporis hæreses, | Svper Evangelia Ferialia Per | Totam Qvadragesimam. | In hac Parte Qvadragesimali | vnius Caluini varia impietas in multis, eisdemq́[ue] | grauissimis fidei dogmatibus aperitur, & | accurate refutatur. | Additus est Index rerum copiosissimus. | . . . (4 lines)

Coloniæ Agrippinæ, | In Officina Birckmannica, sumpti- | bus Arnoldi Mylij. | Anno M.D.XCIIII. | Cum gratia & Priuelegio S.Cæsareæ Maiestatis. | Colophon: Coloniae Agrippinae, | Typis Godefridi Kempensis: Anno Reparatæ Sa- | lutis humanæ, M.D.XCIIII. | Mense Martio. | 16.7x10.3cm.   (16),340,(10)p.
Parts 1 and 3. Part 1 lacks t.p.; title from part 3.

WHITAKER, William. Adversvs | Thomæ Staple- | toni Anglopapistae | In Academia Lova- | niensi Theologiæ Professoris Regij | Defensionem Ecclesiasticæ authoritatis, quam ipse | luculentam & accuratam inscripsit, tri- | busque libris digessit, | Dvplicatio, | Pro authoritate atque αὐτοπιστία S. Scripturæ | Authore Gvilielmo Whitakero, S. Theologiæ in Aca- | demia Cantabrigiensi Doctore ac Professore Regio; & Col- | legio D. Ioannis Evangelistæ in eadem Aca- | demia Præfecto. | . . . (2 lines ; device)

Excudebat Cantabrigiæ Joannes Legatus | Academiæ Typographus. | M.D.XCIV. Aprilis. 20. | 28.2x18.6cm.   (39),654,(5)p.

WILLET, Andrew. Synopsis | Papismi, | That Is, | A Generall Viewe Of Papistrie: | wherein the whole mysterie of iniquitie, and summe of | Antichristian doctrine is set downe, which is maintained this | day by the Synagogue of Rome, against the Church | of Christ, together with | An Antithesis of the true Christian faith, and an Antidotum or counterpoyson | out of the Scriptures, against the whore of Babylons filthy | cuppe of abominations: | Deuided into foure Bookes or Centuries, that is, so many hundreds of | Popish heresies and errors. | Now this second time perused and published by the former Author, and augmented | with a fourth hundred of errors, and other necessarie additions, | to be seene in the end of the Preface. | . . . (13 lines; device).

At London | Printed by the Widdow Orwin, for Thomas Man, dwelling | in Pater noster row at the signe of the Talbot. | 1594. | 20.5x15.3cm. (16),1068,(14)p. 2 sub.t.p.

Dedication to Queen Elizabeth, signed.

1595

BÈZE, Théodore de. Propositions | And Prin- | ciples Of Divinitie, | Propovnded And Di- | sputed in the Vniversitie of Geneva, | by certaine students of Divinitie | there, vnder M.Theod.Be- | za, and M. Anthonie Faivs, | Professors of Divinitie. | Wherein Is Contained, | a Methodicall summarie, or Epi- | tome of the common places of Divi- | nitie: translated out of Latine | into English. | Newlie corrected with sundrie | Additions. |

Imprinted 1595. | 13.x8cm. (16),3–400p.

DICKER, George. Discors Concordia | Papæ: | Vel | Antithesis Antichristi | cum Christo, | Per G.D. | Cvm Responsione Invec- | tiua Terr. Or. Roman. in eadem. | Oratio item pia pro Regina nostra Elizabetha. | Per eund. G.D. | (device).

Londini, | In ædibus Richardi | Iohnes. Typograph. 1595. | 18.7x13.5cm. 15p.
Dedication, signed.

HILDERSAM, Arthur and JOHNSON, Francis. A Treatise | Of the Ministery of the Church | of England. | Wherein is handled this question, | Whether it be to be separated from, | or joyned vnto. | Which is discussed in two letters, the one | written for it, the other against it. | Wherevnto is annexed, after the preface, | A brief declaration of the ordinary officers of the Church of Christ. | And, A few positions. | Also in the end of the treatise, | Some notes touching the Lordes prayer. | Seven Qvestions. | A table of some principal thinges conteyned in this treatise. | (Device) . . . (8 lines).

No imprint. 17.x12.8cm. (8),141,(2)p. Date 1595 at foot of p.137.
Anon.Camb.Univ.Cat.No.6814.

PERKINS, William. A | Case of Conscience, the | greatest that euer vvas; Hovv a | man may know whether he be | the Childe of God, | or no. | Resolued by the word | of God. | Whereunto is added a briefe | discourse, taken out of Hier. | Zanchius. | . . . (4 lines).

London | Printed for John Legat. | 1595. | Lace border. 18.4x12cm. (4),47,(1)p.
Title page for Zanchius' Briefe discourse, after p.18.
To The Godly Reader, signed.

PERKINS, William. An Exposition | Of The Symbole Or | Creed Of The Apostles | According To The Tenovr Of | the Scriptures, and the consent of Orthodoxe | Fathers of the Church: | By | William Perkins. | . . . (2 lines; device).
Printed by Iohn Legatt Printer to the Vniuersitie | of Cambridge. 1595. | And are to be solde at the signe of the Inne in | Pauls Church-yard in London. | 17.8x12.2cm (8),544,(2)p.
T.p. and errata supplied: impf. at ends. A1-Ll7 in eights.

POLANUS, Amandus. The Svbstance Of | Christian Religi- | on, Sovndly Set Forth | in two bookes, by definitions and partitions, | framed according to the rules of a natu- | rall method by Amandus Polanus | professor of Diuinitie. | The first booke concerneth faith. | The second concerneth good workes. | The principall pointes whereof are contained in a | short table hereunto annexed. | Translated out of Latin into English by E. W. | . . . (4 lines; device).
Imprinted at London by R. F. for Iohn Oxenbridge | dwelling in Paules church-yard, at the signe | of the Parrot. 1595. | 15.9x9.8 cm. (9),273,(1)p.

STAPLETON, Thomas. Antidota | Apostolica | Contra Nostri | Temporis Hæreses: | In quibus loca illa explicantur, quæ hæretici hodie | (maximè Caluinus & Beza) vel ad sua placitæ | stabilienda, vel ad Catholicæ Ecclesiæ dogmata in- | firmanda, callidè & impiè de-prauarunt. | In Epistolam B.Pauli ad Romanos: | Tomvs II. | Authore Thoma Stapletono Anglo, S.Theol. | Doctore, & in Academia Louaniensi | S.Scripturarum Professore regio. | (device).
Antverpiæ, | Apud Ioannem Keerbergium. | Anno M.D.XCV. | 15.8x9.8 cm. (32),811,(34)p.

SUTCLIFFE, Matthew. An | Ansvvere Vn- | To a Certaine Ca- | lumnious letter published by M.Iob | Throkmorton, and entituled, | A defence of I. Throkmorton against the | slaunders of M. Svtcliffe, | Wherein the vanitie both of the defence of him- | selfe, and the accusation of others is mani- | festly declared, by Matthevv | Svtcliffe. | . . . (5 lines; device).
Imprinted at London by the Depu- | ties of Christopher Barker, Printer to | the Qveenes most excel- | lent Maiestie. | Anno Dom.1595. | 19.5x14.3cm. (6),84fol.

UDALL, John. A | Commenta- | rie Vpon The | Lamentations | Of Ieremy. | Wherein are contained; first, the Method and | order of euery Chapter laid open in seuerall Tables; | then, a literall interpretation of the Text out of the Hebrew, with a | Paraphrasticall exposition of the sence thereof: Afterward, a collec- | tion of diuers Doctrines, gathered sometimes out of a whole verse in | generall, or from the coherence of the Text; and sometimes out of the | particular words of the same; with examples, now and then, shew- | ing how the same doctrines haue bin verified in experience; | Moreouer, the reason and proofe of euery doctrine; | and lastly the particular vses, that are to be | made of them, for the edification | of the Church of God. | . . . (4 lines; device).

London, | Printed by Peter Short, for Thomas | Man, dwelling in Pater Noster row, at the | Signe of the Talbot. 1595. | 18.1x12.7cm. (8),195p. 3 folded leaves. Anon.Cf.Cambr.Univ.Cat.7370.

1596

BABINGTON, Gervase. A briefe conference, | betwixt mans Frailtie and | Faith. | Wherein is declared the true vse, and comfort of | those blessings pronounced by Christ in the fift of Ma- | thew, that euery Christian man and woman ought to make and | take hold of in theyr seuerall tentations and | conflicts. | VVith a new addition of some comfort against the death | of friends, together with a direction to other strength against other | our frailties, noted in the Booke vpon the | Lords Prayer. | Laid downe in this plaine order of Dialogue, to helpe, if it please | God, the conceit and feeling of the simplest. | By Geruase Babington. | . . . (3 lines).

At London | Printed by Iames Roberts for Thomas Chard, | Anno Dom. 1596. | 17.8x13.6cm.(4),83p
From the library of Walter W. Law.

BABINGTON, Gervase. A Profitable Exposition | of the Lords Prayer, by way of Questions | and Answers for most playnnes: | Together With Many | fruitfull applications to the life and soule, aswell for | the terror of the dull and dead, as for the sweete | comfort of the tender harted. | By Geruase Babington, now Bishop of Exeter. | With a Table of the principall matters conteyned in this Booke, | newly added to this impression. | . . . (3 lines: device).

At London, | Printed by R.Robinson for Thomas Charde. | 1596. | 17.8x13.6cm. (8),279,(4)p.
From the library of Walter W. Law

BABINGTON, Gervase. A Very Frvitfvl | Exposition Of The | Commandements By | way of Questions and | Answers for greater | plainnesse: | Togither with an application of euery one to the | soule and conscience of man, profitable for all, and especially | for them that (being not otherwise furnished) are yet desirous | both to see themselues, and to deliuer to | others some larger speech of eue- | ry point that is but briefly | named in the shorter | Catechismes. | By Geruase Babington, now Bishop of Exeter. | Whereunto is newly annexed a Table; containing | the principall matters of this Booke. | . . . (3 lines ornament).

Imprinted at London by R.Robinson, | for Thomas Charde. | 1596. | 17.8x13.6 cm (23),223p.
From the library of Walter W. Law.

BELL, Thomas. The suruey of Popery | Wherein the reader may | cleerely behold, not onely the | originall and daily incrementes of | Papistrie, with an euident Confutati- | on of the same; but also a succinct and | profitable enarration of the state of Gods | Church from

Adam vntill Christs ascension, | contained in the first and second Part thereof: and | throughout the third Part Poperie is turned | vp-side downe, | . . . (4 lines).

London | Printed by Valentine Sims dwelling | on Adling hill at the signe of the | white Swanne. | 1596 | 18.4x13.5cm. (8),536,(4)p.
Epistle dedicatorie, signed.

CLAPHAM, Henoch. A | Briefe Of | The Bible, | Drawne First | into English Poësy, | and then illustrated by | apte Annotations: | togither vvith some | other necessary | Appendices. | By Henoch Clapham |

Printed By | Robert Walde-graue, Prin- | ter to the Kings Ma- | iestie. 1596. | Cum Priuilegio Regio. | Lace border. 11.4x6.5cm. (12),14–234,(4)p.

DRUSIUS, Joannes. Σοφια Σειραξ | Sive | Ecclesiasticvs, | Græce ad exemplar Romanum, & | Latine ex interpretatione | I.Drusii, | Cum castigationibus siue notis eiusdem, | Ad Reuerendissimum in Christo patrem | D.Iohannem VVhitgiftvm | archiepiscopum Cantuariensem &c. | (device)

Franekeræ | Excudebat Ægidius Radæus, | Ordinum Fresiæ Typographus. | M.D.XCVI. | 18.x14.2cm. (16),147,(1);(158)p.

GIFFORD, George. Sermons | Vpon The | Whole Booke | Of The Reve- | lation. | Set forth by George Gyffard, | Preacher of the word at | Mauldin in Essex. | . . . (6 lines).

London, | Printed for Thomas Man, and Toby | Cooke. 1596. | Arch. border. 20.4x15.5cm. (16),454p.

HAMILTON, Francis. De | Sancto- | rvm Invo- | catione | Demonstratio Dvplex. | Quarum | Priore, Ipsa vindicatur ab omni crimine. | Posteriore, Eiusdem ostenditur Iustitia | & æquitas. | Ad vtramque, pro Baccalaureatus Biblici | gradu responsurus est | Reverendvs Et Religiosvs | Pater F. Franciscvs Hamiltonivs | Scotus, Cœnobij Scotorum S.Iacobi | Herbipoli, Prior. | Præside | D. Petro Thyræo Societatis Iesv. | . . . (4 lines).

Wircebvrgi | Excudebat Georgius Fleischmann. | Anno M.D.XCVI. | Border. 19x14cm. 81p.

JUNIUS, Franciscus. The Apocalyps, | Or | Revelation Of S. Iohn | The Apostle And Evan- | gelist of our Lord Iesvs Christ. | With a briefe and methodicall exposition vp- | on euery chapter by way of a little treatise, ap- | plying the words of S. Iohn to our last | times that are full of spirituall and | corporall troubles and di- | visions in Christen- | dome. | Lately set forth by Fr. Dv Ion, and newly | translated into English for the edification | and consolation of the true members | of our Lord Iesus Christ in his | Catholike Church. | (device).

Printed by Iohn Legat, Printer to the Vni- | versitie of Cambridge. 1596. | Lace border. 18.3x12.2cm. (8),286p.

MORTON, Thomas. Salomon | Or | A treatise declaring the state of the king- | dome of Jsrael, as it was in the daies of | Salomon. | Whereunto is annexed another treatise, of the Church: | or more particularly, | Of the right constitution of a Church: | . . . (1 line; device; 4 lines).

London, | Printed by Robert Robinson for | Robert Dexter. 1596. | 18.3x12.9 cm.   (16),71,144p.   Colophon on p.71.

Two parts, separately paged. Dedication to Queen Elizabeth, signed.

MORTON, Thomas. A | Treatise | of the threefolde state of man | wherein is handled, | 1 His Created holinesse in his innocencie. | 2 His Sinfulnesse since the fall of Adam. | 3 His Renewed holinesse in his regeneration. | . . . (8 lines, device).

Printed at London for Robert Dexter | and Ralph Iackeson. 1596. | 15.x9.8cm.   (29), 426,(1)p.

Epistle dedicatorie, signed.

PERKINS, William. An Exposition | Of The Symbole | Or Creede Of The Apo- | stles, According To The | Tenovr Of The Scriptvres, | and the consent of Orthodoxe Fa- | thers of the Church: | reuewed and corrected | By | William Perkins. | . . . (2 lines; device).

Printed by Iohn Legat Printer | to the Vniuersitie of Cambridge. 1596. | 20.7 x 15.2 cm   (6),441,(1),p. folded leaf.

PISCATOR, Johann. Analysis Logica | Evangelii | Secundum | Lucam. | Una Cum Scholiis Et Ob- | servationibus locorum doctrinæ. | Authore | M. Johanne Piscatore, sacrarum literarum | in illustri schola Nassovica-Sigenensi | Professore. | (device).

Londini, | Excudebat Richardus Field. | 1596. | 15.5x10.4cm.   (12),427p.

A TREATISE | Shewing the possibilitie, and conueniencie of the reall | presence of our Sauiour in the blessed | Sacrament: | The former is declared by similitudes and exam- | ples: the latter by the causes | of the same. | (device).

At Antwerp | Imprinted by Ioachim Trognesius, | 1596. | 13.2x8.5cm.   (8),121, (3)fol.

UDALL, John. Certaine | Sermons, Ta- | ken Ovt Of Se- | verall Places | Of Scrip- | tvre. | . . . (4 lines; device).

London, | Printed by Adam Islip, for | Thomas Man. | 1596. | Lace border. 15.4x9.9cm.   20,69;5,79; 5,163; 2,134;1,68;115 p.

Epistle dedicatorie, signed.

WILLET, Andrew. Tetrastylon | Papisticvm, | That is, | The Fovre Principal Pillars Of | Papistrie, the first conteyning their raylings, slanders, forgeries, | vntruthes: the second their blasphemies, flat contradictions to scrip- | ture, heresies, absurdities: the third their loose arguments, weake solutions, | subtil distinctions: the fourth and last the repugnant opinions of | new Papistes with the old: of the new one with another; | of the same writers with themselues: yea of | Popish religion with and | in it selfe. | Compiled as a necessarie supplement or fit appertinance to the Authors | former worke, intituled Synopsis Papismi: To the glorie of God, for | the disswading of light-minded men from trusting to the sandie foundation | of poperie, and to exhort good Christians stedfastlie to holde | the rockie foundation of faith in the | Gospell. | . . . (6 lines; device).

At London | Printed by the Widdow Orwin for Thomas Man, dwel- | ling in Pater noster row, at the signe of the Talbot. | 1596. | 20.5x15.3cm. (12),156p.
Epistle dedicatorie, signed.

WRIGHT, Leonard. A | Svmmons For | Sleepers. | Wherein most greeuous and notorious | offenders are cited to bring foorth true fruits | of repentance, before the day of the Lord, | now at hand. | Herevnto is annexed a Patterne for Pastors, | deciphering briefly the dueties pertaining | to that function. By L.Wright. | . . . (5 lines ; device).

London | Imprinted by Adam Islip, and are to bee sold by Ed- | ward white, at his shop at the little North | dore of Paules, at the signe of | the Gun. 1596. | 17.8x13.3cm. (4),56p.

1597

An ACTE concerning the | Confirmation and establishment of the De- | priuation of diuers Bishops and Deanes in | the beginning of her Maiesties reigne. |

(1597). Elizabeth, Q. [Statutes] Ann. 39, Chap. 8.

BEARD, Thomas. The Theatre | of Gods Iudgements: | Or, | A Collection Of Histo- | ries out of Sacred, Ecclesiasticall, and pro- | phane Authours, concerning the admirable Iudge- | ments of God vpon the transgressours | of his commandements. | Translated Ovt Of French, And Avgmen- | ted by more than three hundred Examples, by Th.Beard. | (device).

London, | Printed by Adam Islip. | 1597. | 18.3x13.7cm. (16),472p.

CAPITVLA Sive | Constitvtiones | Ecclesiasticæ per Archiepiscopum, | Episcopos, & reliquum Clerum Cantua- | riensis Prouinciæ in Synodo inchoata Londini vi- | cesimo quinto die mensis Octobris, Anno Domini millesi- | mo quingentesimo nonogesimo septimo, regníque Serenissimæ in | Christo Principis, Dominæ Elizabethæ, Dei gratia Angliæ, Franciæ, | & Hiberniæ Reginæ, Fidei defensoris, &c. tricesimo nono, con- | gregatos tractatæ, ac posteà per ipsam Regiam Maiesta- | tem approbatæ & confirmatæ, & vtríque Prouin- | ciæ tam Cantuariensi quàm Eboracensi | vt diligentiùs obseruentur, eadem | Regia authoritate sub magno | Sigillo Angliæ pro- | mulgatæ. | (device).

Londini | Excudebant Deputati Christo- | pheri Barker, Regiæ Maiestatis | Typographi. | Anno Domini 1597. | 17.4x12.7 cm. (1),23p.
Repr. in Sparrow's Collection of Articles: 1661, 1675 and 1684.

DERING, Edward. A | Briefe and necessarie | Catechisme or Instruction, very need- | full to be known of all Householders. | Wherby they may teach and instruct | thevr familie in such poynts of Christian

Re- | ligion as is most meete. | VVith prayers to the same adioyning. | (device) . . . (3 lines)

<small>At London, | Newly imprinted. Anno. Dom. | 1597. | 18x12.7cm. (10,129)p.
Iincluded in his Workes: 1597; with separate register.</small>

DERING, Edward. Certaine godly and comfortable Letters, full of | Christian consolation. VVritten by M. Ed. Dering vnto | sundry of his friends. And nowe published, for the profit | of the Church of God. |

<small>Without t.p. (1597). 18x12.7cm. (60)p
Included in his Workes: 1597; with separate register.</small>

DERING, Edward. M. | Derings | workes. | More at large then | euer hath heere-to-fore | been printed in any one | Volume. |

<small>At London, | Printed by I. R. for Paule | Linley, and Iohn Flasket, and | are to bee solde in Paules Church- | yard, at the signe of the | Black-beare. | 1597. | Arch. border. 18x12.7cm. (10),51,(8,416),(60),(10,129)p
Contains: Sermon, Tower of London, 11 Dec. 1569; XXVII Lectures on Hebrews: 1590: Godly Letters, n.d.; Catechisme, 1597.</small>

ELIZABETH, Queen [Statutes] Anno xxxix. Anno xxxix. Reginæ | Elizabethæ. | At the Parliament | begun and holden at Westminster | the xxiiij. day of October, in the xxxix. | yeere of the Reigne of our most gracious | Soueraigne Lady Elizabeth, by the grace | of God of England, France and Ireland | Queene, defender of the | faith, &c. | And there continued vntill the dissolution | thereof, being the ninth of February | next following, | 1597. | To the high pleasure of Almightie God, and the weale | publique of this Realme, were enacted | as followeth. |

<small>Imprinted at London by the | deputies of Christopher Barker, Printer to | the Queenes most excellent Maiestie. | (1597). Engraved border 27.x18.7cm. (1,88,1) fol.</small>

FOORD, John. Apocalypsis Iesv | Christi, Revelata Per | Angelvm Domini, Excepta | atque conscripta à Ioanne Apostolo | & Euangeliographo; | Breui, perspicua, & methodica temporum & personarum | designatione, exposita | Per Ioannem Foorthe. | . . . (2 lines; device)

<small>Londini, | Excudebat Vidua Thomæ Orwini impensis | Rodulphi Iacksoni & Roberti Dexter. | 1597. | 18.1x14 cm. (8),166p.</small>

GIFFORD, George. Certaine | Sermons, | Vpon Divers | Textes Of Ho- | lie Scrip- | tvre. | Whereof some haue been seuerally before published, | and other some for the greater benefit of the god- | ly reader are here now added. | By M.George Giffard, Preacher of the worde | of God at Mauldon in Essex. | (device)

<small>London. | Printed by the Widowe Orwin, | for Thomas Man. 1597. | 14.7x9.5 cm. 255p.</small>

GUEVARA, Antonio de. Mount Caluarie, | The Second Part: | Compyled by the Reverend Father | Don Anthonio de Gueuara, Bishop of Mon- | donnedo, Chronicler and preacher vnto | Charles the fift. |

In this Booke the Authour treateth of the Seuen | Words which Christ our Redeemer spake hanging | vpon the Crosse. | Translated out of Spanish into English. | (device).

London, | Printed by Adam Islip for Edward White, and | are to bee sold at his shop by the little North dore of | Pouls, at the signe of the Gun. Anno. 1597. | 18.2x14cm.(8),502p.

HAMILTON, Francis. Dispvtatio | Theologica | De | Legitimo | Sanctorvm | Cvltv Per Sa- | cras Imagines: | Deqve | Imaginum eorun- dem multiplici vsu, | fructu, & cultu: | Consecratione item atq; bene- dictione; & ha- | rum iustitia atque emolumentis. | Ad quam pro Baccalaureatu formato, in | celebri & Catholica Academia Herbipo- | lensi responsurus est | Reverendvs Et Religiosvs | Pater F.Franciscvs Hamilitonivs | Scotus, Cœnobij Scotorum S.Iacobi Her- | bipoli, Prior. SS.Theologiæ Bacca- | laureus Biblicus. | . . . (3 lines).

Ex officina Typographica Georgij Fleischmanni. | Anno M.D.XCVII. | 18.8x 14.6cm. (8),75p

HOOKER, Richard. Of | The Lawes | of Ecclesiasticall | Politie. | The fift Booke. | By Richard Hooker. | (device).

London | Printed by John Windet dvvelling at Povvles | wharfe at the signe of the Crosse Keyes and | are there to be soulde. | 1597. | 26. x 18.8 cm. (15),271p.
Appended to his, Of | The Lawes | of Ecclesiasticall | Politie. | Eyght Bookes. | [1594.] and also to 2d ed. 1604.

HOWSON, John. A | Sermon preached at | Paules Crosse the 4. | of December. | 1597. | Wherein is discoursed, | that all buying and sel- | ling of Spirituall pro- | motion is vn- | lawfull. | By Iohn Hovvson, | Student of Christes- | Church in Ox- | ford. | (device).

Imprinted at London by Arn. | Hatfield for Thomas Adams. | 1597. | Lace bor- der. 17.4x13.cm. (1),50p.

MORE, George. A | Demon- | stration of God in his | workes. | Against all such as eyther | in word or life deny there is | a God. | By George More, | . . . (3 lines).

At London | Printed by I. R. for Tho- | mas Charde. | 1597. | Lace border. 19.2x14.4cm. (7),155(157),(5)p.
A leaf without pagination inserted between 18 and 19.

PERKINS, William. A | Declaration Of | The Trve Manner | Of Knovving | Christ crucified. | . . . (3 lines; device).

Printed By Iohn Legat, Printer | to the Vniuersitie of Cambridge, 1597. | 20.7x 15.1cm (2),59–73p.
D2–E2 of his A salve for a sicke man: 1597. To the Reader, signed.

PERKINS, William. A | Direction | For The Government | Of The Tongve. | according to Gods word. | (device).

Printed by Iohn Legat, Printer to the Vniversitie | of Cambridge. 1597. | 20.7x 15.1cm. (1),27p.
Appended to his Tvvo Treatises: 1597. C8–E6.; separate pagination. To the Reader, signed.

PERKINS, William. A | Discovrse Of | Conscience: | VVherin Is Set Dovvne | The Natvre, Properties, And | differences thereof: as also the way | to | Get and keepe good Conscience. | The second Edition. | (device).

    Printed by Iohn Legat, Printer | to the Vniuersitie of Cambridge. 1597. | 20.7x15.1cm. (4),75–145p.
    E3–I8 of his A salve for a sicke man: 1597.
    Dedication, signed.

PERKINS, William. An | Exposition | Of The Lords | Prayer: | In the way of Catechising, seruing | for ignorant people. | Corrected and amended. | Hereunto are adioyned the Prayers of Paul, | taken out of his Epistles. | By W.Perkins. (device).

    London, | Printed by Felix Kingston, for Iohn Porter, | and Ralph Iackson. 1597. | 20.7x15.1cm. (6),183–236p. Folded leaf.
    Appended to his Fovndation Of Christian Religion: 1597, with continuous register and pagination.

PERKINS, William. The | Fovndation | Of Christian | Religion: Gathe- | red Into Sixe | Principles. | And it is to be learned of ignorant | people, that they may be fit to heare | Sermons with profit, and to receiue | the Lords Supper with | comfort. | . . . (4 lines).

    London, | Printed by the Widow Orwin, for | Iohn Porter. 1597. | Arch. border. 20.7x15.1cm. (4),16;(3),20–175;(6),183–236p. Two folded leaves.
    Sub-title, at Mm3: An | Exposition | Of The Lords | Prayer: | In the way of Catechising, seruing | for ignorant people. | Corrected and amended. | Hereunto are adioyned the Prayers of Paul, | taken out of his Epistles. | By W.Perkins. | (device)
    London, | Printed by Felix Kingston, for Iohn Porter, | and Ralph Iackson. 1597. |
    Epistle, signed.

PERKINS, William. A Golden Chaine, | Or | The Descrip- | tion Of Theologie, | Containing The Order Of | the causes of Saluation and Damnati- | on, according to Gods word. A viewe | whereof is to be seene in the | Table annexed. | Written in Latine, and translated by R.H. | Hereunto is adioined the order which | M.Theodore Beza vsed in comforting | afflicted consciences. | The second edition, much enlarged, with | a Table at the end. | (device).

    Printed by Iohn Legat, Printer | to the Vniuersitie of Cambridge. 1597. | 20.7x the sugarloafe | 1598. | 14.5x9.7 cm. (59),207 p.
    Cambr.Univ.Cat:7374. To the Christian Reader, signed W. P.

PERKINS, William. A | Graine Of | Mvstard- | Seed, | Or | The Least Measvre Of Grace | that is or can bee effectuall to | Saluation. | By W.Perkins. | (device).

    London, | Printed by Felix Kingston, for Ralph Iackson | and Hugh Burwell. 1597. | 20.7x15.1cm. (4),241–258p.
    Qq1–Rr3 of his Fovndation Of Christian Religion: 1597.

PERKINS, William. A salve for a sicke man: | Or, | A Treatise Con- | taining The Natvre, | Differences, And Kindes | Of Death; As Also The Right | manner of dying well. | And | It may serue for spirituall instruction | to | 1.Mariners when they goe to sea. | 2.Souldiers when they goe to battell. | 3.Women when they trauell of childe. | (device)

Printed by Iohn Legat, Printer | to the Vniuersitie of Cambridge. 1597. | 20.7x 15.1cm.   (4),56;(2),59–73;(4),75–145;(4),241–258p.
Dedication signed.

PERKINS, William. Tvvo Trea- | tises. | I.Of the nature and practise of Repentance. | II.Of the combat of the flesh and spirit. | A second Edition corrected. | (device).

Printed by Iohn Legate, Printer to the Vniversitie | of Cambridge. 1597. | 20.7x15.1 (5),40p.
To the Reader whosoever, signed.

PISCATOR, Johann. Analysis Logica | Libri S.Lucæ | Qui Inscribitur | Acta Aposto- | lorum. | Una Cum Scholiis Et Ob- | servationibus locorum doctrinæ. | Authore | M.Johanne Piscatore, Sacrarum | literarum in illustri schola Nassovica- | Sigenensi Professore. | (device).

Londini, | Excudebat Felix Kingstonus. | M.D.XCVII. | 15.4x9.8cm.   (21), 262p.

SKENE, John. The | Lavves And Actes | Of Parliament, Maid | Be King Iames The First, And | His Successovrs Kinges Of Scot- | land: Visied, collected and extracted | fourth of the Register. | The Contentes Of This Buik, | are expremed in the leafe following. | (coat of arms).

At Edinbvrgh, | Imprented Be Robert | VValde-graue prenter to the Kinges Majestie. | 15. Martii. Anno Dom. 1597. | 25.3x17.cm.   (5),24,26–162; 1–178,(21) fol. T.p. supplied. Lacks fol. 1–24, and final table fol 5ff.
B M Cat.

SPARKE, Thomas. The | High VVay | To Heaven By | the cleare light of the Gos- | pell cleansed of a number of | most dangerous stumbling | stones thereinto throwen by | Bellarmine and others. | In | A Treatise made vpon the 37. 38. and 39. | verses of the 7. of Iohn: wherein is so | handled the most sweete and comfortable doctrine | of the true vnion and communion of Christ | and his Church, and the contrarie is so | confuted, as that not onely thereby also | summarilie and briefly, and yet plainly all | men may learne rightly to receiue the | sacrament of Christs blessed bodie and | blood, but also how to beleeue and | to liue to saluation. And there- | fore entitled The high way | to Heauen. | By Thomas Sparke Doctor | of Diuinitie. |

Printed by R. R. for Robert Dexter. | 1597. | 15.5x9.8cm.   (14),356,(2)p.

VIREL, Matthieu. A | Learned And | Excellent Trea- | tise containing all the prin- | cipall grounds of Christian | Religion. | Set downe by way of conference in a most | plaine and familiar maner. | Written first in French by maister Mathew | Virell, after translated into Latine, and | now turned into english for the vse of our | Countrymen. | . . .

(3 lines) The fourth and last impression corrected and | amended. | (device)

Imprinted at London by Robert Robinson for | Robert Dexter, dwelling in Paules | Churchyard at the signe of the | brasen Serpent. 1597. | 15.6x10.3cm. (8),280p.

1598

GIFFORD, George. A | Briefe discourse of | certaine points of the | religion, which is among the | common sort of Christians, | which may be termed the | Countrie Diuinitie. | With a manifest confuta- | tion of the same, after the | order of a Dialogue. | Compiled by George | Gifforde. | (device).

Imprinted at London, by | Richard Field, and Felix | Kingston. | 1598. | Lace border. 15x10 cm. (6),137p.

KIMEDONCIUS, Jacobus. Of | The Redemp- | tion Of Mankind | Three Bookes: | Wherein the controuersie of the vni- | uersalitie of Redemption and grace | by Christ, and of his death for all men, | is largely handled. | Herevnto Is Annexed A Trea- | tise of Gods Predestination in one booke. | Written in Latin by Iacob Kimedoncivs D. and | professor of Diuinitie at Heidelberge, and translated | into English by Hvgh Ince Preacher of | the word of God. | (device)

At London | Imprinted by Felix Kingston | for Hvmfrey Lovvnes. | 1598. | 18x12.5 cm. (16),406,(4)p. Incomplete at end.

LOUIS de Granada. Granados Devotion. | Exactly Tea- | ching How A Man | May Trvely Dedicate | and deuote himselfe vnto God: | and so become his accep- | table Votary. | Written In Spa- | nish, by the learned and | reuerend Diuine F. | Lewes of Granada. | Since translated into Latine, | Italian and French. | And now perused, and englished, | by Francis Meres, Master of | Artes, & student in Diuinity. |

London, | Printed by E. Allde. for Cuthbert | Burby, and are to be sold at | his shop at the Royall | Exchange. 1598. | Line border. 12.5x7. cm. (14),576,(55)p.

PARSONS, Robert. A Christian | Directorie | Gviding Men To | Their Salvation | Devided Into Three Bookes. | The first whereof apperteining to Resolution, is | only conteyned in this volume, devided into tvvo | partes, and set forth novv again, with many cor- | rections, and additions by th' Authour him selfe, vvith | reprofe of the corrupt and falsified edition of the | same booke lately published by M.Edmu. Buny. | Ther is added also a methode for the use of al, | vvith tvvo tables, and a preface to the Reader, | vvhich is necessarie to be reade. | . . . (6 lines)

At Lovan, | Imprinted by Laurence Kellam, | cum privilegio. 1598. | 14.9x9.3 cm. 3–20fol; 719,(17)p. Lacks fol 1–2. T.p. supplied by Mr. Edward G. Friehold, of London.

Gillow:V:278.

PISCATOR, Johann. Analysis Logica | Evangelii | Secvndvm | Marcum: | Una Cum Scholiis | Et Observationibvs | locorum doctrinæ. | Authore | M.Johanne Piscatore, | Professore sacrarum literarum | in illustri Schola Nassovica | Sigenensi. | (device).

Londini, | Excudebat Arnoldus Hatfield. | 1598. | 14.6x9.5cm. (6),188p.

RACSTER, John. A Booke | Of The Se- | ven Planets, | Or, | Seuen wandring Motiues, of | William Alablasters wit, | Retrograded or remoued, by | John Racster. | . . . (2 lines ; device).

At London, | Printed by Peter Short for Andrew Wise, dwelling | in Paules Church-yard at the signe of the | Angell . 1598. | 19.5x14cm. (4), 43fol

RAINOLDS, John. Iohannis Rainoldi Angli, | De Romanae | Ecclesiæ | Idololatria, | In Cvltv Sanctorvm, | reliquiarum, imaginum, aquæ, salis, olei, | aliarúmque rerum consecratarum, | & sacramenti Eucharistiæ. | Operis Inchoati Libri II. | In Qvibvs Cvm Alia Mvlta | variorum Papismi patronorum errata patefiunt: tûm in- | primis Bellarmini, Gregoriiq[ue] de Valentia, calumniæ in | Calvinum ac ceteros Protestantes, argutiæq[ue] pro Papisti- | co idolorum cultu discutiuntur & ventilantur. | . . . (3 lines; device).

Excudebat Iacobus Stœr. Anno 1598. | 17.2x10.7 cm. (16),646 p.

RAINOLDS, John. The Svmme Of | The Conference | Betweene Iohn Rainoldes | And Iohn Hart: | Tovching The Head And The | Faith Of The Chvrch. | Wherein by the way are handled sundry points, of the sufficiencie and right | expounding of the Scriptures, the ministerie of the Church, the function | of Priesthood, the sacrifice of the Masse, with other controuersies of | religion: but chiefly and purposely the point of Church-gouern- | ment, opened in the branches of Christs supreme soue- | raintie, of Peters pretended, the Popes | vsurped, the Princes lawfull | Supremacie. | Penned by Iohn Rainoldes, according to the notes set downe in writing | by them both: perused by Iohn Hart, and (after things supplied, | and altered, as he thought good) allowed for the | faithfull report of that which past in | conference betweene | them. | Whereunto is annexed a Treatise intitled, Six Conclvsions | Tovching The Holy Scriptvre And The | Chvrch, Written by Iohn Rainoldes. | With a defence of such things as Thomas Stapleton and Gregorie | Martin haue carped at therein. | . . . (3 lines).

Imprinted at London by George Bishop. | 1598. | 19.5x14.3cm. (19),675p.

SAINT-GERMAIN, Christopher. The | Dialogve In En- | glish, betweene a Doctor of | Diuinitie, and a Student in the | Lawes of England: | Newly corrected and Im- | printed, with new Addi- | tions. | (lace device).

At London, | Printed by Thomas Wight, | and Bonham Norton. | 1598. | Cum Priuilegio Regiæ | Maiestatis. | 13.3x8.8 cm. 176,(4)fol.
Anon.Cf.Cambr.Univ.Cat:540.

STOUGHTON, Thomas. A | Generall Treatise Against | Poperie, And In Defence Of The | Religion By Pvblike Avtho- | ritie Professed In England | And Other Chvrches | Reformed. | VVherein they that either want leisure to read, or | that haue not iudgement to conceiue, or that are not | able to buie the learned treatises of other con- | cerning particular points of religion, | may yet euidently see poperie not | to be of God, and our religi- | on to be acceptable in | his sight. | Very necessarie for these times, for the confirmation and | strengthening of men in our religion, that neither by Je- | suits, nor by any other, they may be drawne to pope- | rie, or any other heresie or sect: and likewise | for the winning of Papists and Atheists | to an vnfained liking and true | profession of our re- | ligion. | By Thomas Stovghton minister of the word. | (device)

Printed By Iohn Legat, | Printer to the Vniuersitie of Cambridge. 1598. | 15.7x10 cm. (27),320p.

VOYON, Simon de. A Discourse | Vpon the Catalogue of | Doctors of Gods Church, to witt, aswell | of those that haue beene from the beginning | of the world, mentioned in the holy scrip- | tures; as of manie which haue si- | thens by order succeeded, | Together with the continuall succession of | the true Church of God vntill the | yeare 1565. | Written in French by Simon de Voyon, | a worthie member and Minister of the same | Church, and novv faithfully translated into English | by Iohn Golburne. | . . . (3 lines; device).

Imprinted at London by Richard Bradocke, | for Iohn Browne, and are to be solde at his | shop in Fleetstreete ouer against the white | Friars, at the signe of the sugarloafe | 1598. | 14.5x9.7 cm. (59),207 p.

WENTWORTH, Peter. A Pithie | Exhortati- | on To Her Maies- | tie For Establi- | shing Her Svc- | cessor To | the crowne. | Wherevnto | Is Added A Discovrse | containing the Authors opinion of | the true and lavvfull successor | to her Maiestie. | Both compiled by | Peter Wentworth | Esquire. | . . . (8 lines).

Imprinted. 1598. | 13.3x9.1cm. (6),121;(1),95p. Sub-title at I7.
Burned by order of Queen Elizabeth.

ZANCHI, Hieronymus. Compendivm | Præcipvo- | rvm Capitvm Do- | ctrinæ Christianæ, | Qvondam A Clarissimo Viro D. Hie- | ronymo Zanchio, S.S. Theologiæ | Doctore, in priuatum vsum | conscriptum: | Nvnc Vero Primvm, | ingratiam & vtilitatem iuuentutis Theo- | logiæ studiosæ, bono animo & studio hære- | dum, in lucem editum. | (device).

Nevstadii In Palatinatv | Apud Viduam VVilhelmi Harnisij. | M.D.XCIIX. | 16.7x10.1 cm. (26),658,(1)p.

1599

BARKER, Laurence. Christs | Checke To S. | Peter for his curious que- | stion, out of those words | in Saint Iohn: | Quid ad te? | Begun in Paules Church on S: | Iohns day the Euangelist. 1597. out of | part of the Gospel appointed for that day, and | prosecuted the same day this yeare 1598. | in the same place, and else where | at other times in sixe seue- | ral Sermons. | (device)

At London | Printed by P. S. for Cuthbert Burbie, | and Thomas Gosson. | 1599. | 14x9.5 cm. (15,317)p.

Dedication, signed, and dated from " Clarkenwell the first of Ianuary. 1598"; To the Reader; " 28. of October, 1600 ".

BILSON, Thomas. The effect of certaine Sermons | Tovching | The Fvll Redemption | of mankind by the death and bloud of | Christ Jesvs: | Wherein | Besides the merite of Christs suffering, the manner | of his offering, the power of his death, the comfort | of his Crosse, the glorie of his resurrection, | Are handled, | What paines Christ suffered in his soule on the Crosse: | Together, | With the place and purpose of his descent to hel after death: | Preached at Paules Crosse and else where in London, | by the right Reuerend Father Thomas Bilson | Bishop of Winchester. | With a conclusion to the Reader for the cleering of cer- | taine obiections made against the said doctrine. | . . . (6 lines).

Imprinted at London by Peter Short for Walter | Burre, and are to be sold in Paules Churchyard at | the signe of the Flower deluce. 1599. | 18.7x14.2 cm. (12),420p.

BRADSHAW, William. A Triall | Of Svbscrip- | tion, By Way Of | A Preface Vnto Cer- | taine Svbscribers; | And, | Reasons for lesse rigour against non- | subscribers. | Both modestly written; | that | Neither should offend. | . . . (5 lines; device).

1599. | 12.8x8.4cm. (12),28p.
Anon. H&L.

BRISTOW, Richard. A Briefe | Treatise | Of Divers Plaine | and sure waies to finde out the | truth in this doubtfull and | dangerous time of Heresie. | Conteyning Svndrie | Worthy Motives Vnto The | Catholike Faith, or Considerati- | ons to moue a man to beleeue | the Catholikes, and not | the Heretikes. | Set out by Richard Bristow | Priest, Licentiat in Diuinitie. | (device)

Printed at Anvverpe with Priuiledge. | 1599. | 13.6x9.3cm (12),176,(4)fol.

CALVIN, John. The | Institution of Christian | Religion, written in Latine | by M.John Caluine, and tran- | slated into English according to the | Authors last edition, with sundry Tables | to finde the principall matters entreated of | in this booke, and also the declaration of places of Scripture | therein expounded, | By | Thomas Norton. | Whereunto there are newly added in the | margent of the booke, notes conteining | in briefe the substance of the matter | handled in each Section. | (device).

Printed at London by Arnold Hatfield, | for Bonham Norton. | 1599. | 21.2x15.7 cm. (11),412,(87)fol.

CARTWRIGHT, Thomas. A | Christian Letter | of certaine English Protestants, vnfained fa- | uourers of the present state of Religion, authorised and | professed in England: vnto that Reverend and lear- | ned man, Mr. R. Hoo. requiring resolution in certaine | matters of doctrine (which seeme to ouerthrow | the foundation of Christian Religion, | and of the church among vs) ex- | preslie contained in his fiue | books of Ecclesiasti- | call Pollicie. | (device).

1599. | 17.4x13. cm. 49,(1)p. Lacks p. 43-44.
Anon.H&L. Bodl.

GIFFORD, George. Sermons Vpon | The Whole Booke Of | The Revelation. | Set forth by George Giffard, Preacher of the | VVord at Mauldin in Essex. | . . . (5 lines; device).

London, | Printed for Thomas Man. | 1599. | 20.3x14.7cm. (16),454p.

HAYWARD, John. The | First Part | Of | The Life And | raigne of King Henrie | the IIII. | Extending to the end of the first | yeare of his raigne. | Written by I.H. | (device)

Imprinted at London by Iohn Wolfe, and | are to be solde at his shop in Popes head Alley, | neere to the Exchange. 1599. | 18.3x14.1cm. (10),149,(1)p. Colophon. Port. frontisp. Imprint supplied. Dedication signed.

JACOB, Henry. A Defence | Of The Chvrches | And Ministery | Of Englande. | Written in two Treatises, against the Reasons and | Obiections of Maister Francis Iohnson, and | others of the separation commonly called | Brownists. | Published, especially, for the benefitt of those in these | partes of the lowe Countries. | (device).

Middelbvrgh, | By Richard Schilders, Printer to the States of Zealand. | 1599. | 18.1x13.5cm 7,91p.

Separate title-page, at p. 84: A | Short Treatise | Concerning The Trvenes | Of A Pastorall Calling In | Pastors Made By | Prælates. | Against the Reasons and Obiections of Maister | Francis Iohnson, with others of the | separation, commonly called | Brownistes. | Device . 1599. | Dexter: 229. Signed on p. 7.

KING, John. Lectvres | Vpon Ionas, | Delivered At | Yorke | In the year of our Lorde 1594. | By John Kinge: | Newlie corrected and amended. | (device).

Printed at Oxford, by Ioseph Barnes, and are to be solde in | Paules Churchyarde at the signe of the Bible. 1599. | 20.6x14.9cm. (9),660;(1),661–683;(1),685–706p.

With two sermons appended.

LOUIS de Granada. A | Memoriall | Of A Christian Life. | Wherin Are Treated | Al Svch | things, as appertaine vnto a Christian to do from the be- | ginning of his cōuersion, vntil the end of his perfection. | Deuided into Seauen Treatises: the particulars whereof | are noted in the page following. | Written first in the Spanish tongue, by the famous Re- | ligious Father, F. Lewis de Granada, Prouinciall of the | holy order of Preachers, in the Prouince of Portugall. | (device)

Imprinted at Rouen, by George Loyselet. | Anno Domini. 1599. | Line border. 14.8x9.1cm. (2),762,(8)p.

MASTER | Brovghtons | Letters, | Especially his last Pamphlet to and against | the Lord Archbishop of Canterbury, about | Sheol and Hades, for the descent into Hell, | answered in their kind. . . . (3 lines; device).

London | Imprinted by Iohn Wolfe. | 1599. | 17.5x12.9cm 48,(2)p

MORNAY, Philippe de. Tractatvs | De Ecclesia, | Qvo Præcipve | quæ hoc nostro tempore | agitatæ fuerunt quæ- | stiones excu- | tiuntur. | Phil. Mornæo Pless. | Avctore. | Postrema Editio, emendatior,

multis locis locupletior: | cui etiam accessit locorum ex veteribus
Theologis | citatorum accurata descriptio. | Rerum item & capitum
Indices. | . . . (4 lines; device)

Excudebat Ioannes le Preux. | M.D.XCIX. | 16.1 x 9.8 cm. (16),527,(31) p.

MORTON, Thomas. A | Treatise | of the Nature of God. | . . . (2
lines; device, griffin)

London | Printed by Tho.Creede for Raphe Iackson, | dwelling in Pauls Churchyard, at the | signe of the Swanne. | 1599. | 14.9x9.3cm. (14),239p.
Anon. Cf.Camb.Univ.Cat. No.7707.

PARSONS, Robert. A | Temperate | VVarn-VVord, To The | Tvrbvlent And Seditiovs | VVach-word of Sir Francis Hastinges knight, |
vvho indeuoreth to slaunder the vvhole | Catholique cause, & all professors | thereof, both at home and | abrode. | Reduced into eight seueral encounters, vvith a particuler speeche | directed to the Lordes of
her Maiesties most honorable Councel. | To vvhome the arbitriment
of the vvhole is remitted. | By N.D. | (device) . . . (4 lines).

Imprinted vvith Licence. | Anno M.D.XCIX. | 18.1x13.4cm. (6),129p.
Anon. Dexter:234. Gillow:V:281.

PRICE, Henry. The | Eagles Flight | Or | Six principall notes, or
sure | markes for euery true Christi- | an, to soare vp to the euerlast- | ing nest of Gods Eternall | kingdome. | (stars) As It Was
Delivered | in a most godly and fruitfull Ser- | mon at Paules Crosse. |
(stars). By Maister Price of S.Iohns in Oxford. | (ornament).

Imprinted at London by Richard | Bradocke for Iohn Busbie, and are to | be
soulde at his shoppe in Paules Church- | yard, at the signe of the Crane. | 1599. |
13.5x9.cm. (1,82)p.

The SACRED | Doctrine | Of Divinitie, Ga- | thered Ovt Of | the
worde of | God | Togither with an explication of the | Lordes Prayer |
(woodcut device)

1599. | 12.9x8.4cm. 3–56,(22)p.
Preface dated: 1. Ianuar. 1589. T.p. supplied by Mr. Edward G. Friehold, of
London. Cf. BMCat. *Sub* Doctrine.

SUTCLIFFE, Matthew. De | Tvrcopapismo, | Hoc est, | De Turcarum & Papistarum aduersùs | Christi ecclesiam & fidem coniuratione,
eo- | rúmq; in religione & moribus consensione | & similitudine, Liber
vnus. | Eidem præterea adiuncti sunt, de Turcopa- | pistarum maledictis & calumnijs, aduersus Gulielmi | Giffordi famosi Pontificum
Rom. & Iebusitarum sup- | parasitastri volumen illud contumeliosissimum, quod | ille Caluinoturcismum inscripsit, | Libri quatuor. | In
quibus non tantùm huius hominis leuissimi, | sed etiam aliorum importunissimorum scurrarum ad- | uersus orthodoxam Christi ecclesiam
continenter la- | trantium, malitia & petulantia reprimitur, hominúmq; | piorum fama ab eorum calumnijs vindicatur. | . . . (3 lines)

Londini, | Excudebant Georgivs Bishop, | Radvlphvs Newberie, & | Robertvs
Barker. | Anno Domini. | 1599. | 20.7x15.3 cm. 86,(1),248p.
Separate title-page for second part of work: L4. Anon. Cambr. Univ. Cat.
1741.

SUTCLIFFE, Matthew. Matthæi | Svtlivii | Adversus | Roberti Bellar- | mini de Purgatorio dis- | putationem, Liber | vnus. | . . . (8 lines ; device)

Londini, | Excudebant Georgivs Bishop, | Radvlphvs Newberie, & | Robertvs Barker. | Anno Domini. | 1599. | 20.7 x 15.3 cm. (8), 103p.

TOPSELL, Edward. Times | Lamentation: | or | An exposition on the prophet Ioel, | in sundry Sermons or | Meditations. | . . . (11 lines; device).

At London, | Printed by Edm. Bollifant, | for George Potter. | 1599. | 17.4x13.5 cm (8),454p.
Epistle dedicatorie, signed.

WHITAKER, William. Prælectiones | Doctissimi Viri | Gvilielmi Whitakeri, Nvper Sa- | cræ Theologiæ In Academia | Cantabrigiensi Doctoris Et | Professoris Regii, Et Collegii | S. Ioannis Evangelistae in eadem | Academia Præfecti . | In quibus tractatur Controversia de Ecclesia | contra Pontificios, imprimis Robertum Bellarminum | Jesuitam ,in septem Quæstiones distributa, quas | sequens pagina indicabit. | Exceptæ Primvm Ab Ore Avthoris, | deinde cum aliis exemplaribus collatæ, & post eius mor- | tem ad breves illius Annotatiunculas examinatæ. | Opera Et Cvra Ioannis Allenson, Sacræ | Theologiæ Baccalavrei, Et Collegii | Praedicti Socii. | His accessit eiusdem Doct. Whitakeri vltima | concio ad clerum, vnà cum descriptione vitæ & mortis, Authore | Abdia Assheton Lancastrensi, sacræ Thologiæ Bac- | calaureo, & euisdem Collegii Socio, quam sequun- | tur carmina funebria. |

Ex Officina Iohannis Legat, | Florentissimæ Academiæ | Cantabrigiensis Typographi. 1599. | 19.8x14.5cm. (8),478,(13)(1),84,(1).p. 1 tab.
Separate title-page preceding Aaaa 1.: Cygnea Cantio | Gvilielmi VVhita- | keri, Hoc Est, Vltima | Illivs Concio Ad Clerum, | habita Cantabrigiæ in templo Beatæ | Mariæ, paulò ante mortem. | Octob.9. An.Dom.1595. | (Device) Cantabrigiæ. | Ex officina Iohannis Legat. 1599. |

ZANCHI, Hieronymus. H.Zanchivs | His | Confession Of | Christian Religion. | Which novve at length being | 70. yeares of age, he caused to bee published | in the name of himselfe & his family. | Englished in sense agreeable, and in words as answe- | rable to his ovvne latine copie, as in so graue a | mans worke is requisite: for the profite of | all the vnlearneder sort, of English | christians, that desire to know | his iudgement in mat- | ters of faith. | . . . (5 lines).

Printed by Iohn Legat, | printer to the Vniuersitie of Cambridge. | 1599. | 15.2x9.7cm. 43,442p.

1600

ALLEN, Robert. A Treasvrie | Of Catechisme, Or Chri- | stian Instrvction. | The first part, which is concerning the morall | Law or ten Commandements of Almightie | God: with certaine Questions and | Aunswers preparatory to | the same. | . . . (device; 5 lines).

London, | Printed by Richard Field for Thomas Man. | 1600. | 19.2x12.3 cm. (10),308,(1)p.
Preface signed by "Robert Allen, a Minister of the word of God."

ARTICLES to be en- | quired of in the visitatiō, in | the First yeere of the Raign | of our most dread Soue- | raign Ladie Elizabeth | by the grace of | God, of | England, France, and Ireland | Queene, Defender of | the Faith, &c. | Anno Dom. 1559. |

Colophon: Imprinted at London by the | Assignement of Robert Barker | Printer to the Queenes most | excellent Maiestie. | Cum Priuilegio Regiæ Maiestatis. | Anno Dom. 1600. | 19.3x15.1 cm. (13)p.

BARCLAY, William. Gvilielmi Barclaii | Illvstrissimi Dvcis | Lotharingiæ Etc. Consiliarii, | Supplicvmque Libellorvm | Magistri, atque in celeberrima Academia Ponti- | mussana I. V. Professoris ac Decani, | De Regno Et Regali Potestate Adversvs | Buchananum, Brutum, Boucherium, & reliquos Monarchomachos, | Libri Sex. | . . . (2 lines; device)

Parisiis, | Apud Gvillielmvm Chavdiere, via Iocobæa, sub signo | Temporis, & Hominis Svluestris. | M.D.C. | Cvm Privilegio Regis Christianissimi. | 23.3x16.cm. (8),542,(18)p.

CANISIUS, Petrus. A Svmme Of | Christian Doctrine: | Composed In Latin, | By the R.Father P.Canisivs, of the | Society of Iesvs. | With an Appendix of the fall of Man | & Iustification, according to the Do- | ctrine of the Councel of Trent. | Newly translated into Englishe. | To which is adioined the explication of cer- | taine Questions not handled at large in | the Booke as shall appeare in the | Table. | (ornament) . . . (6 lines).

No imprint. [1600?]. Border. 14.3x9.2 cm. Pp.(16),687,(1).
The ornamental border contains some blocks like those used by Thomas White, London, 1602, and in Parson's Warn-word, Antwerp? 1602.

HAMILTON, John. A | Facile Traictise, | Contenand, first: ane infallible reul | to discerne trevv from fals religion: | Nixt, a declaration of the Nature, Num- | bre, Vertevv & effects of the sacraments; | togider vvith certaine Prayeres of deuo- | tion. | Dedicat To His Soverain | Prince, the Kings Maiestie of Scotland. | King Iames the Saxt. | Be Maister Ihone Hamilton Doctor in | Theologie. | . . . (4 lines).

At Lovan, | Imprinted be Laurence Kellam, | Anno Dom. M.DC. | 11.7x7.1cm. (36),444,(24)p. (lacks pp. 193-4, 215-220).

HILL, Thomas. A Qvartron Of Rea- | sons Of Catholike Re- | ligion, With As Many | Briefe Reasons of Refv- | sal: collected and composed, | by Thomas Hill Do- | ctour of Diuinitie. . . . (9 lines; device).

Printed at Antwerpe, with Priuiledge. 1600. | 14.1x8.8cm. (13),187p.

INIUNCTIONS giuen | by the Queenes | Maiestie. | Anno Dom. 1559. | The First yeere of the | Raigne of our Soue- | raign Lady Queene | Elizabeth. |

Cum Priuilegio Regiæ | Maiestatis. | [London: Assigns of Robert Barker. 1600] 19.3x15.1 cm. (32)p. Engraved title-page used by "the Assignement of Robert Barker".
Trin. Col. Cambr. Cat. No.796. Camb.Univ.Cat.No.1686.

JACOB, Henry. A Defence | Of A Treatise Tov- | ching The Svf-ferings | And Victorie Of Christ In | The Worke Of Ovr | Redemption. | Wherein is confirmed, | I That Christ suffered for vs, not only Bodily griefe, but also | in his Soule an impression of the proper wrath of God, | which may be called the paines of Hell. | 2 That after his death on the Crosse he went not downe into | Hell. | For Answere to the late writings of Mr Bilson, L.Bi- | shop of Winchester, which he intitleth, The effect of | certaine sermons, &c. Wherein he striueth | mightily against the doctrine | aforesaid. | By Henry Iacob Minister of the worde | of God. | . . . (3 lines; ornament).

1600. | Border. 18.4x13.9 cm. 211,(1)p.

JAMES, Thomas. Bellvm Papale, | Sive | Concordia Discors | Sixti Quinti, Et Cle- | mentis Octavi, Circa | Hieronymianam editionem. | Preterea, In Qvibvsdam Locis | grauioribus habetur comparatio vtriúsq; editionis, | cum postrema & vltima Louaniensium; vbi miri-fica | industria Clementis, & Cardinalium super castiga- | tione Bib-liorum deputatorum, notas dun- | taxat marginales Louaniensium in | textum assumendo, clarè | demonstratur. | Auctore Thoma Iames, Noui Collegij in alma | Academia Oxoniensi socio, & vtriúsq; Academiæ | in Artibus Magistro. | . . . (4 lines).

Londini, | Excudebant Georgius Bishop, Radulphus | Nevvberie, & Robertus Barker. | Anno 1600. | 18.9x14.6cm. (22,56)p.

KING, John. Lectvres | Vpon Ionas, | Delivered At | Yorke | In the yeare of our Lorde 1594. | By John Kinge: | Newly corrected and amended. | (device).

Printed at Oxford, by Ioseph Barnes, and are to be solde in | Paules Church-yarde at the signe of the Bible. 1600. | 20.9x15.cm. (9),1–660,(1),661–706p.

MORNAY, Philippe de. Fowre Bookes, | Of | The Institvtion, Vse | And Doctrine Of The | Holy Sacrament Of The | Evcharist In The Old | Chvrch. | As Likewise, How, When, | And by what Degrees the Masse is brought | in, in place thereof. | By my Lord Philip of Mornai, Lord of Plessis- | Marli; Councellour to the King in his Councell of Estate, Captaine | of fiftie men at armes at the Kings paie, Gouernour of his towne | and Castle of Samur, Ouerseer of his house | and Crowne of Nauarre. | The second edition, reuiewed by the | Author. | . . . (8 lines; device).

London | Printed by Iohn Windet, for I. B. T. M. and W. P. 1600. | 27.2x19.3cm. (35),484p. Several pp. misplaced.

SUTCLIFFE, Matthew. A Briefe Replie To A | certaine odious and slanderous libel, lately | published by a seditious Jesuite, calling himselfe | N.D. in defence both of publike enemies, and disloyall | subiects, and entitled A temperate wardword, to Sir Francis Hastings | turbulent watchword: | Wherein not only the honest, and religious in-tention, and zeale of that | good Knight is defended, but also the cause of true catholike religion, | and the iustice of her Maiesties proceedings against Popish malcontents | and traitors, from diuers malitious im-

putations and slanders cleered, and | our aduersaries glorious declamation answered, and refuted by O.E. de- | fendant in the Challenge, and encounters of N.D. | Hereunto is also added a certaine new Challenge made to N.D. in | fiue encounters, concerning the fundamentall pointes of his former whole | discourse: | Together with a briefe refutation of a certaine calumnious relation | of the conference of Monsieur Plessis and Monsieur d'Eureux before the | French king, lately sent from Rome into England; and an answer to the | fond collections, and demands of the relator. | . . . (8 lines).
    Imprinted at London, by | Arn. Hatfield. | 1600. | 19.2x14.3 cm. (23),237,(6), 132,(6),38 p.
    Camb. Univ. Cat. No. 2074.

SUTCLIFFE, Matthew. Matthæi Svtlivii | De Concilijs, & eorum authoritate, | aduersus Robertum Bellarminum, | & bellos eiusdem sodales | Libri duo. | . . . (10 lines; device)
    Londini, excudebat Edm.Bollifantus. | 1600 | 19. x13.9 cm. 2–83 fol.
    Separate pagination, but with continuation of signatures from his De Vera Christi Ecclesia: 1600.

SUTCLIFFE, Matthew. Matthæi Svtlivii | de Monachis, eorumque institutis & | moribus, aduersus Robertum Bellar- | minum, vniuersamq; mona- | chorum & mendicantium fra- | trum colluuiem disputatio. | . . . (15 lines ; ornament)
    Excusum Londini per Edm. | Bollifantum. | 1600 | 19. x13.9 cm. (1),152fol.
    Separate pagination, but with continuous signatures from his De Vera Christi Ecclesia: 1600.

SUTCLIFFE, Matthew. Matthæi Svtlivii | De Vera Christi Ecclesia | aduersus Rob. Bellarminvm, | aliósque sectæ Jebusiticæ sodales, | eorúmq; errores & hæreses, | Liber vnus. | . . . (8 lines ; device)
    Londini, | Excudebat Edm.Bollifantus. | 1600 | 19. x13.9 cm. 125fol.

TORQUEMADA, Antonio de. The | Spanish Mande- | uile of Miracles. | Or | The Garden of curious | Flowers. | VVherin are handled sundry points | of Humanity, Philosophy, Diuinitie, and | Geography, beautified with many strange | and pleasant Histories. First written in Spanish, by | Anthonio De Torquemada, and out of that tongue | translated into English. | It was dedicated by the Author, to the Right | honourable and reuerent Prelate, Don Diego | Sarmento de soto Maior, Bishop of | Astorga. &c. | It is deuided into sixe Treatises, composed in | manner of a Dialogue, as in the next page | shall appeare. |
    At London, | Printed by I.R. for Edmund Matts, | and are to be solde at his shop, at the signe | of the hand and Plow in Fleet- | streete. 1600. | Lace border. 17.8x13.5cm. (5),158,(2)fol

VALERA, Cipriano de. Two Treatises: | The first, | Of The Lives Of | The Popes, And | Their Doctrine. | The second, | Of The Masse: The One | and the other collected of that, which the | Doctors, and ancient Councels, and | the sacred Scripture do teach. | Also, | A

Swarme of false Miracles, wherewith Marie de | la Visitacion, Prioresse de la Annuntiada of Lisbon, | deceiued very many: and how she was dis- | couered, and condemned. | . . . (4 lines). The Second edition in Spanish augmented by the | Author himselfe, M. Cyprian Valera, and translated | into English by John Golburne. 1600. | (ornament).

Printed at London by Iohn Harison, and are to be | sold at the Grey-hound in Pater noster row. 1600. | 18.6x13.5cm. (12),445,(1)p. Misnumbered: pp. 257-266, 399-400 omitted.

WHITE, Tobias. Theses Theologicæ | De | Veris veræ & visibilis Ecclesiæ | Christi in terris, | Et | De falsis Pontificiæ Ecclesiæ | Notis: | Quas | Deo Opt. Max. Ivvante, | sub præsidio | Cl. V. D. Amandi Polani | à Polansdorf SS. Theo- | logiæ Doctoris & Professoris, in Illu- | stri & pervetusta Academia | Basiliensi | publicè tuebitur | 24. Ianuarij | Tobias Albivs | Londinensis. |

Basileæ | Typis Conradi Waldkirchii. | M DC. | Border. 19.9x15.0 cm. (7)p.

WILLET, Andrew. Synopsis | Papismi, | That Is, | A General View Of | Papistrie: Wherein The Whole | Mysterie Of Iniqvitie, And Svmme Of | Antichristian Doctrine Is Set | downe, which is maintained this day by the Synagogue | of Rome, against the Church of | Christ: | Together With An Antithesis Of The Trve | Christian Faith, And An Antidotvm Or | Covnterpoyson Ovt Of Scripture, Against | the whore of Babylons filthie cuppe of | abominations: | Confvted By Scriptvres. Fathers, Covn- | cells, Imperiall Constitvtions, Pontificiall | decrees, their owne Writers, and our Martyrs. | Divided Into Five Bookes Or Centvries, | that is, so many hundreds of Popish Heresies | and errors. | Now This Third Time Pervsed And | published by the former Author, and augmented with a fift hundred | of errors, and other necessarie additions, to be seene in the | end of the Preface. | . . . (11 lines ; ornament).

At London | Imprinted by Felix Kyngston, for Thomas Man, | dwelling in Pater noster row at the signe of the | Talbot. 1600. | 30.4x20cm. (18),1106p. Defective: lacks sig A1, and after Bbbbb6) Sub-t.p. at p. 963.
Dedication signed.

1601

BAGSHAW, Christopher. A | True relation of the faction begun | at VVisbich, by Fa. Edmonds, alias VVeston, | a Iesuite, 1595. and continued since by Fa. Walley, | alias Garnet, the Prouinciall of the Iesuits in Eng- | land, and by Fa. Parsons in Rome, with | their adherents: | Against vs the Secular Priests their bre- | thren and fellow Prisoners, that disliked of nouel- | ties, and thought it dishonourable to the auncient Eccle- | siasticall Discipline of the Catholicke Church, that | Secular Priests should be gouerned by | Iesuits. | (ornament).

Newly Imprinted. | 1601. | 18x12.3cm. (8),96p.
D N B. 2: 401 b.
Doubtfully ascribed to William Watson. Cambr.Univ.Cat.6843.

BARLOW, William. A Defence of the | Articles of the Protestants Religion, | in aunsweare to a libell lately cast | abroad, intituled |

Certaine Articles, or forcible reasons, discouering the pal- | pable absurdities, and most intricate erronrs of the | Protestantes Religion. | . . . (3 lines; device).

London | Imprinted by Iohn Wolfe, and are to bee sold in Pauls | Church yard by Mathew Law, 1601. | 17x12.7 cm. (12),227p.
Epistle dedicatorie, signed.

BRADSHAW, William. Hvmble | Motives | For Association | To Maintaine Religi- | on Established. | Published as an antidote against the pestilent | treatises of secular Priests | . . . (1 line; ornament).

Imprinted 1601. | 13.2x9. cm. (1),42p.
H&L. Cambr.Univ.Cat.6837. Ascribed to T: Digges: Dexter, 247.

The | COPIES of certaine dis- | courses, which were extorted from diuers, | as their friends desired them, or their aduersaries | driue them to purge themselues of the most gree- | uous crimes of schisme, sedition, rebellion, facti- | on, and such like, most vniustly laid against | them for not subscribing to the late | authoritie at the first sending | thereof into England: | In which discourses are also many things discouered | concerning the proceedings in this | matter abroad. | . . . (3 lines; ornament).

Imprinted at Roane, by the heires of | Ia.Walker. 1601. | 17.2x12.8cm. (8). 186,(1)p.
H&L, new ed., ascribes to W: Bishop, bishop of Chalcedon.

DOVE, John. Of Diuorcement. | A Sermon | Preached At | Pauls Crosse the 10. of | May. 1601. | By Iohn Doue, Doctor of | Diuinitie. | (ornament).

London | Printed by T.C. 1601. | 13.8x8.8cm. (14), 62p.

ELIZABETH, Queen. [Statutes] Anno xliii. Anno xliij. Reginæ | Elizabethæ. | At the Parliament | begun and holden at Westminster | the xxvij. day of October, in the xliij. | yeere of the Reigne of our most gracious | Soueraigne Lady Elizabeth, by | the grace of God of England, France | and Ireland Queene, Defender | of the Faith, &c. | And there continued vntill the disso- | lution thereof, being the xix. of De- | cember next following. | 1601. | To the high pleasure of Almighty God, and the | weale publique of this Realme, were | enacted as followeth, |

Imprinted at London by | Robert Barker, Printer to the | Queenes most excellent Maiestie. | [1601] Engraved border. 27.1 x 18.7 cm. (2,144,1) p.

FULKE, William. The | Text Of The | New Testament | Of Iesvs Christ, | Translated out of the vulgar Latine by | the Papists of the traiterous Semi- | narie at Rhemes. | With Arguments of Bookes, Chapters, and | Annotations, pretending to discouer the cor- | ruptions of diuers Translations, and to cleare | the controuersies of these dayes. | Wherevnto Is, Added | the Translation out of the Original | Greeke, commonly vsed in the | Church of England, | With | A Confvtation Of All Svch | Arguments, Glosses, and Annotations, as con- | teine manifest impietie, of Heresie, Treason, and Slander, | against the Catholike Church of God, and the | true Teachers thereof, or the Translati- | ons vsed in the Church of | England. | The Whole Worke, | perused and enlarged in diuers places by | the Authors owne hand before his death, with | sundry Quotations, and Authorities out of Holy | Scriptures, Counsels, Fathers, and History. | More amply then in the for- | mer Edition. | By W. Fulke D. in Diuinitie. |

Londini | Impensis G.B. | Anno 1601. | Arch. Border. 32.8x21.5cm. (42),914,(9)p.

GIBBONS, Nicholas. Qvestions And | Dispvtations Con- | cerning The Holy Scrip- | tvre; Wherein Are Con- | tained, briefe, faithfull and sound exposi- | tions of the most difficult and har- | dest places: | Approved By The Testimony Of | the Scriptures themselues; fully correspondent to the | analogie of faith, and the consent of the Church of God; | conferred with the iudgement of the Fathers of | the Church, and interpreters of the Scrip- | ture, nevv and old. | Wherein also the euerlasting truth of the word of God, | is freed from the errors and slaunders of Atheists, | Papists, Philosophers, and all | Heretikes. | The first part of the first Tome. | By Nicholas Gibbens, Minister and | Preacher of the word of God. | . . .   (7 lines; ornament)

At London | Imprinted by Felix Kyngston. 1601. | 18.5x14.2cm. (12),545,(14)pp. Folded map of Mesopotamia.

GODWIN, Francis. A Catalogve | of the Bishops of England, since the | first planting of Christian religion in this | Island, together with a briefe History of their | liues and memorable actions, so neere as can | be gathered out of antiquity. | By F.G.Subdeane of Exceter. | . . . (8 lines; ornament).

Londini, | Impensis Geor.Bishop. | 1601. | 18.6x13.1cm. (8),544p. Dedication, signed.

HILL, Robert. Life euerlasting: | Or, | The Trve Know- | ledge Of One Iehovah, | Three Elohim, And Iesvs | Immanvel: | Collected Ovt Of The Best Mo- | derne Diuines, and compiled into one volume by Robert | Hill, Bachelour in Diuinitie, fellow of S.Iohns | Colledge in Cambridge, and preacher | of Gods word in S. Andrewes | in Norwich. | . . . (1 line; device).

Printed by Iohn Legat, Printer to | the Vniuersitie of Cambridge. 1601. | And are to be sold at the signe of the Crowne in Pauls Church- | yard by Simon Waterson. | 21.4x15.5cm. (17),692p.

PAGET, John. A Primer | Of | Christian | Religion, | Or a forme of Catechi- | sing, drawne from the behold- | ing of Gods works in the cre- | ation of the world: | And published for the loue of those | that are children in Christ, to | giue instruction vnto them: | By I.P. | . . . (2 lines; ornament).

London | Printed by Iohn Harison for Thomas | Man, 1601. | 13.9x9.1cm. (10),183fol. Epistle signed.

PARSONS, Robert. The | Second part of the Booke | of Christian Exercise, apper- | tayning to Reso- | lution. | Or | A Christian Directorie, guiding | all men vnto theyr sal- | uation. | Written by the former Au- | thor, R.P. | . . . (6 lines).

At London, | Printed by I. Roberts, for | Simon VVaterson, dwelling | in Paules Church-yard, at the | signe of the Crowne. | 1601. | 12.2x6.9cm. (4,500)p.
Gillow,V:278.

TOPSELL, Edward. The | Revvard Of | Religion. | Deliuered in sundrie Lectures vpon | the Booke of Ruth, wherein the godly may | see their dayly both inward and outward | trials, with the presence of God | to assist them, and his mercies | to recompence them. | Verie profitable for this present time of | dearth, wherein many are most pittifully | tormented with want; and also worthy to bee | considered in this Golden age of the prea- | ching of the word, when some vo- | mit vp the loathsomnes ther- | of, and others fall away | to damnable | security. | . . . (11 lines) Seene and allowed. |

Printed at London by Iohn Windet. | 1601. | 15.7x10 cm. (38),311p.
Epistle dedicatorie, signed

WATSON, William. A Dialogve | Betwixt A Se- | cvlar Priest, | And A Lay Gen- | tleman. | Being an Abstract of the most | important matters that are in con- | trouersie betwixt the Priests and | the Spanish or Iesuiti- | call faction. | (ornament)

Printed at Rhemes. M D C I. | 18.1x12.6cm. (22),134p. A1 blank.
Cf. H&L. Gillow V: 575.

WATSON, William. A | Sparing Discove- | rie Of Ovr English Iesvits, | and of Fa.Parsons proceedings vnder pretence | of promoting the Catholike faith | in England. | For a caueat to all true Catholiks, our very | louing brethren and friends, how they embrace | such very vncatholike, though Iesuiticall | deseignments. | . . . (3 lines ; ornament).

Newly Imprinted. | 1601. | 17.4x11.8cm. (13),70p.
Signed W.W. Gillow.V:576. Ascribed also to Christopher Bagshaw. DNB. 60: 43b.

1602

CARTWRIGHT, Thomas. Σὺν θεῷ ἐν χριστῷ | The | Ansvvere | To The Pre- | face Of The | Rhemish | Testament, | By T. Cartwright. |

At Edinbvrgh | Printed By Ro- | bert Walde-graue, prin- | ter to the Kings Ma- | iestie. 1602. | Cum priuilegio. | Border, with " R.W. " on sides. 12.7x8.4 cm. 213p. Pp. 65–80 omitted in numbering.

CERTAYNE Letters, trans- | lated into English, being first written | in Latine. | Two, by the reverend and learned Mr. Francis Iunius, Divinitie | Reader at Leyden in Holland. | The other, by the exiled English Church, abiding for the pre- | sent at Amsterdam in Holland. | Together with the Confession of faith prefixed: where vpon | the said letters were first written. | . . . (3 lines: ornament).

Printed in the yeare. 1602. | 17. x12.8 cm. (1), 57p. Pp. 13–14 blank.
Dexter:251.

The CONFESSION and pub- | like recantation of thirteene learned | personages, lately conuerted in France, Germanie, and the | Lowe-Countreys, from Poperie, to the Churches refor- | med: wherein they haue zealously and learnedly set | dovvne the reasons that moued them therevnto. | The names and degrees of the Conuerts. | 1.Godefrid Rabin, Fryer and Preacher in Prage, at S.Thomas on | the little side. | 2.Simon Palory, Prior & Prouinciall of the order of the Holy crosse. | 3.Iohn Colleij, a Caputchin, and Guardian of S.Omer. | 4.Melchior Roman, a Spaniard, Proctor for the Iacobins at Rome. | 5.Iohn Norman, Sub-prior of Marestay, a Preacher. | 6.Father Abraham, Prior of Carmes in Arles. | 7. Antony Ginestet, a confessor of the order of S.Francis. | 8. Signeur Lewis of Caransy, a Priest. | 9.Father Edmon, a Iesuite, Doctor of Diuinity. | 10.Leonard Theuenot, Curat of S. Sauin. | 11.Sir Francis a Monke of the order of the Celestins. | 12. Francis Goupil Angeuin, a Fryer in the couent of Chasteau Roux. | 13.Lewys du Boys, Priest, of S.Francis order in Dunkerke. | Translated out of the French and Dutch Printed | copies, by I.M. |

Imprinted at London for G.P. and are to be solde at the | signe of the Bible in Paules Church-yard. 1602. | 18x13.1 cm. (1,116) p.

CRISPIN, Jean. The | Estate of the Church, | With the discourse of times, from the | Apostles vntill this present: | Also of the liues of all the Emperours, Popes of | Rome, and Turkes: As also of the Kings | of Fraunce, England, Scotland, | Spaine, Portugall, Den- | marke, &c. | With all the memorable accidents of | their times. | Translated out of French into English by | Simon Patrike, Gentleman. | (device)

London | Printed by Thomas Creede. | 1602. | 19.4x13.5cm. (16),708,(30)p. Epistle to reader, signed.

FULBECKE, William. The | Pandectes Of | the law of Nations: | Contayning | seuerall discourses of the questi- | ons, points, and matters of Law, wherein | the Nations of the world doe | consent and accord. | Giuing great light to the vnderstanding | and opening of the principall obiects, que- | stions, rules, and cases of the Ciuill Law, | and Common law of this Realme | of England. | Compiled by William Fvlbecke. | . . . (2 lines; ornament).

London | Imprinted by Thomas Wight. | 1602. | 17.9x13.4cm. (4), 90fol.

FULBECKE, William. The | Second Part | Of The Parallele, | Or | Conference Of | the Ciuill Law, the Canon Law, | and the Common Law of this | Realme of England. | Wherein The Agree- | ment and disagreement of these | three Lawes touching diuers matters not | before conferred, is at large debated | and discussed. | Whereunto is annexed a Table contayning the principall | Questions, matters, and pointes of the | Dialogues ensuing. | Handled in seauen Dialogues, by William Fvlbecke. | (ornament).

London | Printed by Thomas Wight, | 1602. | 17.9x13.4 cm. (8),74,(8)fol.

HERREY, Robert F. Tvvo right profitable | and fruitfull Concordances, or | large and ample Tables | Alphabeticall. | The first containing the interpretation of the | Hebrue, Caldean, Greeke, and Latine wordes | and names scatteringly dispersed throughout the whole | Bible, with their common places following euery of them: | and the second comprehending all such other principall | wordes and matters, as concerne the sense and meaning | of the Scriptures, or direct vnto any necessary | and good instruction. | The further contents and vse of both the which | Tables (for breuitie sake) is expressed at large in the | Preface to the Reader: And will serue as well | for the translation called Geneva, as. | for the other authorized to be read | in Churches. | Collected by R. F. H. | (ornament)

Imprinted at London by Robert | Barker, Printer to the Queenes | most excellent Maiestie. 1602. | Cum priuilegio Regiæ Maiestatis. | 20.5x16. cm. (164) p. Colophon.
Signed preface.

HOWSON, John. A | Sermon | Preached At St. | Maries In Oxford, | The 17. Day of No- | vember, 1602. in defence of | the Festivities of the Church | of England, and namely | that of her Maiesties | Coronation. | By | Iohn Hovvson Doctor Of | Diuinitie, one of her Highnes Chaplaines, and | Vicechancellour of the Vniversitie | of Oxforde. | (device)

At Oxford, | Printed by Joseph Barnes, and are to be sold in Fleete- | streete at the signe of the Turkes head | by Iohn Barnes. 1602. | 18.6x13.8cm. (4,30)p.

The | IESUITES Catechisme. | Or | Examination Of | their doctrine. | Published in French this present | yeere 1602. and nowe translated | into English. | VVith a Table at the end, of all the maine poynts that | are disputed and handled therein. | (ornament).

Printed Anno Domini. | 1602. | 18.9x14.1cm. (11),238,(2)fol.
Pollard, Short-Title Cat. attrib. to Etienne Pasquier.

NICHOLS, Josias. Abrahams Faith: | That Is, | The olde Religion. | Wherein Is Tavght, | That The Religion Now | publikely taught and defended by order in the | Church of England, is the onely true Catholicke, | auncient, and vnchangeable faith of | Gods elect. | And The Pretensed | religion of the Sea of Rome is a false, bastard, | new, vpstart, hereticall and variable super- | stitious deuise of man. | Published by Iosias Nicholls, an humble seruant and mi- | nister of the gospell in the Church. | . . . (3 lines ; ornament)

London | Imprinted by Thomas Wight. | 1602. | 17.9x13.1 cm. (16),316p.

NICHOLS, Josias. The Plea Of The | Innocents, | Wherein is auerred | That the Ministers and people | falslie termed Puritanes, are iniu- | riouslie slaundered for enemies | or troublers of the state. | Published for the common good of the | Church and common wealth of this | Realme of England | As A Covntermvre | Against all Sycophantising Papists, Sta- | tising Priestes, Neutralising Atheistes, and | Satanising scorners of all godlinesse, | trueth and honestie. | Written: | By Iosias Nichols, a faithfull Minister | of the Ghospell of Christ: and an | humble seruaunt of the En- | glish Church. | . . . (7 lines; ornament).

1602. | 13.3x9.1cm. (18),1–244p. and 11 p. in Mss. at end.

OPENSHAW, Robert. Short Questions | and answeares, con- | teining the summe of Chri- | stian Religien: | Newly enlarged with the Te- | stimonies of Scripture. | . . . (10 lines)

Imprinted at London at the | three Cranes in the Vintree, by | Thomas Dawson. | 1602. | (Border). 14.2x9 cm. (8,69)p
Signed at end.

PARSONS, Robert. The | Warn-Word | To Sir Francis | Hastinges Wast- | Word: | Conteyning the issue of three former Treateses, the | Watch-word, the Ward-word and the Wast-word | (intituled by Sir Francis, an Apologie or Defence | of his Watch-word) togeather with certaine | admonitions & warnings to thesaid | knight and his followers. | Wherunto is adioyned a breif reiection of an insolent, and vaun- | ting minister masked with the letters O.E. who hath taken | vpon him to wryte of thesame argument in supply of the | knight. | There go also foure seueral Tables, one of the chapters, another of | the controuersies, the third of the cheif shiftes, and deceits, | the fourth of the particular matters conteyned in the whole | book. | By N.D. author of the Ward-word. | . . . (ornament; 3 lines).

Permissu Superiorum. Anno 1602. | 15.2x10. cm. (8),131,138,(11) fol.
Anon. Gillow V: 282.

RAINOLDS, John. Iohannis | Rainoldi | Angli | Sex theses de sacra Scriptura | & Ecclesia: | Ut publicis in Academia Oxoniensi dispu- | tationibus explicatæ, sic editæ, ante an- | nos viginti; nunc autem recognitæ, & | apologia contra Pontificios Elymas, | Stapletonum, Martinum, | Bellarminum, Baronium, | Justum Calvinum Veteracastren- | sem auctæ. 1602. | . . . (3 lines).

Londini, | Impensis Geor. Bishop. | 1602. | 15.1x10.2 cm. (13),479,(1)p.

SMITH, Henry. Fovre | Sermons | Preached By | Maister Henry | Smith. | And published by a more perfect | coppie then heeretofore. | (device).

At London, | Printed by I.R. for William | Leake, at the signe of the Grey- | hound in Paules Church- | yard. 1602. | 18.9x12.9cm (4,92)p.
Included in The | Sermons | Of Master | Henry Smith; 1604 |

SMITH, Henry. Fovre Sermons, | Preached by Master | Henrie Smith, | And published by a more perfect | Copie then hereto- | fore. | (device).

London: | Printed by S.S. for Cutbert | Burby. 1602. | Lace border. 18.9x12.9 cm. (2,65,10) p.
Included in The | Sermons | Of Master | Henry Smith; 1604 |

SMITH, Henry. Two Sermons, | Of | Ionahs Punishment, | Preached by Master | Henrie Smith, | And published by a more perfect | Copie then hereto- | fore. | (device)

London: | Printed by S.S. for Cutbert | Burby. 1602. | Lace border. 18.9x12.9 cm. (1,44)p.
Included in The | Sermons | Of Master | Henry Smith; 1604 |

SMITH, Henry. Two | Sermons preached by | Maister Henry Smith: with | a Prayer for the morning there- | vnto adioyned. | And published by a more | perfect Coppie then heere- | to-fore. | (device).

At London: | Printed by I.R. for VVilliam | Leake, at the signe of the Gray- | hound in Paules Church-yard. | 1602. | Lace border 18.9x12.9cm. (2,34,1)p. First leaf blank.

Included with The | Sermons | Of Master | Henry Smith, 1604 |

SUTCLIFFE, Matthew. A | Challenge | Concerning | the Romish Church, her | doctrine & practises, | Pvblished First Against | Rob. Parsons, and now againe reuiewed, en- | larged, and fortified, and directed to him, to | Frier Garnet, to the Archpriest | Blackevvell and all their | adhærents. | By Matth. Svtcliffe. | Therevnto Also Is Annexed | an answere vnto certeine vaine, and friuolous exceptions, | taken to his former challenge, and to a certeine worthlesse | Pamphlet lately set out by some poore disciple | of Antichrist, and entituled, | A detection of diuers notable vntrueths, contradictions, | corruptions, and falsifications gathered out of | M. Sutcliffes new Challenge, &c. | . . . (7 lines).

At London | Printed by Arnold Hatfield. | 1602. | 19.4x13.6cm. (25),210;230p.

VERHEIDEN, Jacob. Præstantium | aliquot | Theologorum, | qui | Rom. Antichristum | præcipuè oppugnarunt, | Effigies: | Quibus addita | Elogia, | Librorumq. Catalogi; | Operâ | Iac. Verheiden. |

Hagæ — Comitis. | M. D. C. II. | Cum priuilegio. | Colophon: Ex Officina | Bucoldi Cornelii Nieulandii. | 31 x 19.9 cm. (16),226 p.

Engraved title page.

Portraits of Berengarius, John Wiclif, John Hus, Jerome of Prague, Savonarola, Erasmus of Roterdam, Martin Luther, Philip Melanchthon, Johann Bugenhagen, Justus Jonas; Gaspar Cruciger, George prince of Anhalt, Erasmus Sarcerius, Huldreich Zwingli, Johann Oecolampadius, Simon Grynæus, Sebastian Munster, Ambrosius Blaurerus, John Diaz, Martin Bucer, Paul Fagius, Thomas Cranmer, John Alasco, John Knox, Andreas Gerhard, Wolfgang Musculus, Jacob Faber, John Calvin, William Farel, Peter Viret, Augustine Marlorat, Robert Stephens, John Sleidan, Johann Sturm, Philip Marnix de la Sanct-Aldegonde, John Bale, Peter Paul Vergerius, Mathias Flacius, Gaspar Olevianus, Peter Martyr, Jerome Zanchius, Martin Chemnitz, Lambert Danaeus, Aretius Benedictus, Henry Bullinger, Josias Simler, Rudolphus Gualterus, Louis Lavater, Theodore Beza, and Franciscus Junius,

WESTON, Edward. De Triplici | Hominis Officio, | ex notione ipsius | Naturali, Morali, ac | Theologica; | Institutiones orthodoxæ, | contra | Atheos, Politicos, Sectarios | Avthore | Odovardo Westono Anglo | S.T.D. et in collegio Ang | lorum Duaci Professore. |

Antverpiæ | Apud Ioannem Keerbergium. | Anno | M.DC.II. | 19. x13.8cm. (40),248,424,436,(28) p.

Engraved title-page.

WHITE, Richard. Ricardi Viti | Basinstochii | Comitis Palatini, | Historia- | rvm Britanniæ | Insvlæ, Ab Origine | Mundi, ad annum Christi octin- | gentesimum, Libri Nouem | Priores, | Ad Senatvm, Popvlvmq; | Britannvm. | Quorum Argumenta pòst sequuntur. | (device)

Apud Carolvm Boscardvm | Typographum Iuratum. | M.D.CII. | Border. 15 4x 9.9cm. (16),3–469,(3); 123,(2);(8),96;(4),108;(8),174,(1)p.

WILLET, Andrew. A | Catholicon, | that is, | A generall preservative or re- | medie against the Pseudocatholike religion, ga- | thered out of the Catholike epistle of S.Ivde, | briefly expounded, and aptly, according to the | time, applied to more then halfe an hundreth | of popish errours, and as many | corruptions of manners. | With a Preface seruing as a preparatiue to the | Catholicon, and a dyet prescribed after. | . . . (7 lines).

Printed By Iohn Legat, | Printer to the Vniversitie of Cambridge. | 1602. | And are to be sold at the signe of the Crowne in Pauls | Churchyard by Simon Waterson. | 13.8x9.2cm.   (43),217,(1)p.
Epist.Dedicat.signed.

1603

ABBOT, Robert.   Antichristi | Demonstratio, | Contra Fabvlas | Pontificias, & ineptam Roberti | Bellarmini de Antichristo | disputationem. | Authore Roberto Abbatto, Oxoniensi, | olim è Collegio Baliolensi, sacræ | Theologiæ professore. | . . . (3 lines; device).

Londini | Excudebat Robertus Barkerus, Illu- | strissimæ Regiæ Maiestatis | Typographus. | Anno Dom. 1603. | 20.9x15.7 cm.   (16),287 p.

The | ANSVVERE | Of The Vicechan- | celovr, The Doctors, | both the Proctors, and other the | Heads of Houses in the Vniversi- | tie of Oxford: | (Agreeable, vndoubtedly, to the ioint and Vniforme | opinion, of all the Deanes and Chapters, and all other | the learned & obedient Clergy, in the Church of Eng: | And confirmed by the expresse consent of the | Vniversitie of Cambridge.) | To the humble Petition of the Ministers of the | Church of England, desiring Reformation of cer- | taine Ceremonies and Abuses of the Church. | . . . (5 lines ; ornament).

At Oxford, | Printed by Joseph Barnes, and are to be sold in Pauls Church-yard at | the signe of the Crowne by Simon Waterson. 1603. | 18x13.8cm.   (24),32p.
Third edition mentioned in Madan's Oxford Press, 1603: No. 8.

BELL, Thomas.   The Anatomie | Of Popish Ty- | rannie: | Wherein is conteyned a plaine declara- | tion and Christian censure, of all the princi- | pall parts, of the Libels, Letters, Edictes, Pamphlets, | and Bookes, lately published by the Secular- | priests and English hispanized Iesuites, with | their Iesuited Arch-priest, both | pleasant and profitable, to all | well affected readers. | . . . (2 lines; device).

London, | Printed by Iohn Harison, for Richard Bankworth, | dwelling in Paules Churchyard at the signe of | the Sunne. 1603. | 18.7x14 cm.   (24),184,(8)p
Epistle Dedicatorie, signed.

BROUGHTON, Hugh.   Declaration of gene- | rall corruption of Religion, Scri- | pture and all learning; wrought | by D. Bilson. | While he breedeth a new opinion, that our Lord went from | Paradise to Gehenna, to triumph over the | Devills. | To the most reverend Father in God Iohn Wh. | Doct. in Divinitie, and Metropolitan | of England. | By Hvgh Brovghton. | (device).

1603. | 17.2x13.1 cm.   (8)p.

CLAPHAM, Henoch. Three Partes | of Salomon his Song of Songs, | expounded. | The first Part printed before: but now | reprinted and enlarged. | The { Second | and | Third} Partes | Neuer printed before. | All which **Parts are** here expounded and applied | for the Readers good. | By Henoch Clapham. | . . . (2 lines; device).

Printed at London by Valentine Sims for Edmund Mutton | dwelling in Paternoster-Row at the signe of | the Huntes-man. 1603. | 17.8x13.7cm. (16),89;(5), 91–138;(8),141–298,(1)p. Mispagings. Two sub. t.p.

COVELL, William. A Ivst And | Temperate De- | fence Of The Five Books | Of Ecclesiastical Policie: | Written By M. Richard | Hooker: | Against an vncharitable Letter of certain English Pro- | testants (as they tearme themselues) crauing reso- | lution, in some matters of doctrine, which | seeme to ouerthrow the foundation | of religion, and the Church | amongst vs. | Written by William Covel | Doctor in Diuinitie. | The contents whereof are in | the page following. | . . . (2 lines: ornament).

At London | Printed by P. Short for Clement Knight, | dwelling at the signe of the holy Lambe in | Paules church-yard. 1603. | 17.7x13.3 cm. (6),154 p.

DENT, Arthur. The Rvine | Of Rome: | Or | An Exposition | vpon the whole Reuelation. | Wherein is plainly shewed and proued, that the | Popish Religion, together with all the power and au- | thoritie of Rome, shall ebbe and decay still more | and more throughout all the Churches | of Europe, and come to an vtter ouer- | throw euen in this life before | the end of the world. | Written especially for the comfort of Protestants, and | the daunting of Papists, Seminary Priests, Ie- | suites, and all that cursed rabble. | Published by Arthur Dent, Preacher of the word of God, | at South-Shoobery in Essex. | . . . (6 lines; ornament)

London Printed for Simon Waterson and Cutbert Burby, 1603. | 17.2x13.1cm. (14),306p.

DILLINGHAM, Francis. A | Qvartron Of Rea- | sons, composed by Doctor Hill, vn- | quartered, and prooued a quartron of | follies: by Francis Dillingham, Bachelour | of Diuinitie. | . . . (5 lines ; device).

Printed by Iohn Legat, Printer to | the Vniuersitie of Cambridge. 1603. | And are to be sold at the signe of the Crowne in Pauls Church- | yard by Simon Waterson. | 17.5x13.4cm. (5),104p. Misprinted, 204.

A | DISCOVERY of the vnnatu- | rall and traiterous Conspiracie | of Scottish Papists, against God, | his Church, their natiue Countrie, the | Kings Majesties person and | estate. | Set downe, as it was confessed and | subscribed by M.George Ker, then remaining | in prison, and Dauid Grahame of Fentrie, iustly | executed for his treason in | Edinburgh. | Wherevnto are annexed, certaine intercep- | ted Letters, vvritten by sundry of that faction | to the same purpose. | First Printed and published in Edinburgh | at the speciall commaund of the Kings | Majestie. | (ornament).

Printed at London by T. Snodham, and are to | be sould at the house of T.Este. | 1603. | 17.3x12.3cm. (6),25p.

DOVE, John. A | Perswasion | to the English Recusants, to Reconcile | themselues to the Church of | England. | Written for the better satisfaction of | those which be ignorant. | By Iohn Doue Doctor of Diuinitie. | . . . (5 lines; device).

Printed at London by V.S. for Cuthbert Burby dvvelling | in Paules churchyard at the signe of the | Swanne. 1603. | 17.3x13.cm. (4),34,(1)p.

DOWNAME, George. A | Treatise Con- | cerning Anti- | Christ, Divided In- | to Two Bookes, The | Former, Proving That | The Pope Is An- | tichrist: | The Latter, Maintai- | ning the same assertion, against all the | obiections of Robert Bellarmine, | Iesuit and Cardinall of the Church | of Rome. | By George Dovvname, Doctor of Diuinitie, | and lately reader of the Diuinity Lecture | in Paules. | (4 lines ; ornament)

At London | Imprinted for Cuthbert Burbie. 1603. | 17.6x13.7 cm. (8),142, 192 p.

ESTEY, George. Certaine | Godly and learned Ex- | positions vpon diuers parts of | Scripture. | As They Were Prea- | ched, and afterwards more briefly penned by that | vvorthy man of God, Maister George Estey, sometimes | fellovve of Goneuill and Caius Colledge | in Cambridge. | Late Preacher of the word of God in | Saint Edmunds Burie. | (ornament).

At London, | Printed by I.R. for Richard Banck- | worth, and are to be sold in Paules Church- | yard, at the signe of the Sunne. | 1603. | 17.8x13.2cm. (3),74; 156fol.

HAYWARD, John. An | Ansvver To | The First Part | Of A Certaine Con- | ference, Concerning | Svccession, Pvblished | not long since vnder the name | of R.Dolman. | (cut)

At London | Imprinted for Simon Waterson, and | Cuthbert Burbie. | 1603. | 17.5x13.4cm. (6, 24),17–48,(49–152)p.
Epistle Dedicatorie, signed.

HEYDON, Christopher. A | Defence Of Ivdici- | all Astrologie, In | Answer To A Treatise | lately published by M. Iohn Chamber. | Wherein all those places of Scripture, Councells, Fathers, Schoole- | men, later Divines, Philosophers, Histories, Lawes, Constituti- | ons, and reasons drawne out of Sextus Empiricus, Picus, Pere- | rius, Sixtus ab Heminga, and others, against this Arte, are par- | ticularly examined: and the lawfulnes thereof, by equiualent | proofes warranted. | By Sir Christopher Heydon Knight. | (device). Seene and allowed. |

Printed by Iohn Legat, Prin- | ter to the Vniversitie of Cambridge. 1603. | And are to be sold in Pauls Churchyard at the signe of the Crowne | by Simon Waterson. | 18.5x14.3cm. (16),551 , (51)p.

JAMES I. Glaubens Bekantnuss. | Darinnen | Jacob, diss Namens | der Erste, König in Engeland, Schott- | land, &c. Sampt seinen Rhäten, gantzem Köni- | glichem Hause, vnd vnzelichen andern, vor dem Par- | lament vnd versamleten Ständen der | Cron Engelland, | Gott zu Ehren, vnd jedermeniglichem zur | Aufferbauwung, | Zu dem Christlichen wah-

ren Glau- | ben, vnd der reinen Religion, als die in dem | reinen Wort
Gottes durch die H. Propheten vnd | Apostel verfasset, offentlich sich
bekant, geschwo- | ren, vnd selberst vnterschrieben. | Sampt einer
gnedigen Antwort, so Ihre | Mayestet den geflüchtigten Kirchen in
Enge- | land, &c. auff ihr ansuchen wi- | derfahren lassen. | Auss dem
zu Lunden, auss Köni- | glicher Mayest. befelch den 1. Junij 1603. |
gedruckten Exemplar, in diese Spra- | che fleissigst vbergesetzt. | (device).

Getruckt Anno | 1603. | 18.6x14.2cm. 8p.

JEWEL, John. Certaine | Sermons | Preached Be- | fore the Queens
Maiestie, and | at 'Paules crosse, by the reuerend | Father Iohn Ievvel
late | Bishoppe of Salisbury. | Wherunto is added a short Trea- | tise
of the Sacraments, gathered out | of other his Sermons, made vpon that
matter, | in his Cathedrall Church at | Salisburie. | (device).

Imprinted at London for William Leake, dwelling | in Paules Church-yard at
the signe of the Holy | Ghost. 1603. | 15.7x10.4 cm. (10),247,(1),117. Colophon.
Pp (1-2) blank.

JEWEL, John. A | Treatise | Of The Sacra- | ments, gathered out
of certaine | Sermons, which the Reuerend | Father in God, Bishoppe
Iewell, | preached at Salisburie. | (device).

At London, | Printed for VVilliam Leake, dwelling | in Paules Church-yard, at
the Signe | of the Holy Ghost. | 1603. | 15.7x10.4cm. (1),117p.
Appended to his Certaine Sermons: 1603.

MURIELL, Christopher. An | Ansvver | Vnto The | Catholiqves |
Svpplication, Pre- | sented Vnto The Kings | Maiestie, for a tolleration
of Popish | religion in England. | Wherein Is Contained A | confutation
of their vnreasonable petitions, and | slaunderous lyes against our late
Soueraigne Queene | Elizabeth, whose happie and gratious gouerne-
ment, | the Papists in their said supplication do so pe- | remptorilie
traduce. | Together with an information vnto his Maiestie of di- | uers
their wicked and treasonable practices, attempted in | the life time
of our late Queene his worthy predecessor, | whose life they alvvayes
sought meanes | to extinguish. | Wherevnto is annexed the Supplication
of the Pa- | pists, word for word as it was presented vnto the | Kings
Maiestie: With some necessarie an- | notations thereupon. | Written
by Christopher Muriell | the elder. |

Imprinted at London by R.R. for Francis Burton, | and are to be solde in
Paules Church-yard at the | signe of the White-Lyon. 1603. | 17.2x12.7 cm.
(1,26) p.

PARSONS, Robert. A | Brief, And | Cleere, Confvta- | tion, Of A
New, Vaine, | and vaunting Chalenge, made by O.E. | Minister, vnto
N.D. Author of | the Warn-word. | Wherin | Yssue is ioyned vpon the
fiue seueral pointes, | proposed by the Chalenger: and his egregious |
ignorance, falshood, and folly, discouered in | them all. | By W.R. |
The particular pointes and heades of euery | Chalenge, follow in the
second page. | . . . (8 lines).

Imprinted vvith licence. | Anno Domini 1603. | 14.9x9.4cm. (9),218,(13)p.
Cambr.Univ.Cat. 6851.

PARSONS, Robert. The | First Part | Of The Reso- | lvtion Of Religion, De- | vided Into Two Bookes, Con- | tayning a Demonstration of the Ne- | cessity of a Diuine and Super- | naturall Worshippe. | (three stars). | In The First, Against All A- | theists and Epicures: In the second, that Christian Ca- | tholicke Religion is the same in particuler, and more | certaine in euery Article thereof, then any hu- | mane or experimented knowledge, against | Iewes, Mahumetans, Pagans, and | other externall enemies | of Christ. | Manifestly Convincing All | their Sects and Professions, of intollera- | ble errors, and irreligious abuses. | (ornament)

Printed With Licence. 1603. | 13.9x9.5cm. (8),281,(4)p.
Anon.Cambr.Univ.Cat. 6852.

PARSONS, Robert. A Treatise | Of Three | Conversions | Of England | from Paganisme to Christian | Religion. | The First vnder the Apostles, in the first age after | Christ: The Second vnder Pope Eleutherius and | K. Lucius, in the second age. The Third, vnder Pope | Gregory the Great, and K. Ethelbert in the sixth age; | vvith diuers other matters thereunto apperteyning. | Divided | Into three partes, as appeareth in the next page. | The former two whereof are handled in | this booke, and dedicated to the | Catholikes of England. | VVith a new addition to the said Catholikes, vpon the nevvs | of the late Q. death, and succession of his Maiestie of | Scotland, to the crovvne of England. | By N.D. Author of the VVarn-vvord. | . . . 5 lines).

Imprinted with licence, anno. 1603. | 14.x9.3cm (69),658,(28)p. Index after "Roman", Vv8. missing: 4 pages.
Gillow. V: 283.

PERKINS, William. Ευζωια: | hoc est | De Bene Beateqve | Vivendi Ratione | Tractatvs. | Auctore | Gvilielmo Perkinso | Theologo Anglo. | Latinus e Belgico factus a I. H. | Quouis, inprimis autem turbido rerum statu, | seu tempore, maxime vtilis, & necessarius. | (device)

Hanoviæ | Apud Guilielmum Antinium, | M D CIII. | 15.9x9.6cm. 63p.

PERKINS, William. Myrothecivm: | hoc est, | De Natvra | Diversisqve Mor- | tis Generibvs: | Et | De Ratione Bene, | feliciterque moriendi, | Tractatvs. | Auctore | Gvilielmo Perkinso | Theologo Anglo. | Latinus e Belgico factus | a | C. B. Ecclesiæ Belgicæ, quæ est Hanouiæ, | Ministro. | (device).

Hanoviæ | Apud Guilielmum Antonium, M D CIII. | 15.9x9.6cm. 154,(1)p.

POWELL, Gabriel. Der Catholijcken | Svpplicatie | aen de Conicklijcke Majesteyt, | tot Toelatinghe vande Catholijcke Re- | ligie in England. | Met weynighe ende corte aenwysinghen | op de canten ghestelt. | Waer by noch ghevoecht is ghelijck teghen malcandren | ghestelt, Een Supplicerende Teghen-ghewichte, ghedaen | by de Protestanten aende selve Conincklicke | Maiesteyt. | Tsamen met de redenen van beyde zijden, voor ende tegen het | toelaten van verscheyden Religien. | Wt den Enghelschen overgheset door Richard Schilders. | (ornament).

Middelbvrgh, | Ghedruct by Richard Schilders, Drucker der Heeren | Staten van Zeelandt, wonende inden langhen | Delft inden Olyphant. 1603. | 20.7x15.9 cm. 40 p. Mispaged at end.
Tot den Christelicken Leser, signed.

POWELL, Gabriel. The | Catholikes | Svpplication Vn- | to The Kings Maiestie; | For Toleration Of | Catholike Religion in | England: | With Short Notes Or A- | nimaduersions in the margine. | Whereunto is annexed Parallel-wise, a Supplicatorie | Counterpoyse of the Protestants, vnto | the same most excellent | Maiestie. | Together with the reasons of both sides, for | and against toleration of diuers | Religions. | (device).

At London | Imprinted by Felix Kyngston, for Edmund Weauer, | and are to be solde at his shop, at the great | North doore of Paules Church. | 1603. | 17.7x 13.7 cm. 3–39p.
To the Christian Reader, signed.

POWELL, Gabriel. The | Resolved | Christian; | Exhorting to Resolution. | Written, to comfort the Faint-hearted, to | strengthen the faithfull, to recal the world- | ling, and to perswade All Men, so to run, | that they may obtaine. | Corrected and enlarged. | The fourth Edition. | (device).

Printed at London for Thomas | Bushell. 1693. | Line border. 13.3x8.6cm. (16),302p. Lacks pp. 263–266.
Epistle Dedicatorie, signed.

PRICKET, Robert. Vnto The | Most High | And Mightie Prince, his Soueraigne Lord | King Iames. A poore Sub- | iect sendeth, A Souldiors Reso- | lution; humbly to waite vpon | his Maiestie. | In This Little | Booke the godly Vertues of our | Mighty King are specified, with dis- | scription of our late Queene, (and still renow- | ned) Elizas Gouernement: The Pope and | Papists are in their colours set forth, their | purposes laid open, and their hopes | dissolued, the happie peace of England | is well described, and the long | continuance thereof hum- | bly prayed for. | (device).

London | Printed by Iohn Windet, for Walter Burre, dwelling | in Paules Churchyeard at the Signe of the Crane. | 1603. | 17.8x13.5cm. (2),22fol.
Epistle Dedicatorie, signed.

ROGERS, Richard. Seven | Treatises, | Containing Svch | Direction As Is Gathered | Ovt Of The Holie Scriptvres, | leading and guiding to true happines, both in this life, | and in the life to come: and may be called the | practise of Christianitie. | Profitable For All Svch As Hear- | tily Desire The Same: In The Which, | more particularly true Christians may learne how to leade a | godly and comfortable life euery day. | Penned By Richard Rogers, Preacher Of | the word of God at Wethersfield in Essex. | . . . (5 lines; device).

At London | Imprinted by Felix Kyngston, for Thomas Man, | and Robert Dexter, and are to be sold at the brasen | Serpent in Pauls Churchyard. 1603. | 26.6x18.2cm.(24), 597,(32)p.

ROLLOCK, Robert. Analysis Logica | In Epistolam | Pavli Apos- | toli | Ad Galatas. | Authore | D.Roberto Rolloco | Scoto, Ministro Iesu | Christi, & | Rectore Academiæ Edin- | burgensis. | (device)
Excvdebat | Iacobvs Stoer, | M.DCIII. | 14.6x9.7cm. (12),179p.

ROLLOCK, Robert. Lectvres | Vpon The Epi- | stle of Pavl To | The | Colossians. | Preached By That Faithfull | seruant of God, | Maister Robert Rollok, | sometime Rector of the Vniuersitie of | Edenburgh. | . . . (8 lines ; device).
At London | Imprinted by Felix Kyngston, dwelling in Pater-noster | row, ouer against the signe of the Checker. | 1603. | 17.3x12.6cm. (8),442p.

ROLLOCK, Robert. A | Treatise Of | Gods Effectval | Calling: | Written First In The Latine | tongue, by the reuerend and faithfull seruant of | Christ, Maister Robert Rollock, | Preacher of Gods word in | Edenburgh. | And Now Faithfvlly Translated | for the benefite of the vnlearned, into the English | tongue, by Henry Holland, Preacher | in London. | . . . (3 lines: device).
At London | Imprinted by Felix Kyngston. | 1603. | 16.9x12.8cm. (22),253p.

SUTCLIFFE, Matthew. Matthæi Svtlivii | De missa papistica, varijsque synagogæ | Rom, circa Eucharistiæ sacramentum | erroribus & corruptelis, | Aduersus Robertum Bellarminum, & vniuersum Iebu- | sæorum & Cananæorum sodalitium | Libri quinque; | Quorum primus de reali præsentia, secundus de | transubstantiatione, tertius de sacrificio mis- | sæ, quartus de missis priuatis & communi- | one sub vna specie, vltimus de missæ cære- | monijs & partibus controuersias tractat. | . . . (4 lines; ornament).
Londini, | Excusum per Adamum Islip. | 1603. | 18.7x14.2 cm. (8),323 fol.

1604

ABBOT, George. The | Reasons | VVhich Doctovr Hill | Hath Brovght, For The | vpholding of Papistry, which is false- | lie termed the Catholike Religion: | Vnmasked, and shewed to be very weake, and vpon exa- | mination most insufficient for that purpose: | By George Abbot Doctor of Divinity & Deane | of the Cathedrall Church in VVinchester. | The first Part. | Joh.9.4. | . . . (4 lines; ornament).
At Oxford, | Printed by Joseph Barnes, & are to be sold in Paules | Churchyarde at the signe of the Crowne by | Simon VVaterson. 1604. | 17.3x13.2 cm. (5),438,(6)p

The | ANSVVERE | Of The Vicechan- | celovr, The Doctors, | both the Proctors, and other the | Heads of Houses in the Vniversi- | tie of Oxford: | (Agreeable, vndoubtedly, to the ioint and Vniforme | opinion, of all the Deanes and Chapters, and all other | the learned & obedient Cleargy, in the Church of Eng: | And confirmed by the expresse consent of the | Vniversitie of Cambridge.) | To the humble Petition of the Ministers of the | Church of England, desiring Reformation of cer- | taine Ceremonies and Abuses of the Church. | . . . (5 lines ; device).

    At Oxford, | Printed by Ioseph Barnes, and are to bee sold in Paules Churchyard at | the signe of the Crowne by Simon Watetson. 1604. | 17.7x13.4lm. (22, 22) p.

    BABINGTON, Gervase. Comfortable Notes | Vpon the bookes of Exodus and Leui- | ticus, as before vpon Genesis. | Gathered and laid downe still in this plaine | manner, for the good of them that cannot vse better | helpes, and yet are carefull to read the Scriptures, | and verie desirous to finde the comfort in | them. | By | The Reuerend Father in God Geruase | Babington, Doctor of Diuinitie, | and Bishop of Worcester. | With a Table of the principall matters contained in | this Booke. | . . . (3 lines).

    At London, | Printed for Thomas Chard. | Anno Dom. 1604. | 17.8x13.6cm. (20),466,(1) ;(14),223p.   Sub.title for Leviticus.

    From the library of Walter W. Law.

    BARLOW, William. The | Svmme And Svb- | stance Of The Con- | ference, which, it pleased his Excellent | Maiestie to haue with the Lords, Bishops, | and other of his Clergie, (at vvhich the | most of the Lordes of the Councell were pre- | sent) in his Maiesties Priuy-Chamber, at | Hampton Court. Ianuary 14. 1603. | Contracted by VVilliam Barlovv, | Doctor of Diuinity, and Deane of Chester. | Whereunto are added, some Copies, (scattered | abroad,) vnsauory, and vntrue. | (device).

    London | Printed by Iohn Windet, for Mathew Law, | and are to be sold at his shop in Powles | Churchyard, neare S. Austens | Gate. 1604. | 19.4x14.2 cm. (7),103,(5)p.

    First impression.

    BARLOW, William. The | Svmme And Svb- | stance Of The Con- | ference, which, it pleased his Excellent | Maiestie, to haue with the Lords Bishops, | and other of his Clergie, (vvhereat the | most of the Lordes of the Councell were pre- | sent)in his Maiesties Priuy-Chamber, at | Hampton Court. Ianuary 14, 1603. | Contracted by VVilliam Barlovv, | Doctor of Diuinity, and Deane of Chester. | Whereunto are added, some Copies, (scattered | abroad,)vnsauory, and vntrue. | (device)

    London | Printed by Iohn Windet, for Mathew Law, | and are to be sold at his shop in Paules | Churchyard, neare S.Austens | Gate. 1604. | 17.8x13.2cm. (7),103,(5)p.

    Second impression

    BILSON, Thomas. The | Svrvey | Of Christs | Svfferings | For Mans | redemption: | And | Of His Descent | To Hades Or Hel | for our deliuerance: | By Thomas Bilson Bishop | of Winchester. | The Contents whereof may be seene in certaine Resolutions before the | Booke, in the Titles ouer the Pages, and in a | Table made to that end. | 10 lines)   Perused and allowed by publike Authoritie. |

    London, | Printed by Melchisedech Bradwood for Iohn Bill. | M.DC.III. | 28.6x18.9 cm.   (19),678,(12) p.

BISHOP, William. A Reformation | Of A Catho- | like Deformed: By M.W. | Perkins. Wherein The Chiefe | Controversies In Reli- | gion, Are Methodically, | and learnedly handled. | Made by D.B.P. | The Former Part. | . . . (3 lines; lace decoration)

Printed with Priuiledge. 1604. | Lace border. 19.5x14.3cm. (19),119;57p.
Gillow.I:221.

BOWNDE, Nicholas. Medicines For | The Plagve: | That is, | Godly and fruitfull Sermons vpon | part of the twentieth Psalme, full of instru- | ctions and comfort: very fit generally for all | times of affliction, but more particularly ap- | plied to this late visitation of | the Plague. | Preached at the same time at Norton in Suffolke, | by Nicholas Bownd, Doctor of Diuinitie. | And now published for the further good of all | those that loue and feare the Lord. | Perused, and allowed. | . . . (6 lines)

London, | Printed by Adam Islip for Cuthbert Burbie, | and are to be sold at the Swan in Paules | Churchyard. 1604. | 18.8x13.7cm. (12),301p.

BRADSHAW, William. A Shorte | Treatise, Of | the crosse in Baptisme con | tracted into this syllogisme. | No humane ordinance becomming an Idoll, | may lawfully be vsed in the seruice of God. | But the signe of the crosse being a humane | ordinance is become an Idoll: ergo | The signe of the crosse may not lawfully be | vsed in the seruice of God. | (ornament).

Amsterdam | Printed by I.H. 1604. | 13.5x9.cm. (4),1–21,(4)p.
Anon. Camb.Univ.Cat. No.6349

BRADSHAW, William. A Treatise | Of Divine | Worship, Tend- ing | to prove that the Ceremonies im- | posed vpon the Ministers of the Gospell | in England, in present contro- | versie, are in their vse | vnlawfull. | (ornament).

1604. | 13.6x8.8cm. 47p.
H&L. Sometimes ascribed to Henry Jacob. Cambr.Univ.Cat.6468.

BRIDGES, John. Sacro-sanctum Novum | Testamentum Domini Serva- | toris nostri Iesv Christi, in Hex- | ametros versus ad verbum & genui- | num sensum fideliter in Latinam linguam | translatum, per Iohannem Episco- | pum Oxoniensem. | (ornament).

Londini | Excudebat Valentinus Simsius. | M DC III. | Border. 15.8x10.2cm. (45),736,(14)p.

BROUGHTON, Hugh. An | Adverti- | sement Of Cor- | rvption In Ovr | Handling Of | Religion. | To the Kings Majestie. | By Hvgh Brovghton. | (lace device).

1604. | Lace border. 17.8x13.5cm. (1, 109, 1)p

BROUGHTON, Hugh. Two little workes defensiue of our Re- | demption, That our Lord went through | the veile of his flesh into Heaven, to ap- | peare before God for vs. | Which iourney a Talmudist, as the Gospell | would terme, a going vp to Paradise: But Hea- | then Greek, a going down to Hades, and Latin, | Descendere ad inferos. | Wherein the vnlearned barbarous anger God and man, | saying, That Iesus descended to Hell. and yeelde | vnto ihe blasphemous Iewes by sure conse- | quence vpon their words, That he | should not be the Holy one | of God. | By Hvgh Brovghton. | . . . (2 lines; device)

1604. | 17.2x13.1 cm. (8)p. Without register.

CARTWRIGHT, Thomas. Metaphrasis Et | Homiliæ | In Librum | Salomonis, | qui inscribitur | Ecclesiastes: | Authore | Thoma Cartwright, | Anglo. | (device).

Marpurgi Cattorum, | Typis Pauli Egenolphi, Typogr. Acad. | M D CIV. | 14.6x 9.3cm. (8),632p.

CONSTITUTIONES | Sive | Canones Ecclesiastici, | Per Episcopum | Londinensem, | Præsidem Synodi pro Cantuariensi Pro- | vincia, ac reliquos Episcopos, & Clerum ejusdem | Provinciæ ex Regia authoritate tractati, & | conclusi | In ipsorum Synodo inchoata Londini, Anno Salutis | millesimo, sexcentesimo tertio, regnique Sere- | nissimi Principis, Clementissimi Domini nostri | Iacobi Dei gratia Angliæ, Franciae & Hiberniæ | Regis primo, & Scotiæ tricesimo septimo: | Ab eadem Regia Majestate deinceps approbati, ratihabiti, ac | confirmati, ejusdemque authoritate sub magno Sigillo | Angliæ promulgati, per utramque Provinciam tam Cantu- | ariensem quàm Eboracensem diligenter observandi. |

Londini, | Excudebat Johannes Norton, serenissimæ Regiæ | Majestatis in Latinis, Græcis, & Hebraicis Typo- | graphus. Anno 1604. | Border. 19.5x15.2cm. Pp. 301-372 of Sparrow's Collection: 1661. Also in his reprints in 1675 and 1684.

CONSTITVTIONS | And Canons | Ecclesiasticall, | Treated vpon by the Bishop of Lon- | don, President of the Conuocation for the | Prouince of Canterbury, and the rest of the | Bishops and Clergie of the | sayd Prouince: | And agreed vpon with the Kings Maiesties Licence in their Sy. | node begun at London Anno Dom. 1603. And in the | yeere of the raigne of our Soueraigne Lord Iames | by the grace of God King of England, | France and Ireland the first, and | of Scotland the 37. | And now published for the due obseruation of them by his | Maiesties authoritie, vnder the great | Seale of England. | (ornament).

Imprinted At London | by Robert Barker, Printer to the Kings | most Excellent Maiestie. | Anno. 1604. | Colophon. 19.3x15.1 cm. (21,150)p.

CONSTITVTIONS | And Canons | Ecclesiasticall, | Treated vpon by the Bishop of Lon- | don, President of the Conuocation for the | Prouince of Canterbury, and the rest of | the Bishops and Clergie of the | said Prouince: | And agreed vpon with the Kings Maiesties | Licence in their Synode begun at London Anno | Dom. 1603. And in the yeere of the raigne of our | Soueraigne Lord Iames by the grace of God King | of England, France, and Ireland the first, | and of Scotland the 37. | And now published for the due obseruation of | them by his Maiesties authoritie, vnder the | great Seale of England. | (ornament)

Imprinted At London | by Robert Barker, Printer to the Kings | most Excellent Maiestie. | Anno 1604. | Colophon.   18.5x12.8cm.   (21,150)p.
Second edition.

COVELL, William. A Modest and rea- | sonable examination, of some things in | vse in the Church of England, sundrie times here- | tofore misliked, and now lately, in a Booke called the | (Plea of the innocent:) and an Assertion for true and Christian | Church policy, made for a full satisfaction to all those, that | are of iudgement, and not possessed with a preiudice a- | gainst this present Church Gouernment, wherein the | principall poynts are fully, and peaceably aun- swered, | which seeme to bee offensiue in the Ecclesiasti- | call State of this Kingdome. | The Contentes whereof are set downe in the Page | following. | By William Couell, Doctor of Diuinitie. | . . . (3 lines; ornament).

At London, | Printed by Humfrey Lownes for Clement Knight, | and are to be solde at his shop at the Signe of the holy | Lambe in Saint Paules Churchyard. | 1604. | 17.3x13.5cm.   (8),215,(8)p.

DOWNAME, George. The Christians | Sanctvarie: | Whereinto being retired, he may safely be | preserued in the middest of all dangers. | Fit for all men to read at all times, especially for those that | are exercised in the schoole of affliction, in the time of | Gods present Visitation. | Described in two Bookes or Treatises: | I. Of the Christian exercise of Fasting. | II. Of holy Inuocation on Gods name. | By George Dovvname Doctor of Diuinitie. | (device).

London, | Printed by Adam Islip for Thomas Man, | dwelling in Pater-noster Row, at the | signe of the Talbot. 1604. | 19.2x14.3 cm.   (4),102p. 1 folding page.

DOWNAME, George. Lectvres | On The XV. | Psalme: | Read in the Cathedrall Church of | S. Paule, in London. | Wherein besides many other very profitable and | necessarie matters, the question of Vsurie is | plainely and fully decided. | By George Dovvname, Doctor | of Diuinitie. | (ornament)

London, | Printed by Adam Islip for Cuthbert Burbie, | and are to be sold in Paules Church-yard | at the signe of the Swan. | 1604. | 18x13.cm.   (6),362,(1)p.
Also another copy from the library of Walter W. Law. 18.9x12.9cm.

GLANVILLE, Ranulf de. Tractatvs | de Legibus & Consuetudini- | bus regni Angliæ, tempore Regis | Henrici secundi compositus, Iusticiæ gu- | bernacula tenente illustri viro Ranvlpho | De Glanvilla iuris regni & antiqua- | rum consuetudinum eo tempore peritissimo. Et illas | solum Leges continet & consuetudines secundum | quas placitatur in Curia Regia ad | Scaccarium & coram Iusti- | cijs vbicunque fuerint. | Qui nunc imprimitur post 50. annos à pri- | ori & prima Impressione, quia in pluribus | concordat cum antiquo libro Legum Scotię | vocato Regiam Maiestatem precipuè | in locis hoc signo notatis. *. | Cum diuersis manuscriptis nuper examinatis: | Cum duplici Indice; vno

Alphabetice in principio | Libri; Altero summorum Capitulorum in fine. |

In ædibus Thomæ Wight. | 1604. | Cum priuilegio Regiæ Maiestatis. | 13.7x9.2 cm. (10),116,(17)fol. A1 has leaf ornament and " j."
Camb.Univ.Libr.2400.

HOOKER, Richard. Of | The Lavves | of Ecclesiasticall | Politie, | Eight bookes. | By Richard Hooker. | (device).

Printed at London by Iohn Windet, dwelling at the signe of the Crosse- | keyes neare Paules wharffe, and are there to | be solde. 1604. | 26.x18.8cm. (4),207,(1)p. Second edition. Appended is the Fifth Book, in the edition of 1597.

JACOB, Henry. Reasons | Taken Ovt Of Gods | Word And The Best Hvmane | Testimonies Proving A Ne- | cessitie Of Reforming | Ovr Chvrches | In England. | Framed and applied to 4. Assertions wherein | the foresaid purpose is contained. | The 4. Assertations are set downe in the | Page next following. | . . . (3 lines; device).

1604. | Border. 17.3x12.8 cm. (7),83p.
Dedication to James I, signed.

JAMES I. Iacobi Primi | Angliæ, Sco- | tiæ, Franciæ, | Et Hiberniæ | Regis, Fidei Defen- | soris, &c. | Βασιλικον Δωρον, | Sive | Regia Institvtio | ad Henricvm Principem | primogenitum Filium suum, | & hæredem proxi- | mum. | (ornament)

Londini, | Excudebat Iohannes Norton, | Serenissimæ Regiæ Maiestati in | Latinis, Græcis, & Hebraicis | Typographus. | Anno Domini M.DC.IIII. | 16.3x9.9 cm. (34),139p.

JAMES I. The | Kings Maiesties Speech, as | it was deliuered by him in the vpper | house of the Parliament to the Lords | Spirituall and Temporall, and to the | Knights, Citizens and Burgesses | there assembled, | On Munday the 19. day of March 1603. | being the first day of this present Parlia- | ment, and the first Parliament of | his Maiesties Raigne. | (device).

Imprinted at London by Robert | Barker, Printer to the Kings | most Excellent Maiestie. | Anno 1604. | 18.5x14.3cm. (2,25)p.

JOHNSON, Francis and AINSWORTH, Henry. An Apologie | Or Defence | Of Svch Trve Christians | as are commonly (but vniustly) called | Brovvnists: | Against such imputations as are layd vpon | them by the Heads and Doctors of | the Vniversity of Oxford. | In their Answer | To the humble Petition of the Ministers of the | Church of England, desiring reformation | of certayne Ceremonies and abuses | of the Church. | . . . (7 lines).

1604. | 17.6x13 cm. (15),118p.
Dexter: 264. Ascribed to John Robinson by H&L., and to Henry Barrow, John Greenwood, and John Penry by DNB.3:298a.

MORNAY, Philippe de. VVorke Con- | cerning the Trunesse of Chri- | stian Religion, written in French: | Against Atheists, Epicures, Paynims, Iewes, Mahumetists, | and other Infidels. By Philip of

Mornay | Lord of Plessie Marlie. | Begunne to be translated into English by that honourable and wor- | thy Gentleman, Syr Philip Sidney Knight, and at his request | finished by Arthur Golding. | Since which time, it hath bene reviewed, and is now the third time publi- | shed, and purged from sundrie faultes escaped heretofore, tho- | row ignorance, carelesnes, or other corruption. | (device).

At London | Printed for George Potter, dwelling at the great | North doore of S. Pauls Church, at the | Signe of the Bible. | 1604. | 18.8x13.7cm. (21),590,(1)p. Title clipped and mounted

PARKES, Richard. A | Briefe An- | svvere Vnto Cer- | taine Obiections And | Reasons against the descension of Christ | into hell, lately sent in writing vnto a Gen- | tleman in the Countrey. | . . . (4 lines; device).

At Oxford, | Printed by Ioseph Barnes, and are to be sold | in Paules Churchyard at the signe of the | Crowne, by Simon VVaterson. 1604. | 17.4x13.8 cm. (7), 58,(1)p.
Anon. Cambr.Univ.Cat:5268.

PARSONS, Robert. A Relation | Of The Triall | Made before the King of France, vpon | the yeare 1600. betvveene the Bishop | of Eureux, and the L. Plessis Mornay. | Abovt | Certayne pointes of corrupting and falsifying authors, | wherof the said Plessis was openly conuicted. | Newly reuewed, and sett forth againe, with a de- | fence therof, against the impugnations both of | the L.Plessis in France, & of O.E. in England. | By N.D. | . . . (3 lines ; ornament).

Imprinted vvith licence | Anno M.DC.IIII. | 16.3x10.5cm 237p.
Appended to his Third Part of a Treatise. . . The First Six Monehts: 1604. Gillow. V: 283.

PARSONS, Robert. A Review | Of Ten Pvblike | Dispvtations | Or Conferences held vvithin the com- | passe of foure yeares, vnder K.Edward | & Qu.Mary, concerning some principall points in Religion, especially of | the Sacrament & sacrifice of the Altar. | VVherby, | May appeare vpon how vveake groundes both Catholike Religion | vvas changed in England; as also the fore-recounted Foxian | Martyrs did build their new opinions, and offer themselues to | the fire for the same, vvhich vvas chiefly vpon the creditt of the | said Disputation. | By N.D. | . . . (4 lines; ornament).

Imprinted vvith licence | Anno M.DC.IIII. | 16.3x10.8cm. 370p.
Part of the Third Part of his Three Conversions of England: 1604. Gillow. V: 284.

PARSONS, Robert. The | Third Part | Of A Treatise | Intituled | Of Three Conversions | Of England. | Conteyninge an examen of the Calendar or Catalo- | gue of Protestant Saintes, Martyrs and Confessors, de- | uised by Fox, and prefixed before his huge Volume of | Actes and Monuments: VVith a Paralel or Compari- | son thereof to the Catholike Roman Calendar, and | Saintes therin conteyned. | The Last Six Monethes. | VVhervnto is annexed in the end, another seuerall Treatise, cal- | led: A re-view of ten publike Disputations, or

Con- | ferences, held in England about matters of Religion, especial- | ly about the Sacrament and Sacrifice of the Altar, vnder King | Edward and Queene Mary. | By N.D. | (ornament; 7 lines).

   Imprinted with licence, Anno Domini 1604. | 16.3x10.8cm. (116),463,(15) ;370p. Gillow. V: 283.

PARSONS, Robert. The | Third Part | Of A Treatise, | Intituled: of three Conuersions of England: | conteyninge. | An examen of the Calendar or Catalogue of Protestant Saints, | Martyrs and Confessors, diuised by Iohn Fox, and pre- | fixed before his volume of Acts and Monuments. VVith a | Pararell or Comparison therof to the Catholike Roman | Calendar, and Saints therin conteyned. | The First Six Monethes. | Whervnto in the end is annexed a defence of a cer- | taine Triall, made before the King of France vpon | the yeare 1600. betweene Monsieur Peron Bishop of | Eureux, and Monsieur Plessis Mornay Gouernour of | Saumur, about sundry points of Religion. | By N.D. | . . . (ornament; 7 lines).

   Imprinted vvith licence, Anno Dñi. 1604. | 16.3x10.5cm. (144),530,(14) ;237p. Gillow. V: 283.

PERKINS, William. Gvilielmi Perkinsi | Problema | De | Romanæ Fidei E- | mentito Catholicismo. | Estq̃; Antidotum contra Thesaurum | Catholicum Iodoci Coccij. | Προπαιδε´α Iuventutis in Lectione omnium Patrum. | Editum post mortem Authoris operâ & studio | Samuelis Wardi. | (device)

   Cantabrigiæ | Ex officina Ioannis Legat. | Anno Dom. M.D.CIIII. | Extant Londini apud Simonem Waterson in Cœmeterio D. | Pauli ad insigne Coronæ. | Line border. 19x13.8cm. (12),244,(12)p.

PERKINS, William. Lectvres Vpon | The Three First | Chapters Of The Revela- | tion: Preached In Cam- | bridge Anno Dom. 1595. by Master William | Perkins, and now published for | the benefite of this Church, | by Robert Hill Bachelor | in Diuinitie. | To which is added an excellent Sermon, penned at the request | of that noble and wise Councellor, Ambrose, Earle of | Warwicke: in which is proued that Rome | is Babylon, and that Babylon is fallen. | . . . (2 lines; device).

   London, | Printed by Richard Field for Cuthbert Burbie, and are | to be sold at his shop in Paules Church-yard, at the | signe of the Swan. 1604. | 18x13.6cm. (17),373p.

PERKINS, William. Satans | Sophistrie | Ansvvered By Ovr | Saviovr Christ, And | in diuers Sermons further manifested | by that worthy man Maister | William Perkins. | To which is added, a Comfort for the feeble | minded: wherein is set downe the | temptations of a Christian. | . . . (2 lines; device).

   London, | Printed by Richard Field for E.E. and are | to be sold at the signe of the Swanne | in Paules Church-yard. | 1604. | 14.3x9.4cm. (16),186p.

POWELL, Gabriel. A | Consideration Of | the Papists Reasons of State and Reli- | gion, for toleration of Poperie | in England, | Intimated In Their | Supplication vnto the Kings Maie- | stie, & the States of the Pre- | sent Parliament. | . . . (6 lines; device).

At Oxford, | Printed by Joseph Barnes, and are to bee sold | in Paules Churchyarde at the signe of the | Crowne, by Simon VVaterson. 1604. | 17.2x13.9 cm. (4),128p.
To the Christian Reader, signed.

POWELL, Gabriel. The | Svpplication | Of Certaine | Masse-Priests falsely called | Catholikes. | Directed to the Kings most excel- | lent Maiestie, now this time of Parlia- | ment, but scattered in corners, to mooue | mal-contents to mutinie. | Published with a Marginall glosse, | and an answer to the Libellers reasons againe re- | uewed and augmented, and by Sections applied | to the seuerall parts of the supplicatory | declamation. | . . . (5lines).

London | Imprinted for William Aspley. | 1604. | 17.1x12.7cm. (6,120)p.
Anon. D N B. 46: 241 a.

RENECHER, Herman. The | Golden Chayne | of Salvation. | Written by that Reverend | and learned man, Maister | Herman Renecher. | And now translated out of | Latine into English. | . . . (8 lines).

At London | Printed by Valentine Simmes | for Thomas Man, dwelling in Pater | noster row, at the Signe | of the Talbot. | 1604. | Lace border. 18x12.5 cm. (12),275p.

SAINT-GERMAIN, Christopher. The | Dialogve | in English, betweene | a Doctor of Diuinity, and | a Student in the Lawes | of England. | Newly corrected & Im- | printed, with new Addi- | tions. | (Ornament).

At London, | Printed by Thomas | Wight. 1604. | Cum Priuilegio. | Lace border. 14.3x9.5 cm. 176,(4)fol.
Anon. Camb.Univ.Cat. No.2402.

SAINT GERMAIN, Christopher. Dialogvs | de fundamentis | Legum Angliæ et | de conscientia. | Per Christophe- | rvm de Sancto Germano com- | muniter Seyngerman con- | fectus, cuius mentio est in | principio secundi libri Dia- | logorum inter sacræ | Theologiæ Doctorem et | Studentem Legum | Angliæ. | (ornament).

In ædibus Thomæ Wight. | 1604. | Cum priuilegio Regiæ Maiestatis. | 13.2x9.3 cm. (4),73,(2)fol
Cambr.Univ.Cat.2401.

SMITH, Henry. Gods Ar- | row Against | Atheists. | By Henry Smith. | (device).

At London | Imprinted by F.K. for Thomas Pauier, and are | to be sold at his shop entring into | the Exchange. 1604. | 18.9x12.9cm. (3),104p.
Part of The Sermons of Master Henry Smith: 1604.

SMITH, Henry. The | Sermons | Of Master | Henry Smith, | gathered into one | volume. | Printed according to his corrected | copies in

his life time. | Whereunto is added, Gods arrow | against Atheists. | (ornament)
  At London: | Imprinted by Felix Kyngston, for | Thomas Man. 1604. | Border. 18.9x13.cm.   600,3–56;(2,34,1);(4,92);(1,44);(2,76);(3),104p.

STOUGHTON, William. An Assertion | For true and Christian | Church-Policie. | Wherein certaine politike | obiections made against the plan- | ting of Pastours and Elders in every Con- | gregation, are sufficientlie aunswered. And | wherein also sundrie projectes are set downe, | how the Discipline by Pastors & Elders may be planted, | without any derogation to the Kings Royal prerogatiue, | any indignitie to the three Estates in Parleament, or | any greater alteration of the laudable Lawes, | Statutes, or Customes of the Realme, | then may well be made with- | out damage to the | people. | (ornament).
  1604. | 13.9x9.1 cm.   (1),16,3–439,(7)p.
  Anon. Dexter:262.   Camb.Univ.Cat.No.6463.

A | SVPPLICATION | to the Kings most excellent | Maiestie, | Wherein, seuerall reasons of State and Religion | are briefely touched: not vnworthie to be read, | and pondered by the Lords, Knights, | and Burgeses of the present Parliament, | and other of all estates. | Prostrated | At his Highnes feete by true affected | Subiects. | . . . (4 lines; device)
  1604. | 17.3x13.4cm.   (1),49,(1)p.

TOOKER, William. Of The | Fabriqve | of the Church and | Church-mens | liuings. | By William Tooker Doctor in | Diuinitie, his Maiesties Chaplaine | in ordinarie. | . . . (6 lines; device).
  London | Printed by Melchisedech Bradwood | for Iohn Norton. 1604. | 15.6x 10.2cm.   (8),132 p.

VERSTEGEN, Richard. Theatrvm | Crudelitatum Hæreticorum | Nostri Temporis. | Editio altera emendatior. |
  Antverpiæ, | Apud Hadrianum Huberti. | Anno M.DCIIII. | Cvm Privilegio. | 21.5x16.6cm.   95p.   Engr.t.p., and 29 engravings.
  Anon. Cambr.Univ.Cat;6134.

WIDLEY, George. The Doctrine | Of The Sabbath, | Handled In Fovre | Severall Bookes | Or Treatises. | The first of which intreateth of the day of rest. | The second, of the duties of the day. | The third, of the persons whom these duties concerne. | And the fourth, the reasons vsed to perswade all persons | to the practice of these duties vpon that day. | Written by G. W. Master of Arts, and Minister of the | word of God in Portsmouth. | . . . (8 lines; device)
  London, | Imprinted by Felix Kyngston for Thomas Man, dwelling | in Paternoster row, at the signe of the Talbot. 1604. | 17.3x12.1cm.   (12),235p.   Mispaged.
  Epistle Dedicatory, signed.

WILLET, Andrew. Limbo-Ma- | stix: | That is, | A Canuise of Limbus Patrum, shew- | ing by euident places of Scripture, inuincible rea- | sons, and pregnant testimonies of some ancient wri- | ters, that

Christ descended not in soule to | Hell, to deliuer the Fathers | from thence. | Containing also a briefe replie to so much of a Pamphlet lately | published, intituled, An answere to certaine obiections | against the descension &c. as lookes that way, and | is personally directed against some wri- | ters of our Church. | . . . (9 lines: ornament).

London | Printed for Thomas Man. | 1604. | 17.4x12.8 cm. (8),60;(7),58,(1) p. Anon. DNB:61:291b.

1605

An | ABRIDGMENT | Of That Booke Which The Mi- | nisters Of Lincoln Diocess | delivered to his Maiestie upon the first of | December last. | Being | The First Part Of An Apolo- | gye For Themselues And | their brethren that refuse the subscrip- | tion, and conformitie which is required. | VVhervnto Is Annexed, | A Table Of Sondry Poynts Not Handled In This | Abridgment, which are other exceptions they take to the | subscription requyred, and shalbe the Argument of the | second part of their Apology. | . . . (15 lines).

Printed 1605. | 17.8x13.5cm. (7),80p.
Reprinted also in 1617.

ARTICLES to be inquired | Of, in the first Metropoliticall Visita-tion | of the most Reuerend Father: Richarde | by Gods Prouidence, Archbushop of Canterbu- | ry, and Primat of all Englande: in, & for, all thiese Diocesses | following, (Viz.) Exeter Norwich, Chicester, St. Davids, | Landaffe, Heriford, Worcester, Bristol, Bath & Welles | and Coventrie & Litchfielde, in the yeare of our | Lorde God, 1605. and in the first yeare of his | Graces Translation. | (device).

At London Printed by Ralph Blower, for | Thomas Pavier, and are to be solde at his Shop | neare the Royall Exchaung, An.Dom.1605. | 18.6x14.3cm. 22p. Pp. 1-2 blank.

BELL, Thomas. The Popes | Funerall. | Containing a plaine, suc- | cinct, and pithy reply, to a pretensed an- | swere of a shamelesse and foolish Libell, intituled, | The Forerunner of Bels downfall. | VVhich is nothing else indeede, (as the indifferent | Reader shall perceiue by the due peruse thereof,) but | an euident manifestation of his owne folly; | ith the vtter confusion of Poperie, and all po- | pish vassals throughout the Christi- | an world. | . . . (6 lines ; ornament).

London | Printed by T.C. For William Welby, and are to be sold at | his shop in Paules Church-yard, at the signe of the | Grayhound. 1605. | 18x13.8cm. (14, 38;73)p.
Anon. Cambr.Univ.Cat.2736.

BELL, Thomas. Thomas | Bels Motiues: | Concerning | Romish Faith | and Religion. | . . . (1 line). The second Edition: | Newly corrected and inlarged by the Author. | (lace ornament).

Printed by Iohn Legate, prynter to the | Vniuersity of Cambridge. 1605. | And are to be sold at the signe of the Crovvne | in Paules Church-yard. | 17.2x13.3cm. (16),157,(1)p.

BELL, Thomas. The | VVoefull crie of | Rome. | Containing a de-fiance to popery. With Tho- | mas Bells second challenge to all fauorites | of that Romish faction. | Succinctly comprehending much variety of mat- | ter, full of honest recreation, and very profitable | and expedient for all sorts of people: but especially | for all simply seduced Papists. | . . . (2 lines; device).

London. | Printed by T.C. for William Welby, and are to be sold at | his shop in Paules Church-yard, at the signe of the | Grayhound. 1605. | 18.4x14.4cm. (6), 77,(1)p.

BRADSHAW, William. English Pvritanisme | Containe- | ning. | The maine opinions of the rigidest | sort of those that are called Puritanes | In the Realme of England. | . . . (10 lines; ornament).

Printed 1605. | 14.5x9.7cm. (2),35p.
Anon. Camb.Univ.Cat. 6380.

BROUGHTON, Hugh. A Replie | Vpon Ther. R.F. Th. | VVinton | For Heads Of His Di- | vinity In His Ser- | mon And Svrvey: | Hovv he taught à perfect truth, | that our Lord vvent hēce to Pa- | radise: But adding that he vvent | thence to Hades, & striving | to prove that, he inju- | rieth all learning | & Christianitie. | To The Most No- | ble Henry Prin- | ce Of Great Bri- | tany. | (ornament).

1605. | 13.5x8.5cm. 48p.
Signed at end.

BROUGHTON, Hugh and AINSWORTH, Henry. Certayne Qvestions | Concerning | 1. Silk, or vvool, in the High Priests Ephod. | 2. Idol temples, commonly called Churches. | 3. The forme of Prayer, commonly called | the Lords prayer. | 4. Excommunication, &c. | Handled betvveen | Mr Hugh Broughton remayning of late at | Amsterdam in the Low countreyes. | And | Mr Henry Ainsvvorth Teacher of the exiled English | Church at Amsterdam aforesayd. | . . . (device; 2 lines).

1605. | Border. 17.7x13.6 cm. (4),39p.
Edited by F.B.

CALVINUS, Justus. Ivsti Baronii | Veteracastrensis | SS. Th. Et I.V.D.Illmo. Archpo. | Moguntino a consilijs. | Præscripti- | onvm Adversvs | Hæreticos Per Petva- | rum ex SS. Orthodoxis potissimum | Patribus | Tractatvs VI. | Itervm Editi, Ac Vin- | dicijs aduersus Ioan. Rainol- | dvm Anglo Caluinianum | aucti. | . . . (6 lines).

Mogvntiæ | Apvd Ioannem Albinvm. | Anno M.DCV. | 15.x9.2cm. (32),712, (79)p.
Catholic Encycl. III, 204 a.

CERTAINE | Considerations | drawne from the Canons of the | last Sinod, and other the Kings Ecclesia- | sticall and statute law, ad informandum animum Do- | mini Episcopi Wigornensis, seu alterius cuiusuis iudicis | ecclesiastici, ne temere & inconsulto prosiliant ad depriua- | tionem Ministrorum Ecclesiæ: for not subscription, for | the not exact vse of the order and forme of the booke | of common prayer, heeretofore provided by the | Parishioners of any parish Church, within | the Diocesse of Worcester, or for the | not precise practise of the rites, | ceremonies, & ornaments | of the Church. | . . . (9 lines; device).

1605. | Border. 17.8x13.3 cm. (16),52p.

CERTAINE | Demandes With | their grounds, drawne out of holy | Writ, and propounded in foro conscientiæ by | some religious Gentl. vnto the reverend Fathers, | Richard Archbishop of Canterbury, Richard Bishop of | London, William Bishop of Lincolne, Garvase Bishop of | Worcester, William Bishop of Exeter, & Thomas Bishop | of Peterbourough, wherevnto the said Gentl. re- | quire that it would please their Lord- | ships to make a true, plaine, di- | rect, honest and resolute | aunswere. | . . . (10 lines; device)

1605. | Border. 18.5x14.8 cm. 68p.

GREENHAM, Richard. The | Workes | Of The Reverend | And Faithfvll Ser- | vant Of Iesvs Christ | M.Richard Greenham, Minister | And Preacher Of The Word | of God, collected into one | volume: | Revised, Corrected, | And Pvblished, For The Fvr- | ther Bvilding Of All Svch As Love | the trueth, and desire to know the power of | godlinesse. | The Fovrth And Last Edition: | In Which Is Added Sixe Severall Treatises | of the same Author, neuer before published: | By H.H.(olland) | . . . (3 lines; device).

At London | Imprinted by Felix Kyngston, for Cvthbert Bvrbie, | and are to be solde at his shop in Paules Church-yard at the | signe of the Swanne. 1605. | 27x18cm. (22),875p. (4 parts: Pt. 2, 3d ed. Pts. 3–4, 1st ed. 6 sub.t.p. Table misplaced, in front of book, and imperfect, containing only first 4p, Ffff 1–2.

HIERON, Samuel. A | Short Dialogve | Proving That The Ceremo- | nyes, And Some Other Corrvpti- | ons now in question, are defended, by none other | Arguments then such as the Papists haue here | tofore vsed; And our Protestant writers haue | long since answered | VVherevnto Are Annexed, | Certayne Considerations | Why The Ministers Shovld Not | be removed for the Subscription & Ceremonies. | . . . (10 lines).

Printed 1605. | 17.5x13 cm. (5),69p.
Dexter:282.

HUTTEN, Leonard. An | Ansvvere To A Cer- | taine Treatise Of The | Crosse In Baptisme. | Intituled | A Short Treatise of the Crosse in Baptisme, con- | tracted into this Syllogisme. | No humane ordinance becomming an Idoll may law- | fully be vsed in the service of God. | But the signe of the Crosse, being a humane ordinance | is become an Idoll. Ergo: | The signe of the Crosse, may not lawfully bee vsed in the | service of God. | VVherein not only the weaknesse of the Syllogisme it | selfe, but also of the grounds and proofes there- | of, are plainely discovered. | By L.H. Doct. of Divinitie. | . . . (5 lines; ornament).

Printed at Oxford by Ioseph Barnes, and are to be | sold in Paules Church-yard at the signe of the | Crowne, by Simon Waterson. 1605. | 18.5x14.5cm. (7), 139p.

Epistle dedicatory, signed

HUTTON, Thomas. Reasons For Refvsal | Of Svbscription To The | booke of Common praier vnder the | hands of certaine Ministers of Devon and | Cornwall word for word as they were ex- | hibited by them to the Right Reverend | Father in God William Co- | ton Doctor of Diuinitie, | L. Bishop of Exceter. | VVith an Amsvvere At Se- | verall times returned them in publike conference | and in diverse sermons vpon occasion prea- | ched in the Cathedrall Church of Exceter, | by Thomas Hvtton, Bachi- | ler of Divinitie & fellow of | St. Iohns Coll. in Oxon. | And Now Pvblished At | the very earnest intreatie of some especiall | friends for a farther contentment of o- | ther the Kings Maiesties good | and loyall Subiects. | . . . (3 lines; device).

Printed at Oxford by Joseph Barnes, and are to be | sold in Paules Church-yard at the signe of the | Crowne by Simon VVaterson. 1605. | 18.3x14.4 cm.   200p.

JEFFERY, Richard. The | Sonne Of Gods | entertainment by the | sonnes of men. | Set forth in a Sermon at Paules | Crosse the seauenth of | October. 1604. | By Richard Iefferay of Magdalen | Colledge in Oxford. | . . . (5 lines ; ornament).

At London | Printed by T.P. for Henrie Tomes, and are to be | sold at his shop at Graies Inne new gate | in Holborne. 1605. | 17.4x12.7cm.   (2),47p.

KELLISON, Matthew. [A | S]vrvey Of The | New Religion, Detecting | Many Grosse Absvrdities | Which It Implieth. | Set forth by Matthevv Kellison, | Doctor and Professor of Diuinitie. | Divided Into Eight Bookes. | Nevvly augmented by the Author. | . . . (4 lines; device).

Printed at Doway by Lavrence Kellam, | at the signe of the holie Lambe. | M. DC. V. | 19.7x14.3 cm. 16,(17-52),404,(12)p.
Dexter:260.

MORTON, Thomas. Apologia | Catholica Ex | Meris Iesvitarvm Con- | tradictionibus conflata, in qua Paradoxa, | Hæreses, Blasphemiæ, Scelera, quæ a | Pontificijs obijci Protestantibus solent, | ex ipsorum Pontificiorum | testimonijs diluuntur | omnia. | Eius Libri duo | De Notis Ecclesiæ. | Autore Thoma Mortono Sacræ Theologiæ Baccalaureo, | & quondam in celeberrima Academia Cantabrigiensi | Collegij Iohannis Euangelistæ, Socio. | . . . (2 lines ; device).

Londini, | Excudebat Iohannes Norton, Serenissimæ | Regiæ Maiestatis in Latinis, Græcis, & Hebraicis | Typographus. | Anno Salvtis M.DC.V. | 17.5x13cm.   (18),438,(5)p.

MORTON, Thomas. An | Exact Disco- | verie Of Romish | Doctrine In The Case | Of Conspiracie And | Rebellion, by pregnant | obseruations: | Collected (not without direction from | our Superiours) out of the expresse | dogmaticall principles of Popish Priests | and Doctors. | . . . (3 lines; device).

At London | Imprinted by Felix Kyngston, for C.B. and E.W. | and are to be sould in Paules Church-yard | at the signe of the Swan. 1605. | 17.1x13.3cm.   (4), 54p.

Camb.Univ.Cat.No.7468; cf. Nos.2938-2939. Signed T.M. at end.

ORMEROD, Oliver. The | Pictvre | of a Puritane: | Or, | A Relation of the opinions, qualities, | and practises of the Anabaptists | in Germanie, and of the Puritanes | in England. | VVherein is firmely prooued, that the | Puritanes doe resemble the Anabap- | tists, in aboue fourescore seuerall | thinges. | By O. O. of Emmanuel. | Wherunto is annexed a short treatise, entituled, Pu | ritano-papismus: or a discouerie of Puritan- | Papisme. | . . . (4 lines).

London | Printed by E.A. for Nathaniel Fosbroke, and | are to be solde at his Shop, at the West end | of Paules. 1605. | 17.5x12.3 cm. (14,107)p.
Cambr.Univ.Cat.2018.

PHILIPS, Edward. Certaine | Godly And Lear- | ned Sermons: Preached | by that worthy seruant of Christ | M.Ed.Philips, as they were | deliuered by him in Saint Sauiors | in Southwarke. | And were taken by the pen of H.Yeluerton | of Grayes Inne Gentleman. | . . . (3 lines; device).

London, | Printed by Richard Field for Cuthbert Burbie, and are | to be sold at his shop in Paules church-yard | at the signe of the Swanne. | 1605. | 18.1x13.6 cm. (22),462p.

POWELL, Gabriel. Gabrielis Poueli Ordovicis | Britanni, Davidis F. | Dispvtationvm | Theologicarvm | & Scholasticarum de An- | tichristo & eius Ecclesia, | Libri II. | In Qvibus Certissimis Argvmen- | tis, clarissimisque Testimoniis irrefutabi- | liter demonstratur Papam Romanum Magnum | illum esse Antichristum, & Papanam Ec- | clesiam ipsissimam Antichristi | Synagogam; | Monachorvm Blasphemae So- | cietatis Examini, Disquisitioni & | Considerationi humiliter | Submissi. | Cum triplici Indice, 1.Capitum. 2.Au- | ctorum citatorum. 3.Rerum. | Ad Illustriss. & invictiss. D.Iacobvm potētiss. | Britanniæ Maioris Monarcham, Gallia- | rum & Hiberniæ Regem, &c. |

Londini | Ex Typographeîo Ioan.Windeti, Impensis | Thomæ Man, Bibliopolæ Londinensis. | Anno M. DC. V. | 16.2 x 10. cm. (13),459,(36)p. Colophon.

POWELL, Gabriel. A | Refvtation | Of An Epistle | Apologeticall Written by a Puritan-Papist | to perswade the Permission of the | promiscuous Vse and Profes- | sion of all Sects and | Heresies: | Wherein the vnlawfulnesse and danger of such wicked | Licence is fully declared by auctoritie of Scriptures, | Canons, Councels, Fathers, Lawes of Chri- | stian Emperours, and iudge- | ment of Reason. | Together | With the Punishment of Heretiques | and Idolaters. | (device)

London | Printed by Arnold Hatfield for Thomas Man Iunior | dwelling in Pater-noster-Row at the signe | of the Talbot. 1605. | 17.2x12.9 cm. (11),115p.
To the Christian Reader, signed.

RADFORD, John. A | Directorie | Teaching The | Way To The Trvth In A | Briefe And Plaine | Discovrse Against | the heresies of this time. | Wherevnto Is Added, | A Short Treatise Against | Adiaphorists, Nevters, and such as | say they may be saued in any Sect or | Religion, and would make | of many diuers sects one | Church. | . . . (8 lines)

Printed with licence. 1605. | 13.4x9.2cm. (23),608p.
Epistola dedicatoria, signed.

SALUSTE du Bartas, Guillaume de. Bartas | His | Deuine Weekes & Workes | Translated: | & | Dedicated | To the Kings most excellent | Maiestie | by | Iosvah Sylvester. |

Engraved t.p., without imprint. 18.3x13.3cm. (34),(1),662,(20); (3),674–715p. 8 sub t.p. Imprint of The | Second Weeke: | . . . At London, | Printed by Humfrey Lownes dwelling on Bred- | streete hill at the signe of the Starre. | 1605. | Camb.Univ.Cat. 2476. Lacks Posthumous Bartas, after p.716.

SANDYS, Edwin. A | Relation | Of The State Of | Religion: and with what Hopes and | Policies it hath beene framed, and is maintai- | ned in the severall states of these westerne | parts of the world. | (device)

London, | Printed for Simon Waterson dwel- | ling in Paules Churchyard at the | signe of the Crowne. | 1605. | Line border. 19.1x14.5 cm. (1,180)p. Anon. Cambr.Univ.Cat.2111.

SOUTHWELL, Robert. An | Epistle Of | Comfort: To The Reverend Priests, And | To The Honovrable | Worshipfull, and other of | the lay sort, restrayned in | durance for the Catho- | like Faith. | . . . (5 lines; ornament).

Printed with Licence. 1605. | 14.4x9.6 cm. 419,(3) p. Anon. Cf.Cambr.Univ.Cat.6217.

SYMONDS, William. Pisgah | Evangelica. | By the Method of the Reuelation, presenting | to publike view those Cananites ouer whom our | Lord Iesus Christ and his holie Church shall | triumph after seuerall Battailes. | That Which Is Past Is Shewed In | a briefe Ecclesiasticall Historie, containing most of the Mu- | tations which haue befallen the Church, from the | yeere of our Lord 97, vnto the yeere 1603. as | they haue been shewed vnto S.Iohn in | Patmos, and recorded by such Hi- | storiographers as are of least | suspected faith. | Gathered by William Symonds, sometimes Fellow of | Magdalen Colledge in Oxford. | . . . (9 lines: ornament).

Imprinted at London by Felix Kyngston, for | Edmund Weauer, and are to be sold at his shop at the great | North-doore of S.Pauls Church. 1605. | 18.5x14.2cm. (25),266,(1)p.

TEMPLE, William. A | Logicall | Analysis Of | Twentie Se- | lect Psalmes, | Performed by W.Temple. | . . . (4 lines: device).

Imprinted at London by Felix Kyngston, for | Thomas Man, and are to be sold at his shop in | Pater-noster row, at the signe of the | Talbot. 1605. | 17.2x13.2cm. (18),208p. impf. ends with Dd4.

VERSTEGEN, Richard. A | Restitvtion | of | Decayed Intelligence: | In antiquities. | Concerning the most noble and renovv- | med English nation. | By the studie and trauaile of R.V. | Dedicated vnto the Kings most excellent Maiestie. | (Cut: Nationum Origo).

Printed at Antvverp by Robert Bruney. | 1605. | And to be sold at London in Paules-Churchyeard, | by Iohn Norton and Iohn Bill. | 18.5x13.6cm. (24),338, (13)p. 10 engravings, T.p. in red and black
Dedications, signed.

WHITE, Thomas. A | Discoverie | of Brownisme: | Or | A briefe declaration of some of the | errors and abhominations daily | practised and increased among the Eng- | lish company of the seperation remayning | for the present at Amsterdam in | Holland. | . . . (2 lines). By Thomas White. | (device)

London | Printed by E. A. for Nathaniell Fosbroke and | are to be solde at his Shop at the West end | of Paules. 1605. | 17.3x12.8 cm. (5),26,(3)p.

WILLET, Andrew. Hexapla in Genesin: | That Is, | A Sixfold Commentarie Vp- | on Genesis, wherein sixe seuerall translations, that is, | the Septuagint, and the Chalde, two Latin, of Hierome and | Tremellius, two English, the great Bible, and the Geneva edition are compared, | where they differ, with the Originall Hebrew, and Pagnine, and | Montanus interlinearie interpretation: | Together with a sixfold vse of euery chapter, shewing 1. | the Method or argument, 2. the diuers readings, 3. the explanation of difficult | questions and doubtfull places, 4. the places of doctrine, | 5. places of confutation, 6. morall obseruations: | Wherein aboue | A thousand Theologicall questions are discussed: and is comprised | together, whatsoeuer worthie of note, either Mercerus out of the Rabbins, Pererius out | of the Fathers, Marlorat out of the new writers haue in their | learned Commentaries collected. | Divided Into Two Tomes, And Pvblished To The | glorie of God, and the furtherance of all those that desire to read the | Scripture with profit, | by Andrevv Willet, Minister of the | Gospel of Iesus Christ. | . . . (7 lines).

Printed by Iohn Legat, Printer to the Vniuersitie | of Cambridge. 1605. | 27.5 x 18.3 cm. (8,4),263;(4),265-363; (5),365-470,(2) p.

WOTTON, Anthony. An | Ansvvere | to a popish Pamphlet, of late newly | forbished, and the second time Printed, | Entituled: | Certaine articles, or forcible rea- | sons discouering the palpable absur- | dities, and most notorious errors of the | Protestants religion. | By Anthony Wotton. | . . . (14 lines).

Imprinted at London by G. Eld, for William Timme, dwel- | ling in Paternoster rowe, at the signe of the Flower de Luce | and Crovvne, neere Cheapeside. 1605. | 17.9x13.2 cm. (4),159p.

1606

ABBOT, Robert. A | Defence Of The | Reformed Catho- | licke of M.W.Perkins, | lately deceased, against the bastard | Counter-Catholicke of | D.Bishop, Seminary | Priest. | The First Part: | For answer to his calumniations generally framed against the same, | and against the whole Religion and state of our Church, | in his Epistle Dedicatory to the Kings most | excellent Maiesty. | Wherein is to be seene the audaciousnesse and impudencie of these | Romish brokers in their Supplications and Dedications to his | Highnesse: their religion is dismasked of that antiquity | which they pretend for it: the religion established in | our Church by law is iustified to be no other | but what was anciently receiued in the | Church, and namely in the an- | cient

Church of | Rome. | By Robert Abbot Doct. of Diuinitie. | . . . (6 lines).
    Londini | Impensis Georgii Bishop. | 1606. | 19.2x13.6cm. (14),244;(16),1241p. Two parts: sep. t.p.

ALLEN, Robert. The | Doctrine | Of The Gospel. | By A Plaine and Fami- | liar Interpretation Of The Par- | ticular points or Articles thereof: with the Promises, | Comforts, and Duties, seuerally belong- ing | to the same. | VVherevnto is added, a declaration of | the danger of not knowing, not beleeuing, or not | obeying any one of them. | Likewise, A Rehearsal Of The Ma- | nifold heresies, wherein many haue erred con- | trary to them all. | Diuided into three Bookes. | The First Whereof, Is Of Beliefe In God The | Father, the first Person of the most holy, glorious, and vndiuided Trinitie: | one onely true God, to be blessed and praised for euer. | . . . (8 lines; device).
    London, | Printed by Thomas Creede. 1606. | 26.3x18.2cm. (14),257,(1); (10), 619; (4),122,(5)p. Three books: each with separate t.p.
    Inscription dedicatorie, signed.

ANDREWES, Lancelot. A Sermon | Preached Before | the Kings Maiestie, at | Hampton Court, | Concerning the Right and Power | of calling Assemblies, | On Sunday the 28. of September, | Anno 1606. | By the Bishop of Chichester. | (ornament).
    Imprinted at London by Robert | Barker, Printer to the Kings most | Excellent Maiestie. 1606. | 18.7x14.8 cm. (1), 55p.
    Cambr.Univ.Libr.2591.

BARLOW, William. One Of | the foure Sermons | Preached | Be- fore The Kings | Maiestie, at Hampton Court | in September last. | This | Concerning the Antiquitie and Superio- | ritie of Bishops. Sept. 21. 1606. | By | The Reuerend Father in God William | Lord Bishop of Rochester. | (device).
    London | Imprinted by I. W. for Matthew Law | 1606. | 17.5x13.8 cm. (10,36)p.

BARLOW, William. The | Sermon Preached at | Paules Crosse, the tenth day of No- | vember, being the next Sunday af- | ter the Discoverie of this late | Horrible | Treason. | Preached | By the right Reverend Father in God William | Lord Bishop of Rochester. | . . . (3 lines; ornament).
    Printed for Mathew Lawe. | 1606. | 18.2x13.cm. (5,31)p.

BARROW, Henry, and GREENWOOD, John. A Plaine | Refvta- tion | Of M. Giffards Booke, | intituled, Ashort treatise | gainst the Donatistes of | England. | Wherein is discouered | 1 The forgery of the vvhole Ministerie, | 2 The confusion, | 3 False vvorship, | 4 And Antichristian disorder, | Of these Parish assemblies, called the Church of England. | Here also is prefixed a summe of the causes of our separati- | on, & of our purposes in practise, vvhich M. Gif- | fard hath tvvise sought to confute, and | hath novv tvvise receiued an- svver, | By Henry Barrovve. | Here is furder inserted a brief refutation of M. Giff. suppo- | sed consimilitude betvvixt the Donatistes & vs. | VVherin is shevved hovv his Arguments | haue bē & may be by the Papists more | iustly retorted against him- | self & the preset estate | of their Church. By | Io. Greenwood. | Here are also annexed a fevv obseruations of M. Giff. his last | Reply, not printed heretofore: as the other afore- | said vvere in the yeare | 1591. |

No imprint. [Amsterdam: 1606] 17.9x13.9 cm. (20),260p.
Dexter: 190 and 284
The original edition of 1591 was burned in Holland and destroyed with the exception of a single copy.

BELL, Thomas. The | Regiment of the | Church: | As It Is Agreable With | Scriptures, all Antiquities of the Fathers, and mo- | derne Writers, from the Apostles themselues, | vnto this present age. | . . . (6 lines; device).

London, | Imprinted by T. C. for William Welby, and are to be sold | at his Shop in Paules Church-yard, at the Signe of | the Grayhound. 1606. | 17.5x12.4 cm. (8),223,(1) p.
Epistle Dedicatorie, signed.

BODIN, Jean. The | Six Bookes | Of A Common- | Weale. | Written by I. Bodin | a famous Lawyer, and a man | of great Experience in mat- | ters of State. | Out of the French and Latine Copies, | done into English, by | Richard Knolles. |

London | Impensis G.Bishop. | 1606. | Pillar and vine border. 28.4x18.9cm. (10),794p. Colophon: Imprinted at London by | Adam Islip. 1606. |

BOWNDE, Nicholas. Sabbathvm | Veteris Et Novi | Testamenti: | Or | The true doctrine of the Sabbath, held and pra- | ctised of the Church of God, both before, and vnder the | Law; and in the time of the Gospel: plainly laid foorth and | soundly prooued by testimonies both of holie Scripture, | and also of old and new ecclesiasticall Writers: Fa- | thers and Councels, and lawes of all sorts, both | Ciuill, Canon, and Common. | Declaring first from what things God would haue vs straitly to rest | vpon the Lords day: and then by what meanes we ought pub- | likely and priuately to sanctifie the same. | Together with the sundrie abuses of men in both these kindes: and | how they ought to be reformed. | Diuided into two Bookes by Nicolas Bovvnd | Doctor of Diuinitie: | And now by him the second time perused, and inlarged with an | interpretation of sundrie points belonging to the Sabbath: and a more ample | proofe of such things, as haue bin gainsaid, or doubted of by some Di- | uines of our time: and a more full answere vnto certaine. obie- | ctions made against the same: with some other things | not impertinent to this argument. . . . 7 lines).

Imprinted at London by Felix Kyngston, for Thomas | Man and Iohn Porter. 1606. | 18x14.1 cm. (18),283;(16),285–479p.
Following page 283 is a second title: Sabbathvm | Veteris et Novi | Testamenti. | Or | The Second Booke Of | the doctrine of the Sabbath, held and practiced | of the Church of God, both before and | vnder the law, and in the time | of the Gospel. | Declaring The Severall | partes of Gods worship, with other duties of | charitie, whereby we ought in soule and body | publikely and priuately, to sanctifie and | keepe holy the Lords day from | morning to morning, with o- | thers

and by ourselues. | Together With The Svndry Abv- | ses of all sorts of men in these kinds, and how | they ought to be reformed. | By Nicolas Bownd Doctor | in Diuinitie. | . . . (2 lines)

BRADSHAW, William. Myld And | Ivst Defence Of Certeyne Ar- | gvments, At The Last Session Of | Parliament directed to that most Honorable High | Court, in behalfe of the Ministers suspended and | deprived &c: for not Subscribing and Conforming | themselues etc. | Against An Intemperat And Vnivst Considerati- | on of them by M.Gabril Powell. The chiefe and generall | contents wherof are breefly layd downe immediately after | the Epistle. | . . . (11 lines).

Imprinted, 1606. | 17.4x13.9cm. (6),163,(1)p.
Anon. DNB:6:184b. Cf. Dexter: 313.

BROUGHTON, Hugh. Tvvo Epistles | Vnto | Great Men Of | Britanie, | In The Yeare | 1599. | Requesting them to put their neckes | vnto the work of theyr Lord: | To break the bread of the soule unto the hungry Iewes, by | theyr writinges, or by theyr charges, through such | as be ready to declare all that theyr ne- | cessity doth require. |

Printed now the second time, in the yeare synce the | creation of the world | 5532. | Or yeare of the Lord | 1606. | Translated by the Auctour for | the use of such as would | & should know what | in this cause ought | to be per- | formed. | 17.5x13.3 cm. (20)p.
Dedication, signed.

BUCANUS, Guilielmus. Gvilielmi | Bvcani, S.S. Theologiæ | In Ecclesia Et Acade- | mia Lavsannensi | Ecclesiastæ, | In Dominicam Orationem. | Homiliarvm | Sylvæ. | (device)

Excudebat | Iacobvs Stoer, | M.DCVI. | 17.x10.2cm. 264p.

BUCANUS, Guilielmus. Institvtions | Of Christian Re- | ligion, framed out of Gods word, and the | writings of the best Diuines, methodi- | cally handled by Questions and Answers, fit for | all such as desire to know, or practise | the will of God. | Written in Latin by William Bvcanvs | Professor of Diuinitie in the Vniuersitie of | Lavsanna. | And published in English by Robert Hill, Bachelor | in Diuinitie, and Fellow of Saint Iohns Colledge in | Cambridge, for the benefit of our English Na- | tion, to which is added in the end the practise | of Papists against Protestant | Princes. | . . . (3 lines; ornament).

Printed at London, by George Snowdon, | and Leonell Snowdon. 1606. | Red line border. 18x13.2cm. (16), 908p. Frequent mispagings.

BUCKERIDGE, John. A Sermon | Preached At | Hampton Court before | the Kings Maiestie, | On Tuesday the 23. of September, | Anno 1606. | By Iohn Bvckeridge, | D. of Diuinitie. | (ornament).

Imprinted At | London by Robert Bar- | ker, Printer to the Kings most | Excellent Maiestie. 1606. | 17.3x13.2cm (1),42p.
Also another copy, 17x13.5cm. (1),1–39,42p. from which pp 39–40 have been omitted.

BULKELEY, Edward. Specvlvm Ecclesiæ | Pontificiæ | Nicolavs Cle- | mangis Archidiaco- | nvs Baiocensis, Doctor | S. Theologiæ Parisiensis, de cor- | rupto Ecclesiæ statu. | Huic accesserunt duæ eiusdem Epistolæ super | materla Concilij generalis: Tractatus Petri de Aliaco | Cardinalis Cameracensis, de reformatione Ecclesiæ | Concilio Constantiensi oblatus, aliaq́; ex D. Gersono, | Bernardo, Iohanne Sarisburiensi Episcopo Carno- | tensi, Marsilio Patauino, Aluaro Pelagio Episcopo | Syluensi, Theodorico de Niem Episcopo Verdensi, | & aliis, eiusdem argumenti ad detegendam Ecclesiæ | Pontificię fœditatem, collecta & edita opera & studio | Edvvardi Bvlklei S. Theologiæ Doctoris. | . . . (6 lines; ornament).

Londini, | Impensis Georg.Bishop. | 1606. | 14.3x9.3cm. (16),300p.

CAMPIAN, Edmund. (Ornament). Edmvndi | Campiani So- | cietatis Iesv The- | ologi, qui non ita pridem pro | Catholica religione in Anglia | mortē oppetiit, oblati cer- | taminis in causa fidei | rationes decē red- | ditę Academicis | Angliæ. | (device, IHS)

Rorschachii, | Excudebat Bartholomæus | Schnell. Anno 1606. | 11.2x7.1cm. (10),149,(2)p.

CARLETON, George. Tithes | Examined and pro- | ued to bee due to the | Clergie by a diuine | right. | VVhereby the contentious and | prophane Atheists, as also the dissembling | Hypocrites of this age, may learne to honour | the Ministers and not to defraude | them, and to Rob the Church. | The Contents heereof is set downe in the Page | next following. | Written by George Carleton Batchelour in Diuinitie. | (ornament)

Printed at London by T. Este, for Clement Knight | dwelling in Paules Churchyard at the signe | of the Holy Lambe. 1606. | 18.5 x 14.2 cm (3),39fol.

CASMAN, Otho. Vade mecum. | Goe with mee: | Dear Pietie, and rare Charitie. | VVhose flame is stirred vp, to dispell | the cold out of the minde. | By Otho Casmanne, | Preacher in Stoade. | Translated out of Latine, by H.T. | Minister. | The Contents appeare in the | Page following. | . . . 6 lines).

London | Imprinted for Thomas Charde. | 1606. | 14.3x9.8cm. (32,235)p.

CECIL, Robert. An | Answere | To Certaine | scandalous Papers, | Scattered abroad vnder colour | of a Catholicke Ad- | monition. | . . . (1 line; ornament).

Jmprinted at London by Robert | Barker, Printer to the Kings most | Excellent Maiestie. | Anno 1606. | 18.3x12.6 cm. (16,25) p.
Anon. Camb.Univ.Cat.No.2597.

CERTAINE | Argvments To Per- | swade And Provoke The Most | Honorable And High Covrt Of Par- | liament now assembled, and also all other in any high au- | thority, or in any grace, and creditewith them that are in | high authority, to promote and advance the sincere Ministery of | the Gospell; as also Zealously to speake for the Ministers therof | now degraded, deprived, silenced, or admonished, or after-

ward | like to be called into question, for Subscription, Ceremonyes, | strict observation of the booke of common prayer, or for | other conformitie. | . . . (10 lines).
Imprinted 1606. | 18.6 x 13.4 cm (6),31p.

COVELL, William. A Briefe An- | svver Vnto Cer- | taine Reasons by way of an Apologie | deliuered to the Right Reuerend Father in God, the | L. Bishop of Lincolne, by Mr. Iohn Bvrges: | wherein he laboureth to prooue, that hauing hereto- | fore subscribed foure times, and now re- | fusing (as a thing vnlawfull) that he | hath notwithstanding done | lawfully in both. | Written by VVilliam Couell, Doc- | tor in Diuinitie. | . . . (2 lines ; device).
At London, | Printed by G.S. for Clement Knight, and are | to be sold at his shop in Paules Churchyard | at the Signe of the Holy Lambe. | 1606. | 18.8x14.5 cm. (14),160,(1)pp.

A | DECLARA- | TION Of The | iust causes of his Maisties pro- | ceeding against those | Ministers, | Who are now lying in prison, | attainted of high | Treason. | Set foorth by his Maiesties Counsell | of his kingdome of Scotland. | (device).
Imprinted at London by Robert | Barker, Printer to the Kings most | Excellent Maiestie. | Anno 1606. | 18. x 13.4 cm (1), 45p.

DOD, John. A | Plaine And | familiar Exposition of | the Ten Commaundements, with a me- | thodicall short Catechisme, containing brief- | lie all the principall grounds of Christian | Religion. | Newly corrected by the Author. | . . . (3 lines ; ornament).
At London | Printed by Humfrey Lownes for Thomas Man, dwel- | ling in Pater-noster-Rowe, at the signe of | the Talbot. 1606. | 18.3x13.6cm. (7),374,(19)p.
Dedication, signed John Dod and Robert Cleaver.

DOVE, John. A Defence Of | Church Gouernment. | Dedicated to the high Court of Parliament. | Wherein, The Chvrch Go- | uernment established in England, is directly proued | to be consonant to the word of God, and that subiects | ought of dutie to conforme themselues to the | state Ecclesiasticall. | Together with, | A Defence Of The Crosse In | Baptisme; as it is vsed in our Church, being not repugnant | to the word: and by a consequent, the brethren which are | silenced, ought to subscribe vnto it, rather | then to burie their Talents in | the ground. | By Iohn Dove, Doctour of Diuinity. | (device).
At London, | Printed by T.C. for Henry Rockit, and are to be sold by Iohn | Hodgets in Pauls Churchyeard. 1606. | 17.8x12.7cm. (6),72p.

FAIRLAMBE, Peter. The Recan- | tation of a Brownist. | Or | A Reformed Pvritan. | Written By One That Hath | altogether, bin led in the same erronious op- | pinions for many yeeres together: and | therevpon banished this Realme. And now since his | conuersion, hath and doth approue, the holy Disci- | pline, by the auncient Pastors, Doctors and Elders | (which Disciplinarian malecontents would ob- | trude vpon our Church,) and hath found it far shor- | ter, then the

Discipline vsed either in the Primitiue | Church, or in this our Church of England. | (device).

At London printed for Henry Gosson, and are to be sold | at the signe of the Sunne, in Paternoster rowe. 1606. | 18.1x13.4 cm. (14,43)p.

Dedications, signed.

FIELD, Richard. Of | The Chvrch, | Five Bookes. | By Richard Feild, Doctor | of Diuinitie. | (device)

At London | Imprinted by Humfrey Lownes, for | Simon Waterson. 1606. | 20.6x16 cm. (16),275,(1),23pp.

FITZHERBERT, Thomas. The | First Part | Of A Treatise Concer | ning Policy, And | Religion. | Wherein the infirmitie of humane wit is amply declared, with | the necessitie of Gods grace, and true Religion for the perfe- | ction of policy; And by the way some political matters are | treated: Diuers principles of Macchiauel confuted; And ma- | ny aduises geuen, tending no lesse to religious piety, then to | true policy; With a confutation of the arguments of Atheists, | against the prouidence of God, which is clearly proued | throughout the whole. | Written by Thomas Fitzherbert Esquire, | and Catholique priest, for the benefite | of young Statists. | . . . (6 lines).

VVith permission of Superiors. | M.DC.VI. | Lace border. 18.7x13.5cm. (52), 461,(1)p.

HACKET, Roger. A | Sermon Prin- | cipally Entrea- | ting Of The Crosse | In Baptisme: | Wherein Also It Is | proued, against the vnaduised re- | prouers, that it is no Popish error, | to say; that Austine sent from | Gregorie the Great, was the | conuerter of the English | in this Iland: | And Fvrther That | the Britaines did not receiue | their first faith from the | Church of Rome. | By R.H. D. |

At London | Imprinted by F.K. for Cuthbert Burbie | dwelling in Pauls Churchyard, at | the signe of the Swanne. 1606. | 13x8.1cm. (10),52p.

Cambr.Univ.Cat:I:p.514.

HAYWARD, John. A | Reporte | Of A Discovrse | Concerning Sv- | preme power in affaires of | Religion. | Manifesting | That this power is a right of Regalitie, in- | separably annexed to the Soueraigntie of euery State: | and that it is a thing both extreamely dangerous, | and contrarie to the vse of all auncient Em- | pires and Commonwealths, to ac- | knowledge the same in a for- | raigne Prince. | . . . (1 line; device).

At London | Imprinted by F. K. for Iohn Hardie, and are to be | sold by Iohn Flasket, dwelling at the signe of the blacke | Beare in Paules Church yeard. 1606. | 16.9x11.6 cm. (4),52p.

Anon. Cambr.Univ.Cat:2942.

HIERON, Samuel. The | Doctrine | Of The Beginning | of Christ. | Short for memorie, plaine | for capacity, deliuered almost in | the expresse words of the Text, | for the more Au- | thority. | By Samuell Hieron, Minister | of the Gospel. | . . . (5 lines).

Imprinted at London for Sa- | muel Macham, and Mat. Cooke, | and are to be sold at their shop in | Paules Churchyard, at the signe | of the Tygers head, 1606. | Border. 13.9x8.7 cm. (6,26)p.

HOLLAND, Henry. The | Historie of Adam, or | the foure-fold state of Man, | VVell formed in his Creation, | Deformed in his Corruption, | Reformed in Grace, and | Perfected in Glory. | By | M.Henry Holland, late Preacher at | Saint Brides Church in London. | (ornament).

London | Printed by T.E. for Thomas Man, dwelling in Pater- | noster-Row at the signe of the Talbot. 1606. | 17.5x13.1cm. (3),182fol.

HUBBARD, William. Great Brit- | taines Resvr- | rection: Or the Parliaments | passing Bell. | By VVay Of Psalmodie, Against | the tryumphing of the Papists, in their | seuen Psalmes. | And in imitation of the song of the three Nobles | of Israel, deliuered out of the fierie Ouen | of Babell. | By VVilliam Hubbard, Chaplaine to the Kings Maiestie, | in his Highnes Tower of London. | . . . (4 lines). Seene and allowed. | (lace ornament)

At London, | Printed by T. C. for Arthur Iohnson, and are to be | sold at his shop in Pauls Churchyard, at the signe of | the white Horse. | 1606. | 18x13.5 cm. (15,47)p.

HUTTON, Thomas. The | Second And Last | part of Reasons for Refusall of Subscrip- | tion to the Booke of Common prayer, vnder | the hands of certaine Ministers of Deuon. | and Cornwall, as they were exhibited by | them to the right Reuerend Father in | God William Cotton | Doctor of Diuinitie, and Lord | Bishop of Exceter. | As also an Appendix, or Compendious | Briefe of all other Exceptions taken by others | against the Bookes of Communion, Homilies, | and Ordination, word for word, as it came to | the hands of an Honorable | Personage. | VVith an Ansvvere to both at seuerall | times returned them in publike conference, and in diuerse | Sermons vpon occasion preached in the Cathredrall | Church of Exceter by Thomas Hutton Bachiler | of Diuinitie, and Fellow of S. Iohns | Colledge in Oxon. | . . . (5 lines).

London. | Printed by Iohn Windet for the Com- | panie of Stationers. 1606. | 18.8x14.5 cm. (16),1–56,37–260 p.

JACOB, Henry. A | Christian | And Modest Offer | Of A Most Indifferent Confe- | rence, Or Dispvtation, Abovt | the maine and principall Controversies betwixt the | Prelats, and the late silenced and deprived Ministers | in England: | Tendered By Some Of The Said Ministers To The | Archbishops, and Bishops, and all their adherents. | (ornament). . . . (8 lines)

Imprinted. 1606. | 17.5x13cm. (9),42p.
Anon. Dexter, 303.

KING, John. The | Fovrth | Sermon Preached At | Hampton Covrt On | Tuesday the last of Sept. 1606. | By | John Kinge Doctor of Divinity, and | Deane of Christ-Church in Oxon. | (device).

At Oxford, | Printed by Joseph Barnes Printer to the | Vniversitie. 1606. | Line border. 17.7x13.8 cm. (1),49 p.

MEREDITH, Richard. Tvvo | Sermons | Preached before his Maiestie, in | his Chappell at Whitehall, the one, | the xi. of Februarie,

the other the | xxv. of the same moneth. | By Richard Meredeth, one of his Maiesties | Chaplaines in ordinarie. | (cut)
   At London | Printed by G.Eld, for Simon Waterson. | 1606. | 17.3x12.5cm. (1),46p.

MORTON, Thomas.   Apologiae | Catholicæ, | In Qva | Paradoxa, Hæreses, | Blasphemiæ, Scele- | ra, quæ | Iesuitæ, & Pontificij alij Protestantibus impin- | gunt, ferè omnia, ex ipsorum Pontificiorum te- | stimoniis apertis diluuntur, | Libri Dvo. | De Notis Ecclesiæ. | Autore Thoma Mortono Sacræ Theologiæ Baccalaureo, | quondam in celeberrima Academia Canta- | brigiensi Collegij Iohannis E- | uangelistæ, Socio. | Editio castigatior & Index locupletior. | . . . (2 lines, ornament)
   Londini, | Excudebat Iohannes Norton, Serenissimæ Re- | giæ Maiestatis in Latinis, Grȩcis, & He- | braicis Typographus. | Anno Salvtis M DC VI. | 16.7x10.8 cm.   (24),1–112,103–558,(6)p.

MORTON, Thomas.   A Fvll | Satisfaction | Concerning A | Dovble Romish Iniqvitie; | hainous Rebellion, and more then | heathenish Æquiuocation. | Containing three Parts: | The two former belong to the Reply vpon the Moderate An- | swerer; the first for Confirmation of the Discouerie in these | two points, Treason and Æquiuocation: the second is a Iu- | stification of Protestants, touching the same points. | The third Part is a large Discourse confuting the Reasons and | grounds of other Priests, both in the case of Rebellion, and | Æquiuocation. | . . . (3 lines; device).
   London, | Printed by Richard Field for Edmond | Weauer. 1606. | 17.1x13.3cm. (11),131;103p.

ORMEROD, Oliver.   Pagano-Papismus: | Or, | A Discouery of Popish Paganisme: wherein is plainelie | shewed that the Papistes doo resemble the idolatrous | Heathen in aboue sixscore particulars: and that in | many things they are worse then they, and are whollye | departed from the very principles of Philosophy, rea- | son, and outward sence: made Dialogue-wise in a | most plaine and familiar manner. |
   No t.p. 17.2x12.2cm. 1–56p. Impf. at end.
   Part of his Pictvre Of a Papist: 1606; with separate register and pagination.

ORMEROD, Oliver.   The | Pictvre Of | a Papist: | Or, | A Relation of the damnable heresies, dete- | stable qualities, and diabolicall prac- tises of sundry here- | ticks in former ages, and of the papists in this age. | Wherein is plainly shewed, that there is scarce any | heresie which the auncient Church knew, and withal condem- | ned to the pit of hell, which the Romish Church hath not | raked up againe, and pro- pounded to the world with new | Varnish and fresh Colours. | Together with a discourse of the late treason, and of the | late execution of some of the Traitors: wherein is shewed | the haynousnesse of their crime, and the lawfulnesse | of their punishment. | Written to stop the mouthes of those, that com- | plaine of rigour, and scandalize the state of cruelty, | in their just severitie. | Whereunto is annexed a certain treatise, intituled | Pagano-Papismus: wherein is prooved by irrefragable | demonstrations, that Papisme is flat Paganisme: and | that the Papists doe resemble the very Pagans, in | above sevenscore severall things. |

>At London | Printed for Nathaniel Fosbrooke, and are to be sold | at his shop, at the west end of Paules. | 1606. | 17.2x12.2cm. 3–83,90–137,168–275;1–56p. 84–89, 138–167, and 204–263 omitted in numbering. Lacks t.p., prefatory matter, and pages 1–2.
>Anon. Camb.Univ.Cat.No.3616. T.p. supplied by Mr. Edward G. Friehold, of London.

OSIANDER, Lucas. A | Manvell | Or briefe volume of | Controuersies of Religion betweene | the Protestants and the Papists: wherein the | Arguments of both sides are briefely set downe, | and the Aduersaries Sophismes are | plainely refuted. | Written in Latine in a briefe and perspi- | cuous method by Lvcas Osiander, and | now Englished with some additions | and corrections. (device).

>At London Printed by Humfrey Lownes: | 1606. | 15.3x10.4cm. (8),486p.

PARRY, Henry. De | Regno Dei, | Et | Victoria Christia- | na, Conciones Dvæ: | Auctore D.Henrico Parraeo S. | Theologiæ Doctore, & Decano Cestrensi. | (Device).

>Londini | Ex Typographeío Felix Kyngstoniano, Impensis | Cuthberti Burbæi & Edmundi Weauer. | Anno Domini, 1606. | 18.x13.1cm. (7),24; (6)26p. Subtitle.

PARRY, Henry. Victoria | Christiana. | Concio Ad Clerum: | Habita Oxonii, Anno | 1591. Edita Et Inscripta | Nobilissimo Gvlielmo Her- | berto, tum Cardidiæ despotæ, | nunc Pembrochiæ Comiti | honoratissimo. | (device)

>Londini | Ex Typographeío Kyngstoniano, Impensis Cuth- | berti Burbæi & Edmundi Weauer. | Anno Domini, 1606. | 18x13.1cm. (6),26p.
>Part of his De Regno Dei: 1606. Sep. t.p. and pag.

PARSONS, Robert. An | Ansvvere | To The Fifth Part | Of Reportes | Lately set forth | By | Syr Edvvard Cooke Knight, the Kings | Attorney generall. | Concerning | The ancient & moderne Municipall lawes of England, | vvhich do apperteyne to Spirituall | Power & Iurisdiction. | By occasion vvherof, & of the principall Question set dovvne in | the sequent page, there is laid forth en euident, plaine & perspi- | cuous Dem nstration of the continuance of Catholicke Religion in | England, from our first Kings christened, vnto these dayes. | By a Catholicke Deuyne. | . . . (4 lines; ornament).

>Imprinted vvith licence, | Anno Domini 1606. | 18.5x12.9cm. (72),386,(14)p.
>Anon. Gillow. V: 284.

The REMOOUALL | Of certaine Imputati- | ons laid vpon the Ministers of Deuon: | and Cornwall by one M. T. H. | and in them, vpon all other Mi- | nisters els-where, refusing to | Subscribe. | . . . (7 lines; device)

>1606. | Line border. 18. x13.9 cm. (6),66p.

ROLLOCK, Robert. In | Epistolam | S. Pavli Apostoli | Ad Ephesios, | Roberti Rolloci | Scoti, Ecclesiæ Edinburgensis Ministri, | Commentarius. | Altera Editio, cui accesserunt Notæ, quæ | Epistolæ & Commentarij methodum | per breuem quandam Synopsin | ostendunt. | (device).

Genevæ, | Apud Iacobum Stœr, | M.DCVI. | 14.4x9.4cm. (12),420,(8)p.

ROLLOCK, Robert. Lectvres Vpon | the First And Second | Epistles Of Pavl To The | Thessalonians: | Preached by that faithfull ser- | uant of God M. Robert Rollock, some-tyme | Minister of the Euangell of Iesus Christ, and | Rector of the Colledge in Edinbvrgh. | (device). |

Edinbvrgh | Printed by Robert Charteris | Printer to the Kings most Excellent Majestie. | An. Dom. M.D.C.VI. | Cum Priuilegio Regiæ Majestatis. | 18.5x13.3cm. (8),346, (2), 171p.

SMITH, Richard. An Answer | To Thomas Bels | Late Challeng Named | By Him The Dovvnfal | Of Popery | Wherin Al His Argvments | are answered, his manifold vntruths, slaun- | ders, ignorance, contradictions, and | corruption of Scripture, & Fathers | discouered and disproued: | VVith One Table Of The | Articles and Chapters, and an other of the | more markable things conteyned | in this booke. | VVhat controuersies be here handled is | declared in the next page. | By S. R. | . . . (9 lines).

At Doway, | Imprinted by Lavrence Kellam, at | the signe of the holie Lambe. | M.DC.VI. | 15.4x9.5 cm. (64),446,(34) p.
Gillow:V:512.

SMITH, William. The | Black-Smith. | A | Sermon Preached | at White-Hall before the Kings most | excellent Majestie, the young | Prince, the Councell, &c. On Loe-Sunday. 1606. and by com- | maundment put to | print. | By | W. S. Doct. in Diuinitie Chaplaine to | his Majestie. | (ornament).

London | Printed by Ed.Allde for Nicholas | Ling. 1606. | Line border. 13.3x8.9 cm. (8),56p.
B.M.Cat.

A | SVPPLICATI- | ON Of The Fa- | mily of Loue (said to be presen- | ted into the Kings royall hands, know- | en to be dispersed among his Loyall | Subiectes) for grace and | fauour. | Examined, and found to be derogato- | rie in an hie degree, vnto the glorie of God, the honour | of our King, and the Religion in this Realme | both soundly professed & firm- | ly established. | . . . (4 lines; device).

Printed for Iohn Legate, Printer to the Vniuersitie of | Cambridge. 1606. | 18.1x 13.6 cm. (1),65 p.

SUTCLIFFE, Matthew. An | Abridgement | Or | Svrvey Of | Poperie, | Conteining a compendious declaration, of the grounds, | doctrines, beginnings, proceedings, impieties, | falsities, contradictions, absurdities, fooleries, | and other manifold abuses of that religion, | which the Pope and his complices doe now | mainteine, and vvhere-vvith they haue | corrupted and deformed the true | Christian faith, | Opposed vnto Matthew Kellisons Suruey of the new | Religion, as he calleth it, and all his malicious | inuectiues and lies, | By | Matthevv Svtcliffe. | (ornament)

London | Printed by Melchisedech Bradwood for | Cuthbert Burbie. | 1606. | 18.6x13.9 cm.   (11),330,(4)p.

SUTCLIFFE, Matthew. The Examination | and Confutation | Of | A certaine scurrilous treatise entituled, | The Suruey of the newe Religion, | Published by Matthew Kellison, in | disgrace of true religion pro- | fessed in the Church | of England. | . . . (8 lines; device).

London | Printed by E. Allde for Richard Serger and Edmund Weauer, | & are to be solde at the great north dore of S. Paules | Church. 1606. | 18.2x13.6 cm. (27),113,(2)p.
Epistle Dedicatory, signed.

SUTCLIFFE, Matthew. The | Svbversion | Of | Robert Parsons | His confused and worthlesse worke, | Entitvled, | A treatise of three Conuersions of England | from Paganisme to Christian | Religion. | . . . (3 lines; device).

London, | Printed for Iohn Norton. | 1606. | 17.3x13.2 cm.   (16),144,(2) p.
Epistle Dedicatory, signed.

SUTCLIFFE, Matthew. A | Threefold Answer | Vnto The Third Part Of A | Certaine Triobolar Treatise | of Three supposed Conuersions of England to the mo- | derne Romish Religion published by Rob. Parsons | vnder the continued Maske of N.D. | The first Part whereof conteineth a defence of the Martyrs and | Confessors of the true faith against the heresies and impie- | ties of Poperie, and of their acts, sayings, and sufferings by | him wickedly traduced. | The second examineth some part of the Romish Martyrologies | and Legends, and of the impious doctrine and practise of | Papists in worshipping of Saints and Angels, by him | weakely defended. | The third refuteth his exorbitant Discourses, relations, and ob- | seruations, and discouereth his grosse leasings, falsities, foo- | leries and other enormities. | . . . (4 lines ; ornament).

London, | Printed for Iohn Norton. | 1606. | 18.1x13.5cm.   (9),317p. P. 7 repeated.
Epistle Dedicatorie, signed.

SYMONDS, William. A | Heavenly | Voyce. | A Sermon tending to call the people of God | from among the Romish Babylonians: | Preached at Paules Crosse the | 12 of Ianuarie. 1606. | By William Symonds. | . . . (3 lines ; ornament).

At London Printed by I.R. for Edmund VVea- | uer, and are to be solde at his shoppe, at | the great North-doore of Paules | Church. 1606. | 18.2x13.1cm. (4,30)p.

A TRVE And | Perfect Rela- | tion Of The Whole | proceedings against the late most | barbarous Traitors, Garnet a Iesuite, | and his Confederats: | Contayning sundry Speeches deliuered | by the Lords

Commissioners at their Arraign- | ments, for the better satisfaction of those that were | hearers, as occasion was offered; | The Earle of Northamptons Speech hauing | bene enlarged vpon those grounds which | are set downe. | And lastly all that passed at Garnets | Execution. | (ornament).

Imprinted at London by Robert | Barker, Printer to the Kings most | Excellent Maiestie. 1606. | 18.8x14.3cm. (6,410)p.

TURNBULL, Richard. An | Exposition | vpon the Canonicall | Epistle of Saint | Iames, | With the Analysis and Resolution | both of the whole Epistle, and of euery | Chapter therof, with the particular re- | solution of euery singular place. | Diuided into 28. Lectures or Sermons, | Made by Richard Turnbul, sometime, Fel- | low of Corpus Christi Colledge in Oxford, | and sometime Preacher and Minister of | the word of God and of the holy Sacra- | ments in the Citty of London. |

Imprinted at London by John | Windet, and are to be solde by | Richard Bankworth in Paules | Churchyeard, 1606. | Engraved border; title in oval. 18.5x13.2 cm. (4),375,(55)fol.

Contains also, with continuous paging An Exposition Vpon . . . Iude: 1606; And four sermons on Psalm xv, 1–5.

TURNBULL, Richard. An | Exposition V- | pon the Canonicall Epistle of | Saint Iude. | With the Analysis and resolution, both generall of the | whole Epistle; and particular of euerie | Lecture. | Diuided into tenne Sermons or | Lectures. | Made and written by Richard Turnbull Preacher, | in the Cittie of London. | (device).

London | Imprinted by Iohn Windet, 1606. | 18.5x13.2cm. fol. 241–375, of his Exposition vpon . . Iames: 1606.

V., T. A | Briefe Viewe | of the weake Grounds | of Popery; | As it was propounded to D. | Norrice, Priest, by T. V. Gent: | and returned without | answere. | (ornament).

At Londn | Imprinted by Humfrey Lownes, for Sa- | muel Macham, and Mathew Cooke, and are | to be sold in Pauls Church-yard, at | the signe of the Tigers | head. 1606. | 14.3x9.cm. (24),101,(7)p.

Ms. attribution to Thomas Vicars.

WETENHALL, Thomas. A | Discovrse | Of The Abvses Novv | In Qvestion In The Chvrches | Of Christ, Of Their Creeping In, Gro- | wing vp, and flowrishing in the Babilonish Church of Rome, | how they are spoken against not only by the scriptures, | but also by the ancient Fathers as long as there remayned | any face of a true Church maintained by publique autho- | rity. And likewise by the lights of the Gospell, and bles- | sed Martyrs of late in the middest of the Antichristi- | an darknes. | By Thomas Whetenhall Esquier. | . . . (ornament; 5 lines).

Imprinted. 1606. | 16.9x13.2 cm. (8),194,(1) p. Pp. 142, 143 double numbered.

WHITAKER, William. An | Answere To | The Ten Reasons Of | Edmvnd Campian The Iesvit, | In Confidence Whereof He | offered disputation to the Ministers of the | Church of England, in the contro- | uersie of faith. | Wherevnto Is Added In | Briefe Marginall Notes, The | summe of the defence of those reasons by | Iohn Dvrævs the Scot, being a | Priest and a Iesuit, with a reply | vnto it. | Written First In The Latine | Tongve By The Reverend And | faithfull seruant of Christ and his Church, William | Whitakers, Doctor in Diuinitie, and the Kings | Professor and publike Reader of Diuinitie | in the Vniuersitie of Cam- | bridge. | And Now Faithfvlly Translated For | the benefit of the vnlearned (at the appointment and desire | of some in authoritie) into the English tongue; by | Richard Stocke, Preacher | in London. | In This Treatise, Most Of The | Controuersies betwixt vs and the Church of Rome are | briefely and and plainely handled. | The Principall Things In Every Answere | are gathered into a short summe, and are set downe after | the Epistle to the Reader. |

Imprinted at London by Felix Kyngston, for | Cuthbert Burby and Edmund Weauer. 1606. | 17.4x12.9cm. (32),326pp.

WOTTON, Anthony. A | Defence | Of M. Perkins | Booke, Called | A Reformed Ca- | tholike: | Against the cauils of a Popish writer, | one D.B.P. or W.B. in his defor- | med Reformation. | By Antony Wotton. | (device)

At London, | Imprinted by Felix Kyngston, for | Cuthbert Burby, and are to be sold at his shop in | Paules Church-yard at the signe of | the Swan. 1606. | 18.5x13.9cm. (10),600p.

1607

ABBOT, Robert. The | Second Part | Of The Defence | Of The Reformed | Catholicke. | VVherein the Religion established in our Church | of England (for the points here handled) is apparently iusti- | fied by authoritie of Scripture, and testimonie of the aunci- | ent Church, against the vaine cauillations collected by Do- | ctor Bishop Seminary Priest, as out of other Popish writers, | so specially out of Bellarmine, and published vnder the name | of The marrow and pith of many large volumes, | for the oppugning thereof. | By Robert Abbot Doctor of Diuinitie. | . . . (3 lines; device)

Londini, | Impensis Georg.Bishop. | 1607. | 19.2x13.6cm. (16),1241p.

ARTICLES, | To Be Enqui- | red of within the Dioces of Lon- | don, in the first generall Visitation | of the Reuerend Father in God, | Thomas Lord Bishop | of London. | Holden in the yeere of our Lord God, | 1607. In the fifth yeere of the Raigne of our | most gracious Soueraigne Lord Iames, by | the grace of God King of great Bri- | taine, France and Ireland, defen- | der of the faith, &c. | (ornament).

London | Printed by Henry Ballard. | Lace border. 17.3x12.6cm. (20)p.

BARLOW, William. The | First Of | the foure Sermons | Preached | Before The Kings | Maiestie, at Hampton Court | in September last. | This | Concerning the Antiquity and Superio- | ritie of Bishoppes.

Sept. 21. 1606. | By | The Reuerend Father in God William | Lord Bishop of Rochester. | (device).

London | Imprinted by I.W. for Matthew Law. | 1607. | 17.8x13.8cm. (10,36)p.

BERNARD, Richard. The Faithfvll | Shepheard: | Or | The Shepheards | Faithfulnesse: | Wherein is for the matter largely, but for | the maner, in few words, set forth the excel- | lencie and necessitie of the Ministerie; A Ministers | properties and dutie; His entrance into this function and | charge; How to begin fitly to instruct his people; | Catechising and Preaching; And a good | plaine order and method there- | in: Not so as yet pub- | lished. | Very profitable both for yoong Students, who intend the | studie of Theologie (heerein being also declared what | Arts and tongues first to be learned, what kinde of Authours | to be read and books necessarie in the beginning, and which | in the first place) as also for such Ministers as yet haue not | atteined to a distinct order to studie, write, meditate, | and to preach methodically, both for their bet- | ter course in deliuering the Word, and | the peoples vnderstanding in | hearing and memorie | in reteining the | same. | By Richard Bernard, Preacher | of Gods Word. | . . . (4 lines).

London | Printed by Arnold Hatfield for Iohn Bill. | 1607. | 18. x13.8 cm. (8), 95p.

BLACKWELL, George. Mr.George | Blackwel, | (Made by Pope Clement 8. Arch- | priest of England) his Answeres | vpon sundry his Examinations: | Together, with his Approbation and | taking of the Oath of Allegeance: | And his Letter written to his Assistants, | and brethren, moouing them not onely | to take the said Oath, but to aduise | all Romish Catholikes so | to doe. |

Imprinted at | London by Robert Barker, | Printer to the Kings most | Excellent Maiestie. | 1607. | 16.3x12.4cm. (1),39p.

CARPENTER, John. The | Plaine Mans | Spirituall Plough. | Containing The Godly | and Spirituall Husbandrie. | VVherein euery Christian | ought to be exercised, for the happie en- | crease of fruite, to eternall life. | By I.C.Preacher of the Word. | . . (3 lines; device)

London | Printed by Thomas Creede. | 1607. | 18.2x12.5cm. (8),246p. Epistle Dedicatorie, signed.

DENT, Arthur. The Rvine | Of Rome. | Or | An | Exposition | vpon the whole Reuelation. | VVherein is plainely shewed and proued, that the | Popish Religion, together with all the power and authority | of Rome, shall ebbe and decay still more and more through- | out all the Churches of Europe, and come to an vtter | ouerthrow euen in this life, before the end | of the world. | Written especially for the comfort of Protestants, and the | daunting of Papists, Seminary Priests, Iesuites, | and all that cursed rabble. | Published by Arthur Dent, Preacher of the word of God | at South-Shoobery in Essex. | . . . (6 lines: ornament)

London | printed by W.I. for Simon Waterson and Richard | Banckworth. 1607. | 17.8x13.5cm (18),300pp.

FULLER, Nicholas. The Argv- | ment Of Master Ni- | cholas Fvller, In The Case Of | Thomas Lad, And Richard Mavn- | sell, his Clients. Wherein it is plainely proved, that the | Ecclesiasticall Commissioners haue no power, by vertue | of their Commission, to Imprison, to put to the Oath | Ex Officio, or to fine any of his Maiesties | Subiects. | . . . (device; 14 lines).
Imprinted 1607. | 16.5x13.2cm. (4,32)p.

HANMER, Meredith. Transl. The | Avncient | Ecclesiastical | Histories Of The First Six | Hvndred Yeares After Christ, | written in the Greeke tongue by three learned Historiogra- | phers, Eusebius, Socrates, and Euagrius. | Evsebivs Pamphilvs Bishop of Cæsarea in Palæstina wrote 10. bookes. | Socrates Scholasticvs of Constantinople wrote 7. bookes. | Evagrivs Scholasticvs of Antioch wrote 6. bookes. Whereunto | is annexed Dorothevs Bishop of Tyrus, of the liues and ends | of the Prophets, Apostles, and 70. Disciples. | All which Authors are faithfully translated out of the Greeke tongue | by Meredith Hanmer, Doctor of Diuinitie. | Last of all, herein is contained a briefe Chronographie collected by the said Translator, | with a copious Index of the principall matters throughout all the Histories. | The third Edition, corrected and amended. | (device)
London, | Printed by Richard Field, dwelling in the Blackfriers. | 1607. | 26x18 cm. (12),1–191,202–598,(18)p. Four sub.t.p.

HIERON, Samuel. The | Christians | Iovrnall: | Shewing both the course to be held, | and the way to be shund by all those, | who desire (as they ought) to | enter into life. | In three Sermons vpon Mat- | thew 7. 13. 14. | By | Samvel Hieron. | . . . (4 lines ; ornament).
At London, | Printed by Felix Kyngston for | Thomas Man. 1607. | 13.4x8.5cm. (4),99p.

HIERON, Samuel. A Defence | Of The Ministers Reasons, For | Refvsall Of Svbscription To The | Booke of Common prayer, and of Conformitie. | Against The Severall Ansvvers. | Of | T. Hutton Bachiler of Divinity, in his two Bookes a- | gainst the Minist: of Dev. and Cornwell. | William Covel. D. in Diuinitie, in his Booke against | M. I. Burges. | Tho: Spark. D. in Diuinitie, in his Brotherly perswasion | to Vnitie and Vniformitie. | So Farr As Any Thing Is Sayd By Them | concerning the holy Scriptures, and Apocrypha. | Devided into two partes. | The first parte, concerning the holy Scriptures. | The second parte, concerning the holy Scriptures and | Apocrypha. | . . . (8 lines).
Imprinted. 1607. | 17.7x13.2 cm. (8),226 p.
Anon. Camb.Univ.Cat.No.6385.

JAMES I. His | Maiesties | Speech To Both | the Houses of Parliament, in | his Highnesse great Cham- | ber at Whitehall, the day of | the Adiournement of the | last Session, | Which was the last day of | March 1607. | (device)
Imprinted At | London by Robert Barker, | Printer to the Kings most Ex- | cellent Maiestie. | (1607). 17.x12.6cm (4,52)p.

JAMES I. Triplici nodo, triplex cuneus. | Or | An Apologie | For The Oath | of Allegiance, | Against the two Breues of Pope | Pavlvs Qvintvs, and the | late Letter of Cardinal Bellar- | mine to G. Black-vvel | the Arch-priest. | . . . (2 lines). Authoritate Regiâ. |
   Imprinted at London by Ro- | bert Barker, Printer to the Kings | most Excellent Maiestie. | Anno 1607. | Border. 17.6x13.6 cm. (2),112 p.
   Anon.Cambr.Univ.Cat.2605.

KECKERMANN, Bartholomew. Systema | Ethicæ, | Tribvs Libris Adorna- | tum & publicis prælectionibus traditum | in Gymnasio Dantiscano, | à | Bartholomæo Kecker- | manno Dantiscano, Philosophiæ | ibidem Professore. | (device).
   Londini, | Ex Officina Nortoniana. | 1607. | 15.8x10.5cm. (6),288p.

KING, John. The | Fovrth | Sermon Preached At | Hampton Covrt On | Tuesday the Last of Sept. 1606. | By John Kinge Doctor of Divinity, and | Deane of Christ-Church in Oxon. | (device).
   At Oxford, | Printed by Joseph Barnes Printer to the | Vniversitie. 1607. | Line border. 17.8x13.8cm. (1),49p.

KING, John. A | Sermon | Preached In Oxon: | the 5. of November. 1607. | By | John Kinge Doctor of Divinity, Deane | of Christ Church, and Vicechancellor | of the Vniversity. | AC: (Device) OX.
   At Oxford, | Printed by Ioseph Barnes. 1607. | Line border. 17.7 x 13.7 cm. (1),35p.

A | LARGE Exami- | nation Taken | at Lambeth, according to his | Maiesties direction, point by point, | of M. George Blakwell, made Arch- | priest of England, by Pope Clement 8. | Vpon occasion of a certaine answere of his, | without the priuitie of the State, to a | Letter lately sent vnto him from Cardinall | Bellarmine, blaming him for taking | the oath of Allegeance. | Together with the Cardinals Letter, and | M. Blakwels said answere vnto it. | Also M. Blakwels Letter to the Romish | Catholickes in England, as well Ec- | clesiasticall, as Lay. | (ornament).
   Imprinted at London by Robert | Barker, Printer to the Kings most | Excellent Maiestie. | 1607. | 17.3x12.3 cm. (48),170 p.
   DNB. 5: 146a

MASON, Francis. The | Avthoritie | Of The Chvrch | in making Canons and | Constitutions concerning | things indifferent, | And the obedience thereto required: with particular | application to the present estate of the | Church of England. | Deliuered in a Sermon preached in the Greene yard | at Norwich the third Sunday after | Trinitie. 1605. | By Fran. Mason, Bacheler of Diuinitie, and | sometime fellovv of Merton College | in Oxford. | And now in sundrie points by him | enlarged. | . . . (3 lines; device)
   London | Printed for Iohn Norton. 1607. | 19x14.3cm. (6),72p.

MERITON, George. A | Sermon | Of | Nobilitie. | Preached at White-hall, be- | fore the King in February 1606. | By George Meriton

Doctor of Diuini- | ty, one of his Maiesties Chaplianes in Or- | dinary;
and Parson of Hadleigh | in Suffolke. | . . . (3 lines; ornament).

Imprinted at London for Thomas Clarke, and are to | be sold at the signe of
the Angell in Saint | Paules Church-yard. | 1607. | 18.2x13.cm.   (6),32p.

MILBORNE, Richard.   Concerning | Imposition of hands. | A |
Sermon at the Lord Archbi- | shop his visitation Metropolitical, held, |
at Saint Marie Cray in Kent, by | the Bishop of Rochester his | Graces
Commissioner, the 7 | of September last, | Preached by Richard Mil-
borne Doctor | of Diuinitie, and Parson of Seuen- | oke in Kent. |

London | Printed for Matthew Law, and are to bee | sold at his shop dwelling
at the signe | of the Fox in Pauls Church yard. | Colophon. London | Printed by
I.VV for | Mathew Law, and are to | besolde at his shoppe at the | signe of the
Foxe in | Paules Churchyearde, | 1607. | 14.7x9.5 cm.   (4,48) p.

NARRATIO | Fidelis Et Svccincta | De Nvpera Illa | Proditione
Longe | Immanissima, A Iesvitis | Et Conivratis In Magnvm | Magnæ
Britanniæ Regem | Intentata, | Ex Commentarijs Anglicis, publica
authoritate | editis, in unum Historiæ corpus congesta. | (device).

Lvgdvni Batavorvm, | Prostant apud Ioannem Orlers, | Anno MDCVII. | 18.2x
14.3 cm.   38p.

PARKER, Robert.   A | Scholasticall | Discovrse Against | Symboliz-
ing With An- | tichrist In Ceremonies: | Especially In The | Signe Of
The | Crosse. | (device).

Anno Domini, | 1607. | 28.8x18.6 cm.   (6),196,(14),136,(8)p.   Mispagings.
Anon. Camb.Univ.Cat. No.6383.

PARSONS, Robert.   The | Dolefvll | Knell, Of Thomas Bell. | That
Is | A full and sounde ansvver, to his Pamphlet, Inti- | tuled. The
Popes Fvneral. VVhich | he published, against a Treatise of myne, |
called. The Fore-Rvnner Of | Bels Dovvnefal. | VVherein his manifest
vntruthes, grosse corruptions, cunning slightes, | vaine cavils, immodest
railing, insolent challenging, and idle ex- | cursions, be noted, exam-
ined, and refuted. | By B. C. Student in Diuinitye. | Diuided into two
bookes, and seuerall chapters: according | to Bels method. The par-
ticuler contents whereof, are | to be founde in the end of this booke. |
. . . (6 lines).

Printed at Roane. 1607. | 16.4x11.3cm.   (112),416p.   Pp. 230–240 irregular; Two
extra pages.
Gillow. V: 285.

PARSONS, Robert.   A | Treatise | Tending To | Mitigation | to-
vvardes Catholicke-Subiectes | in England. | VVherin Is Declared, |
That it is not impossible for Subiects of different Religion, | (espe-
cially Catholickes and Protestantes) to line togeather | in dutifull
obedience and subiection, vnder the | gouernment of his Maiesty of
Great Britany. | Against | The seditious wrytings of Thomas Morton |
Minister, & some others to the contrary. | Whose two false and slaun-
derous groundes, pretended to be | dravvne from Catholicke doctrine
& practice, concerning | Rebellion and Eqvivocation, are | ouerthrowne,

and cast vpon himselfe. | Dedicated to the learned Schoole-Deuines, Cyuill and Canon Lavvyers | of the tvvo Vniuersities of England. | By P.R. | . . . (3 lines).

Permissu Superiorum. 1607. | 17x11.2cm. (28),556,(14)p.
Gillow. V: 285.

PELLING, John. A Sermon Of | The Providence | Of God. | Preached at Paules Crosse, the | 25. of October. 1607. | By Iohn Pelling Bacchalaur of | Diuinitie. | . . . (3 lines; device).

London, | Printed by Nicholas Okes for Nathaniell Butter, dwel- | ling at the signe of the Pide Bull neere | S. Austins gate. 1607. | 17.8x13.9 cm. (6),46p.

RIDLEY, Thomas. A | View Of The | Civile And Eccle- | siastical Law, And | wherein the practise of them is | streitned, and may be relieued | within this Land. | Written by Thomas Ridley | Doctor of the Ciuile Law. | . . . (2 lines; ornament).

London, | Printed for the Company of Stationers | Anno. 1607. | 18.7x13.8cm. (16),230p.

ROGERS, Thomas. The | Faith, Doctrine, | and religion, professed, & protected | in the Realme of England, and dominions of | the same: | Expressed in 39 Articles, concorda- | blie agreed vpon by the reuerend Bishops, and Clergie of this | Kingdome, at two seuerall meetings, or Conuocations of | theirs, in the yeares of our Lord, 1562, | and 1604: | The Said Articles Analised Into | Propositions, and the Propositions prooued to be agreeable both to | the written word of God, and to the extant Confessions of all | the neighbour Churches, Christianlie | re-formed: | The Adversaries Also Of Note, And | name, which from the Apostles daies, and primitiue Church | hetherto, haue crossed, or con-tradicted the said Articles | in generall, or any particle, or proposition arising from a- | nie of them in particular, heereby are discouered, | laid open, and so confuted. | Perused, and by the lawfull authoritie of the Church of | England, allowed to be publique. | . . . (4 lines).

Printed by Iohn Legatt, Printer | to the Vniuersitie of Cambridge. 1607. | 18.7x 14.8cm. (36),222,(2)p.
Preface, signed.

SMITH, Henry. Gods Arrow | Againste | Atheists. | By Henrie Smith. | (Device)

At London, | Imprinted by R.B. for Thomas Pauier, and are to bee sold | at his shop entring into the Exchange. 1607. | 17.3x12.3cm. (3),100p.

SMITH, Henry. Fovre Sermons. | Preached by Maister | Henry Smith. | And published by a more | perfect Copie then heretofore. | (device)

London | Printed by T.D. for Cuthbert | Burby. 1607. | Lace border. 17.9x13.1 cm. (2,49)p.
Appended to his Sermons: 1609; without pagination; register continued from his Two Sermons: 1607.

SMITH, Henry. Three | Sermons | Made By Ma- | ster Henry Smith. | I. The Benefit of Contentation. | II. The Affinitie of the faithfull. | III. The lost Sheepe is found. | (ornament)

At London | Imprinted by F.K. for Nicolas Ling, and are to be sold at his | shop in S.Dunstanes Churchyard. 1607. | 17.9x13.1cm. 56p.
Appended to his Sermons: 1609; with separate register and pagination

SMITH, Henry. Two Sermons, | Of | Ionahs punishment. | Preached by Maister | Henry Smith. | And published by a more | perfect Copie then heretofore. | (device)

London | Printed by T.D. for Cuthbert | Burby. 1607. | Lace border. 17.9x13.1 cm. (1,44)p.
Appended to his Sermons: 1609; with separate register; without pagination.

SPARKE, Thomas. A | Brotherly Per- | swasion To Vnitie, | And Vniformitie In Ivdgement, | And Practise Tovching The Received | and present Ecclesiasticall gouernment, and the authorised | rites and ceremonies of the Church of England. | VVritten by Thomas Sparke Doctor | in Diuinitie. | And seene, allowed, and commanded by publike au- | thoritie to be printed. | . . . (5 lines; device).

London, | Printed by Nicholas Okes for Roger Iackson, and are to be sold | at his shop in Fleet-street neere to the great | Conduit. 1607. | 17.2x12.8 cm. (16), 83p. Paging irregular.

STANFORD, William. An Exposition of the | Kings Prerogatiue, collected | out of the great Abridgement of Iu- | stice Fitzherbert, and other | old Writers of the Lawes of England, | by the right Worshipfull Sir William | Stanford Knight, lately one of | the Iustices of the late Queenes | Maiesties Court of Com- | mon Plees. | Whereunto is annexed the Proces | to the same Prerogatiue appertaining. |

London | Printed for the Company of | Stationers. 1607. | Cum priuilegio. | 19.1x13.6 cm. fol.(1–5),1,6–85.
Appended to the French edition, 1607.

STANFORD, William. Les | Plees Del Co- | rone, Divisees | in plusors titles & Com- | mon lieux. | Per queux home pluis redement & ple- | nairement trouera quelq; chose que il quira, touchant | les dits Plees, composes per le tresreuerend Iudge, Monsieur | Gvilliavlme Stavndford | Chiualer, dernierment corrigee. | Auecques vn Table parfaicte des choses nota- | bles contenus in ycelle, nouelment reueu & cor- | rigee, oue ascun nouel additions. |

Londini | Ex Typographia Societatis Stationari- | orum. Anno Domini 1607. | Cum Priuilegio. | 19.1x13.6 cm. (12),198. fol.

VIGNIER, Nicolas. Concerning the Excommunication of | the Venetians | A | Discovrse | Against Cæsar Baronivs | Cardinall of the Church | of Rome. | In which the true nature and vse of Excommuni- | cation | is briefly and cleerly demonstrated, both by Testi- | monies of Holy Scripture, and from the old | Records of Christs Church. | Written in Latine by Nicolas Vignier, and | translated into English after the Copie | printed at Samur 1606. | Whereunto is added the Bull of Pope Pavlvs the | Fift, against the Duke, Senate and Commonwealth | of Venice: With the protestation of | the sayd Duke and Senate. | As also an Apologie of Frier Pavl of the | Order of Serui in Venice. | (ornament)

London | Printed by M.B. for C.B. and are to be sold in Pauls | Church-yard at the signe of the White-svvan. | 1607. | 17.8x13.6cm. (1),49;23p.

VIREL, Matthieu. A Learned | and excellent Treatise, | Conteining all the | principall grounds | of Christian re- | ligion: | Set dovvne by vvay of conference, | in a most plaine and fa- | miliar maner. | Written first in French, by M.Matth. | Virel: after, translated into La- | tine: and then into English, for the | vse of our Countreymen. | The seuenth impression: | Now newly reuised, and very much amen- | ded, according to the best and per- | fectest Copy: with a Table | thereunto annexed. | . . . (3 lines).

London, | Printed for Edward Bishop, and are to | be sold in Pauls Churchyard, | at the signe of the brasen | Serpent. 1607. | Lace border. 17x10.8cm. (6),260,(5)p.

WILKINSON, Robert. The | Merchant Royall. | A | Sermon | Preached at White-Hall before the King's Majestie, | at the Nuptials of the Right Honourable the Lord | Hay and his Lady, vpon the Twelfe day last, being | Ianuar.6.1607. | (cut).

At London. | Printed by Felix Kyngston for John Flasket, and are to be | sold at his Shop at the Signe of the Black Beare. 1607. | 20.4x12.5cm. vi,43p.
Anon. H&L. Reprint, without date.

WILLET, Andrew. Loidoromastix: | That Is, | A Scovrge For A | Rayler; Containing A Fvll | And Svfficient Answer Vnto | the Vnchristian raylings, slaunders, vntruths, and other in- | iurious Imputations, vented of late by one Richard | Parkes master of Arts, against the author | of Limbomastix. | Wherein three hundred raylings, | errors, contradictions, falsifications of Fathers, | corruptions of Scripture, with other grosse | ouersights, are obserued out of the said | vncharitable discourse, | by | Andrevv Willet Professor of Diuinitie. | . . . (9 lines).

Printed by Cantrell Legge, | Printer to the Vniversitie of Cambridge. 1607. | And are to be sold in Pauls Churchyard by Richard | Bankevvorth at the signe of the Sunne. | 17.4x12.9 cm. (39),195,(3) p.

1608

AINSWORTH, Henry. An Epistle | Sent Vnto Tvvo | daughters of VVarwick | from H. N. | The Oldest | Father of the Fami- | lie of Love. | VVith a refutation of the | errors that are therin; | by H. A. | . . . (3 lines; device).

Imprinted at Amsterdam | by Giles Thorp. | 1608. | 18.3x13.1cm. 64p.
Cambr.Univ.Cat.6352.

ANDERTON, James. The | Protestants | Apologie | For The | Roman Chvrch. | Deuided into three seuerall Tractes. | VVherof | The First {Concerneth the Antiquity & Continuance of the Ro- | man

Church & Religion, euer since the Apostles times. | The Second {1. That the Protestants Religion was not so much as | in being, at, or before Luthers first appearing. | {2. That the Marks of the true Church are apperteyning | to the Roman, and wholy wanting to the seuerall | Churches, begun by Luther & Caluin. | The Third {That Catholicks are no lesse loyall, and dutifull to | their Soueraigne, than Protestants. | All which is vndertaken, & proued by testimonies of the learned | Protestants themselues. | VVith | A Conclusion to the Reuerend Iudges, and other the graue | and learned Sages of the law. | By Iohn Brereley Priest. | . . . (4 lines).

Permissu Superiorum. Anno M.D.C.VIII. | 18.6x13.1 cm. (26),1–56,(4),57–751, (72)p. 715–719 are folioed.
Anon. Gillow. I: 36.

BELL, Thomas. The Jesuites Antepast, | Conteining, | A Reply against a pretensed aun- | swere to the Downe-Fall Of Po- | perie, lately published by a masked Iesuite | Robert Parsons by name, though he hide himselfe | couertly vnder the letters S.R. which may | fitly be interpreted (A Sawcy Rebell.) | . . . (device; 3 lines).

At London | Printed by William Iaggard dwel- | ling in Barbican. 1608. | Border. 17.7x13.5 cm. (7),227p. Pp. 185-192 skipped.
Epistle Dedicatory, signed.

BELL, Thomas. The | Tryall of the New | Religion. | Contayning a plaine Demonstra- | tion, that the late Faith and Doctrine of the | Church of Rome, is indeede the | New Religion. | By Thomas Bell. | (device)

At London | Printed by William Iaggard dwel- | ling in Barbican. 1608. | 17.8x 12.7 cm. (9,44)p.

BROUGHTON, Hugh. A | Petition | To The Lords, To | examine the religion | and cariage of D. | Ban. Archb. | By Hugh Broughton. | (ornament).

An° 1608. | 13.x8.4cm. (1),14p.

BULKELEY, Edward. An | Apologie | For | The Religion | established in the Church of | England. | Being An Answer to T. W. His | 12. Articles of the last edition. In this impres- | sion recognized and much inlarged. | Also | Answers to three other writings of three | seuerall Papists. | By Ed: Bvlkley Doctor of Diuinitie. | . . . (8 lines; ornament).

At London | Printed by George Eld for Arthur Iohnson, and are to be | sold at his shop at the signe of the white Horse, ouer- | against the great North doore of S. Paules | Church. 1608. | 18x14.1 cm. (10),270 p.

CHAUNCY, Maurice. Commentariolvs | De Vitae | Ratione Et | Martyrio Octo Decim | Cartvsianorvm Qvi In An- | glia sub Rege Hērico VIII. ob Ecclesię defen- | sionem ac nefarii Schismatis detesta- | tionem crudeliter trucidati sunt. | Editvs | Primum à V. P. F. Mauritio Chancæo Anglo eiusdem | ordinis Priore domus Shene, pari fide ac pietate; nunc | verò recenter recognitus, & paulùlum illustratus me- | lioriq̇[*ue*] stilo digestus. | Vna cum noua Historica relatione duodecim Mar- | tyrum Cartusianorum Ruræmundensium | qui Anno M. D. LXXII. Angonem | suum compleuerunt. | Auctore V. P. Arnoldo Hauensio priore Cartusiæ | Gandensis. |

Gandavi. | Apud Gualterum Manilium. | Anno 1608. | Permissu Superiorum. | 14.3x9.2cm. (8),111;(16),77,(3)p. Folded frontisp. and 1 engr.

CHAUNCY, Maurice. Innocentia, | Et Constantia Victrix; | Siue | Commentariolus; | De vitæ ratione, et Martyrio. 18. Cartusianorum; | qui in Angliæ Regno, sub Henrico octauo, ob Ecclesiæ | defensionem, et nefarij Schismatis detestationem, | crudeliter trucidati sunt. | Edita | Primum á R. P. F. Mauricio Chancæo, Anglo, | eiusdem Ordinis, pari fide ac Pietate; | Nunc recensita, distincta et mendis purgata, | in Cartusiâ, Horti Angelorum Wirceburgi, | in Orientali Franconiâ. |

Anno M.D.C.VIII. | Permissu Superiorum. | Engr. t.p. 15.3x9.6cm (22),111p. Title in round space.

CRASHAW, William. The | Sermon | Preached At | the Crosse, Feb .xiiij. 1607. | By W.Crashawe, Batchelour | of Diuinitie, and preacher at the | Temple; | Iustified by the Authour, both against Papist, | and Brownist, to be the truth. | Wherein, this point is principally followed; namely, that | the religion of Rome, as now it stands established, is | worse then euer it was. | . . . (3 lines; device).

Imprinted at London by H.L. for Edmond Weauer: and are | to be solde at the great North-gate of S.Paules | Church. 1608. | 17.8x13.7cm. (15),174p.

DOWNAME, George. A | Sermon defending the | honourable function of | Bishops, | Preached, April. 17. Anno | D. 1608. at the Consecration of | the right reuerend Father in God, | the L. Bishoppe of Bath | and Wells. | By George Downame, Doctor | of Divinitie. |

At London, | Printed by H.L. for Mathew | Lownes, and Felix Kyngston. | Anno D.1608. | Wood-cut border. 18.1x13.7cm. (14),100p.

First of his Two Sermons: 1608.

DOWNAME, George. Two | Sermons, | The One Com- | mending The Ministe- | rie In Generall: | The Other Defending | The Office Of Bishops | in particular: | Both Preached, and since enlarged by | George Dovvname | Doctor of Diuinitie. | . . . (4 lines; ornament).

At London | Imprinted by Felix Kyngston, and are to be sold in | Paules Churchyard by Matthew | Lownes. 1608. | 18.1x13.7cm. (3),(14),100,103p.

DOWNAME, John. Lectvres | Vpon The Fovre | First Chapters Of | The Prophecie | Of Hosea. | Wherein The Text Is Expovn- | ded and cleered, and such profitable instructions | obserued, and applied, as naturally arise out of | this holie Scripture, and are fit for | these times. | By Iohn Dovvname Bachelor in Diuinitie, and | Preacher of Gods word. | . . . (4 lines; ornament).

At London, | Imprinted by Felix Kyngston, for William Welby and are to be sold | at his shop in Pauls Churchyard at the signe of the | Greyhound. 1608. | 17.2x13.6 cm. (8),320,347p.

Also another copy from the library of Walter W. Law. 18.9x12.9cm.

DRAXE, Thomas. The | Chvrches | Securitie, | Togither with the Anti- | dote or preservative of ever | waking Faith. | A treatise conteyning many fruitefull instructions, | moralities and consolations fit for the time | and age wherein wee live. | Hereunto is annexed a sound and profitable trea- | tise of the generall signes and fore-runners | of the last judgement. | By Thomas Drax. | . . . (2 lines).

At London | Imprinted by George Eld, and are to be sold by | John Wright at his shoppe at Christ- | church Gate. 1608. | 17.5x12.7cm. 62,(16)p.
Lacks sig.A. T.p. supplied by Mr. Edward G. Friehold, of London.

DRAXE, Thomas. The | VVorldes | Resvrrection, | Or | The generall calling of | the Iewes. | A familiar Commentary vpon the | eleuenth Chapter of Saint Paul to the Romaines, accord- | ing to the sence of Scripture, and the consent of the | most iudicious interpreters, wherein aboue fiftie | notable questions are soundly answered, and | the particular doctrines, reasons and vses | of euery verse, are profitably and | plainly deliuered. | By Thomas Draxe Minister of | the word of God. | (ornament).

At London | Printed by G. Eld, for Iohn Wright, and are to be sold | at his shop neere Christ Church gate. | Anno. 1608. | 17.3x13.7 cm. (14),124 p.

GUILD, William. A | Yong Mans | Inqvisition, | Or Triall. | Whereby all young men | (as of all ages) may know how to re- | dresse and direct their waies, according | to Gods word, and if they bee in the | way of life to saluation, or in | the way of death, to | condemnation. | Together with a godly and most com- | fortable Meditation and Praier | ioyned thereunto. | . . . (2 lines). By William Guilde. | (ornament).

At London, | Printed by R. Raworth, for Iohn Bache, and | are to be sold at his shop in Popes- | head Pallace. 1608. | Line border. 14x9.1cm. (13),270p.

HALL, Joseph. Characters | Of | Vertves | And | Vices. | In two Bookes. | By | Ioseph Hall. |

London | Printed by Melch. Bradwood, for | Eleazer Edgar and Samuel Macham, | and are to be solde at their | shops in Pauls Church- | yard. | Anno | 1608. | Arch. border. 16.6x10.8cm. (13),173p.

HALL, Joseph. Epistles, | The | First (-Third) | Volume: | Conteining two (I–VI) | Decades | By | Ioseph Hall. |

London | Printed by A.H. for | Eleazar Edgar & Samuel | Macham: & are to be | sold at their shops | in Pavls | church-yard. | Anno 1608. | Arch. border. 16.6x 10.8cm. (12),190; (8),215; (8),120;(1),114p.
Impf. Vol. 1. mutilated to p. 6.; vol. 3, lacks t.p. and first leaf of preface.

HALL, Joseph. Pharisaisme | And | Christianitie: | Compared and set forth | in a Sermon at Paules | Crosse, May 1. | 1608. | By I.H. | . . . (4 lines).

London, | Printed by H.L. for Samuel Ma- | cham, and are to be sold at his | shop in Paules Church-yard | at the signe of the | Bul-head. | Anno | 1608. | Border. 16.6x10.8cm. (5),87p.
Epistle Dedicatory, signed.

HAVENS, Arnold. Historica Relatio | Dvodecim | Martyrvm | Cartvsianorvm, Qvi | Ruræmvndæ Indvcatv | Geldriæ Anno M. D. LXXII. Agonem | suum fœliciter comple- | uerunt. | Avctore | Vener. P. D. Arnoldo Havensio, | SS. Theologiæ Doctore, Cartusiæq[ue] Gan- | densis Priore. | Accessit Eivsdem Exhortatio | ad Cartusianos, de obseruantia disciplinæ Regu- | laris, vitæque Solitariæ commen- | datione. | . . . (2 lines; device).

Permissu Superiorum. 1608. | 14.3x9.2cm. (16),77,(3)p.
Appendix to Maurice Chauncey's Commentariolus: 1608.

HAVENS, Arnold. Specvlvm | Haereticae | Crvdelitatis: | In quo | Tam Vetervm Qvam | recentium Hæreticorum, ingenia, mores, immanisque sæuitia, in Antistites maximè ac Religio- | sorum hominum familias, varijs in locis desig- | nata, proprijs suis coloribus depicta | exhibentur. | Auctore | Rever.P.D.Arnoldo Haven- | sio, Cartusiæ Gandansis Præfecto. | Permissu Superiorum. | (device).

Coloniæ, | Imprimebat Seruatius Erffens, | Anno M.DC.VIII. | 14.3x9.2cm. (16), 245,(3)p.

HIERON, Samuel. An Answere to a | Popish Ryme, lately scattered | abroad in the West parts, and | much relyed vpon by some | simply-seduced. | By Samuel Hieron, Minister of | the word of God, at Modbury | in Deuon. | . . . (4 lines) | The second Edition | . (ornament)

London | Printed by H.L. for Samuel Macham, and are to be | sold at his shop in Paules Churchyard, at the | signe of the Bull-head, 1608. | 17x12.7 cm. (8,37)p.

HIERON, Samuel. A Dispvte | Vpon The Qvestion Of Kneeling, | In The Acte Of Receiving The Sa- | cramentall bread and wine, proving it to be unlawfull. | Or A Third Parte | Of The Defence Of The Ministers | reasons, for refusall of the Subscription and Conformitie | requyred. | Against the severall answers, | Of | 1. D. Spark, in his brotherly perswasion to unitie &c: | 2. D. Covel, in his booke against M. Iohn Burges, | 3. Thomas Hutton, in his 2. booke against the Ministers of | Devonshire and Cornwell. | 4. Thomas Rogers, in his two Dialogues, printed this yeare | 1608. | . . . (5 lines).

Printed. Anno 1608. | 17.5x13.6 cm. (8),166p.
Anon. Dexter: 347.

HIERON, Samuel. The | Second | Parte Of The | Defence of the Ministers Reasons | For refusal of Subscription & Confor- | mitie to the book of Common prayer. | Against The Several Answers | Of | Th. Hutton Bachiler of Divinity, in his two bookes | against the Minist. of Dev & Cornwel. | William Covel D. in Divinitie, in his Book against | M. Iohn Burges. | Th. Spark, D. in Divinity, in his Brotherly perswasion | to Vnitie & Vniformitie. | Fran. Mason Bachiler in Divinitie in his sermon | upon I Cor. 14. 40. | Concerning the holy Scriptures and | Apocrypha. | . . . (7 lines). | The Contents of the Book are in the Preface. |

Imprinted. 1608. | 17.7x13.2 cm. (16),243p.
Attribution doubtful; cf. Camb.Univ.Cat:6385. DNB. 26: 363 b.

INFORMATIONS, | Or | A Protestation, And | A Treatise from Scotland. | Seconded With | D. Reignoldes His Letter To Sir | Francis Knollis. | And | Sir Francis Knollis his speach in Par- | liament. | All | Suggesting the vsurpation of Papal Bishops. | . . . (6 lines).
Imprinted 1608. | 13.7 x 8.6 cm. (6),94p.

JAMES, Thomas. An | Apologie For Iohn | Wickliffe, shewing his conformitie | with the now Church of England; with an- | swere to such slaunderous obiections, | as haue beene lately vrged against him | by Father Parsons, the Apolo- | gists, and others. | Collected Chiefly Ovt Of | diuerse works of his in written hand, by Gods e- | speciall providence remaining in the Publike | Library at Oxford, of the Honorable foun- | dation of Sr. Thomas BodleY Knight: | By | Thomas James keeper of the same. | . . . (3 lines; device)
At Oxford, | Printed by Ioseph Barnes, printer to the | Vniversitie. 1608. | 17.6x 13.7cm. (8),75,(4)p.

KING, John. A | Sermon | Preached At White- | Hall The 5. Day Of No- | vember. ann. 1608. | By | John King Doctor of Divinity, Deane of | Christ-Church in Oxon. and Vicechauncel- | lor of the Vniversity. | Published by commandement. | (device).
At Oxford, | Printed by Joseph Barnes Printer to the | Vniversitie. 1608. | Line border. 18.8x14.3cm. (1),40p.

KING, John. A | Sermon | Preached In St. Maries | at Oxford the 24. of March being the | day of his sacred Maiesties inauguration | and Maundie thursday. | By | John Kinge Doctor of Divinity, Deane | of Christ Church, and Vicechancellor | of the Vniversitie. | (device).
At Oxford, | Printed by Ioseph Barnes. 1608. | Line border. 17.2x12.9cm. (1), 30p.

LEVER, Christopher. Heauen and Earth, | Religion and Policy. | Or, | The maine difference betweene | Religion and Policy. | Written by C.L. | . . . (device; 1 line).
Printed by H.B. for Ieffrey Chorlton, | and are to be sold at his shop, at the great | North dore of Paules Church. 1608. | Lace border. 15.5x10.1cm. (6),116, (1)p.
Camb.Univ.Cat.No.2900. Epistle dedicatory, signed.

MAIHEW, Edward. A | Treatise Of | The Grovndes | Of The Old And | Newe Reli- | gion. | Devided Into Two Parts, | Whereunto is added an Appendix, containing a briefe con- | futation of William Crashaw his first | Tome of Romish forgeries and | falsifications. | . . . (3 lines; ornament).
Anno Domini M.D.C.VIII. | 18.3x13.2 cm. (7),32,146,232p.
Anon. Gillow:IV:552. Camb.Univ.Cat:6875.

MORTON, Thomas. A | Preamble | Vnto | An Incovnter | With P.R. The Avthor | of the deceitfull Treatise of | Mitigation: | Concerning the Romish doctrine both in question of | Rebellion and of Aequiuocation: | By | Thomas Morton. | . . . (3 lines, ornament).

London, | Printed by Melch. Bradwood for Iohn Bill | and Edmond Weauer. | 1608. | 17.6x13.2cm. (13),128p.

P., B. The | Prentises | Practise In Godli- | nesse, and his true | freedome. | Diuided into ten Chapters. Written by | B. P. | . . . (4 lines; device).

London | Printed by Nicholas Okes, for Iohn Bach, and | are to be sold at his shop in Popes | head Palace. 1608. | Line border. 13.9x8.7 cm. (15),71,(13) fol.

PANKE, John. The Fal Of Babel. | By the confusion of tongues, directly proving against the | Papists of this, and former ages; that a view of their wri- | tings, and bookes being taken, it cannot be discerned by any man | living, what they would say, or how be vnderstoode, in the | question of the sacrifice of the Masse, the Reall pre- | sence or transubstantiation, but in explaining | their mindes, they fall vpon such termes, | as the Protestants vse and allow. | Fvrther | In the question of the Popes supremacy is shewed, how they | abuse an authority of the auncient father St.Cyprian, A Canon of | the I.Niceene counsell, And the Ecclesiasticall historie of Socra- | tes, and Sozomen. And lastly is set downe a briefe of the suc- | cession of Popes in the sea of Rome for these 1600 yeeres | together; what diversity there is in their accompt, what here- | sies, schismes, and intrusions there hath bin in that sea, | deliuered in opposition against their tables, where- | with now adaies they are very busie, and o- | ther things discovered against them. | By | Iohn Panke. | . . . (4 lines; ornament)

Printed at Oxford by Ioseph Barnes. 1608. | 17.2x13.3cm. (31),147,(2)p.

PARSONS, Robert. The | Ivdgment | Of A Catholicke | English-Man, Living In | Banishment For His Religion: | VVritten to his priuate friend | in England. | Concerning A late Booke set forth, and entituled; Triplici nodo, triplex cuneus, | Or, An Apologie for the Oath of Allegiance. | Against two Breves of Pope Pavlvs V. to the Catho- | lickes of England; & a Letter of Cardinall Bellarmine | to M.George Blackwell Arch-priest. | VVherin, the said Oath is shewed to be vnlawfull vnto a Catholicke | Conscience; for so much, as it conteyneth sundry clauses | repugnant to his Religion. | . . . (Lace ornament; 3 lines).

Permissu Superiorum. Anno 1608. | Line border. 17.5x13.7 cm. (6),128p.
Anon. Cambr. Univ. Cat: 6517.

PERKINS, William. Clarissimi Viri | D. Gvilielmi Perkinsi, | Theologi Angli, | Catechesis: | In qua initiò sex firma & immota totius religionis | Christianæ iacta sunt fundamenta, instar | breuis ac succinctæ alicuius in opus | ipsum introductionis. | Deinde omnia & singula Christianæ Religionis Capita, | (vtpote Symbolvm Apostolicvm, vtrum- | que Noui Testamenti Sacramentum, Baptismvs | nimirum, & Coena Domini, Decalogvs & | Oratio Dominica,) perspicuo commentario | illustrata, & nunc primum Latinitate donata, | à | Iohanne Lotichio Solitariensi, | Ministro verbi diuini apud Ostheimenses in | Illustri Comitatu Hanouico. | . . . (2 lines; device)

MDCVIII. | Hanoviæ | Apud Guilielmum Antonium. | 17. x 10.2 cm. 35,821, (2)p.

PERKINS, William. A | Clovd Of | Faithfvll | Witnesses, Lea- | ding To The Heavenly | Canaan: | Or | A Commentarie vpon the II. Chap- | ter to the Hebrewes, preached in Cambridge | by that Godly, and iudicious Divine, | M. William Perkins: | Long expected and desired; and therefore pub- | lished at the request of his Executours, by Will. Cra- | shawe, and Tho. Pierson, Preachers of Gods Word: | who heard him preach it, and wrote it | from his mouth. | . . . (6 lines).

At London, | Printed by Humfrey Lownes, for Leo. Greene. | 1608. | 18.3x13.cm (7),592p.

ROGERS, Thomas (editor). A | Methode | vnto Mortification: | Called heretofore, | The contempt of the | world, and the vanitie | thereof. | Written at the first in the Spa- | nish, afterward translated into the Itali- | an, English, and Latine tongues; now | last of all perused at the request | of some of his godly | friends, and | as may bee most for the benefite of | this Church, reformed | and published | by | Thomas Rogers. | Allowed by authoritie. | . . . (3 lines)

Imprinted at London by | Iohn Windet. | 1608. | 12.4x6.8cm (19),471p. (impf. after X 8.)

ROGERS, Thomas. Two | Dialogves, | Or | Conferences (Abovt | an old question lately renued, and by the | Schismaticall company, both by printed Pamphlets, | and othervvise to the disturbance of the Churches | quiet, and of peaceable minds, very | hotly pursued.) | Concerning Kneeling in the very act of recei- | uing the Sacramentall bread and wine, | in the Supper of the Lord. | The former | Betvveene tvvo Ministers of the vvord, the one refracta- | rie, and depriued; the other not so. | The latter | Betweene an humorous Schismatike and a setled professor. | . . . (6 lines, ornament).

Printed by Henry Ballard. | 1608. | Lace border. 18.6x14cm. (12, 30; 2, 88) p. Sub t.p.

Cambr.Univ.Cat:2901. Preface to the bishop of London, signed.

ROLLOCK, Robert. In | Epistolam | S. Pavli Apostoli | Ad Romanos, | Roberti Rolloci | Scoti, Edinbvrgensis | Ecclesiæ Ministri, | Commentarivs, Ana- | lytica methodo conscriptus. | Altera editio emendatior, & Indice auctior. | (device).

Geneuæ, apud Iacobum Stœr. | M.DCVIII. | 15.5x9.8cm. (24),407p.

ROLLOCK, Robert. In | Evangelivm | Domini Nostri | Iesv Christi | secundum Sanctum | Iohannem, | Commentarivs Roberti | Rolloci Scoti, Ecclesiæ | Edinburgensis Ministri: | Nunc denuò in lucem editus. | Accessit Harmonia ex Quatuor Euangelistis in Hi- | storiam

Mortis, Resurrectionis, & Ascensionis Domini: | ab eodem Rolloco concinnata & luculenter exposita. | Index item Analyticus. | (device)

Apud Iacobvm Stoer. | M.DCVIII. | 16.8x10.2cm.   (31),1195,(4)p.

SMITH, Henry. Fovre | Sermons | Preached | By Maister | Henry Smith. | And published by a | more perfect Copie then | heeretofore. | (device)

At London, | Printed for William Leake, | dwelling in Pauls Churchyard, | at the signe of the Holy- | Ghost. 1608. | Lace border. 17.9x13.1cm. (4,93)p.

Appended to his Sermons: 1609. Without page numbers; register continuous from his Two Sermons preached: 1608.

SMITH, Henry. Two | Sermons | preached by Maister | Henry Smith: With a | Prayer for the morning | thereunto adioyning. | And published by a| more perfect Copie then | heretofore. | (device)

At London, | Printed for William Leake, | dwelling in Pauls Churchyard, | at the signe of the Holy- | Ghost. 1608. | Lace border. 17.9x13.1cm. (2,35)p.

Appended to his Sermons: 1609. With separate register and pagination

STAPLETON, Thomas. Thomae | Stapletoni, | Angli, S.Theo- | logiae Doctoris, Et | Professoris Regii | Lovanii, | Promptvarivm | Catholicvm, | Ad instructionem Concionatorum contra | hæreticos nostri temporis, | Svper Omnia Evangelia Totivs Anni | Tam Dominicalia, Qvam De Festis; | In Qvo Inveniet Concionator, Vnde Ex | litera Euangelica, vel plerasq[ue] hæreses aptè refutet; vel contra hæreti- | corum hodie fraudes & mendacia, fidem Catholicam prætex- | tu Euangelij plausibiliter ab illis impugnatam, | solidè defendat. | Hac vltima editione plurimis in locis nouis additionibus ab au- | ctore recens locupletatum. | Additus est Index rerum copiosissimus. | . . . (4 lines)

Coloniae Agrippinae, | In Officina Birckmannica, sumptibus | Hermanni Mylij. | Anno M.DC.VIII. | Cum gratia & Priuilegio S. Cæsareæ Maiestatis. | 16.2x10.3cm. (30),325;321,(13);(16),340,(10)p. 3 pts with separate title pages.

TWYNE, Brian. Antiqvi- | tatis Academiæ Oxo- | niensis Apologia. | In tres libros divisa. | Avthore | Briano Twyno in facultate Artium Ma- | gistro, & Collegij Corporis Christi in eâdem | Academia Socio. | (device).

Oxoniæ, | Excudebat Iosephus Barnesius. | Anno Dom. 1608. | 18.3x13.3cm.   (6), 384,(72)p.

UDALL, John. A | Commenta- | rie Vpon The | Lamentations | Of Ieremie: | VVherein are contained; first, the method and order of | euery Chapter layd open in seueral Tables; then a litterall inter- | pretation of the text out of the Hebrevv, vvith a Paraphrasticall exposition of | the sense thereof: Aftervvard, a collection of diuers doctrines, gathered some- | times out of a vvhole verse in generall, or from the coherence of the text; | and sometimes out of the particular vvords of the same: vvith examples, | novv and then, shevving hovv the same doctrines haue bene veri- | fied in experience: Moreouer, the reason or proofe of e- | uery doctrine: and lastly, the particular vses, that | are to be made of them, for the edificati- | on of the Church of God. | . . . (4 lines; device).

London | Imprinted by T.C. for Thomas Man. 1608. | 17.8x12.cm. (8),195p. Cf.Cambr.Univ.Cat.7370.

WHITE, John. The Way | To The Trve | Chvrch: | wherein | The principall Motiues perswading to Romanisme; | and | Questions touching the nature and authoritie | of the Church and Scriptures, are familiarly dispu- | ted, and driuen to their issues, where, this day they | sticke betweene the Papists and vs: | Contriued into an Answer to a Popish Discourse, concerning the | Rule of Faith and the marks of the Church, And published to | admonish such as decline to Papistrie of the weake and vncer- | taine grounds, whereupon they haue ventured their soules. | Directed to all that seeke for resolution: and especially | to his louing countrimen of Lancashire. | By Iohn White Minister of Gods word at Eccles. | For the finding out of the matter and questions handled, there are three Ta- | bles: two in the beginning, and one in the end of the Boooke. | . . . (2 lines; ornament).

London, | Printed for Iohn Bill and Wil- | liam Barret. | 1608. | 18.8x14.cm (46), 454,(10)p.

WOODCOKE, Richard. A Godly And | Learned Answer, | To a lewd and vnlear- | ned Pamphlet: | Intituled, | A few, plaine and forcible Reasons for the Catholike | Faith, against the Religion of the | Protestants. | By Richard Woodcoke Batchellor | of Diuinitie. | . . . (4 lines: device)

London, | Printed by N.O. for Iohn Bache and Nicholas Bourne, and | are to be sold at his shop vnder the Royall | Exchange. 1608. | 18. x13.2 cm. (7),114p.

WOTTON, Anthony. A Trial Of | The Romish Cler- | gies Title To The Chvrch: | By way of answer to a Popish Pamphlet | written by one A.D. and entituled | A Treatise of Faith, wherein is briefly and plainly shewed | a direct way, by which euery man may resolue and settle | his mind in all doubts, questions and controuersies, con- | cerning matters of Faith. | By Antonie Wotton. | In the end you haue three Tables: one of the texts of Scripture | expounded or alledged in this booke: another of the Testi- | monies of ancient and later Writers, with a Chro- | nologie of the times in which they liued: a | third of the chiefe matters contained | in the Treatise and Answer. | . . . (6 lines; ornament).

London, | Printed for Elizabeth Burby Widow, and are to be sold | at the signe of the Swan in Pauls Churchyard. | 1608. | 17.9x13.8 cm. (5),420,(15) p.

WYCLIFFE, John. Tvvo Short Trea- | tises, Against The | Orders of the Begging Friars, | compiled by | That | Famovs Doctovr Of The Chvrch, | and Preacher of Gods word John Wickliffe, | sometime fellow of Merton, and Master of | Ballioll Coll. in Oxford, and afterwards | Parson of Lutterworth in Lece- | stershire. | Faithfully Printed according to two ancient | Manuscript Copies, extant, the one in | Benet

Colledge in Cambridge, the o- | ther remaining in the Publike Li- | brarie at Oxford. | . . . (3 lines).

At Oxford, | Printed by Joseph Barnes, Printer to the University. 1609. | 18.6x 13.5cm. (8),62,(2)p.
Part of impr. supplied; lacks page containing Faults escaped in the printing, and pp. 17–18.
Madan: Oxford Press, 1608:18.

1609

ANDREWES, Lancelot. Tortvra Torti: | Sive, | Ad Matthaei | Torti Librvm | Responsio, qui nuper editus | contra Apologiam | Serenissimi Poten- | tissimiqve Principis, | Iacobi, Dei Gratia, | Magnæ Britanniæ, Franciæ, | & Hiberniæ Regis, | Pro | Ivramento Fidelitatis. | (ornament and head-piece).

Londini | Excudebat Robertvs Barkervs, | Serenissæ. Regiæ Maiestatis | Typographvs. | Anno 1609. | 21.4x15.2cm. (8),402p.
Anon. Cambr.Univ.Cat:2612.

An ANSVVERE | To A Sermon Prea- | ched The 17 Of April | Anno D. 1608, By George Dow- | name Doctovr Of Divi- | nitie And Intituled, | A Sermon defendinge the honorable function | of Bishops; wherein, | All his reasons, brought to prove the | honorable function of our L. | Bishops, to be of divine insti- | tution; are answered | and refuted. | . . . (7 lines).

Imprinted anno 1609. | 17.6 x 14.5 cm. 58, (1), 166 p.
H&L, new ed., attributes to —— Sheerwood.

BARLOW, William. An Ansvver | To | A Catholike | English-Man (So By | Himselfe Entitvled) Who, | without a Name, passed his Censure | vpon the Apology, made by the Right | High and mightie Prince Iames by the | Grace of God King of Great Brittaine, | France, and Ireland &c. for the | Oath of Alle- | geance; | Which Censvre Is Heere | Examined And Refuted | By the Bishop of Lincoln. | . . . (3 lines).

London, | Printed by Thomas Haueland for Mathew Law, and are to be sold | in Paules-Church-yard at the signe of the Fox neere | Saint Austines-gate. 1609. | Head piece and line border. 19.6x14.2cm. (12),370p.

BOYS, John. An | Exposition | Of Al The Princi- | pall Scriptvres Vsed | in our English Liturgie. | Together With A Reason | why the Church did chuse the same. | By Iohn Boys Doctor of | Diuinitie. | . . . (6 lines ; ornament).

At London, | Imprinted by F.K. for Martin C[lark, and are to be sold] | by William Aspley, at the signe of the Parot in | Pauls Churchyard. 1609. | Imprint stained. 18x13.8cm. (5),126p.

BROUGHTON, Hugh. Principall Positions | for groundes of the holy Bible. | A Short Oration Of The | Bibles Translation. | Positions Historiqve: | and of the Apocrypha. | Tobit Particvlarly | handled. | Ivdith Severally | handled. | By Hvgh Brovghton. | (ornament).

Printed in the yeare of our Lord, | 1609. | 17.2x13.3cm. 31p.

BUDDLE, George. A Short | And Plaine | Discourse. | Fully containing the vvhole | doctrine of Euangelicall | Fastes. | By George Bvddle, Bachelour of | Diuinitie, and Parson of Whikkenby | in Lincolne-shire. | . . . (1 line; device).

London | Printed for Mathevv Lavv, and are to be sold at his | Shop in Pauls Church-yard, neere vnto Saint | Austines Gate, at the Signe of | the Foxe. 1609. | 17.7x13.4cm. (8),87p.

CALVIN, John. A | Commentary | Vpon The Prophecie | Of Isaiah. | By | Mr. Iohn Calvin. | Wherevnto Are Added Fovre Tables: | The first touching places of Scripture alleaged: The second, of the principall | matters handled: The third, of Authors and diuers names mentioned: The | fourth, of certaine texts cited out of Isaiah in the new Testament, | which by the Author in the Commentarie are | compared and reconciled. | Translated Ovt Of French | Into English: By C.C. | . . . (5 lines; ornament).

At London | Imprinted by Felix Kyngston, and are to be sold by | William Cotton, dwelling in Pater noster Row, at the signe of | the golden Lion. 1609. | 27.4x17.7cm. (22),674,(40)p.

CAWDRAY, Robert. A | Treasvrie | Or Store-Hovse | of Similies: | Both pleasaunt, delightfull, | and profitable, for all estates of men | in generall. | Newly collected into Heades and | Common places. | By Robert Cawdray. | (device).

London, | Printed by Thomas Creede. | 1609. | 18.3x14.1cm. (12),860,(8)p.

COOPER, Thomas. The | Chvrches | Deliverance, | Contayning | Meditations and short notes vppon | The booke of Hester. | In remembrance of the wonderfull deliue- | rance from the Gunpoulder-Treason. | By | Thomas Cooper. | (device).

At London. | Imprinted by G.Eld for T.Adams, and are to be sold | at the white Lyon in Paules Church-yard. | 1609. | 17.8x14.cm. (20),219p.

DOD, John and CLEAVER, Robert. A | Plaine And | Familiar Expo- | sition Of The | Fifteenth, Sixteenth, and Se- | uenteenth Chapters of | the Prouerbs of | Salomon. | (device).

London, | Printed by Thomas Haveland | for Thomas Man, | 1609. | 17.5x13.7 cm. (24),157p.
Dedication, signed.

DOD, John and CLEAVER, Robert. Ten | Sermons | tending chiefely to | the fitting of men for the wor- | thy receiuing of the Lords | Supper. | Wherein amongst many other holy | instructions: the Doctrines of sound repen- | tance and humiliation, and of Gods speciall fa- | uours vnto penitent sinners, and worthy | Communicants are largely and | effectually handled. | The six first, by I. Dod. | The foure last, by R. Cleauer. | Whereunto is annexed, a plaine and learned | metaphrase on the Epistle to the Collossi- | ans, written by a godly and iudicious | Preacher. | There is also set before the Sermons, a short Dialogue | of Preparation: containing the chiefe points that concerne |

the worthy receiuing of the Lords Supper, taken for | the most part, out of the Sermons following: and | collected into a method for the benefit and | ease of those that desire directi- | on in this matter. |

London | Printed by William Hall for Roger Iackson, and are to bee | sold at his shop, neere the Conduitin | Fleet-street. 1609. | 17.4x13.4 cm. (13),170,105p.

DOWNAME, John. The | Christian | Warfare. | Wherein Is First Generally | Shewed The Malice, Power And | politike stratagems of the spirituall enemies of our saluation, | Satan and his assistants the world and the flesh; with the | meanes also whereby the Christian may withstand | and defeate them. | And Afterwards More Speci- | allie Their Particular Temptati- | ons, against the seuerall causes and meanes of our saluation, | whereby on the one side, they allure vs to securitie and | presumption, and on the other side, draw vs | to doubting and desperation, are expres- | sed and answered. | Written Especially For Their Sakes | who are exercised in the spirituall conflict of temptations, and | are afflicted in conscience in the sight and sense | of their sinnes. | By I. Dovvname, Bacheler in diuinitie and | Preacher of Gods word. | The Second Edition, Corrected And | much enlarged by the Author, as further appeareth in the | Epistle to the Reader. | . . . (2 lines).

At London | Imprinted by Felix Kyngston, for Elizabeth Burby, | widow, and are to be sold at her shop in Paules Church- | yard at the signe of the Swan. 1609. | 18x12.8cm. (24),744p.

DVTIFVLL | And | Respective | Considerations | Vpon Fovre Severall | Heads Of Proofe And Triall | In Matters Of Religion. | Proposed | By the High and Mighty Prince, Iames King of Great | Britayne, France and Ireland &c. in his late Booke | of Premonition to all Christian Princes, for clearing | his Royall Person from the imputation | of Heresy. | By a late Minister & Preacher in England. | . . . (ornament: 6 lines).

[St.Omer]. Permissu Superiorum. M.DC.IX. | 18.5x13.5cm. (16),243,(1)p. Camb.Univ.Cat.Nos.6519,6520. Gillow ascribes to Robert Parsons.

EBURNE, Richard. The Mainte- | nance of the Mi- | nisterie. | Wherein Is Plainly Decla- | red how the Ministers of the Gospell ought | to be maintained: And the true and aunci- | ent practize of our Church in this | case, shewed to be agreeable to | the word of God, and | all Antiquitie. | Necessarie in these times to be read and considered | of all sortes of Christians, but specially of | such as liue in Townes and Cities. | By Richard Eburne, Minister of the word. | . . . (3 lines; ornament).

London, | Printed by T. C. for Eleazar Edgar, and are | to be solde at his shop in Paules Church-yard, | at the signe of the Wind-mill. 1609. | 17.5x13.8cm. (12), 175 p.

EGERTON, Thomas. The Speech | Of The Lord | Chancellor Of | England, in the Eschequer | Chamber, touching the | Post-nati. | (ornaments).

London, | Printed for the Societie of | Stationers. An. 1609. | Head piece and line border. 19x13.7 cm. (10),118 p.
Camb.Univ.Cat. No.3237.

HALL, Joseph. The | Art | Of Divine | Meditation: | Profitable for all Chri- | stians to know and | Practise. | Exemplified with a large | Meditation of eternall | life. | By Ios: Hall. |
At London, | Printed by Tho:Purfoot | for Samuell Macham, and | Lawrence Lyle. | 1609. | Lace border. 12x7cm. (18),193p.

HALL, Joseph. Heaven | Vpon | Earth: | Or, | Of true Peace | and Tranquillity of | minde. | By Ios: Hall. |
At London, | Printed by Tho:Purfoot | for Samuell Macham, and | Lawrence Lyle. | 1609. | Lace border. 12x7cm. (5),220p.

HALL, Joseph. Holy | Obseruations. | Lib. I. | Also, | Some fewe of Da- | vids Psalmes Meta- | phrased, for a taste of | the rest. | By Ios: Hall. |
At London, | Printed by Tho:Purfoot | for Samuell Macham: and are | to be sold at his shop in Paules | Churchyard, at the signe | of the Bull-head. 1609. | Lace border. 12x7cm. (7),129;(16,33)p. Sub-title, at F11.

HALL, Joseph. An | Open And | plaine Paraphrase, | vpon the | Song Of Songs, | Which is | Salomons. | By Ios.Hall. | (ornament).
Anno Domini, 1609. | 16.6x10.8cm. (5),87p.
Part of his Salomons Divine Arts: 1609.

HALL, Joseph. The | Passion | Sermon, | Preached At | Pavles Crosse | on Good-Friday. | Apr.14.1609. | By I.H. |
London | Printed by W.S. for Eleazer | Edgar, and are to be sold at | his Shop in Pauls Church- | yard at the Signe of | the Wind-mill. | Anno | 1609. | Arch. border. 16.6x10.8cm. (6),96p.

HALL, Joseph. The | Peace Of | Rome. | Proclaimed To | All the world, by her famous | Cardinall Bellarmine, | and the no lesse famous Casuist | Navarre. | Whereof the one acknowled- | geth, and numbers vp aboue three | hundred differences of Opinion, maintai- | ned in the Popish Church. The other | confesses neere threescore differen- | ces amongst their owne Doctors | in one onely point of their | Religion. | Gathered faithfully out of their writings | in their own words, and diuided into foure | Bookes, and those into seuerall | Decads. | Whereto Is Prefixed A | Serious Disswasiue from Poperie. | By J. H. |
London | Printed for Sam. Macham. 1609. | Arch border. 17.6x13.7 cm. (7), 39,(4),195,(21)p.
Dedication to Prince Henry, signed.

HALL, Joseph. Salomons | Diuine Arts, | Of | 1. Ethickes, | 2. Politickes, | 3. Oeconomicks: | That is; the Gouernment | Of {1. Behaviovr, | 2. Common-vvealth, | 3. Familie. | Drawne into Method, out of his | Prouerbs & Ecclesiastes. | With an open and plaine Para- | phrase, vpon the | Song of Songs. | By Ioseph Hall. |
At London, | Printed by H.L. for | Eleazar Edgar, and | Samuel Macham. | 1609. | Arch. border. 15.1x10.1cm. (7) 174;(5),87p.

HALL, Joseph. Some | few of Dauids | Psalmes Metaphra- | sed for a taste | of the rest. | By Ios:Hall. | (Lace ornament).

At London, | Printed by Tho:Purfoot | for Samuell Macham; and are | to be sold at his shop in Paules | Churchyard, at the signe | of the Bull-head. 1609. | Lace border. 12x7cm. (16,33)p.
Appended to his Holy Obseruations.Lib.I.1609.

HIERON, Samuel. The | Discoverie | Of Hypocrisie, | In Two Sermons, | Vpon Mathevv. | 3. verse.10. | And Three Other, Cal- | led the perfect patterne of true Con- | uersion, vpon Matth.13.ver.44. | By Samuel Hieron, Minister of the Gospel. | . . . (8 lines; ornament).

London, | Printed by T.C. for Thomas Man. | 1609. | 17.5x13.3cm. (4),82p.

HIGGONS, Theophilus. The | First Motive | Of T.H. Maister Of Arts, | And Lately Minister, To | Svspect The Integrity Of His | Religion: | Which was | Detection Of Falsehood in D. Hum- | frey, D. Field, & other learned Protestants, touching the question | of Purgatory, and Prayer for the dead. | VVith his | Particvlar Considerations | perswading him to embrace the Catholick do- | ctrine in theis, and other points. | (three asterisks) An Appendix | intituled, | Try Before Yov Trvst. | Wherein | Some notable vntruths of D. Field, | and D. Morton are discouered. | (ornament).

Printed 1609. | 15.6x10.8cm. (16),172,(4) ; (8),70,(1)p.
Epistle, signed.

HIGGONS, Theophilus. Try | Before Yov | Trvst. | Or | An Admonition | Vnto the credulous, and seduced Pro- | testants, to examine the fidelity | of their vvriters, and parti- | cularly of tvvo princi- | pall Doctours; viz. | D. Field, & D. | Morton. | A | Detection of their falsehood in some mat- | ters of great importāce: and a dis- | covery of sondry vanities in the | new Gospell according | to Lvther, | Zvingl. | and others. | By | T.H. Maister of Arts, | and lately Minister. | Added by way of Appendix vnto his | First Motive. |

1609. | 15.6x10.8cm. (8),70,(1)p.
Appendix to his First Motive: 1609; with separate register and pagination.
Epistle, signed T.H.

HOSKIN, John. A Sermon | upon the Parable of the | King that taketh an accompt | of his seruants. | Math,18.23. | Wherein is declared, the justice, | mercy, and seueritie of God: the crueltie | of man, and his reward for the same. | Rising upon St.Peters question to Christ, | Viz. How oft shall I forgive my bro- | ther? seauen times? 21 vers. | By John Hoskin, Minister | of Gods holy word, student in | Diuinitie. | . . . (4 lines)

At London | Printed by G.E. for John Wright | 1609. | Wood-cut border. 13.4x 8.5cm. (6,51)p. T.p. supplied by Mr. Edward G. Friehold, of London.

INGMETHORPE, Thomas. A | Sermon Vpon | Part Of The Second | Chapter of the first Epistle of Saint | Iohn: wherein the present State of the Pa- | pacie, is in part but vnpartially repre- | sented, and

shewed to be nothing | lesse then Catholique, euen | plaine Antichristian. | By Thomas Ingmethorp. | . . . (10 lines; device).
London, | Printed by Thomas Creede. | 1609. | 17.3x13.2 cm.   (8,30)p.

JACOB, Henry. To the right High | and mightie Prince, Iames | by the grace of God, King of great | Britannie, France, and Irelande, De- | fender of the faith, &c. | An humble Supplication for Toleration and li- | bertie to enioy and observe the ordinances of | Christ Iesvs in th'administration of | his Churches in lieu of hu- | mane constitutions. | . . . (13 lines).
1609. | Border.   18.4x14 cm.   2–48 p.   Lacks fly-leaf.
Anon. Dexter:358.

JAMES I. Apologia Pro | Ivramento | Fidelitatis, | Primùm quidem Aνωνυμos : Nunc | verò ab Ipso Avctore, Serenissimo ac | Potentiss. Principe, Iacobo Dei gratiâ | Magnæ Britanniæ, Franciæ & | Hiberniæ Rege, Fidei Defensore, | denuò edita. | Cui præmissa est Præfatio Mo- | nitoria Sacratiss. Cæsari Rodolpho II. | Semper Avgvsto, Cæterisque Christiani Orbis | Sereniss. ac Potentiss. Monarchis ac Regibus: | Illustriss. Celsissimisq[ue] Liberis Principibus, | Rebus publicis atq[ue] Ordinibus inscripta, | eodem Avctore. | . . . (5 lines).
Londini | Excudebat Ioannes Norton, Serenis- | simæ Regiæ Maiestatis in Latinis, Græcis, | & Hebraicis Typographus. 1609. | Cum priuilegio Regali. | Ornam. head-piece.   20.6x15.4cm.   (4),141;(11,2),116p.

JAMES I. An Apologie for the Oath | of Allegiance. | First Set | Foorth Withovt | a name; And now acknowledged by the | Author, the Right High and Mightie Prince, | Iames, by the Grace of God, King of | Great Britaine, France and Ireland; | Defender of the Faith, &c. | Together with a Premonition | of his Maiesties, to all most Mightie | Monarches, Kings, free Princes | and States of Christendome. | . . . (5 lines)
Imprinted at London by Robert | Barker, Printer to the Kings most | Excellent Maiestie. | April. 8. Anno 1609. | Cum priuilegio Regali. | Orn. head-piece.   19x14.2 cm.   (4),135,(11);(2),112p.

JAMES I. Triplici nodo, triplex cuneus. | Or | An Apologie | For The Oath | of Allegiance. | Against the two Breues of Pope | Pavlvs Qvintvs, and the late | Letter of Cardinall Bellar- | mine to G. Black- vvel | the Arch-priest. | . . . (2 lines)   Authoritate Regiâ | (ornament).
Imprinted at London by Robert | Barker, Printer to the Kings most | Excellent Maiestie. | Anno 1609. | 19.x14.1cm.   (2),112p.
Sub-title of his Apologie for the Oath of Allegiance: 1609.

JAMES I. Triplici nodo triplex cuneus. | Sive | Apologia Pro | Ivramento | Fidelitatis, | Adversvs Dvo Brevia | PP.Pavli Qvinti, & Epistolam | Cardinalis Bellarmini, ad | G.Blackvellvm Archi- | presbyterum nuper | scriptam. | . . . (3 lines).   Editio altera. | (ornament)
Londini | Excudebat Ioannes Norton, | Serenissimæ Regiæ Maiestatis, in Latinis | Græcis, & Hebraicis Typographus. | Anno 1609. | Orn. head-piece, line border. 20.6x15.4cm.   (2),116p.
Sub-title of his Apologia Pro Ivramento Fidelitatis: 1609. With separate register and pagination.

MORTON, Thomas. A | Catholike | Appeale For | Protestants, | Out of the confessions of the Romane Doctors; | particularly answering the mis-named Catholike | Apologie for the Romane faith, out of the Protestants: | Manifesting the Antiquitie of our Religion, and | satisfying all scrupulous Obiections which haue | bene vrged against it. | Written by Th. Morton Doctor of Diuinitie. | . . . (4 lines ; device).

Londini, | Impensis Georg. Bishop & Ioh. Norton. | 1609. | 29x18.4cm. (22),680, (20)p.

MORTON, Thomas. A Direct | Answer | Vnto | The Scandalovs Excep- | tions, which Theophilus Higgons hath lately | obiected against D. Morton. | In the which there is principally discussed, | Two of the most notorious Obiections vsed by the Ro- | manists, viz. | 1. M. Luthers conference with the diuell, and | 2. The sence of the Article of Christ his descension into hell. | . . . (device; 3 lines).

London, | Printed for Edmvnd Weaver. | 1609. | 17.1x12.9cm. (6),31p. Dedication, signed.

MOULIN, Pierre du. Apologie | Povr La Saincte | Cene Dv Seignevr: | Contre | La Presence Corporelle, | Et Transsvbstantiation. | Item, Contre les Messes sans communians. | Et contre la Communion sous vne espece. | Par Pierre Dv Movlin, Ministre de | la Parole de Dieu en l'Eglise de Paris. | Quatriesme edition reueuë & corrigée, en laquelle | est satisfait à toutes les accusations des | aduersaires. | (device)

A Geneve, | Povr Isaie Le Preux. | M.DCIX. | 17.4x10.4cm. (16),486p.

PARSONS, Robert. A | Qviet And Sober | Reckoning | VVith | M. Thomas Morton | somewhat set in choler by his | Aduersary P. R. | Concerning | Certaine imputations of wilfull falsities obiected to the said | T. M. in a Treatise of P. R. intituled Of Mitigation, some | part wherof he hath lately attempted to answere in a large | Preamble to a more ample Reioynder promised by him. | But heere in the meane space the said imputations are iustified, and | confirmed, & with much increase of new vntruthes on his part retur- | ned vpon him againe: So as finally the Reckoning being made, the | Verdict of the Angell, interpreted by Daniel, is verified of him. | . . . (3 lines; ornament) There is also adioyned a peece of a Reckoning with Syr Edward Cooke, | now L. Chief Iustice of the Cōmon Pleas, about a Nihil dicit, & some | other points vttered by him in two late Preambles, to his sixt and | seauenth Partes of Reportes. |

Permissu Superiorum. M.DC.IX. | 17.9x12.7 cm. (39),688,(16)p.
Anon. Gillow.V:286.

PENRY, John. The | Historic | of Corah, Dathan, and Abiram, &c. | Numb.16.Chap. | Applied to the Prelacy Ministerie and | Church-assemblies of England. | By Mr Iohn Penry, a Martyr | of Iesus Christ. | . . . (8 lines; ornament).

Imprinted in the yeare, 1609. | 17x12.7 cm. (4),45p.

PLAYFERE, Thomas.   A | Fvnerall Ser- | mon Preached In S. | Maries. 10. May. | 1605. | By that eloquent Diuine of famous | memorie, Th. Playfere Doctor | in Diuinitie. | . . . (3 lines ; device)

   Printed by Cantrell Legge, | Printer to the Vniuersitie of Cam- | bridge. 1609. | Line border. 17.8x13.8cm. (1),41–64p.
   Camb.Univ.Cat.No.7708. Begins with F3.

PLAYFERE, Thomas.   A | Sermon Prea- | ched Before The Kings | Maiestie at Drayton in Northampton- | shire the sixt day of August. | 1605. | By that eloquent Diuine of famous | memorie, Th. Playfere Doctor | in Diuinitie. | . . . (3 lines; device)

   Printed By Cantrell Legge, | Printer to the Vniuersitie of Cam- | bridge. 1609. | And are to be sold by Samvel Macham in Pauls | Churchyard at the signe of the Bullhead. | Line border 17.8x13.8cm. (1),21, T.p. trimmed and mounted.
   Camb.Univ.Cat.No:7708. Contains three other sermons: even date.

PLAYFERE, Thomas.   A | Sermon Prea- | ched Before The Kings | Maiestie that day he entered into Ox- | ford, at Woodstocke, beeing the | 27. of August. | 1605. | By that eloquent Diuine of famous | memorie, Th. Playfere Doctor | in Diuinitie. | . . . (3 lines; device).

   Printed By Cantrell Legge, | Printer to the Vniuersitie of Cam- | bridge. 1609. | Line border. 17.8x13.8cm. (1),23–39p.
   Camb.Univ.Cat.No:7708. Begins with D1.

PLAYFERE, Thomas.   A | Sermon | Preached | By that eloquent Diuine of famous | memorie, Th. Playfere Doctor | in Diuinitie. | . . . (3 lines ; device).

   Printed by Cantrell Legge, | Printer to the Vniuersitie of Cam- | bridge. 1609. | Line border. 17.8x13.8cm. (1),65–87p.
   Camb.Univ.Cat.No.7708. Begins with I4.

RAINOLDS, John.   The Svmme Of | The Conference | Betvveene Iohn Rai- | noldes And Iohn Hart: | Tovching The Head And The | Faith Of The Chvrch | Wherein by the way are handled sundry points, of the sufficiencie | and right expounding of the Scriptures, the ministerie of the Church, the | function of Priest-hood, the sacrifice of the Masse, with other con- | trouersies of religion: but chiefly and purposely the point of | Church-gouernment, opened in the branches of Christs | supreme soueraintie, of Peters pretended, the | Popes vsurped, the Princes | lawfull Supre- | macie. | Penned by Iohn Rainoldes, according to the notes set downe in writing | by them both: perused by Iohn Hart, and (after things supplied, | and altered, as he thought good) allowed for the | faithfull report of that which past | in conference betweene | them. | Whereunto is annexed a Treatise intituled, Six Conclusions Tou- | ching The Holy Scripture, and the Church, | Written by Iohn Rainoldes. | With a defence of such things as Thomas Stapleton and Gregorie | Martin haue carped at therein. | . . . (3 lines).

   London. | Printed by W.Hall for Thomas Adams. | 1609. | 18.7x14.5cm.   (19), 675p. Colophon.
   T.p. torn; supplied by Mr. Edward G. Friehold, of London.

RAWLINSON, John. Fishermen | Fishers of Men. | A | Sermon Prea- | ched At Mercers | Chapell on Mid-Lent | Sunday the 26. of | March 1609. | By | Iohn Ravvlinson Doctour | of Diuinitie. | . . . (4 lines)

London, | Printed by Arnold Hatfield for Edward Blount | and William Barret. | 1609 | 18.7x14.2cm. (6),40p.

SMITH, Henry. Gods | Arrow | Against | Atheists. | By Henrie Smith. | (device).

At London | Imprinted by F.K. for Thomas Pauier, and are to | be sold at his shop entring into the | Exchange. 1609. | 17.9x13.1cm. (3),96p.
Appended to his Sermons: 1609; with separate register and pagination

SMITH, Henry. The Sermons Of Master Henry Smith, gathered into one volume.

At London, | Imprinted by F.K. for Thomas Pauier, and are to | be sold at his shop entring into the | Exchange. 1609. | 17.9x13.1cm. (4),9–600;(3),96;56;(2,35); (4,92);(1,44),(2,49)p. Lacks t.p., and pp. 1–4.
Imprint from Gods Arrow Against Atheists: 1609.

SMITH, Richard. The Prvdentiall | Ballance Of | Religion, | Wherin the Catholike and Protestant religion are | weighed together with the weights of | Prudence, and right Reason. | The First Part, | In which the foresaide Religions are weighed together with | the weights of Prudence and right Reason accordinge to | their first founders in our Englishe Nation, S. Austin and Mar. Luther. And the Catholike religion euidently de- | duced through all our Kings and Archbishopps of Can- | terburie from S. Austin to our time, and the valour and | vertue of our Kings, and the great learninge and Sanctitie | of our Archbishopps, together with diuers Saints and | miracles which in their times proued the Catholike faith; | so sett downe as it may seeme also an abridgment of our | Ecclesiasticall Histories. | With a Table of the Bookes and Chapters con- | teyned in this Volume. | . . . (2 lines).

Printed vvith Licence. 1609. | 14.9x9.2 cm. (48),598p. 343–352, repeated.
Anon. Gillow. V: 513.

SMYTH, John. The Character Of The Beast: | Or | The False Constitvtion Of The Chvrch. | Discovered | In Certayne Passages Betwixt Mr.R.Clifton | & Iohn Smyth, concerning true Christian baptisme of New Creatures, | or New borne Babes in Christ: &nd false Baptisme of infants | borne after the Flesh. | Referred to two Propositions. | 1. That infants are not to bee Baptized. | 2. That Antichristians converted are to bee admitted into the true Church | by baptisme. | . . . (6 lines).

Printed. 1609. | 18x13.8cm. (8),71p.
Epistle to the Reader, signed. Whitley, 6–609.

STOCK, Richard. A | Sermon | Preached At | Paules Crosse, the se- | cond of Nouember. | 1606. | By Richard Stocke, Prea- | cher of Al-hallowes, | Bread-streete, | London. | (ornament)

London, | Printed by T.C. for Ed- | mond Weauer, and William | Welby. 1609. | Lace border. 15.5x9.9cm. (14),75,(1)p.

TOPSELL, Edward. The | House-holder: | Or, | Perfect Man. | In the | commenda | tion of | Wisedome. | Diligence. | Knowledge. | Frugality, and | Liberall House-keeping. | And the | discommē- | dation of {Folly, Naturall & Spirituall. | Negligence. | Ignorance. | Vnthriftinesse, and | Illiberall House-keeping. | Preached in three Sermons lately at | Hartfield in Svssex, by | Ed: Topsell. |

Printed for Henry Rockyt, and are to be sold at his | shop in the Poultry, vnder the Diall. 1609. | Line border. 13.4x8.5cm. (30),173p.

TYNLEY, Robert. Two | Learned Ser- | mons. | The one, of the mis- | chieuous subtiltie, and barbarous cru- | eltie, the other of the false Doctrines, and | refined Hæresis of the Romish | Synagogue. | Preached, the one at Paules Crosse the 5. of Nouember, 1608. | The other at the Spittle the 17. of Aprill. 1609. | In the first, are examined diuers passages of that lewde | English Libell, written by a Prophane Fugitiue, against | the Apologie for the Oath of Allegeance. | In the seconde, are answered many of the arguments pub- | lished by Rob. Chambers Priest, concerning Popish Mira- | cles; and Dedicated (forsooth) to the Kings | most excellent Maiestie. | By Robert Tynley, Doctor of Diuinitie, and Arch- | deacon of Ely. |

London | Printed by W. Hall for Thomas Adams. 1609. | Line border. 17.3x13.6 cm. (8),72p.

WALSINGHAM, Francis. A | Search | Made Into Matters | Of Religion, | By | Francis VValsingham | Deacon of the Protestants Church, before his | change to the Catholicke. | VVherein | Is related, how first he fell into his doubts: And how for finall | resolution therof he repayred vnto his Maiesty, who remitted | him to the L. of Canterbury that now is, and he to other | learned men. And what the issue was of all | those Conferences. | And | How after this againe he betooke himselfe to the reading of Protestant and | Catholicke Authors for better finding out the truth: As also for discer- | ning where, & on what side true or false dealing was to be found: | and what the successe of this Search hath beene. | Dedicated to the Kings most Ex- | cellent Maiesty. | (ornament) . . . (2 lines).

Permissu Superiorum. Anno M.DC.IX. | 17.7x12cm. (24),512,(8)p

WOTTON, Anthony. Sermons Vpon | A Part Of The | First Chap. Of The | Gospell Of S.Iohn. | Preached By Antony | Wotton, in the Parish Church of | Alhallowes Barking in London, | and now by him published. | . . . (2 lines; ornament).

At London, | Printed by H.L. for Samvell Macham, | and are to be sould at his shop in Pauls Church-yard, | at the signe of the Bull-head. An.1609. | 17.7x13.3cm. (4),474p.

1610

ABBOT, Robert. The Old | Waye. | A | Sermon Prea- | ched At Oxford, | The eight day of Iuly, | being the Act Sunday. | 1610. | By Robert Abbott, Doctor | of Diuinitie, and Maister of Baliol | Colledge. | (device).

London | Printed for Eleazar Edgar, and Ambrose Garbrand, and | are to bee solde at their Shop in Pauls Church-yard, | at the Signe of the Wind-mill. | 1610. | 17.8x13.7cm. (9),59p. T.p. supplied.

ANDREWES, Lancelot. Responsio | Ad Apologiam | Cardinalis | Bellarmini, Quam nuper | edidit contra Præfationem | Monitoriam. | Serenissimi Ac | Potentissimi Principis | Iacobi, Dei Gratia | Magnæ Britanniæ, Franciæ, | & Hiberniæ Regis, | Fidei Defensoris, | Omnibvs Christianis | Monarchis, Principibvs, | atque Ordinibus | inscriptam. | (ornament).

Londini | Excudebat Robertvs Barkervs, | Serenissæ Regiæ Maiestatis | Typographvs. | Anno 1610. | 22.5x16cm. (18),362,(1)p.

Cambr.Univ.Cat:2622. Epistola dedicatorie, signed L.Eliensis.

AUGUSTINE, St. St. | Avgvstine, | Of | The Citie Of God: | With The Learned | Comments | Of | Io.Lod.Vives. | Englished by J.H. | (device).

Printed by George Eld. | 1610. | 27.9x18.5cm. (18),921,(8)p.

BECANUS, Martinus. R.P. | Martini | Becani | Societatis Jesv | Theologi, | Opvscvlorvm | Theologicorvm, | Tomus Primus. | (- Tertius). (device) Cum Gratia & Priuilegio Sac. Cæs. Maiestatis. |

Mogvntiæ | Ex Officina Ioannis Albini | Anno M.DC.X. | 18.7 x 11.8 cm. I. (16),678; II. (16),694; III. (16),416 p. Imperfect.

BECANUS, Martinus. Refvtatio | Tortv | rae Torti | Seu | Contra Sacellannm Regis An- | gliæ, quod causam sui Regis | negligenter egerit. | Authore | R.P.Martino Becano, | Societatis Iesv Theologo. | (device) Cum licentia superiorum. |

Mogvntiæ, | Typis Ioannis Albini. | Anno M,DC.X. | 16.5 x 10.1 cm. (4),67 p.

BECANUS, Martinus. Serenissimi | Iacobi | Angliæ Regis | Apologiæ, & monitoriæ Præfatio- | nis ad Imparatorem, Reges | & Principes, | Refvtatio. | Authore | Martino Becano | Societatis Iesv | Theologo. | (device)

Mogvntiæ, | Typis Iohannis Albini. | Anno M.DC.X. | 16.5x10.1cm. 174p.

BENEFIELD, Sebastian. Doctrinæ Christianæ | Sex Capita, | Totidem Prælectionibvs | in Scholâ Theologicâ Oxoniæ pro formâ | habitis discussa, & | disceptata. | Accessit Appendix Ad Ca- | put secundum, de Consiliis Evangelicis, in | quâ ad omnes SS.Patrvm autorita- | tes, ab Hvmphredo Leechio | pro iisdem asserendis citatas, | respondetur. | Avtore | Sebastiano Benefield. | SS,Theologiæ D. Collegii | Corporis Christi Socio. | . . . (2 lines; ornament).

Oxoniæ, | Excudebat Iosephus Barnesius. 1610. | 18.5x14.cm. (20),208,(12)p. Subtitle at p.145.

BILSON, Thomas. The Perpetvall | Government Of | Christs Chvrch: | Wherein are handled, | The fatherly superioritie which God first established in the | Patriarkes for the guiding of his Church, and after conti- | nued in the Tribe of Levi and the Prophets: and | lastly confirmed in the New Testament | to the Apostles and their | successors: | As also the points in question at this day. | Touching the Jewish Synedrion: the true kingdome of Christ: the Apostles | commission: the Lay Presbyterie: the Distinction of Bishops from Presby- | ters, and their succession from the Apostles times and hands: the | calling and moderating of Prouinciall Synods by Primates | and Metropolitanes: the allotting of Diœceses, | and the Popular electing of such as | must feede and watch | the flock. | And diuers other points concerning the pastorall regiment | of the house of God: | By Tho.Bilson Warden of Winchester | College. | Perused and allowed by publike authority. | . . . (5 lines; ornament).

London, | Printed for Thomas Adams, | 1610. | 18.2x14.1cm. (28),414p.

BOYS, John. An | Exposition | Of Al The Princi- | pal Scriptvres Vsed | in our English Liturgie: | Together With A Reason | why the Church did chuse the same. | By Iohn Boys Doctor of | Diuinitie. | . . . (6 lines; ornament).

At London | Imprinted by Felix Kyngston, and are to be sold | by William Aspley, at the signe of the Parot in | Pauls Churchyard. 1610. | Line border. 18.7x 13.6cm. (5),126; (4),202; (4),246; (4),247; (3),227p.
Contains also : An | Exposition | Of The Dominical | Epistles And Gospels | vsed in our English Liturgie | . . . London. 1610–1612. Four parts.

BOYS, John. An | Exposition | Of The Dominical | Epistles And Gospels | vsed in our English Liturgie | throughout the whole yeere. | Together With A Rea- | son Why The Chvrch | did chuse the same. | By Iohn Boys, Doctor | of Diuinitie. | The Spring-part from the first in Lent to | Whitsunday. | . . . (4 lines; ornament.)

At London | Imprinted by Felix Kyngston, for | William Aspley. 1610. | Line border. 18.7x13.6cm.(4), 246p. Separate register and pagination

BOYS, John. An | Exposition | Of The Dominical | Epistles And Gospels | vsed in our English Liturgie | throughout the whole yeare. | Together With A Rea- | son Why The Chvrch | did chuse the same. | By John Boys, Doctor | of Diuinitie. | The Winter part from the first Aduentuall | Sunday to Lent. | . . . (5 lines: ornament.)

At London | Printed by Felix Kyngston, for | William Aspley. 1610. | Line border. 18.7x13.6cm. (4), 302p. Separate register and pagination.

BRADSHAW, William. Puritanismus | Anglicanvs, | Sive | Præcipva Dogmata | eorum, qui inter vulgo dictos Puri- | tanos in Anglia, rigidiores | habentur. | Quibus annectitur scholastica disceptatio de circulo | pontificio & eorum omnium ἀκαταληψία qui in scriptu- | ris non acquiescunt. | . . . (8 lines ; device).

Francofvrti. | Prostat in Bibliopolio Aubriano. | M. DC. X. | 16.x10.3 cm. (28), 92p.
The preface is signed: Gvilielmvs Amesivs. Cf.Cambr.Univ.Cat.6380.

BRIGHTMAN, Thomas. Antichri- | stus. | Disputatio bipartita: | I.Papam Romanum reverâ, magnum illum, & | propriè-dictum Antichristum esse, in Sacris lite- | ris prædictum: | Autore Daniele Tileno, |

Theologo Sedanensi. | II. Antichristum Pontificiorum & Jesuitarum, fi- | ctitium, & contra veritatem Sacrarum litera- | rum ementitum monstrum esse; adversus Rob. | Bellarmini de Antichristo disputationem: | Autore Thoma Brightmanno, | Theologo Anglo. | In Gratiam Veritatis | Et Pietatis Studiosorum, | nunc iterum & conjunctim, | edita, | curâ & studio | M.Lvdovici Lvcii | Basileensis. | (ornament).

Ambergâe, | Typis Johannis Schönfeldii. | M DC X. | 15.x9.cm. (16),259,(2)p.

BROCARD, James. The | Revelation | Of Saint John reuealed. | Opening by Conference of time | and place many poyntes very necessa- | ry for the time present. | Especially against the Papacy. | By | Iames Brocard. | . . . (4 lines)

At London Imprinted. | 1610. | 18.6x14.1cm. (1),170,(1)fol.

BROUGHTON, Hugh. A | Revelation | Of The Holy | Apocalyps. | By Hvgh Broughton. | . . . (12 lines).

Printed 1610. | Engraved border. 18. x13.6cm. 339, (7) p.

C., M. A | Briefe | Admonition | To All English | Catholikes, | Concerning | A late Proclamation set forth against them. | Dedicated To The | Queenes most Excellent Maiesty. | Togeather with the Confutation of a Pamphlet, newly pu- | blished, cōcerning a Decree of the Sorbon at Paris &c. | And | An Epistle to Doctor King, in the behalfe | of the Iesuites. | By M.C.P. | . . . (ornament; 4 lines)

Permissu Superiorum. M.DC.X. | 17.2x12.9cm. (12),135p.
Preface signed M.C.

CALVIN, John. A | Harmonie | Vpon The Three | Euangelistes Matthewe, Marke, | and Luke, with the Com- | mentarie of M Iohn | Caluine: | Faithfully translated out of | Latine into English | by E.P. | Whereunto is also added a | Commentarie vpon the Euan- | gelist S.Iohn, by the same | authour. |

Londoni | Impensis Thom.Adams. | 1610. | Engr.border. 18.7x14.1cm. (47),806; (6),464,(21)p.

CAPELLO, Marco Antonio. F. M. Antonii | Capelli | Franciscani Conuentualis | Adversvs Prætensvm | Primatum Ecclesiasticum Regis Angliæ | Liber | In quo Iacobi Regis, & eius Eleemosynarij | confutantur Scripta | De{Captioso Iuramento Proposito Anglis Catholicis. | Vsurpata Potestate Spirituali eiusdem Regis. | Exaggerata, & Impossibili Hominum, & Reddituum | sacrorum copia in vniuersa Republica Christiana. | Ad Illustriss. & Reuerendiss. Dominum, | D. Benedictum S. R. E. Presbyt. | Card. Iustinianum, | Pro Sanctissimo D. N. Pavlo Papa Quinto | Bononiæ de Latere Legatum, &c. | . . . (3 lines)

Bononiæ, Ex Typographia Bartholomæi Cocchij. 1610. | De Superiorum licentia. | 19.9x14.2 cm. (16),283,(1) p.

CARLETON, George. Ivrisdiction | Regall, | Episcopall, | Papall. Wherein Is Declared | How The Pope Hath Intrvded | Vpon the Iurisdiction of Temporall Princes, and | of the Church. The instrusion is dicouered, and the | peculiar and distinct Iurisdiction to | each properly belonging, | recouered. | Written by George Carleton. | . . . (3 lines; ornament).

Londini | Impensis Iohannis Norton. 1610. | 18.8x14.5 cm. (16),302p.

CLIFTON, Richard. The | Plea For Infants | And Elder People, | concerning their Baptisme. | Or | A Processe Of The Passages | between M.Iohn Smyth and Richard Clyfton: | Wherein, first is proved, | That the baptising of Infants of beleevers, is an ordinance of God. | Secondly, | That the rebaptising of such, as have been formerly baptised in | the Apostate Churches of Christians, is utterly unlawful. | Also, | The reasons and objections to the contrairie, | answered. | Divided into two principal heads. | I. | Of the first Position, concerning the baptising of infants. | II. | Of the second Position, concerning the rebaptising | of Elder People. | . . . (9 lines).

Printed at Amsterdam by Gyles Thorp. | Anno 1610. | 18x14cm. (19),226,(2)p. Preface signed.

The | COPIE Of A | Late Decree Of | the Sorbone at Paris, for the | condemning of that impious and | hæreticall opinion, touching the | murthering of Princes; | Generally maintained by the Iesuites, | And amongst the rest, of late by | Ioannes Mariana, | a Spaniard: | Together, with the Arrest of the Parlia- | ment, for the confirmation of that Decree, | And the condemning of the said Marianas | Booke, to be publiquely burnt by | the Executioner. | Taken out of the Register of the Parliament, and | translated into English. | (ornament).

Imprinted At | London by R.B. | Anno 1610. | 17.2x13.cm. (12,29)p. Trimmed.

DOD, John and CLEAVER, Robert. Two | Sermons | On The Third | Of The Lamenta- | tions. | Preached at Hanwell in the first yeere of | his Maiesties reigne, 1602. The one | by I.D. the other by R.C. | . . . (5 lines; ornament).

At London | Imprinted by Felix Kyngston, for Thomas Man, and | are to be sold at the signe of the Talbot in | Pater noster row. 1610. | 17.8x14.3cm. 71p.
Cf. DNB. 15: 145 b.

DONNE, John. Psevdo- | Martyr. | Wherein | Ovt Of Certaine | Propositions and Gradations, This | Conclusion is euicted. | That Those Which Are | of the Romane Religion in this Kingdome, | may and ought to take the Oath of | Allegeance. | . . . (9 lines).

London | Printed by W.Stansby for Walter Burre. | 1610. | Line border. 19.1x 13.8cm. (29), 392p.
Epistle Dedicatory to James I, signed.

DOVE, John. An | Advertise- | ment To The Eng- | lish Seminaries, Amd | Iesvites: | Shewing their loose kind of writing, | and negligent handling the cause | of Religion, in the whole course | of their workes. | By Iohn Dove Doctor in Diuinity. | . . . (2 lines; device).

London, | Printed for Simon Waterson dwelling in Pauls | Church-yard at the signe of the Crowne. 1610. | 17.6x13.cm. (5),78p.
At p.65, a sub t.p.: The | Ansvver To A | Treatise Intitv- | led: A Search Made

In- | to matters of Religion: | By Francis Walsingham, Deacon of | the Protestants Church, before his change to | the Catholike. Dedicated to the | Kings Maiestie. | Against Luther, Caluin, Zuinglius, Beza, Iewel, Williat, | Doue, Rogers, and other Protestants. | . . . (2 lines; device). London, | . . . 1610.

FITZHERBERT, Thomas. The | Second Part | Of A Treatise Concerning | Policy, And Religion. | Wherein the necessity, fruite, and dignity of christian religion, | in common welth, is euidently showed, with the absurdity of | false religions, and the danger, and damage, that ensueth | thereof to all states; And by the way somme philosophical, | moral, and politicall matters are treated: dyuers pious lessons, | & instructions geeuen, tending to christian perfection: many | controuersyes in religion debated, and discussed: and the ob- | iections of politykes, and heretyks answered; Finally it is | clearely proued, that the catholique Roman religion only doth | make a happy common welth. | Written by Thomas Fitzherbert Esquyre, | and Catholique priest. | . . . (4 lines).

Printed with Licence of Superiors. | Anno Domini 1610. | Lace border. 19.1x14.3 cm. (24),1–467,450–654,685–697,(19)p.

The HELLISH and hor- | ribble Councell, practised and | vsed by the Iesuites, (in their priuate | Consultations) when they would | haue a man to murther a | King. | According to those damnable instru- | ctions, giuen (by them) to that bloody villaine | Francis Ravilliacke, who murdered | Henry the fourth, the late | French King. | Sent to the Queene Regent, in answere of | that impudent Pamphlet published by Peter Cotton Iesuite, in defence of the Iesuites, | and their doctrine; which also is | hereunto annexed. | Translated out of the French. | . . . (3 lines).

London, | Printed for T.B. and are to be sold by Iohn Wright at his | shop by Christs-Church-gate. | 1610. | 17.6x12.9cm. (5,18)p.

IRELAND, Thomas. The Oath Of | Allegeance, | Defended by a Sermon preached at | a Synode in the Metropoliticall Church | of Yorke; | By Thomas Ireland, Bachelour | in Diuinitie. | . . . (4 lines ; device).

London, | Printed by Nicholas Okes for Edward Aggas, and are to be | sold at his shop vpon Snore hill neere Holborne | Conduit. 1610. | 17.9x13.5cm. (6,39)p.

JAMES I. Apologia | Pro Juramento | Fidelitatis, | Primùm quidem Aνωνυμos, | Nunc verò ab ipso | Avctore, | Serenissimo ac potentissimo Principe, | Jacobo Dei Gra- | tia Magnæ Britan- | niæ, Franciæ Et Hi- | berniæ Rege, | Fidei Defensore, | denuò edita, | Cui præmissa est | Præfatio Monitoria, | Sacratiss. Cæsari | Rodolpho II. | Semper Augusto, | Cæterisq[ue] Christiani Orbis Sereniss. & Potentiss. | Monarchis Ac Regibvs: | Illustris. Celsissimisq[ue] Liberis Principibvs, | Rebvs-pvblicis Atqve Ordinibvs | inscripta, eodem Avctore. |

Anno M D CX. | 13.3x7.8 cm. (4),330p.

JAMES I. Triplici Nodo | Triplex Cuneus. | Sive | Apologia | Pro Juramento | Fidelitatis. | Adversus duo Brevia | PP. Pauli Quinti, | Et

Epistolam | Cardinalis Bellarmini, | ad G. Blackvellum Ar- | chipresbyterum, | Nuper scriptam | . . . (4 lines).
 Anno M D CX. | 13.3x7.7 cm. p.195–330, of his Apologia | Pro Juramento | Fidelitatis, | : 1610.

KNIGHT, William. A | Concordance | Axiomaticall: | Containing | A Svrvey of Theolo- | gicall Propositions: | With Their Reasons And | vses in holie Scripture. | Taken At First By | Attent Reading, | And after | Digested into an Alphabeticall order for the be- | nefit of the Church, especially for such as labour | in the Word and Doctrine. | Whereunto is annexed (after the Preface) a Practise teaching the vse | and application of the whole Worke. | By William Knight. | . . . (7 lines; device)
 At London, | Printed for Iohn Bill. | 1610. | Line border. 28.6x19cm. (27),606p.

MORTON, Thomas. A | Catholike | Appeale For | Protestants, | Out of the confessions of the Romane Doctors; | particularly answering the mis-named Catholike | Apologie for the Romane faith, out of the Protestants: | Manifesting the Antiquitie of our Religion, and | satisfying all scrupulous Obiections which haue | been vrged against it. | Written by Th.Morton Doctor of Diuinitie. | . . . (4 lines; device).
 Londini, | Impensis Georg.Bishop & Ioh.Norton. | 1610. | 28.3x18.6cm. (22),680,(20)p

MOULIN, Pierre du. A | Defence | Of | The Catho- | licke Faith: | Contained In The | Booke Of The Most | Mightie, and most Gracious King | Iames the first, King of Great | Britaine, France and Ireland, Defen- | der of the Faith. | Against The Answere Of | N.Coeffeteau, Doctour of Diuinitie, and Vicar | Generall of the Dominican Preaching | Friars. | Written in French, by Pierre Dv Movlin, | Minister of the word of God in the Church | of Paris. | Translated into English according to his first | Coppie, by himselfe reuiewed and | corrected. |
 London | Printed by W.Stansby for Nathaniel Butter and | Martin Clerke. 1610. | Line border. 19.7x13.9 cm. (12),493,(1)p.

OWEN, David. Herod and Pilate reconciled: | Or, | The Concord Of | Papist And Pvritan (A- | gainst Scripture, Fathers, Councels, and other | Orthodoxall Writers) for the Coercion, | Deposition, and Killing | of Kings. | Discouered by | David Owen Batchelour of Diuinitie, | and Chaplaine to the right Honourable Lord Vicount | Hadington. | . . . (3 lines; device).
 Printed By Cantrell Legge, | Printer to the Vniversitie of Cambridge. | 1610. | 17.2x13 cm. (14), 57 p.

RAINOLDS, John. A | Defence | Of The Ivdg- | ment Of The | Reformed churches. That a man | may lawfullie not onelie put | awaie his wife for her ad- | ulterie, but also marrie | another. | Wherin hoth Robert Bellarmin the Jesuits Latin treatise, and an Eng | lish pamphlet of a namelesse author mainteyning the contrarie are confuted | by Iohn Raynolds. | A taste of Bellarmins dealing in controversies of

Religion: how | he depraveth Scripturs, misalleageth Fathers, and abuseth Reasōs | to the perverting of the truth of God, and poysoning of his Chur | che with errour. | (triangular lace ornament) The faultes escaped in the first impression, are here in this carefully | corrected by the Printer. Fare-well. |

Printed by George Walters, 1610. | 19.2x 14.4 cm. (4),78p. Mispagings.

ROBINSON, John. A | Ivstification | Of | Separation from the Church of | England. | Against Mr Richard Bernard his invective, | Intitvled; | The Separatists schisme. | By Iohn Robinson. | . . . (5 lines; device).

Anno D. 1610. | Border. 17.4x13.6 cm. 483p. Misnumbered 479

ROLLOCK, Robert. In Selectos | Aliqvot Psalmos | Davidis, | Roberti Rolloci | Scoti, Ecclesiæ Edimburgensis | Ministri, | Commentarivs, | Editio Secunda. | (device).

Genevæ | Apud Iacobum Stœr, | M.DCX. | 15x9.4cm. (8),338p.

S., T. The Key Of | David, | That openeth the Gates | to the Citie of | God: | Also, | Of Faith and Repentance, | and how they are wrought, and | brought to passe: whether | Faith be commanded in the | Law, or not. | (ornament)

London | Printed by Thomas Haueland for | Nathaniel Fosbrooke. | 1610. | Line border. 14.5x9.5cm. (7),78p.
From the library of Walter W. Law.

SANDERS, Nicholas. Nicolai | Sanderi | Angli Doct. Theol. | De | Origine Ac Progressv | Schismatis Anglicani, | Libri Tres: | Qvibvs Historia Continetvr | maximè Ecclesiastica, Annorum circiter | 60. lectu dignissima; Aucti priùs per Edovar- | dvm Rishtonvm, Romæq[ue] | impressi; | Nvnc Vero Addita Appendice, | R. P. Petri Ribadeneirae Soc. Iesu, | iterum in Germania locupletiùs & castiga- | tiùs editi. | Cuiusq[ue] Libri Argumenta, vide post præfationem. | (device).

Coloniæ Agrippinæ, | Sumptibus Petri Henningi, sub | signo Cuniculi, M.D.CX. | 15.9x9.2cm. (16),456,(24),(4),182,(1) p.

SARAVIA, Hadrian. De Imperandi | Avthoritate, | Et Christiana | Obedientia, | Libri Quatuor. | Authore | Hadriano Saravia. | . . . (3 lines; device).

M DC X. | 29.4x18.4cm. (1),109–314p.
Part of his Diversi Tractatus: 1610 ; with continuous register and pagination

SARAVIA, Hadrian. Defensio | Tractationis | De Diversis Mini- | strorvm Evange- | lii Gradibus: | Contra | Responsionem Claris- | simi viri D. Theodori Bezæ: | Ab ipso Authore | Hadriano Saravia recognita, & nunc | tertiò edita. | (device)

M DC X. | 29.4x18.4cm. (14),382p.
Part of his Diversi Tractatus: 1610; with continuous register, but separate pagination

SARAVIA, Hadrian. Examen Trac- | tatvs De Episco- | patvvm Triplici | Genere: | Ab | Hadriano Saravia | æditum. | . . . (4 lines; device).
M DC X. | 29.4x18.4cm. (10),105p.
Part of his Diversi Tractatus: 1610 ; with continuous register but separate pagination.

SEMPILL, James. Sacrilege | Sacredly | Handled. | That is, | According to Scripture onely. | Diuided into two parts: | I. For the Law. | 2. {For the Gospell. | An Appendix Also Added; An- | swering some Obiections mooued, namely against this | Treatise: and some others, I finde in Ios. Scaligers | Diatribe, and Ioh. Seldens Historie | of Tithes. | For The Vse Of All Chvrches In | generall: but more especially for those of | North-Britaine. | . . . (6 lines).
London, | Printed by William Iones, for Edmvnd Weaver, and are to | be sold at his Shop at the great North-doore of Saint | Pauls. 1610. | 17.5x13.6cm. (16), 100,54p.
Cf.Cambr.Univ.Cat.3331.

A SURUEY | Of the Booke of Com- | mon Prayer, | By way | Of 197. Quæres grounded vpon 58. places, | ministring iust matter of question, with | a view of London Ministers excep- | tions. All humbly pro- | pounded, | That | They may be syncerely answered: | Or els | Offences Religiously remoued. | Reviewed, corected, and augmented, | As is to be seene in the next page. | . . . (5 lines).
Anno Dñi 1610. | Border. 13.8x9. cm. (7),3-204,(36)p.

WHITE, John. The VVay | To The Trve | Chvrch: | wherin | The principall Motiues perswa- | ding to Romanisme, | and | Questions touching the nature and authoritie | of the Church and Scriptures, are familiarly dispu- | ted, and driuen to their issues, where, this day they | sticke betweene the Papists and vs: | Contriued into an Answer to a Popish Discourse, concerning the | Rule of Faith, and the marks of the Church. And published to | admonish such as decline to Papistrie, of the weake and vncer- | taine ground, whereupon they haue ventured their soules. | Directed to all that seeke for resolution: and especially | to his louing countrimen of Lancashire. | The second impression corrected and augmented. | By Iohn White Minister of Gods word at Eccles. | . . . (2 lines; ornament).
London, | Printed for Iohn Bill and Wil- | liam Barret. | 1610. 18.9x14.4cm. (60),456,(8)p. Impf. at end of index: lacks sig. Gg

WILLET, Andrew. Hexapla | In Danielem: | That Is, | A Six-Fold Commentarie | vpon the most diuine prophesie of Daniel, wherein | according to the method propounded in Hexapla vpon Genesis and Exodus, | sixe things are obserued in euery Chapter. 1. The Argument and Method. 2. The | diuers readings. 3. The Questions discussed. 4. Doctrines noted. | 5. Controversies handled. 6. Morall observations | applyed. | Wherein many obscure visions, and diuine Prophesies are | opened, and difficult questions handled with great breuitie, perspicuitie, and | varietie, which are summed to the number of 536. beside the Controversies | 134. in the Table, in the end of the booke: and the best | Interpreters both old and new are therein | abridged. | Diuided into two bookes: the first containing the hi- | storicall part of this Prophesie, in the 6. first Chapters: the | propheticall, in the 6. last. | By Andrevv Willet Professour of Diuinitie. | The First Booke. | . . . (3 lines; ornament).

Printed by Cantrell Legge, Printer to the | Vniuersitie of Cambridge. | 1610. | 26.8 x 17.5 cm.   (6),196;(4),197-520,(16) p.

WILSON, Thomas. A | Dialogve | About | Ivstification | by Faith: | Wherein the nature and | office, the property and pow- | er of Faith is | Plainely taught, against such as | deny the certainety or parti- | cularity and powerfulnesse | of Faith. | Especially, against a late errour, deni- | ing the necessity of Faith vnto | Ivstification. | (stars).

London | Printed by William Hall, and are to bee | sold by Nathaniel Butter at the signe | of the pide Bull, neere St. Austens | gate. 1610. | 13.6x8.3 cm.   (9), 173p.

Republished with his Jacobs Ladder: 1611 , which see for other things included under continuous register, but separate pagination.   Epistle dedicatorie, signed.

1611

ABBOT, Robert. A | Defence Of The | Reformed Catho- | licke of M.W.Perkins, | lately deceased, against the bastard | Counter-Catholicke of D. | Bishop, Seminary | Priest. | The First Part: | For answere to his calumniations generally framed against the | same, and against the whole Religion and state of our | Church, in his Epistle Dedicatory to the Kings | most excellent Maiesty. | Wherin is to bee seene the audatiousnesse and impudencie of these | Romish bookes in their Supplications and Dedications to his | Highnesse: their religion is dismasked of that antiquity | which they pretend for it: the religion established in | our Church by law is iustified to be no other | but what was anciently receiued in the | Church, and namely in the an- | cient Church of | Rome. | By Robert Abbot Doct. of Diuinitie. | . . . (5 lines)

Londini. | Impensis Thomæ Adams. | 1611 | 18.8x14.1 cm.   (12),244p.

ABBOT, Robert. The | Second Part | Of The Defence | Of The Reformed | Catholicke. | Wherein the Religion established in our Church | of England (for the points here handled) is apparently iu- | stified by authoritie of Scripture, & testimonie of the anci- | ent church, against the vaine cauillations collected by Do- | ctor Bishop Seminary Priest, as out of other Popish writers, | so specially out of Bellarmin, & published vnder the name | of The marrow and pith of many large volumes, | for the oppugning thereof. | By Robert Abbot Doctor of Diuinitie. | . . . (3 lines ; ornament)

Londini, | Impensis Thomæ Adams. | 1611. | 18.8x14.1 cm.   (16),838p. Mispaged at end. Incomplete after Ggg6.   Separate register and pagination

ABBOT, Robert. The Trve | Ancient Ro- | man Catho- | like. | Being An Apology | Or Covnterproofe Against | Doctor Bishops Re-proofe | of the defence of the Reformed | Catholike. | The First Part. | Wherein the name of Catholikes is vindicated from Popish abuse, | and thence is shewed that the faith of the Church of Rome as now | it is, is not the Catholike faith, nor the same with the faith com- | mended in the Epistles of St.Peter and St.Paul, and that confir- | med by the testimony of the ancient Bishops of Rome, and other | Writers of that Church. | By Robert Abbot Doctor of Diuinity, Master | of Balioll Colledge in Oxford. | . . . (3 lines).

London, | Printed by William Stansby for Ambrose Garbrand, and are to be sold | at the signe of the Wind-mill in Pauls Church-yard, 1611. | 18.3x13.9cm. (20),402,(1)p.

ANDREWES, Lancelot. A Sermon | Preached Be- | fore His Maj-estie at | White-Hall, | On the 24. of March last, be- | ing Easter day, and being also the day | of the Beginning of His Maiesties | most Gracious Reigne. | By the Bishop of Elie His | Maiesties Almoner. | (ornament).

Imprinted at London by Ro- | bert Barker, Printer to the Kings | most Excellent Maiestie. | Anno 1611. | Orn. head-piece. 17.7x13.5cm. (1),42p.

BARCLAY, William. Gvil. Barclaii J. C. | Of The Av- | thoritie Of | The Pope: Whether, | And How Farre Forth, | he hath power and authoritie | ouer Temporall Kings | and Princes, | Liber posthumus. | (ornament).

At London | Imprinted by Arnold Hatfield, | for VVilliam Aspley. 1611. | 17.9x 13.4 cm. (14),229 p.

BENEFIELD, Sebastian. A | Sermon | Preached In St Maries | Church in Oxford, March xxiv. MDCX. | at the solemnizing of the happy in- | auguration of our gracious sove- | raigne King Iames. | Wherein Is Proved That Kings Doe | hold their kingdomes immediately from God. | By | Sebastian Benefield D. of Divinitie | Fellow of Corpus Christi College. | (device)

At Oxford, | printed by Joseph Barnes. 1611. | 17.5x13.7cm. (4),18pp.

BILSON, Thomas. De Perpetva | Ecclesiæ Chri- | sti Gvbernatione. | In Qva Tractantvr | Patria potestas quam Deus primùm in Patriarchis pro re- | genda Ecclesia sua instituit; Deinde in Tribu Leui & | Prophctis continuauit: Postremo in nouo Te- | stamento Apostolis eorumque succes- | soribus confirmauit. | Vt etiam quæ hodiè in quæstione versantur de Iudæorum Synedrio; vero | Christi regno; authoritate & legatione Apostolica: laico Presbyterio: | Episcoporum à Presbyteris distinctione: eorumq́[ue] ab Apostolorum tem- | poribus Potestate ac Successione: Diœcesium assignatione; populari Pa- | storum electione: Synodorum in Ecclesia Dei antiquitate & neces- | sitate; atque earundem in quauis Prouincia conuocatione | & moderatione per Metropolis Episcopum: | Cum multis alijs quæ ad Pastoralem domus Dei | procurationem pertinent. | Liber ad vtilitatem Patriæ primùm Anglicè scriptus, nunc demum ab Authore | Thom. Bilsono Episcopo Wintoniensi recognitus, auctus, & in | publicum Ecclesiæ bonum Latinè redditus. | . . . (6 lines: ornament).

Londini, | Impensis Iohannis Billij. | 1611. | 19.2x14.2cm. (16),494,(1) p.

BOYS, John. An | Exposition | Of The Dominical | Epistles And Gospels, | vsed in our English Liturgie, | throughout the whole yeere. | Together With A Rea- | son Why The Chvrch | did chuse the same. | By Iohn Boys, Doctor | of Diuinitie. | The Summer-part from Whit-sunday to the | twelfth after Trinitie. | . . . (3 lines: ornament).

At London | Imprinted by Felix Kyngston, for | VVilliam Aspley. 1611. | Line border. 18.7x13.6cm. (4),247p.
Separate register and pagination

BROUGHTON, Hugh. A | Reqvire | Of | Agreement | To the groundes of Diuinitie | studie: wherin great Scho- | lers falling, & being caught of | Iewes disgrace the Gospel: | & trap them to de- | struction. | By H.B. | (ornament).

1611. | Lace border. 17.2x13.3cm. (12),91p.
Epistle Dedicatorie, signed.

BUNNY, Edmund. Of The | Head-Corner-Stone: | by Builders still ouer- | much omitted: | That is; a forme of teaching Iesvs Christ, | out of all the Holy Scriptvres, both of the Old Testa- | ment (that are Canonicall) and of the New; Gathered into | one entire Bodie: in Substance, all one, with that which is | commonly vsed by all; But in Forme or manner, as it were, a | neerer & plainer path, not yet (that the Author knoweth of) | troden by any. | The whole Worke being digested into Two seuerall Tomes: eyther of which | Tomes, hauing two Bookes therevnto appertaining: as more at | large is to be seene in the next Leafe. | Togither with certaine Tables of diuers sorts, for the better vnder- | standing, and vse of these Bookes; One, of Method, in the begin- | ning; and three others in the end: the first of the Scrip-tures, in two | parts; the next, of other Authors, and their Authorities; the thirde, of | the more speciall & principall matters, contained in the whole worke. | By Edm: Bvnny, Batche- | ler of Diuinitie. | . . . (4 lines).

Printed by W. Iaggard, 1611. | Border. 28.0x18.7cm. (20),577 p.

CALVIN, John. The | Institvtion | of Christian Religion, written in Latine | by M.Iohn Calvine, | Translated into English according to | the Authors last edition; | With sundry Tables to finde the prin-cipall | matters intreated of in this | Booke, | And also the declaration of places | of Scripture therein ex- | pounded: | By Thomas Norton. | Whereunto there are newly added in the | margin of the Booke, Notes contei- | ning in briefe the substance of the | matter handled in ech | section. |

Imprinted at London for | Iohn Norton. | 1611. | Column & arch border. 28.5 x 18.9cm. (20),749,(159) p.

CARTWRIGHT, Thomas. Christian | Religion: | Svbstantially, Metho- | dicallie, plainlie, and profitablie | Treatised. | (device).
London, | Printed by Felix Kingston for | Thomas Man, | 1611| 18.6x13.6 cm. (1), 315p. Pp. 141–159 omitted.
First edition of his Treatise Of Christian Religion: 1616.

COQUÆUS, Leonardus. Examen | Praefatio- | nis Monitoriae, | Iacobi I.Magnae Britan- | niae Et Hiberniae Regis, Praemissae | Apologiae Svae Pro Ivramento Fide- | litatis, Expresso Nomine Ipsivs | Avthoris Denvò Editæ. | Christianis Omnibvs Monarchis, | Principibvs, Atqve Ordinibvs, Firmissimis Fidei Ca- | tholicæ & S.Romanæ Ecclesiæ columinibus & propugnacu- | lis, in sui erga Deum & eamdem fidem Zeli pignus, | Dicat & Vovet | F.Leonardvs Coquævs Avrelivs, | Eremita Augustinianus. | In quo Examine refellitur & Apologia ipsa Regis, | & summi Pontificis Brevia ad Catholicos Anglos | defendentur. | . . . (7 lines). Cum Sacræ Cæsar. Maiest. Priuilegio perpetuo. |
Fribvrgi Brisgoiæ. | Apud Ioannem Strasservm. | Anno M.DC.XI. | Line border. 31.6x20.2cm. 509,(1)p.

COWPER, William. The | Anatomie | Of A Christian | Man. | VVherein Is Plainelie | shewed out of the Word of God, what | manner of man a true Christian is in all his | conuersation, both inward, and outward. | Fvll Of Heavenly Instrv- | ctions, by practise whereof we may behold | in the life to come, our Creator in his glory, | and our Redeemer at his right hand. | By M.William Covvper, | Minister of Gods Word. | . . . (3 lines).
London: | Printed by T.S. for Iohn Budge, and are to be sould | at the great south dore of Paules, and at | Brittaynes Bursse. 1611. | Line border. 17.4x13.5cm. (20),284, (4)p. Lacks sig. A4.

DENISON, John. The | Christian | Petitioner. | Shewing how we must sue in the | Courts of Heauen, both for re- | ward and remission. | (decoration) A | Sermon Preached | At Oxford, The | Seventh Day Of Ivly, | Being The Act | Sunday.1611. | By Iohn Denison, Doctor of Diuinity, some- | times of Balioll Colledge. | (device).
London. | Printed by William Stansby. 1611. | Line border. 17.5x13.3cm. (8), 46p.

DENISON, John. The | Sinne | Against The | Holy Ghost | Plainly De- | scribed. | By {The Authoritie of Scriptures. | The Testimonie of Fathers. | The consent of Schoolemen. | In a Sermon Preached at Pavles | Crosse, April 14. | 1611. | By Iohn Denison Bachelor | of Diuinitie. | (device).
London. | Printed by William Stansby, and are to be sold by Iohn Budge, at | the great South dore of Paules, and at Brittaines | Bursse. 1611. | Line border. 17.7x13.7 cm. (6),64p.

The | DOCTRINE | of the Bible: | Or, | Rvles Of | Discipline: | Briefely Gathered | through the whole course of | the Scripture, by way of | Questions and Answers. | . . . (3 lines; ornament).
London: | Printed by T. Snodham, for Thomas Pauier, | and are to be sold at the signe of the | Cat and Parrets neare the | Exchange. 1611. | 11.7x6.7 cm. Fol (2),1–69,82–119,(1),120–227,226–235,237. 70–81 missing; some folios unnumbered.

DOWNAME, George. A | Defence | Of The Sermon | Preached at the Consecration of the | Bishop of Bath and VVelles, against a | confutation thereof by a namelesse Author. | Diuided into 4 Bookes: | The first, prouing chiefly that the lay or onely-gouerning Elders haue no | warrant either in the Scriptures or other monuments of Antiquity. | The second, shewing that the primatiue Churches indued with power | of Ecclesiasticall gouernment, were not Parishes properly but Dio- | ceses, and consequently that the Angels of the Churches or ancient | Bishops were not parishionall but Diocesan Bishops. | The third, defending the superioritie of Bishops aboue other Ministers, | and prouing that Bishops alwayes had a prioritie not onely in order, | but also in degree, and a maioritie of power both for ordination and | iurisdiction. | The fourth, maintayning that the Episcopall function is of Apostoli- | call and diuine institution. | By George Downame Doctor | of Diuinitie. | (line ornament).

London: | Printed by Thomas Creed, William Hall, and | Thomas Snodham. 1611. | 18.8x14.2cm. (9),238,(1); 148; 154; 168p. (Colophon at end of part I).

DU COIGNET, Pierre. Anti-Coton, | Or | A Refvtation Of | Cottons Letter Declaratorie: lately | directed to the Queene Regent, for the Apolo- | gizing of the Iesuites Doctrine, touching | the killing of Kings. | A Booke, | In which it is proued that the Ie- | suites are guiltie, and were the Authors of the late | execrable Parricide, committed vpon the Person of the | French King, Henry the fourth, | of happie memorie. | To Which Is Added, | A Supplication of the Vniuersitie of Paris, for the | preuenting of the Iesuites opening their Schooles | among them: in which their King-killing | Doctrine is also notably discouered, and confuted. | Both translated out of the French, by G. H. Together with the Translators animaduersions | vpon Cottons Letter. | (line ornament).

London, | Printed by T. S. for Richard Boyle, and are to be | sold at his shop in the blacke Fryers. | 1611. | 17.2x13 cm. (6),76,(6)p.

Anon.Brit.Mus.Cat. Attributed also to Pierre du Moulin. Cath Enc: IV, 422b. G.H. supposed to be George Hakewill. DNB.24:8b.

FULKE, William. The | Woman | Of | Canaan. | A comfortable Sermon of faith in | temptations and afflictions. | Preached at Saint Buttolphes without Alders- | gate in London, the 15. of February. | 1573. | By Maister William Fulke Doctor of Diuinity and | Maister of Pembrooke Hall in Cambridge. | Now newly reuiued, corrected, and amended: and | published at the request of certaine well | affected persons. | . . . (3 lines; device).

At London | Imprinted for Thomas Adams. | 1611. | Line border. 18. x14. cm. (8),38p.

GORDON, John. Orthodoxo- | Iacobvs: | Et | Papapostaticvs. | Sive | Theses Confirmatæ | Testimoniis Græcorvm, Et | Latinorum Patrum, qui vixerunt vsque ad millesimum à | Christo annum; quibus probatur Serenissimum Regem maxi- | mæ Britanniæ &c. esse Catholicæ fidei, verum Defen- | sorem & Propugnatorem: Papasq[ue]

Cardinalitios defecisse à | fide Sanctæ Trinitatis, & Iuramento Baptismi. | Per | Ioannem Gordonivm, Sacræ | Theologiæ Doctorem, et Eccle- | siæ Salisburiensis in Anglo-Britan- | nia, Decanum. | (device).
   Londini, | Excudebat Felix Kyngston. | 1161. | [1611]. | 17.6x14.2cm. 81p.

HALL, Joseph. Epistles, | The | Third | And Last | Volvme, | Containing | Two Decades. | By Ioseph Hall | Doctor of Di- | uinitie. |
   London | Printed for E.Edgar, | and A.Garbrand at | the Wind-mill in | Pauls Church | yard. 1611. | Arch border. 16.6x10.8cm. (12),124;(1),114p.

HAMPTON, Christopher. A | Sermon | Preached In | the Cittie of Glasco in Scotland, | on the Tenth day of June, 1610. | At the holding of a generall | Assembly there. | By Christopher Hampton, Doctor | in Diuinitie, and Chaplaine to the Kings most | Excellent Maiestie. | (ornament).
   London: | Printed by T.S. for Henry Fetherstone, dwelling in | Paules Churchyard at the signe of the Rose. | 1611. | Line border. 18.3x14cm. (4),32 .

HIERON, Samuel. The Spiritvall | Sonne-ship: | As | Jt hath beene collected out of | 1 Iohn 3.1. and deliuered in | two Sermons: | By Samvel Hieron. | Hereunto is annexed, The Mariage-blessing, | preached at a Wedding. | . . . (2 lines; device).
   At London | Printed by VVilliam Hall for Samuel | Macham, and are to be sold at his shop in | Pauls Church-yard at the signe of | the Bull-head. | 1611. | Line border. 17.6x13.4cm. (6),81p.

HOOKER, Richard. Of The | Lawes | of | Ecclesiastical | Politie, | Eight Bookes | By Richard Hooker. |
   Imprinted at Lond: by Will: Stansby. | Will: Hole fecit | Engraved t.p. (1611). 29x18.7 cm. (52),453p.
   Books I–IV, and V with separate t.p. at p. 169. Third ed. of I–IV, and second of Book V. Date on sub-title.

JAMES, Thomas. A | Treatise | Of The Corrvp- | tion of Scripture, Councels, and Fa- | thers, by the Prelats, Pastors, and Pillars of | the Church of Rome, for maintenance | of Popery and irreligion. | By Thomas Iames, | Student in Diuinitie, and chiefe Keeper of | the Publique Librarie in the Vniuersitie of | Oxford; of the Honorable foundation of | Sir Thomas Bodley, Knight. | Together with a sufficient answere vnto James | Gretser, and Antonie Posseuine Iesuites, and | the vnknowne Author of the Grounds | of the old religion & the new. | Diuided into V Parts. | (device).
   At London, | Printed by H. L. for Mathew Lownes: and are to be | sold in Pauls Church-yard, at the signe of the | Bishops-head. 1611. | Line border. 19x14.8 cm. (22),71,(12);103,(1);59;102,(1);35,(1) p.
   Each part has separate register and pagination, without sub-titles.

JEWEL, John. A | Defence Of | The Apologie | of the Church of | England, | Conteining an Answer to a certaine | Booke lately set forth by M.Harding, | and entituled, A Confutation of &c. | Whereunto there is also newly added an Answer | vnto another like Booke, written by the said M.Harding, | entituled, A Detection of sundrie foule errours,

&c. Printed at | Louain, Anno 1568, and inserted into the former | Answer, as occasion and place required, | as by speciall Notes added to the | Margine it may appeare. | By Iohn Ievvel Bishop of Sarisburie. | . . . (3 lines).

London, | Printed by Iohn Norton, | Printer to the Kings most ex- | cellent Maiestie. | 1611. | Arch. border. 31.2x20.7cm. (35),652;(40),472,(7)p
Part of his Workes: 1611. Sig *g1–Hhh8, ¶1–Rr6.

JEWEL, John. A Replie | Vnto M. | Hardings | Answer: | By perusing whereof, the discreet and diligent | Reader may easily see the weake and | vnstable grounds of the Roman reli- | gion, which of late hath been ac- | counted Catholike: | By Iohn Ievvel Bishop of Sarisburie. | . . . (9 lines).

London, | Printed by Iohn Norton, | Printer to the Kings most ex- | cellent Maiestie. | 1611. | Arch. border. 31.2x20.7cm. (40),472,(7)p.
Part of his Workes: 1611. Sig ¶1–Rr6.

JEWEL, John. A | View Of A | Seditiovs | Bull sent into England, | from Pius Quintus Bi- | shop of Rome, | 1569. | Taken by the reuerend Father in God, | Iohn Iewel, late Bishop | of Sarisbvrie. | Whereunto is added a | short Treatise of the holy | Scriptures. | Both which he deliuered in diuers Sermons | in his Cathedrall Church of | Sarisburie, 1570. |

London, | Printed by Iohn Norton, | Printer to the Kings most ex- | cellent Maiestie. | 1611. | Arch. border. 31.2x20.7cm. 48p.
Appended, with continuous pagination: An | Exposition | Vpon The Two | Epistles Of The | Apostle Paul to the | Thessalonians: | *and* Certaine | Sermons | Preached Before The Qveens | Maiestie, at Pauls Crosse, and else- | where: . . . Whereunto is added a short | Treatise of the Sacraments, gathered | out of other his Sermons, made | vpon that matter, in his Cathedrall | Church at Sarisbury. | (Pages 49–291).
Part of his Workes: 1611.

JEWEL, John. The | Workes | Of The Very | Learned And | Reuerend Father in God | Iohn Ievvel, | not long since Bishop of | Sarisbvrie. | Newly set forth with some | amendment of diuers quota- | tions: | And a briefe discourse | of his life. |

London, | Printed by Iohn Norton, | Printer to the Kings most ex- | cellent Maiestie. | 1611. | Arch. border. 31.2x20.7cm. (34), 62; (35),652; (40), 472,(7); 291p.

KING, John. Lfctvres | Vpon Ionas, | Delivered At | Yorke, | In the yeare of our Lond 1594. | By Iohn Kinge: | Newly corrected and amended. (device)

At London | Imprinted by H.L. and are to be sould by | Arthur Iohnson, at the signe of the white horse, | neere the great North doore of | Paules Church. | 1611. | 20.6x15.7cm. (9),706p. A1 blank. Two sermons at end.
From the library of Walter W. Law.

PERKINS, William. The Whole Trea- | tise Of The Cases Of | Conscience, Distingvished Into | Three Bookes. | Taught and deliuered by M.W.Perkins in | his Holy-day Lectures, examined by his owne | Briefes, and published for the common good, by T.Picke- | ring Bach-

elour of Diuinitie. | Newly corrected, with the two Tables set before |
the first booke; one of the Heades and Number of the Questions |
propounded and resolued: another of the principall Texts of | Scripture, which are either explaned, or vindicated | from corrupt interpretation. | . . . (2 lines ; device)

Printed at London by Iohn Legatt, | Printer to the Vniversity of Cambridge.
1611. | And are to be sold in Pauls Church-yard, at the signe | of the Crowne, by
Simon Waterson. | 18.2x14 cm. (30),373pp.
Imprint clipped; supplied.

RAWLINSON, John. The Romish Ivdas. | A | Sermon | Preached
At | Saint Maries In | Oxford The Fifth | Of November, | 1610. | By |
Iohn Ravvlinson Doctour | of Diuinitie. | . . . (3 lines; ornament).

London, | Printed by William Hall for | Iohn Hodgets, 1611. | 17.7x13.7cm.
(8),40p.

SANFORD, Hugh. De | Descensv | Domini Nostri | Iesv Christi |
ad Inferos. | Libri Qvatvor. | Ab auctore doctissimo, Hvgone Sanfordo, | Coomflorio, Anglo, | Inchoati. | Opera veró et studio Roberti
Parkeri, ad | umbilicum perducti, ac jam tandem | In Lucem editi. |
Cum duplici Indice Sectionum, | & Rerum. | In quibus non pauca,
Poetica, Historica, Philosophica, Theologica, | ad veritatem divinam
illustrandam, ex Hebraicis, Arabicis, | Græcis, Latinisque scriptoribus,
jam | primùm orbi Christiano | evulgantur. | (ornament).

Amstelrodami. | In ædibus Ægidij Thorpij. Anno. 1611. | 18.9x14.2cm. (8),51,
165,(1),249,213,(2) p.
Four books: each with separate register and pagination.

SARAVIA, Hadrian. Diversi | Tractatvs | Theologici, | Ab Hadriano Saravia editi: | Quorum titulos sequens pagina indicabit. | . . . (3
lines; device).

Londini, | Ex Typographia Societatis Stationariorum. | 1611. | 29.3x18.4cm. (14),
29; (14),382; (1),21; (10),314p.
Contains: De diuersis gradibus Ministrorum Euangelij. | De honore Præsulibus
& Presbyteris debito. | De Sacrilegis & Sacrilegorum pœnis. | Defensio Tractatus
de diuersis Ministrorum gradibus. | Responsio ad conuitia quædam Gretseri
Iesuitæ, in quibus Hadriani Sara- | uiæ nomine abutitur. | N.fratri & amico. |
Examen Tractatus D.Bezæ de triplici Episcoporum genere. | De imperandi authoritate & Christiana obedientia libri quatuor. |)

SCHOPPE, Caspar. Gasp.Scioppii | Ecclesiasticvs | Auctoritate |
Serenissimi D.Iacobi | Magnæ Britanniæ Regis | Oppositvs. | In quo
cùm Argumento magnam partem Nouo, | tùm Exemplo nemini adhuc
vsitato disputatur | De amplitudine potestatis & Iurisdictionis Ecclesiasticæ tàm in tempora- | libus quàm in spiritualibus. | De Regum ac
Principum Christianorum erga Ecclesiam eiusque Antisti- | tes seu
Prælatos officio. | De natura & ingenio Ecclesiæ Rebellium, siue
Hæreticorum, variisq[ue] eo- | rundem ad Ecclesiæ obedientiam reducendorum modis. | De Charactere, siue signis ac Notis Ecclesiæ, ex
quibus eam tam Ethnici, | quàm Hæretici à quibuscumque Hæreticorum conuenticulis queant | internoscere. | (ornament).

Hartbergæ | Anno M.DCXI. | 20.x15.5cm. (39),565,(4)p.

SCLATER, William. A | Key To The | Key Of Scriptvre: | Or | An Exposition | with Notes, vpon the Epistle to the | Romanes; the three first Chapters: | Begun in Walsall in Staffordshire, con- | tinued at Pitmister in Somerset. | By William Sclater Batchelar in Diuinitie, | and Minister of the Word of God at | Pitmister in Somerset. | (ornament).

London: | printed by T.S. for Richard Bonian, dwelling in Paules | Church- yard at the signe of the Floure de luce. | 1611. | Line border. 17.2x13.6cm. (6), 388,(2)pp.

SHELDON, Richard. Certain | General Rea- | sons, Proving The Law- | fulnesse of the Oath of Allegiance, | written by R.S. Priest, to his priuat | Friend. | (ornament).

At London | Imprinted by Felix Kyngston, for | William Aspley. 1611. | Line border. 18.7x12.7 cm. (12),77p.
DNB.52:27b. Preface signed B. S. Priest, Prisoner.

The | TOCSIN, | Or, | Watch-Bell: | Sent | To The King, Qveene | Regent, Princes of blood, to all the Par- | laments, Magistrates, Offi- cers, and loyall | Subiects of France. | Against the booke of the Popes temporall po- | wer, not long since set forth by Cardinall | Bellarmine Iesuite. | By Memnons Statue. | With the permission of the best Genie of Fraunce. | And done into English by I.R. | . . . (4 lines).

London, | Printed for Edward White the younger, and are to be sold at the | little North doore of Paules, at the signe of the Gunne. | 1611. | 19.3x14.8cm. (8,50)p.

URSINUS, Zacharias. The | Svmme Of | Christian | Religion | De- liuered by Zacharias Vrsinvs | in his Lectures vpon the Catechisme, au- | thorised by the noble Prince Frederick | throughout his do- minions. | Wherein are debated and resolued the Questions of what- | soeuer points of moment, which haue beene or are | controuersed in Diuinitie. | Translated into English by D.Henrie Parrie, | and lately conferred with the last and best Latine Edi- | tion of D.David Parevs, Professor of | Diuinity in Heidelberge. | . . . (device).

At London, | Imprinted by H.L. and are to be sold by Arthur | Iohnson, at the signe of the white horse, neere | the great North doore of Paules | Church. 1611. | Line border. 19.7x14.7cm. (10), 1113, (13)p.

WILLET, Andrew. Hexapla: | That Is, | A Six-Fold Commentarie | vpon the most Diuine Epistle of the holy Apostle S. | Pavl to the Romanes: wherein according to the Authors former me- | thod sixe things are observed in euery Chapter. 1. The Text with the diuers | readings. 2. Argument and method. 3. the Questions dis- | cussed. 4. Doctrines noted. 5. Controversies handled. | 6. Morall vses observed. | Wherein are handled the greatest points of Christian reli- | gion: con- cerning iustification by faith, c.3,4. the fall of man, c.5. the combat | betweene the flesh and the spirit, c.7. Election, c.9. the vocation of the Iewes, | C.11. with many other Questions and Controversies | summed in the ende of the Table. | Diuided into two bookes: the first vnto the 12. | chapter, containing matter of Doctrine: the second | belonging to

Exhoration, in the five | last Chapters. | The First Booke. | . . . (7 lines; device).

Printed By Cantrell Legge, Printer To | the Vniversitie of Cambridge. 1611. | 27.5x17.7cm. (5),531, (4), 533–746,(21)p.
Dedication to James I, signed.

WILSON, Thomas. A | Dialogve | About | Ivstification | by Faith: | Wherein the nature and | office, the property and pow- | er of Faith is | Plainely taught, against such as | deny the certainety or parti- | cularity and powerfulnesse | of Faith. | Especially, against a late errour, deni- | ing the necessity of Faith vnto | Iustification. |

London | Printed by William Hall, and are to bee | sold by Nathaniel Butter at the signe | of the pide Bull, neere St.Austens | gate, 1611. | 14x8.7cm. (9),173; (4),18;(4),40;(7),58p.
Contains also: A | Receite | Against | Heresie, | For | Preuention or purging | out (if it be entred) that | spirit of Hereticall | prauity. | No impr. (4),18p; A | Sermon Of | Sanctification | or new Creation. | (wh.see); and, A | Sermon Of | The Spirituall | Combat, beetweene the two | Lawes of sinne, and of a mind | renewed by grace: | Or, | Of The Strife Be- | tweene the flesh and the Spirit, | preached in S.Georges in Canter- | bury, Aug.8.1609. | Without impr. (7),58p.
Continuous register throughout, but separate paginations.
Epistle dedicatory, signed.
Re-dated edition, part of his Jacobs Ladder: 1611; with separate register and paging.

WILSON, Thomas. Jacobs Ladder, | Or | A Short Trea- | tise Laying Forth | distinctly the seuerall degrees | of Gods eternall purpose, where- | by his grace descends vpon the e- | lect, and the elect ascend to | the predestinate | glory. | (ornament)

London | Printed by William Hall, for | Nathaniel Butter. | 1611. | 13.6x8.3cm. (17),9;(9),173;(4),18;(4),40;(7),58p. A1 blank.
Contains also a publication dated the previous year: A | Dialogve | About | Ivstification | by Faith. | London: 1610. (which see); And also the following: A | Receite | Against | Heresie, | For | Preuention or purging | out (if it be entred) that | spirit of Hereticall | prauity. | No date. (4),18p. A | Sermon On | Sanctification | or new Creation. | Preached on Ianv- | arie the first, beeing Newyeares | day, in the Chapter house of the | Cathedrall Church in | Canterburie. | (Same size and imprint) (4),40p. and A | Sermon Of | The Spirituall | Combat, beetweene the two | Lawes of sinne, and of a mind | renewed by grace: | Or, | Of The Strife Be- | tweene the flesh and the Spirit, | preached in S.Georges in Canter- | bury, Aug.8.1609. | (No date) (7),58p.
The added portion has continuous register, but separate pagination.
Epistle to the Reader, signed.

WILSON, Thomas. A | Sermon Of | Sanctification | or new Creation. | Preached On Ianv- arie the first, beeing Newyeares | day, in the Chapter house of the | Cathedrall Church in | Canterburie. | (device)

London | Printed by William Hall for | Nathaniel Butter, | 1611. | 14.8x8.7cm. (4),40p.
Included in his Jacobs Ladder: 1611; with continuous register.
Epistle dedicatorie, signed.

1612

ADAMS, Thomas. The | Gallants Burden. | A | Sermon preached at | Pavles Crosse, The | twentie nine of March, being | the fift Sunday in Lent. | 1612. | By Tho.Adams, Preacher | of Gods Word at Willington | in Bedford-shire. | Published by authority. | (device).

London | Printed by W.W. for Clement Knight, and are to | be sold at his Shoppe in Paules Church-yard | at the Signe of the Holy Lambe. 1612. | Border. 17.8x13.2cm. (2),34fol.

ARMINIUS, James. Iacobi | Arminii | Veteraqvinatis Batavi, | S. Theologiæ Doctoris eximij, | Examen Modestvm | Libelli, quem | D. Gvlielmvs Perkinsivs | apprimé doctus Theologus, | edidit ante aliquot annos | De | Prædestinationis modo & ordine, | itemque de | Amplitudine gratiæ divinæ. | Addita est propter argumenti convenientiam Analy- | sis Cap.IX.Ad Roman. ante multos annos ab eo- | dem ipso D.Arminio delineata. | Cum Indice rerum contentarum. | (device).

Lugduni Batavorum | Ex Officinâ Godefridi Basson. | M.D.CXII. | 17.8x11.9 cm. (23),312p.

ARTICLES | Whereupon it was agreed by the | Archbishops and Bishops of both Pro- | uinces, and the whole Cleargie: | In the Conuocation holden at London | in the yeere of our Lord God 1562. | According to the computation of the | Church of England. | For the auoyding of the diuersities of | opinions, and for the stablishing of | consent touching true Religion. | (ornament).

Imprinted at London by Robert | Barker, Printer to the Kings most | Excellent Maiestie. | Anno 1612. | 17.9x13.1cm. (1,21)p.

ATTERSOLL, William. A | Commentarie | Vpon The Epistle Of | Saint Pavle To | Philemon. | Wherein, the Apostle handling a meane and low subiect, intreating for a Fraudulent and Fugitiue Seruant, | mounteth aloft vnto God, and deli- | uereth sundry high Misteries of true | Religion, and the practise of Duties} {œconomicall. | Politicall. | Ecclesiasticall. | As {Of Persecution for Righteousnesse sake. | Of Christian Equity, and Moderation. | Of Gods free Grace forgiuing offences. | Of Houshold Gouernment, and priuate possesions. | Of the Conuersion of Sinners, and Communion of Saints. | Of Faith, and good workes. | Of Friendship, and Suretiship. | Of Prayer, and Hospitality. | Of the Gospell, and Almes-deedes. | Of Gods Prouidence. | And of the force and fruit of the Ministery. | Mouing all the Ministers of the Gospell, to a diligent labouring in the spirituall Haruest, | and the people, to a conscionable attending to the word of Saluation, as to Gods high and | holy ordinance for our conuersion, with assured hope of his wonderfull blessing; | vpon the sound Preaching of the one, and the sauing hearing | of the other. | Written by William Attersoll, Minister of the word | of God, at Isfield in Sussex. | . . . (3 lines).

Printed at London by William Iaggard. 1612. | Line border. 28.1x18cm. (1), 560, 6p.

BARCLAY, William. Gvilielmi Barclaii | De | Potestate | Papæ: | An & quatenus in Reges & Principes secu- | lares ius & imperium habeat. | Liber Posthumus. | Eiusdem | De Regno Et Regali | Potestate: | Aduersus | Bvchananvm, Brvtvm, Bovcherivm, | & reliquos Monarchomachos, | Libri VI. | Editio | Nunc primùm in Germaniâ adornata emendatior. | (device)

Hanoviæ, | Impensis ac Typis Willerianis, & consort. | M DC XII. | 16.3 x 10.4 cm. (16),825,(19) p.

BOYS, John. The | Avtvmne | Part From | The Twelfth Svnday | after Trinitie, to the last in the | whole yeere. | Dedicated Vnto The Mvch | honoured and most worthie Doctor | Iohn Overal Deane | of Pauls. | . . . (2 lines: ornament).

At London | Imprinted by Felix Kyngston for VVilliam | Aspley, and are to be solde at his shop in Pauls | Church-yard, at the signe of the | Parrot. 1612. | Line border. 18.7x13.6cm. (3), 227p.
Separate pagination, and register, beginning with A3.

BROUGHTON, Hugh. A Letter to a | Friende, touching | Mardochai | his age; | Which helpeth much to holde the | trueth, for that chiefe Prophecie of | our saluation in Gabriels Seuenties: | which shew, that most exactly 490. | yeares after the Angels speach, | Christ the most Holy should be | killed, to giue life. Dan.9.23. | . . . (3 lines).

Imprinted at London by Wil. | VVhite, in Cow-lane. 1612. | Engr. border. . 17.2x13.3cm.   (4,12)p.
Signed at end.

BROUGHTON, Hugh. Obseruations | Vpon | The first ten | Fathers | By H.Brovghton. | (device).

Imprinted at London by W.White | dwelling in Cow-lane. | 1612. | Lace border. 17.2x13.3cm. (1),21p.

CARTWRIGHT, Thomas. A | Commentary | Vpon The Epistle | of Saint Paule written to the | Colossians. | Preached | By Thomas Cartwright, and now | Published for the further vse of | the Church of God. | . . . (3 lines: ornament).

London | Printed by Nicholas Okes, and are to be sold by George | Norton, dwelling neere Temple-barre. | 1612. | Line border. 18x13.1cm. (1),248p.

CONSTITVTIONS | And Canons | Ecclesiasticall. | Treated vpon by the Bishop of Lon- | don, President of the Conuocation for the | Prouince of Canterbury, and the rest of the | Bishops and Clergie of the | sayd Prouince: | And agreed vpon with the Kings Maiesties Licence in their | Synode begun at London Anno Dom. 1603 And in the | yeere of the raigne of our Soueraigne Lord Iames | by the grace of God King of England, | France, and Ireland the first, and | of Scotland the 37. | And now published for the due obseruation of them by his | Maiesties authority, vnder the great | Seale of England. | (Line ornament).

Imprinted At London | by Robert Barker, Printer to the Kings | most Excellent Maiestie. | Anno. 1612. | 18.3x13.8 cm.   (16,104)p.

COPLEY, John. Doctrinall | And Morall | Observations | Concerning | Religion: | Wherein The Av- | thor Declareth The | Reasons of his late vn-enforced departure from the | Church of Rome; and of his incorporation to the present | Church of England: teaching, maintaining and | defending the true Christian Catholike and Apostolike | Faith, professed by the ancient Primitiue Church, most | conspicuous in the outward vertues and constant sufferings | of many holy Bishops and other good Christi- | ans, glorious in the crowne of | Martyrdome. | By Iohn Copley Seminarie Priest. | . . . (5 lines).

London, | Imprinted by W. S. for Richard Moore, and are to be sold at | his Shop in Fleet-street, in Saint Dunstans | Church-yard. 1612. | Line border. 18.3x 13.1 cm. (12),242,(1) p.

COWPER, William. Three | Heavenly | Treatises, | concerning Christ: | {I. His Genealogie. | 2. His Baptisme. | 3. His Combat with Sathan. | Together VVith | deuout Meditations, for Christian | Consolation and Instruction. | By Mr. William Cowper, Minister | of Gods Word. |

London: | Printed by T.S. for Iohn Budge, and | are to be sold at the great South doore | of Paules, and at Brittaines | Bursse. 1612. | Line border. 14.4x9.3 cm. (25),48,(1),49–326, (15)p.

DISCOVRS | En Forme De | lettre missiue, sur le su- | jet d'vne Epistre du | Sieur Casaubon. | (ornament).

Without place. M.DC.XII. | 16.6x10.2cm. (4),52p.

DOWNAME, John. The | Christian | Warfare. | Wherein Is First General- | lie Shewed The Malice, Power | and politike stratagems of the spirituall enemies of our saluation, | Satan and his assistants the world and the flesh: with the | meanes also whereby the Christian may withstand | and defeate them. | And Afterwards More Speci- | allie Their Particvlar Tentati- | ons, against the seuerall causes and meanes of our saluation, | whereby on the one side, they allure vs to securitie | and presumption, and on the other side, draw vs to doubting and desperation, are ex- | pressed and answered. | Written Especially For Their Sakes | who are exercised in the spirituall conflict of tentations, and | are afflicted in conscience in the sight and sense | of their sinnes. | By I. Dovvname, Batcheler in Diuinitie and | Preacher of Gods word. | The Third Edition, Corrected And | much enlarged by the Author, as further appeareth in | the next leafe. | . . . (2 lines).

At London | Imprinted by Felix Kyngston, for William Welby | and are to be sold at his shop in Paules Churchyard | at the signe of the Swan. 1612. | 17.6x13.5 cm (29),829p.

From the library of Walter W. Law.

FLOYD, John. The | Overthrovv | Of The | Protestants | Pvlpit-Babels, | Convincing | their Preachers of Lying & Rayling, | to make the Church of Rome seeme | mysticall Babell. | Particvlarly | confuting VV.Crashawes Sermon at the Crosse, prin- | ted as the patterne to iustify the rest. | VVith | a Preface to the Gentlemen of the Innes of Court, shewing | what vse may be made of this Treatise. | Togeather |

with a discouery of M.Crashawes spirit: and an Answere | to his Iesuites Ghospell. | By I.R. Student in Diuinity. | . . . (3 lines).
    Imprinted Anno M.DC.XII. | 18.6x13.1cm. 328,(4)p.
    Anon.Gillow.II:302.

GREENHAM, Richard. The | Workes | Of The Reverend | And Faithfvll Ser- | vant Of Iesvs Christ | M. Richard Greenham, Minister | And Preacher Of The Word | of God, collected into one | Volume: | Revised, Corrected, | And Pvblished, For The Fvr- | ther Bvilding Of All Svch As Love | the truth, and desire to know the power of | godlinesse. | By H.H. | The Fift And Last Edition: | In Which, Matters Dispersed Before Throvgh | the whole booke, are methodically drawne to their seuerall | places, and the hundred and nineteenth Psalme perfected: | with a more exact Table annexed. | . . . (2 lines ; device).
    London: | Printed for VVilliam VVelby, and are to be solde at his shop | in Paules Church-yard, at the signe of the Swanne. 1612. | Line border. 28.3x18.4 cm. (18),880,(16)p.

HIERON, Samuel. A Helpe vnto | Deuotion: | Containing | Certain Moulds or Forms | of Prayer, fitted to seueral oc- | casions; and penned for the fur- | therance of those, who haue more | desire then skill, to poure out their | soules by petition vnto | God. | By Sam. Hieron. | The fourth Edition. | . . . (4 lines ; ornament).
    At London, | Printed by H.L. for Samuel | Macham, 1612. | Border. 11.9x6.3cm. (32),453,(6)p. Pp. 1–2 blank; engr border on each page.

HOOKER, Richard. The | Ansvvere | Of | Mr. Richard Hooker To A | Svpplication Preferred | by Mr Walter Travers to | the HH. Lords of the Pri- | vie Counsell. | (device).
    At Oxford, | Printed by Ioseph Barnes, and are to be | sold by John Barnes dwelling neere | Holborne Conduit. 1612. | 20.5x15.4 cm. (1),32p.

HOOKER, Richard. A | Learned | And Comforta- | ble Sermon Of The | certaintie and perpetuitie of | faith in the Elect; especially | of the Prophet Habak- | kuks faith. | By | Richard Hooker, Some- | times fellow of Corpus Christi | College in Oxford. | (device).
    At Oxford, | Printed by Ioseph Barnes, and are to be | sold by John Barnes dwelling neere | Holborne Conduit. 1612. | 16.8x12.7cm. (1),17p.

HOOKER, Richard. A | Learned | Sermon Of | The Natvre | Of Pride, | By | Richard Hooker, Some- | times fellow of Corpus Christi | College in Oxford. | (device).
    At Oxford, | Printed by Ioseph Barnes, and are to be | sold by John Barnes dwelling neere | Holborne Conduit. 1612. | 18.1x13.8cm. (1),17p.

HOOKER, Richard. A | Remedie | Against Sor- | row And Feare, | delivered in a funerall | Sermon, | By | Richard Hooker, Some- | times fellow of Corpus Christi | College in Oxford. | (device).
    At Oxford, | Printed by Ioseph Barnes, and are to be | sold by John Barnes dwelling neere | Holborne Conduit. 1612. | 18.1x13.8cm. (1),14p.

HULL, William. The | Third Worke | Of Mercy. | Or, | The Sinners Enter- | tainement of harbourlesse | Christ. | Set forth in sixe Sermons, whereof the | {1.is, The Patterne of Patience. | 2.The Knocke of the Spirit. | 3.The Bride-groomes Voyce. | 4.Mans Heart Christs home. | 5.The blessed Inne-mate. | 6.Mutuall Loue-feasts betweene God | and Man. | By W.Hvll Doctor of Diuinity. | . . . (9 lines).

London, | Printed by N.O. for Samuel Rand, dwelling neare | Holborne bridge. 1612. | Line border. 14.2x9.4cm. (8),107fol.

JACOB, Henry. A | Declaration | And | Plainer Opening | Of | Certain Points, | With | A Sovnd Confirmation | Of Some Other, | Contained In A Treatise | Intitvled, | The Divine Beginning | and institution of Christes true visible | and ministeriall Church. | Written in a Letter by the Author of the | said Treatise, out of the Low Coun- | tryes, to a friend of his in England. | (device).

Printed | Anno Dom. 1612. | 14x9 cm. 44 p. Mispaged 45.
Anon. Dexter:391.

JAMES I. His Maiesties | Declaration | concerning His Proceedings | with the States generall of the Vni- | ted Prouinces of the Low | Countreys, | In the cause of D. Conradvs | Vorstivs. | . . . (coat of arms; 2 lines).

Imprinted At London | by Robert Barker, Printer to the Kings | most Excellent Maiestie. | Anno Dom. 1612. | 16.6x12.4 cm. (2),89p.

JAMES, Thomas. The Iesuites Downefall, | Threatened | Against Them | By The Secvlar | Priests for their wicked liues, accur- | sed manners, Hereticall doctrine, | and more then Matchiavil- | lian Policie. | Together | With The Life Of Father | Parsons An English | Iesuite. | . . . (4 lines; ornament).

At Oxford, | Printed by Ioseph Barnes, and are to bee soldby | John Barnes dwelling neere Hol- | borne Conduit. 1612. | 18.8x14.9cm. (12),72p.
Epistle dedicatory, signed.

LAWNE, Christopher and others. The | Prophane | Schisme Of The | Brownists Or | Separatists. | With The | Jmpietie, | Dissensions, Levvd, And Abhominable | Vices of that impure Sect. | Discouered by {Christopher Lavvne, | Iohn Fovvler, | Clement Sanders, | Robert Bvlvvard. | Lately returned from the Companie of M. | Iohnson, that wicked Brother, into the bo- | some of the Church of England, | their true Mother. | . . . (5 lines).

M.D.C.XII. | Line border. 18.4x14.6cm. (8),88pp.

MARTELIERE, Pierre de la. The | Argvment | of Mr. Peter de la Marte- | liere Aduocate in the Court of Parlia- | ment of Paris, made in Parliament, | the Chambers thereof being | assembled. | For The Rector And Vniversitie | of Paris, Defendants and Opponents, against the | Iesuits Demandants, and requiring the approbation | of the Letters Patents which they had obtained, giuing | them power to reade and to teach publikely | in the aforesaid Vniuersities. | Translated out of the French Copie set forth | by publike Authoritie. | (royal arms).

Jmprinted at London, and are | to be sold neere S. Austins | Gate. 1612. | 17.5x 13.4cm. (16),111p.

MATTHIEU, Pierre. The | Heroyk Life | And | Deplorable Death | Of | The most Christian King | Henry the Fourth. | Adressed to his Immortal Memory; | By | P.Mathiev, | Counceller and Historiographer of France. | Translated | By | Ed: Grimeston, Esquire. |

London | Printed by George Eld. | 1612. | 18.6x14.cm. (8),190p.
Contains only The Deplorable Death, etc; lacks the Heroyk Life, and the "Trophies" in verse. T.p. supplied.

MORNAY, Philippe de. The Mysterie Of | Iniqvitie: | That is to say, | The Historie of the Papacie. | Declaring by what degrees it is now mounted to this height, | and what Oppositions the better sort from time to time haue made against it. | Where is also defended the right of Emperours, Kings, and Christian Princes, | against the assertions of the Cardinals, Bellarmine and Baronius. | By Philip Morney, Knight, Lord du Plesis, &c. | Englished by Samson Lennard. | . . . (cut; 2 lines).

London | Printed by Adam Islip, Anno Dom. 1612. | 28x18.5cm. (18),661,(1)p.

MOULIN, Pierre du. An | Apology | For The Holy | Svpper Of The | Lord. | Against {The Corporall presence. | Transubstantiation. | Masses without Communicants. | The Communion vnder one kinde. | Together With | Certaine Analiticall and Orthodoxe Propositions, | vpon the Lords Svpper. | VVritten in French, by Pierre Dv Movlin, | Minister of the word of God in the Church | of Paris. | Translated into English, according to his last Copie, by him- | selfe reuiewed and corrected, wherein all the Accusations | of the Aduersaries are answered. | By Edward Skipwith, Esquire. |

London: | Printed by T.S. for Nathaniell Butter, and are to | be solde at the signe of the Pide-Bull, neere | S.Austins Gate, 1612. | 18.9x13.7cm. (20),49,254, 111p.

MOULIN, Pierre du. Theophilvs, | Or | Love Divine. | A Treatise containing | Five } Degrees, | Markes, | Aides, | Of the Loue of God. | Translated by Richard Goring,out | of the third French edition: re- | newed, corrected and augmented by the | Author Mr. Peter Moulin, Preacher | to the reformed Church | of Paris. | Newly corrected and amended. |

At London, | Printed for Samuel Macham, and | are to be sold at his shop in Pauls church- | yard, at the signe of the Bull- | head. 1612. | Line border. 11.8x6.7 cm. (30),280p.

MOULIN, Pierre du. The Waters Of Siloe. | To Qvench | The Fire Of Purgatory | and to drowne the traditions, Lim- | boes, mans satisfactionsand all Popish | Indulgences, against the rea- | sons and allegations of a Portu- | gall Frier of the order of | St.Frances, suppor- | ted by three | treatises. | The one written by the same Franciscan and |

entituled The fierie torrent, &c. | The other two by two Doctors of Sorbon. | The one intituled The burning furnasse. The | other The fire of Helle. | By | Peter Dv Movlin Minister of | Gods word. | . . . (3 lines). Faithfully translated out of French by I.B. |

Printed at Oxford for Iohn Barnes | dwelling neere Holborne | Conduit. 1612. | 14.6x9.1cm. (32), 406p.

NIXON, Anthony. The | Dignitie | Of Man, | Both | In The Perfections | Of His Sovle And | Bodie. | Shewing As Well The Fa- | culties in the disposition of the one: as the | Senses and Organs, in the composi- | tion of the other. | By A.N. . . . (2 lines; ornament).

London, | Printed by Edward Allde dwelling vppon | Lambert-hill, neere old Fish-street. | 1612. | 18.x13.7cm. (5),125p.
Epistle Dedicatory, signed.

PARSONS, Robert. A | Discvssion | Of The | Ansvvere | Of | M. VVilliam Barlovv, | D. of Diuinity, to the Booke intituled: | The Iudgment of a Catholike Englishman liuing | in banishment for his Religion &c. | Concerning | The Apology of the new Oath of Allegiance. | VVritten | By the R. Father, F. Robert Persons of the Society of Iesvs. | VVhervnto | since the said Fathers death, is annexed a generall Preface, lay- | ing open the Insufficiency, Rayling, Lying, and other | Misdemeanour of M. Barlow in his writing. | (ornament ; 2 lines).

Permissu Superiorum. M.DC.XII. | 18.9x13.9cm. (124),543,(9)p.

PAULE, George. The | Life Of The | Most Reverend | And Religiovs Pre- | late John Whitgift, Lord Arch- | bishop of Canterbury. | VVritten by Sir George Paule | Knight, Comptroller of his | Graces Householde. | . . . (4 lines; ornament).

London; | Printed by Thomas Snodham. | 1612. | Line border. 17.9x14. cm. (6),94p

PRESTON, Thomas. Rogeri | Widdringtoni | Catholici Angli | Responsio Apolo- | getica. | ad | Libellum cuiusdam Doctoris Theologi, qui | eius pro iure Principum Apologiam tanquam | fidei Catholicæ apertè repugnantem, atque | Ethnicismum sapientem, falsò, indoctè, | & seditiosè criminatur. | . . . (3 lines; device).

Cosmopoli | Apud Pratum. | 1612. | 15.6x10.1cm. (88),216p.
Pseud. Gillow.V:365.

RAWLINSON, John. Mercy To A Beast. | A | Sermon | Preached At Saint | Maries Spittle In | London on Tuseday in | Easter weeke. 1612. | By | Iohn Rawlinson Doctor | of Divinitie. | (Oxford arms)

At Oxford, | Printed by Ioseph Barnes. 1612. | 17.6x13.3cm. (6),52p.

RICHARDSON, Charles. The | Repentance | Of Peter | And Ivdas. | Together With | The Frailtie Of The | Faithfull, and the feare- | full ende of wicked | Hypocrites. | . . . (3 lines).

London | Printed by William Stansby, for | Ioseph Browne. | Anno Domini, | 1612. | Arch. border. 18.2x13.4cm. (8),285p. Mispaged.
Epistle Dedicatorie, signed.

RICHER, Edmond. De | Ecclesiastica | Et Politica | potestate Liber vnus. | Ecclesia, Est Politia Mo- | narchia, ad finem supernaturalem instituta: | regimine aristocratico, quod omnium opti- | mum & naturæ conuenientissimum est, tem- | perata à summo animarum pastore Domino | nostro Iesu Christo. | De La Pvissance Eccle- | siastiqve Et Politiqve. | L'Eglise est vne police Monarchique, instituée à vne | fin supernaturelle: conduite d'vn gouuernement | Aristocratique, par le souuerain Pasteur des ames | nostre Seigneur Iesus Christi. |

A Caen, | Iouxte la copie Imprimee à Paris. | M.DC.XII. | 16.6 x 10.2 cm. 95 p.
Cf.Cambr.Univ.Cat.3083

RICHER, Edmund. A | Treatise | of Ecclesiasticall and | Politike povver. | Shewing, | The Church is a Monarchicall go- | uernment, ordained to a supernaturall and spiri- | tuall end, tempered with an aristocraticall or- | der, (which is the best of all and most | conformable to nature) by the great | Pastor of soules Iesus | Christ. | Faithfully translated out of the Latin originall, of late pu- | blikely printed and allowed in Paris. | Now set foorth for a further warrant | and encouragement to the Romish Catholikes of En- | gland, for theyr taking of the Oath of Allegiance; seeing so | many others of their owne profession in other Coun- | tries doe deny the Popes infalibility in iudge- | ment and temporall power ouer Prin- | ces, directly against the do- | ctrine of Iesuits. | To the Prince. |

Printed by VV.S. and are to be sold by Iohn Budge, at the great | South doore of Paules, and at Britaines Bursse. | 1612. | Line border. 18.6x14.5cm. (28,33)p.
Cambr.Univ.Cat:3083.

ROLLENSON, Francis. Twelve | Prophetical | Legacies. | Or | Twelve Sermons Vpon Iacobs Last | Will and Testament, Recorded by Moses, in the | 49. Chapt. of Genesis: containing his Be- | quests and Blessings, bestowed vpon | his twelue Sonnes. | . . . (12 names arranged in four sets of three, bracket before each set) Preached | by Francis Rollenson, Bach: of Diuinitie, | and sometimes Fellow of S. Iohn | the Euang: Colledge in | Cambridge. | (ornament)

London. | Imprinted by T.C. for Arthur Iohnson, | dwelling at the signe of the white horse, | by the great North doore of Paules. | 1612. | 17.6x13. cm. (6), 287 pp.

RUYTINCK, Simeon. Gvlden Legende | vande Roomsche Kercke: | Mitsgaders | Hare Heylighdommen, | Ende | Aflaten, | Aenden | Toetsteen der Waerheyd | beproeft. | Door | Symeon Ruytinck, Dienaer des | H. Euangeliums. | . . . (3 lines ; ornament).

Tot Londen, | By Thomas Snodham. 1612. | Line border. 17.8 x 13.9 cm. (40),225,(5),62,(1) p.

SHELDON, Richard. The First | Sermon | Of R. Sheldon Priest, | after his Conuersion from the | Romish Church: Preached before an ho- | nourable Assembly at S. Martins | in the Field, vpon Passion | Sunday, &c. | . . . (4 lines). Published by Authoritie. | (ornament)

London. | Printed by I. B. for Nathanael | Bvtter. 1612. | Head-piece. 18.7x12.7 cm. (4),67p.

SHELDON, Richard. The | Motives | of Richard Sheldon Pr. for his | iust, voluntary, and free renoun- | cing of Communion with the Bi- | shop of Rome, Pavl the 5. | and his Church. | . . . (6 lines) Published by Authority. | (device)

London printed for Nathaniel Bvtter, | and are to be sold at his shop neere S. Austines | gate. 1612. | 18.7x12.7 cm. (32),160,55p.
Two parts, with separate pagination and register; lacks A1 of second part.

SMITH, Henry. Six | Sermons | Preached by Maister | Henry Smith. | 1 2 of Ionahs punish- | ment. | 3 The Trumpet of the | Soule. | 4 The sinfull mans search | 5 Maries choyce. | 6 Noahs drunkennesse. | Two zealous Prayers. | And published by a more | perfect Copie then heretofore. |

London | Printed by T. D. for Nicholas | Bourne, and are to be sould | at his Shop at the Royall | Exchange. 1612. | Border. 18.5x14.2 cm. (1,44; 1, 74) p.
Sub-title after p.34: Fovre | Sermons | Preached by Maister | Henry Smith. | The remainder of page identical with that above.

TAYLOR, Thomas. A | Commentarie | Vpon The Epistle | of S. Paul written to | Titvs. | Preached in Cambridge by Thomas | Taylor, and now published for the further | vse of the Church of God. | With three short Tables in the end for the easier finding | of 1.Doctrines, 2.Obseruations, 3.Questions | contained in the same. | . . . (3 lines: device).

Printed by Cantrell Legge, | Printer to the Vniversitie of Cambridge. | 1612. | Line border. 20.8x15.8cm. (14),751,(12)p. Folded plate.
From the library of Walter W. Law.

TAYLOR, Thomas. Iaphets First | Pvbliqve Perswasion | into Sems tents: | Or | Peters Sermon, | Which Was The First Ge- | nerall calling of the Gentiles, preached | before Cornelius. | Expounded in Cambridge by Thomas | Taylor, and now published for the | further vse of the Church of God. | (device)

Printed By Cantrell Legge | Printer to the Vniuersitie of | Cambridge. 1612. | And are to be sold by Raph Mab at the signe | of the Angel in Pauls Churchyard. | Line border. 18.3x14.3 cm. (8),366 p.

TRAVERS, Walter. A | Svpplicati- | on Made To The | Privy Covnsel | By | Mr Walter Travers. | (device).

At Oxford, | Printed by Ioseph Barnes, and are to be | sold by John Barnes dwelling neere | Holborne Conduit. 1612. | 20.5x15.4 cm. (1),25p.

WARMINGTON, William. A Moderate | Defence Of The | Oath Of Allegiance: | Wherein the Author proueth the | said Oath to be most lawful, notwithstanding | the Popes Breues prohibiting the same; and solueth the | chiefest obiections that are vsually made against it; perswading | the Catholickes not to resist soueraigne Authoritie | in refusing it. | Together with the Oration of Sixtus 5. in the Consistory | at Rome, vpon the murther of Henrie 3. the | French King by a Friar. | Whereunto also is annexed strange Reports or | newes from Rome. | By

William Warmington Catholicke Priest, | and Oblate of the holy congregation of S.Ambrose. | . . . (4 lines ; device).
Permissu Superiorum. | An. Dom. 1612. | 18.3x13.9cm. (12),170p.

WEBBE, George. The | Pathway | To Honor. | Declaring the honora- | ble estate of those that feare | the Lord. | And the vile and damnable estate of | those that are contemners of | the Word. | Preached at Paules Crosse, Ivne 21. | Anno Domini | 1612. | By George Webbe Master of | Arts, and Preacher of Gods word | at Steeple Ashton in | Wiltshire. |
Imprinted by W.S. for Ralphe Mabbe, | and are to be sold at his shop in | Paules Church-yard, at the | signe of the Angell. | 1612. | Line border. 13.5x9.cm. (8),122p.

WHITE, John. The VVay | To The Trve | Chvrch: | wherein | The principall Motiues perswa- | ding to Romanisme, | and | Questions touching the nature and authority | of the Church and Scriptures, are familiarly dispu- | ted, and driuen to their issues, where, this day they | sticke betweene the Papists and vs: | Contriued into an Answer to a Popish Discourse, concerning the | Rule of Faith, and the marks of the Church. And published to | admonish such as decline to Papistrie, of the weake and vncer- | taine grounds, whereupon they haue ventured their soules. | Directed to all that seeke for resolution: and especially | to his louing countrimen of Lancashire. | The third impression corrected and augmented. | By Iohn White Minister of Gods word at Eccles. | . . . (2 lines; ornament).
London, | Printed for Iohn Bill and Wil- | liam Barret. | 1612. | 18.3x12.8 cm. (60),456,(10) p.
First edition, 1610. Reprinted 1616, and in Works: 1624.

WILLET, Andrew. A | Treatise | Of Salomons | Mariage, | Or, | A Congratvlation For | The Happie And Hopefvll Mariage | betweene the most illustrious and Noble Prince Fre- | derike the V. Count Palatine of Rhine, Elector of the Sacred | Romane Empire, and Arch-Sewer, and in the vacancie | thereof Vicar Generall: Duke of Bauaria, &c. | Knight of the most noble order | of the Garter. | And The Most Gratiovs And Ex- | cellent Princesse, the Ladie Elizabeth, sole daughter vnto | the High and Mighty Prince Iames, by the grace of God, | King of Great Britaine, France and Ireland. Ioyfully | solemnized vpon the 14. day of Februarie, | 1612. In the Kings Pallace of White- | hall in Westminster. | . . . (2 lines; device).
At London | Imprinted by F.K. for Thomas Man the elder, and William | Welby, and are to be sold at the Swanne in | Pauls Church-yard, 1612. | 17.1x13.8 cm. (14),56p.

WRIGHT, Samuel. Divers | Godly And | Learned Sermons Of A | Reverend And Faithfvll Ser- | uant of God. Mr. Samvel Wright, Bachelor of Diuinitie, late President of Sidney | Colledge in Cambridge, deceased: ten- | ding to the same ends with the for- | mer, verie profitable and fit for | these times. | . . . (3 lines; device).
At London, | Imprinted by Felix Kyngston, for Thomas Man. | 1612. | 17.2x12.8 cm. (4),300p. Lacks p.5–16.

WYCLIFFE, John. Wickliffes Wicket, | Or | A Learned And | Godly Treatise Of | The Sacrament, | Made by | John Wickliffe. | Set forth according to an ancient | Printed Copie. | (3 stars; device).

At Oxford, | Printed by Joseph Barnes, and are to be sold by John | Barnes, dwelling neere Holborne | Conduit. 1612. | 17. x 12.4 cm. (8),18 p.

1613

ABBOT, George. An | Exposition | Vpon The Pro- | phet Ionah: | Contained in certaine Sermons, preached | in S.Maries Church in Oxford: | By George Abbot Professor of Diuinitie, | and Maister of Vniuersitie Colledge. | . . . (2 lines: device).

London, | Imprinted by Richard Field, | 1613. | 19.1x14.1cm. (6),612,(2)p.

ABBOT, Robert. Antilogia | Adversvs Apolo- | giam Andreæ Evdæ- | mon-Ioannis Iesvitæ Pro | Henrico Garneto Iesuita Proditore. | Qua mendacissimi Monachi aduersus Eccle- | siam & remp. Anglicanam violatæ religionis & iusti- | tiæ nomine calumniæ refutantur; & Iesuitarum, Garneti | verò maximè, Proditoria consilia & coniurationes | exploratissima veritate referuntur. | Authore Rob. Abbotto sacræ Theologiæ in Aca- | demia Oxoniensi Professore Regio. | . . . (2 lines; device)

Londini, | Ex officina Thomæ Adams. | 1613. | 21.5x15.5cm. (9),201fol.

ADAMS, Thomas. Heaven | and Earth | Reconciled. | A Sermon preached at Saint Paules | Church in Bedford, October.3.1612. | At the visitation of the right | Wor.M.Eland, Arch- | deacon of Bedford. | By | Tho.Adams Minister of the | Gospell at Willington. | . . .(5 lines).

London, | Printed by W.W. for Clement Knight, and are | to be sold at his Shop in Paules Church- | yard at the signe of the holy | Lambe. 1613. | Lace border. 18.2x13.5cm. (4),23,(1)p.

ADAMS, Thomas. The | VVhite Devil, | Or | The Hypocrite | Vncased: | In A Sermon | Preached at Pavls | Crosse, March 7. | 1612. | By | Thomas Adams Minister of | the Gospell at Willington, in | Bedford-shire. | . . . (3 lines). The second edition. |

London, | Printed by Thomas Snodham for Ralph Mab, | and are to be sold in Pauls-Church-yard, | at the signe of the Angell. | 1613. | Line border. 18x14.1cm. (8),62p.

BAKER, John. Lectvres | Vpon | The twelue Articles of | our Christian Faith: | Written | For the comfort of the Godly, and | instruction of the Simple, | By Iohn Baker. | Whereunto is annexed a cleare Con- | fession of our Christian Faith, contained | in an hundred Articles, according to | the order of the Creed of | the Apostles. | By Iohn Hooper, Martyr; and some- | times Bishop of Glocester. |

London, | Printed by Nicholas Okes, by the Assignment | of Robert Barker, Printer to the Kings | Maiesty, 1613. | Line border. 14.8x9cm (16),605p.

BECANUS, Martinus. Controversia | Anglicana | De | Potestate | Pontificis Et | Regis; | Recognita Et Avcta. | Contra Lancellottum,

Sacellanum Regis Angliæ, | qui se Episcopum Eliensem vocat, Vbi etiam | defenditur Illustrissimus Cardinalis | Belarmanis,&c. | Avtore | R. P. Martino Becano | Societatis Iesu Theologo & Profes- | sore Ordinario. | (device).

Mogvntiæ, | Apud Ioannem Albinum, Anno 1613. | 16. x 10. cm. 272p.

BENEFIELD, Sebastian. A | Commentarie | Or | Exposition Vpon The First | Chapter of the Prophecy of Amos, delivered | in xxi. Sermons in the Parish Church of | Meisey Hampton in the Di- | ocesse of Gloucester, | By | Sebastian Benefield Doctor | of Divinity and fellow of Corpus Christi | College in Oxford. | Herevnto Is Added A Sermon | upon I. Cor. 9. 19. wherein is touched the law- | full vse of things indifferent. | . . . (2 lines; ornament)

Printed at Oxford by Ioseph Barnes, and are to be | sold by Iohn Barnes dwelling neere Hol- | borne Conduit. 1613. | 17.5x13.7cm. (7),280,(7)pp. Subtitle at p. 265; continuous register.

BENEFIELD, Sebastian. A | Sermon | Preached At Wotton | Vnder Edge in the Diocesse of | Gloucester before the Clergy there assem- | bled at the Episcopall Visitation of | Thomas Ravis, late Bishop | of Gloucester. 1605. | By | Sebastian Benefield. | . . . (2 lines; lace ornament)

Printed at Oxford by Ioseph Barnes. 1613. | 18x13.8cm. 17.5x13.7cm Pp. 265-280 of Commentaie . . vpon . . Amos i: 1613. With continuous register and pagination

BENEFIELD, Sebastian. A | Sermon | Preached In St. | Maries Church in Oxford, | March xxiv, MDCXII. at the so- | lemnizing of the happy inaugu- | ration of our gracious Soue- | raigne King James. | Wherein is prooued, that Kinges | doe hold their Kingdomes im- | mediately from God. | By | Sebastian Benefield D. of | Diuinitie, Fellow of Corpus | Christi College. |

At Oxford | Printed by Ioseph Barnes, and are to be | sold by Iohn Barnes dwelling neere | Holborne Conduit. 1613. | Border. 17.4x13.2 cm. (4),18p.

BOYS, John. An | Exposition | Of The Festivall | Epistles And Gos- | pels, vsed in our English | Liturgie. | Together With A Reason Why The Chvrch | did chuse the same. | By Iohn Boys, Doctor | of Diuinitie. | The first part from the Feast of S.Andrew the | Apostle to the purification of blessed | Mary the Virgin. | . . . (2 lines; ornament).

At London | Imprinted by Felix Kyngston, for | VVilliam Aspley. 1613. | Line border. 18.4x14.3cm. (4),156; (4),159,(1);(1),147;(1)26,(14)p.

Parts II and III, dated 1614 and 1615.

BROUGHTON, Hugh. A | Seder Olam, | that is: | Order of the VVorld, | or yeares from the Fall to the | Restoring, | A seconde Apologie for the Angell Gabriels pro- | prietie of truth, in his holy and healthy message, of | the cleernes & certainty for our Redempton: | and a further answere to some, litle think- | ing that all humane Libraries may by | them selues, and must by Scrip- | ture be controld: |

With a long Preface touching the humanitie of | the Gentry of Cambridge, and higher, in | fauour of ancient Learning. | . . . (3 lines).

Imprinted at Lodon by W.White, | dwelling in Cow-lane. | 1613. | Lace border. 17.2x13.3cm. (10),29p.
Epistle signed.

BUCER, Martin. Constans | Defensio, | Ex S.Scriptvra, Et | Vera Catholica Doctri- | na, Atqve Observatione | Vniuersalis Christianæ Ecclesiæ Deli- | berationis de Christiana | Reformatione, | Quam Reuerendissimus in Deo Pater, Princeps & Dominus D. | Hermannvs Archiepiscopus Coloniensis, & Princeps Elector, &c. | iam antè publicauit: Cum firmissima confutatione eorum omnium | quæ Clementiæ eius aduersarij, sub titulo Antididagmatis, & sub | nomine Capituli Coloniensis, contra eandem Clementiæ suæ Deli- | berationem produxerunt, & in lucem emiserunt. | Auctore D.Martino Bvcero. | . . . (4 lines). Nunc primò è manuscripto Buceri in lucem editus. | (device)

Genevæ, | Sumptibus Ian Ant. Saraceni, & Alexandri Pernet. | M.DC.XIII. | 22.7 x 15.8 cm. (16),483 p.

CARLETON, George. Consensvs | Ecclesiæ | Catholicæ | Contra Tri- | dentinos. | Demonstrans Vnam Ac Per- | petuam doctrinam è sacris Scripturis excerptam, | & in Ecclesia Catholica conseruatam vsque ad | Concilium Tridentinum, in grauissimis fidei | controuersiis, quæ sunt | De { Scripturis, siue regula fidei. | Ecclesia. | Fide iustificante. | Gratia. | Opvs | Prælectionibvs Oxoniensibvs | inchoatum, deinde auctum, & in publi- | cum editum. | Auctore | Georgio Carletano, Anglo. | . . . (4 lines).

Prostat | Francofvrti, | apud Rulandios. | Anno M.DC XIII. | 16.1x10.cm. (22), 455p.

DOWNAME, John. Consola- | tions For The | Afflicted: | Or, | The Third Part Of The | Christian Warfare: wherein is shewed, | how the Christian may be armed and strengthened against | the tentations of the World on the left hand, arising from | trouble and affliction; and inabled to beare all crosses and | miseries with patience, comfort and | thanksgiuing. | By I. Dovvname, Batchelar in Diuinitie, | and Preacher of Gods word. | . . . (5 lines: device)

At London | Printed by Iohn Beale, for W.Welby, and | are to be sold at his shop in Pauls Churchyard at the | signe of the Swan. 1613. | 17.4x13.cm. (35), 717pp.

DRAXE, Thomas. The | Earnest | Of Ovr Inhe- | ritance: | Together With A De- | scription Of The New Heaven | and of the New earth, and a demonstration of | the glorious Resurrection of the bodie in | the same substance. | Preached at Pauls Crosse the second | day of August. 1612. | By Thomas Draxe Bachelour of Diuinity. | (device).

At London, | Imprinted by F. K. for George Norton. 1613. | Line border. 17.4x 13.5 cm. (7),60p.

FITZHERBERT, Thomas. An | Adioynder | To The | Svpplement | Of | Father Robert Persons | His Discvssion | of M.Doctor Barlowes

Ansvvere &c. | Contayning | A Discouery, and Confutation of very many foule Absur- | dityes, Falsities, and Lyes in M.D.Andrewes his La- | tin Booke intituled, Responsio ad Apologiam Car- | dinalis Bellarmini &c. An Answere to the A- | pology of Card.Bellarmine. | Written | By F.T.Authour of the Supplement, to iustify certaine places, and autho- | rities alleaged, as well by him in the said Supplement, as by | the Cardinall in his Apology, and pretended to be | answered by M.D.Andrewes. | Also | an Appendix touching a Register alleaged by M.Franc.Mason for the | lawfull Ordayning of Protestant Bishops in Q.Elizabeths Raigne. | . . . (2 lines).
 Imprinted with Licence, M.DC.XIII. | 18.1x13.7cm. (8),495,(6)p.
 Separate register and pagination. Cambr. Univ. Cat. 6529. Cf. Gillow.II:287.

FITZHERBERT, Thomas. A | Svpplement | To The | Discvssion | Of M.D.Barlowes | Ansvvere | To the Iudgment of a Catholike Englishman &c. | interrupted by the death of the Author F. | Robert Persons of | the Society of Iesvs. | Wherein | Many foule Absurdities, Ignorances, and Falsities are | discouered in M.D.Barlow. | And | By the way is briefly censured M.Iohn Dunnes Booke, | intituled Psevdo-Martyr. | Also | An Adioynder, contayning a Confutation of certaine Absurdities, | Falsities, and Follies vttered by M.D.Andrewes in his Answere | to Cardinall Bellarmines Apology, concerning certaine points | incident to matters treated in this Supplement. Togeather with | the Censure of the whole Worke. | By F.T. | . . . (3 lines).
 Permissu Superiorum. M.DC.XIII. | 18.5x13.5cm. (8),400,(6)p.
 Gillow. II: 287. Cambr. Univ. Cat. 6528.

FORBES, Patrick. An | Exqvisite | Commentarie | Vpon The Reve- | lation Of Saint | Iohn. | VVherein, Both The | course of the whole Booke, as also | the more abstruse and hard places thereof not | heretofore opened; are now at last most | cleerely and euidently | explaned. | By Patrik Forbes of Corse. | . . . (3 lines; device)
 London | Printed by W.Hall, for Francis Burton, and are to bee | sold at his shop in Pauls Churchyeard, at the | signe of the Greene Dragon. | 1613. | 17.6 x 12.4 cm. (28),5–269,(17) p.

GREENWOOD, Henry. The Race | Celestiall. | By Henry Greene- | vvood, Maister of Arts, | and Preacher of the | Word of God. | The second Impression, corrected | and inlarged by the Authour. | . . . (2 lines; ornament).
 London, | Printed by N. O. for Henry Bell, and | are to be sold at his shop within | Bishops-gate. 1613. | Lace border. 13.1x8.7cm. (5),81,(9) p.

GREENWOOD, Henry. A | Treatise, | of the great and Generall | day of Iudgement. | Necessary for euery Christian, that | wisheth good successe to his soule, | at that great and terrible day. | By Henry Greenvvood, Maister of | Arts, and Preacher of the word of God. | The fifth Impression, Corrected and A- | mended, by the Author. | Whereunto is added a Comfortable | Exposition of the Lords Prayer, | by the same Authour. | . . . (4 lines).

London, | Printed by Nicholas Okes, for Henry Bell, | and are to bee sold at his Shop, within | Bishops-gate. 1613. | 13.5x8.4cm. (6),103p. Impf: lacks Pp. 27–42, 59–74.

HAKEWILL, George. The | Avncient | Ecclesiasticall Practise | Of | Confirmation. | Confirmed by Arguments drawne from | Scripture, Reason, Councels, Fathers, | and later Writers. | VVritten, | Vpon occasion of the Confirmation of the Prince | his Highnesse, performed on Munday in Easter-weeke, | 1613. in the Chappell at White-hall, by the right Re- | uerend Father in God, the Bishop of Bath and | Wels, Deane of his Maiesties | Chappell. | By | George Hakevvill, Doctor of Diuinitie, his | Highnesse Chaplaine in ordinarie. | Published by Authoritie. |

London: | Printed by Thomas Snodham, for Mathew Lownes, | and are to be solde at his Shop, at the Signe of the | Bishops-head in Pauls Church-yard. | 1613. | 19.5x15.4cm. (4),27p.

HIERON, Samuel. The Life And | Death Of | Dorcas. | VVherein, Hee | That Pleaseth To | reade, may finde both good | direction for the or- | dering of his | Course: | And | A Necessary | warning to be prepared | for his End. | By Samvel Hieron. | . . . (2 lines).

London, | Printed by Melch. Bradwood | for Samvel Macham, and are | to be sould at his shop in Pauls Church- | yard at the signe of the | Bull-head. | 1613. | Line border. 17.6x13.8cm. (5),21p.

HOOPER, John. A | Briefe | And | Cleare Confession of | the Christian Faith, con- | taining an hundred Articles, | according to the order of | the Creed of the Apostles. | Written, | By that Learned and Godly Mar- | tyr, Iohn Hooper, some- | times Bishop of Glocester | in his life time. |

London, | Printed by Nicholas Okes, by the | Assignement of Robert Barker, | Printer the Kings most | excellent Maiesty. | 1613. | Line border. 13.2x8.6 cm. p. 497–606. 606 blank. Sigs. Kk to Qg7.
Part of J: Baker's Lectvres: 1613.

HUTTON, Matthew. Brevis & dilucida explicatio, ve- | ræ, certæ, & consolationis plenæ | doctrinæ, | De | Electione, Præ- | destinatione Ac Re- | probatione, | Authore | Matthæo, Eboracensi Archie- | piscopo, Theologo Eximio. | Cui accesserunt & aliorum Clariss.Theologorum in- | clytæ Cantabrigiensis Academiæ,D D.Estaei, | Somi, Chatertoni, Et VVilleti, | Eiusdem argumenti scripta. | Nec non Lambethani Articuli, seu assertiones | Orthodoxæ, cum Anglicana confessio- | ne, & Patrum, maximè Augusti- | ni, sententia collatæ. | . . . (4 lines; ornament).

Hardrovici, Ex Typographéo Thoma Henrici, | Impensis Henrici Lavrentii Amstero- | damensis Librarii. | An.M.DC.XIII. | 16.9x10.8cm (48),256p.

JACOB, Henry. An Attestation | of many Learned, Godly, | and famous Divines, Lightes of | Religion, and pillars of the Gospell, | iustifying this doctrine, viz. | That the Church-governement ought to bee | always with the peoples free consent. | Also this; | That a true

Church vnder the Gospell contay- | neth no more ordinary Congregations but | one. | In the discourse whereof, specially Doctor | Downames & also D. Bilsons chiefe mat- | ters in their writings against | the same, are answered. | . . . (5 lines).

Anno Dom. 1613. | 13.7x9 cm. 323,(10) p.
Epistle Dedicatorie, signed.

KILBY, Richard. The | Bvrthen Of | a loaden conscience: | Or | The Miserie Of | Sinne: | Set forth by the confes- | sion of a miserable | sinner. | (device).

Printed by Cantrell Legge | Printer to the Vniversitie | of Cambridge. 1613. | And are to be sold by Matthevv Lavv in | Pauls Churchyard at the signe of | the Foxe. | 13.6x8.4cm. (1),98p. Imperfect: Lacks pp. 11–12, 25–6, 43–4, 57–8.
Cf. Cambr.Univ.Cat:5671.

LEIGH, William. The | Dampe Of | Death: Beaten | backe with the glorious light | and life of Iesus Christ. | In a Sermon Preached at Lan- | caster Assises in Lent last, to the con- | demned Prisoners there, and before | the Honourable Iudges, and | Worshipfull of that | Countie. | By William Leigh, Bachelor in Diui- | nitie, and Pastor at Standish. | . . . (3 lines).

London | Printed by Tho: Creede, for Arthur | Iohnson, dwelling in Pauls Church- | yard at the signe of the white | Horse. 1613. | 13.5x9. cm. (7),53 p.

MASON, Francis. Of | The Conse- | cration Of The | Bishops In The Chvrch | Of England: | With their Succession, Jurisdiction, and other | things incident to their calling: | As Also | Of The Ordination | of Priests and Deacons. | Five Bookes: | Wherein they are cleared from the slanders and odious | imputations of Bellarmine, Sanders, Bristow, | Harding, Allen, Stapleton, Parsons, | Kellison, Evdemon, Becanvs, | And other Romanists: | And iustified to containe nothing contrary to the Scriptures, | Councels, Fathers, or approued examples of Primi- | tiue Antiquitie. | By Francis Mason, Batchelour of Diuinitie, and sometimes | Fellow of Merton Colledge in Oxeford. | . . . (2 lines; ornament).

Imprinted at London | by Robert Barker, Printer to the Kings | most Excellent Maiestie. Anno 1613. | 29.3x18.5 cm. (10),269,(1) p.

MAXWELL, James. A Monvment | of Remembrance, | Erected In Albion, In | Honor Of The Magnificent | Departvre From Britannie, | and honorable receiuing in Germany, | namely at Heidelberge, of the | two most Noble Princes | Fredericke, | First Prince of the Im- | periall bloud, sprung | from glorious Char- | lemaigne, Count Pala- | tine of Rhine, Duke of | Bauier, Elector and | Arch-sewer of the ho- | ly Romane Empire, | and Knight of the Re- | nowned order of the | Garter. } (device) & { Elizabeth | Infanta of Al- | bion, Princesse Pa- | latine, and Dut- | chesse of Bavier, | the onely Daughter | of our most gratious | and Soueraigne Lord | Charles-Iames, | and of his most Noble | and vertuous Wife, | Queene Anne. | Both of them being almost in one and the same degree of lineall descent | from 25 Emperours of the East and West, of Romanes, Greekes, and | Germans, and from 30 Kings of diuers countries. | By Iames Maxvvel. |

London, | Printed by Nicholas Okes, for Henry Bell, and are to be sold | at his shop within Bishops-gate. 1613. | Border. 18x14cm. (15,40)p.

N., R. The | Christians | Manna. | Or | A Treatise | Of the most Blessed and Reuerend Sacrament | of the Evcharist. | Deuided into tvvo Tracts. | Written by a Catholike Deuine, through occasion of Monsieur | Casaubon his Epistle to Cardinal Peron, expressing therin | the Graue and Approued Iudgment of the Kings | Maiesty, touching the doctrine of the Reall | Presence in the Evcharist. | . . . (5 lines)

Imprinted with Licence, Anno 1613. | 16.9x12.8 cm. (32),244p. Epistle dedicatory, signed R.N.

NICCOLS, Richard. A | Day-Starre | For | Darke-wandring Soules: | Shewing the Light, by a | Christian Controuersie: | Or | Briefely and plainely setting forth | the Mysterie of our Salvation. | Divided Into | Principles, Obiections, and Answeres. | By | Richard Niccolls, th' elder, of the | Inner Temple London, Gent. deceased, | Pvblished | For the generall benefit of all those who | heartily, and with a true Faith, desire | their ovvne Saluation: by I.C. |

London: | Printed for Iohn Budge, and are to be solde at | the great South-doore of Paules. 1613. | Line border. 13.x9 cm. (12),83 p.

PRICE, Daniel. Spiritvall | Odovrs To The | Memory Of Prince | Henry | In Fovre Of The Last Ser- | mons preached in St James after his High- | nesse death, the last being the Sermon be- | fore the body, the day before | the Funerall. | By | Daniel Price then Chaplaine in Attendance. | . . . (3 lines; device).

At Oxford | Printed by Ioseph Barnes and are to be sold by Iohn Barnes | dwelling neere Holborne Conduit. 1613. | Line border. 18x14cm. (3),52p.

PURCHAS, Samuel. Pvrchas his Pilgrimage. | Or | Relations | Of The World | And The Religions | Observed In All Ages | And places discouered, from the | Creation vnto this | Present. | In foure Partes. | This First Contai- | neth A Theologicall And | Geographicall Historie of Asia, Africa, | and America, with the Ilands | Adiacent. | Declaring the Ancient Religions before the Flovd, the | Heathnish, Jewish, and Saracenicall in all Ages since, in those | parts professed, with their seuerall Opinions, Idols, Oracles, Temples, | Priestes, Fasts, Feasts, Sacrifices, and Rites Religious: Their | beginnings, Proceedings, Alter-ations, Sects, | Orders and Successions. | With briefe Descriptions of the Countries, Nations, States, Discoueries, | Priuate and Publike Cus-tomes, and the most Remarkable Rarities of | Nature, or Humane Industrie, in the same. | By Samvel Pvrchas, Minister at Estwood in Essex. | . . . (1 line).

London, | Printed by William Stansby for Henrie Fetherstone, and are to be | sold at his Shoppe in Pauls Church-yard at the | Signe of the Rose. 1613. | Line border. 28.4x18.8cm. (28), 752,(20)p.

RAINOLDS, John. The | Prophecie | Of Obadiah | Opened And Applyed In | Svndry Learned And Gra- | ciovs Sermons Preached | at All-Hallowes and St | Maries in Oxford, | By | That Famovs And Ivdici- | ous Divine Iohn Rainolds D. | of Divinity and late President of | Corp.Chr. Coll. | Published for the honour and vse of that famous Vni- | versity, and for the benefit of the Churches of | Christ abroad in the Country, | By W.H. | . . . (device).

At Oxford, | Printed by Joseph Barnes. 1613. | Line border. 17.2x13.2cm. (8), 136; (4),20p.

RAINOLDS, John. A | Sermon | Vpon Part Of The | eighteenth Psalme. | Preached To The Pvblike | assembly of Scholers in the Vniversity of | Oxford the last day of August, 1586. | By | John Rainolds: | Vpon occasion of their meeting to giue thankes to God | for the detection and apprehension of Trai- | tours, who wickedly conspired against | the Queenes Maiestie and | the state of the Realme. | . . . (4 lines; ornament).

Printed at Oxford by Ioseph Barnes. 1613. | Line border. 18.4x13.8cm. (4), 20p.

Appendix to his Prophecie Of Obadiah: 1613, with separate pagination but continuous register.

REUTER, Adam. Libertatis | Anglicanae | Defensio, | Sev | Demonstratio: | Regnum Angliæ non | esse feudum Pontificis: | In Nobilissima & Antiquissima Oxoniensi | Academia, publicè opposita | Martino Becano Societatis Iesu Theologo | & Professori ordinario | Ab Adamo Revter. Cotb.L. | (device).

Londini | Excudebat Iohannes Beale, 1613. | 18x13.7cm. (4),32p.

ROBARTES, Foulk. The | Revenve Of | The Gospel Is | Tythes, | Due to the Ministerie of the word, | by that word. | Written by Fovlke Robartes Batchelour | of Diuinitie. | (device); . . . (6 lines , double column).

Printed by Cantrel Legge | Printer to the Vniuersitie of Cambridge. | 1613. | 17.5x13.4cm. (8),142,(1)p.

SAINT-GERMAIN, Christopher. The | Dialogve | in English, betweene | a Doctor of Diuinitie, | and a Student in the | Lawes of Eng- | land. | Newly corrected and | Imprinted, with new | Additions. |

London | Printed for the Com- | pany of Stationers. | 1613. | Cum Priuilegio. | Lace border. 14.1x8.9cm. (1),176,(4)fol. Impf. at end.

Anon. Cambr.Univ.Cat.No.3257.

SALKELD, John. A | Treatise | Of | Angels. | Of The Natvre, | Essence, Place, Power, Sci- | ence, VVill, Apparitions, Grace, | Sinne, and all other Proprie- | ties of Angels. | Collected Ovt Of | the holy Scriptures, ancient Fathers, | and Schoole-Diuines. | By Iohn Salkeld, lately Fellow of the | Iesuites Colledges in the Vniuersities | of Conimbra, Corduba, and | Complutum. | Assistant in studies to the famous Iesuites, | Franciscvs Svarivs, and | Michael Vasqvez. |

London: | Printed by T.S. with authoritie of Superiours, | for Nathaniel Butter. 1613. | Line border. 15.9x10.4 cm. (24),365,(1)p.

SIMSON, Patrick. A Short | Compend | Of The Historie | Of The First Ten | Persecvtions Mo- | ved Against Christi- | ans, Divided Into | III. Centvries. | Wherevnto Are Ad- | ded in the end of euery Centurie treatises a- | rising vpon occasion offered in the historie, clearely | declaring the noveltie of Popish Religion, and that it | neither flowed from the mouthes of Christs holy A- | postles, neither was it confirmed by the blood of the holy | Martyrs who died in these ten persecutions. | . . . (7 lines; crown-device)

Edinbvrgh, | Printed by Andro Hart, and are to be solde at his shop on | the North side of the high streete a little beneath the Crosse, | Anno Dom. 1613. | 18.9x14.3cm.   (12),231,(1)p.

Faultes escaped, pasted on Q2 *verso*.
Also another copy with IV–IX Centuries appended; published in 1615 and 1616; with separate registers and pagination.
Epistle dedicatorie, signed P.Symson.

SMITH, Henry. Three | Sermons | Made By Mr. | Henrie Smith. | I. The Benefit of Contentation. | II. The Affinitie of the Faithfull. | III. The lost Sheepe is found. | . . . (device).

London, | Printed for Iohn Smethwick, and are to be sold at | his shop in S. Dunstanes Church-yard. | 1613. | 17.5x13.1cm.56p.

Bound up with his Sermons: 1614; with separate pagination and register.

SPELMAN, Henry. De non temerandis Ecclesijs. | A Tract | Of the Rights and Respect | due vnto Chvrches. | Written to a Gentleman, who hauing an Appro- | priat Parsonage, imploied the Church to prophane | vses, and left the Parishioners vncertainly proui- | ded of diuine seruice, in a Parish neere | there adioyning. | By Sr.Henry Spelman Knight. | (device).

At London | Printed by Iohn Beale. 1613. | Line border. 14.2x9.cm.   (7),111p.

SUTTON, Thomas. Englands | Svmmons. | A Sermon preached at Pauls | Crosse the third of | Ianuary, 1612. | By Thomas Sutton, Master of Arts | and fellow of Queenes Colledge | in Oxford. | . . . (5 lines).

London, | Printed by William Hall for Mathew | Law, and are to be sold at his Shop | in Pauls Church yarde at the signe | of the Foxe. 1613. | Line border. 14.9x9.6cm.   (13),128p.

USSHER, James. Gravissimae | Quæstionis, | De | Christianarvm | Ecclesiarvm, In | Occidentis præsertim partibus, | Ab | Apostolicis Temporibvs | ad nostram usq; ætatem, continuâ successione | & statu, Historica Explicatio. | Avthore | Jacobo Usserio, | S.æ Theologiæ in Dvbliniensi | Academiâ apud Hibernos, | Professore. | . . . (6 lines).

Londini | Excudebat Bonham Norton, | Serenissimæ Regiæ Maiestatis in Latinis, Græ- | cis & Hebraicis Typographus. | Ann. MDCXIII. | 18.1x13.8cm. (16),372p.

WILLIAMSON, Thomas. The | Sword | of the spirit to smite in | pieces that Antichristian | Goliah, | Who Daily Defieth | the Lords people the host | of Israel. | Drawen forth by Tho.Williamson, | Gentleman. | . . . (6 lines; ornament).

London | Printed by Edw.Griffin. | 1613. | 14.1x9.2cm.   (19),124p.

1614

ADAMS, Thomas. The | Diuells Banket. | Described in sixe Sermons. | {1.The Banket propounded; begunne. | 2.The second Seruice. | 3.The breaking vp of the Feast. | 4.The Shot or Reckoning. | 5.The Sinners Passing-Bell. | 6.Phisicke from Heauen.} Published by Thomas Adams, Preacher of | Gods Word at Willington in Bedfordshire. | . . . (12 lines).

London: | Printed by Thomas Snodham for Ralph Mab, and are to be | sold in Paules Churchyard, at the signe of the | Grayhound. 1614. | Line border. 18.2x 13.5cm. (8),341p.
Five sub. t.p. Continuous register and pagination

ATTERSOLL, William. The | Nevv Covenant, | Or | A Treatise of the Sacraments. | Whereby the last Testament of our Lord and | Sauiour Iesus Christ, through the shedding of | his Pure and Precious Blood, is ratified and applyed vn- | to the Conscience of euery true | Beleeuer. | Diuided into three Bookes }I. Of the Sacraments in Generall. | 2. Of Baptisme. | 3. Of the Lords Supper. | Verie Necessarie and Profitable for these | Times: wherein we may behold | The{ Truth it selfe plainly prooued, | Doctrine of the Reformed Churches clearely maintained, | Errors of the Church of Rome soundly conuinced, | Right maner of the Receiuing of thē comfortably declared | And sundry doubts and difficult Questions decided. | By William Attersoll, Minister of Gods word | at Isfield in Sussex. | . . . (3 lines). The second Edition, Newly Corrected | and Enlarged. |

Printed at London by W.Iaggard, and are to be solde by Ni- | cholas Bourne, at his Shop at the entrance of the Roy- | all Exchange, 1614. | 18.7x14cm. (29), 576,(6)p.

BAUGHE, Thomas. A | Svmmons | To Ivdgement. | Or | A Sermon Appointed | For The Crosse, Bvt Delive- | red vpon occasion in the Cathedrall Church of | S. Paul London: the 6. day of Iune, 1613. | beeing the first Sunday of Mid- | sommer Terme. | By Thomas Bavghe, student of Christ- | Church in Oxford. | . . . (3 lines).

London, | Printed by G.Eld, for William Iones, and are | to bee sold at his shop neere Holborne Conduit, | at the Signe of the Gunne. 1614. | Line border. 17.3x13. cm. (6),59p.

BENEFIELD, Sebastian. Eight Ser- | mons Pvblikely | Preached In The V- | niversity Of Oxford, | the second at St. Peters in the East, | the rest at St Maries Church. Be- | gunne in the yeare 1595. | Decemb. XIIII. | Now First Pvblished By Sebas- | tian Benefield Doctor, and Professour of | Divinity for the Lady Margaret. | . . . (3 lines; device)

At Oxford, | Printed by Ioseph Barnes. 1614. | 17.5x13.7cm. (4),153,(5)pp.

BOYS, John. An | Exposition | Of The Festivall | Epistles And Gos- | pels, vsed in our English | Liturgie. | Together With A Rea- | son Why The Chvrch | did chuse the same. | By Iohn Boys, Doctor | of

Diuinitie. | The second part from the Purification of bles- | sed Mary the Virgin, to the feast of | S.Iohn the Baptist. | . . . (4 lines; ornament).

At London | Imprinted for VVilliam Aspley. 1614. | Line border. 18.4x14.3cm. (4),159,(1)p.

BREREWOOD, Edward. Enqviries | Tovching | The Diversity | of Langvages, and | Religions through the | chiefe parts of the | world. | Written | By Edw.Brerewood | lately professor of Astronomy | in Gresham Colledge in | London. |

London | Printed for Iohn Bill. | 1614. | Arch. border. 18.6x14.2cm. (24),198p.

BUCKERIDGE, John. De | Potestate | Papæ In Rebvs | Temporalibvs, | Sive in Regibvs | Deponendis Vsvr- | pata; | Adversus Robertvm Cardinalem | Bellarminvm, | Libri Dvo. | In quibus respondetur Authoribus, Scripturis, | Rationibus, Exemplis, contra Gvlielmvm | Barclaivm allatis. | Necnon sex, vel verius quinque exemplis: quibus, morte præ- | ventus, non responderat G.B. | Authore Ioanne Episcopo Roffensi. | . . . (5 lines; ornament).

Londini, | Ex Officina Nortoniana apud Ioannem Billivm. | M.D.C.XIIII. | Cum Privilegio Regis. | 22.x16.4cm. (20),1113,(5)p. Misnumbered.

CAMDEN, William. Remaines, | concerning | Britaine: | But especially England, and the | Inhabitants thereof. | Their | Languages | Names | Surnames. | Allusions | Anagrammes | Armories | Monies | Empresses | Apparell | Artillarie | Wise Speeches | Proverbs | Poesies | Epitaphes. | Reviewed, corrected, and encreased. | (device)

Printed at London by Iohn Legatt for Simon | Waterson. 1614. | 17.7x13.2cm. (4),386pp.
Dedication signed N.M. See H&L. III: 2132 . T.p. supplied by Edward G. Friehold.

CHAMPNEY, Anthony. A Manval | Of Contro- | versies. | wherin the Catholique Romane faith in all | the cheefe pointes of controuersies of these | daies is proued by holy Scripture. | By A.C.S. | . . . (5 lines; ornament).

Printed at Paris by Peter Buray. | M.D.C.XIV. | 13.1x7.6cm. (4),166,5p.
Gillow:I:464.

CLEAVER, Robert. Bathshebaes | Instrvctions | to her Sonne Lemvel: | Containing a fruitfull and plaine | Exposition of the last Chapter of the | Proverbs. | Describing the duties of a Great-man, | And | The vertues of a Gracious Woman. | Penned by a godly and learned man, | now with God. | Perused, and published for the vse of Gods Church, | By { Iohn Dod, | And | Williæm Hinde. | (device).

Printed at London by Iohn Beale, for Roger Iackson, | and are to be sold at his shop neere the great | Cunduit in Fleet-streete. 1614. | Line border. 17.9x13.7 cm. (12),78p. Table lacks first leaf .
Cf. DNB. 15: 146a

CLEAVER, Robert. A | Plaine | And Familiar | Exposition Of The | First and Second Chapters | of the Prouerbes of | Salomon. | By Robert Clever. | . . . (5 lines; device)

London: | Printed by T.S. for Thomas Man. | 1614. | 17.7x13.7cm (2),155p. Lacks Sig. A.
T.p. supplied by Mr. Edward G. Friehold.

CROOKE, Samuel. A | Briefe Direc- | tion To Trve | Happinesse. | Abridged Ovt Of | the larger Treatise, for the more | conuenient vse of priuate Fa- | milies, and instruction of | the yonger sort. | By Sam. Crooke. | . . . (4 lines; ornament).

London | Printed by Edward Griffin, for Nathaniel | Butter, and are to be sold at his shop neere | S. Austins gate, at the signe of the | Pyed Bull. 1614. | Line border. 15.8x10 cm. (8),67p.

CROOKE, Samuel. The | Gvide Vnto | Trve Blessed- | nesse. | Or, | A Body Of The Do- | ctrine of the Scriptures, directing | man to the sauing know- | ledge of God. | Collected | By Sam. Crooke. | The second Edition. | . . . (5 lines).

London, | Printed by Edw. Griffin, for Nathaniel Butter, | and are to be sold at his shop neere S. Austins gate, at | the signe of the Pyde Bull. 1614. | Border. 15.8x10.cm. (45),244p.

DAY, John. Day's Dyall | Or, | His Twelve Howres | That Is, | Twelve Severall Lectvres | By Way Of Catechisme, As | they were delivered by him in the Chappel of | Oriell Colledge in Ox- | ford, in the yeeres of our Lord | God 1612, and 1613. | . . . (device; 5 lines).

At Oxford, | Printed by Ioseph Barnes, 1614. | 18.5x13.9cm. (8),329,(2)p.

A | FAITHFVLL | Admonition | Of The Paltsgraves | Churches, to all other | Protestant Churches in | Dutchland. | That They Wovld Consi- | der the great danger that hangeth ouer their | heads as well as ours by the Popedome, and | therefore Christianly and brotherly cease the | priuate vnnecessary and now too | much growne strife with vs. | Together With A Short Abstract | of the warning about the Iesuites bloodthirsty plots publi- | shed in print at Tubing. | Published by Authoritie. | According to the Originall Printed in the Electors Pals- | graues Country at Nustadt vpon the Hardt, | Englished by Iohn Rolte. |

Imprinted at London by Edward Griffin for George | Gibbes, and are to be sould at his shop in Poules- | church-yard at the signe of the | Flowerdeluce. 1614. | 18.2x14.cm. (8),31p.

FORBES, Patrick. A Defence | Of The Lawfvl | Calling Of The Ministers | Of Reformed Chvrches, Against | The Cavillations Of Romanists. | Whereto is subjoined, | An Epistle To A Recvsant, For | Clearing And Maintaining Some Points | of the former treatise of defence, challenged by | a Roman Elymas Bar-Iesus-it. | With A Short Discovery Of The Adversarie | his dottage in his impertinent and rediculously deceitfull demands. | By | Patrik Forbes, of Coirse. | . . . (3 lines: ornament).

Printed at Middelburgh, by Richard Schilders, dwelling in the | langen Delft, at the signe of the Olyphant. | Anno 1614. | 18.2x14.4cm.(6), 66; 30; 25p.

Appended to his Learned Commentarie: 1614, with separate register and pagination.

FORBES, Patrick. An | Learned | Commentarie | Vpon The Revelation | Of Saint Iohn, Wherein Both | The Covrse Of The Whole Booke, As Also | the more abstruse and hard places thereof, are more cleerly | and euidently explaned then heretofore they haue | bene. Newly corrected, and the defectes | and errors of the first Edition, sup- | plied & amended. | By Patrik Forbes of Cotharis | Wherevnto Is Added An Profitable | Treatise of the Author, in defence of the lawfull calling of the Ministers | of reformed Churches, against the cauillations of Romanistes: | And an Epistle to a Recusant, cleering and maintayning | some pointes of the said Treatise, chalenged by a | Roman Elymas Bar-Iesvs-it. | . . . (2 lines: ornament).

Printed at Middelburg, by Richard Schilders, dwelling in the | langen Delft at the signe of the Olyphant. | 1614. | 18.2x14.4cm.(28),256,(15); (6),66;30; 25p.

GIBSON, Thomas. The | Blessing | Of | A Good King. | Deliuered in Eight Sermons vp- | on the storie of the Queene of | the South, her words to Salomon, | magnifying the gouernment of | his familie and kingdome. | By | Thomas Gibson, Minister. | . . . (3 lines).

At London. | Printed by Tho:Creede, for Arthur Iohnson, | Dwelling at the signe of the white | Horse in Pauls Church-yard. | 1614. | 14.3x9.cm. (30),326, (7);117p.

Seventh and eighth sermons have separate pagination.

GOODWIN, William. A | Sermon | Preached Before | The Kings Most | Excellent Maies- | tie At Woodstocke, | Avg. 28. 1614. | By | William Goodwin, Deane of Christ's | Church and Vice-Chancellor of the Vni- | versity of Oxon. | Published by Commandement. | (device).

At Oxford, | Printedby Joseph Barnes. 1614. | 17.3x13.3 cm. (1),38p.

HALL, Joseph. Meditations | And | Vowes, | Divine and Morall; | Serving | For Direction In | Christian and ciuill practice. | 3. Centuries. | By Ios. Hall. Dr. of Diuinity. | (device)

At London | Printed by Humfrey Lownes, for Arthur Iohnson, | Samuell Macham, and Lawrence | Lisle. 1614. | Line border. 28.2x18.cm. (5),1114p.

HIERON, Samuel. All | The Sermons | Of Samvel Hieron, | Minister Of Gods | Word, At Modbvry In | Deuon, heretofore sunderly published, | now diligently reuised, and collected | together into one Volume. | Herevnto are An- | nexed Of The Same Avthors, | 1 The Preachers Plea. | 2 An Answer to a Popish Rime. | 3 The Doctrine of the Beginning of Christ, in forme of a | Catechisme. | 4 An Helpe vnto Deuotion. | . . . (6 lines: device).

Printed at London by Iohn Legatt, Printer to the | Vniuersitie of Cambridge. 1614. | 27.9x17.7cm. (12,3), 1–163, (3), 165–195, (3), 197–231, (3), 233–392, (3),

393–427, (3), 429–447, (3), 449–466, (3), 467–475, (4), 477–551, (5), 553–576, (4), 577–584, (8), 585–659p.

Lacks engr. fore t.p.: Workes. 20 Sub. t.p. all dated 1613. Contents: Christians Iovrnall; Minoritie of the Saints; Trvths Pvrchase; Dignitie Of The Scriptvre; Abridgement of the Gospel; Back-Parts Of Iehovah; Worth of the Water of Life; Davids longing and Davids loue; The good Fight; Discouerie of Hypocrisie; Baptizing Of The Evnvch; Triall Of Adoption; Spiritvall Sonne-ship; Life And Death Of Dorcas; Spiritvall Tillage; Remedie Of Secvritie; World-lings Dovvne-fall; Bride-Groome; Preachers Plea; Answer To A Popish Rime; Doctrine Of The Beginning Of Christ; Helpe Vnto Devotion;

KING, John. Vitis Palatina. | A Sermon | Appointed To | be preached at VVhitehall | vpon the Tuesday after the mariage of the | Ladie Elizabeth | her Grace. | By the B. of London. | (device)

London, | Printed for Iohn Bill. | 1614. | Line border. 17.8x13.9cm. (13),39p.

LAMBARDE, William. The Dvties | Of | Constables, Borsholders, | Tythingmen, and such o- | ther lowe and Lay Mini- | sters of the Peace. | Whereunto be adioyned, the se- | uerall offices of Church Ministers, | and Churchwardens, and Ouerseers | for the Poore, Surueyours of the | highwaies, and Distributors | of the prouision against | noisome fowle and | vermine. | First collected by William Lambard | Of Lincolnes Inne Gent. | And enlarged in the yeare. | 1610. | (ornament).

London, | Printed for the Companie of Stationers. | 1614. | Cum Priuilegio. | 16.4x10.8 cm. 94 p.

Appended to his Eirenarcha, with separate register and pagination.

LAMBARDE, William. Eirenarcha, | Or | Of The Office | of the Iustices of Peace, in | foure Bookes. | Reuised, corrected, and enlar- | ged, in the eighth yeere of the | peaceable Raigne of our most | gracious King, | Iames. | First collected by Wil- | liam Lambard of Lin- | colnes Inne Gent. | . . . (1 line).

London, | Printed for the Companie | of Stationers. | 1614. | Cum Priuilegio. | Lace border. 16.4x10.8 cm. (1),634,(83) p. Pp. 303–319, mispaged and misfolded.

LOE, William. Come and see. | The Blisse | Of Brightest | Beavtie: | Shining Ovt Of Sion In | Perfect Glorie. | Being the summe of foure sermons preached in | the Cathedrall Church of Glocester at com- | mandment of superiours. | By William Loe. | (device).

Imprinted at London by Richard Field | for Mathew Law. | 1614. | Line border. 18x14. cm. (12),57p.

LOUIS de Granada. The Sinners | Gvide. | A VVorke Contay- | ning the whole regiment of a Christian | life, deuided into two Bookes: | Wherein Sinners Are Recalled From | the by-path of vice and destruction, and brought into the high- | way of euerlasting happinesse. | Compiled In The Spanish Tovng | by the learned and reuerend Diuine F.Lewes | of Granada. | Since translated into Latine, Italian, and French. | And now perused, and digested into English by Francis |

Meres, Maister of Artes, and student in Diuinitie. | . . . (3 lines: ornament).

At London, | Printed by Richard Field, for Edward Blovnt | and are to be sold in Paules Church-yard, at the signe | of the Beare. 1614. | 18.9x14.4cm.(7),525,(26)p.

A | MANVDIC- | TION For Mr. | Robinson, And | such as consent with him in privat commu- | nion, to lead them on to publick. | Breifly Comprized In A | letter written to Mr.R.W. | (device)

At Dort, | Printed by George Waters, And are to be sould at | his shop at the signe of the Snuffers, on the fish-market, | 1614. | 18.4x12.6cm. (10),84p. Lacks pp. 23–24.

Ascribed to William Ames: DNB. 49: 22; Dexter, No. 429. Also attributed to W: Bradshaw.

MOSSE, Miles. Iustifying | And Saving | Faith Distingvished | from the faith of the Deuils. | In | A Sermon preached at Pauls crosse | in London, May 9. 1613. | By Miles Mosse Pastor Of | the Church of God at Combes in Suffolke, | and Doctor of Diuinitie. | . . . (5 lines; ornament).

Printed by Cantrell Legge, | Printer to the Vniuersitie of Cambridge. | 1614. | And are to be sold by Matthevv Lavv in Pauls | Churchyard at the signe of the Foxe. | 20.x14.5 cm. (10),85p.

MOULIN, Pierre du. Father | Cotton | A Iesvite, | The Kings Confessovr, | His two and thirtie Demands, | to the Ministers of France, | with the Answeres added at | the end of euerie | Demand. | Also three-score and foure Demands proposed to Fa- | ther Cotton, by way of Counter-change. | By Peter Movlin, Minister of the word of | God in the Church of Paris. | Printed according to the French Copie, | printed in Paris. | Also a new late Chalenge, by a learned Diuine, to all | Papists, in 24. other Popish Articles. | . . . (3 lines).

London: | Printed for Iohn Barnes, and are to be sould by Iohn Budge, | at the great South dore of Paules, and at Brittaines-Bursse. 1614. | Line border. 17.6x13.8cm. (8),60p.

PRIDEAUX, John. Ephesvs Backsliding | Conside- | red And Apply- | ed To These | times, in a Sermon preached at | Oxford, in St. Maries, the | tenth of Iuly, being the Act | Sunday. 1614. | By | Iohn Prideavx, Doctor of Divinity, | and Rector of Exceter College. | . . . (2 lines; device).

At Oxford, | Printed by Ioseph Barnes. 1614. | 18.3x13.9 cm. (6),37p.

RAINOLDS, John. The | Discovery | Of The Man Of Sinne: | Wherein Is Set Forth The | Changes Of Gods Chvrch, | In her { Afflictions by his Raigne. | Consolations by his Ruine. | First preached in divers Sermons to the Vniver- | sitie and Cittie of Oxon, by a Reverend & Iu- | dicious Divine I R. D. of Divinity and some- | times of Queenes College. | And now published for the farther vse of both, and | comfort of all that hate Antichrist and loue | the Lord Iesus Christ wheresoever: | By W H. | . . . (3 lines; device).

At Oxford, | Printed by Ioseph Barnes. 1614. | 18.4x14. cm. (6),50p.
Madan: Oxford Press, 1614: 14.

RAINOLDS, John. The Second Part | Of | A Reply, | Answering | A Defence Of A | Sermon Preached At The | Consecration of the Bishop of Bathe and Welles, | by George Downame, Doctor of | Divinitie. | In defence of an Ansvvere to the foresayd Sermon | imprinted anno 1609. | . . . (2 lines; ornament).

Imprinted, Anno 1614. | 18.2x13.5 cm. (7),91,164p. Pp. 17–64 of Lib. I. misplaced.
Cf.Cambr.Univ.Cat:6501.

SMITH, Henry. Gods | Arrow | Against | Atheists. | By Henry Smith. | (device).

At London | Imprinted by H.L. for Thomas Pauier, | 1614. | 17.5x13.1cm. (3), 96p.
Part of his Sermons: 1614, with separate pagination and register.

SMITH, Henry. The | Sermons | Of Master | Henry Smith, | gathered into one | volume. | Printed According to His | corrected copie in his life time. | Wherevnto Is Added, Gods Arrow | against Atheists. | . . . (device).

At London | Imprinted by Hvmfrey Lownes, for | Thomas Man, dwelling in Pater-noster | Row, at the signe of the Talbot. | 1614. | 17.5x13.1cm. 600;(3),96p.

SMITH, Henry. Six | Sermons | Preached by Maister | Henry Smith. | 1 2 of Ionahs punish- | ment. | 3 The Trumpet of the | Soule. | 4 The sinfull mans search | 5 Maries choyce- | 6 Noahs drunkennesse. | Two zealous Prayers. | And published by a more | perfect Copie then heretofore, |

London | Printed by T.D. for Nicholas | Bourne, and are to be sould | at his shop at the Royall | Exchange.1614. | Lace border. 17.5x13.1cm.(1, 122)p.

SPEED, John. The | History | Of | Great Britaine | Under the Conquests of ye | Romans, Saxons, | Danes and | Normans. | Their Originals, Manners, | Warres, Coines & Seales: with ye | Successions, Lives, acts & Issues of the | English Monarchs from Iulius Cæsar, to our most gracious | Soueraigne King Iames. | by | Iohn Speed |

Imprinted At London | Anno | Cum Privilegio | 1614 | And are to be solde by Iohn Sudbury & Georg | Humble, in Popes-head alley at ye signe of ye white Horse. | 41.5x26.5cm. (8),151–894,(51)p. Egr. title mounted. Lacks geographical portion.

TYMME, Thomas. A Silver | Watch-Bell. | The Sound whereof is able | (by the Grace of God) to winne the | most profane worldling, and carelesse liuer, | (if there be but the least sparke of Grace | remayning in him) to become a true | Christian indeed; that in the | end he may obtaine euer- | lasting Saluation. | Whereunto is adioyned a Treatise of the holy | Sacrament of the Lords Svpper, | in part augmented. | By Thomas Tymme. | The tenth Impression. |

At London: | Printed for Clement Knight, dwelling in Paules- | Churchyard, at the signe of the Holy | Lambe. 1614. | Line border. 14.3x9.8cm.(12),288p.

WALKER, William. A | Sermon | Preached At | The Fvnerals Of | the Right Honourable, William, | Lord Rvssell, Baron of Thornhaugh, |

at Thornhaugh, in Northampton-shire, | the 16. of September, 1613. | VVherein is briefely set downe his Godly Life, | together with his Christian Death. | By | William Walker, Batchelour of Diuinitie, | and Preacher of the word of God at Cheswicke | in Middlesex. | . . . (5 lines).

London: | Printed for Iohn Hodgets. 1614. | Line border. 18.1x13.9cm.(7),62p.

WHITE, John. A | Defence | Of The Way To | The Trve Chvrch | against A. D. his Reply. | Wherein | The Motives leading to Papistry, | And Qvestions, touching the Rvle of Faith, | The Avthoritie of the Church, | The Svccession of the Truth, and | The Beginning of Romish Innouations: | are handled and fully disputed. | By Iohn White Doctor of Diuinity, sometime | of Gunwell and Caius Coll. in Cambridge. | . . . (3 lines; device).

London, | Printed for William Barret dwelling in Pauls | Church-yard at the signe of the three Pigeons. | 1614. | 18.3x12.8 cm. (43),557 p.

WILLET, Andrew. An | Harmonie | Vpon | The First Booke | Of Samvel, Wherein According | To The Methode And Order Observed | in Hexapla vpon Genesis and Exodvs, but more com- | pendiously abridged, these speciall things are ob- | serued upon euery Chapter. | The Divers Readings | compared, doubtfull questions explaned, | places of Scripture reconciled, controversies briefly touched, | and morall collections applyed. | Wherein aboue fowre hundred Theologicall | questions are handled, with great breuitie, | and much varietie, by the former author of Hexapla | on Genesis and Exodvs. | (ornaments).

Printed by Cantrell Legge, for | Leonard Greene. | 1614. | 28.1x18.5cm.(6), 176, (13); (5,9), 1-33, (6), 33-83; (4), 85-155, (6)p. Part 2 has sep. t.p. & pagination, and 3 Subtitles.

Epistola dedicatoria, signed.

WILSON, Thomas. Christs | Farewell | to Jerusalem, | And | last Prophesie. | A Sermon | Preached in the Quier of | the Cathedrall Church of Can- | terburie, at the Funerall of that | Reuerend and worthy man, Mr. | Doctor Colfe, Vice-Deane of | the said Church. Octob. 12. | 1613. | By Thomas Wilson, Minister | of Gods word. | (device).

London: | Printed for Francis Burton, and are to bee | sould at the signe of the greene Dragon | in Paules Church-yard. 1614. | 13.7x9 cm. (18,59)p.

WILSON, Thomas. A | Commentarie | vpon the most Diuine Epistle of | S. Paul to the Romanes. | Containing | For Matter, the degeneration of our Na- | ture by Adams Fall; and the restauration there- | of, by the Grace of Christ. Together with the per- | fection of Faith, and the imbecillity of Workes, in the | cause of Iustification of elect sinners | before God. | {For forme and | maner of hand- | ling, it hath The Coherence and Method, | The Svmme and Scope, | The Interpretations & Doctrines | The Reasons and Vses, of most Texts.} All which, are set downe very Familiarly and Compendiously, | in forme of a Dialogue, betweene Timothevs and Silas, | By Thomas Wilson, one of the six Preachers in the | Cathedrall Church of Canterbury. | . . . (7 lines).

London | Printed by W. Iaggard, dwelling in Barbican, 1614. | 17.1x13.6cm. (7),1260,(12)p.

1615

ABERNETHY, John. A | Christian | And Heavenly | Treatise. | Containing, | Physicke for the Soule: | Wherein { 1 The diseases of the Soule are largely described. | 2 The Faculties affected are shortly touched. | 3 The Causes are distinctly set downe | 4 The Signes and Symptomes are particularly specified. | 5 The Prognosticks are plainely pointed out. | 6 The remedies are methodically prescribed. | Very necessary for all those which are trou- | bled in conscience. | By Mr. I.A. Minister of Gods word. | . . . (device).

At London, | Printed by I.Beale for Iohn Budge, and are to be sold | at his shop at the great South-doore of Paules, and | at Britannes bursse.1615. | Line border. 18.1x13.4cm. (16),374;(16)p.
Dedication signed Io. Abrenethy.

ADAMS, Thomas. The | Blacke Devill | Or | The Apostate. | Together | With { The Wolfe Worrying the Lambes. | And | The Spiritvall Navigator, | Bovnd | For the Holy Land. | In three Sermons. | By Thomas Adams. | . . . (7 lines).

London, | Printed by William Iaggard, 1615. | Line border. 18.2x13.5cm. (6), 78;(5),2-34;(4),58p. With separate registers and pagination.

ADAMS, Thomas. Englands | Sicknes, | Comparatively | Conferred with Israels. | Diuided into two Sermons, | By | Tho:Adams. | . . . (3 lines; ornament).

London | Imprinted by E:G: for Iohn Budge, and | Ralph Mab, 1615. | Line border. 18.2x13.5cm. (4),101p.

ADAMS, Thomas. Mystical | Bedlam, | Or | The VVorld Of | Mad-Men. | By | Tho:Adams. | . . . (4 lines; ornament).

London | Printed by George Purslowe, for Clement Knight, and are | to be sold at his shoppe in Paules Church-yard, | at the Signe of the Holy Lambe. | 1615. | Line border. 18.2x13.5cm. (6),82p.

ADAMS, Thomas. The | VVhite Devill | Or | The Hypocrite | Vncased: | To this fourth Impression are | newly added, | 1 The Two Sonnes | Or | The dissolute conferred | VVith | The Hypocrite. | 2 The Leaven, | Or | A medicine for them both. | By | Tho. Adams. |

London, | Printed by Thomas Dawson, for VVilliam | Arondell, and are to be sold in Pauls | Church-yard, at the signe | of the Angell. | 1615. | Line border. 18.2x13.5cm. (10),121p. Lacks pp 65–68.

AINSWORTH, John and AINSWORTH, Henry. The | Trying | Ovt Of The | Trvth: | Begvnn And Proseqvvted In Certayn | Letters or Passages between Iohn Aynsworth and Henry | Aynsworth, the one pleading for, the other | against the present religion of the | Church of Rome. | The chief things here handled, are, | 1. Of Gods word and scriptures, whither they be a sufficient rule | of our faith. | 2. Of the

Scriptures expounded by the Church; and of unwrit- | ten traditions. | 3. Of the Church of Rome, whither it be the true Catholike | Church, and her sentence to be received, as the cer- | tayn truth. |
Published for the good of others by E. P. | in the yeare 1615. | 16.8x13. cm. 190p.

ANDROTIUS, Fulvius. Certaine | Devovt Consi- | derations Of | Freqventing The | Blessed Sacrament: | Written | By the reuerent Father Fvlvivs Andro- | tivs of the Societie of Iesvs. | With | Svndrie Other Preceptes | and rules of direction, composed for the | benefit of such as seeke to attaine to | the perfection of vertue. | Firste written in Italian: after turned into La- | tin: and now translated into English. | . . . (2 lines: device).
[Douay? 1615:] Permissu Superiorum. | 12.6x7cm. (23), 296 13p. Lacks p. 145-192.

BABINGTON, Gervase. Comfortable | Notes Vpon The | Bookes of Nvmbers And | Devteronomie. | VVith An Exposition Of | the Catholike Faith: | Or, | The twelue Articles of the Apostles Creed: | Neuer before published. | By | The right Reuerend Father in God Gervase Babington, late | Bishop of Worcester. | With an Alphabeticall Table of the principall matters | contained in them. | (device)
London, | Printed by George Eld, for Henry Fetherstone. | 1615. | 27.6x18.1cm. (4),332,(8)p.

BABINGTON, Gervase. A | Profitable | Exposition Of The | Lords Prayer, by way of Questions and | Answers for most Plainnesse. | Together | VVith Many Frvitfvll | applications to the Life and Soule, as well for the | terror of the dull and dead, as for the sweet comfort | of the tender-hearted. | By the Right Reuerend Father in God Gervase Babington, | late Bishop of Worcester. | With a Table of the principall matters in this booke, newly | added to this Impression. | . . . (2 lines; device).
London, | Printed by George Eld. 1615. | 27.6x18.1cm. (8),156p.
Appended, without t.p.: Conference betwixt | mans Frailtie and Faith | 48p.; Sermon | Preached At Paules Crosse, the second Sunday | in Michaelmas Tearme. 1590. | 49-78p.; A Funerall Sermon: | 79-95p.

BABINGTON, Gervase. A | Verie Frvitfvll | Exposition Of The | Commandements, By | way of Questions and Answers for | greater plainnesse. | Together With | An Application Of Eve- | ry One To The Sovle And Con- | science Of Man, Profitable For All, And | especially for them that (being not otherwise furnished) are yet desirous | both to see themselues, and to deliuer to others some larger speech | of euery point, that is but breefely named in the | shorter Catechismes. | By the Right Reuerend Father in God, Gervase | Babington, late Bishop of Worcester. | VVhereunto is newly annexed a Table; containing the principall | Matters in this Booke. | . . . (3 lines; ornament).
London, | Printed by George Eld for Thomas | Charde. 1615. | 27.6x18.1cm. (12),118,(2)p.

BENEFIELD, Sebastian. The | Sinne | Against The Holy | Ghost Discovered: | And Other Christi- | an doctrines delivered: | In | Twelve Sermons Vpon Part | of the tenth Chapter of the Epistle to | the Hebrewes. | By | Sebastian Benefield Doctor of Divinity | and Professour for the Lady Margaret, | in the Vniversitie of Oxford. | . . . (2 lines, device)

At Oxford, | printed by Ioseph Barnes Printer to the | Vniversitie. 1615. | 17.5x 13. 7cm. (4),181,(3)pp.

BOYS, John. An | Exposition | Of The Dominicall | Epistles And Gospels, | vsed in our English Liturgie, | throughout the whole yeere. | Together With A Rea- | son Why The Chvrch | did chuse the same. | By Iohn Boys, Doctor | of Diuinitie. | (The Winter-part Advent to Quinquagesima Sunday). | . . . (3 lines: ornament).

At London | Imprinted by Felix Kyngston, for | VVilliam Aspley. 1615. | Line border. 18x13.2cm. (1),302p.
From the library of Walter W. Law.

BOYS, John. An | Exposition | Of The Dominical | Epistles And Gospels, | vsed in our English Liturgie, | throughout the whole yeere. | Together With A Rea- | son Why The Chvrch | did chuse the same. | By Iohn Boys, Doctor | of Diuinitie. | The Spring-part from the first in Lent to | Whitsunday. | . . . (4 lines: ornament)

London, | Printed by Edvvard Griffin for | William Aspley. 1615. | Line border. 18x13.2cm. (4),246p.
From the library of Walter W. Law.

BOYS, John. An | Exposition | Of The Last | Psalme. | Delivered In A Sermon | Preached At Pavles | Crosse the fifth of Nouember 1613. | Which I haue ioyned to the Festiuals | as a short Apologie for our | Holy daies in the Church | of England. | Dedicated Vnto My Honorable | friend and most respected kinsman Sir William | Monins Baronet. | By Iohn Boys, Doctor | of Diuinitie. | (ornament).

At London | Imprinted by Felix Kyngston, for | VVilliam Aspley.1615. | Line border. 18.4x14.3cm. (1),26p.
Separate register and pagination

BOYS, John. The | Third Part | From S.Iohn Bap- | tists Nativitie To | the last Holy-day in the | whole yeere. | Dedicated Vnto The | Right Religiovs And Re- | solute Doctor, Matthevv Svt- | cliffe, Deane of Exeter. | By Iohn Boys, Doctor | of Diuinitie. | . . . (3 lines; ornament).

At London | Imprinted by Felix Kyngston, | for William Aspley. 1615. | Line border. 18.4x14.3cm. (1),147p.
Part of his Exposition of the Festival Epistles:1613 .

BRIGHTMAN, Thomas. A Revelation | of the Reuelation | that is. | The Revelation | of St. John opened clearely | with a logicall Resolution | and Exposition. | Wherein The Sense | is cleared, out of the | scripture, the euent | also of thinges foretold | is Discussed out of the | Church-Historyes. | By Thomas Brightman. |

Anno Dni. imprinted at Amsterdam. 1615. | Engr. t.p., with eight panels. 19.8x 15.2cm (16),921,(1)pp.
Said to have been burned by the bishops: doubtful.

BYFIELD, Nicholas. An | Exposition | Vpon The Epistle | To The Colossians. | Wherein, | Not Onely The Text Is | Methodically Analysed, and the sence of | the words, by the help of VVriters, both ancient | and moderne is explayned: | But also, | By Doctrine and Vse, the intent of the holy Ghost is in | euery place more fully vnfolded and vrged. | And besides, | The very marrow of most Common-places is aptly diffused through- | out the body of this Exposition, as the nature of | of this kinde of Teaching would beare. | And further, | Many chiefe Cases of Conscience are here resolued. | All | With conuenient Varietie and Breuitie. | Being, | The substance of neare seauen yeeres VVeeke-dayes Sermons, | of N.Byfield, | late one of the Preachers for the Citie of Chester. | . . . (4 lines).

London: | Printed by T.S. for Nathaniel Bvtter, and are to be sould | at his Shop at the signe of the Pide-Bull in Pauls Church-yard, | neare S.Austins Gate. 1615. | Line border. 28.6x18.8cm. (22),179;(8),90;(10),137;(8),157-202p.

A | CATECHISME | Of Christian | Religion. | Appointed | to be printed for the | vse of the Kirke of | Edinbvrgh. | (device).

Edinbvrgh, | Printed by Andro Hart. | Anno Dom. 1615. | Border. 12mo. Repr. in Bonar's Catechisms of the Scottish Reformation. London: 1866. Pp. 113-170. The so-called Palatine Catechism .

CERTAINE | Advertisements | For The Good Of The | Chvrch And Common-Wealth, | Well Worthy The Seriovs | consideration of the most Honourable High | Court of Parliament late assembled, and | hereafter to be assembled | againe. | . . . (8 lines)

Without imprint. [1615] 19.3x14.6cm. (1),80p.

CHRISTS | Kingdome | Discovered. | Or, | That the true Church of God is | in England, clearely made manifest | against all Sectaries what- | soeuer. | . . . (5 lines)

London, | Printed by Thomas Creede. for Iosias | Harrison; and are to be sold in Pater- | Noster-Row, at the Signe of the | Golden Anker. 1615. | Line border. 14.5x9.5cm (5),67,(1)p.
From the library of Walter W. Law.

CLEAVER, Robert. A | Briefe | Explanation | Of The Whole Booke | of the Prouerbs of Salomon. | By Robert Cleaver. | (device).

At London | Imprinted by Felix Kyngston for Thomas Man, | and Roger Iackson. 1615. | 16.5x12.6cm. (4),558p.

COOPER, Thomas. A | Familiar | Treatise, laying downe | Cases Of Conscience, | Furthering to perseuerance in | Sanctification. | By Thomas Cooper, preacher of Gods word. | (device)

Printed at London by Iohn Beale, for William Welby, | and are to be sold at his shop, at the signe | of the Swan in Paules Church- | yard. 1615. | 16.8x13. cm. (28),92p.

DAY, John. Concio Ad Clervm | In Secvndi, Vel Qvarti, Re- | gvm, Capitis Sexti, Ver- | svm Primvm, Secvndvm, | Tertivm, Et Qvartvm. | Habita in Templo B.Mariæ Oxon. | Iunij 25°. Ann. Dom. 1612. | Per Ioannem Dayvm Baccalav- | reum in Theologia, et Collegij Orielen- | sis apud Oxonienses Socium. | Editio Secvnda. | . . . (device; 6 lines).

Oxoniæ, | Excudebat Iosephus Barnesius, 1615. | 18.5x13.9cm. (4),26,(2)p.

DAY, John. David's Desire | To Goe To Chvrch: As It | was published in two Sermons | in St Maries in | Oxford. | The One, the Fift of November, in the Afternoone | to the Vniversitie, in the Yeare of our Lord | God 1609. the Other, on Christmas | Day next following, to the Pa- | rishioners of that | place. | . . . (device; 10 lines).

Printed at Oxford by Ioseph Barnes 1615. | 18.5x13.9cm. (8),48p.
Dedication signed.

DYKE, Daniel. The | Mystery | Of Selfe-Deceiving. | Or | A Discovrse | and discouery of the deceitful- | nesse of Mans Heart. | Written | By the late faithfull Minister of Gods Word | Daniel Dyke, Bachelour in | Diuinity. | Published | Since his death, by his Brother I.D. Minister of | Gods Word. | . . . (5 lines).

London: | Printed by Thomas Snodham for Ralph Mab, | and are to be solde at the signe of the Grey-hound | in Pauls Church-yard. 1615. | Line border. 17.8x 13.8cm.(16),426p.

ELTON, Edward. An | Exposition | Of The Epistle | of St Paule to the Colossians, | deliuered in sundry Sermons, | Preached by Edvvard Elton | Minister of Gods word at St.Mary | Magdalens Bermondsey neare London. | And now by him published intending the | further good of his charge, and the profit | of as many as shall please to read it. | . . . (5 lines: ornament)

London | Printed by Edward Griffin for Ralph Mab and are to be sold | at his shop, at the signe of the Grey-hound, | in Pauls-Church-yard. 1615. | 16.9x13.3cm. (27),1471p.
From the library of Walter W. Law.

FINCH, Henry. An | Exposition | Of The | Song of Solomon: | called Canticles. | Together with | Profitable Observations, | collected out of the same. | ¶Perused and published by William | Govge, Preacher of Gods Word in | Black-Friers, London. | . . . (2 lines ; device).

London, | Printed by Iohn Beale dwelling in Alders- | gate streete and there to be solde. | . . . (trimmed). Colophon: ¶Jmprinted at London by John | Beale, dwelling in Alders- | gate streete 1615. | 17.2x13cm. (12),129,(1)p.
Anon. H&L.

FORSYTH, James. The | Bitter | Waters Of | Babylon, | Or | The Miserable | Estate of the Citizens of | Sion: Considered by | the confusion of all | things in this world. | . . . (6 lines).

London, | Printed by Edw.Griffin for Ralph Mab, and are | to bee sold in Pauls Church-yard, at | the signe of the Grey-hound, 1615. | 17.7x13.2cm.(8),32p.
Epistle Dedicatory, signed.

GODWIN, Francis. A Catalogve | of the Bishops of England, since the | first planting of Christian Religion in this | Island, Together with a brief History of | their liues and memorable actions, so neere as | can be gathered out of antiquity. | Wherevnto Is | prefixed a discourse concerning the first | conuersion of our Britaine vnto Chri- | stian Religion. | By | Francis Godwin now | Bishop of Landaff. | . . . (3 lines: ornament).

London | Printed for Thomas Adams. | 1615. | 18.7x14.3cm. (12),703,(1)p. Mispaged.

HAKEWILL, George. The | Vanitie Of | The Eye, | First beganne for the Comfort of a | Gentlewoman bereaved of her | sight, and since upon occa- | sion enlarged & pub- | lished for the | Common | good. | By | George Hakewill Master | of Arts, and fellow of Exeter | Coll. in Oxford. | The third Edition augmented by | the Author. | . . . (2 lines: ornament).

At Oxford, | Printed by Ioseph Barnes, Printer | to the Vniversitie.1615. | 11.8x 6.8cm. (6),170,(18)p.

HALL, Joseph. A | Recollection | of such Treatises as | haue bene heretofore | severally published, and | are nowe reuised, correc- | ted, augmented. | By | Jos:Hall Dr of Diuinity. | With addition of some | others not hitherto | extant. |

London | Printed for Arthur Iohnson, Samuel | Macham, and Laurence Lisle. 1615. | 28.1x18.5cm. (8,5),1114p. Engr.t.p.
Contains 25 sub-title pages, all dated 1614.

HOSKINS, John. Sermons | Preached | At Pavls Crosse | And Elsewhere, | By Iohn Hoskins, Some- | Times Fellow Of | New-Colledge in Oxford, Minister and | Doctor of Law. | (device)

London, | Printed by William Stansby for Nathaniel Butter, and are to be | sold at his shop at Saint Austens gate. | 1615. | Line border. 18.x13.8cm. (6),71p.

HOSKINS, John. Two | Sermons | Preached At | Oxford: | The One At New | Colledge, The Other | at Saint Maries. | By Iohn Hoskins, Minister and | Doctor of the Law. | (device)

London, | Printed by William Stansby for Nathaniel Butter, and are to be | sold at his shop at Saint Austens gate. | 1615. | Line border. 17x13cm (4),51p.

HOSKINS, John. Two | Sermons | Preached: | The One At Hereford, The Other At | Pavls Crosse. | By Iohn Hoskins, Minister and | Doctor of the Law. | (device)

London, | Printed by William Stansby for Nathaniel Butter, and are to be | sold at his shop at Saint Austens gate. | 1615. | Line border. 17x13cm. (4),61p.

HOSKINS, John. Two | Sermons | Preached: | The One At Saint | Maries In Oxford, The | Other Being the Conclvsion | of the Rehearsall Sermon at Pauls | Crosse. 1614. | By Iohn Hoskins, Minister and | Doctor of the Law. | (device)

London, | Printed by William Stansby for Nathaniel Butter, and are to be | sold at his shop at Saint Austens gate. | 1615. | Line border. 17x13cm. (4),42p.

HULL, William. The | Mirrovr Of | Maiestie. | Wherein the Mother-Church inviteth | her Damsels to Contemplate the | Harbourlesse Ghest, yet waiting at the doore | of mans heart for entertainment. | Set forth in fiue Sermons: | }1 The Blamelesse Separatist. | 2 Sweete Contemplation. | 3 Salomons Royaltie. | 4 Christs Coronation. | 5 The Saints Dignitie. | Preached in Ascension weeke, by W. Hvll | Doctor in Diuinitie. | . . . (12 lines).

London, | Printed by Nicholas Okes, for William Timme and Iohn Robinson, and are to | bee sold at their shop in Pater-noster-row. 1615. | Line border. 18. x13.8 cm. (16),140,(1) p.

MASON, Thomas. Christs | Victorie | Over Sathans | Tyrannie. | Wherin Js Contained A | Catalogve Of All Christs Faith- | fvll Sovldiers That The Divell | either by his grand Captaines the Empe- | rovrs, or by his most deerly beloued sonnes | and heyres the Popes, haue most cruel- | ly Martyred for the | Trvth. | With All The Poysoned Doctrins | Wherewith That Grat Redde | Dragon hath made drunken the Kings and In- | habitants of the Earth; with the confuta- | tions of them | Together | With All His Trayterovs Practi- | ses and Designes, Against All Christian | Princes to this day, especially against our late | Queen Elizabeth of famous memorie, and | our most religious Soueraigne | Lord King Iames. | Faithfully abstracted out of the Book of Martyrs, and | diuers other Books. | By Thomas Mason Preacher of Gods Word. |

London, | Printed by George Eld and Ralph Blower. | 1615. | Line border. 26.4x16.7cm. (10),418,(12)p.

MAXWELL, James. Admirable | And | Notable Pro- | phesies, vttered in former | times by 24. famous Romain- | Catholickes, concerning the | Church of Romes defection, Tri- | bulation, and reformation. | Written First In | Latine, & now published in the Eng- | lish tongue, both by Iames Maxwell | A Researcher of Antiquities. |

London, | Printed by Ed:Allde for Clement | Knight, and are to be sold at | the holy Lambe in S.Paules | Churchyard. | Anno Dom. 1615. | Wood cut border. 17.7x12.8cm. (20),164,(1)p.

MOCKET, Richard. God | and the | King: | Or, | A Dialogue shewing that | our Soueraigne Lord King Iames, | being immediate vnder God within | his Dominions, | Doth rightfully claime whatsoeuer | is required by the Oath of | Allegeance. |

London: | Imprinted by his Maiesties speciall | priuiledge and command. 1615. | 13.4x9.cm. (6),93p. Frontisp.

Anon. DNB. 38: 91 a.

MURTON, John. Obiections | Answered by way of Dialo- | gue, wherein is proved | By the Law of God: | By the law of our Land: | And by his Ma[ties] many testimonies | That no man ought to be persecuted | for his religion, so he testifie his alle- | geance by the Oath, appointed by Law. | . . . (10 lines; ornament).

Printed 1615. | 13.4x9.1 cm. (8),80p.
Anon. Dexter 436.

NORRIS, Sylvester. An | Antidote | Or | Soveraigne | Remedie | Against | The Pestiferovs Writings | Of All English Sectaries. | And | In particular against D. Whitaker, D. Fvlke, D. | Bilson, D. Reynolds, D. Sparkes, and | D. Field, the chiefe vpholders, some of Pro- | testancy, some of Puritanisme. | Deuided into three Partes. | In which the true Catholike Doctrine, in the chiefest points of Faith, called in | Question by the Protestants of our time, is explained, defended, | and their principall Obiections answered. | By S.N. Doctour of Diuinity. | The First Part | . . . (4 lines).

Permissu Superiorum. M.DC.XV. | 18.3x13.6 cm. (20),322,(2) p. Gillow.V:190.

A | NUNNES Prophesie, | Or. | The fall of Friers. | Contayning the downefall of the Pope, by the | Vnicorne of the West; prophesied 300. yeares | agone, and fulfilled in this present age 1615. | First read, and then iudge. | (cut).

Imprinted at London by W. White, and are to be | sold by E. Marchant at Pauls Crosse 1615. | 17.6x13. cm. (4,18)p.

PARR, Elnathan. The | Grovnds | Of Diuinitie, | Plainely discouering the Mysteries | of Christian Religion, propounded fami- | liarly in diuers Questions and Answeres: | Substantially proued by Scriptures; Ex- | pounded faithfully, according to the Writings | of the best Diuines, and euidently applyed | by profitable vses, for the helpe and be- | nefit of the Vnlearned which | desire Knowledge. | To the which is prefixed a very profita- | ble Treatise, contayning an Exhortation | to the Studie of the Word, with singular | directions for the Hearing and Reading | of the same. | Newly corrected, augmented, and enlarged | by Elnathan Parr, Minister of | the Word at Palgraue in Suffolke. | The second Edition. | . . . (5 lines).

London, | Printed by Thomas Snodham for Samuell Man, and are to | be solde at his Shop in Pauls Church-yard, at the | signe of the Ball.1615. | 13.4x8.7cm. (16),366p. Lacks 161–178p.

PULTON, Ferdinand. De Pace Regis | Et Regni, | viz. | A Treatise declaring which be | the great and generall Offences of the | Realme, and the chiefe impediments of the peace of | the King and the Kingdome, as Treasons, Homicides, and Felonies, Me- | naces, Assaults, Batteries, Ryots, Routs, Vnlawfull assemblies, Forcible entries, For- | geries, Periuries, Maintenance, Deceit, Extortion, Oppression: And how many, | and what sorts of them there be, and by whom and what | meanes the said Offences, and the Offendors therein | are to be restrained, repressed, or | punished. | Which being reformed or duly checked, | Florebit pax Regis & Regni. | Collected out of the Reports of the Common Lawes of this | Realme, and of the Statutes in force, and out of the painefull workes of the | Reuerend Iudges, Sir Anthonie Fitzharbert, Sir Robert Brooke, Sir William | Stanford, Sir Iames Dyer, Sir Edward Coke, Knights, and other | learned Writers of our Lawes, By | Ferdinando Pvlton of Lincolnes Inne, Esquier. |

London. | Printed for the Companie of Stationers, | An.Dom. 1615. | Cum Priuilegio. | 28.7x18.8cm. (5),243,(17) fol.

REMONSTRANCES | Made By The Kings | Maiesties Ambassadovr, | vnto the French King and the Queene | his Mother, Iune last past, | 1615; | Concerning the marriages with Spaine; | As also certayne Diabolicall opinions maintayned by Cardinall Perron, about the deposing | and murthering of | Kings. | Together with the French Kings Letter to | the Prince of Conde, Dated the 26. | of Iuly last, 1615. and the Prince | his Answere thereunto. | Translated according to the French Copie. | (ornament).

London, | Printed by William Stansby for Nathaniel Butter, and are to | be sold at his shop vnder Saint Augustines | Gate. 1615. | 16.5x12.2cm. (1,30)p.

ROGERS, Richard. A | Commentary | Vpon The Whole | Booke Of Ivdges. | Preached First And Delive- | red In Svndrie Lectvres; Since | collected, and diligently perused, and now published. | For the benefit generally of all such as desire to grow in faith | and Repentance, and especially of them, who would | more cleerely vnderstand and make vse of the | worthie examples of the Saints, re- | corded in diuine history. | Penned By Richard Rogers Preacher | of Gods word at Wethersfield in Essex. | . . . (5 lines; device).

London, | Imprinted by Felix Kyngston for Thomas | Man, and are to be sold at his shop in Pater-noster | Row, at the signe of the Talbot.1615. | 27.2x17.7cm. (16), 970p.

SIMSON, Patrick. A Short | Compend, | Of The | Arrian and Evtychian | Persecvtions, | Comprised in the IIII. V. and VI. | Centvries. | Whereunto is added, | Treatises, Declaring The | noueltie of Popish Religion. | (ornament).

Edinburgh, | Printed By Andro Hart, | Anno Dom. 1615. | 18.8x14.6cm. 150, 70, 71 p.
Second part of his Short Compend Of the Historie, etc. 1613.
Epistle Dedicatorie, signed.

SMITH, Henry. Sixe | Sermons, | Preached By | Mr.Henry Smith: | with Prayers, both for the | Morning and Euening, | thereunto adioyned: | And published by a more | perfect Copie then here- | tofore. | . . . (4 lines).

London, | Printed by Will. Stansby for William | Barret, dwelling in Pauls Church- | yard at the signe of the three | Pidgeons. 1615. | Arch. border. 17.5x13.1 cm.(4,132)p.

WAKE, Isaac. Rex Platonicvs: | Sive, | De Potentis- | simi Principis Ia- | cobi Britanniarvm | Regis, ad illustrissimam Aca- | demiam Oxoniensem, | adventu, Aug.27. | An.1605. | Narratio | Ab Isaaco Wake, Pvbli- | co Academiæ ejusdem Oratore, | tunc temporis conscripta, nunc i- | terum in lucem edita, multis | in locis auctior & e- | mendatior. | Editio tertia. | (ornament).

Oxoniæ, | Excudebat Iosephus Barnesius | Academiæ Typographus. | 1615. | 12.6x7.2cm. (7),224,(19)p.

WALKINGTON, Thomas. Theologicall Rules, | To Gvide | Vs In The Vn- | derstanding and practise | of holy Scriptures: | Two Centuries: | Drawne partly out of Scriptures | themselues: Partly out of Eccle- | siasticall writers old and new. | Also | Ænigmata Sacra, Holy Riddles; Or | Misticall Cases and Secrets of | Diuinitie, with their Re- | solutions. | Foure Centuries: | The vnfolding whereof layeth open that | Truth that concerneth Saluation. | By T. W. Preacher of the word. | (monogram).

London | Printed by Edw. Griffin for Fran. Burton, | and are to be solde in Pauls Church-yard | at the signe of the greene Dragon. | 1615. | 14.3x9.3 cm. (8),125;(12),206p.

DNB.59:91b. Ænigmata Sacra has separate t.p. and pagination; register continuous.

WALSINGHAM, Francis. A | Search | Made Into Matters | Of Religion, | By | Francis VValsingham | Deacon of the Protestants Church, before his | Change to the Catholike. | VVherein | Is related, how first he fell into his doubts: And how for finall reso- | lution therof he repaired vnto his Maiesty, who remitted him | to the L. of Canterbury, and he to other learned men. And | what the issue was of all those Conferences. | And | How after this againe he betooke himselfe to the reading of Protestant and | Catholike Authors, for better finding out the truth: As also for discer- | ning where, & on what side true or false dealing was to be found: | and what the successe of this Search hath byn. | Dedicated to the Kings most Excellent Ma^{ty}. | The Second Edition. | (ornament) . . . (2 lines).

Permissu Superiorum. Anno M.DC.XV. | 18.2x14cm. (24),504,(8)p. Cambr.Univ.Cat:6532.

The | VVAY To Trve | Happines : | Leading to the Gate of | Knovvledge. | Or , | An entrance to Faith: | without which it is vnpossible | to please God. | By | Questions and Answers, opening | briefly the meaning of euery | seuerall Booke and Chapter of | the Bible, from the begin- | ning of Genesis, to the | end of the Revelation. |

London: | Printed by Thomas Snodham, for | Thomas Pauier, and are to be | sold at his shop in Iuy-lane. | 1615. | Lace border. 16.1x10.6 cm. (1),124 p. Mispaged 130.

WORSHIP, William. The Christians | Movrning Garment. | Aarons Bels. | The Fisher. | Earth Raining Vpon | Heaven. | Foure Sermons, | Preached at foure seuerall times: | The first three preached at three | seuerall Visitations, at Hore-castle | in Lincoln-shire. The fourth prea- | ched at the Assises holden in Not- | tingham, August 5. | 1614. | By | William Worship, Doctor | of Diuinitie. | . . . (2 lines).

London, | Printed by L.S. for Thomas Pauier, | and are to be sold at his shop | in Iuy-Lane. 1615. | Line border. 14.5x9.5cm. (4),133p.

From the library of Walter W. Law.

WRIGHT, Leonard. A | Svmmons For | Sleepers. | VVherein Most | grieuous and notorious offen- | ders are cited to bring forth | true fruits of repentance, be- | fore the day of the Lord | now at hand. | Hereunto is annexed, A Patterne | for Pastors, deciphering briefly the duties |

pertaining to that function. | By | Leonard VVright. | Newly corrected and augmented. | . . . (6 lines; device).
London, | Imprinted by George Purslowe. 1615. | 17.7x13.7 cm. (6),58p.

YATES, John. Gods | Arraignement | Of Hypocrites: | With | An Inlargement | concerning Gods decree in | ordering sinne. | As | Likewise A Defence | of Mr. Calvine against Bellarmine; | and of M. Perkins against | Arminivs. | . . . (4 lines; ornament).
Printed by Cantrell Legge, | Printer to the Vniuersitie of Cambridge. | 1615. | 18.3 x 13.5 cm. (13),413,(2) p.
Epistle dedicatorie, signed.

1616

ADAMS, Thomas. A Divine | Herball | Together with | A Forrest of Thornes. | In Five Sermons. | { 1. The Garden of Graces. | 2.The prayse of Fertilitie. | 3. The Contemplation of the Herbes. } { 4. The Forrest of Thornes. | 5. The end of Thornes. By Tho.Adams. | . . . (5 lines; ornament).
London, | Printed by George Purslowe, for Iohn Budge, and are to be | solde at his shop, at the great South-dore of Pauls, | and at Brittaines Burse. 1616. | Line border. 18.2x13.5cm. (6),157p.

ADAMS, Thomas. The | Gallants Burden. | A | Sermon preached at Paules | Crosse, the twentie nine of March, | being the fift Sunday in Lent. | 1612. | By Thomas Adams. | Published by Authoritie. | (ornaments).
London, | Printed by W. W. for Clement Knight, and are to be | sold at his Shop in Paules Church-yard at the | Signe of the Holy Lambe. 1616. | Border. 18.2x13.5cm   (4),67p.

ADAMS, Thomas. The | Sacrifice Of | Thankefulnesse. | A Sermon preached at Pauls Crosse, | the third of December, being the | first Aduentuall Sunday, | Anno 1615. | By Tho.Adams. | . . . (2 lines). Whereunto are annexed Fiue other of his Sermons prea- | ched in London, and else-where; neuer before Prin- | ted. The Titles whereof follow in the next Page. | (ornament).
London, | Printed by Thomas Purfoot, for Clement Knight, and are to | be sold at his shop in Pauls Church-yard, at the | Signe of the Holy Lambe. 1616. | Line border. 18.2x13.5cm. (4),103;(1),25;(1),18p.
Lacks the last of the Five Sermons: The Taming of the Tongue . 2 sub.t.p. With separate registers and pagination.

B., J. A | Sermon | Preached At | Mapple-Dvrham | in Oxfordshire: | And Pvblished | at the request of Sir | Richard Blovnt. | By J.B.D.D. and Chapleine | in Ordinary to his Maiestie. | . . . (1 line; ornament)
London: | Printed by T.S. for Iohn Hodgets. | 1616. | Line border. 19.7x14.8cm. (1),28p.
B.M.Cat. attributes to J.Bowle?

BEARD, Thomas. A | Retractive | From The Romish | Religion: | Contayning | Thirteene Forcible Motives, | disswading from communion with | the Chvrch of | Rome: | Wherein is demonstratiuely proued, that the | now Romish Religion (so farre forth as it is | Romish) is not the true Catholike | Religion of Christ, but the seduction | of Antichrist: | By Tho. Beard, Doctor in Diuinity, and Preacher | of Gods holy Word in the Towne of | Hvntington. | . . . (3 lines).

London, | Printed by William Stansby, and are | to be sold by Henrie Fetherstone. | 1616. | 19x14.1 cm. (16),543,(1) p.

BOYS, John. The | Avtvmne | Part From | The Tvvelfth | Sunday after Trinity, | to the last in the | whole yeere. | Dedicated | Vnto the much honoured and | most worthy Doctor, Iohn | Overal Deane of | Pavls. | . . . (2 lines: ornament).

London, | Printed by Edvvard Griffin, for | William Aspley. | 1616. | Line border. 18x13.2cm. (3),227p.
From the library of Walter W. Law.

BOYS, John. An | Exposition | Of The Dominicall | Epistles And Gospels, | vsed in our English Liturgie, | throughout the whole yeere. | Together With A Rea- | son Why The Chvrch | did chuse the same. | By Iohn Boys, Doctor | of Diuinitie. | The Summer-part from Whitsunday to the | twelfth after Trinitie. | . . . (3 lines: ornament).

At London | Imprinted by Felix Kyngston, for | VVilliam Aspley. 1616. | Line border. 18.6x14.2cm.(4), 247p.
Also another copy from the library of Walter W. Law. 18x13.2cm.(1),302p.

BRIGHTMAN, Thomas. The | Revelation | of S.Iohn illustrated | with an Analysis | & scholions. | Wherein the sence is | opened by the Scriptu: | re, & the euent of things | forê-told, shewed by | Histories. | The third Edition Corrected & amended, | With supply of many things | formerly left out. | By Thomas Brightman. |

Imprinted at Leyden by John Class, A'1616. | Engr. t.p., with 8 panels. 18.2x 11.7cm. (16), 1143p.

CAMDEN, William. Annales | Rervm Angli- | carvm, Et Hibernicarum regnante | Elizabetha, | Ad | Annvm Salvtis | M.D. LXXXIX. | Gvilielmo Cambdeno Avthore. | Item Eivsdem Avthoris | Britannia. | Siue Angliæ, Scotiæ, Hiberniæ, & Insularum adiacentium, ex intima | antiquitate, Chorographica descriptio. | (device).

Francofurti ad Mœnum, curantibus Rulandijs, | Typis Ioannis Bringeri, 1616. | 18.2x11.4cm.523,(25)p.

CAMDEN, William. Britannia; | Sive | Florentissimo- | rvm Regnorvm, | Angliæ, Scotiæ, Hiberniæ, | & Insularum adiacentium ex intima | antiquitate Chorographica | descriptio; | Avthore | Gvilielmo Camdeno. | Nunc tertio recognita, & magna accessione adaucta. | (device).

Francofurti ad Mœnum, Curantibus Rulandiis, | Typis Ioannis Bringeri. | M.DC.XVI. | 18.2x11.4cm.(8),762,(19)p.
Appended to his Annales:1616, with separate register and pagination

CARTWRIGHT, Thomas. A | Treatise | Of Christian | Religion. | Or, | The Whole Bodie And | substance of Diuinitie. | By T.C. | (device).

At London, | Imprinted by Felix Kyngston, | for Thomas Man. | 1616. | 17.6x 13.5 cm.   (8),360p.   Second edition.
Dexter:454.

CHAMPNEY, Anthony. A | Treatise Of | The Vocation Of | Bishops, And Other | Ecclesiasticall | Ministers. | Proving The Ministers | Of The Pretended Reformed | Chvrches In Generall, To Have | No Calling: Against Monsieur | du Plessis, and Mr. Doctour | Feild: | And in particuler the pretended Bishops in | England, to be no true Bishops. | Against Mr. Mason. | By Anth. Champ. P. and D. of Sorbonne. | . . . (8 lines: ornament).

At Dovay, | by Iohn Heigham. With Licence | of Superiours. Anno | 1616. | 19x13.3 cm.   (16),326,(4) p.   Mispaged 90-94, 7 pages.   Imperfect: lacks pp. 215-222.

DENISON, John. A | Three-fold | Resolvtion, | very necessary to | Saluation. | Describing | Earths Vanitie. | Hels Horror. | Heavens Felicitie. | . . . (3 lines).   By Iohn Denison. | The fourth Edition. |

London, | Printed for Nicholas Bourne | Anno. Dom. | 1616. | Line border. 12.4x6.8cm.(10),579p.

DOMINIS, Marco Antonio de. A | Manifes- | tation Of | The Motives, | Whereupon the most Reuerend | Father, Marcvs Antonivs | De Dominis, Archbishop of Spalato, | (in the Territorie of Venice) | Vndertooke his departure | thence. | Englished out of his Latine Copy. | (device).

At London | Printed by Iohn Bill, | Anno 1616. | 18.8x13.cm.   (1),56;5;6;(14)p.
Contains also Latin Decretum, placing the book on the Index, with translation and observations on the Decree.
The works of De Dominis were burned at Rome, Dec. 21, 1624.

DOMINIS, Marco Antonio de.   Marcvs | Antonivs | De Dominis, | Archiepiscopvs | Spalatensis, Svæ | Profectionis | Consilivm | Exponit. | (device).

Londini, | Apud Ioannem Billivm. | Anno 1616. | Cum Priuilegio. | 18.2x13.7cm. (1),40,5p.   Blank fly-leaf.

DYKE, Daniel.   Certaine | Comfortable | Sermons Vpon | the 124. Psalme: | Tending to stirre up to Thankefulnesse | for our Deliverance from the late | Gunpowder-Treason: | Preached before the Lady Elizabeth | her Grace, at Combe: | By Daniel Dike Preacher of the | Word of God. | . . . (6 lines).   Seene and allowed. |

London: | Printed by Thomas Snodham for Henry Fetherstone | dwelling in Pauls Church-yard at the Signe | of the Rose. 1616. | 17.2x13.3cm.   (12),98p.
T.p. supplied by Mr. Edward G. Friehold, of London.

EBURNE, Richard.   The | Royal | Lavv: | Or, | The Rvle Of | Eqvitie Prescribed | Vs By Ovr Saviovr | Christ. Math.7.12. | Teaching All Men Most | Plainly And Briefely, How | to behaue themselues iustly, consciona- | bly, and vprightly, in all their dealings, | toward all men. | To The Glory Of God, And | good of Gods Church, explained: | By | Ricaard Ebvrne Minister of the Gospel | at Hengstridge in Somersetshire. | . . . (3 lines)

London, | Printed for Thomas Adams. | 1616. | Line border. 18.9x13.8cm. (7), 68p.

FORBES, John. A Treatise | Tending To Cleare | The Doctrine Of | Ivstification. | Written by Io. Forbes, Pastour of the English | Church at Middelbvrgh, for the instru- | ction of his flocke: And now published | by some of them for the good | of others. | . . . (7 lines ; ornament).

At Middelburgh, | Printed by Richard Schilders. 1616. | 17.8x13.5cm. (12), 189,(1)p.

FOTHERBY, J. The | Covenant | Betweene | God And Man. | Playnely declared in laying | open the chiefest points | of Christian | Religion. | Diuided into foure Parts. | The Contents whereof are in the | page next after the | Epistle. | . . . (2 lines).

London | Printed by W. Stansby for Richard Meighen, | and are to bee sold at his shop neere | Saint Clements Church without | Temple Barre. 1616. | Line border. 14.4x9.2 cm. (16),453,(11)p. Pp. 147-176 omitted in numbering .
Signed I.F. in heading of dedication. H&L, new edition.

FULLER, Nicholas. Miscellaneorvm | Theologicorum, | Quibvs Non | Modo Scriptvræ Divinæ, | Sed Et Aliorum Classico- | rum Auctorum plurima monumenta explican- | tur atque illustrantur: | Libri Tres, | Plurimarum observationum, in hac Editione, insigni | auctario Locupletati: | His insuper accessit, consimilis argumenti, Liber | item Quartus, antehac nunquam pervulgatus. | Avctore | Nicolao Fvllero antiquæ & | inclytæ Ecclesiæ Cathedralis | Sarisbvriensis | Canonico. | (ornament).

Oxoniæ, | Excudebat Iosephus Barnesius. 1616. | 18.6x14.3cm.(16), 1–452, (8), 453–645,(1)p.

GOSTWYKE, Roger. Deo & Ecclesiæ | D. D. | The | Anatomie Of | Ananias: | Or, | Gods Censure against Sacri- | ledge. | With | A Briefe Scholie Vpon | Psalm. 83. concerning the same subject. | By Roger Gostvvyke Batchelour of Diui- | nitie, and Minister of Sampford Courtnie | in the Countie of Deuonsh. | . . . (4 lines; ornament)

Printed by Cantrell Legge, | Printer to the Vniuersitie of Cambridge. | 1616. | 17.7x13.2cm (7),183pp.

GOUFFIER, Henri Marc de. A | Declaration | Of Henry Marc De | Gouffier Marquise of Boniuet, | Lord of Creuecœur, &c. | Made in the Consistorie of Rochell, | in the presence of the Pastors and Elders of the said | Towne; as also of Monsieur de la Violette and | Thevenot, Pastors of the Churches of Marans and | Benet, on Wednesday being the third of August, 1616. | The which very same protestation likewise hath beene | made by the said Lord Marquise in the presence of the | whole Church of Rochel, on Sunday being | the seuenth of the said

moneth, after | the morning Sermon in the | great Church. | At Rochell, | Printed for H. Havltin, by Cornelis | Hertman. 1616. | (device).
London, | Printed by Edward Griffin for Nathaniel Butter, dwel- | ling neere S. Austens gate, at the signe of | the Pide-Bull. 1616. | 16.9x13.1 cm. (4),14p.

GOUGE, William. Πανοπλια Του Θεου. | The | VVhole-Armor of God | Or | The Spiritvall Fvrnitvre | which God hath prouided to keepe safe euery | Christian Sovldier from all the | assaults of Satan. | First Preached, and now published for | the good of all such as well vse it: | By | VVilliam Gouge B.D. and Preacher | of Gods word in Blackfryers London. | . . . (2 lines ; device).
At London | Printed by Iohn Beale. 1616. | 17.9x13.4cm. (16),523, (15)p.

HAKEWILL, George. An Answere | To A Treatise Writ- | ten By Dr. Carier, | By way of Letter to his Maiestie: | Wherein He Layeth | Downe Svndry Politike | Considerations, | By which hee pretendeth himselfe was moued, | And endeuoureth to moue others to be reconciled to the | Church of Rome, and imbrace that Religion, | which he calleth Catholike. | By George Hakewil, Doctour of Diuinity, | And Chapleine to the Prince his Highnesse. | . . . (6 lines; 11 in margin).
Imprinted at London | by Iohn Bill. | 1616. | Cum Priuilegio. | 18x13.3cm. (1), 30,306,26,(1) p.
After p. 130, two leaves containing facsimile of the Spanish title-page of Juan de la Puente's Conveniencie Of The Tvvo Catholike Monarchies, with translation. Folded plate after p. 138.

HALL, Joseph. Meditations | & | Vovves, | Diuine and Moral | Seruing for direction in | Christian and Ciuill | Practice. | Diuided into two bookes. | Newely enlarged with 10. | Vowes and Meditations. | By Ios: Hall. |
London | Printed by Humfrey | Lownes, for Henry | Fetherston. | 1616. | Lace border. 12.2x6.8cm. (8),1–401,(5),409–618:(16),637–837,(6),845–946,(8),957–979p. 5 Sub. t.p. Portr.frontisp.
Contains also: Heaven | Vpon | Earth: | ; The Art of | Diuine Meditation; | Holy | Observa- | tions. | Lib.I. | ; and, Some Few | of Dauids Psalmes | Metaphrased, for a taste | of the rest. |

HAY, Peter. A | Vision Of | Balaams | Asse. | VVherein Hee | did perfectly see the present estate | of the Church of Rome. | Written by Peter Hay Gentleman | of North-Britaine, for the reformation | of his Countrymen. | Specially Of That Trvly | Noble and sincere Lord, Francis Earle | of Errol, Lord Hay, and great | Constable of Scotland. | . . . (2 lines; ornament).
London | Printed for Iohn Bill. | Cum Priuilegio. | 1616. | 18.2x13.3cm. (24), 286p.

HUNGERFORD, Anthony. The | Advise Of | A Sonne, Novv Pro- | fessing The Religi- | on Established In | the present Church of England, | to his deare Mother, yet a Ro- | man Catholike. | (device).
At Oxford, | Printed by Ioseph Barnes, Printer to the Vni- | versitie. 1616. | 17.4x13.5 cm. (1),38p.
Cf. DNB. 28: 253b.

JAMES I. His | Maiesties | Speach In | The Starre- | Chamber, | The xx. Of Ivne, | Anno 1616. | (device)

¶Imprinted at London by Ro- | bert Barker, Printer to the | Kings most Excellent Maiestie. | [1616]. 18.5x14.2cm. (4 , 59)p.

JAMES I. The | VVorkes Of | The Most High | And Mightie | Prince, | Iames | By The Grace Of | God, King Of Great | Britaine, France And | Ireland, Defender | of the Faith, &c. | Pvblished By Iames, Bishop | of Winton, and Deane of his Maiesties | Chappel Royall. | . . . (2 lines; device)

London | Printed By Robert Barker And | Iohn Bill, Printers To The Kings | most Excellent Maiestie. | Anno 1616. | Cum Priuilegio. | 32.5x20.7cm. (38),621,(1)p.
Colophon dated 1620.

La | LITVRGIE | Angloise. | Ov | Le Livre Des | Prieres Pvbliqves, | de l'Administration des Sa- | cremens, & autres Ordres & | Ceremonies de l'Eglise | d'Angleterre. | Nouuellement traduit en François | par l'Ordonnance de sa Maiesté de | la Grande Bretaigne. |

A Londres, | Par Iehan Bill, | Imprimeur du Roy. | M.DC.XVI. | Auec priuilege de sa Majesté. | Engraved border. 19x14.2cm. (39, 502)p. Le | Livre Des | Pseavmes | De David. | p. 319.

PARKER, Robert. De | Politeia Ecclesiastica | Christi, | Et | Hierarchica Opposita, | Libri Tres. | In quibus tam veræ disciplinæ fundamenta: | quam omnes ferè de eadem controversiæ, | summo cum judicio & doctrina methodicè | pertractantur. | Authore | Roberto Parkero Anglo, | Theologo ad regnum Dei doctissimo. | Argumenta Librorum & Capitum præpositus | Index ostendet. | . . . (4 lines; ornament)

Prostant Francofvrti | Apud | Godefridvm Basson. | M.D.C.XVI. | 18.7x14.2 cm. (18),368,456p.

PERKINS, William. The | VVorkes Of That | Famovs And VVor- | thy Minister Of Christ | in the Vniuersitie of Cambridge, | Mr. William Perkins. | The First Volvme: | Newly corrected according to his owne Copies. | With Distinct Chapters, And Contents | of euery Booke, and two Tables of the whole: one, of the matter and | questions, the other of choice places of Scripture. | . . . (6 lines ; device).

Printed at London by Iohn Legatt Printer to | the Vniuersitie of Cambridge. | 1616. | Line border. 3 vols. I, 1616, 33.1x22.2cm; (7),779,(16)p; II, 1617, 33.6x21.5 cm; (16),727,(28)p; III, 1609, 32.7x22.cm; (6),264,(9);(4),206; (12),207-370;(10), 371-408;(5),411-439; (4),441-463;(4),465-477;(8),479-605;(9),607-667;(7),669-700, (14)p.

PERKINS, William. Zungenleitter | das ist, | Ein edler vnd herzlicher | Vnterricht, wie man die Zunge zu | Gottes Ehre, dess Nechsten vnd eines | jeglichen selbst eygenen Nutzen recht | brauchen könne vnd solle. | Erstlich | Beschrieben in Englisher Spraache | von Herrn Guilielmo Perkinso, | und demnach in Lateinische Zunge vrbersetzet | von Thoma Draxo, newlich | aber verteutschet. | Durch | Henricum Springlium | von Zürich in der Eydgnossschafft. | (ornament)

Gedruckt zu Oppenheim bey Hieronymo | Gallern, In Vorlegung Levini Husii Woctib | M D C X V I. | 12.3x8cm. 143p.

POWELL, Gabriel. The | Resolved | Christian; | Exhorting to Res-
olution. | Written, | {To comfort the Faint-hearted. | To strengthen the
Faithful. | To recall the Worldling: | And | To perswade All Men, so
to run | that they may obtaine. } (Line ornament)

London, | Printed by T.S. for Richard Moore, | and are to bee sould at his
shop | in St. Dunstans Churchyard | in Fleet-streete. | 1616. | Line border. 14.4x9.5
cm. (16),302,(1)p.
Epistle dedicatorie, signed.

PRESTON, Thomas. Appendix | ad Disputationem Theologicam |
de Iuramento Fidelitatis. | In Qvo | Omnia Argumenta, quæ à Fran-
cisco Suarez | celeberrimo Societatis Iesv Theologo | pro potestate
Papali Principes deponendi, | & contra recens Fidelitatis Iura- | mentū
allata sunt, dilucidè | examinantur. | A | Rogero Widdringtono | Ca-
tholico Anglo. | (device). . . . (2 lines).

Albionopoli | Apud Rvardvm Phigrvm. | Anno Salutis. 1616. | 14. x9. cm.   (21),
284p. Imperfect: Sig. F, pp 43-58 repeated; Sig. G, 59-74 missing.
Anon. Gillow. V: 365.

PRESTON, Thomas. Rogeri Widdringtoni, | Catholici Angli Ad |
Sanctissimum Dominum Pavlvm | Quintvn, Pontificem Max. | humil-
lima Supplicatio. | Cui | Adiungitur Appendix, in quo plurimæ calum-
niæ | cum insigni fraude, & maledicentia coniunctæ, quas Adolphus |
Schulckenius Doctor Theologus eidem Widdringtono ad | eū hæreseωs
accusandum falsò, summamq́[ue] periniuri- | am imposuit, perspicuè
deteguntur, | Et | Idem Schulckenius in ius vocatur, atq́; in manifestæ
calumniæ | iudicium a Widdringtono adducitur. | . . . (3 lines ; de-
vice).

Albionopoli | Apud Rufum Lipsium, 1616. | 14.x9. cm.   (1),94;(4),1-76,75-262,
(1)p.
Appendix has separate title-page, register and pagination. Gillow. V, 365.

RAWLINSON, John. The | Vnmasking | Of The | Hypocrite. | A
Sermon preached in St Maries | in Oxford, Maij 12. | [1616.] | By |
Iohn Ravvlinson Doctor of Diuinitie. | . . . (3 lines; ornament)

London, | Printed by Edw: Griffin for Ralph Mabbe, | and are to be sold at the
signe of the Gray-hound | in Paules Church-yard. 1616. | 16.5x12.8cm.   (6),37p.

ROUS, Francis. Meditations | Of Instrvction, | Of Exhortation, | Of
Reprofe: | Indeavovring The | edification and reparation of | the house
of God. | . . . (4 lines ; ornament).

London, | Printed by I.L. for George | Gibbs and Francis Consta- | ble, 1616. |
Line border.   11.4x6.7cm.   (7),468,(11)p
Cambr.Univ.Cat:3761. Epistle dedicatorie, signed F.R.

SANDYS, Edwin. Sermons | Of the most Reuerend | Father In
God, | Edwin Arch-bishop of Yorke, | Primat and Metropolitane of |
England. | Some whereof were preached in the parts beyond | the Seas,
in the time of his exile, in the raigne | of Queene Marie. | The residue,
in such places of preferment as he enioyed vn- | der her late Maiestie,
Queene Elizabeth, of famous memo- | rie: viz . He was in Anno D.1559.

first consecrated Bishop of | Worcester; and thence translated to London, in Anno | D.1570. and then remooued to Yorke, | in Anno D. 1576. | VVith a Preface to the Christian Readers of their | vse and benefit; by a most reuerend Father | now liuing. | . . . (4 lines).

At London | Printed by Iohn Beale, for Thomas | Chard. 1616. | Line border. 17.7x14cm. (4), 194 fol. fol. numbers begin on 2d leaf of Sermons.

SCOTT, Thomas. Christs | Politician, | And Salomons | Pvritan. | Deliuered in two Sermons preached | before the Kings Maiestie. | By | Thomas Scot Bachelour of | Diuinitie and one of his Maiesties Chapleines. | These two Sermons Epitomiz'de. | . . . (4 lines).

London | Printed by Edward Griffin for Francis Constable, and are to be | sold at his shop at the signe of the White Lion in | Paules Church-yard. 1616. | 17.2x 12.8 cm. (4),34,23p.

SHELDON, Richard. A | Svrvey Of | The Miracles | Of The Chvrch | of Rome, prouing them to be | Antichristian. | Wherein Are | examined and refuted the six funda- | mentall Reasons of Iohn Flood Ignatian, published by him in defence | of Popish Miracles. | By Richard Sheldon Ca- | tholike Priest, and sometimes in the | Church of Rome Mr. Floods | Colleagve. | . . . (4 lines).

London, | Printed by Edward Griffin for Nathaniel Butter, and are to | be sold at his shop at S. Austens Gate, at the signe | of the Pyde Bull. 1616. | 18.7x12.7 cm. (20),336,(6)p.

SIMSON, Patrick. A Short | Compend, | of the grouth of the | Romane Antichrist, | Comprised in the VII. VIII. and IX. | Centuries. | Wherevnto Are Added | Treatises, Clearly | declaring the noueltie of | Popish Religion. | (ornament)

Edinbvrgh, | Printed by Andro Hart, | Anno 1616. | Head-piece. 18.2x13.7cm. (8),238p.

Epistle dedicatorie, signed.

SPELMAN, Henry. De non temerandis Ecclesiis. | A | Tract Of | The Rights And | Respect Dve Vn- | to Churches. | Written to a Gentleman, who hauing | an Appropriate Parsonage, imploied the | Church to prophane vses, and left the Pari- | shioners vncertainely prouided of | diuine seruice, in a parish neere | there adioyning. | The second Edition enlarged with an | Appendix. | By Sr. Henry Spelman | Knight. |

At London | Imprinted by Iohn Beale, and are | to be sold by William Welby. | 1616. | 12.9x8.7cm. (10),196p.

WHITE, John. The | VVay To The | Trve Chvrch: | Wherein | The Principall Motives | perswading to Romanisme, | and | Questions touching the nature and authority of the | Church and Scriptures, are familiarly disputed, | and driuen to their issues, where, this day they | sticke betweene the Papists and vs: | Contriued into an Answer to a Popish Discourse, concerning the Rule | of Faith, and the marks of the Church. And published to ad- | monish such as decline to Papistry, of the weake and vncertaine | grounds, whereupon they haue ventured their soules. | Directed to all that seeke for resolution: and especially to his | louing countrimen of Lancashire. | By Iohn White Minister of Gods word at Eccles. | The fourth impression, to which is annexed the Authors Protestation made | vpon his deathbed, touching his opinion in the present controuersies. | . . . (2 lines; ornament).

London, | Printed by Richard Field for Iohn Bill and | William Barret. 1616. | 18x13.9cm   (64),456,(10)pp.

1617

An | ABRIDGEMENT | Of That Booke Which | The Ministers Of Lin- | colne Diocesse De- | liuered to his Maiestie vpon the | first of December 1605. | Being The First Part Of | An Apologie For Them- | selves And Their Bre- | thren That Refvse The | Subscription and Conformitie | which is required. | Wherevnto Is Annexed, | A Table of sundry Poynts not handled in this A- | bridgement, which are other exceptions they take to | the Subscription required, and shall be the Ar- | gument of the second part of their | Apologie. | . . . (12 lines).

Reprinted, Anno Dom. 1617. | 14x8.5cm.(14),102p.

AINSWORTH, Henry. Annotations | Upon the Book of | Psalmes. | Wherin the Hebrew words and sentences are compared with, and | explained by the ancient Greek and Chaldee versions: | but chiefly by conference with the | holy Scriptures. | By Henry Ainsworth. | . . . (6 lines; ornament).

The second edition: in the yere | 1617. | Line border. 20.x15.6cm.   (4.279,8)p.
Part of his Annotations Vpon The Five Bookes Of Moses: 1622; with separate register.

BARCLAY, John. Ioannis | Barclaii | Parænesis | Ad | Sectarios | Libri II. | (device)

Svperiorvm Permissv. | Coloniæ, | Apud Ioannem Kinckivm. | Anno M.DC.-XVII. | 15.6x9.2cm.   (16),296p.

BERNARD, Richard. A Key Of Knowledge | For The Opening Of The | Secret Mysteries Of St Iohns | Mysticall Revelation. | By Ric. Bernard, preacher | of Gods word at Batcombe, | in Somersetshire. | The Contents ar in the next | page before the booke. | . . . (3 lines)

At London | imprinted by Felix Kyngston. | 1617. | 18.6x14.2cm.   (60), 351pp.
Engraved title-page: nine vignettes . Pp. 1–4, 13–16 in duplicate.

BRUCE, Robert. The | Way To Trve | Peace And Rest. | Delivered At Edinborovgh | In XVI. Sermons: on the Lords Supper: Hezechiahs | Sicknesse: and other select Scriptures. | By that reuerend & faithfull Preacher of Gods word: | Mr. Robert Brvce, for the present, | Minister of the Word in Scotland. | . . . (5 lines; device).

London. | Printed by R.Field for Thomas Man and Ionas | Man, dwelling in Pater-noster row at | the signe of the Talbot. 1617. | 17.6 x 13. cm.   (12),367p.

BYFIELD, Nicholas. An | Exposition | Vpon The Epistle | To The Colossians. | Wherein, | Not Onely The Text Is | Methodically Ana-lysed, and the sence of | the words, by the help of Writers, both ancient | and moderne is explayned: | But also, | By Doctrine and Vse, the intent of the holy Ghost is in | euery place more fully vnfolded and vrged. | And besides, | The very marrow of most Common-places is aptly diffused through- | out the body of this Exposition, as the nature of | this kinde of Teaching would beare. | And further, | Many chiefe Cases of Conscience are here resolued. | All | With conuenient Varietie and Breuitie. | Being, | The substance of neare seuen yeeres Weeke-dayes Sermons, | of N. Byfield, | late one of the Preachers for the Citie of Chester. | Corrected and amended. | . . . (4 lines).

London: | Printed by E.G. for Nathaniel Bvtter, and are to be sould | at his Shop at the signe of the Pide-Bull in Pauls Church-yard, | neare to S. Austins Gate. 1617. | Line border. 28x18.3cm. (28),179,(8),90,(10),137,(8),157–202p.

BYFIELD, Nicholas. Sermons | Vpon The | first Chapter of the first | Epistle generall of Peter. | Wherein | Method, Sense, | Doctrine and Vse is with great | varietie of matter profitably | handled. | By Nicholas Byfeild Preacher | of Gods word at Isleworth in | Middlesex. | The rest of the Epistle may be published in | due time, if God will. | . . . (4 lines).

London, | Printed by Edward Griffin for Nathaniel Butter, and | are to be sold at the signe of the Pyde Bull | at S.Austins gate. 1617. | Line border. 18.7x14.2cm. (30),512p.

CARTWRIGHT, Thomas. Commentarii | Succincti & Dilucidi | In | Proverbia Salomonis. | Avthore | Thoma Cartvvrighto | SS.Theologiæ in Academia Can- | tabrigiensi quondam | Professore. | Quibus adhibita est Præfatio clarissimi viri | Iohannis Polyandri. | S.Theologiæ Professoris Leidensis. | (ornament).

Lvgdvni Batavorvm. | Apud Guiljelmum Brevvsterum, | In vico Chorali. | 1617. | 19.7x14.2cm. (11)p,1–225,246–907,910–911,910–1133,1135–1514columns,(23)p.

COLLINS, Samuel. Epphata | to F.T. | Or, | The Defence | of the Right Reuerend Father in God, | the Lord Bishop of Elie, Lord High-Almoner and | Priuie Counsellour to the Kings | Most Excellent | Maiestie. | Concerning His Answer | to Cardinall Bellarmines Apologie: | Against the slaunderous cauills of a namelesse Adioyner; | entitling his Booke in euery page of it, | A Discouerie of many fowle absurdities, falsities, lyes, &c. | Wherein | These Things Cheifely | are discussed, (besides many other incident.) | 1.The Popes false Primacie, clayming by Peter. | 2. Invocation of Saints, with Worship of creatures, and Faith in them. | 3. The Supremacie of Kings both in Temporall and Ecclesiasticall mat- | ters and causes, ouer all states and persons, &c. within their Realmes | and Dominions. | By Dr. Collins, chapleine to His Maiestie. | . . . (1 line).

Printed By Cantrell Legge, | Printer to the Vniuersitie of Cambridge. | 1617. | 18x13.3cm. (46),554,(19)p. Sub-title before p. 223.

CRASHAW, William, Trans. Fiscus Papalis. | Sive, | Catalogus Indulgentiarum & Reli- | quiarum septem principalium Ec- | clesiarum vrbis Romæ. | Ex vetusto Manuscripto codice vere & | fideliter descriptus. | A part of the Popes Exchequer, | That is | A Catalogue of the

Indulgences and Reliques be- | longing to the seauen principall Churches | in Rome. | Laying downe the spirituall riches and infinite treasure | which (as sure as the Pope is holy & true) are tobe found | in the Catholike Roman Church, whereof the poore | Heretikes in England haue not one Mite. | Taken out of an antient Manuscript, and translated | Together with | Certaine notes and Comments explaining the more difficult | place, for the ease and helpe of good Catholikes, who | had best goe to Rome, to trie the vertue of | the glorious Indulgences. | By a Catholike Diuine. |

London, | Printed by Nicholas Okes, for George Norton, and are | to be sold at his Shop neere Temple-barre | Gate. 1617. | 18.5x13.5 cm. (16,92) p. Colophon.
Cambr. Univ. Cat: 3669.

DARRELL, John. A | Treatise Of | The Chvrch. | VVritten Against | them of the Separation, commonly | called Brownists. | Wherein the true Doctrine of a visible Church | is taught, and the Church of England, proued to be | a true Church. The Brownists false doctrine of the | visible Church is conuinced; their shamefull peruer- | ting of the holy Scriptures discouered, their | Arguments to proue the Church of | England a false | Church answered. | . . . (6 lines).

London, | Printed by William Iones, dwelling in Red-crosse | streete. 1617. | 16.9x13.5cm (15),266p.
Cambr.Univ.Cat:3323. Epistle Dedicatory, signed.

DELAUNE, Nathaniel. The | Christians | Tryvmph. | Manifested | By the Certitude of | Saluation. | Deliuered | In a Sermon at Pauls-Crosse on Trinity | Sunday, the 15. of Iune. 1617. | By Nathanael Delavne, Mi- | nister of the word of God at Saint Se- | pulchers. And Chaplein in Or- | dinarie to the Kings | Maiestie. |

London, | Printed by N.O. for Iohn Pyper, and are | to be sold at his shop at Pauls gate | next Cheap-side at the signe | of the Crosse-keyes. | 1617. | Line border. 14.5x9.5cm. (10),86p.
From the library of Walter W. Law.

DOMINIS, Marco Antonio de. De | Repvblica | Ecclesiastica | Libri X | Auctore | Marco Antonio | de Dominis | Archiepiscopo Spalatensi. | Cum suis Indicibus. |

Londini | Ex Officina | Nortoniana | Apud | Io:Billivm. | MDCXVII. | Engraved titlepage. 2 v. 33.8 x 21.5 cm. I, (32),773,(34) : II, (8),1009,(28)p. Portr. Vol. 2, dated 1620

DOMINIS, Marco Antonio de. Papatvs | Romanvs: | Liber | De Origine, Pro- | gressu, atque extinctione | ipsius. | (device).

Londini, | Ex Officina Nortoniana, Apud | Iohannem Billvm. | 1617. | 18.5x14.7 cm. (10),206p.
Anon. Cambr.Univ.Cat:3477.

DOMINIS, Marco Antonio de. A Sermon | Preached In | Italian, | By the most Reuerend father, Marc | Antony De Dominis, Archb. | of Spalato, the first Sunday in | Aduent, Anno 1617. | In the Mercers Chappel in London, to the | Italians in that City, and many other Hono- | rable auditors then assembled. | Vpon the 12. Verse of the 13.

Chapter to the | Romanes, being part of the Epistle | for that day. | First published in Italian by the Author, | and thereout Translated into English. | (ornament). |
   London. | Printed by Iohn Bill, | M.DC.XVII. | 17.7x13.4cm. (1),81p.

EPISTOLA | Ecclesiastarvm, | Quos in Belgio Remonstrantes | vocant, | Ad | Exterarvm Ecclesiarvm | Reformatos Doctores, | Pastores, Theologos: | Qua | Sententiam suam de Prædestinatione | & annexis ei capitibus exponunt, & enati aliquot ab hinc | annis ob hæc ipsa in Ecclesiis Belgicis, ac indies magis | magisque gliscentis dissidij fontes causaque | aperiunt, | Opposita Epistolæ Delegatorum Classis VValachrianæ | ad eosdem Doctores singulatim directæ. | (device)
   Lvgdvni Batavorvm, | Excudit Ioannes Patius, Iuratus & Ordinarius Academiæ | Typographus, Anno 1617. | 18.1x13.9cm. (4),133p.

FIELD, John and WILCOX, Thomas. An | Admonition | To The Parliament | Holden In The 13. Yeare | Of The Reigne Of Qveene | Elizabeth Of Blessed | Memorie. | Begun Anno 1570. and ended 1571. | (9 lines ; ornament).
   Imprinted, Anno 1617. | 19.5x14.6 cm. (4),68p.
   Anon. cf Cambr. Univ. Lib. 5895.
   Contains also An Exhortation To The Bishops To deale brotherlie with their Brethren; An Exhortation To The Bishops and their Clergie, to answer a little Booke that came foorth the last Parliament, and to other Brethren to iudge of it by Gods word, vntill they see it answered, and not to be carried away with any respect of man; and A Second Admonition To The Parliament, [by Thomas Cartwright].

HALL, Joseph. Contemplations. | Vpon The | Principall | Passages Of The | Holy Storie. | The first Volume, | In Fovre Bookes. | By I.H. D.D. |
   London | Printed by William Stansby for | Henry Fetherstone. | 1617. | "Grape and column" border. 29.8x19cm.(8),188p.
   Sub-title in his Recollection of such Treatises..1617.

HALL, Joseph. Meditations | And | Vowes, | Divine & Morall: | Serving | For Direction In | Christian and ciuill practise. | III. Centuries. | By Jos. Hall Doctor of | Diuinitie. | (device).
   London, | Printed by Edward Griffin for Henry Fetherstone | at the signe of the Rose in Paules Churchyard. 1617. | Line border. 29.8x19cm. (10), 728p.
   First sub-title in A Recollection of such Treatises.. : 1617.

HALL, Joseph. A | Recollection | of such Treatises as | haue bene heretofore | seuerally published, and | are nowe reuised, correc- | ted, augmented. | By | Jos:Hall Dr of Diuinity. | With addition of some | others not hitherto | extant. |
   London. Printed for Hen: Fetherstone | in Paul's-church-yeard, at ye signe of the rose. | (1617). Engr. t.p. 29.8x19.cm (10),728;(8),188p.
   A collected edition of works, with 29 separate title pages,

HOOKER, Richard. Of The | Lawes | of | Ecclesiastical | Politie, | Eight Bookes, | By Richard Hooker. |

London | Printed by Will:Stansby, and are | to be sold by Mat:Lownes. | Año D 1617. | Engr. t.p. 28.6x18.7cm. (58),453p.
The volume contains also his Certayne Divine Tractates, etc. dated 1618.

JACKSON, Thomas. Nazareth And Bethlehem, | Or, | Israels | Portion In The Sonne | Of Iesse. | And, | Mankinds Comfort | From The Weaker Sexe. | Tvvo Sermons Preached In | St Maryes Church in Oxford. | By | Thomas Iackson, Bachelour of Divinitie, and | Fellow of Corpus Christi College | in Oxford. | . . . (3 lines; device).
At Oxford, | Printed by Iohn Lichfield, and william Wrench. | 1617. | Line border. 17.3x13.2cm. (4),75p.

JOHNSON, Francis. A | Christian | Plea | Conteyning three Treatises. | I. | The first, touching the Anabaptists, & others main- | teyning some like errours with them. | II. | The second, touching such Christians, as now are here, com- | monly called Remonstrants or Arminians. | III. | The third, touching the Reformed Churches, with vvhom my self agree in | the faith of the Gospel of our Lord Iesus Christ. | Made by Francis Iohnson, Pastour of the aun- | cient English Church, now sojourning at Amsterdam | in the Low Countreyes. | . . . (15 lines)
Printed, | In the yeere of our Lord 1617. | 4 ornaments 17.4x13.8cm. (8),324p.

KELLISON, Matthew. The | Right And | Ivrisdiction | Of The Prelate, | and the Prince. | Or, | A Treatise Of | Ecclesiasticall, | and Regall | authoritie. | Compyled | By I. E. Stvdent In Divinitie | for the ful Instruction and appeacemēt of the con- | sciences of English Catholikes, cōcerning the late | Oath of pretended Allegeance. Togeather with a | cleere & Ample declaratiō, of euery clause thereof. | . . . (6 lines)
Imprinted with licence of | Superiours. Anno Dom. 1617. | 16.4x9.7 cm. 317, (2)p.
Anon. Gillow.III:682.

MAXWELL, James. A | Demonstra- | tive Defence Or | Tenfold Probation | Of The Doctrine Of The | Chvrch Of England Tovching | one of the most important points of our Creed, | necessary to be vnderstood of all Christians, | which is of our Sauiours descending into | hell after death, to binde and sub- | due Sathan, &c. | Written for the information and sa- | tisfaction of many mens mindes touching so weighty | a matter, but especially for the furthering of the | Church of Scotlands full conformitie with | that of England. | By | Iames Maxvvell Master of Artes, &c. | . . . (3 lines; ornament)
London, | Printed by Iohn Legatt, Printer to the Vniuer- | sitie of Cambridge. 1617. | 18.4x13.8cm. (2),27p.
Part of his: A Nevv Eight-Fold Probation: 1617. With continuous register, but separate pagination.

MAXWELL, James. A | Nevv Eight- | Fold Probation | Of The Chvrch Of | Englands Divine Constitv- | tion, Prooved By Many Preg- | nant arguments, to be much more com- | plete then any Geneuian in the world | against the contrary assertion of the fifty | three petitioner-preachers of Scotland | in their petition presented in the | late Parliament to the Kings | most excellent Maiesty. | With a ten-folde probation of the | same Churches doctrine touching one of the most | important points of our Creede, which is | of our Sauiours descending into Hell, | By | Iames Maxvvell Master of Artes, &c. | (ornament).

London, | Printed by Iohn Legatt, Printer to the Vniuer- | sitie of Cambridge. 1617. | 18.4x13.8cm. (16),74;(2),27p.

MOCKET, Richard. Doctrina, | Et Politia | Ecclesiae Angli- | canæ, A Beatissimæ | Memoriæ Principibvs | Edovardo Sexto, Regina | Elizabetha Stabilitæ, Et A | Religiosissimo, & Potentissimo Monarcha Iacobo, | Magnæ Britan. &c. Rege continuatæ. | Quibvs Eivsdem Ecclesiæ, | Apologia præfigitur pro sua discessione in vtraque | à grauissimis Romanæ Ecclesiæ, corruptelis, Tyrannide, Ido- | lolatria, Erroribus, & quod ad Concilium Tridenti- | num non accesserit. | Varia totius operis capita pagina quinta indicat. | (device).

Londini, | Apud Ioannem Billivm.1617. | Cum Priuilegio. | 20.6x16.7cm.(8),350p. Folded Sheet at end.
DNB. 38: 91 a.
The edition of 1616 was burned and destroyed by order of James I.

MOORE, John. A | Mappe Of | Mans Mortalitie. | Clearely manifesting the originall of | Death, with the Nature, Fruits, and | Effects thereof, both to the Vnregenerate, | and Elect Children of God. | Diuided into three Bookes; and published for the | furtherance of the wise in practise, the humbling of the | strong in conceit, and for the comfort and confirma- | tion of weake Christians, against the combat of | Death, that they may wisely and seasonably | be prepared against the same. | Whereunto are annexed two Consolatory Sermons; for | afflicted Christians, in their greatest Conflicts. | By | Iohn Moore, Minister of the Word of God, at Shearsbie | in Leicester-Shire. | . . . (11 lines).

London: | Printed by T.S. for George Edvvards, and are to be sold | at the signe of the Greyhound in Paules Church-yard. 1617. | Line border. 18.1x13.2cm. (34),264;(8),45p. Subtitle.

MOORE, John. A | Two-Fold Cord | Of | Consolation, | for afflicted Christians in their | greatest Conflicts. | Seruing to strengthen their Faith, and | to support their Patience, in the | day of Triall. | Deliuered in two Sermons. | The first whereof, contayneth, The effect of | the true knowledge of Gods Word. | The second, contayneth, The power of | faithfull and feruent Prayer. | By | Iohn Moore, Minister of Gods word at Shearsby, | in Leicester-Shire. |

London: Printed by T.S. for George Edvvards, and | are to be sould at the signe of the Greyhound in | Paules Church-yard. 1617. | Line border. 18.1x13.2cm. (8),45p.
Part of his Mappe Of Mans Mortalitie: 1617, with separate register and pagination.

MORNAY, Philippe de. A | Worke | Concerning the trunesse | of Christian Religion: | Against, | Atheists, Epicures, Paynims, Iewes, | Mahumetists, and other Infidels. | Written in French, by Philip of Mornay | Lord of Plessie and Marly. | Begunne to be translated into English, by that honourable and | worthy Gentleman, Sir Philip Sidney Knight, and at his | request finished by Arthvr Golding. | Since which time, it hath beene reuiewed, and is the fourth time pub- | lished, and purged from sundry faults escaped heretofore, | thorow ignorance, carelesnesse, or other | corruption. | (device)

London, | Printed by George Purslowe. 1617. | 18.6 x 14.2 cm. (24),605,(3) p.

URSINUS, Zacharias. The | Svmme Of | Christian | Religion, | De- liuered by Zacharias Vrsinvs | in his Lectures vpon the Catechisme, au- | thorised by the noble Prince Frederick | throughout his domin- ions. | Wherein are debated and resolued the Questions of vvhat- | so- euer points of moment, vvhich haue beene or are | controuersed in Diuinitie. | Translated into English first by D.Henrie Parrie, | and lately conferred with the last and best Latine Edi- | tion of D.David Parevs, Professor of | Diuinitie in Heidelberge. | (device).

At London, | Imprinted by H.L. and are to be sold by Arthur | Iohnson, at the signe of the white horse, neere | the great North doore of Paules | Church. 1617. | Line border. 21x16cm.(10), 1111,(12)p.

WHITAKER, William. Edmvndi | Campiani | Iesuitæ Ra- | tiones Decem, | Quibus Fretus, Certamen | Anglicanæ Ecclesiæ, Et | Omnibus Orthodoxis Evan- | gelii Ministris Obtu- | lit In Causa Fidei: | Et Ad Eas | Gvil. Withakeri | Theologiæ in Academia Can- | tabrigiensi pro- fessoris Re- | gij Responsio. |

Per VVilhelmum VVesselium. | Prostat Francofurti apud Iohannem Caro- | lum Vnckelium. | Anno M DC XVII. | Lace border. 19.8x14.9cm.(17),2-198,(3)p. T.p. in red and black.

WHITE, Francis. The | Orthodox | Faith And Way | To The Chvrch Ex- | planed And Iustified: | In Answer To A Popish Treatise, | en- tituled, White Died Blacke; wherein T. W. P. in | his triple accusation of D. White for impostures, vntruths, and | absurd illations, is proued a trifler: And the present con- | trouersies betweene vs and the Roman- ists are | more fully deliuered and cleared. | By Francis White Bach- elour in Diuinitie, and elder | Brother of Doctor Iohn White. | . . . (6 lines; ornament).

London, | Printed by Richard Field for William Barret, | and are to be sold at his shop in Pauls Church-yard | at the signe of the three Pigeons. 1617. | 18.2x13.7 cm. (44),405,(3) p.

WORSHIP, William. The | Christians | Iewell. | Or, | The Treasvre Of | a Good Conscience. | By William Worship, | Doctor of Diuinitie. | . . . (4 lines).

London, | Printed by William Stansby, | for Iohn Parker. 1617. | Line border. 13.4x8. cm. (20),243p.

1618

ADAMSON, Patrick. Apocalypsis | S.Ioannis Theologi, | Latino Carmine reddita. | Patricio Adamsono, Scoto, | Sanctiandreæ Archiepiscopo | Authore. | (device).
Londini, | Apud Ioannem Billivm. | Anno 1618. | 18.9x14cm. (10),57p.
Incorporated with his: Poëmata...1619; with continuous register, but separate pagination.

ADAMSON, Patrick. Catechismvs | Latino Carmine | Redditvs, Et In Li- | bros Qvatvor Digestvs, | Patricij Adamsoni Scoti, poetæ | elegantissimi opera, at- | que industria: | Ac Nunc Denvo Per Tho- | man Volvsenvm Recog- | nitus & expolitus. | (ornament).
Londini, | Apud Ioannem Billivm. | Anno 1618. | 18.9x14cm. (4),36 fol
Incorporated with his: Genethliacum; with continuous register, but separate pagination.

ADAMSON, Patrick. Confessio Fidei, Et | Doctrinæ, Per Ecclesiam Re- | formatam Regni Scotiæ receptæ; Exhibitæ | ordinibus Regni euisdem in publicis Par- | liamenti (vt vocant) comitijs, & eorum | communi consensu approbatæ, vti | certissimis fundamentis verbi | Dei innixæ, & con- | sentaneæ, | Per Patricium Adamsonum descripta, | Anno salutis nostræ millesimo quingentesimo | septuagesimo secundo. | ... (4 lines; ornament).
Londini | Apud Ioannem Billium. | Anno 1618. | 18.9x14.cm. (3),42–60 fol.
Incorporated with his Genethliacum; with continuous register and pagination.

ADAMSON, Patrick. De Papistarvm | Svperstitiosis | Ineptiis. | Patricij Adamsonij Scoti, | Poetæ carmen. | ... (3 lines; ornament).
Londini | Apud Ioannem Billium, | Anno 1618. | 18.9x14cm. (1),37–41fol.
Incorporated with his: Genethliacum; with continuous register and pagination.

ADAMSON, Patrick. Serenissimi Ac No- | bilissimi, Scotiæ, Angliæ, Franciæ, & | Hyberniæ Principis, Henrici | Stvardi Illustrissimi Herois, ac | Mariæ Reginæ amplissimæ filij, | Genethliacum. | A Patricio Adamsono Scoto, Poeta or- | natissimo Parisijs conscriptum, & ibidem Typis audaciùs commissum, | 25. Iunij, sexto à partu die. | 1566. | (device).
No Imprint. (1618). (4,7)p.
Incorporated with his: Poëmata...1619; with separate register and pagination.

ADAMSON, Patrick. Threnorvm Sive | Lamentationvm | Ieremiæ Prophetæ | F.Elciæ | Libellus, Latino Carmine redditus, | A Patricio Adamsono, Scoto, | Sanctiandreæ Archiepiscopo. Et nunc denuò per | Thomam Volvsenvm I.C. | recognitus & expolitus. | (device).
Londini, | Apud Ioannem Billivm. | Anno 1618. | 18.9x14cm. (8),19p.
Incorporated with his: Poëmata...1619; with separate pagination, but continuous register.

AINSWORTH, Henry. Annotations | Upon The Third Book | Of Moses, | Called | Leviticvs. | Wherin, By Conferring | the holy Scriptures, by comparing the Greek | and Chaldee Versions, and moniments of the | Hebrewes: the Sacrifices, and other legal | ordinances heretofore cōmanded | of God, to the Church of | Israel, are explain- | ed. | By Henry Ainsworth. | . . . (ornament; 7 lines).

Imprinted in the yere 1618. | Line border. 20.x15.6cm. (2,274)p.

Part of his Annotations Vpon The Five Bookes Of Moses: 1622; with separate register.

AIRAY, Henry. Lectvres | Vpon The VVhole | Epistle of St.Pavl to the | Philippians. | Deliuered in St.Peters Church | in Oxford: | By the reuerend and faithfull seruant of | Christ Henry Airay Doctor of | Diuinitie and late Prouost of Queenes | Colledge. | And now published for the vse of Gods Church | by C.P. Master of Arts and Fellow of | the same Colledge. | (ornament).

London | Printed by Edw: Griffin for William Bladen, and are to | be sold at his shoppe in Pauls Church-yard at the signe of | the Bible neere the great north doore. 1618. | Line border. 18.7x13.8cm.(20),1–864,721–950p.T.p. & pp. 1–2 of Preface in MS facsimile.

ANDREWES, Lancelot. A Sermon | Preached | before His Maiestie, | At White hall the fift of | Nouember last, | 1617. | By the Bishop of Elie, His | Maiesties Almoner. | (device).

London | Printed by Iohn Bill, | M.DC.XVIII. | 17.6x14 cm. (2),50p.

ATTERSOLL, William. A | Commentarie | vpon the Fourth Booke of Moses, | called Nvmbers. | Containing, | The Foundation of the Church and Common-wealth of the Israelites, | while they walked and wandered in the | Wildernesse. | Laying before vs the vnchangeable loue of God promised and exhibited to this | people; The comely order established and obserued among them; Sundry exam- | ples of his horrible iudgements against obstinate sinners; The Fatherly chastisements and | corrections of the faithfull offending; and the dangerous plottings | and diuellish policies of the Churches enemies, are | detected and discouered. | Wherein | the whole | body of Di- | uinity is | handled | touching | matters (Dogmaticall: Of God, of Christ, of the Gospel, of the Law, of Sin, of Faith and Iustification, of the Scrip- | tures, of the Sabbath, of Magistrates and of the Ministery, of the Resurrection, of Prayer and the lawfulnesse | of set formes, of Tythes and Impropriations, of the Sacraments in generall, and in speciall of Baptisme and the | Lords Supper, of Duelles and Duellists, of Excommunication, of Repentance and remission of sinnes, of restitu- | tion, of Warre, and of the lawfulnesse of the marriage of Cozengermans. | Ceremoniall: Of the calling of the Priests and Leuites, and of the first borne, of the waters of iealousie, of | the vow of the Nazarites, of the daily sacrifice, of the Iewish Feasts, of the yeare of Iubile, of the new Moones, | of afficting the soule, of the Feast of the Passeouer and Pentecost, of the Trumpets and of the Tabernacles, of | the Vrim and Thummim, of the seuen Lampes and the making of the two siluer Trumpets, of the pillar of Fire | and the Cloud, of the meate Offering and drinke Offering, with the vses of them all toward our selues, together | with a description of sundry waights and measures vsed of the Iewes. | Polemicall: Or Controuersies betweene the Church of Rome and vs, as of the Scriptures, of the Church and | the notes of it, of the supremacy of the Byshop of Rome, of the Masse, of Purgatory, of Free-will, of Prayer in a | strange tongue, of iustification by Workes, of the Sacraments, of Vowes, of auricular Confession, of Reliques, of | binding and loosing, of Temples, of Tapers and wax Candles, of Sanctuaries, and of Images and Idolatry. | Heerein also the Reader shall finde more then fiue hundred Theolo- | gicall Questions, decided and determined | By William Attersoll, Minister of the word. |

London, | Printed by William Iaggard, 1618. | Line border. 32.6x21.3cm. (14), 1271p.

BAYNES, Paul. A | Caveat | For Cold | Christians. | In | A Sermon Preached | By Mr. Pavl Bayne, Somtimes | Minister of Gods Word at St. An- | drewes, in Cambridge. | Wherein The Common Dis- | ease of Christians, with the remedie, is plain- | ly and excellently set downe for | all that will vse it. | . . . (3 lines; device)

At London | Imprinted by Felix Kyngston, for Nathanael Newbery, | and are to be sold at his shop vnder St. Peters | Church in Cornhill, and in Popes-head | Alley, right against the signe of | the white horse. 1618. | 18.3x13.9 cm. (5),20p.

BAYNES, Paul. A | Commentarie | Vpon The First | Chapter of the Epistle of | Saint Pavl, written to | the Ephesians. | Wherein, Besides | the Text fruitfully explained: some | principall Controuersies about Pre- | destination are handled, and diuers | Arguments of Arminius | are examined. | By Mr Pavl Bayne, sometimes Preacher | of Gods Word at Saint Andrevves | in Cambridge. | . . . (5 lines)

London: | Printed by Thomas Snodham, for Robert | Mylbovrne, and are to be sold in Pauls Church- | yard, at the Signe of the Beare. 1618. | 18x13.4cm (20), 409p.

BAYNES, Paul. A | Covnterbane | against | Earthly Carefvlnes. | In a Sermon preached at Crane- | brooke in Kent. 1617. | By Mr. Paul Baine sometimes Preacher of Gods | Word at Saint Andrewes in | Cambridge. | . . . (2 lines; device).

London | Printed by H.L. for Nathanaell Newbery, and are to | be solde at his Shop vnder St.Peters church in | Cornehill and in Popes-head Alley. | 1618. | 17.3x 13.2cm. (6),25,(2)p.

BRADWARDINE, Thomas. Thomæ | Bradwardini | Archiepiscopi Olim | Cantvariensis, | De Cavssa Dei, | Contra Pelagivm, | Et De Virtvte Cavssarvm, | Ad suos Mertonenses, | Libri Tres: | Jussu Reverendiss. Georgii | Abbot Cantuariensis Archiepiscopi; | Opera Et Stvdio Di. Henrici | Savilii, Equitis aurati, Collegij Mertonensis in | Academia Oxoniensi Custodis, | Ex scriptis Codicibus nunc primum editi. | (device)

Londini, | Ex Officina Nortoniana, | Apud Ioannem Billivm. | M.DC.XVIII. | 34.2x22.2cm. (11),876p.

BUCER, Gerson. Dissertatio | De | Gvbernatio- | ne Ecclesiæ, | maximéque de | Presbyterio, & Episcopatv, | præcipuas hujus argumenti controversias placidè | pertractans, amicâ collatione institutâ cum Doctissimi Clarissimique Viri D. | Georgii Downami, S. Theologiæ Doctoris Concione, quondam | de hoc eodem subjecto Anglicè editâ, nunc verò in Latinum sermonem | versâ; non contentionis studio, sed justæ defensionis cau- | sâ, ad veritatis illustrationem suscepta, | à Gersomo Bvcero, verbi divini Administro in Ecclesia Veriana | . . . (2 lines: device).

Middelbvrgi Zelandorvm, | Apud Symonem Moulert. Anno M. DC. XVIII. | 21.3x15.9cm. (20),622,(2)p.

BUCKERIDGE, John. A Sermon | Preached | before His Maiestie | At Whitehall, March 22. 1617. | being Passion-Sunday, | Touching Prostration, and Kneeling | in the worship of God. | To which is added a Discourse con- | cerning Kneeling at the Communion. | By Iohn, Bishop of Rochester. | (device)

London | Printed by Iohn Bill, | 1618. | 18x14 cm. 248,(2) p.

CARLETON, Dudley. The | Speech Of | Sir Dvdly | Carlton Lord | Ambassadovr For The | King Of Great Britaine, | Made In The Assembly | of the Lords the Estates Generall of the | vnited Prouinces of the Low | Countries. | Being assembled at the Haghe. | Tovching The Discord | And Trovbles Of The | Church and Policie, caused by the | Scismaticall Doctrine of | Arminivs. | Exhibited the 6. of October. 1617. | Set forth by Authoritie. | (ornament)

London, | Printed by William Iones, for Nathaniel Browne, | and are to be sold at the great North doore | of Saint Paules Church. 1618. | 20.3x16cm. (1),9p.

CARTWRIGHT, Thomas. A | Confvtation | Of The | Rhemists | Translation, Glosses | And Annotations | On The | New Testament, | So Farre As They Containe | Manifest Impieties, Heresies, | Idolatries, Superstitions, Prophanesse, Treasons, Slanders, | Absurdities, Falsehoods and other evills. | By Occasion Whereof The Trve Sence, Scope, | and Doctrine of the Scriptures, and humane Authors, by them | abused, is now given. | VVritten Long Since By Order From The Chiefe In- | struments of the late Queene and State, and at the speciall request and | encouragement of many godly-learned Preachers of England, | as the ensuing Epistles shew. | By that Reverend, Learned, and Iudicious Divine, | Thomas Cartvvright, | sometime Divinitie Reader of | Cambridge . | (device).

Printed in the yeare 1618. | 29.2x19. cm. (58),761,(18)p.

A | COMMISSION | With Instrvcti- | ons And Directions, | granted by his Maiestie to the Master | and Counsaile of the Court of Wards | and Liueries, | For compounding for Wards, Ideots, | and Lunaticks, | And giuen vnder His Highnesse great | Seale of England | The eleuenth day of December 1618. | (ornament)

London, | Printed by Bonham Norton | and Iohn Bill, Printers to the | Kings most Excellent Maiestie. | M.DC.XVIII. | 17.2x13.4 cm. (1),30p.

COWPER, William. The | Triumph of a Christian, | Containing three excellent and | heauenly Treatises | {1. Iacobs wrestling with God. | 2. The Conduit of comfort. | 3. A Preparatiue for the Lords

Supper. | Full of sweet consolations for all that | desire the comfortable sweetnesse of Iesus | Christ; and necessary for those who are | troubled in Conscience. | Written by that worthy man, Mr. | William Cowper, Minister of Gods word. | The 7.Impression, Corrected and | amended: with two Prayers to be vsed | in priuate Families hereunto added. | (ornament).

London, | Printed by H.L. for Iohn Budge, | and are to be sold at his shop in Pauls | Churchyard, at the signe of the | Greene Dragon. 1618. | Line border. 14x 8.5cm.(6),368,(6)p. 2 Sub.t.p.

DIGHTON, Thomas. Certain | Reasons | Of A Private | Christian | Against Con- | formitie to kneeling in | the very act of recei- | ving the Lords | Supper. | By Tho:Dighton Gent. | . . . (4 lines; ornament).

Anno 1618. | Lace border . 13.2x9.cm. (17),143p.

DOD, John. A | Remedy | Against Privat | Contentions. | A Godly And Frvitfvll | Sermon on Iames, 4. 1. &c. | Wherein Is At Large Discove- | red the hatefulnes, and perniciousnesse of priuate Iars | and Contentions, with manifold remedies | against the same. | By Mr. Iohn Dod. | . . . (2 lines; device).

At London | Printed by Felix Kyngston for Thomas Man, and are | to be sold at the signe of the Talbot in Pa- | ter-noster row. 1618. | 18.1x14.1cm. 32p.

DOMINIS, Marco Antonio de. The Rockes | Of Christian | Shipwracke, | Discouered by the holy Church of Christ | to her beloued Children, that they may keepe | aloofe from them. | Written In Italian By The | Most Reverend Father, Marc' Ant. | De Dominis, Archb. of Spalato, | And thereout translated into English. | (cut) . . . (1 line).

London, | Printed by Iohn Bill. M.DC.XVIII. | 18.8x13.cm. (14),171p.

DOWNAME, John. The | Conflict | Betvveene The | Flesh and the Spirit. | Or | The Last Part Of | The Christian Warfare: | Wherein is described the nature of these Combatants, | the malice and power of the Flesh and fleshly lusts, with | the meanes whereby we may subdue and | ouercome them. | By Iohn Downame Batchelar in Diuinitie, and | Preacher of Gods Word. | . . . (4 lines: ornament).

London, | Printed by William Iones, dwelling in Red-crosse streete, neere | Saint Gyles Church without Cripple-gate. | 1618. | 17.8x12.6cm.(27),394p. 122-135 mispaged.

DRAXE, Thomas. Αντερώ τήματα Thomæ Draki. | Ten Covnter- | Demavnds Pro- | pounded to those of the Separati- | on, (or English Donatists) to be directly and | distinctly answered. |

Without t.p. [1618] 16.8x12.cm. 7p. Photographic copy.
Dexter, 485.

EVERARD, John. The | Arriereban: | A Sermon | preached to the Company | of the Military | Yarde, | At St Andrewes Church in Holborne | on St. Iames his day last. | By Iohn Everarde Student in | Diuinity, and Lecturer at Saint | Martins in the fields. | . . . (3 lines).

London, | Printed by E.G. for Thomas Walkley, and | are to be sold at his shop at the Eagle | and Childe in Brittaines | Burse. 1618. | Line border. 15.6x9.6cm. (16), 104p.

FOWNS, Richard. Trisagion | Or, | The Three Holy | Offices Of Iesvs | Christ, The Sonne Of God, | Priestly, Propheticall, | and Regall; how they ought of all | his Church to be receiued. | With a Declaration of the violence and | iniuries offered vnto the same, by the Spirituall and | Romish Babylon; as well in her publique Missals, Breuia- | ries, Portuses, Rosaries, Liturgies, Psalters, Primers, | Manuels of prayers and Suffrages, as in their best | and most approued priuate Writings. | Reuealing many blasphemous Mysteries | vnknowne to the Vulgar. | By Richard Fovvns, Doctor of Diuinitie, and Chap- | laine Domesticall to the late illustrious | Prince Henry. |

London, | Printed by Hvmfrey Lovvnes for Mathevv | Lovvnes: and are to bee sold at his Shop in | Pauls Church yard, at the signe of the | Bishops head. 1618. | Line border. 18.6x14.3cm. (43),346;(8),347–504;(5),503–782p. Two subtitles.

FULBECKE, William. A | Parallele Or | Conference Of The | Civil Law, the Canon Law, | and the Common Law of this | Realme of England. | Wherein the agreement and | disagreement of these three Lawes, and | the causes and reasons of the said agree- | ment and disagreement, are ope- | ned and discussed. | Digested in sundry Dia- logues | By William Fvlbecke. | At the end of these Dialogues is an- | nexed a Table of the Sections or Di- | uisions of the principall points, mat | ters, and questions, which are hand- | led in euery Dialogue. |

At London | Printed for the Company of | Stationers. | Anno Domini 1618. | 17.9x13.4cm. (12),104,(8) fol. Fol. 25–26; 31–32 lacking.
Cambr. Univ. Cat. 3271.

GORDON, James. A Svmmary | Of | Controversies. | Wherein | Are briefly treated the cheefe Questions of | Diuinity, now a dayes in dis- pute betweene | Catholikes & Protestants: especially | out of the holy Scripture. | Written In Latin | By the R.Father, Iames Gordon Huntley of | Scotland, Doctour of Diuinity, of the | Society of Iesvs. | And translated into English by I.L. of the | same Society. | The I.Tome, deuided into two Controuersies. | The Second Edition. | (device).

Permissu Superiorum. M.DC.XVIII. | 13.9x8.8cm.(8),367,(1)p.
DNB. 22: 205 b.

GUEVARA, Antonio de. The Mount of Caluarie. | Compiled | By The Reverend | Father In God, | Lord Anthonie de Gueuara, Bishop | of Mondonnedo, Preacher, Chronicler, | and Councellor, vnto Charles the fift, | Emperour. | Wherein are handled all the Myste- | ries of the Mount of Caluarie, from the time that | Christ was condemned by Pilat, vntill | hee was put into the Sepulcher, | by Ioseph and Nicho- demus. | (ornament).

At London, | Printed by Edw. All-dé for Iohn Grismond, and are to be | sold at his shop, at the little North dore of Paules, | at the signe of the Gunne. | 1618. | 18.2x14cm. (23),415,(5)p

HOOKER, Richard. Certayne | Divine | Tractates, | And other Godly | Sermons. | By | Richard Hooker, some- | times Fellow of Corpvs | Christi Colledge in | Oxford. | The Contents follow. |

London | Printed for Henrie Fetherstone. | 1618. | " Grape and column " border. 28.7x18.7 cm. (4),1–96,(6),95–120p.

Contains: The | Answere | Of | Mr. Richard Hooker | To a Svpplication, | Preferred by Master Walter | Trauers, to the Hono- | rable Lords of the | Priuie Councell. | ; A | Learned | Discovrse Of | Justification, .. | ; Three | Learned | Sermons, | ; and Two | Sermons | Vpon Part | Of S. Ivdes | Epistle. | All dated 1618, and with " grape and column " border.

JAMES I. The | King's Maiesties | Declaration | To His Subjects, | Concerning | Lawful Sports | To Be Used. |

London: | Printed by Bonham Norton and John Bill, Deputie Printers for the | King's most Excellent Maiestie. | M.DC.XVIII. | Reprinted by G.Smeeton, St. Martin's Church Yard, Charing Cross. | 1817. | 19.4x15.8cm. 11p.

MAXEY, Anthony. The Copie | Of | A Sermon Prea- | ched in Lent before the | Lords of the Councell, at | Whiee-Hall. | By D. Maxe, Deane of | Windesore. | (device)

London: | Printed by H.L. for Clement Knight, dwelling in | Pauls Church yard, at the signe | of the holy Lambe, 1618. | Line border. 16.6x10.3cm. (1),53p.
First of his Certaine Sermons: 1619.

MONGINOT, Francis. A | Resolvtion | Of Dovbts. | Or | A Svmmarie Decision | of Controuersies betwixt the Refor- | med Church and the Romaine. | By | Francis Monginot Phisitian to the | King of France. | A Treatise containing the causes and reasons mouing | the sayde Fr. Monginot to forsake the Romane Church | betaking himselfe to the Reformed. | At Rochel. | Faithfully rendred according to the | French Copie. 1618. |

London, | Imprinted by Bernard Alsop, for George Norton, and | are to be solde at his shoppe at the Signe | of the Red Bull, neere Temple | Barre. 1618. | 17.6x 13.8cm. (22),55p. Misnumbered.

MORTON, Thomas. A | Defence | Of | The Innocencie | Of The Three Ceremo- | nies Of The Chvrch Of | England. | viz. | The Surplice, Crosse after Baptisme, and Kneeling | at the receiuing of the blessed Sacrament. | Diuided into two Parts: | In the former whereof the Generall Arguments vrged | by the Non-conformists; and, in the second Part, | their Particular Accusations, against these | III. Ceremonies seuerally, are an- | swered, and refuted. | . . . (3 lines) Published by Authoritie. | (ornament)

London, | Imprinted for William Barret. | 1618. | 18x14 cm. (20),308p.
Cf Camb.Univ.Cat. No 3740. Dedication signed Tho.Cestren.

PAGET, John. An | Arrow | Against the Separation | Of The | Brownists. | Also an | Admonition | Tovching | Talmudique & Rabbinical allegations. | By Iohn Paget. | (device).

Printed at Amsterdam, | By George Veseler, dwelling by the | South-Church at the signe of the Hope. | Anno M.DC.XVIII. | 19.9x15.3cm. 476pp. Title and preface supplied.

PICKFORD, John Jerome. The | Safegarde | From Ship-Wracke, | Or | Heavens Haven | . . . (12 lines). Compiled by I.P.Priest. | (ornament)

Printed at Dovay, | By Peter Telv, at the signe of the | Natiuitie Anno 1618. | Superiorum Permissu. | 16.4x10.2cm. (56),285p.
Gillow:V:309.

ROGERS, John. The | Glory And | Happines of a true | Christian. | A Sermon Preached By | Master Rogers at Needham in | Norfolke the 28 of Iune. 1617. | (device)

London | Printed by W.I. for T.P. dwelling | in Iuie laine. 1618. | Line border. 15.6x9.6cm. (1),63p.

SALVIANUS, Quis Diues Saluus. | How | A Rich Man | May Be Saved. | Written | To the Catholike Church, by Saluianus | Priest, afterwards Bishop of Massilia | in France, about the yeare of | Christ 480. | With Annotations out of the Holy Fathers. | Translated into English by N.T. | . . . (5 lines: ornament: 1 line)

Permissu Superiorum. M.DC.XVIII. | 13.8x8.9cm.(16), 314, (5)p.

SCULTETUS, Abraham. A | Secvlar | Sermon Con- | cerning The Do- | ctrine of the Gospell by the goodnes | and power of God restored in the fifteenth | age from the birth of our Lord | Iesus Christ. | Made by the Reverend And Wor- | thy Preacher Mr.Abraham Scvltetvs, | in the High-dutch tongue. | After By Another Transla- | ted into Latin, and now out of Latin | into English. | (ornament)

London, | Printed by William Iones, dwelling in Red-crosse | streete neare S. Giles Church, Anno 1618. | 17.2x12.5cm. 41,(3)p.

SELDEN, John. The | Historie | of | Tithes | That is, | The Practice of Payment of them. | The Positiue Laws made for them. | The Opinions touching the Right of them. | A Review of it | Is also annext, which both Confirmes it and di- | rects in the Vse of it. | By I.Selden. | . . . (2 lines).

M.DC.XVIII. | 18.9x14.cm. (6),XXII,(11),491,(5)p.

SELDEN, John. The | History | Of | Tythes. | That is, | The Practice of Payment of them. | The Positive Laws made for them. | The Opinions touching the Right of them. | A Review of it | Is also annext, which both Confirms it, and | directs in the use of it. | By J.Selden. | . . . (2 lines).

M.DC.XVIII. | 18.x14.3cm. (6),i–ii,v–xxii,(11),491,(5)p. Lacks pp. iii–iv. Title page in black and red. Second edition, with list of Faults, on final page.

SPRINT, John. Cassander | Anglicanvs; | Shewing | The Necessity Of | Conformitie To The | Prescribed Ceremonies | Of Ovr Chvrch, | In Case of Depriuation. | By Iohn Sprint, Minister of Thornbury | in Glocester-Shire, sometimes of Christ- | Church in Oxon. | . . . (2 lines; ornament).

London | Imprinted by Iohn Bill. | Anno M.DC.XVIII. | 18.5x13.5 cm. (21), 277,(3) p. Fly leaf blank.

STOW, John. The | Abridgement of the | English Chronicle, | First collected by M. Iohn Stow, | and after him augmented with | very many memorable Anti- | quities, and continued with | matters forreine and dome- | sticall, vnto the beginning | of the yeare, 1618. | By E[dmond] H[owes] Gentleman. | There is a briefe Table at the end | of the Booke. |

Imprinted at London for the Com- | pany of Stationers, 1618. | Engr. border. 16.3x10.8cm. (11),568,(41)p.

TAYLOR, Thomas. Christs | Combate And | Conquest: | Or, | The Lyon of the tribe of Ivdah, | vanquishing the Roaring Lyon, assaulting him in | three most fierce and hellish | Temptations. | Expovnded, And | now (at the request of sundry per- | sons) published for the common good, by Tho, | Taylor, Preacher of the Word of | God, at Reeding in Barkeshire. | . . . (5 lines).

Printed By Cantrell Legge, For | Thomas Man. 1618. | Line border. 19.6x14.6 cm.(8), 413, (10)p.

TAYLOR, Thomas. Davids | Learning, | Or | The Way To | True Happinesse: | In a Commentarie vpon the | XXXII. Psalme. | Preached and now published by T.Taylor, | late Fellow of Christs Colledge in | Cambridge. | To which is prefixed the Table of method of the | whole Psalme, and annexed an Alphabeticall | Table of the chiefe matters in the | Commentarie. | The second time Corrected. |

London | Printed by W.Stansby, for Henry Fetherstone, | and are to be sold at his shop in Pauls Church- | yard, at the signe of the Rose. | 1618. | Line border. 17.7x13.8cm.(20),406,(10)p. Folded leaf.

TORQUEMADA, Antonio de. The | Spanish | Mandevile | Of Myr- | acles. | Or | The Garden of curious | Flowers. | Wherein Are Handled | sundry points of Humanity, Philosophy, | Divinity, and Geography, beautified with | many strange and pleasant Histories: First | written in Spanish by Anthonio de Tor- | quemeda, and translated out of that | Tongue into English. | It is diuided into sixe Treatises, composed in man- | ner of a Dialogue, as in the next Page shall appeare. |

London, | Imprinted by Bernard Alsop, by the Assigne of | Richard Hawkins, and are to be solde at his | house by Saint Annes Church neere | Aldersgate. 1618. | Line border. 18.8x14.2cm.(6),325p.

1619

ABBOT, Robert. De Svprema | Potestate Regia | Exercitationes habitæ in Academiâ | Oxoniensi, | Contra Rob. Bellarminvm, & | Francisc. Svarez. | Auctore Rob. Abbot ibidem tunc Pro- | fessore Regio, nuper Sarisburiensi | Episcopo. | . . . (2 lines; device).

Londini, | Ex Officina Nortoniana, | Apud Ioannem Billivm. | M.DC.XIX. | Colophon. 22.3x15.2 cm. (17),197,(1)p.

ADAMS, Thomas. The | Happines | of the Church. | Or, | A Description of those Spiritual Prerogatiues | vvherewith Christ hath endowed her. | Considered in some contemplations vpon part of | the 12.

Chapter to the Hebrewes. | Together with certain other Meditations and Discour- | ses vpon other portions of holy Scriptures: the titles | wherof immediately precede the Booke. | Being the Summe of diuerse Sermons preached in | S. Gregories London: By Thomas Adams, | Preacher there. | . . . (2lines)

London, | Printed by G.P. for Iohn Grismand, and are to be sold | at his shop neere vnto the little North dore | of Saint Pauls, at the signe of | the Gun. 1619. | Line border. 18.1x13.8cm 2v. in 1. (10), 441, 367 and 14supplied in MS. Mispaged. I, 269–278, 327–8 omitted; II, 35, 51 repeated, 238 omitted.

ADAMSON, Patrick. Reverendissimi | In Christo | Patris, | Patricii Adamsoni, | Sancti-Andreæ | In Scotia Archiepiscopi, dignissimi | ac doctissimi, | Poëmata Sacra, cum alijs opusculis. | Studio ac industria Tho. Volvseni | I.C. Expolita & Recognita. | (device).

Londini, | Apud Ioannem Billivm, | Anno M.DC.XIX. | 18.9x14cm. (58),102; (10),57; (11) ; (8),36fol; (2),37–41fol; (16),42–69fol; (8),70–77,74–79fol; (2)p.
The other pieces are dated 1618.

AINSWORTH, Henry. Annotations | Upon The Fifth Book | Of Moses Called | Devteronomie. | Wherein, By Conference Of The | Holy Scriptvres, By Comparing The Greek | and Chaldee Versions, and testimonies of Hebrew writers; the | Histories, Lawes and Ordinances, which Moses (a litle | before his death) repeated and enlarged | unto Israel in this Book, | are explained. | By Henry Ainsworth. | . . . (lace ornament; 6 lines; ornament).

Imprinted in the yere 1619. | Line border. 20.x15.6cm. (2,290)p.
Part of his Annotations Vpon The Five Bookes Of Moses: 1622; separate register.

AINSWORTH, Henry. Annotations | Upon The Fourth Book | Of Moses, Called | Numbers. | Wherein, By Conference Of The | Scriptvres, By Comparing The Greek And | Chaldee Versions, and testimonies of Hebrew writers; | the Lawes and Ordinances given of old unto | Israel in this book, are explained. | By Henry Ainsworth. | . . . (lace ornament; 11 lines).

Imprinted in the yere 1619. | Line border. 20.x15.6cm. (2,310)p.
Part of his Annotations Vpon The Five Bookes Of Moses: 1622; with separate register.

BAYNES, Paul. The | Mirrovr | Or Miracle | Of Gods Love Vnto | the world of his Elect. | Preached On The | third of Iohn, verse the sixteenth: | Wherein the said Scripture is very lear- | nedly expounded, and the rich treasures of | Gods grace in Christ are | accurately opened. | By that faithfull seruant of Christ, and preacher of his | Gospell, Mr. Pavl Baine. | . . . (5 lines).

London, printed by H.L. for Nathanael Newbery: and are | to be sold at his shop vnder St. Peters Church in | Cornhill, and in Popes head Alley, at | the signe of the Starre. 1619. | 17.3x13.2cm. (7),70p.

BEDE, John. The | Masse Dis- | played. | VVritten In French | by Mr John Bede, advocate to | the Parliament of Paris, and | now translated into | English. | . . . (4 lines ; device).

At Oxford, | Printed by John Lichfield, and James | Short, Printers to the famous | Vniversitie. 1619. | 18.6x14cm. (13),112p.

BUNTING, Henry.   Itinerarivm | Totivs Sacræ | Scriptvræ. | Or, | The Trauels of the Holy Pa- | triarchs, Prophets, Iudges, Kings, our | Sauiour Christ, and his Apostles, as they | are related in the Old and New | Testaments. | With a Description of the Townes and | Places to which they Trauelled, and how | many English miles they stood from | Iervsalem. | Also a short Treatise of the Weights, Monies, and | Measures mentioned in the Scriptures, reduced to our | English valuations, quantitie, and weight. | Collected out of the Workes of Henry Bvnting, | and done into English by R.B. | (ornament).
 London, | Printed by Adam Islip. | 1619. | Line border. 20.3x14.8cm.(6),562,(5)p.

CALDERWOOD, David.   A | Solvtion | Of | Doctor Resolvtvs, | His | Resolutions for kneeling. | . . . (10 lines; device).
 M.DC.XIX. | 17.4x12.7 cm. 55p.
 Anon. Cambr.Univ.Cat:7806.

COOPER, Thomas.   The | Sacred | Mysterie Of The | Government Of | the Thoughts: | Discovering | Their Nature and Differences, | and together, | Resoluing such speciall Doubts, | which are incident hereunto. | Very necessary for the Tryall and | safe keping of the Heart. | And Also, | For the well ordering and com- | fort of a Christian Life. |
 London, | Printed by Ber: Alsop, and are to be sold by | Thomas Iones at his shop in Chancery | Lane, ouer against the Rowles. | 1619. | Line border. 12.1x7. cm. (21),487p.
 Epistle Dedicatorie, signed.

COWPER, William.   Pathmos: | Or, | A Commentary | On The Revelation | of Saint Iohn, diuided into | three seuerall Prophecies. | The First Prophecie | contained in the fourth, fift, sixt, | and seuenth Chapters. | By Mr. William Cowper, | Bishop of Galloway. | . . . (4 lines; ornament)
 London, | Printed by George Purslow, for Iohn Budge, and are to be | sold at the signe of the greene Dragon in Pauls | Church-yard. 1619. | Line border. 18.5 x 13.3 cm. (14),346,(10) p.

The | DOCTRINE | of the Bible: | Or, | Rvles Of | Discipline: | Briefly Gathered | through the whole course of | the Scripture, by way of | Questions and Answers. | . . . (3 lines ; ornaments).
 London: | Printed by T.Snodham for Thomas Pauier, | and are to be solde at his Shop | in Iuie Lane. 1619. | 11.8x6.7cm. (2),236fol.

DYKE, Jeremiah.   A | Caveat For | Archippvs. | A Sermon preached at a Visitation | at White-Chappel Church in London, | Septemb.23. 1618. | By Ier.Dyke Minister of Gods word | at Epping in Essex. | . . . (6 lines; device).
 London, | Printed for Robert Mylbovrne, and are to be | sold at his shop at the great South-doore of Pauls. | 1619. | 18x13.5cm. (1),45p.

FAVOUR, John.   Antiqvitie | Trivmphing | Over Noveltie: | Whereby It Is Proved That Antiqvi- | tie is a true and certaine Note of the Christian Catholicke Church | and verity, against all new and late vpstart heresies, aduancing | themselues against the religious honour of old Rome, whose ancient | faith was so much commended by S. Pauls pen, and after | sealed with the bloud of many Martyrs and | worthy Bishops of that Sea. | With other necessarie and important questions incident and proper | to the same subiect: | By Iohn Favovr Doctor of the Lawes, sometimes Fellow of New | Colledge in Oxford, now Vicar of Halifax. | . . . (7 lines; ornament).

London, | Printed by Richard Field dwelling in Great | Woodstreete. 1619. | 17.6x13.8 cm. (16),602,(1) p.

FOWNS, Richard. Trisagion | Or, | The Three Holy | Offices Of Iesvs | Christ, The Sonne Of God, | Priestly, Propheticall, | and Regall; how they ought of all | his Church to be receiued. | With a Declaration of the violence and | iniuries offered vnto the same, by the Spirituall and | Romish Babylon; as well in her publique Missals, Breuia- | ries, Portuses, Rosaries, Liturgies, Psalters, Primers, | Manuels of prayers and Suffrages, as in their best | and most approued priuate Writings. | Reuealing many blasphemous Mysteries | vnknowne to the Vulgar. | By Richard Fovvns, Doctor of Diuinitie, and Chap- | laine Domesticall to the late illustrious | Prince Henry. |

London, | Printed by Hvmfrey Lovvnes for Matthevv | Lovvnes and are to bee sold at his Shop in | Pauls Church yard, at the signe of the | Bishops head. 1619. | Line border. 18.9x14.2cm. (38),782p.

Separate sub-title pages for second and third partes.

GATAKER, Thomas. Of the | Natvre And Vse | Of | Lots; | A Treatise | Historicall | And | Theologicall; | Written | By Thomas Gataker B. of D. | sometime Preacher at Lincolnes Inne, | and now Pastor | of Rotherhith. | . . . (ornament).

London | Printed by Edward Griffin and are to be | sold by William Bladen at the signe of | the Bible at the great north dore | of Paules. 1619. | 19.1x14.5cm (14),360p.

T.p. actually on Q2 of his Spiritvall Watch, but counted at ¶1 of a new signature, which with a blank leaf goes only to ¶3. Afterward separate register and pagination.

GATAKER, Thomas. The | Spiritvall | Watch, | Or | Christs Generall | Watch-Word. | A Meditation | On | Mark.13.37. | . . . (2 lines). By Thomas Gataker B. of D. | and Pastor of Rotherhith. |

London | Printed by Edward Griffin for William | Bladen at the signe of the Bible at the great | north dore of Paules. 1619. | 19.1x14.2cm. (8),114p.

HORNE, Robert. Of | The Rich | Man And | Lazarvs. | Certaine Sermons, | By Robert Horne. | . . . (7 lines; ornament).

London, | Printed by Ber: Alsop for Iohn Hodgets. | 1619. | Line border. 17.9x 13.9cm.(4),140p.

JAMES I. The Peace-Maker: | Or, | Great Brittaines Blessing. | Fram'd | For the continuance of that mighty Happinesse | wherein this Kingdome excels many Empires. | Shewing the Idlenesse of a Quarrelling Reputation, | wherein consists neither Manhood nor | Wisdome. | Necessary for all Magistrates, Officers of Peace, Masters of |

Families, for the confirmation of youth, and for all his | Majesties most true and faithfull Subiects. | To the generall auoiding of all Contention | and Bloud-shedding. | (line ornament)

London | Printed by Iohn Beale. An. Dom. 1619. | Cum Privilegio. | 16.8x12.5 cm. (6,33)p.

Head-piece. Royal arms on fly-leaf. Anon. Cf. Cambr. Univ. Cat: 4141.

JAMES I. Serenissimi Et Potentissimi | Principis Iacobi, | Dei gratia, magnæ Britanniæ, | Franciæ, & Hiberniæ Regis, | Fidei defensoris, &c. | Meditatio In Orationem | Dominicam; | Ad Subditos suos, eos præ- | sertim, qui aulam sequuntur. | . . . (3 lines)

Londini | Apud Bonhamvm Nortonivm, & | Ioannem Billivm Typographos | Regios. M.DC.XIX. | 14.8x9.3cm (20),140,(1)p. T.p. supplied. Colophon.

The IVDGEMENT | Of The | Synode | Holden at | Dort, | Concerning the fiue Articles: | As also their sentence touching | Conradvs Vorstivs. | (device) . . . (2 lines).

London | Printed by Iohn Bill. | M.DC.XIX. | 17.8x14.3 cm. (17),106p.

JVDICIA | Theologo- | rvm Provincia- | livm, | De | Quinqve Controversis | Remonstrantivm | Articulis. | Synodo Dordrechtanae | Exhibita. | (device).

Anno M DC XIX. | 21x16.3cm. 453p.
Running head: Acta Synodi Nationalis Dordrechtanæ.

KING, John. A | Sermon | Of Pvblicke | Thanks-Giving | for the happy recouery of | his Maiesty from his late | dangerous sicknesse: | Preached at Pavls-Crosse | the 11. of Aprill, 1619. | By | the B. of London. | Published by commandement. | (ornament).

London, | Printed for Thomas Adams. | 1619. | Line border. 17.7x13.1cm. (1), 55p.

LILY, Peter. Two Sermons: | Viz. | 1. A Preseruatiue Lilie to cure Soules. | And | 2. How to Seeke to finde Christ. | Preached by that famous and iudi- | cious Diuine, Peter Lilie, Doctor | of Diuinitie, and sometime Fellow | of Iesus Colledge in | Cambridge. | . . . (2 lines; device).

London, | Printed by Thomas Snodham. | 1619. | Line border. 17.9x13.8cm. (8), 65p.

MANDEVILL, Robert. Timothies | Taske: | Or | A Christian Sea-Card, | guiding through the coastes of a peaceable con- | science to a peace constant, and a | Crowne immortall. | Wherein I. Pastors are put in minde of their | double dutie, and how to discharge it. I. Personall, | as watchfull men. 2. Pastorall, as faithfull watch- | men. II. True doctrine is advanced. III. Tradi- | tions discountenanced, & their rancour discovered. | In two Synodoll assemblies at Carliell, out of two seuerall, but | sutable Scriptures. This of 1 Timoth. 4. 16. and | that of Actes 20. 28. | Since concorporate, and couched with augmentation | vnder their prime Head: | By | Robert Mandevill, sometimes of

Queenes Colledge | in Oxford, and Preacher of Gods word at | Abbey-holme in Cumberland. | . . . (2 lines; device).

At Oxford, | Printed by John Lichfield, and James | Short. An. Dom. 1619. | 18.2x13.5 cm. (8),64p.

MAXEY, Anthony. Certaine | Sermons Prea- | ched Before The | Kings Maiestie, and else where, by | that Reuerend Diuine Anthony | Maxey, Doctor in Diuinitie, and | late Deane of Windsor, deceased: some | of them neuer before in Print. | (Viz.) | 1 The Golden Chaine of mans Saluation. | 2 The fearefull point of Hardning. | 3 The Churches Sleepe. | 4 The Agonie of Christ. | 5 The vexation of Saul. | 6 The Sacrifice of Abraham. | 7 Hallelu-iah. | 8 A Marriage Sermon. | 9 The Wise-men guided by a Starre. | The sixt Edition. | The points handled in these Sermons are set downe in | the next Pages following |

At London printed by H.L. for Clement Knight, | dwelling in Pauls Church-yard, at the signe | of the Holy Lambe. 1619. | Line border. 16.6x10.3cm. (1), 388,(1),29p. T.p. supplied.

MAXEY, Anthony. A | Sermon | Preached | before his Maiestie at | Bagshot, September 1. | Anno Dom. 1616. | By A.Maxy.D.D. | . . . (14 lines).

At London printed by H. L. for Clement Knight, | dwelling in Pauls Church-yard, at the | signe of the Holy Lambe. 1619. | Line border. 16.6x10.3cm.(1),29p.

Ninth of his Certaine Sermons: 1619. With separate register and pagination.

NEGUS, William. Mans | Active | Obedience, Or | The Power Of Godlines, | especially in the Commandement of the | Gospell, which requireth faith in | euerie Christian: | Or | A Treatise Of Faith, Wor- | thily Called Preciovs | faith, as being in it selfe a most rare iewell | of ioy, and peerelesse Pearle, that excelleth | in worth the highest price. | Wherein is plainly declared what faith in Christ is, what | properly is the obiect of it, what is the speciall operation of faith, | by which it may bee discerned; and the worke about which, it | is principally im-ployed, the subiect wherein it is placed; what | things are needfull to the making it vp, what to the being, and | what to the wel-being of it; with the differences that | are betweene true beleeuers and fained | in all of them, and the vses | thereof. | By Master William Negvs, lately Minister of | Gods Word at Lee in Essex. |

London, | Imprinted by Felix Kyngston for Nathaniel Newbery, and are to | be sold at his shop vnder S. Peters Church in Cornehill, and in | Popes head Alley, at the signe of the Starre. 1619. | Line border. 17.3x12.7cm. (22),341p.

PARR, Elnathan. The | Grovnds | Of Diuinitie, | Plainely discouer-ing the Mysteries | of Christian Religion, propounded fami- | liarly in diuers Questions and Answeres: | Substantially proued by Scriptures; Ex- | pounded faithfully, according to the Writings | of the best Di-uines, and euidently applyed | by profitable vses, for the helpe and be- | nefit of the Vnlearned which | desire Knowledge. | To the which is prefixed a very profita- | ble Treatise, contayning an Exhortation | to the Studie of the Word, with singular | directions for the Hearing and Reading | of the same. | Newly corrected, augmented, and enlarged | by Elnathan Parr, Minister of | the Word at Palgraue in Suffolke. | The Third Edition. | . . . (5 lines).

London, | Printed by Edward Griffin for Samuell Man, and are to | be sold at his Shop in Pauls Church-yard, at the | Signe of the Svvanne. 1619. | 13.8x9.1 cm. (16),354p. Pp. 221–222 omitted in numbering.

PEMBERTON, William. The | Charge Of | God and the King, | To Iudges and Magistrates, | for execution of Iustice. | In a Sermon preached before | Sr Henry Hobart Knight and | Baronet, Lord Chiefe Iustice of the | Common Pleas: and Sr Robert | Havghton Knight, one of the | Iudges of the Kings Bench, | At the Assises at Hartford. | By William Pemberton, B.D. and | Minister at high-Ongar in Essex. | . . . (8 lines).

London, | Printed by Edward Griffin for Samuel Man, dvvel- | ling in Paules Church-yard at the signe | of the Svvan. 1619. | Line border. 16.2x9.8cm. (19), 108p. Misnumberings

PONT, Robert. De | Sabbatico- | rvm Annorvm | Periodis Chronolo- | gica A Mvndi Exordio Ad | Nostra Vsque Secvla Et | Porro Digestio. | Per Robertum Pontanum, Caledo- | nium Britannum. | (device).

Excusum per Gvlielmvm Iones. | MDCXIX. | 19x13.9cm.(15),203p.

RICHOME, Lewis. Holy Pictvres | of the mysticall Figures of the most | holy Sacrifice and Sacrament of the | Evcharist: | Set forth in French | by | Lewis Richome, | Prouinciall of the Societie | of Jesvs; | And | Translated into English for the benefit of | those of that Nation, aswell Protestants | as Catholikes. | By C.A. | (ornament).

[Douay?] Printed with Licence. 1619. | 18.3x13.3cm. (13),300,(12)p.

ROUS, Francis. The Arte | Of | Happines. | Consi- | sting of | three | parts, | whereof | {The first searcheth out the hap- | pinesse of man. | The second, particularly disco- | uers and approues it- | The third, sheweth the meanes | to attayne and increase it. | By Francis Rovs. | . . . (4 lines).

London | Printed by W.Stansby for Iohn Parker, | and are to be sold at his shop in Pauls | Church-yard at the signe of the | Ball. 1619. | Line border. 12.5x 7.3cm. (17),506p.

SCLATER, William. An | Exposition | with Notes vpon the | first Epistle to the | Thessalonians. | By | William Sclater D.D. | and Minister of the Word | of God at Pitmister in | Sommerset. | (ornament).

London | Printed by W.Stansby for Iohn | Parker, and are to be sold at | his Shop in Pauls Church | yard at the signe of | the Ball. 1619. | 17.5x13.2cm. (8), 598p.

T.p. supplied by Mr. Edward G. Friehold.

SEMPILL, James. Sacrilege | Sacredly | Handled. | That is, | According to Scripture onely. | Diuided into two parts: | 1. {For the Law. | 2. For the Gospell. | An Appendix Also Added; An- | swering some Obiections mooued, namely, against this | Treatise: and some others, I finde in Ios. Scaligers | Diatribe, and Ioh. Seldens Historie |

of Tithes. | For The Vse Of All Chvrches In | generall: but more especially for those of | North-Britaine. | . . . (6 lines).

London, | Printed by William Iones, for Edmvnd Weaver, and are to | be sold at his Shop at the great North-doore of Saint | Pauls, 1619. | 19.1x14.3cm. (16), 100,54 p.
Cambr.Univ.Cat:3331. Dedication to James I, signed.

SMITH, Richard. De | Avctore | Et Essentia | Protestanticæ | Ecclesiæ Et Religionis. | Libri Dvo. | Auctore Richardo Smithæo, | Lincolniense S. Theologiæ Doctore. | Quid potissimum in hoc opere continea- | tur sequens pagina indicat. | . . . (2 lines; ornament).

Parisiis, | Apud Mathvrinvm Mavperlier, viâ ⌈Iacobeâ, sub scuto Britanniæ. | M.DC.XIX. | Cum Priuilegio Regis. | 17. x11. cm. (64),496p.

SYNODVS | (Cut). (Page 3) Ivdicivm | Synodi | Nationalis, | Reformatarvm | Ecclesiarvm Belgicarvm, | habitæ | Dordrechti, | Anno 1618. & 1619. | Cui etiam interfuerunt plurimi insignes Theologi | Reformatarum Ecclesiarum Magnæ Britanniæ, | Palatinatus Electoralis, Hassiæ, Helvetiæ, Cor- | respondentiæ VVedderavicæ, Genevensis, Bre- | mensis, & Emdanæ, | De | Qvinqve Doctrinæ | Capitibus in Ecclesiis Belgicis Controversis. | Promulgatum VI. May, M.DC.XIX. | Cum Privilegio. |

Dordrechti, Apud Ioannem Berewout, & Franciscum | Bosselaer, Socios Caninij 1619. | 18.8x14.5 cm. (12),128p.

TAYLOR, Thomas. A | Commentarie | Vpon The Epistle | of Saint Paul written to | Titvs. | Preached in Cambridge by Thomas | Taylor, and now published for the further | vse of the Church of God. | Reviewed By The Avthor, | and enlarged with some notes, and besides the addition of many | hundreths of places of Scripture, with an Alphabe- | ticall table of the cheife and most obseruable | points contained in the | Booke. | . . . (3 lines; ornament)

Printed By Cantrell Legge, Prin- | ter to the Vniuersitie of Cambridge. 1619. | Line border. 20.2x15.6 cm. (14),751,(14)p.
Also another copy from the library of Walter W. Law. 20.4x16cm.(14),751, (1 4)p. 2 folding plates.

TAYLOR, Thomas. A | Mappe Of | Rome: | Lively Exhibiting Her | Mercilesse Meeknesse, | and cruell mercies to the Church | of God: | Preached in fiue Sermons, on occasion of the | Gunpowder Treason, by T.T. and now published | by W.I. Minister. | 1.The Romish Furnace. | 2. The Romish Edom. | 3.The Romish Fowler. | 4.The Romish Conception. | To which is added, | 5.The English Gratulation. | . . . (3 lines).

At London. | Imprinted by Felix Kyngston, for Iohn Bartlet, and are | to be sould at the signe of the Talbot in Pater | noster Row. 1619. | Line border. 17.2x 13.3cm. (8),100p.
Author's Apologie, signed.

TILLESLEY, Richard. Animadversions | vpon M.Seldens | History | Of Tithes, | And His | Review Thereof: | Before which (in lieu of the two first | Chapters purposely pretermitted) is premised a Cata- |

logue of seuenty two Authours, before the | yeere 1215. | Maintaining the Ius diuinum of Tythes or more, | to be payed to the Priesthood vnder the | Gospell: | By Richard Tillesley Doctor in | Diuinity, and Archdeacon of Rochester. | . . . (2 lines).

London, | Printed by Iohn Bill. | M.DC.XIX. | 18.2x13.7 cm. (44),236p.

The | WONDERFVL | Discoverie Of The | Witchcrafts of Margaret and Phillip | Flower, daughters of Joan Flower neere Beuer | Castle: executed at Lincolne, March 11. 1618. | Who were specially arraigned & condemned before | Sir Henry Hobart, and Sir Edward Bromley, Judges | of Assize, for confessing themselues actors in the destruc- | tion of Henry, Lord Rosse, with their damnable prac- | tises against others the Children of the Right | Honourable Francis Earle of Rutland. | Together with the seuerall Examinations and Confessions of Anne | Baker, Ioan Willimot, and Ellen Greene, Witches in Leicestershire. | (cut).

Printed at London by G.Eld for I.Barnes, dwelling in the long Walke | neere Christ-Church. 1619. | 22.2x13.3cm. 26p.

Reprint: without date .

1620

ABBREGE Des | Controverses | Ov | Sommaire | Des Errevrs | des Religionnaires | de nostre temps. | Auec leur refuation par | textes exprés de la Bible | de Geneue. | (device).

A Bovrdeavs, | Par Iacq.Millang. Imprimeur | ordinaire du Roy, & Clavde | Mongirovd Marchand | Libraire. | M.DC.XX. | 11.1x5.6cm. 108,(5)p.

ACTA Et Scripta | Synodalia | Dordracena | Ministrorvm | Remonstrantivm | In Foederato Belgio. | . . . (3 lines; device; 1 line)

Herdervviici | Ex Officina Typographi Synodalis. | Anno M.DC.XX. | (16),211; (2),370,349p.

ACTA | Synodi Na- | tionalis, In Nomi- | ne Domini Nostri Iesv | Christi, | Autoritate. | Illvstr. Et Praepotentvm | DD. Ordinvm Generalivm Foederati | Belgij Prouinciarum, | Dordrechti Habitæ | Anno M.DC.XVIII. & M.DC.XIX. | Accedunt plenissima, de Quinque Articulis, tam Exterorum quam | Prouincialium Theologorum Iudicia. | Accessit In Calce Index Cvm Rervm | tum verborum Locorumque communium in hoc opere con- | tentorum locupletissimus. | (ornaments).

Hanoviæ, | Impensis Egenolphi Emmelii, | Anno M.DC.XX. | Line border. 20.8x 16.2cm. (56),858, (44)p.

Dexter 499

AINSWORTH, Henry. A Reply | To A Pretended | Christian Plea For The Anti- | Christian Chvrch of Rome: | published by Mr. Francis Iohnson | a°. 1617. | Wherin the weakness of the sayd Plea is manifested, and | arguments alleaged for the Church of Rome, | and Baptisme therein, are refuted; | By Henry Ainsworth. | Anno 1618. | . . . (4 lines; device).

Printed in the yere 1620. | 17.3x13.4 cm. (4),184p.

ANDERTON, James. The | Lytvrgie Of | The Masse: | Wherein Are Treated Three | Principall Points Of Faith. | 1. {That in the Sacrament of the Eucharist are truly and really | contained the body and bloud of Christ. | 2. {That the Masse is a true and proper sacrifice of the body and | bloud of Christ, offered to God by Preistes. | 3. }That Communion of the Eucharist to the Laity vnder one kind | is lawful. | The ceremonies also of the Masse now vsed in the Catho- | licke Church, are al of them deriued from the Pri- | mitiue Church. | By Iohn Brereley | Preist. | . . . (5 lines).

printed at Colen. 1620. | 18.7x14.1 cm (6),9–469 p. Gillow:I:37.

AUGUSTINE, St. Saint | Avgvstine, | Of | The Citie Of God: | With | The Learned Comments | Of | Io.Lodovicvs Vives. | Englished first by J.H. And now in this second Edition | compared with the Latine Originall, and in very many | places corrected and amended. | . . . (2 lines; device).

London, | Printed by G.Eld and M.Flesher. | 1620. | Line border. 32.3x21.1cm. (18),861,(4)p.

BENEFIELD, Sebastian. A | Commen- | tarie, | Or | Exposition | Vpon The Second | Chapter of the Prophecie of | Amos. | Deliuered | In XXI. Sermons in the Parish Church | of Meysey-Hampton in the | Diocesse of Glocester. | By | Sebastian Benefield Doctor of Diuini- tie, | and Professor for the Lady Margaret | in the Uniuersitie of Oxford. | . . . (2 lines).

London, | Printed by Edward Griffin for Iohn Parker, | and are to be sold in Paules Church-yard at the signe of | the three Pigeons. 1620. | 18x13.8cm.(4),375, (8)p.

BOUGHEN, Edward. A | Sermon | Of | Confirma- | tion, Preached In | Oxford, At The First | Visitation of the Right reuerend Father in | God, Iohn Lord Bishop of Oxford. | September, 27, 1619. | By Edward Boughen, Chaplaine to the | Lord Bishop of Oxford. | . . . (5 lines; ornament).

London, | Printed by Bernard Alsop, for Elizabeth A- | dams, and are to be sold at her shop, in | Pauls Church-yard, 1620- | 18 x 13.8 cm. (4),72p.

BRADSHAW, William. A | Plaine | And Pithy Ex- | position Of The | Second Epistle To The | Thessalonians. | By that learned & judi- cious Diuine | Mr William Bradshaw, some- | time Fellow of Sidney Colledge | in Cambridge. | Published since his Deceasse | By | Thomas Gataker B. of D. and | Pastor of Rotherhith. | (ornament)

London | Printed by Edward Griffin for William Bladen, and are | to be sold at his shop at the signe of the Bible, at | the great North dore of Paules. 1620. | Line border. 18.3x13.6cm. (10),208pp.

CALDERWOOD, David. A | Defence | Of Our Arguments | against kneeling in the act of re- | ceiuing the Sacramentall ele- | ments of bread and wine | impugned by Mr. | Michelsone. | . . . (9 lines)

Imprinted Anno. M DC XX. | Lace border. 13.6x9. cm. (4),75p. Anon. DNB. 8: 245 b. (3)

CALDERWOOD, David. A | Dialogve | Betwixt Cosmophi- | lus And Theophi- | lus Anent The | Urging of new ceremonies | upon the Kirke of | Scotland. | . . . (5 lines).

MDCXX. | Lace border. 13.7x8.5 cm. (4),43 p.
Anon. DNB. 8: 245 b. (4)

CALDERWOOD, David. The | Speach Of The Kirk | Of | Scotland | To Her Beloved | Children. | . . . (16 lines)

Imprinted in the yere 1620. | 13.7x8.5 cm. (1),125 p.
Anon. DNB. 8: 245 b. (5)

CALDERWOOD, David, and MELVILLE, Andrew. Parasynagma Perthense | Et | Ivramentvm Ecclesiæ | Scoticanæ | Et | A.M.Antitamica- | micategoria. | (device).

Anno M.DC.XX. | 17x13.5cm. 46p.
Cf.Cambr.Univ.Cat.7682. DNB. 8: 245 b (2).

CHAMPNEY, Anthony. Mr. Pilkinton | His Parallela | Disparalled. | And | The Catholicke Roman faith main- | tained against Protestantisme. | By Ant.Champney Sorbonist, and | Author of the Manuall of Controuersies, | impugned by the said Mr. Pilkinton. | Wee Wish That Those Wovld | departe from their owne frowardnes, who against | Christ, carry the ensigne of Christ, and against the | Gospell, bragge of the Gospell which they vnderstande | not. Aug. ep.61. ad Dulcit. | Cited by Mr. Pilkinton against himselfe. | (lace ornament).

At S. Omers, | For Iohn Heigham. | With permission, Anno 1620. | 15.1x9.5cm. 220,(2)p.

CROY, Francis de. The three Conformities. | Or | The Harmony | And Agreement | Of The Romish | Church with Gentilisme, | Ivdaisme and auncient | Heresies. | Written in French by Francis | De Croy G. Arth. and newly | translated into English. | Seene, perused and allowed. | (lace ornament).

London. | Printed by Edvvard Griffin, | 1620. | Line border. 16.6x12.7cm.(27) 130;(6)131–177; (23), 179–258p. 3 parts

DENISON, John. Fovre | Sermons: | Viz. | { 1.The blessednesse of Peace-makers. | 2.The aduancement of Gods Children.} Preached before the King. | 3.The Sinne against the holy Ghost. | Preached at Pauls Crosse. | 4.The Christian Petitioner. | Preached at Oxford on the Act Sunday. | By Iohn Denison Doctor of Diuinity, | and one of his Maiesties Chaplaynes. | (ornament).

London: | Printed by T.S. for Iohn Budge, and are to | be sold at the signe of the greene-Dragon | in Paules Church-yard. 1620. | Line border. 16x10.9cm. (12), 1–96;(6),97–205,(2); (1),209–278p. 3 sub-t.p.

DOWNAME, George. Papa Antichristvs, | Sive | Diatriba | De Antichristo, | Cvivs Dvae Partes: | Prior, |Κατασκευη, quâ Orthodo- |xa Serenissimi Regis Iacobi, de An- | tichristo sententia demonstratur; | Posterior, | Ανασκευη, quâ Leonardi Lessii sedecim Demonstrationes, monito- | riæ Regis Præfationi oppositæ, refutantur. | Auctore Reuerendo in Christo Patre, Georgio | Dovnamo Episcopo Derensi. | (ornament)

Londini, | Ex Officina Nortoniana, | Apud Ioan. Billivm. | M.DC.XX. | 21.5x 15.8 cm. (16),653,(2)p. Colophon.

DYKE, Daniel. The | Mystery | Of Selfe-Deceiving. | Or | A Discovrse | and discouery of the deceitful- | nesse of Mans Heart. | Written by the late faithful Minister of Gods Word | Danyel Dyke, Batchelour in Diuinitie. | Published since his death, by his Brother I.D. | Minister of Gods Word. | And now by him augmented and inlarged, and there- | vnto two exquisite Tables added, enlightning | much the whole Treatise. | The seauenth Edition. | . . . (5 lines).

London, | Printed by Thomas Snodham. | [1620?] Line border. 18.8x14.7cm. (16), 1–308, 321–388, 401–438, (24)p. Mispaged.

DYKE, Jeremiah. A | Covnterpoison | Against Cove- | tovsnes: | In a Sermon preached at Pauls- | Crosse, May 23. 1619. | By Ier. Dyke Minister of Gods word | at Epping in Essex. | . . . (6 lines). The second impression. | (device).

London, | Printed for Robert Mylbovrne, and are to | be sold at his shop at the great South | doore of Pauls. | 1620. | 18.x13.4cm. (1),58p.

GATAKER, Thomas. The | Benefit | Of | A Good Name, | And | A Good End. | A Funerall Sermon | On Eccles. 7.1. | By T.G. B. of D. | (device).

London, | Printed by Edward Griffin for William Bladen, and are to | be sold at his shop at the signe of the Bible, | neere the great North dore of | Paules. 1620. | 18.5x14.3cm (6),28p.
Second of his Two Funeral Sermons: 1620.

GATAKER, Thomas. A Good Wife Gods | Gift. | A | Mariage | Sermon | On | Prov.19.14. | By Thomas Gataker B. of D. | and Pastor of Rotherhith. | (device).

London, | Printed by Edward Griffin for | Fvlke Clifton. 1620. | 18.1x14.3cm. (8),23p.

GATAKER, Thomas. Gods | Parley | VVith Princes: | With | An Appeale | from Them to Him. | The Svmme of two Sermons on | the 3. last Verses of the 82. Psalme, | Preached at Sergeants-Inne in | Fleet-Streete. | By | Thomas Gataker B. of D. | and Pastor of Rotherhith. | (ornament).

London | Printed by Edw. Griffin, and are to be sold by | Timothy Barlow, at his shop in Pauls-Church-yard at | the signe of the Bull-head. 1620. | 18.5x14.3 cm (6),86p.

GATAKER, Thomas. Marriage | Dvties Briefe- | ly Covched | Togither: | Ovt Of | Colossians,3. 18,19. | By | Thomas Gataker Bachelar of Diuinitie and | Pastor of Rotherhith. | (ornament).

London, | Printed by William Iones, for William Bladen, | and are to be sold at his shop at the signe of the Bible | in Pauls Church-yard. | 1620. | 18.5x14.3cm (8),48p. Pp (2–4) blank.

GATAKER, Thomas. משכיל לדוד | Dauids Instructer. | A | Sermon | Preached At | The Visitation Of | the Free-Schole at Tvnbridge | in Kent, by the Wardens of the | Worshipfull Companie of | Skinners: | By | Thomas Gataker B. of D. | and Pastor of Rotherhith. | (ornament).

London, | Printed by Edward Griffin. | 1620. | 18.1x14.4cm. (7),34p.

GATAKER, Thomas. Pavls | Desire Of | Dissolution, | And | Deaths Advan- | tage. | A | Sermon Preached | at the Funerall of that right vertuous and | religious Gentlewoman Mrs Rebekka Crisp, | togither with the Testimonie then | giuen vnto her. | By T.G. B. of D. |

London, | Printed by Edward Griffin for William Bladen, and are to | be sold at his shop at the signe of the Bible, | neere the great North dore of | Paules. 1620. | 18.1x14.4cm. (14),29,(1)p.
Sub title of his Two Funeral Sermons: 1620.

GATAKER, Thomas. Trve | Content- | ment | In | The Gaine Of | Godlines, | With its | Self-Svfficiencie. | A Meditation | On | I. Timoth. 6.6. | By Thomas Gataker B. of D. | and Pastor of Rotherhith. |

London | Printed by Edward Griffin for William Bladen, and are to be | sold at his shop at the signe of the Bible, neere the | great North dore of Paules. 1620. | 18.1x14.4cm. (7),87p.

GATAKER, Thomas. Two | Funeral | Sermons, | Mvch Of One And | the same Subiect; | To Wit, | The Benefit of Death. | The Former | On | Philip.1.23. | The Latter | On | Eccles.7.1. | By Thomas Gataker B. of D. | and Pastor of Rotherhith. |

London | Printed by Edward Griffin for William Bladen, and are to be | sold at his shop at the signe of the Bible at the great | North dore of Paules. 1620. | 18.5x14.3cm. (1,14),29,(1) ; (6),28p.
Being: Pauls Desire of Dissolution, and The Benefit of a Good Name. Separate register and pagination.

GEE, Edward. Two | Sermons. | One, | The Curse and Crime of Meroz. | Preached at the Assises at Exon. | The other, | A Sermon of Patience. | At St Maries in Oxford. | By | Edward Gee, | Doctor in Diuinitie, and Chaplaine to | his Maiestie. | Published since his death, by his | two | brethren, | {Iohn Gee | and | George Gee,} Ministers of Gods Word. |

London, | Printed by W. S. for Nathaniel Butter, and are to be sold | at his shop neere S. Austins-gate, at the signe of | the Pyde Bull. 1620. | 18.5x14.4 cm. (4),62p. Sub-title.

GIBSON, Samuel. A | Sermon | Of Ecclesiasti- | cal Benediction: | Preached at Oundle at a Visitation, Apr.14.1619. | by Master Samvel Gibson, Minister | at Burleigh in Rutland. | . . . (4 lines; device).

At London | Imprinted by F.K. for William Barringer, at the great | Northdoore of Pauls. 1620. | Line border. 18.5x13.8cm. (4),38p. Mispaged.

GIFFORD, George. Fifteene | Sermons | Vpon The Song | Of Salomon. | Written by George Gyffard, Preacher of | the Word at Maulden in Essex. | (device).

At London | Printed by Barnard Alsop, by the assignes | of I.M. and G.N. and are to be sold at | his house, by Saint Annes Church, | neere Aldersgate. | 1620. | Line border. 14.5x9.5cm.(8),377p.

GORDON, James. Contro- | versiarvm | Christianae Fidei Adver-svs | Hvivs Temporis Hae- | reticos | Epitome: | Auctore | R.P. Iacobo Gordono Hvntlaeo Scoto, | Societatis Iesv Doctore Theologo : | In Qua De Qvaestionibvs Theologicis | hac nostrâ ætate controuersis breuiter disputatur; | idq́[ue] ex sacris præsertim litteris. | Ad S.D.N. Pavlvm V. Pont. Max. | (device).
Coloniae Agrippenae, | Apud Ioannem Kinchivm ad intersigne | Monocerotis, Anno M.DC.XX. | Permissu Superiorum & priuilegio. | 17.3x10.5cm. (18),410,(1); (8),352,(12)p. Subtitle. 3 pts.
DNB. 22: 205b.

GRANGER, Thomas. Syntagma | Logicvm. | Or, | The Divine | Logike. | Seruing especially for the vse of Di- | uines in the practise of preaching, and for the | further helpe of iudicious Hearers, and | generally for all. | By Thomas Granger Preacher | of Gods Word. | . . . (7 lines; ornament).
London, | Printed by William Iones, and are to be sold by Arthur Iohnson, | dwelling in Pauls Church-yard at the signe of the | white Horse. 1620. | 18.7x14.1 cm.(16),387p. 1 folded leaf.

GREENWOOD, Henry. The | Iaylers | Iayl-Delivery. | Preached at Great Saint Maries | in Cambridge, the 6. of | February. 1619. | By Henry Greenwood; Master of | Art, and Preacher of the Word of God. | . . . (2 lines; device).
At London. | Printed by George Purslow, for Henry Bell, and | are to be sold at his Shop, at the sign of the | Sunne in Bethlem. 1620. | Line border. 17.3x13.2 cm. (6),27,(4)p.

HIERON, Samuel. The | Doctrines | Triall: | Shewing both the ne- | cessitie and the way of | trying what is | taught; | In a Sermon vpon | I. Thess. 5. 21. | . . . (2 lines)
London | Printed by W.Stansby. | 1620. | Vine and pillar border. 28x19cm. (6),500,(11)p. No general t.p. Lacking?
Contains: The Christians Live-Loode; Penance For Sinne; and Fovre Learned And Godly Sermons.
From the library of Walter W. Law.

HIERON, Samuel. The | Sermons | Of Master | Samvel Hieron, | Formerly Collected | Together By Himselfe, And | Pvblished In One Volvme | In His Life Time. | Herevnto Are Annexed | Of The Same Avthors. | 1.The Preachers Plea. | 2.An Answer to a Popish Rime. | 3.Meditations touching death. | 4. The Doctrine of the Beginning of Christ, in forme of a | Catechisme. | 5.An Helpe vnto deuotion. | With fiue Sermons not heretofore published. | . . . (6 lines; device)
London, | Printed by Iohn Legatt. 1620. | 27.6x18.2cm.
Sub-title of his Workes: 1620, wh.see.
Also another copy from the library of Walter W. Law. 27.8x17.5cm. (16),1-163; (3),165-195; (3),197-231; (3),233-392; (3),393-427; (3),429-447; (3),449-466; (3), 467-475; (4),477-551; (6),553-576; (1),577-763,(14)p.

HIERON, Samuel. The | Workes | Of | Mr Sam. Hieron | late Pastor of | Modbury in | Deuon. | . . . (3 lines).

London | Printed by William | Stansby and Iohn | Beale. | (1620). Engr. t.p. with cuts. 27.6x18.2cm.(15), 1–65, (1),71–163, (3), 165–195, (3), 197–231, (3), 233–392, (1), 393–427, (3), 429–447,(3),449–466,(3),467–475,(4),477–551,(6),553–576,(3), 577–763(14)p. 22 Sub. t.p. dated 1619.

HOWARD, Henry. A | Defensative | against the poyson of supposed | Prophecies. | Not hitherto confuted by the Pen of any man, | which being grounded, either vpon the warrant | and Authority of Old painted Bookes, Expositions of Dreames, Ora- | cles, Reuelations, Inuocations of damned Spirits, Iudicials of Astrolo- | gie, or any other kinde of pretended knowledge whatsoeuer, | De futuris contingentibus; haue beene causes of great | disorder in the Common-wealth, especially | among the simple and vnlear- | ned people. | Very needfull to be published, considering the great offence, which | grew by most palpable and grosse errors | in Astrologie. | Written by Henry Howard, late Earle of Northampton, Lord | Priuy Seale, &c. Now newly reuised, and diuided into diuers seue- | rall Heads and Chapters. | (ornament).

Printed by Iohn Charlewood, seruant to the right Honorable Philip | Earle of Arundell, 1583. And reprinted by W. Iaggard, and to be sold by Ma- | thew Lownes in Pauls church-yard, at the signe | of the Bishops head, 1620. | Broad border. 27.5x18.3 cm. (7),149 fol.

KING, John. A | Sermon | At | Paules Crosse, | On Behalfe Of | Pavles Chvrch, | March 26. 1620. | By the B. of London. | Both preached and published by his Ma- | jesties commandement. | (ornament).

London | Printed by Edward Griffin for | Elizabeth Adams. 1620. | Line border. 18.7x14.4cm. (1),51p.

MICHAELSON, John. The Lawfulnes | Of | Kneeling | In The Act | Of receiuing the Sacrament | of the Lordes Supper. | Written by M.Iohn Michelsone | Preacher Of Gods Word | At Bvrnt-Yland. | . . . (4 lines; device).

Printed by Edvvard Raban, | Printer to the Vniversitie of | Sainct-Andrewes: | And are to bee solde at his Printing-house, in | the South-street of the Citie: At the signe | of the A B C. 1620. | Line border. Frontisp. 13.4x9.cm. (10), 130p

MORTON, Thomas. Cavsa Regia, | Sive, | De Avthoritate | Et Dignitate | Principum Christianorum, | Dissertatio; | Aduersus | Rob. Cardinalis Bellarmini | Tractatum, | De officio Principis Christiani | inscriptum, edita. | Authore Reuerendo Patre Thoma Mortono, | Couentriensi & Lichfeldensi Episcopo. | (device).

Londini, | Apud Ioannem Billivm Typographum Regium | MDCXX. | 20.6x 15.4cm. (32),301,(2)p. Colophon: idem.

MOULIN, Pierre du. The | Anatomy | Of | Arminianisme: | Or | The opening of the Controversies | lately handled in the Low-Countryes, | Concerning the Doctrine of Prouidence, | of Predestination, of the Death of | Christ, of Nature and | Grace. | By | Peter Movlin, Pastor of the Church | at Paris. | Carefully translated out of the originall Latine Copy. | (ornament).

London: | Printed by T.S. for Nathaniel Newbery, and are to | be sold at the signe of the Starre vnder Saint | Peters Church in Cornehill, and in | Popes head Alley. 1620. | 18.x13.3cm. (18),504p. Pp. 166-75, 279 misnumbered; 369-398 skipped; 441-2 repeated .

MOULIN, Pierre du. The | Bvckler | Of The Faith: | Or, | A Defence Of The | Confession Of Faith Of The | reformed Churches in France, against the Ob- | iections of M. Arnoux the Iesuite. | Wherein all the principall Controuersies betweene | the reformed Churches and the Church of Rome | are decided. | Written in French by Peter du Moulin Minister of the word | of God in Paris: and now translated into English. | (device).

London, | Printed by R. F. for Nathanael Newbery, and are to be sold | at the signe of the Starre vnder Saint Peters Church in | Cornhill, and in Popes head Alley. 1620. | 17.1x13.2 cm. (30),560,(6) p.

MURTON, John. A Most Humble Supplication Of Many Of The King's Majesty's Loyal Subjects, Ready To Testify All Civil Obedience, By The Oath Of Allegiance, Or Otherwise, And That Of Conscience; Who Are Persecuted (Only For Differing In Religion), Contrary To Divine And Human Testimonies. As followeth.

Printed 1620.
Repr. in the Hanserd Knollys Society's Tracts on Liberty of Conscience: 1846.

PAOLO, Servita. The | Historie Of | The Covncel | Of Trent. | Conteining eight Bookes. | In which (besides the ordinarie Actes of the Councell) | are declared many notable occurrences, which happened in | Christendome, during the space of fourtie | yeeres and more. | And, particularly, the practises of the Court of Rome, to | hinder the reformation of their errors, and to main- | taine their greatnesse. | Written in Italian by Pietro Soaue Polano, and faithfully translated | into English by Nathanael Brent. | (Royal arms).

London | Printed by Robert Barker, and Iohn Bill, | Printers to the Kings most Excellent | Maiestie. | Anno Dom.M.DC.XX. | 32.4x20.7cm.(10), 825,(16)p. Colophon.

PARR, Elnathan. A | Plaine | Exposition | vpon the whole eighth, ninth, | tenth, eleuenth, twelfth Chapters of | the Epistle of Saint Pavl to | the Romanes. | Wherein the Text is diligently and Methodically | resolued, the sence giuen: and many Doctrines thence | gathered, are by liuely vses applyed, for the benefit | of Gods Children. | Performed with much variety, and conuenient breuitie: | being the substance of neere fiue yeeres Weeke- | dayes Sermons: | The second Edition corrected, with the twelfth | Chapter not before printed. | By Elnathan Parr, Bachelor in Diuinity, | and Preacher of Gods Word. | . . . (4 lines).

London, | Printed by George Purslowe for Samuel Man, | dwelling in Pauls Church-yard at the | signe of the Swanne. 1620. | 18.8x13.8cm.(26),619p.

Also another edition, lacking sig. A, and containing An Exposition | vpon the eighth, ninth, tenth, and the | eleuenth Chapters of the Epistle to the | Romanes. | 18.3x13.2cm. (2),305,138p. The section on the xi. chapter, has separate register and pagination.

PRESTON, Thomas. A New-Yeares | Gift For English | Catholikes, | Or | A Briefe and cleare Explication of the | New Oath of Allegiance. | By E.I. Student in Diuinitie; | For a more full Instruction, and appeasement | of the consciences of English Catholikes, con- | cerning the said Oath, then hath beene | giuen them by I.E. Student in Di- | uinitie, who compiled the Trea- | tise of the Prelate and | the Prince. | . . . (2 lines; cross ornament; 4 lines).

With licence of Superiours. | 1620. | 14.1x9.3 cm. (29),208[174],(1) p. Pp. 65–68, and 149–178 omitted in numbering.
DNB. 61: 182 a.

ROGERS, Nehemiah. The | Trve Con- | vert. | Or | An Exposition | Vpon The Whole | Parable of the Prodigall. | Lvke. 15. 11. 12. &c. | Wherein is ma- | nifestly shewed; { 1. Mans miserable estate by forsaking of God. | 2. Mans happie estate by returning to God. | Deliuered in sundry Sermons, by Nehemiah Ro- | gers, Preacher of Gods Word, at St Margarets Fish- | street. And now by him published, intending the farther | benefit of so many as then heard it; And the | profit of so many as shall please to read it. | . . . (4 lines).

London | Printed by Edward Griffin for Edward Brewster, and | are to be sold at his Shop, at the West gate of Pauls, | at the signe of the Starre. 1620. | Line border. 18.9x14.5cm.(18), 343,(9)p. Folded leaf.

ROGERS, Richard. Samuels | Encovn- | ter With | Saul. | I.Sam. Chap.15. from ver. | 13. to ver.30. | Preached and penned, | by that worthy seruant of | God, Mr. Richard | Rogers, late Preacher | of Wetherfield | in Essex. | And published word for | word, according to his owne | coppy, finished before | his Death. |

London, | Printed by Edw. Griffin, for | Samuel Man, dwelling in | Pauls Church-yard at the signe | of the Svvan. 1620. | Line border. 14.1x8cm.(29),354p.

SCOTT, Thomas. Vox Popvli. | Or | Nevves From Spayne, | translated according to the Spanish coppie. | Which may serue to forwarne both England | and the Vnited Provinces how farre to | trust to Spanish pretences. | (lace ornament).

Imprinted in the yeare 1620. | 18.5x14.2cm. (1,25)p.
Anon.Cambr.Univ.Cat. 6648.

SCUDDER, Henry. A | Key Of | Heaven: | The Lords Prayer | opened, and so applied, that a | Christian may learne how to pro- | cure all things which may make for | the glorie of God, and the good of | himself, and of his neighbour. | Containing likewise such Do- | ctrines of faith and godlinesse, as may | be very vsefull to all that desire to | liue godly in Christ Iesus. | By Henrie Scvdder | preacher of the word. | . . . (4 lines).

London, | Printed by R.Field, for Tho.Man, | and are to be sold at the signe of the Tal- | bot in Pater noster row. 1620. | Line border. 14.4x8.1 cm. (33), 538p.

STAPLETON, Thomas. Thomæ | Stapletoni | Angli, Sacrae | Theologiæ Doctoris, | Et Professoris Regii, | Dvaci Primo; Deinde Lovanii | Opera quæ extant omnia, | Nonnvlla Avctivs Et Emendativs, | quædam iam anteà Anglicè scripta, nunc primùm studio & diligentia | Doctorum virorum Anglorum Latinè reddita. | In Qvatvor Tomos Distribvta, Qvorvm | Elenchum Pagina decima-nona indicabit. | (Portrait in ornamental engr. border)

Lvtetiæ Parisiorvm, | M.DCXX. | Cvm Privilegio Christianissimi Regis. | 4 v. in 5. 40.x 25.cm. I, (48),1293,(17) :II,(7),1653,(19) ;III,(32),993,(14) :IV,(32),1065, (13) p.

TILENUS, Daniel. Parænesis | Ad | Scotos, | Geneuensis Disciplinæ | Zelotas. | Autore | Dan.Tileno Silesio. | (device).

Londini | Typis Gul.Stansby, pro Nathaniele Buttero. | M.D.C.XX. | 14.8x10. cm. 3–72p.

VALLE de Moura, Emanuel do. De Incanta- | tionibvs Sev | Ensalmis. | Opvscvlvm Primvm, Avctore Ema- | nuele do Valle de Moura Doctore Theologo, ac Sanctæ | Inquisitionis Deputato Lusitano. | Patria Calantica. | Precipva, Qvæ Agvntvr | in hoc Opusculo, refert Elenchus ad calcem Epis- | tolæ ad Lectorem. | (device)

Eboræ. | Typis Laurentij Crasbeeck. Anno 1620. | (1 line) 26x18.7cm. (6),1–11 fol,12–552,553–589,589–609,(1)p. Blank page between 552 and 553 .

WASTELL, Simon. Microbiblion | Or | The Bibles | Epitome: | In Verse. | Digested according to the | Alphabet, that the Scriptures | we reade may more happily | be remembred, and things | forgotten more ea- | sily recalled. | By Simon Wastell sometimes of | Queenes Colledge in Oxford. | . . . (6 lines).

London, | Printed for Robert Mylbourne, | and are to be sold at his shop | at the signe of the Greyhound | in Paules Churchyard. | 1620. | Border. 13.8x7.9 cm. (12),506,(8)p.

(Error in date; should be 1629. Figure blurred).

WHITTELL, Robert. The | Way To The | Celestiall Paradise. | Declaring how a Sinner may be | saued, and come to life euerlasting. | Contained in three bookes. | The { First | Second | Third { sheweth that | a Sinner may | be saued, & | come to life | euerlasting.{ By {Faith, apprehending | Christ for his iustifi- | cation, & applying to |} himselfe the promises | of the Gospell made in | Iesus Christ. | Repentance, hauing | his sins washed away | in the bloud of the | Lambe Iesus Christ. | Prayer, calling vpon | God in the name of | Iesus Christ. | By Robert Whittell, Minister | of the Gospell. | . . . (4 lines).

London, | Printed by Edw. Griffin, for Ralph Rounthwaite, | and are to be sold at his shop in Pauls Church- | yard at the signe of the golden Lyon. 1620. | Line border. 17.6x13.5cm.(58),398p.

WILLET, Andrew. Hexapla; | That Is | A Six-Fold Commentarie | vpon the most Diuine Epistle of the holy Apostle S. | Pavl to the Romanes: wherein according to the Authors former me- | thod sixe things are obserued in euery Chapter. I. the Text with the di- | uers readings. 2. Argument and method. 3. the Questions discussed. | 4.

Doctrines noted. 5. Controuersies handled. | 6. Morall vses obserued. | Wherein are handled the greatest points of Christian | Religion: concerning iustification by faith. c.3,4. the fall of man, c.5. the | combat betweene the flesh and the spirit, c.7. Election, c.9. the vocation of | the Iewes, c.11. with many other Questions and Controuersies | summed in the end of the Table. | Diuided into two Bookes: the first vnto the 12. | Chapter, containing matter of Doctrine: the second belonging to Ex- | hortation, in the fiue last Chapters. | The First Booke. | . . . (7 lines: ornaments)

Printed for Leonard Greene. | 1620. | 28.5 x 19.2 cm. (6),746,(20) p. Dedication to James I, signed.

WILLIAMS, John. A | Sermon | Of | Apparell, | Preached before the Kings Ma- | iestie and the Prince | his Highnesse at Theobalds, | the 22. of February, | 1619 | By Iohn Williams, Dr. in Diuinitie, Deane | of Salisbury, and one of his Maiesties | Chaplaines then in Attendance. | Published by his Maiesties | especiall Commandement. | (device).

London, | Printed by Robert Barker, and | Iohn Bill, Printers to the Kings | most Excellent Maiestie. | M.DC.XX. | 18.3x14.2cm. (1),32p.

WILSON, Thomas. Saints by Calling: | Or | Called to be Saints. | A Godly Treatise of our holy Calling to | Christ, by the Gospell. | With the seuerall gifts proper vnto the | Called: And their Counterfeits in the | Hypocrites which are not partakers of | this Effectuall Cal- | ling. | Written by Thomas Wilson, Minister of Gods Word, at | S. Georges Church in Canterbury. | . . . (4 lines; ornament).

Printed by W. Iaggard, dwelling in Barbican, 1620. | Line border. 19.1x14.5cm. (15),413p.

1621

AINSWORTH, Henry. Annotations | Upon the first book of Moses, | called | Genesis. | Wherein the Hebrew words and sentences, are compared with, & | explained by the ancient Greek and Chaldee versions: | but chiefly, by conference with the | holy Scriptures. | By H.A. | (lace ornament) . . . (5 lines; 6 stars).

Imprinted in the yeare | 1621. | Line border. 20.x15.6cm. (12 , 262)p. Cf.Cambr.Univ.Cat:6382.

BAYNES, Paul. The | Diocesans Tryall. | Wherein | All The Sinnewes | Of Doctor | Dovvnhams Defence | Are brought into three heads, and | orderly dissolved. | By | M.Pavl Baynes. | Published by | Dr. William Amis. | The questions discussed in this Diocesans tryall | are these: | 1.Whether Christ did institute, or the Apostles frame | any Diocesan forme of Churches, or parishionall | onely, pag.1. | 2.Whether Christ ordained by himselfe, or by his A- | postles, any ordinary Pastours, as our Bishops, ha- | ving both precedency of order, and majority of | power over others, pag.24. | 3.Whether Christ did immediately commit ordinary | power Ecclesiasticall, and the exercise of it,

to any | one singular person, or to an united multitude of | Presbyters, pag.78. |
Imprinted 1621.| 18.7x13.8cm. (12),89p.

BEDFORD, Thomas. The | Sinne Vnto | Death. | Or | An Ample Dis- | couery Of That | Fearefvll Sinne, | The Sinne against the holy Ghost, | Together with the signes, de- | grees and preseruatiues | thereof. | In | A Sermon Preached | at Pauls Crosse. August 26. | 1621. | By | Tho:Bedford,Mr of Arts in Queenes Col- | ledge in Cambridge. |

London, | Printed by Iohn Dawson for William Sheffard, | and are to be sold at the signe of the Starre vn- | der St Peters-Church in Corne-hill, and in Popeshead Alley, 1621. | 18.3x13.2 cm. (24),86p.

BERNARD, Richard. The | Faithfvll | Shepherd: | Wholy in a manner trans- | posed, and made anew, and very | much inlarged both with precepts | and examples, to further young | Diuines in the studie of | Diuinitie. | With | The Shepherds Practise in | the end. | By Richard Bernard Mi- | nister and Preacher of Gods word at | Batcombe in Sommerset- | shire, | . . . (5 lines)

London | Printed for Thomas Pavier. | 1621. | Border. 14.2 x8.1cm. (28),413p Subtitle at p. 357.

BRADSHAW, William. A | Meditation | Of Mans | Mortalitie. | Containing An | Exposition of the Ninetieth | Psalme. | By that Reuerned and Religious Seruant | of God Mr William Bradshavv, | sometime Fellow of Sidney Col- | ledge in Cambridge. | Published since his decease by Thomas | Gataker B. of D. and Pastor of | Rotherhith. |

London | Printed by Iohn Dawson for Fulke Clifton, | and are to be sold on New-fish streete hill | vnder Saint Margrets Church. | 1621. | Line border. 16.9x 13.4cm. (6),73p.

CADE, Anthony. A | Sermon | Of | The Natvre | Of Conscience Which | may well be tearmed, | A Tragedy Of Conscience | In Her. | First, a Wakning. | Secondly, Wrastling. | Thirdly, Scourging. | Preached before the Right Honourable Sir Henry Ho- | bart Knight and Baronet, Lord Chiefe Iustice of the | Common Pleas: and Sir Edward Bromley Knight, | one of the Barons of the Exchequer, at the Assises | at Leicester. 1620. Iuly, 25. | By Anthony Cade Batchelour in Diuinity. | (ornament).

London, | Printed by Bernard Alsop for Thomas Iones, and are to be | solde at his shop in Chancery Lane, and in | Westminster hall. 1621. | Line border. 17 8x 13.8cm.(4),46p.

CARTER, Bezaleel. Christ | His Last VVill, | And | Iohn His Legacy. | In a Sermon preached at Clare in | Suffolke, | By Bezaleel Carter Preacher of the word of God at | Canham neere to Saint Edmunds Bury. | . . . (4 lines; ornament).

London, | Printed by Bernard Alsop for Edward Blackemore and | are to be sold at his shop at the signe of the Blazing- | Starre in Paules Church yard. | 1621. | Line border. 17.4x13.9cm. (7),86p.

CASAUBON, Meric. Merici | Casavboni | Is.F. | Pietas | contra maledicos Patrij | nominis, & religionis | hostes. (device).
Londini | Ex Officinia Bibliopolarum. | M.DC.XXI. | 15.7x10.cm. (16),167p.

COOKE, Alexander. More | VVorke | For | À Masse- | Priest. | . . . (3 lines; cut of printing press).
London, | Printed by William Iones, | dwelling in Red-crosse streete. | 1621. | 18.1x13.8cm. (4),74p.
Anon. Cambr. Univ. Cat. 3338.

CRAKANTHORP, Richard. The | Defence | Of | Constantine: | VVith A Treatise Of | the Popes temporall Monarchie. | Wherein, besides diuers passages, touching | other Counsels, both Generall and Prouinciall, | the second Roman Synod, vnder Siluester, is | declared to be a meere Fiction | and Forgery. | By Richard Crakanthorp, Doctor | of Divinity. |
London, | Printed by Bernard Alsop, for Iohn Teage, and | are to besold at his Shop in Pauls Church- | yard, at the signe of the Golden-Ball. | 1621. | 18.1x14.2 cm.(16),380; 283,(1)p. 2 pts.

CRASHAW, William. The | Iesvites | Gospell: | VVritten by them-selues. | Discouered and published by W. Crashaw, B. of Diuinity, | and preacher at White-chappell. | The second Impression Corrected and enlarged by | the Author. | (ornament).
London, | Printed by Bernard Alsop, and are to be sold at his house, be- | ing the next house to Saint Annes Church | 1621. | 17.2x13.9cm. (9),106p.

DENISON, John. De | Confessionis | Avricvlaris | Vanitate, Ad- | versus Cardinalis | Bellarmini | Sophismata, | Et De | Sigilli Confes-sionis Impie- | tate, contra Scholasticorum , & Neoterico- | rum quo-rundam dogmata | Disputatio. | Avthore | Ioanne Denisono Oxoniensi | Sacræ Theologiæ Doctore. | . . . (2 lines; ornament).
Oxonii, | Excudebant Iohannes Lichfield, | & Iacobvs Short. 1621. | 17.2x12.8 cm. (10),126p.

ENGLISH | Protestants Plea, | And Petition, For English | Preists and Papists, To The | present Court of Parlament, and all perse- | cutors of them: diuided into two parts. | In The First Is Proved | by the learned protestants of England, that | these Preists and Catholicks, haue hitherto | been vniustly persecuted, though they haue | often and publickly offered soe much, as any | Christians in conscience might doe. | In The Second Part, Is Proved | by the same protestants, that the same preistly sacri- | ficeing function, acknowledgeing and prac-tize of the | same supreame spirituall Iurisdiction of the Apostolick | See of Rome, and other Catholick doctrines, in the | same sence wee now defend them, and for which | wee ar at this present persecuted, continued and were | practized in this Iland without interruption in al ages, | from S.Peter the Apostle, to these our tymes. | (device; 2 lines).
With permission, Anno 1621. | 13.8x8.9cm. 1-98,83-109,(1)p. Top margin trimmed.

FINCH, Henry. The Calling of the Ievves. | A | Present | To Ivdah And | The Children Of | Israel that ioyned with him, | and to Ioseph (the valiant tribe | of Ephraim) and all the | house of Israel that | ioyned with him. | The Lord giue them grace that they | may returne and seeke Iehovah | their God, and David their | King, in these latter dayes. | There is prefixed an Epistle vnto them, | written for their sake in the Hebrue tongue, | and translated into English. | Published by William Gouge, B. of D. and | Preacher of Gods word in Blackefryers. London. |

London | Printed by Edvvard Griffin for | William Bladen, aud are to be sold at his Shop | neare the great North dore of Pauls, at the signe | of the Bible. 1621. | 17.7x13.5 cm.   (4)234,(1)p.

Sub t.p. of his The VVorlds Great Restavration. 1621. Cf. DNB. 19: 13a.

FINCH, Henry. The | VVorlds | Great Restavration. | Or | The Calling Of | The Ievves, and (with them) | of all the Nations and King- | domes of the earth, to the faith | of Christ. | Published by William Gouge, B. of D. and | Preacher of Gods Word in Black-fryers. London. | (ornament).

London | Printed by Edvvard Griffin for | William Bladen, and are to be sold at his Shop | neare the great North dore of Pauls, at the signe | of the Bible. 1621. | 17.5x13.5cm.   (12),234,(1)p.   Pp. 25-32 wanting: Pp. 82 and 178 blank .

Anon. H&L.   DNB. 19: 13 a.   Ascribed to Gouge, DNB.22:372a(3).

The FIRST And | Second Booke Of | Discipline. | Together with some | Acts Of The Generall | Assemblies, | Clearing and confirming the same: And | An Act Of Parliament. | . . . (4 lines; device).

Printed Anno 1621. | 18.4x13.8 cm.   (16),92p.

GATAKER, Thomas. A | Sparke | Toward The | Kindling Of | Sorrow for Sion. | A Meditation on Amos 6.6. | Being The Svmme Of | A Sermon preached at Sergeants Inne | in Fleet-Street. | By Thomas Gataker B. of D. | and Pastor of Rotherhith. | (device).

London, | Printed by I.H. for William Sheffard, and are to be | sold at the signe of the Starre in Corne-hill, and | in Popes-head Alley. 1621. | 18.5x14.3cm.(10), 39p.

GERHARD, John. The Souls VVatch: | Or, | A Day-Booke for the | Deuout Sovle. | Consisting of 52. heauenly | Meditations, and diuers godly | Prayers, fitted to all the dayes | of the Weeke. | Being holy Exercises for a | sanctified conuersation and | spirituall riches for the | Inward Man. | By Iohn Gerhard Dr of | Diuinitie, and suporintendent of | Heldburge. | . . . (2 lines).   Englished by R.B. With the Lords Prayer | expounded by him. | The third Edition. |

Lōdon printed for R. Iackson. 1621. | Vignette border.   12.9x7.8cm.   (24),512p.

GRANGER, Thomas. A | Familiar | Exposition | or Commentarie on | Ecclesiastes. | VVherein the worlds vanity, | and the true felicitie are plainely | deciphered. | By | Thomas Granger, Preacher of | the Word at Butterwike in East- | holland, Lincolne. |

London: | Printed by T.S. for Thomas Pauier, | dwelling in Iuie-Lane. 1621. | Engraved border; title in oval panel.   18.6x14. cm.   (16),344,(7) p.

HAKEWILL, George. King Davids | Vow | For Reformation | of | Himselfe. | his Family. | his Kingdome. | (Orn. scroll). Deliuered in twelue ser- | mons before the Prince his | Highnesse vpon Psalm 101. | By George Hakewill | Dr. in Divinity. |

London printed for | Mathew Lownes | 1621. | Engr. t.p. and Border. 15.8x10.2 cm.(23),335p.

JAMES I. His | Maiesties | Declaration, | Touching his proceedings in the | late Assemblie and Conuention | of Parliament. | (Coat of Arms).

Imprinted at London by Bonham | Norton and Iohn Bill, | Printers to the Kings most Excellent | Maiestie. 1621. | 17.6x13.1cm. (1),63p.

JAMES I. His | Maiesties | Speach In The | Vpper House of | Parliament, | On Munday the 26. of March, 1621. | (device)

London | Printed by Bonham Norton and | Iohn Bill, Printers to the | Kings most Excellent | Maiestie. | 1621. | 17.4x13.1cm. (2),15p.

KING, Henry. A | Sermon | Preached At | Pavls Crosse, | The 25. Of Novem- | ber. 1621. | Vpon occasion of that false and scandalous | Report (lately Printed) touching the sup- | posed Apostasie of the right Reuerend Father | in God, Iohn King, late Lord | Bishop of London. | By Henry King, his eldest | Sonne. | Whereunto is annexed the Examination, and | Answere of Thomas Preston, P. taken before my | Lords Grace of Canterbury, touching | this Scandall. | Published by Authority. | (ornament).

At London, | Imprinted by Felix Kyngston, | for William Barret. 1621. | Line border. 18.8x14.6 cm. (6),77,(9)p. Lacks Sig A1, fly leaf.

LANGFORD, George. Manassehs | Miracvlovs | Metamorphosis: | Representing to euery Sinne-loaden (if | Sinne-loathing) Soule, | {1 A Conduit of Consolation. | 2 A Comfort against Desperation. | 3 A Conduct to Deuotion. } A Sermon Preached Before The | the thrice-famous Vniuersity of Cambridge, at Great | Saint Maries, Septemb. 10. Anno Dom. 1620. | By George Langford, Master of Arts, Preacher of | Gods Word, and Chaplaine to the Right Honourable | Thomas Earle of Exceter. | . . . (9 lines).

London, | Printed by G.Eld for Iohn Clarke, and are to be sold at his shop | vnder S.Peters Church in Cornhill. 1621. | Line border. 17.9x13.3cm. (6),34p.

LINDSAY, David. A | Trve Narration | Of All The Passages | Of The Proceedings In | the generall Assembly of the Church | of Scotland, | Holden at Perth the 25. of August, | Anno Dom. 1618. | Wherein is set downe the Copy of his | Maiesties Letters to the said | Assembly: | Together with a iust defence of the Articles | therein concluded, against a seditious | Pamphlet. | By Dr. Lyndesay, Bishop of Brechen. | . . . (3 lines; ornament).

London | Printed by William Stansby for Ralph Rounthwait | dwelling at the signe of the golden Lyon | in Pauls Church-yard. | 1621. | 18x14.3 cm. (28),136, 152,125 p. 3 pts

LOE, William. Vox | clamantis. | Mark.1.3. | A | Stil Voice, | To The Three | Thrice-honourable Estates | Of | Parliament | And in them, to all the Soules | of this our Nation, of what state or | condition soeuer they be. | By William Loe, Doctor of Di- | uinitie, and Chaplaine to the Kings | most excellent Maiestie. |

Printed by T.S. for John Teage, and are | to be sold at the Signe of the Golden- | Ball in Pauls Church-yard, 1621. | Engraved border. 18.9x14.6cm. (10), 72p.

A | LOOKING-GLASSE | For Papists: | To see their owne Deformities in matters of Faith, and Religion: | And for formall Protestants, to make them more carefull of | the true profession of Iesvs Christ: lest | at any time they fall away from the sinceritie | of the Gospell of Christ. | With a briefe History of the Popes liues, from the first three hundred | yeeres after Christ, vntill Paul the fift. | . . . (2 lines; cut).

Printed at London by T.S. for Nathaniel Newbery. 1621. | 17.5x13.3cm. (8), 107p.

MAIE, Edward. A | Sermon | Of The Com- | mvnion Of Saints; | Preached By Edward | Maie, Chaplaine To | the Honorable Societie of Lin- | colnes Inne. | . . . (4 lines; ornament, 3 and 5 lines, *double column.*)

London, | Printed by Iohn Legatt for George Lathum, and are to | be sold at his shoppe in Pauls Church-yard, at | the signe of the Brasen Serpent. | 1621. | 18.5x14.cm. (12),26,(1)p.

MOULIN, Pierre du. A | Letter | Vnto Them | Of | The Romish Church, | By Peter du Movlin, Minister | in the reformed Church at | Paris. | Together with a true Iubile or generall | Pardon of Indulgence by the | same Author. | (device).

London, | Printed by H.L. for Mathew Lownes, | dwelling in Paules Church-yard. | 1621. | Line border. 17.x10.4cm. (5),55p.

MONTAGU, Richard. Diatribæ | Vpon The First | Part Of The Late | History of Tithes. | By Richard Movntagv. |

At London, | Imprinted by Felix Kyngston, for Matthevv | Lovvnes. 1621. | 18.7x13.7cm. (9),579p.

NICHOLAS y SACHARLES, Juan de. The | Reformed | Spaniard: | To all reformed Churches, embracing the true | Faith, wheresoeuer dispersed on the | Face of the Earth: | In speciall, To the most Reuerend Arch- | Bishops, Reuerend Bishops, and Worshipfull Doctors, | and Pastors, now gathered together in the venerable Synode | at London, this yeare of our Lord, 1621. | John de Nicholas & Sacharles, Doctor of | Physicke, wisheth health in our | Lord. | First published by the Author in Latine, and | now thence faithfully Translated | into English. | (device).

London, | Printed for Walter Burre, and are to be sold | at his shop in Paules Church-yard, at the signe | of the Crane, 1621. | 18x14cm. (1,33)p

ROGERS, Nehemiah. Christian Curtesie: | Or, | St.Pavls Vltimum Vale. | Deliuered in two Sermons, on 2.Cor. | 13.11. at St.Margarets on |

Fish-stret-hill in London. | By N.Rogers (sometimes Prea- | cher there) at his Farewel, vpon his remoueal | thence to a Pastoral charge elsewhere. | . . . (2 lines; ornament).

London, | Printed by H.L. for Edward Brewster: and are to bee | sould at his shop, at the west end of Pauls, at | the signe of the Star. 1621. | Line border. 18.4x14.2cm. (8),77p.

ROGERS, Thomas. The | Faith, Doctrine, | And Religion, | Professed, | And Protected In The | Realme Of England, And | Dominions of the same. | Expressed in thirty nine Articles, concordably | agreed vpon by the reuerend Bishops, and Clergie of this King- | dome, at two seuerall meetings, or Conuocations of theirs, | in the yeeres of our Lord, 1562. and 1604. | The Said Articles Analised Into | Propositions, and the Propositions proued to be agreeable both | to the written word of God, and to the extant Con- | fessions of all the neighbour Churches | Christianly Reformed. | The Adversaries Also Of Note, And Name | which from the Apostles daies, and Primitiue Church hitherto, haue | crossed, or contradicted the said Articles in generall, or any par- | ticle, or proposition arising from any of them in particular, hereby | are discouered, laid open, and so confuted. | . . . (4 lines; ornament).

London, | Printed by Iohn Legatt. | 1621. | 18.4x13.8cm. (36),222p. Preface, signed.

ROGERS, Thomas. A | Pretiovs Booke Of | Heavenly Meditations. | Called, A private talk of the soule | with God. | Which, whoso zealously will vse and per- | vse, shall feele in his minde an vnspeak- | able sweetnes of the ever- | lasting happinesse. | Written (as some think) by that reuerend and | religious Father, S. Augustine; and not | translated onely, but purified also, & | with most ample and necessary | sentences of holy scrip- | ture adorned, | By | Thomas Rogers. | . . . (3 lines).

At London, | Printed for the Companie of | the Stationers. | 1621. | 11.9x7cm. (17),205; (15),213,(21); (12),92,(3)p.

Contains also . . . S.Augustines Praiers, and Saint Avgvstines Manval; with continuous register, but separate pagination.

ROGERS, Thomas. A right Christian Treatise, | entituled S. Augustines Praiers: | Published in more ample sort | then hath bin yet in the English tongue: | purged from divers superstitious | points, and adorned with mani- | fold places of the holy | Scripture, | by | Thomas Rogers. | Whereunto is annexed Saint Augu- | stines Psalter, | Translated and quoted by the | same T.R. | . . . (2 lines).

Imprinted | At London for the Compa- | ny of the Stationers. | 1621. | 11.9x7 cm.(15),213,(21)p.

Appended to his Pretiovs Booke: 1621.; with continuous register, but sep. pagination.

ROGERS, Thomas. Saint Avgvstines | Manval: | Containing speciall, and picked | Meditations, and god- | lie Prayers. | Drawne out of the word of God, and | writings of the holy Fathers for the | exercise of the soule. | Corrected, translated and adorned, | By | Thomas Rogers. | . . . (2 lines: ornament).

At London, | Printed for the Company | of Stationers. | 1621. | 11.9x7cm.(12), 92,(3)p.

Appended to his Pretiovs Booke: 1621; with continuous register, but separate pagination.

ROGERS, Timothy. The | Roman-Catharist: | Or, | The Papist Is A | Pvritane. | A Declaration, shewing that they of | the Religion and Church of Rome, are | notorious Pvritans. | By Timothy Rogers, Preacher of the word of God | at Steple in Essex. | . . . (2 lines; device).

At London, | Printed for Edward Brewster, and are to be sold at | his shop, at the west end of Pauls, at the | signe of the Starre. | 1621. | Line border. 17.9x13.7 cm. (1),42p.

SMITH, Richard. Of | The Avthor | And | Svbstance | Of The | Protestant Chvrch | And Religion, | Two Bookes. | Written first in Latin by R. S. | Doctour of Diuinity, | And | Now reuiewed by the Author, and transla- | ted into English by VV. Bas. | . . . (ornament; 2 lines).

Permissu Superiorum, M.DC.XXI. | 16x10.7 cm. (32),329,(5) p. Gillow,V:516.

TAYLOR, Thomas. The | Parable | Of The Sower | And Of The | Seed. | Declaring in Fovre Seve- | rall grounds, among other things: | 1. How farre an Hypocrite may goe in the way towards heauen, | and wherein the sound Christian goeth beyond him. | And | 2. In the last and best ground, largely discourseth of a good | heart, describing it by very many signes of it, digested into a | familiar method: which of it selfe is an entire Treatise. | And also | 3. From the constant fruit of the good ground, iustifieth the | doctrine of the perseuerance of Saints: oppugneth the fifth | Article of the late Arminians; and shortly and plainly an- | swereth their most colourable Arguments and euasions. | By Thomas Taylor, late Fellow of Christs Col- | ledge in Cambridge, and Preacher of the Word of | God, at Reding in Bark-shire. |

Imprinted at London by Felix Kyngston, for Iohn | Bartlet, and are to be sold at the signe of the gilded | Cup, in the Goldsmiths Rowe in | Cheapside. 1621. | Line border. 18.4x14.2cm. (16),453,(11)p. 2 folded tables.

TEELINCK, William. Pavls | Complaint | Against His | Natvrall | Corrvption. | With | The Meanes | How To Bee | Delivered From | the power of the same. | Set forth in two Sermons vpon | the 24 verse of the 7.Chapter of | his Epistle to the Romanes. | . . . (2 lines). By me William Teelinck, Preacher of the | Word of God at Middlebvrgh. |

London | Printed by Iohn Dawson for Iohn Bellamie. | 1621. | Line border. 17.9x13.9cm. (8),66p.

TILLESLEY, Richard. Animadversions | vpon M.Seldens | History | Of Tythes, | And His | Review Thereof: | Before which (in lieu of the two first | Chapters purposely pretermitted) is premised | a Catalogue of 72. Authors, before | the yeare 1215. | Maintaining the Ius diuinum of Tythes, or more, to be payd | to the Priesthood vnder the Gospell. | The second Edition newly corrected and much augmented, | together with an Answer to an vnprinted Pamphlet di- | vulged against the former. | By Richard Tillesley Doctor in diuinity, | and Archdeacon of Rochester, and sometimes fellow of | Saint Iohn Baptist's Colledge in Oxford. | . . . (2 lines).

London, | Printed by N.Okes for Arthur Iohnson. | MDCXXI. | 18.3x14.3cm (42),263; 137, (1)p. 2 pts

USSHER, James. The | Svbstance | Of That Which | Was Delivered In A Ser- | mon before the Commons House of | Parliament, in St. Margarets | Church at Westminster, the | 18. of February, | 1620. | By Iames Vssher, Profes- | sor Of Divinity In The | Vniuersity of Dvblin, | in Ireland. | (device)

Imprinted at London by Felix Kyngston, for Iohn | Bartlet: and are to be sold at the signe of the gilded | Cup, in the Goldsmiths Rowe in | Cheapside. 1621. | Line border. 18.5x14.1cm. (4),50p.
Also inserted in his Answer to a Challenge: 1625.

WATS, James. The | Controversie | Debated | About the Reuerend ge- | sture of Kneeling, in the Act of | Receiuing the Holy | Com- munion. | By Iames Wats, Minister of | Gods Word at Woodnos- borough in Kent: | And sometime fellow of Mag- | dalene Colledge in | Cambridge. | (device).

London, | Printed by W. I. for Walter Burre, and are | to be sold at his shop in Paules Church- | yard, at the signe of the Crane, | 1621. | 18.4x14.8 cm. (6,36)p.

1622

AINSWORTH, Henry. Annotations | Vpon The | Five Bookes of | Moses, And The | Booke of the Psalmes. | Wherein The Hebrew Words | and sentences are compared with, and explained by the | ancient Greeke and Chaldee versions, and other Records and Monu- ments | of the Hebrewes: But chiefly by conference with the holy Scriptures, | Moses his words, lawes and ordinances, the Sacrifices and other Legall | ceremonies heretofore commanded by God to the Church | of Israel are explained. | With an Advertisement touching some objections made against | the sinceritie of the Hebrew Text, and allegation of the Rabbines | in these Annotations. | As also Tables directing unto such principall things as are | observed in the Annota- tions upon each severall Booke. | By H.A. | . . . (3 lines: ornament).

London, | Printed by Iohn Haviland for Beniamin Fisher, and | are to be sold at the signe of the Talbot in Pater noster | Row. M.DC.XXII. | Line border. 20.x15.6cm.
General title-page of series, signed: Genesis, dated 1621; Exodus, 1622; Leviti- cus, 1618; Numbers, 1619; Deuteronomy 1619; and Psalmes, 1617. Each part has separate register

AINSWORTH, Henry. Annotations | Vpon the second Booke of | Moses, Called | Exodus. | VVherein, by conferring the holy Scriptures, | comparing the Chaldee and Greeke versions, and other | Records of the Hebrewes; Moses his words, lawes, | and ordinances are explained. | By H.A. | . . . (8 lines; ornament).

Printed by Iohn Haviland for Iohn Bellamie and Beniamin Fisher, | and are to be sold at the two Greyhounds in Cornhill, and at the | Talbot in Pater Noster Row. 1622. | Line border. 20.x15.6cm. (2,239)p.

Part of his Annotations Vpon The Five Bookes of Moses: 1622; with separate register.

General preface, signed.

AMES, William. A | Reply | To | Dr. Mortons | Generall Defence | Of Three Nocent | Ceremonies. | Viz. | The Surplice, Crosse in Baptisme, and kneeling at | the receiving of the sacramentall elements | of Bread and Wine. | (device).

Printed in yeare 1622. | 18.3x13.8 cm. (10),114p. (Mispaging).

Anon. Dexter 520. Camb.Univ.Cat.6929. Attributed to David Calderwood. DNB.8:245b.

BARNES, Thomas. The Gales | Of Grace: | Or, | The Spirituall VVinde: | Wherein the Mysterie of | Sanctification is opened | and handled. | By Thomas Barnes, | Preacher of Gods word at | Much-Waltham | in Essex. | . . . (3 lines).

London | Printed by H.L. for Nathanael Newbery, and | are to be sold at his shop in Cornehil, | neere S.Peters church and in | Popes-head Alley. 1622. | Line border. 14.7x9.1cm. (16),249p.

From the library of Walter W. Law.

BOURNE, Immanuel. The | Trve VVay Of | A Christian, To The | Nevv Iervsalem. | Or, | A Three-Folde De- | monstration: | First, of the Excellencie of the true and sauing Knowledge of | Christ; and the meanes to attaine it: with the Antiquitie, | necessitie, and benefit of Catechisme. | Secondly, of our Vnion and Communion with Christ, and his | Church. | Thirdly, of our new Creation in Christ, by the blessed Spirit. | With diuers Questions, and Cases of Conscience, most comfor- | table for a Christian. | Deliuered first in Briefe, in a Sermon Preached at | Paules-Crosse, the first Sunday in the new | yeere, 1617. | And newly reuised and enlarged by Immanvel Bovrne | Master of Artes, and now Parson of Ashouer | in the Countie of Derby. | (ornament).

London, | Printed for George Fayerbeard, and are to be sold at his shop | at the North doore of the Royall Exchange. | 1622. | 18.2x14.2cm. (8),120p.

BOYS, John. The | Workes Of | Iohn Boys | Doctor in Diuinitie | and Deane of | Canterburie. |

Imprinted for William Aspley | Anno 1622. | Engr. t.p. 29.3x19.5cm. (4,4), 1-562, (4), 563-790, (4); 791-948, (1), 949-988, (10)p. 5 Sub. t.p.

BREREWOOD, Edward. Enqviries | Tovching | the diuersity of Langvages, | and Religions, through | the chiefe parts of the | World. | VVritten by Edvv. Brerevvood lately | professour of Astronomy in Gresham Colledge | in London. | (device).

London, | Printed by Iohn Bill. | M.DC.XXII. | 18x13.2cm. (24),203p.

BRINSLEY, John. The | Third Part | Of | The Trve Watch, | Containing the call of the Lord, to awake | all sorts to meet him with intreatie of peace, and to | turne unto him by true repentance: shewing what | causes we have forthwith to betake our selves | to Watching and Prayer. | Taken out of the Vision of Ezekiel, Chap.9. | By Iohn Brinsley. | . . . (11 lines)

London, | Printed by Iohn Haviland for Thomas Pavier, and are to | be sold at his shop in Ivie lane. 1622. | 19.4x13.8cm. (54),568,(42)p. Lacks engr. t.p.

BUGGS, Samuel. Davids | Strait. | A Sermon Preached | at Pauls-Crosse, July 8. 1621. | By | Samvel Bvggs Bachelor of Diuinitie, | sometime Fellow of Sidney-Sussex Colledge | in Cambridge: | And now Minister of the Word of God | in Coventrie. | . . . (4 lines; ornament).

London, | Printed by G. Eld for Nathanael Butter, and are | to be sold at his shop at the signe of the pyde | Bull neare S. Austins Gate. 1622. | Line border. 18. x13.9 cm. (6),58p.

BYFIELD, Nicholas. The | Principles | Or, | The Patterne of | wholesome Words. | Containing a Collection of such | Truths as are of necessity to be be- | lieued vnto saluation, separated | out of the body of all | Theologie. | Made euident by infallible and | plaine proofes of Scripture. | And withall, | The seueral vses such Principles should | be put to, are abundantly shewed. | A Proiect much desired, and of singu- | lar vse for all sorts of Christians. | By, | N.Byfeild, Preacher of Gods Word | at Isleworth in Middlesex. | The second Edition, corrected | and amended. |

London: | Printed by T.S. for Samuel Man, | dwelling in Pauls Church-yard, at | the signe of the Swan. 1622. | Line border. 13.6x7.6cm. (21),500,(1)p. Colophon. From the library of Walter W. Law.

CAMPION, Edmund. Edmvndi | Campiani | Societatis | Iesv Martyris | In Anglia, | Opuscula omnia nunc pri- | mùm è M.S. edita. | (device)

Mvssiponti, | Apud Sebastianvm Cramoisy, | Serenissimi Dvcis & Vniuersita- | tis Typographum auratum. | M.DC.XXII. | 10.6x5.5cm. (24),476p.

COOKE, Alexander. Yet More | Worke | For | A Masse- | Priest. | . . . (3 lines; cut).

London, | Printed by William Iones, and | are to be sold by William Sheffard at his shop | in Popes head Ally. 1622. | 18.7x14.2 cm. (4),42p. Cf.Cambr.Univ.Cat. 3337-3338. Dedication signed.

COTTON, Clement. The Christians | Concordance: | Containing The Most | materiall words in the New Testament. | By the helpe whereof he may (onely by calling to | mind some one such word in a sentence) readily attaine to any | passage therein, seruing his present vse. | As also by conferring one place with another he may easily discerne the | diuerse acceptations of one and the same word. | . . . (4 lines; device).

London, | Printed by Richard Field for Nathanael Newbery, and are to be | sold at the signe of the Starre vnder S.Peters Church | in Cornhill, and in Popes head Alley. | 1622. | 25.2x16.5cm.(8, 450, 13)p. Dedication signed.

DALECHAMP, Caleb. Vindiciæ | Salomonis: | Sive, | Dispvtatio Bipartita | De Lapsv Statvqve | Æterno Regis | Salomonis: | Quâ eius

& omnium Sanctorum perse- | uerantia in fide defenditur. | Authore | Calebo Dalechampio Sedanensi, | S.Theologiæ Studioso. | . . . (8 lines).
Londini, | Excusum per Gvlielmvm Iones, | Impensis Leonardi Greene Cantabrigiensis. | 1622. | 17.9x13.8cm.(13), 37p.

DOD, John and CLEAVER, Richard. A Plaine | And Familiar | Exposition Of The | Ten Commandements. | With A Methodicall Short | Catechisme, containing briefly the principall grounds of Christian Religion. | The fifteenth Edition: | Newly corrected and amended by the Author. | . . . (3 lines; device).
London, | Printed by Richard Field, for Thomas Man, | dwelling in Pater-noster row, at the signe | of the Talbot. 1622. | 17.7x13 cm. (6),365,(28)p.
Epistle Dedicatorie, signed.

DONNE, John. A | Sermon | Vpon | The XV. Verse | Of The XX. Chap- | ter Of The Booke | Of Ivdges | Wherein occasion was iustly taken for the Publication | of some Reasons, which his Sacred Maiestie | had beene pleased to giue, of those Directions | for Preachers, which he had | formerly sent forth. | Preached at the Crosse the 15th of September. | 1622. | By Iohn Donne, Doctor of Diuinitie and Deane | of Saint Pavls, London. | And now by commandement of his Majestie | published, as it was then preached. |
London | Printed by William Stansby for Thomas Iones, and are to | be sold at his shop in the Strand at the blacke | Rauen, neere vnto Saint Cle- | ments Church. | 1622. | Line border. 17.6x13.1 cm. (6),68p.
The text is given as Ivdges.5.20.

DOWNAME, John. A Gvide To | Godlynesse | Or a Treatise of a | Christian Life | Shewing the duties wherein it | Consisteth, the helpes Inabling & | the Reasons parswading vnto it | ye Impediments hindering ye Prac- | tise of it, and the best meanes | to Remoue them | Whereunto are added diuers Prayers | And | a Treatise of Carnall Securitie | By John Dovname | Batcheler in Diuinitie | and Minister of Gods Word | . . . (4 lines).
Printed at London | by Felix Kingstone For Ed: | Weuer & W: Bladen | at the North dore | of Pauls. | [1622]. Engraved t.p. 32.1x20.5cm. (36),961,(1) ;(14), 103p.

DOWNAME, John. A | Treatise | Of Secvritie: | Diuided into two Bookes. | The Former, Intreating | Of Carnall Secvritie And | Hardnes Of Heart; | Wherein the Nature, Originall and Causes of it are displayed and | described, the Kinds of it distinguished, and the Differences betweene | them expressed, the Signes whereby it may be knowne, shewed, | with the Preseruatiues and Remedies, whereby we may | be kept from falling into this dangerous disease, or | recouered if we be alreadie fallen. | The Latter, Intreating Of | Spiritvall And Christian | Secvritie; | Wherein is shewed what it is, the Causes and Effects of it, and the | Meanes whereby it may be obtayned and preserued. | Published as an Antidote against the dangerous Securitie | of these last Times: | By Iohn Downame, Batchelar in Diuinitie, and | Preacher of Gods Word. | . . . (4 lines ; ornament).

London | Printed by William Stansby. | 1622. | Line border. 32.1x20.5cm. (14), 103p.

Appended to his: A Gvide To Godlynesse ... 1622; with separate register and pagination.

ELTON, Edward. The | Complaint | Of A Sancti- | fied Sinner | Answered: | Or | An Explanation of the seuenth Chapter | of the Epistle of Saint Paul to the Romans, | deliuered in diuers Sermon, | Preached by Edvvard Elton, Bachelor in Diuinitie, | and Preacher of Gods word at Saint Mary Magdalens | Barmondsey neere London. | And now by him published, intending the common | good and profit of Gods Church. | The second Edition. | . . . (3 lines):

London, | Printed by G.Eld for Robert Mylbovrne, | and are to be sold at the great South doore of | Pauls. 1622. | Line border. 18.8x13.9cm.(6),509,(9)p.

FOTHERBY, Martin. Atheomastix: | Clearing foure Truthes, | Against Atheists and Infidels: | 1. That, There is a God. | 2. That, There is but one God. | 3. That, Jehouah, our God, is that one God. | 4. That, The Holy Scripture is the Word of that God. | All of them proued, by Naturall Reasons, and Secular | Autorities; for the reducing of Infidels: and, by Scriptures, and | Fathers, for the confirming of Christians. | By the R. Reuerend Father in God, Martin Fotherby, | late Bishop of Salisbury. | The Contents followes, next after the Preface. | . . . (5 lines; ornaments).

London, | Printed by Nicholas Okes, dwelling in Foster-Lane. | 1622. | Line border. 28.6x18.7cm. (36),1–68,99–362p. 69–98 omitted in numbering.

The | FRENCH | Heravld | Sent To The | Princes Of | Christendome. | (devices)

Printed according to the | French Copie. | 1622. | 18.9x14.6cm. 3–21p. 1–2, fly-leaf, missing.

GATAKER, Thomas. מזכיר לדויד | Davids | Remembrancer. | A | Meditation | On | Psalme 13.1. | Deliuered in a Sermon at Serjeants | Jnne in Fleet-street. | By | Thomas Gataker, Bachelor in Di- | uinitie, and Pastor of Rotherhith. | . . . (4 lines).

London, | Printed by Iohn Haviland. | 1622. | 18.1x14.4cm. (6),77p. Sub title in his Two Sermons: 1623.

GATAKER, Thomas. The | Spiritvall | Watch, | Or | Christs Generall | Watch-Word. | A Meditation | On | Mark.13.37. | What I say vnto You, I say vnto All, | Watch. | By Thomas Gataker B. of D. | and Pastor of Rotherhith. | The second Edition; Amended and | Enlarged. | (ornament).

London, | Printed by Iohn Haviland for William Bladen, and | are to be sold at the signe of the Bible, at the great | North doore of Pauls. 1622. | 18.5x14.3cm. (8),130p.

GOUGE, William. Of | Domesticall | Dvties | Eight Treatises. | I. An Exposition of that part of Scripture out of which Dome- | sticall Duties are raised. | II. {1. A right Coniunction of Man and Wife. | 2. Common-mutuall Duties betwixt Man and Wife. | III. Particular

Duties of Wiues. | IV. Particular Duties of Husbands. | V. Duties of Children. | VI. Duties of Parents. | VII. Duties of Seruants. | VIII. Duties of Masters. | By William Govge. | (ornament).

London, | Printed by Iohn Haviland for William Bladen, and | are to be sold at the signe of the Bible neere the great North | doore of Pauls. 1622. | Line border. 18.7x14cm. (24),693,(1)p.

HARPSFIELD, Nicholas. Historia | Anglicana | Ecclesiastica | A Primis Gentis Svsceptae Fidei | Incvnabvlis Ad Nostra Fere | Tempora Dedvcta. | Et In Qvindecim Centvrias Distribvta: | Avctore | Nicolao Harpsfeldio | Archidiacono Cantvariensi. | Adiecta breui narratione de Diuortio Henrici VIII. Regis ab vxore | Catherina, & ab Ecclesia Catholica Romana discessione, | Scripta ab | Edmvndo Campiano. | Nunc primum in lucem producta Studio & Opera | R.P.Richardi Gibboni Angli Societatis Iesv Theologi, | (device)

Dvaci, | Symptibus Marci Wyon, Typographi Iurati, | sub signo Phœnicis. | Anno M.DC.XXII. | Cum gratia et Priuilegio. [34.6 x 20.8 cm. (24),779,(1) p

HARRIS, Robert. Gods | Goodnes | And Mercy. | Layd Open In A | Sermon, Preached | At Pavls-Crosse | On The Last | Of Ivne. | 1622. | By | Mr Robert Harris, Pastour of the Church | of God at Hanvvell in Oxfordshire. | . . . (4 lines; device).

London | Printed by Iohn Davvson for Iohn Bartlet, | and are to be sold at the Guilt Cup in the | Gold-smiths Row in Cheap-side. | 1622. | 17.2x13.2 cm. (8),29p.

MAYER, John. A | Treasvry | Of Ecclesiasticall | Expositions, vpon the difficult | and doubtfull places of the Scriptures, | Collected out of the best esteemed | Interpreters, both auncient and mo- | derne, together with the Authors | judgement, and various | Observations. | Conteining 270. Texts, throughout | the Gospels of Mathew, Marke, Luke, | and Iohn, and the Acts of the Apostles. | The very pith, and choicest streines of | many Bookes in one, and a fully satisfying | Resolution of aboue a thousand | Questions in solid Diuinitie. | The next page sheweth the names of the Writers, | whose Expositions follow in this Booke. | By Iohn Mayer, B.D. |

London | Printed by I.D. for Iohn Bellamie, | and are to be sold at his Shop at the | two Grey hounds in Corne-hill, | nere the Royall Exchange. | 1622. | Arch. border. 18.7x14.7 (20),704p.

Also another copy from the library of Walter Law. 17.5x13.8cm.

MONTAGU, Richard. Analecta | Eccle- | siasticarum | Exercitationum: | Collectore | Richardo Montacutio. | 1622. |

Londini, | Pro Societate Bibliopolarum. | Column and vine border. 28.2x18.3cm. (30),390p.

The | NEVV Man | Or, | A Svpplication From An | vnknowne Person, a Roman Catholike vnto | Iames, the Monarch of Great Brittaine, and | from him to the Emperour, Kings, and Prin- | ces of the Christian World. | Touching | The causes and reasons that will argue a necessity | of a Generall Councell to be forthwith assembled a- | gainst him that now vsurps the papall Chaire | vnder the name of Pavl the fifth. |

Wherein are discouered more of the secret Iniqui- | ties of that Chaire and Court, then hitherto their friends | feared, or their very aduersaries did suspect. | Translated into English by William Crashaw, Batchelour in Di- | uinity, according toe the Latine Copy, sent from | Rome into England. | (ornament)

London, | Printed by Bernard Alsop, for George Norton, and are | to bee sold in Distaffe-lane, at the signe of | the Dolphin. 1622. | 17.3x12.1cm (22),56p.
First edition ?
The Latin edition, Novus Homo, was burned in Italy in 1613.

The | NEVV Man | Or, | A Svpplication From An | vnknowne Person, a Roman Catholike vnto | Iames, the Monarch of Great Brittaine, and | from him to the Emperour, Kings and Prin- | ces of the Christian World. | Touching | The causes and reasons that wil argue a necessity | of a Generall Councell to be forthwith assembled against | him that now vsurps the Papall Chaire, | vnder the name of Paul the fifth. | Wherein are discouered more of the secret Ini- | quities of that Chaire and Court, then hitherto their friends | feared, or their very aduersaries did suspect. | Translated into English by William Crashaw Batchelour in | Diuinity, according to the Latine Copy, sent from | Rome into England. | (ornament).

London, | Printed by Barnard Alsop, for George Norton, and are | to be sold in Distaffe-lane, at the signe of | the Dolphin. 1622. | 17.7x13.4cm. (22),56p.
Cambr. Univ. Cat. 4173. Ascribed to Martin Becan.

NORRIS, Sylvester. An | Antidote | Or | Treatise Of | Thirty Controversies: | VVith a large Discourse of the Church. | In Which | The soueraigne truth of Catholike doctrine, is | faythfully deliuered: against the pestiferous | writinges of all English Sectaryes. | And | In particular, against D. Whitaker, D. Fvlke, D. | Reynolds, D. Bilson, D. Robert Abbot, D. | Sparkes, and D. Field, the chiefe vpholders, some | of Protestancy, some of Puritanisme, some of both. | Deuided into three Partes. | By S.N. Doctour of Diuinity. | . . . (5.lines).

Permissu Superiorum, M.DC.XXII. | 18.6x13.7cm. (20),335(2); (8),307(2)p.
Two parts, with separate t.p., register and pagination
Cambr Univ Cat 6546.

PARR, Elnathan. A | Plaine | Exposition | vpon the whole thirteenth, four- | teenth, fifteenth, and sixteenth Chap- | ters of the Epistle of Saint Pavl to | the Romanes. | Wherein the text is diligently and methodi- | cally resolued, the sense giuen, and many Do- | ctrines thence gathered, are by liuely vses applied | for the benefit of Gods Children. | Performed with much varietie, and conuenient breuitie, | By | Elnathan Parr Bachelor in Diuinity, and | Preacher of Gods word. | To which is prefixed an Alphabetical Table, containing the | chiefe Points and Doctrines handled in the Booke. | . . . (2 lines)

London, | Printed by G. Eld for Samvel Man, dwelling | in Pauls Church-yard at the signe of | the Swanne. 1622. | 18.8x13.8cm. (16),349p.

PARSONS, Robert. A | Christian | Directory, | Guiding men to Eternall Saluation: com- | monly called the Resolvtion. | Deuided into three Bookes. | The first wherof, teacheth how to make | a good Resolution. The second, how | to begin well. The third, how to per- | seuere, and end happily. | Written | By the R.Father Robert Persons, | Priest of the Society of Iesvs. | The Sixt. and last Edition. | . . . (device: 1 line).

Permissu Superiorum, M.DC.XXII. | 14.5x7.8cm. (24),826p.

RANDALL, John. The | Description | Of Fleshly Lvsts. | Or | A Profitable And | Frvitfvll Sermon | Vpon the first Epistle of Saint Peter, | Chap.2.vers.11.12. Preached and Penned by | that famous, learned, iudicious, Orthodoxall, holy, wise, | and skilfull Preacher and servant of God, now | deceased, and with his God triumphing | in Heaven, Iohn Randall, | Batchelour of Divinitie, Pastour of | St.Andrewes Hubbart in little | East-cheape London, | Sometimes Fellow of | Lincolne Colledge in | Oxford: | And now published, to the glory of God, | the edification of his Church, and the honou- | rable Memoriall of the Author, by | William Holbrooke, | Preacher of the Word of God in | the Church aforesaid. |

London | Printed by I.D. for Nathaniel Newbery and William Sheffard, | and are to be sold at their Shops in Popes-head Alley. | 1622. | 18x13.6cm.(8),22p.

RANDALL, John. The | Necessitie | Of | Righteovsnes. | Or | A Profitable And | Frvitfvll Sermon | Vpon the fift Chapter of the Gospell | of S.Mathew.Vers.20. Preached and Penned by | that famous, learned, iudicious, Orthodoxall, holy, wise, | and skilfull Preacher and servant of God, now | deceased, and with his God triumphing | in Heaven, Iohn Randall, | Batchelour of Divinitie, Pastour of | St Andrewes Hubbart in little | East-cheape London, | Sometimes Fellow of | Lincolne Colledge in | Oxford. | And now published, to the glory of God, | the edification of his Church, and the honou- | rable Memoriall of the Author, by | William Holbrooke, | Preacher of the Word of God in | the Church aforesaid. |

London | Printed by I.D. for Nathaniel Newbery and William Sheffard, | and are to be sold at their Shops in Popes-head Alley. | 1622. | 18.3x13.9cm. (8),24p.

SCOT, William. The | Course of Conformitie, | As it| Hath proceeded, | Is concluded, | Should be refused. | . . . (3 lines; lace ornament).

Printed in the yeare 1622. | 17.2x13.2cm. (23),168pp.
Ascription by David Laing. Usually ascribed to David Calderwood. DNB.8: 245b.

SCOTT, Thomas. The | Belgicke | Pismire: | Stinging the slothfull Sleeper, | And | Avvaking the Diligent | To | Fast, Watch, Pray; | And | Worke Ovt Their Owne | Temporall and Eternall Salvation | With | Feare and Trembling. | . . . (3 lines).

Printed at London. 1622. | 16.4x12. cm. (12),100p.
Anon.Cambr.Univ.Cat. 6933.

SEMPILL, James. Scoti τοῦ τυχόντου Paraclesis | Contra | Danielis Tileni | Silesii Paraenesin. | Ad Scotos Genevensis Dis- | ciplinæ Zelotas conscriptam, | Cuius pars prima est, | De Episcopali Ecclesiæ | Regimine. | (ornament).

Anno. 1622. | 18.6x13.6 cm. (4),232p.
Anon. DNB.51:236b.

SWIFT, William. A | Sermon | Preached At | The Fvnerall | Of That Painfvll | And faithfull seruant of Iesus Christ, | Mr Thomas Wilson, in his | owne Churche at St. Georges, in | Canterbury the 25. day of | Ianuary. In the yeare of | our Lord God | 1621. | By William Svvift, Preacher of Gods | Word, at St Andrevves, within the Citie | of Canterbury. | . . . (4 lines)

London | Printed by I.D. for Fulke Clifton. | 1622. | Line border. 17.2x13.4 cm. (6), 22, (3) p.

TILENUS, Daniel. De | Disciplina | Ecclesiastica | Brevis & modesta dissertatio, | Ad Ecclesiam Scoticam. | Autore | Gallo quodam Theologo, | Verbi Divini Ministro. | (lace orn.)

Abredoniæ, | Excudebat Eduardus Rabanus, | Impensis Davidis Melvill, 1622. | Cum privilegio. | 13.6x8.3 cm. Pp. (1), 5–142 (1). Lacks Ai.
Anon. Cambr.Univ.Cat.5998.

WARD, Samuel. VVoe To | Drvnkards. | A Sermon by Samvel Ward | Preacher of Ipswich. | (cut, in two parts)

London | Printed by A.Math. for Iohn Marriott, and | Iohn Grismand, and are to be sold at their Shops in | St.Dunstons Church-yard, and in Pauls Alley | at the Signe of the Gunne. 1622. | Line border. 15x10cm. (1),51p.

WHATELY, William. Gods | Hvsbandry | The First Part. | Tending To Shew The | Difference Betwixt The | Hypocrite and the truehearted | Christian. | As It Was Delivered In | Certaine Sermons, And | is now published | By William Whately Preacher of the | Word of God in Banbury in Oxfordsheire. | . . . (4 lines: ornament).

London, | Imprinted by Bernard Alsop for Thomas Man, and are | to be sold at his shop in Pater-noster-row, at the signe | of the Talbot. 1622. | Line border. 18.8x13.6cm.(8),152; (8),158p.
2 Pts, with separate t.p., register and pagination.

WILLAN, Robert. Conspiracie | Against | Kings, | Heavens | Scorne. | A Sermon preached at Westmin- | ster-Abbey before the Iudges, vpon | the fifth of Novemb. | 1622. | By | Ro:Willan, Doctor in Diuinity. | . . . (5 lines)

London, | Printed by Iohn Bill. 1622. | 18.x13.9cm. (6),46,(1)p.

WORTHINGTON, Thomas. An | Anker | Of Christian | Doctrine. | Wherein the most principal Points of Catholike | Religion, are proued: by the only written | Word of God. | Not rejecting Diuine, nor Apostolical Traditions; au- | thentical Councels; Popes Decrees; ancient Fa- | thers; nor other ordinarie Proofes; but | abstracting from them in this | Encounter. | For better satisfaction of those, who wil admit | no other trial of true Religion, but | Scriptures onely. | Auctore T.W. S.T.D.P.A. | . . . (3lines).

Printed at Doway | By Laurence Kellam, at the signe of the | holy Lambe. | M. DC. XXII. | Permissu Superiorum. | Line border. 18.1x13.8cm. 496p. Camb.Univ.Cat.No.6575.

YATES, John. A | Modell Of | Divinitie | Catechistically | Composed. | Wherein Is Delive- | red The Matter And | Methode of Religion, according | to the Creed, ten Commandements, | Lords Prayer, and the | Sacraments. | By | Iohn Yates, Bachelour in Diuinitie, and | Minister of Gods Word in St Andrewes | in Norvvich. | . . . (6 lines).
London | Printed by Iohn Dawson for Fulke Clifton, and are to be | sold on New-fish streete hill, vnder St Margrets | Church. 1622. | 18.3x14cm. (36),335pp.

1623

ADAMS, Thomas. The | Barren | Tree. | A | Sermon Preached at Pauls Crosse | October 26. 1623. | By | Tho.Adams. | (device).
London, | Printed by Avg:Mathevvs for | Iohn Grismand, and are to be sold | at his Shop in Pauls Alley, at the signe | of the Gunne. 1623. | Line border. 18.7x 14.6cm. (6),56p.

AILESBURY, Thomas. A | Sermon | Preached At | Pavles-Crosse | the second day of June, be- | ing the last Sunday in | Easter Terme. | 1623. | By | Thomas Ailesbvry Student | in Diuinitie. | . . . (3 lines).
London, | Printed by George Eld for Leonard Becket and | Robert Wilson, and are to be be sold neere the | Temple Church, and at Graies Inne | new Gate. 1623. | Line border. 17.7x13.9cm (8),40p.

AINSWORTH, Henry. A | Censvre | Upon A Dialogve Of The | Anabaptists, Intituled, A Description of | what God hath Predestinated concer- | ning man, &c. | By Henry Ainsvvorth. | . . . (8 lines).
Printed in the yeare of our Lord, | 1623. | Head and tail lace ornaments. 18.6x 14.2 cm. (4),64p.

AINSWORTH, Henry. Solomons | Song Of Songs. | In English Metre: | With Annotations And | References to other Scriptures, for the | easier understanding of it. | By Henry Ainsvvorth. | . . . (11 lines; ornament).
Printed in the yeare of our Lord, 1623. | Line border. 20.x15.6cm. (4,90)p.
Appended to his Annotations Vpon The Five Bookes Of Moses: 1622; with separate register

AMES, William. A | Reply | To | Dr. Mortons | Particvlar Defence | Of Three Nocent | Ceremonies. | Viz. | The Surplice, Crosse in Baptisme, and kneeling at | the receiving of the sacramentall elements | of Bread and Wine. | (device).
Printed in the yeare 1623. | 18.3x13.8 cm. (4),71,(4)p.
Anon. Dexter:524. Attributed to David Calderwood. DNB.8:245b.

ANDERSON, Patrick. The | Grovnd | Of The | Catholike And | Roman Religion | In The Word | Of God. | With the Antiquity and Continuance therof, | throughout all Kingdomes and Ages. | Collected | Out of diuers Conferences, Discourses, and Disputes, which | M. Patricke Anderson of the Society of Iesvs, had at seuerall | tymes, with sundry Bishops and Ministers of Scotland, at | his last imprisonment in Edenburgh, for the Catholike Faith, | in the yeares of our Lord 1620. and 1621. | Sent vnto an Honourable Personage, by the Compyler, | and Prisoner himselfe. | . . . (5 lines).

Permissu Superiorum, Anno M DC XXIII. | 17.9x12.7cm. (1),60; (6),3–152; (6),3–174(1)p.
Three parts, with separate register and pagination.

BRINSLEY, John. The | third part of | The Trve-watch | or | The Call of ye Lord | to awake all sorts to | meete him speedely | with intreaty of | peace, & to turne | vnto him by true | repentance: shew- | ing what causes | we haue forthwith | to betake orselu's, | to watching & prayer. | Taken out of ye vision | of Ezekiel Chap:9. | By Jo: Brinsley. | The secound edition. |

Imprinted | at London for | Thomas Pauier. | 1623. | 19.2x14.7cm. (72), 501, (41)p. Engr. t.p., title in central panel.

BYFIELD, Nicholas. A | Commentary: | Or, | Sermons Vpon | The Second Chap- | ter Of The First | Epistle of Saint Peter: | Wherein Method, | Sense, Doctrine, and Vse, is, with great | variety of matter, profitably handled; | and sundry heads of Diuinity largely | discussed. | By Nicholas Byfield, late Preacher of | God's Word at Isle-worth in Middlesex. |

London, | Printed by Humfrey Lownes for George Latham, and are | to be sould at his shop in Paul's Church-yard, at the | Signe of the brazen Serpent. 1623. | Line border. 19.2 x 13.9 cm. (13),922,(6) p.

CALDERWOOD, David. Altare | Damascenvm | Ceu | Politia Ecclesiæ Anglica- | næ obtrusa Ecclesiæ Scoticanæ, a formalista | quodam delineata, illustrata & examinata | studio & opera | Edwardi Didoclavij. | Cvi | Locis suis interserta | Confutatio Paræneseos | Tileni ad Scotos Genevensis, ut ait, disciplinæ zelotas | Et adjecta | Epistola Hieronymi Phila- | delphi de Regimine Ecclesiæ Scoticanæ. | Ejusque | Vindiciæ Contra Calum- | nias Iohannis Spotsuodi Fani Andreæ | Pseudoarchiepiscopi per anonymum. | . . . (9 lines).

Anno MDC XXIII. | 19.2x14.1cm. (8),953,(9),108p.
Anon.Cf.H&L.
Burned by the order of the convocation of the University of Oxford, July 1683.

CAMERON, John. Traicte | Avqvel Sont | Examinez Les Pre- | jugez de ceux de l'Egli- | se Romaine, | Contre la Religion Reformee. | Par I. Cameron Ministre de | l'Eglise de Bourdeaux. | (device)

A La Rochelle, | Par Iean Hebert. | M.DC.XXIII. | 17 x 10.6 cm. 6,(4),257 p.

CHIBALD, William. A | Defence Of | The Treatise | Called, A Tryall | Of Faith. | Concerning The | Doctrine Of Ivstifi- | cation By Faith In | Christ, As It Is There | Delivered. | By William Chibald. | . . . (3 lines).

London, | Printed by G.P. for Samuel Man: and | are to be sold at his shop in Pauls Church- | yard, at the Signe of the Swanne. | 1623. | Line border. 16.1x10cm. (5),42p.

COOKE, Robert. Censvra | Qvorvndam | Scriptorvm, Qvæ | Svb Nominibvs Sancto- | rum & veterum Auctorum, à Ponti- | ficijs (in quæstionibus potissimùm | hodie controuersis) citari | solent. | In qua ostenditur, scripta illa, vel esse supposititia, | vel dubiæ saltem fidei. | Auctore Roberto Coco Ecclesiæ Leodiensis, in agro Ebo- | racensi pastore, & olim in florentissima Academia | Oxoniensi, Collegij Ænæi-nasi socio. | . . . (1 line; device).

Londini, | Excudebat Richardus Field, impensis | Guilielmi Barret. | 1623. | 17.7x13.9 cm. (16),247,(1)p.

CRAKANTHORPE, Richard. De | Providentia | Dei | Tractatus. | Avthore | Ri. Crakanthorp. | (ornament).

Cantabrigiæ, | Impensis Leonardi Greene | vnius ex Typographis Academiæ. | Ann.Dom. 1623. | 17.9x13.8cm.(7),48p.

CRAKANTHORPE, Richard. A | Sermon | Of Predesti- | nation, | Preached at Saint Maries in | Oxford: | By Ri: Crakanthorp. | (device).

London, | Printed for Thomas Lownes, and are to be sold at | his shop in Pauls Churchyard, at the Signe of | the Golden Ball. 1623. | 17.7x13.7cm. (4),46p.

CROIX, Jean de la. The | Catholiqve | Ivdge: | Or | A Moderator Of The | Catholique Moderator. | Where in forme or manner of a Plea or | Suite at Law, the differences betweene those | of the Reformed Church, and them of the Romish | Church are decided; and without partia- | litie is shewed which is the true Religion | and Catholique Church, for the in- | struction of either partie. | Together with eight strong Arguments or Reasons, | why the Popes cannot be competent Iudges in these con- | troversies. | Written in the Dutch and French tongue, by Iohn of the | Crosse, a Catholique Gentleman. | Translated out of French into English, by the Right worshipfull | and learned Knight Sir A.A. | . . . (2 lines).

London, | Printed by I.D. for Robert Mylbourne; and are to be | sold at his shop, at the great South-doore of Pauls. | 1623. | Line border. 19.3x14.7 cm. (8), 87p.

Cambr.Univ.Cat. 3851. Bodl.

DOMINIS, Marco Antonio de. Marcvs | Antonivs | De Dominis | Archiepisc. Spalaten. | Svi Reditvs Ex | Anglia Consilium exponit. | (device)

Parisiis, | Apud Sebastianvm Cramoisy, | via Iacobæa sub Ciconiis. | M.DC. XXIII. | Cum Approbatione. | 16.6 x 10.2 cm. 64 p.

Ascribed to Edward Coffin. DNB.11:216a.

DOWNING, Thomas. The | Catechisers | Holy | Encovragement, | To the profitable exercise of Cate- | chising in the Church of | England. | . . . (7 lines; device).

London, | Printed by VV. I. dwelling in Red-crosse- | street. 1623. | 16.4x12.4 cm. (4),28p.

Dedication signed.

DU PERRON, Jacques Davy. The | Catholike | Moderator: | Or | A Moderate | Examination | Of The Doctrine | of the Protestants. |

Prouing against the too rigid Catholikes | of these times, and against the Arguments especially, | of that booke called, The Answer to the Catholike Apologie, That we | who are members of the Catholike, Apostolike, & Roman | Chvrch, ought not to condeme the Protestants for | Heretikes, vntill further proofe be made. | First written in French by a Catholike Gentleman, | and now faithfully translated. | See the occasion of the name of Hvgvenots, | after the Translaters Epistle. |

London, | Printed for.Nathaniel Bvtter. | 1623. | 16.8x12.2cm. (16),68p. T.p. trimmed; date cut away.

Camb. Univ. Cat. No. 3514. 3d ed.

DYKE, Jeremiah. A | Sermon | Dedicatory. | Preached | At The Consecra- | tion Of The Chap- | pell of Epping in Essex Octo- | ber, 28. 1622. | By Ier. Dyke, Minister there. | . . . (4 lines; ornament).

London, | Printed by I.D. for Nathanael Newbery, and | are to be sold at his Shop vnder Saint Peters | Church in Cornehill, and in Popes-head | Alley, at the signe of the Stare. | 1623. | 17.7x13.7cm. (4),29p.

EADMER. Eadmeri | Monachi | Cantvariensis | Historiæ | Novorum | Siue | Sui Sæculi | Libri VI | Res gestas (quibus ipse non modò spectator diligens sed comes etiam | & actor plerunq[ue] interfuit) sub Guilielmis I & II & Hen- | rico I Angliæ Regibus, ab anno nempè Salutis M LXVI ad | MCXXII potissimùm complexi. | In lucem ex Bibliotheca Cottoniana emisit Ioannes Seldenvs, | & Notas porrò adjecit & Spicilegium. | . . . (2 lines).

Londini, | Typis & Impensis Guilielmi Stanesbeij, ex officinis | Richardi Meighen & Thomæ Dew. | M.DC.XXIII. | 31.7x20.8cm.(6),xvi, 218p.

ELTON, Edward. The | Trivmph | Of A True Chri- | stian Described: | Or, | An Explication Of The | Eight Chapter Of The Epistle | of Saint Paul to the Romans, wherein the sancti- | fied sinners heauen vpon earth is layed | open, with explication of the comfort of it to | as many as are so qualified. | Deliuered in sundrie Sermons by Edward Elton, | Bachelour in Diuinitie, and Preacher of Gods | word at Saint Mary Magdalens Barmondsey | neare London. | And now by him published, intending the good and sauing | comfort of euery true beleeuing soule that shall | please to reade it. | . . . (5 lines)

London, | Printed by Richard Field for Robert Mylburne | and are to be sold at the great South doore | of Pauls. 1623. | Line border 18.1x13.6cm. (6),890, (13)p.

GATAKER, Thomas. A | Good VVife | Gods Gift: | And, | A Wife Indeed. | Two Marriage Sermons. | By Thomas Gataker B. of D. | and Pastor of Rotherhith. | . . . (3 lines; ornament).

London, | Printed by Iohn Haviland for | Fvlke Clifton. 1623. | 18.1x14.4cm. (8),24; (4),67p.

Continuous register, but separate pagination.

GATAKER, Thomas. The Ioy | Of The Ivst; | VVith | The Signes of Such. | A | Discovrse Ten- | ding To The Com- | fort Of The Deiected | and Afflicted; | And | To the Triall of Sinceritie. | Being The

Enlargement | of a Sermon preached at Black-Friers | London; on Psal. 95.11. | By Thomas Gataker B. of D. | and Pastor of Rotherhith. |

London, | Printed by Iohn Haviland for Fvlke Clifton | dwelling on New Fish-street Hill at the signe of | the Lambe. 1623. | 18.1x14.4cm. (9),163p.

GATAKER, Thomas. A | Iust Defence | Of Certaine Passages | in a former Treatise concerning the | Nature and Vse of Lots, | Against such Exceptions and Opposi- | tions as haue been made thereunto | by Mr.I.B. | Wherein the insufficiencie of his Answers | giuen to the Arguments brought in defence | of a Lusorious Lot is manifested; | The imbecillitie of his Arguments produced | against the same further discouered; | And the Point it selfe in Controuersie more | fully cleared; | By | Thomas Gataker B. of D. and Author | of the former Treatise. |

London, | Printed by Iohn Haviland for Robert Bird, and are | to be sold at his shop at the signe of the Bible in | Cheapside. 1623. | 17.8x13.4cm. (8),270, (5)p.

GATAKER, Thomas. Noah | His | Obedience, | With | The Grovnd Of It: | Or | His Faith, Feare, and Care. | A Meditation | On | Hebrewes 11.7. | Deliuered in a Sermon at Lincolnes-Inne: | By Thomas Gataker, Batcheler of Diuinitie; | sometime Preacher there: | And now Pastor of Rotherhith. |

London, | Printed by Iohn Haviland. | 1623. | 18.1x14.4cm. (9),81–130p.
Second of his Two Sermons: 1623.

GATAKER, Thomas. Tvvo Sermons: | Tending | To Direction | For Christian | Cariage, | Both in | Afflictions Incvmbent, | And in | Ivdgements Imminent. | The Former | on Psalm.13.1. | The Latter | on Hebr. 11.7. | By Thomas Gataker B. in D. | and Pastor of Rotherhith. |

London, | Printed by Iohn Haviland. | 1623. | 18.1x14.4cm. (1,6),77;(9),81–130p.
Being: Davids Remembrancer; and Noah his Obedience.

GOAD, Thomas. The | Dolefvll | Euen-Song, | Or | A Trve, Particv- | lar And Impartiall | narration of that fearefull and sudden | calamity, which befell the Preacher Mr. Drvry | a Iesuite, and the greater part of his Auditory, | by the downefall of the floore at an assembly | in the Black-Friers on Sunday the 26. | of Octob. last, in the after noone. | Together With The Rehear- | sall of Master Drvrie his Text, and the diuision there- | of, as also an exact Catalogue of the names of such | as perished by this lamentable accident: And | a briefe application thereupon. | . . . (2 lines)

London, | Printed by Iohn Hauiland, for William Barret, and | Richard Whitaker, and are to be sold at the signe | of the Kings head, 1623. | 17.6 x 14.3 cm (6,51)p.
Cambr.Univ.Cat.4781. Bloom, Engl. Tracts, I: 397. To the Reader, signed T.G.

GOAD, Thomas (editor). The | Friers | Chronicle: | Or, | The Trve Legend | Of Priests And | Monkes Liues. | . . . (1 line; device).

London, | Printed for Iohn Budge: and are to be sold at his | Shop in Pauls Churchyard, at the Signe of the | Greene Dragon. 1623. | Line border. 17.5x12.7 cm. (5,63)p.

D N B. 22: 21 b. Bloom, Engl. Tracts, I: 398. Doubtfully assigned also to Thomas Gainsford. cf.DNB.20:368b.
Dedication signed T.G.

GOSSELIN, Peter. transl. The | State-Mysteries | Of The Iesvites, | By way of | Questions and Answers. | Faithfully extracted out of their owne | Writings by themselues published. | And | A Catalogue prefixed of the Authors names | which are cited in this Booke. | Written for a Premonition in these times both to | the Publike and Particular. | Translated out of French. | . . . (3 lines ; ornaments).

London, | Printed by G.E. for Nicholas Bourne. | 1623. | 17.2x13.8cm. (8),54p. Epistle Dedicatorie, signed.

HART, John. The | Bvrning-Bvsh, | Not | Consvmed: | Wherein, either vnder all deepe sense | of Wrath, or hardnesse of Heart, one | may iudge, whether he be the Childe | of God, or not, &c. | Chiefly receiuing full satisfaction, concerning | the sinne against the Holy Ghost. | Perused by J. D. and diuers other Diuinies. | . . . (5 lines). The fourth Edition. |

London, | Printed by Iohn Haviland for Roger Iackson, and are | to be sold at his shop in Fleet-street, ouer | against the great Conduit. 1623. | Line border. 14.8x9.3 cm. (22),153p.
Epistle Dedicatory signed I.Hart. Pollard, Short-Title Catalogue.

HIERON, Samuel. Aarons Bells | A-Sounding. | In A Sermon, tending cheiftly to | admonish the ministerie, of their charge, & duty. | Preached by M.Samvel Hieron at a ge- | nerall visitation neere Bristow. | And now published by them to whom his coppy | was entrusted after his death. | . . . (2 lines ; device).

Printed. | 1623. | 17.7x13.2cm. (6),37p.

HINDE, William. The | Office | And Vse Of | the Morall Law of God in the | dayes of the Gospell, | Iustified, and explained at large by Scripture, Fathers, | and other Orthodoxe Diuines, | So Farre As Occasion | was giuen by a scandalous Pamphlet sent abroad | of late into the hands of diuers good Christians, pretending | great reason and reading for the vtter abrogating and | abolishing of the whole Law of Moses since | the death of Christ. | By William Hinde, sometimes Fellow of Queenes | Colledge in Oxford, and now Preacher of Gods Word | at Bvnbvry in Cheshire. | . . . (4 lines).

London, | Printed by Iohn Haviland for Thomas Pavier, and are to be | sold at his shop in Ivy Lane. 1623. | 18.3x14.5cm. (18),140p.
T.p. supplied.

JACKSON, Thomas. The raging Tempest stilled. | The Historie | of Christ his passage, with his Disci- | ples, over the Sea of Galilee, and the memo- | rable and miraculous occurrents therein. | Opened and explaned in weekly Lectures (and the | Doctrines and Vses fitly applied to these times, for the direction | and comfort of all such as feare Gods Iudgements) in | the Cathedrall and Metropoliticall Church | of

Christ, Canterb. | By Thomas Iackson, Doctor of Divinitie, and one | of the Prebends, and Lecturer there. | (cut of armada).

London, | Printed by Iohn Haviland for Godfrey Emondson and | Nicolas Vavasour. 1623. | Line border. 17.3x13.4cm. (7),344p. folded sheet.

JESSOP, Edmond. A | Discovery | Of The Errors | Of The English | Anabaptists. | As also an Admonition to all such | as are led by the like spirit of error. | Wherein is set downe all their seuerall and maine | points of error, which they hold. | With a full answer to euery one of them seuerally, | wherein the truth is manifested. | By Edmond Iessop who sometime walked | in the said errors with them. | . . . (10 lines ; ornament).

London, | Printed by W.Iones for Robert Bird, and are to be sold at | his shop in Cheapside at the signe of the Bible. | 1623. | 18x14cm. (12), 103p.

LOE, William. The | Kings Shoe. | Made, And Ordained | To Trample On, And To | Treade Downe Edomites; | To teach in briefe, what is Edoms doome; | what the carefull condition of a King; | what the Loyall submission of a sub- | iect, and what Proiects are | onely to best purpose. | Deliuered in a Sermon before the | King at Theobalds, October the ninth, 1622. by | William Loe, Doctour of Diuinity, | Chaplaine to his Sacred Maiestiy | in ordinary. | . . . (2 lines ; device).

London, | Printed by I.L. for William Sheffard, and are to bee sold | at his shop, at the entring in of Popes head Allie out | of Lumbard street. 1623. | 17.5x13.8 cm. (7),45p.

MAYER, John. The | English | Catechisme | Explained. | Or, | A Comentarie | On The Short Catechime | set forth in the Booke of Com- | mon Prayer. | Wherein Divers Necessarie | Questions touching the Christian Faith are inserted, | moderne Controuersies handled, doubts resolued, | and many Cases of Conscience | cleared. | Profitable for Ministers in their Churches, for Schoole- | Masters in their Schooles, and for Housholders | in their Families. | By Iohn Mayer, Bachelour of Diuinitie. | The third Edition reviewed. | Published by Command. |

London, | Printed by Aug.Mathewes for Iohn Marriot, and are to be | sold by Iohn Grismand, at his Shop at the signe of the Gun | in Pauls Alley. 1623. | Line border. 18.7x14.2 cm. (30),575p.

PATTENSON, Matthew. The Image | Of Bothe Chvrches, | Hiervsalem and Babel, | Vnitie And Confvsion. | Obedienc and Sedition. | By, P. D. M. | (ornament)

Printed at Tornay, By Adrian Quinqve: | M.DC.XXIII. | VVith Licence. | 15x 9.5 cm. (8),461,(2)p.
H&L. Gillow,V:250. Dexter: 527.

PHILLIPS, Jerome. The | Fisher- | Man. | A Sermon preached at a Synode | held at Southwell in Nottinghamshire. | Shewing | 1.The necessitie of calling and gifts enabling in a | Minister. | 2. The danger intruders are in. | 3.Whose fault it is that such are in the Church. |

4.A good life requisite in all that professe Chri- | stianitie, but especially in Ministers. | 5.Wisedome and learning absolutely necessary in | Preachers. | 6.Vnlearned & frothy preaching doth much hurt. | 7.Gods worke goeth best forward when his work- | men agree well amongst themselues. | 8.Contempt of Gods Ministers shall not be vnpu- | nished. With other points of moment. | By Ierom Phillips Bachelour in Diuinitie. |

London, | Printed for W.I. for Robert Bird, and are to be sold | in Ivie Lane. 1623. | Border. 18.x13.3cm. (6),26p.

RANDALL, John. Saint Pavls | Trivmph, | Or | Cygnea illa & dulcissima Cantio, | That | Swan-like and most sweet Song, of that | Learned and faithfull Seruant of God, | Mr. Iohn Randall, Bachelor of | Diuinitie: | Vttered by him (in an Eleauen Sermons, | vpon the Eight Chapter of St.Pavl his Epistle to | the Romans, Vers.38.39.) lately before his death, | in the time of his great and heauy Affliction, and | vpon the Communion-dayes, either | altogether, or for the most part. | And | Now published for the glory of God, the edification of | his Church and people, and the hononrable memoriall | of the Author, by William Holbrooke, | Preacher of the word of God. |

London: | Printed by T.S. for Richard Redmer, and Nathanael Newbery, | and are to bee sould at the signe of the Starre vnder | St.Peters Church in Cornehill, and in | Popes-head Alley, 1623. | Line border. 17.8x13.7cm. (8),239,(1)p. Lacks pp.9–16

ROUS, Francis. Oile Of | Scorpions. | The Miseries of these | Times turned into Me- | dicines and Curing | themselues. | By Francis Rous. | . . . (4 lines)

London | Printed by W.Stansby for Iohn Parker, | and are to bee sould at his Shop | in Pauls Church-yard at | the signe of the | three Pigeons. | 1623. | Line border. 13.2x7.7 cm (14),317p.

SAINT ALDEGONDE, Philips van Marnix. The | Bee Hive Of | The Romish | Chvrch. | A Worke Of All | good Catholikes to be read, | and most necessary to bee | vnderstood. | Wherein the Catholike Religion is | substantially confirmed, and the Here- | tikes finely fetchd ouer the coales. | Translated into English by George | Gilpin the Elder. | . . . (2 lines)

London. | Printed by Iohn Dawson. 1623. | 14.x9.1 cm. (49), 364 fol.
Anon. Cambr.Univ.Cat. 3853.

SCOTT, Thomas. The | Proiector. | Teaching A Direct, Svre, | and ready vvay to restore the decayes of | the Church and State both in | Honour and Revenue. | Delivered In A Sermon | before the Iudges in Norvvich, at Summer | Assises there holden, | Anno 1620. | By Thomas Scot Batchelor in Diuinity. | . . . (5 lines; device).

Printed at London. 1623. | 17.3x14. cm. (6),39p.

SCOTT, Thomas. A | Tongve-Combat, | Lately Happening Be- | tvveene tvvo English Souldiers in the | Tilt-boat of Grauesend, | The One Going To Serue | the King of Spaine, the other to serue | the States Generall of the Vnited Provinces. | Wherein the Cause, Course, and

Continuance of those | Warres, is debated, and declared. | . . . (1 line; ornament).

Printed at London. 1623. | 17.9x13.3cm. (8),104p.
Anon. DNB.Suppl.2:418b. Ascribed also to Henry Hexham.

SCOTT, Thomas. Vox Dei: | Inivstice Cast | And Condemned. | In a Sermon preached the | twentieth of March 1622. At the | Assises holden in St. Edmunds | Bury in Suffolke. | By Thomas Scot Batchelar in | Diuinity, and Minister of the Word | at S.Clements in Ipswitch. | . . . (4 lines: ornament).

London, | Printed by I.L. for Ralph Rounthwait, at the | Golden Lyon in Paules Church-yard. | 1623. | Line border. 15.6x9.6cm.(1), 53p.

WARBURTON, G——. King Melchizedech. | A Sermon | Preached At | the Court, at East-Hamsted, | in His Maiesties last | Summer progresse, | On Tuesday, the second of September.1623. | By G.Warbvrton. | . . . (4 lines).

London, | Printed by Bonham Norton and Iohn Bill, | Printers to the Kings most Excellent | Maiestie. 1623. | 17.2x13.3cm. (8),56p.

WEEMSE, John. The | Christian | Synagogue. | Wherein is contained the diverse Reading, | The right Poynting, Translation, and Collation of | Scripture with Scripture. | With the Customes of the Hebrewes and Proselytes, and of all | those Nations, with whom they were conversant. | Digested into three Bookes. | The First, shewing the meanes both inward and outward, to attaine to the know- | ledge of the Sense of the whole Scripture. | The Second, vnfolding the true sense of the Scripture it selfe, as also teaching the | right way of gathering Doctrines from any Text of Scripture. | The Third, teaching the true manner of Confirmation, Illustration, and Appli- | cation of Doctrines, rightly gathered from the true Sense of Scripture. | Serving generally for a helpe to the vnderstanding of all, that desire to | know and obey the vvill of God in holy Writ: But more specially for all young Stu- | dents in Diuinitie, that they may more easily vnderstand the Languages of Canaan, | and Greece, and make a profitable vse of them in Preaching. | The Second Edition, corrected, and amended. | By Iohn Weemse, of Lathoquar, in Scotland, Preacher | of Christs Gospell. | . . . (5 lines).

London, | Printed by I.D. for Iohn Bellamie, and are to be sold at his Shop, | at the two Grey-hounds in Cornehill, neare the Royall Exchange. 1623. | Line border 22.2x16cm. (18),308p.

WHATELY, William. A | Bride- | Bvsh. | Or, | A Direction For | Married Persons. | Plainely describing the duties common to | both, and peculiar to each of them. | By Performing Of Which, | Marriage shall prooue a great helpe to such, | as now for want of performing them, | doe finde it a little hell. | Compiled and published by William Whately, | Minister and Preacher of Gods Word, | in Banbury in Oxford-shiere. | . . . (3 lines).

London, | Printed by Bernard Alsop for Beniamin Fisher, and are | to be sold at his shop in Pater noster Rowe, | at the Signe of the Talbot. | 1623. | Line border. 18x14.1cm. (12), 220p.

WRIGHT, William. A | Svmmary | Of | Controversies. | Wherein the chiefest points of the Holy | Catholike Roman fayth, are compen- | diously, and methodically proued, | against the Sectaryes of this age. | By C.VV. | The II. Edition. | . . . (ornament: 5 lines).

At S. Omers, for Iohn Heigham. | With permission of Superiours, | Anno 1623. | 14.5x9.5cm. 370, (1)p.
Gillow, V: 597.

1624

ABBOT, George. A | Treatise | Of The | Perpetuall Visibilitie, | And | Succession of the True Chvrch | in all Ages. | (device)

At London, | Printed by Hvmfrey Lovvnes, for | Robert Milbovrne. | 1624. | Line border. 18.5x14.2cm. (7),116p.
Anon. Camb.Univ.Cat. No.2545.

ARTICLES | Agreed On | In The | Nationall Synode | of the Re- | formed Churches of | France, | Held at Charenton neere Paris, in the Moneth | of September, 1623. | Which the same ordaineth to be in- | uiolably kept | in all the Chvrches and Vniversi- | ties of that Realme. | Wherein, their iudgement touching the principall Contro- | versies now on foote betwixt the Remonstrantes | and Contra-remonstrantes, is | briefly declared. | (ornament).

At Oxford, | Printed by Iohn Lichfield, and Iames Short, | Printers to the famous Vniuersity. 1624. | 17.9x13.2 cm. (1),34p.

ARTICLES | Wherevpon | It Was Agreed By | the Archbishops and Bishops of | both Prouinces, and the | whole Cleargie: | In the Conuo- cation holden at London | in the yeere of our Lord God 1562. | Ac- cording to the computation of | the Church of England: | For the auoyding of the diuersities of | opinions, and for the stablishing of con- | sent touching true Religion. | (ornament).

Imprinted at London by Bonham Norton | and Iohn Bill, Printers to the Kings most | Excellent Maiestie. 1624. | 18.4x14cm. (1,21)p.

BAILY, Richard. An | Ansvvere | To Mr. Fishers Re- | lation of a Third Confe- | rence betweene a certaine | B. (as he stiles him) | and himselfe. | The Conference was very pri- | uate, till Mr. Fisher spread | certaine Papers of it, which | in many respects deserued | an Answere. | Which is here giuen by R.B. Chapleine | to the B. that was imployed in | the Conference. |

London, | Printed by Adam Islip. | 1624. | Column & vine border. 28.7x18.7cm. (4), 74p.
Appended to Francis White's Replie: 1624; with separate register and pagina- tion. DNB.32:194b.

BARGRAVE, Isaac. A | Sermon | Preached | Before the Honorable Assembly; | of Knights, Cittizens, and Burgesses, | of the lower House of Parliament: | February the last. 1623. | Thomas Crevv, Knight,

Speaker. | By | Isaac Bargrave: | Doctor in Divinitie; Chaplayne | to the Prince's Highnes; and Pastor | of St Margarets Church | in Westminster. | (device)

London | Printed by I.D. for Iohn Bartlett, and Iohn | Spencer: and are to be sould at the Gilded | Cupp in Cheap-side. 1624. | Line border. 17.7x13.6cm. (5), 37p.

BERNARD, Richard. Looke beyond Luther: | Or An | Answere | To That Qvesti- | on, So Often And So | Insvltingly Proposed By | our Aduersaries, asking vs; Where this | our Religion was before Lu- |thers time? | Whereto Are Added | Sovnd Props To Beare | vp honesthearted Protestants, that | they fall not from their sa- | uing-faith. | By Richard Bernard, Of | Batcombe in Sommersetshire. | (device).

London, | Imprinted by Felix Kyngston, and are to be sold by Edmund | Weauer, at his shop, at the great North-doore | of Pauls. 1624. | 18.4x14.1cm. (6),55p.

BRINSLEY, John. The | Fovrth Part | Of The | Trve Watch: | Containing | Prayers And Teares | for the Chvrches. | Or | A helpe to hold up the hearts | and hands of the poorest servants of | God, untill our Lord Iesus Christ shall | have rescued his Glorie, Kingdome, | and People in all the world, and | fully prepared the way to his | most glorious ap- | pearing. | . . . (6 lines).

London, | Printed for Thomas Pavier. | 1624. | Line border. 14.4 x 7.9 cm. (106),420,(35)p.
Epistle Dedicatorie, signed.

CALDERWOOD, David. A | Dispvte | Vpon | Commvni- | cating At Ovr | Confused Communions. | . . . (16 lines).

Printed Anno 1624. | 13.9x9.4 cm. 74p.
Anon.H&L. Advoc.Libr.

CALDERWOOD, David. An | Epistle | Of A | Christian | Brother | Exhorting an other to keepe him- | selfe vndefiled from the present | corruptions brought in to | the ministration of the | Lords Supper. | (lace ornament)

Printed Anno 1624. | 13.9x9.4 cm. (1),27p.
Anon. DNB. 8: 245 b (13).

CAMERON, John. Defensio | Ioh. Cameronis | S. Evangelii Ministri | & S.Theologiæ Professoris. | Opposita Libello cui titulus est | Epistola viri docti ad amicum, in qua expendi- | tur sententia Ioannis Cameronis | de Gratia & Libero arbitrio. | (device)

Salmvrii, | Apud Clavd. Girardvm & Dan. | Lerpinerivm. M.DC.XXIV. | 17.8 x 11.5 cm. (24),338 p.

CARLETON, George. A | Thankfvll | Remembrance | Of Gods mercy. | In an Historicall Collection of the | great and mercifull Deliverances of the | Church and State of England, since the Gospell | began here to flourish, from the beginning | of Queene Elizabeth. | Collected by Geo:Carleton, | Doctor of Divinitie, and Bishop | of Chichester. | . . . (3 lines)

London. | Printed by I.D. for Robert Mylbourne, and | Humphrey Robinson, and are to be sold at | the great South doore of Pavls. | 1624. | Line border. 18.8x 13.7 cm. (1: engraved title),(12),227p.

CAWDREY, Daniel. Hvmilitie, | The Saints | Liverie; | Or, | The Habit Of Hvmili- | tie, The Grace Of Graces: | Fetched out of the Wardrobe of | Saint Pavl. | As it was deliuered (for Substance) in two | Sermons at Blacke-Fryers in London, the one, | September 22. the other, October 6. 1624. | By Daniel Cavvdrey Minister of the | Word of God, at little Ilford in Essex. | . . . (5 lines).

London, | Printed by Iohn Haviland, for Edward Brewster, and | are to be sold at the great West doore of Saint | Pauls. 1624. | Line border. 17.2x13.6cm. (8), 51p.

CHAMPNEY, Anthony. A Defence of the Appendix. | Or | A Reply | To Certaine Avthorities | alleaged in Answere to a Catalogue of Catholike | Professors, called, An Appendix to the Antidote. | VVherein | Also the Booke fondly intituled, The Fisher catched in his | owne Net, is censured. And the sleights of D.Featly, | and D.VVhite in shifting off the Catalogue of | their owne Professors, which they vn- | dertooke to shew, are plainly | discouered. | By L.D. | To the Rt. VVorshipfull Syr Humphry Lynde. | . . . (ornament; 3 lines).

Permissu Superiorum. M.DC.XXIIII. | 17.2x12.8cm. 72p.
H&L, new ed. Gillow, I. 465.
Attributed by Edward Gee to John Sweet, jesuit. Cf.Gillow:V.191 (2).

CROMPTON, William. Saint | Avstins | Religion. | VVherein is Ma- | nifestly proued out of the Works | of that Learned Father, that he dissen- | ted from Popery, and agreed with the | Religion of the Protestants in all the | maine Points of Faith and | Doctrine. | Contrary to that Impudent, Er- | ronious, and Slanderous Position of | the bragging Papists of our Times, who | falsely affirme, we had no Religion | before the Times of Luther | and Caluine. |

London, | Printed by A. M. and are to be Sold | in Saint Dunstons Church- | yard. 1624. | Line border. 18.7x14.1 cm. (8),32p.
Anon. H&L. Mendham; also attributed to Alexander Cooke. DNB.XII:76

DENISON, John. The | Sinners | Acqvittance. | A Checke to Curiositie. | The safest Seruice. | Deliuered in three Sermons | at the Court. | By | Iohn Denison Doctor of Diui- | nity, and one of his Maiesties | Chaplaines then in | Attendance. |

London, | Printed by Iohn Legatt, and are to | be sold by Iohn Budge, at the signe of | the Greene Dragon in Paules | Church-yard. 1624. | Line border. 15.6x 9.6cm. (8),126p. 3 sub-t.p.

FEATLEY, Daniel. An | Appendix | To | The Fishers | Net: | Together vvith a Description | of the Romish Wheele, | or Circle. | By | Daniel Featly, Doctor | of Diuinitie. | . . . (2 lines ; ornament).

London, | Printed for Robert Milbourne, and are to be sold | at his Shop at the Great South-doore | of Pauls Church. 1624. | Line border. 19x14.5cm. (12),190p.
Appended: A True | Relation | Of That Which | Passed In A Con- | ference, at the end of Pater- | noster-Rowe, called | Amen: | Touching Transubstantiation. | April 18. 1623. | and A Conference | By VVriting, | Betweene D.Featly, Doctor of | Diuinity, and M.Svveet, Iesuite: | Touching the ground and last resolution | of Faith. | Or, | The Wheele of Popery turned round. |

FEATLEY, Daniel. The | Romish | Fisher | Cavght | And | Held | In His Owne Net. | Or, | A True Relation of the Protestant | Conference and Popish Difference. | A Iustification of the one, and a Refutation | of the other. | In matter of {Fact. | Faith. | By Daniel Featly, Doctor in Diuinity. | . . . (3 lines).

London, | Printed by H.L. for Robert Milbourne, and are | to bee sold at the great South-dore of Pauls. | 1624. | border. 19x14.5cm. (22),46,(80),176p.

A | GAGGE For | The Pope, And | The Iesvits: | Or | The Arraignement, | And Execvtion | Of Antichrist. | Shevving plainely, | that Antichrist shall be discouered, | and punished in this VVorld: | to the amasement of all obstinate | Papists. | (device)

London | Printed by I.D. for Edward Blackmore, and are | to be sould at his Shop, at the Great | South-dore of Paules. | 1624. | 17.8x14 cm. (6),82p.

GATAKER, Thomas. Christian | Constancy | Crowned By | Christ. | A | Funerall Sermon on | Apocalyps 2.10. | Preached at the buriall of M.William | Winter, Citizen of London; | Together with the Testimonie then giuen | vnto Him: | By Thomas Gataker, B. of D. and | Pastor of Rotherhith. | (ornament).

London, | Printed by Iohn Haviland for William Bladen, | and are to be sold at the signe of the Bible, at the great | North doore of Pauls. 1624. | 18.5x14.3cm. (6),31p.

GATAKER, Thomas. The | Christian | Mans Care. | A Sermon On | Matth. 6. 33. | Together with | A Short Catechisme | for the Simpler Sort. | By | Thomas Gataker, B. of D. | and Pastor of Rotherhith. | (ornament).

London, | Printed by Iohn Haviland, for Fvlke Clifton, | and are to be sold at his Shop upon new Fish- | street Hill. 1624. | 18.4x14.3cm. (12),53,(6) p.

GATAKER, Thomas. A | Discvssion | Of The Popish | Doctrine Of | Transubstantiation: | Wherein the same is declared, by the | Confession of their owne Writers, | to haue no necessary ground in | Gods Word: | As also it is further demonstrated to be | against Scripture, Nature, Sense, Reason, | Religion, the Iudgement of the Aunci- | ents, and the Faith of our | Auncestours: | Written by Thomas Gataker B. of D. | and Pastor of Rotherhith. | (ornament).

London, | Printed by I. L. for William Sheffard, and are | to bee sold at his shoppe at the entring in of | Popes-head Alley out of Lumbard-streete. | 1624. | 18.2x13.2cm. (5),233p.

GATAKER, Thomas. A | Good VVife | Gods Gift: | And, | A VVife Indeed. | Two Mariage Sermons. | By Thomas Gataker B. of D. | and Pastor of Rotherhith. | . . . (3 lines: ornament).

London, | Printed by Iohn Haviland for | Fvlke Clifton. 1624. | 18.5x14.3cm. (8),24; (4),67p.

GATAKER, Thomas. Iacobs | Thankfvlnesse | To God, | For | Gods Goodnesse | To Jacob. | A Meditation On | Genesis 32.10. | Wherein by the way also the Popish | Doctrine of Mans Merite is |

discussed. | By | Thomas Gataker, B. of D. and Pastor | of Rotherhith. |

London, | Printed by Iohn Havilamd, for Fvlke Clifton, | and are to be sold at his Shop upon new Fish- | street Hill. 1624. | 18.6x13.6cm. (7), 97,(4)p.

GATAKER, Thomas. A | Mariage | Praier, | Or | Succinct Meditations: | Delivered In A Ser- | mon On The Praier Of | Eleazer the Seruant of Abra- | ham, Genes. 24.12,13,14. | By Thomas Gataker B. of D. | and Pastor of Rotherhith. | (ornament).

London, | Printed by Iohn Hauiland for Fulke Clifton and | Iames Bowler, 1624. | 18.5x14.3 cm. (6),22p.

GEE, John. The | Foot out of the Snare: | With | A Detection Of | Svndry Late | practices and Impostures of the | Priests and Iesuits in England. | Whereunto is added a Catalogue of | such bookes as in this Authors knowledge | haue beene vented within two yeeres last | past in London, by the Priests and | their Agents. | By Iohn Gee, Master of Arts, of Exon-Colledge | in Oxford. |

At London, | Printed by H. L. for Robert Milbourne, and are to bee sold | at his shop at the great South doore of | Pauls, 1624. | Line border. 17.6x13.2 cm. (10),99,(8)p.
[First edition]

GEE, John. The | Foot out of the Snare: | With | A Detection Of | Svndry Late | practices and impostures of the | Priests and Iesuites in England. | Whereunto is | added a Cata- | logue of {Popish Bookes lately dispersed in | our Kingdome. | The Printers, Binders, sellers and | dispersers of such bookes. | Romish Priests and Iesuites resi- | dent about London. | Popish Physicians practising about | London | The Fourth Edition, carrying also a gentle Excuse vnto Master | Musket for stiling him Iesuite. | By Iohn Gee, Master of Arts, of Exon-Colledge | in Oxford. |

London, | Printed by H.L. for Robert Milbourne, and are to be sold at his shop at the great | South-dore of Pauls, 1624. | Line border. 17.2x13.8cm. (10),116, (30)p. Colophon. Title in red and black.

GEE, John. Hold | Fast, | A | Sermon Preached at Pavls | Crosse vpon Sunday being | the xxxi. of October, | Anno Domini | 1624. | By Iohn Gee, Master of | Arts, late of Exon Colledge | in Oxford. |

London. | Printed by A.M. and I.N. for Robert | Mylbovrne, and are to be sold at his | Shop at the great South doore | of Pauls. 1624. | Line border. 18.2x14.3 cm. (6),66p.

GEE, John. New | Shreds | Of The | Old Snare. | Containing | The Apparitions of two new female Ghosts. | The Copies of diuers Letters of late intercourse | concerning Romish affaires. | Speciall Indulgences purchased at Rome, granted | to diuers English gentle-beleeuing Catholiques | for their ready money. | A Catalogue of English Nunnes of the late trans- | portations within these two or three yeares. | By Iohn Gee, Master of Arts, | late of Exon-Colledge in Oxford. |

London, | Printed for Robert Mylbourne. | 1624. | Line border. 17.4x13.7 cm. (4),121p. Title in red and black

HALL, Joseph. Columba Noæ | Olivam Ad- | ferens Iacta- | tissimæ Christi | Arcæ. | Concio Synodica, ad Clerum Anglicanum | (Prouinciæ præsertim Cantuariensis) | habita, in Æde Pavlina | Londinensi. | Feb. 20. 1623. | A. Ios.Hallo, S.T.D. Decano | Wigorniensi. | (ornament)

Londini | Per Guil. Stansby impensis Guillelmi Barret. | 1624. | Line border. 18.4 x 14.3 cm. (6),47, (1)p.

HARRIS, Robert. God's | Goodnes | And Mercie. | Layd Open | In A Sermon, | Preached At | Pavls-Crosse | On The Last | Of Ivne. | 1622. | By Mr. Robert Harris, Pastour of the | Church of God at Hanwell in Orford-shire. | The second Edition, corrected, amended, and much | enlarged by the same Author. | . . . (3 lines).

London, | Printed by Iohn Dawson for Iohn Bartlet, and are | to be sould at the golden Cup in the Gold- | smiths Rowe in Cheap-side. | 1624. | 17.3x13.3cm. (7),29,(1)p.

HARRIS, Robert. Peters | Enlargement | Vpon The Pray- | ers Of The | Chvrch. | By Master Harris. | The third Edition. | . . . (3 lines; device).

London, | Printed by John Haviland for John Bartlet, and | are to be sold at the Golden Cup, in the Gold- | smiths Row in Cheapside. 1624. | 17.8x13.8cm. (8),23p.

HAYWARD, John. Of | Svpremacie | In Affaires | Of | Religion. | By | Sir Iohn Hayvvard, Knight, | Doctor of Lawe. | (device).

London, | Printed by Iohn Bill, Printer to the | Kings most Excellent Maiestie. | M.DC.XXIIII. | Line border. 16.8x12.2cm. (8),88p. Colophon.

HERBERT, Edward. De | Veritate | Provt Distingvitur | A Revelatione, A Veri- | simili, A Possibili, Et | A Falso. | Hoc Opvs Condidit | Ed. Herbert, Miles Ord. Bal. | et Leg. S^{mi}. Regis M.Brittanniæ | In Gallia. | Et | Vniverso Hvmano Generi | Dicavit. |

M.DC.XXIV. | 24.7x18cm. (1),227p.

HUMPHREYS, Richard. Iob's | Pietie, | Or, | The Patterne | Of A Perfect | Man. | Containing An Absolvte | Historie of all the Excellencies which | ought to be in a perfect Man: And being | drawne from Diuine Writ, may serue as a | Patterne for euery reasonable Bodie, whe- | ther Reall or Representatiue, being | eyther Mightie or Meane, | Rich or Poore. | A Worke Worthie The | consideration of all Men; euen from the | Kings Pallace, to the poore mans Cottage; from | the high House of Parliament, to the lowest Seat of | the meanest Magistrate; and from the greatest | Generall, to the humblest Launce-pessado that | euer commanded in Armies. | . . . (4 lines)

London, | Printed for George Norton, and are to be | sold in Distaffe Lane, at the Signe of | the Dolphin. 1624. | 18.4x13.8cm. (6),235pp.

Pollard, Short-Title Catalogue.

JACKSON, Thomas. An | Helpe To | the best Bargaine. | A Sermon on Mat.13. | 46. Preached on Sunday, | the 26 of Octob. 1623. in the |

Cathedrall Church of | Christ, Canterbury. | By Thomas Iackson, | Doct. of Divinitie, and one | of the Prebends, and | Lecturer there. |

London Printed by | Nich. Okes, for | Mat. Walbanke, and are | to be sold in Graies- | Inne Gate, | 1624. | Arch. border. 15.6x9.6cm.(10), 62p. Lacks pp 24–33.

LEIGHTON, Alexander. Speculum Belli sacri: | or The | Looking-glasse | Of The Holy War. | Wherein is discovered: | {The Evill of War. | The Good of Warr. | The Guide of War. | In The | Last Of These I Give A | Scantling Of The Christian | Tackticks, from the levying of the Souldier, to the | sounding of the Retrait; together with a modell | of the carryage, both of Conquerour and con- | quered. I haue applyed the generall | rules warranted by the Word, to | the particular necessity | of our present | times. | . . . (8 lines).

Printed, Anno 1624. | 19x15cm. (20),316p.
Camb.Univ.Cat.No.6952. Dedications signed A.L.

MAHOMET | Vnmasked. | Or | A Discoverie Of | the manifold Forgeries, Fals- | hoods, and horrible Impieties of | the Blasphemous Seducer | Mahomet. | VVith a demonstration of the In- | sufficiencie of his Law, contained | in the cursed Alcoran | Written long since in Arabicke: and now | done into English by William Bedwell. | Whereunto is annexed the Arabian Trudg- | man, Interpreting certaine Arabicke | termes vsed by Historians. | Together with an Index of the Chapters of | the Alkoran, for the vnderstanding of | the confutation of the Booke. |

London, | Printed for Thomas Dewe, and are to | be sold at his shop in Saint Dunstons Church- | yard. 1624. | Line border. 21x15.3cm (10,66;4,26;6,5)p. Impf. at end. Two sub t.p. dated 1615.

MASON, Henry. The | New Art | Of Lying | Covered By | Iesvites vnder the Vaile of | Eqvivocation, | Discovered And Disproved | By | Henry Mason. | (device).

London: | Printed by George Purslowe for Iohn Clarke, and | are to be sold at his Shop vnder Saint Peters | Church in Cornehill. 1624. | 17.7x13.3cm. (22),106p.

MONTAGU, Richard. A Gagg for the new Gospell? | No: | A Nevv Gagg | For | An Old Goose. | VVho would needes vndertake to stop | all Protestants mouths for euer, | with 276. places out of their owne | English Bibles. | Or | An Ansvvere | to a late Abridger of Controuersies, | and Belyar of the Protestants | Doctrine. | By Richard Mountagu. | Published by Avthoritie. |

London, | Printed by Thomas Snodham for Matthew Lownes | and William Barret. | 1624. | 18.4x14.2 cm. (48),328p. 173–176 omitted.

MUSKET, George: alias Fisher. The | Bishop | Of | London | His Legacy. | Or | Certaine Motiues of D.King, late Bishop | of London, for his change of Religion, | and dying in the Catholike, and | Roman Church. | VVith a Conclusion to his Brethren, the LL. | Bishops of England. | . . . (ornament; 2 lines).

Permissu Superiorum, M.DC.XXIIII. | 18.1x13.5cm. Fol.i–iv,pp.v–xvi,1–24, 33–174. Complete.
Anon. Cambr.Univ.Cat.6549. DNB.39:433a

NEYLE, Richard. M. Ant. De Dñis | Arch-Bishop Of | Spalato, his Shiftings | in Religion. | A Man for many Masters. | . . . (2 lines ; ornament).
    London, | Printed by Iohn Bill. | MDCXXIV. | 17.6 x 13.8 cm. (4),91p.
    Cf.Cambr.Univ.Cat.3518.

The | ORIGINALL | Of Idolatries: | Or, | The Birth | Of Heresies: | A true, Sincere, and exact description of all such Sa- | cred Signes, Sacrifices, and Sacraments as | haue been instituted and ordained of God | since Adam; | with the true source and liuely Anatomy of the Sacrifice | of the Masse. | First faithfully gathered out of sundry Greeke and Latine | Authors, as also out of diuers learned Fathers; | By that famous and learned Isaac Casavbon, and by him Pub- | lished in French, for the good of Gods Church: And now | translated into English for the benefit of this | Monarchy; | By Abraham Darcie. |
    London | Printed by Authoritie, for Nathaniel Bvtter. | Anno Dom. MDCXXIV. | Line border. 18.6x14cm. (16),108p.
    Translator's attribution was erroneous. BMCat.

PERRIN, Jean Paul. The | Blovdy Rage | Of That Great | Antechrist Of Rome And | his superstitious adherents, against the true | Church of Christ and the faithfull professors | of his Gospell. | Declared At Large In The | Historie of the Waldenses and Albingenses, apparent- | ly manifesting vnto the world the visibilitie of our | Church of England, and of all the reformed Churches | throughout Christendome, for aboue foure hun- | dred and fiftie yeares last past. | Diuided into three parts. | The first concernes their originall beginning, the puritie of their Re- | ligion, the persecutions which they haue suffered throughout all | Europe, for the space of aboue foure hundred and fiftie yeares. | The second containes the historie of the Waldenses called Albin- | genses. | The third concerneth the doctrine and discipline which hath bene | common amongst them, and the confutation of the doctrine of their | aduersaries. | All which hath bene faithfully collected out of the Authors | named in the page following the Preface, | By I.P.P.M. | Translated out of French by Samson Lennard. |
    London, | Printed for Nathanael Newbery, and are to be sold at the signe | of the Starre vnder Saint Peters Church in Corn- | hill, and in Popes-head Alley. 1624. | 18.8x13.5cm. (14),66,(2) ;144;143;103p.
    Four parts: with interrupted register, and separate pagination.
    Author's Epistle, signed.

PERRIN, Jean Paul. Lvthers | Fore-Rvnners: | Or, | A Clovd Of Witnesses, De- | posing for the Protestant faith. | Gathered together in the Historie of the Waldenses: | Who for diuers hundred yeares before Luther successiuely op- | posed Popery, professed the truth of the Gospell, | and sealed it with their bloud: | Being most grieuously persecuted, and many thousands of them | martyred, by the tyrannie of that Man of sinne, and his | superstitious Adherents and cruell instruments. | Diuided into three parts. | The first concernes their originall beginning, the puritie of their Re- | ligion; the persecutions which they haue suffered throughout all | Europe, for the space of aboue foure hundred and fiftie yeares. | The second containes the historie of the Waldenses called Albin- | genses. | The third concerneth the doctrine and discipline which hath bene | common amongst them, and the confutation of the doctrine of their | aduersaries. | All which hath bene faithfully collected out of the Authors | named in the page following the Preface, | By I.P.P.L. | Translated out of French by Samson Lennard. |

London, | Printed for Nathanael Newbery, and are to be sold at the signe | of the Starre vnder Saint Peters Church in Corn- | hill, and in Popes-head Alley. 1624. | 18.6x13.6cm. (14),66,(2);144;143;103p. Engraving of Luther laid in . Title in red and black. Three parts, with interrupted register, and separate pagination Same as the preceding, with different t.p.
Author's Epistle, signed.

A | PILL To Pvrge | Ovt Popery: | Or | A Catechisme for Romish | Catholikes; | Shewing, | That Popery is contrary to the grounds of | the Catholike Religion, and that there- | fore Papists cannot bee good | Catholikes. | (device).

London | Printed for Beniamin Fisher, and are to | be sold at his shop in Paternoster-Row, at the | Signe of the Talbot. 1624. | Cum Priuilegio. | 15.1x9.9cm. (1),45p.
Cf.Camb.Univ.Cat.No.2543: ascribed to I.M.

RANDALL, John. The | Great | Mystery Of | Godlines: | Or, | A Treatise | Opening Vnto Vs, | First, what God; Secondly, | What Christ is. | Penned by that learned and Faithfull | seruant of God, Iohn Randall | Batchelour of Diuinitie. | And now published to the glory of God, the edifica- | tion of his Church, and the Honourable | memoriall of the Author. | By William Holbrooke, Preacher of | the Word of God. |

London, | Printed by Iohn Legatt, for Richard Redmer, | and William Sheffard, and are to be sold at the entring | in of Popes-head Alley out of Lumbardstreete. | 1624. | 18.x13.6cm (6),100p.

REEVE, Thomas. Mephibosheths | Hearts-Ioy | Vpon his | Soveraignes | Safetie. | To be imitated by the Sub- | jects of this Land vpon the hap- | py Returne of our Prince | Charles. | Deliuered in a Sermon in the | Church of Great Yarmouth in | Norfolke, the 19. day of | October. 1623. | By Tho: Reeve Preacher of | Gods Word there. |

London | Printed by Aug: Math: for Robert Milbourne | and are to be sold at his Shop at the great | South doore of Saint Paules. 1624. | 15.6x9.6cm.(3), 42p.

ROBINSON, John. A | Defence | Of The Doc- | trine Propovn- | ded By The Synode | At Dort: | Against | Iohn Mvrton And | His Associates, In A | Treatise intuled; A Description | what God, &c. | With | The Refvtation Of | their Answer to a Writing touching | Baptism. | By Iohn Robinson. | (lace ornament).

Printed in the year, 1624. | 19.2x14. cm. (4),203p.

SCOTT, Thomas. Aphorismes | Of State: | Or | Certaine secret Articles for the re- | edifying of the Romish Chvrch agreed vpon, | and approued in Councell, by the Colledge | of Cardinalls in Rome, shewed and deliuered | vnto Pope Gregory the 15. a little | before his death. |

Whereunto is annexed a censure vpon the chiefe | points of that which the Cardinalls | had concluded. | By Tho.Scott. | Very needfull and profitable for all those, who are de- | sirous to vnderstand the euent of the restitution of the | Palatinate: And of the state of the Prince- | Electors, of Saxon and Brandenburgh, | in the behalfe of the Clergie | in Rome. | Fit for the British Nation, especially to take notice of, | that they may euidently see, the issue of all our Treaties, | Ambassages, and Promises, with other hopes depending: | wherein we haue beene long held in suspence, | and are still like to be, to our vnre- | couerable losse. | Faithfully Translated according to the Latine, and | Netherlandish Dutch, into English. |

Printed at Vtrech. 1624. | 16.8x12.2cm. (1),28 p.

SCOTT, Thomas. The | Belgick | Sovldier: | VVarre VVas | A Blessing. | . . . (5 lines).

Printed 1624. | 16.4x12. cm. (1,38,2)p. Trimmed .
Anon. Cambr.Univ.Cat:6513.

SCOTT, Thomas. Boanerges. | Or | The Hvmble | Svpplication Of | The Ministers Of | Scotland, | To | The High Covrt | Of Parliament | In England. | . . . (2 lines, device).

Printed in Edenburgh. | 1624. | 16.5 x 12.4 cm. (2),34p. Mispaged.
Also another edition: Printed in Edinburgh. | 1624. | 18.6 x 14.1 cm. (2),34p. Differently mispaged.
Anon. DNB.51:69a(14).

SCOTT, Thomas. Certaine | Reasons | And | Argvments | Of Policie, | Why the King of England | should hereafter give over all further | Treatie, and enter into warre with | the Spaniard. |

Printed M.DC.XXIV. | 17.9x13.8cm. (1),14p.
Anon. Cambr.Univ.Cat:6956.

SCOTT, Thomas. A Second | Part Of Spanish | Practises. | Or, | A Relation Of More | Particular wicked plots, and cruell, in | humane, perfidious, and vnnaturall | practises of the Spaniards. | With, | More Excellent reasons of greater consequence, de- | liuered to the Kings Maiesty to dissolue the two trea- | ties both of the Match and the Pallatinate, | and enter into Warre with the | Spaniards. | Wherevnto | Is Adioyned A Worthy Ora- | tion Appropriated, vnto the most Mighty and Illu- | strious Princes of Christendome, wherein the right and | lawfulnesse of the Netherlandish warre against Phillip | King of Spayne is approued and | demonstrated. | . . . (3 lines).

Printed. M.DC.XXIV. | 17.6x13.9cm. (45)p.
Anon. H&L.

SCOTT, Thomas. Votivæ Angliæ: | Or, | The Desires | And VVishes | Of England. | Contained in a Patheticall Discourse, presented | to the King on New-yeares | Day last. | Wherein are vnfolded and represented, many strong Rea- | sons, and true and solide Motiues, to perswade his Ma- | jestie to drawe his Royall Sword, for the restoring of the | Pallatynat, and Electorat, to his Sonne in Law | Prince Fredericke, to his onely Daughter the Lady | Elizabeth, and their Princely Issue. | Against | The Treacherovs Vsvrpa- | tion, and formidable Ambition and Power | of the Emperour, the King of Spaine, and the | Duke of Bavaria, who unjustlie possesse | and detaine the same. | Together with some Aphorismes returned (with | a Large interest) to the Pope in Answer | of his. | Written by S.R.N.I. |

Printed at Vtrecht. MDCXXIIII. | 17.5x13.5cm. (8,36)p.
First edition.
Anon. Cambr. Univ. Cat: 6645.

SCOTT, Thomas. Votivæ Angliæ: | Or | The Desires | And VVishes | Of England. | Contayned in a Patheticall Discourse, presented | to the King on New-yeares | Day last. | Wherein are vnfolded and represented, manie strong | Reasons, and true and solide Motives, to perswade his | Majestie to drawe his Royall Sword, for the restoring | of the Pallatynat, and Electorat, to his Sonne in Lawe | Prince Fredericke, to his onlie Daughter the | Ladie Elizabeth, and theyr Princelie Issue. | Against | The Treacherovs Vsvrpa- | tion, and formidable Ambition and Power | of the Emperour, the King of Spayne, and the | Duke of Bavaria, whoe unjustlie Possesse | and detayne the same. | Together with some Aphorismes returned (with | a Large interest) to the Pope in Answer | of his. | Written by S. R. N. I. |

Printed at Vtrecht. MDCXXIIII. | 17.9x13.8 cm. (8,36)p.
Corrected edition.
Anon. Cambr. Univ. Cat: 6646 A

SCOTT, Thomas. Vox Cœli, | Or, | Newes From | Heaven, | Of | A Consvltation | There Held By The High | and mighty Princes, King Hen.8. King Edw.6. | Prince Henry. Queene Mary. Queene Elizabeth, | and Queene Anne; wherein Spaines ambition and | treacheries to most Kingdomes and free Estates of Evrope, | are vnmask'd and truly represented, but more particularly | towards England, and now more especi- | ally vnder the pretended match of Prince Charles, | with the Infanta Dona | Maria. | Whereunto is annexed two Letters written by | Queene Mary from Heauen, the one to Count Gondomar, | the Ambassadour of Spaine, the other to all | the Romane Catholiques of | England. | Written by S.R.N.I. |

Printed in Elisium. 1624. | 19.2x14.5cm. (10),60p. Misnumbered.
Anon. Cambr. Univ. Cat. 6963.

SCOTT, Thomas. Vox | Regis. |
n.p.n.d. [1624] 17.4x13.2 cm. (9),74 p.
Title on fly-leaf, and on engraved second leaf. Preface signed T.S.
Anon. Cambr. Univ. Cat. 6964. DNB.51:69a (No. 15).

SIMSON, Patrick. The | Historie | Of The Chvrch | Since The Dayes Of | Our Saviour Iesus Christ, | vntill this present Age. | Devided into foure Bookes. | 1. The first containeth the whole proceedings and practices of the Empe- | rours, both of the West and East for, or against the Church: as also the | wonderfull loue of God towards it, by whom it was so preserved, that nei- | ther by Tyranny it could be subdued, nor by policie circumvented. | 2. The second containeth a breefe Catalogue of the beginnings, and procee- | dings; of all the Bishops, Popes, Patriarchs, Doctors, Pastors, and | other learned men; in Europe, Asia and Affrica, with or against the | Church, together with their deaths. | 3. The third containeth a short summe of all the Heretiques, which haue | beene in the Church: the time when, and the place where they lived; as | also the persons by whom they were subdued. | 4. The fourth containeth a short compend of all the Councels Generall, | Nationall, and Provinciall: together with their severall Canons, | which haue beene established, either with, or against the Church. | Devided into 16. centuries. | By all which is clearely shewed and proved, the Antiquitie, Visibilitie, and Perpetu- | itie, of our Church; euer since Christs dayes, vntill this present Age. | Collected out of sundry Authors both ancient and moderne; by the famous and | worthy Preacher of Gods word, Master Patrick Symson, late Mini- | ster at Striueling in Scotland. |

London | Printed by I.D. for Iohn Bellamie, and are to be sold at his Shop, at | the three Golden Lions in Corne-hill neere the Royall Exchange: | and for William Sheffard, at the entering in of Popes-head | Alley, out of Lumbard streete. 1624. | 18.3x14cm. (15),700 pp.

SMITH, John. A | Paterne | Of Trve | Prayer. | A Learned And | Comfortable Exposition | or Commentarie vpon the | Lords Prayer: wherein the | Doctrine of the substance and | circumstances of true in- | uocation is euidently and | fully declared out of the | holy Scriptures. | By Iohn Smith, Minister | and Preacher of the | Word of God. |

London | Printed by I.D. for Thomas Man, and | are to be sold by William Sheffard, | Iohn Bellamie, and Beniamine | Fisher. 1624. | Line border. 14. x8.3 cm. (14),452p. Mispaged.

SMITH, Samuel. The | Great Assize, | Or, | Day Of Ivbilee. | Deliuered in Foure Sermons, vp- | on the 20. Chapter of the Reue. | Verse 12,13,14,15. | Whereunto are Annexed two | Sermons vpon the 1. Chapter of the | Canticles, verse 6,7. | The Fourth Impression, Cor- | rected and Amended by the Au- | thour Samvel Smith, | Minister of the Word | of God at Prittle- | well in Essex. | . . . (4 lines).

London, | Printed by N.O. and are to be sold by | Francis Falkner, dwelling neare St. Mar- | garets Hill in Southwarke. 1624. | Line border. 14.7x9.7cm. (14), 332p.

TAYLOR, Thomas. An | Everlasting | Record | Of | The Vtter Rvine | of Romish Amaleck. | Delivered in a Sermon at Black-Friers | in London, By Thomas Taylor. | (device)

London, | Printed by J.H. for Iohn Bartlet, | and are to be sold at the Golden Cup in | the Gold-Smiths row in Cheapside. 1624. | Line border. 18.x13.8cm. (1), 26p.

Part of his Two Sermons: 1624.

TAYLOR, Thomas. Two Sermons: | The One | A Heavenly | Voice, | Calling All Gods | people out of Romish | Babylon. | The Other | An Everlasting | Record of the utter ruine of | Romish Amalek. | By

Thomas Taylor, Preacher of the Word at | Redding in Berkshire. | (device).

London, | Printed by J. H. for Iohn Bartlet, | and are to be sold at the Golden Cup in | the Gold-Smiths row in Cheapside. 1624. | Line border. 18. x13.8 cm. (8),35;(1),26p. Sub-title.

USSHER, James. An | Answer | To A Challenge | Made By A Iesuite | in Jreland. | Wherein | The Iudgement Of | Antiquity in the points questioned | is truely delivered, and the Noveltie of the | now Romish doctrine | plainly discovered | By Iames Vssher Bishop of Meath. | . . . (2 lines; crown and harp device).

Dublin, | Printed by the Societie of Stationers. 1624. | Line border. 19.2x14.3cm. (22), 527, (9)p.

USSHER, James. A Briefe | Declaration | Of The Vniversali- | tie Of The Chvrch | of Christ, and the Vnitie | of the Catholike Faith pro- | fessed therein: | Delivered In A Sermon | before His Majestie the 20th of Iune, | 1624. at Wansted, | By Iames Vssher, Bishop of Meath. | (device).

London, | Printed by Robert Young for Thomas Downes and | Ephraim Dawson, and are to be sold at the | Rain-bow neere the Inner Temple | Gate in Fleet-street. | [1624] Line border. 18.5x14.2cm. (1),65p.
First ed.?

WADSWORTH, James and BEDELL, William. The | Copies Of | Certaine Let- | ters Which Have | passed betweene Spaine and | England in matter of | Religion. | Concerning the generall Motiues to the | Romane obedience. | Betweene Master Iames Wadesworth, | a late Pensioner of the Holy Inquisition in | Siuill, and W.Bedell, a Minister of | the Gospell of Iesus Christ in | Svffolke. | (device).

London, | Printed by William Stansby for William Barret and | Robert Milbourne. 1624. | Line border. 18.8x13.4cm. (10),162,(1)p.

WALKER, George. Fishers folly unfolded: | Or | The Vavnting | Iesvites Vanity | discovered in a challenge of his(by | him proudly made, but on his part | poorely performed.) | Vndertaken And | answered by George VValker | Pastor of S.Iohn Euangelist in | Watling-street London. | (device)

M. DC. XXIIII. | 17.6x13.4 cm. (1),49p.

WALKER, George. The | Svmme Of | A Dispvtation, | Betweene Mr.VVal- | ker Pastor of St. Iohn Euanglists in | Watling-street London; and a popish Priest, | calling himselfe Mr.Smith, but indeed | Norrice, assisted by other Priests | and Papists. | Held In The Presence Of | some worthy Knights; with other | Gentlemen of both | Religions. | (devices)

Printed. 1624. | 17.5x13.3 cm. (1,40)p

WEBBE, George. Catalogus Protestantium: | Or, | The | Protestants | Kalender. | Containing | A Svrview Of The | Protestants Religion long before | Luthers dayes, euen to the time of | the Apostles,

and in the | Primitiue Church. | By | George Web D. of Diuinity, | and Preacher of the Word of | God at the Bathe. | (ornament).
  London, | Printed for Nathaniel Butter. | 1624. | 18.6x14cm.   (2),97p.
  Two title-pages, slightly different: above in red and black .

WHITE, Francis.   The | Orthodox | Faith And Way | To The Chvrch | Explained and iustified: | In Answer To A Popish | Treatise, entituled, White Died Blacke; | wherein T.W.P. in his triple accusation of D. White for im- | postures, vntruths, and absurd illations, is proued a trifler: And the | present controuersies betweene vs and the Romanists are | more fully deliuered and cleared. | By Francis White Doctor in Diuinitie and Deane of Carlile, | elder brother of Doctor Iohn White. | The Second Edition, enlarged by the Author. | . . . (7 lines ; device).
  Printed at London by John Hauiland for | William Barret. 1624. | (28),190, (2)p.
  Incorporated with: White, John. The Workes . . . 1624; with separate register and pagination.

WHITE, Francis.   A | Replie To | Iesuit Fishers | answere to certain | questions propoūded | by his most grati- | ous Ma:tie King | Iames. | By Francis White | D: of Div. Deane of | Carlile, Chaplaine to | his Matie. | Hereunto is annexed, a | Conference of the right: | R: B: of St Dauids wth the | same Iesuit. | . . . (2 lines).
  London | Printed by Adam Islip. 1624. | Engraved t.p. 28.5x19. cm.   (32),592, (4),(4),74 p.   Subtitle-page.

WHITE, John.   A | Defence | Of The Way To | The Trve Chvrch, | against A.D. his Reply. | Wherein | The Motives leading to Papistry, | And Qvestions, touching the Rvle of Faith, | The Avthoritie of the Church, | The Svccession of the Truth, and | The Beginning of Romish Innouations, | are handled and fully disputed. | By Iohn White, Doctor of Diuinity, sometime of | Gunwell and Caius Coll. in Cambridge. | . . . (3 lines ; device).
  At London | Imprinted by Felix Kyngston for William | Barret. 1624. | 28.3x 18.6cm.   (22),316p.
  Incorporated in his: The Workes . . . 1624; with separate register and pagination.

WHITE, John.   Two Sermons: | The Former | Delivered At Pavls | Crosse The Fovre And | twentieth of March, 1615. being the anni- | uersarie commemoration of the Kings most | happy succession in the Crowne of | England. | The Latter At The | Spittle On Monday | in Easter weeke, 1613. | By Iohn White D.D. | . . . (3 lines ; device).
  Printed at London by John Hauiland for | William Barret. 1624. | (4),36p.
  Incorporated in his: The Workes . . . 1624; with separate register and pagination

WHITE, John.   The | Workes | Of That Learned | and reuerend Diuine, | Iohn White | Doctor in Diuinitie: | Together With A | Defence of the Way To The | Trve Chvrch; in answer to a | Popish Treatise written by T.W.P. | intituled White Died | Blacke. | By Francis White Doctor in Diui- | nitie and Deane of Carlile. |

London, | Printed for William | Barret,| Anno 1624. | colum and vine t.p. 28.3x 18.5cm. (1),(34),239,(5) ; (22),316p; (4),36;(28),190,(2)p.

WILCOX, Thomas. The | Works | Of That Late | Reverend | And Learned | Divine, | Mr.Thomas Wilcocks, Minister | of Gods Word: | Containing An Exposition | vpon the whole booke of Davids Psalmes, | Salomons Prouerbs, the Canticles, and part of | the 8.Chapter of St. Pavls Epistle to | the Romans. | (device).

London, | Printed by Iohn Haviland. | 1624. | 28.8x17.8cm. (12),447; (11),93; (6),55p.
Three separate title pages.

WILLIAMS, Griffith. Seven Govlden | Candlestickes | Houlding The Seauen Greatest | lights of Christian Religion; | Shewing vnto all men | what they should beleeue, | & how they ought to walke | in this life, that they may | attayne vnto eternall life | By Gr:Williams Doctor of Divinity | . . . (2 lines). 16 24.

Printed for Nathaniell Butter. | (1624) Engraved title-page. 19.1x14.3cm. (34),744,(29)p. Pp.611,614,618–9,621 misnumbered; 618-9 repeated .

WING, John. The | Saints | Advantage: | Or | The VVell-Fare Of | The Faithfvll, In The | Worst Times. | A Sermon, | Preached at the Hage the 18. of May, | Before the most High, and Mighty Princesse, | Elizabeth, by the Grace of God, | Queene of Bohemia, Countesse Palatine of | the Rhene, Dutches of Bavaria, &c. | And onely Daughter to our Sove- | raigne Lord King Iames. | By Iohn Wing, an vnworthy Minister of the Gos- | pell, and Pastour to the English Church at Flushing | in Zealand. | . . . (6 lines).

London, | Printed by Iohn Dawson for Iohn Bellamie, and are to be | sold at his Shop at the three Golden Lyons, neere the | Royall Exchange. 1624. | 17x13.4 cm. (8),79p. Mispaging .

WOTTON, Anthony. Rvnne | From Rome. | Or, | A Treatise | Shevving The | necessitie of Separating from | the Church of Rome. | Disputed in these Termes: | Everie Man Is | bound vpon paine of Damnation | to refuse the Faith of the Church | of Rome. | By Anthony Wotton. B.D. | . . . (3 lines).

London, | Printed by W.J. for Nicholas Bourne, and are | to be sold at his Shop at the South side of | the Royall-Exchange. 1624. | Line border. 17.6x13.1cm. (8),88,(1)p.

1625

ABBOT, Robert. The | Danger | Of Popery: | Or, | A Sermon Preached | at a Visitation at Ashford in | Kent, vpon 2.Thess.2.12. | Wherein the marks of Antichristianisme | and signes of truth are opened and applied, | and the Question of the sauing and dam- | ning of those that follow Antichrist is ex- | planed by the Scriptures. | By

Robert Abbott, Preacher of the | Word of God at Cranebrook in Kent. | . . . (2 lines).

London, | Printed by I.L. for Philemon Stephens, and Christopher | Meredith, and are to be sold at the Golden Lyon | in Paules Church-yard. 1625. | Line border. 19x14.2cm. (11),42p.

BARLOW, William. The | Svmme | And | Svbstance | Of | The Conference, | which it pleased his Excellent Maiestie to haue | with the Lords Bishops, and other of his Clergie | (at which the most of the Lords of the Coun- | cell were present) in his Maiesties Privie- | Chamber, at Hampton Court, | Ianuary 14. 1603. | Contracted by William Barlovv, | Doctor of Diuinitie, and Deane of Chester. | Whereunto are added some Copies (scattered | abroad) vnsauory, and vntrue. | (royal arms)

London, | Printed by Iohn Bill, Printer to the Kings | most Excellent Maiestie. 1625. | 17.3x13.3cm. (8),106,(5)p. Impr. trimmed.

BARNES, John. Dissertatio | Contra | Æqvivocationes. | Avctore. | Ioanne Barnesio Benedictino, Ar- | tium & S.Theologiæ Doctore. | . . . (4 lines; ornament).

Parisiis, | Apud Rollinum Baragne & Iacobum Villery, | veneunt in Palatio. | M.DC.XXV. | Cum approbatione & Priuilegio Regis. | 17.x10.5cm. (20), 542p.

BEARD, Thomas. Antichrist | the Pope of Rome: | Or, | The Pope of Rome is Antichrist. | Proued in two Treatises. | In the first | Treatise, {1. By a full and cleere definition of Antichrist, taken | from Scripture onely. | 2. By a plaine application of euery part of his defini- | tion agreeing onely with the Pope. | 3. By the weaknesse of the Arguments of Bellarmine, | Florimond Reymond, and others; which they bring | to proue the contrary. All which are heere plain- | ly and fully answered. | In the second Treatise, {By a Description {1. Of his Person. | 2. Of his Kingdome. | 3. Of his Delusions. | In all which, the great Questions and Doubts about | Antichrist, are pithily and briefely handled, yet | fully and amply cleered. | By Tho: Beard, Doctor in Diuinity, and Preacher of Gods | Word in Huntington. | . . . (3 lines).

Printed by Isaac Iaggard for Iohn Bellamie, and are to be sold at his | Shop at the three golden Lyons in Cornhill, neere the | Royall Exchange, 1625. | Line border. 17.7x13.5 cm. (22),425,(1) p. Title in red and black

BEDINGFIELD, Robert. A | Sermon | Preached At | Pavls Crosse | The 24. Of Octo- | ber. 1624. | By | Robert Bedingfield Master | of Arts, and Student of | Christ-Church in | Oxford. | (device).

Oxford, | Printed by Iohn Lichfield and | William Tvrner, for | Henry Cripps. 1625. | Line border. 18.8x14.7cm. (4),43p.

BURGESS, Cornelius. The | Fire Of | The | Sanctvarie | newly vncouered, | Or, | A Compleat Tract of | Zeale. | By C. Burges. | . . . (2 lines; ornament)

London, | Printed by George Miller, and | Richard Badger. 1625. | 13x7.7cm. (30),492p.

BYFIELD, Nicholas. The | Beginning | Of The Doctrine | Of Christ. | Or, | A Catalogue of Sinnes: | Shewing how a Christian may | finde out the euils he must | take notice of in his | Repentance. | With Rules, that shew a course, | how any Christian may be de- | liuered from the guilt and | power of all his sinnes. | By N. Bifield, late Preacher of | God word at Isleworth in Middlesex. | . . . (3 lines).

London, | Printed by George Miller, | and Richard Badger. | 1625. | Line border. 13.7x8 cm. (16),767p.

CARLETON, George. A | Thankfvll | Remembrance | Of Gods Mercy. | In an Historicall Collection of the | great and mercifull Deliverances of the | Church and State of England, since the Gospell | began here to flourish, from the beginning | of Queene Elizabeth. | Collected by Geo:Carleton, | Doctor of Diuinitie, and Bishop | of Chichester. | The second Edition, revised, and enlarged. | . . . (3 lines).

London | Printed by I.D. for Robert Mylbourne, and | Humphrey Robinson, and are to be sold at | the great South doore of Pavls. | 1625. | Line border. 18x 13.3cm. (14),261p.

CHALONER, Edward. Credo | Ecclesiam Sanctam | Catholicam. | I beleeue the holy Catho- | like Church. | The | Avthoritie, | Vniversalitie, | And Visibilitie | of the Chvrch, | handled and | discussed. | By | Edward Chaloner, | Dr. in Diuinitie, and Princi- | pall of Alban Hall in | Oxford. |

London | Printed by William Stansby. | 1625. | Arch. border 18.7x13.5cm. (8), 141p.

Contains also his Vnde Zizania? | The | Originall | And | Progresse | of Heresie | . . . pp. 103–141; with continuous register and pagination.

COOKE, Alexander. Pope Joane. | A | Dialogve | Betvveene a Pro- | testant And A | Papist. | Manifestly prouing, that a woman | called Ioane, was Pope of Rome: against the | surmises and obiections made to the contra- | rie, by Robert Bellarmine and Cæsar Baronius Car- | dinals: Florimondus Ræmondus, N.D. | and other Popish writers, impudent- | ly denying the same. | By Alexander Cooke. | (device).

London, | Printed by Iohn Haviland, for William Garrat, and | are to be sold at his Shop in Pauls Church-yard, | at the signe of the Buls Head. 1625. | 17.5x 13.5cm. (8),131p.

COOKE, Alexander. The | Weather-Cocke | Of | Romes | Religion: | With Her Seve- | rall Changes. | Or: | The World Tvrn'd | Topsie-Tvrvie | By | Papists. | (device).

London: | Printed by George Purslowe for Iohn Marriot, and are to | be sold at his Shop in Saint Dunstanes Church- | yard in Fleet-streete. 1625. | 18.6x14. cm. (1),16p. (Misnumbered: pp. 7–8 omitted).

Anon. Camb. Univ. Cat: 4087.

CRAKANTHORP, Richard. Defensio | Ecclesiæ | Anglicanæ, | Contra | M.Antonii De | Dominis, D.Archiepiscopi | Spalatensis Iniurias: | Viri omni virtute, doctrináque Spectatissimi, | D.Rich.Crakanthorp,S.T.D. | & Regiæ M. nuper Sacellani, Opus | Posthumum. | A.D.

Iohanne Barkham, S.T.D. | in Lucem editum. | . . . (2 lines; ornament).

Londini, | Ex Typographia Bibliopolarum: | M.DC.XXV. | 20.7x15.5cm. (18), 645,(2)p.

CRASHAW, William. A | Mittimvs | To The Ivbile | At Rome: | Or, | The Rates Of The | Popes Cvstome-Hovse. | Sent | To the Pope, as a New-yeeres-gift | from England, this Yeere of | Ivbile, 1625. | And faithfully published out of the old Latine | Copie, with Obseruations vpon the Romish Text, | By William Crashavv, Batchelor of | Diuinity and Pastor at White-Chappell. |

London: | Printed by G. P. for Iohn White, and | are to be sold at his Shop at the Signe of the | Holy-Lambe, in Little-Brittaine, neere | Aldersgate-Street, M.DC.XXV. | 17.8x13.7 cm. (18),44;(1),70p. Title in red and black. Separate title-page for Second Part.

CRASHAW, William. The | Rates Of | The Popes | Cvstome-Hovse: | The Second Part. | Which Is, | Of Transgressions | Against Lawes Partly | Diuine; but for the most part | Ecclesiasticall. | (device).

London: | Printed by George Purslow, for Iohn White, and | are to bee sold at his Shop in Little-Brittaine, at | the Signe of the Holy Lambe, neere St. | Buttolphs Church. 1625. | 17.8x13.7cm (1),70p.
Second part of his Mittimvs To The Ivbile At Rome: 1625.

CROMPTON, William. Saint | Avstins | Religion: | Wherein Is Mani- | festly proued out of the Workes of | that Learned Father, who liued neere twelue | hundred yeares before the time of Lvther; | that he dissented from Poperie, and agreed | with the Religion of the Protestants, | in all the maine Poynts of Faith | and Doctrine: | Contrary to that Impudent, Erronious, | and Slanderous Position of the bragging | Papists of our Times, who falsly affirme, | Wee had no Religion, before the | Times of Lvther and | Calvine. | Wherevnto is newly added, Saint Austins | Svmmes; in Answer to Mr. Iohn | Breerely, Priest. |

London. | Printed for Iohn Marriott, and are to be sold at his Shop | in St. Dunstane's Churchyard, in Fleet-street. 1625. | Line border. 20x15.3cm (8),30; (18),206,(2)pp.
Attributed also to Alexander Cooke. Camb.Cat.4085.
Title of second part signed.

CROMPTON, William. Saint | Avstins | Svmmes: | Or, | The Svmme Of Saint | Avstins Religion: | Collected Verbatim from his owne | vndoubted Writings, wherein the Reader may | plainely and euidently see this Conclusion proued, | that S.Avstin (who liued neere Twelue Hun- | dred Yeeres before the time of Lvther) | agreed with the Church of England, | in all the maine Poynts of Faith | and Doctrine. | In Answer to Mr. John Breereley, Priest. | By William Crompton, Mr. | of Arts, of Brazen-nose Colledge in Oxford, | and Preacher of the Word of God, at | Little-Kymbell in Buckingham-shire. | . . . (3 lines).

London. | Printed for Iohn Marriot, and are to be sold at his Shop | in St. Dunstane's Churchyard in Fleet-street. 1625. | Line border. 20x15.3cm.(18), 206, (2)p.

Appended to his Saint Avstins Religion: 1625, with continuous register, but separate pagination.

DIFFERENCES | In Matters | Of Religion, Be- | tweene the Easterne and | Westerne Churches. | VVherein the Romane Church | may see her selfe charged with | as many Errours, as shee falsly | layeth to the charge of other | Churches in Europe. | Gathered by Irenæus Rodoginus. | . . . (2 lines).

London, | Printed by Avgvstine Mathevves | for Iohn Budge, and are to be sold | at the signe of the Windmill in | Britaines Burse. 1625. | Line border. 17.8x 14.8cm (40),45p.

DONNE, John. The First | Sermon | Preached | To King | Charles, | At Saint Iames: 3º. April. | 1625. | By Iohn Donne, Deane of | Saint Pauls, London. |

London, | Printed by A. M. for Thomas Iones, | and are to bee sold at his Shop at the | Signe of the Blacke Rauen in | the Strand. 1625. | Line border. 18. x14.4 cm. (1),59p.

DOWNAME, George. An | Abstract | Of The Dvties Com- | manded, And Sinnes | forbidden in the Law | of God. | By The Right Reverend | Father In God, George Dovvname, | Doctor of Diuinity, and Lord Bishop | of Derry. | . . . (3 lines; device).

At London, | Imprinted by Felix Kyngston. | 1625. | 16.2x10.cm. (12,174)p.

An | ECCLESIASTICAL | Protestant Historie, | Of The High Pastoral | And Fatherly Charge | and care of the Popes f Rome, ouer | the church of Britanie. | From the first planting of the Christian faith | there, by S.Peter the Apostle, and his Disciples: | continued in euery age, and hundred of yeares, | by holy Bishops, and cleargie men, sent hither | and consecrated by them, his Successors in the | See Apostolicke. | Euidently deduced and proued by historicall | narration, from the published and priuiledged | writings (to appease all protestants) of the most | learned and allowed English protestant preten- | ded Bishops, Doctors, Antiquaries, and others | of that Religion. | (ornament) . . . (4 lines).

With licence. 1625. | 15.3x9.3cm. 249,(1)p.

Part of Second Part of the Protestants Plea: 1625; with separate register and pagination

EGERTON, Stephen. A Briefe | Method Of | Catechizing. | Wherein are handled these | foure Points. | I. How miserable all men are by nature. | 2. What remedie God hath appointed for | their deliuerance. | 3. How they must live that are deliuered. | 4. What helpes they must vse to that end. | The same points are also contracted, and a | forme of examining Communicants added, | with Graces before and after meate. | . . . (4 lines). The 33. Edition. |

London, | Printed by W.S. for Henry Fetherstone, | dwelling in Pauls Churchyard, at the signe | of the Rose. 1625. | 14. x9.3cm. (8),53p.

To the Christian Reader, signed.

A | FORME Of | Common Prayer, | Together with | An Order of Fasting: | For | The auerting of Gods heauy Visitation vpon | many places of this Kingdome, and for the drawing | downe of his Blessings vpon vs, and our Ar- | mies by Sea and Land. | The Prayers are to be read euery Wednesday during | this Visitation. | Set foorth by His Maiesties Authority. | (coat of arms).

Imprinted at London by Bonham Norton and Iohn Bill, | Printers to the Kings most Excellent | Maiestie. Anno 1625. | 17.7x14.5 cm. (6,101)p. Colophon.

FULLER, William. A | Sermon | Preached | Before his Maiestie | At Dover Castle, On Tuesday | the seauenth of June 1625. | By VVilliam Fvller, | B.D. His Maiesties Chaplaine | then attending in Ordinary. | Published by Commaund. | (device)

London | Printed by Edw:Allde for Iohn Hodgets. | 1625. | 17.9x13.4cm. (1,26)p.

GUILD, William. Ignis Fatvvs. | Or, | The Elf-Fire | Of | Pvrgatorie. | Wherein Bellarmine is confuted | by Arguments both out of the Old | and New Testament, and by his | owne Proofes out of Scriptures | and Fathers. | Also an Annexe to this Treatise | of Purgatorie, concerning the di- | stinction of Sinne in Mortall | and Veniall. | By M. William Gvild, Minister | at King-Edvvard. |

London, | Printed by Avgvstine Mathevves, | and are to bee sold at Britaines | Burse. 1625. | Line border. 17.8x14.6 cm. (12),57p.

HODSON, Phineas. The Last | Sermon | Preached Be- | fore His Maiesties | Funerals, at Denmark house: | On Tuesday the third of May. | By | Phinees Hodson Dr of Diuinitie, | one of his Maiesties Chaplaines. | (device).

London | Printed by M. F. for Hannah Barret, 1625. | 17.7x13.5 cm. (1),26p.

JACKSON, Thomas. A | Treatise | Containing | The Originall | of Vnbeliefe, Misbeliefe, or Mis- | perswasions concerning the Veritie, | Vnitie, and Attributes of the Deitie: | with Directions for recifying our | beliefe or knowledge in the | fore-mentioned points. | By Thomas Iackson Dr. in | Diuinitie, Vicar of Saint Nicholas Church | in the famous Towne of New-castle upon Tine, | and late Fellow of Corpus Christi Colledge | in Oxford. | . . . (3 lines).

London | Printed by I.D. for Iohn Clarke, and are to be | sold at his Shop vnder St Peters Church in Cornehill. | 1625. | Line border. 18.8x15cm.(14), 464p.

JAMES, Thomas. An | Explanation | Or | Enlarging Of | the ten Articles in the Supplication of | Doctor Iames, lately exhibi- | ted to the Clergy of | England. | Or | A manifest proofe that they are both rea- | sonable and faisible within the | time mentioned. | . . . (2 lines; device).

Oxford, | Printed by Iohn Lichfield and William | Tvrner, Printers to the famous Vniuersity. | Anno Dom. 1625. | 17.5x13.4 cm. (1),36p.

JAMES, Thomas. A Manvdv- | ction, Or Intro- | dvction Vnto | Diuinitie: | Containing | A Confutation of Papists by Pa- | pists, throughout the important Articles | of our Religion; their testimonies taken | either out of the Indices Expurgatorii, | or out of the Fathers, and ancient | Records; | But especially the Manuscripts. | By Tho. Iames, Doctor of Diuinitie, late | Fellow of New-Colledge in Oxford, and Sub-Deane | of the Cathedrall Church of Welles. | This marke † noteth the places that are taken out of the Indices Expur- | gatorij: And this ☞ , a note of the places in the Parchments. |

Imprinted for Henry Cripps, and Henry Curteyne | at Oxford. 1625. | 17.5x13 cm. (8),136,(8)p.

JENISON, Robert. The | Christians | Apparelling | By Christ. | Where is shewed in three parts: | I.The Happinesse, Honour, and comfortable | estate of all true Christians: with the wret- | ched estate of all others. | 2.The Duetie it selfe, with particular Di- | rections. | 3. The Triall and Examination of our selues | by distinctiue Notes. | By R.I.B.D. | . . . (2 lines)

London, | Printed by A.M. and I.N. for Iohn | Browne, and are to bee sold at the | Signe of the Crane in Pauls | Churchyard. 1625. | Line border. 14.3x9.5 cm. (26).546p.

Epistle Dedicatorie, signed.

LEE, Richard. The Spirituall Spring. | A | Sermon | Preached At Pavls, | Wherein is declared the necessity of | growing in Grace, and the goodly | gaine that comes thereby, &c. | By Richard Lee, Preacher of the word of | God at Woluerhampton in Staffordshire. | . . . (4 lines; device)

London: | Printed by T. S. for Samvel Man, dwelling in Pauls | Church-yard, at the signe of the Swan, 1625. | 18.4x14.3 cm (4),19p.

MASON, Francis. Vindiciæ Ecclesiæ Anglicanæ; | Sive De Le- | gitimo Eivsdem | Ministerio, Id Est, De Episcoporvm | Successione, Consecratione, Electione, & | Confirmatione: | Item, | De Presbytero- | rum, & Diaconorum Ordinatione, | Libri V. | Jn quibus Ecclesia Anglicana à Bellarmini, Sanderi, | Bristoi, Hardingi, Alani, Stapletoni, Parsonij, Kellisoni, | Eudæmonis, Becani, aliorúmque Romanistarum calumnijs, | & contumelijs vindicatur. | Editio secunda, priori Anglicanâ longè auctior, & emendatior. | Cui inter alia accesserunt ad Fitzherberti Presbyteri, Fitz-Simonis Iesuitæ, D. | Kellisoni, Champnæi Sorbonistæ, Fluddi, & nescio cuius Anonymi | Exceptiones suis quæque locis intertextæ Responsiones. | Opus ex Idiomate Anglicano traductum, & locupletatum ab ipso Authore | Franc. Masono, in S. Theologia Bacchal. Archidiacono | Norfolc. Et Socio Colleg. Mertonensis apud | Oxonienses. | (device).

Londini, | Impressum per Felicem Kyngstonum. | 1625. | 27.4x18.5cm. (26), 680,(1)p.

MASON, Henry. Christian | Hvmiliation, | Or, | A Treatise Of | Fasting: | Declaring the Nature, Kindes, Ends, | Vses, and Properties of a Religious | Fast: | Together with a brief Discourse concerning | the Fast of Lent. | By Henry Mason, Pastor of Saint | Andrews-Vndershaft London. | (device).

London: | Printed by G.P. for Iohn Clarke, and are to be sold | at his Shop vnder S. Peters Church in Corne-hill. | 1625. | 19.1x15.5cm.(6),163p.

MAYER, John. An | Antidote | Against | Popery: | Confected out of Scriptures, Fathers, | Councels, and Histories. | Wherein Dialogve- | wise are shewed, the points, grounds, and | antiquitie of the Protestant Religion; and the | first springing vp of the points of Popery: | together with the Antichristianisme | thereof. | Being alone sufficient to inable any Protestant of | meane capacitie, to vnderstand and yeeld a reason | of his Religion, and to incounter with and | foyle the Aduersary. | By Iohn Mayer, B.D. and Pastor of the Church of | little Wratting in Suffolke. |

London, | Printed by M.F. for Iohn Grismand: and are to be | sold at his Shop in Pauls Alley, at the signe | of the Gunne. 1625. | Line border. 18.5x13.7cm. (12),81p.

MONTAGU, Richard. Appello Cæsarem. | A Ivst | Appeale | From | Two Vniust | Informers. | By | Richard Mountagu. | (ornament).

London, | Printed by H.L. for Mathew Lownes. | M.DC.XXV. | Floral headpiece. 18.2x13.6cm. (26),322p.
Suppressed and burned? by proclamation.

MONTANO, Reginald Gonsalvo. A | Fvll, Ample And | Pvnctvall Disco- | very of the Barbarous, Bloudy, | and inhumane practises of the | Spanish Inquisition, | against Protestants: | With the originall thereof. | Manifested in their proceedings against | sundry particular persons, aswell English | as others, upon whom they have | executed their Diabolicall | Tyrannie. | A Worke fit for these times, serving to with- | draw the affections of all good Christians from | that Religion, which cannot be maintayned | without those Props of Hell. | First written in Latin by Reginaldus Gonsaluius | Montanus, and after translated into English. | . . . (2 lines).

London, | Printed for Iohn Bellamy, and are to be sold at the three | golden Lions in Corne-hill, neere the Royall | Exchange. 1625. | 18. x12 cm. (31),198p. Title in red and black.

NETTLES, Stephen. An | Ansvver To | The Ievvish | Part Of Mr Selden's | History Of Tithes. | By Stephen Nettles, | B. of Divinity. | . . . (7 lines: device).

At Oxford, | Printed by Iohn Lichfield, & William Tvrner, | Printers to the famous Vniuersity. 1625. | Line border. 18.8x14.7cm.(11),189,(1)p.

PHILLIPS, John. The | Way To | Heaven: | Shevving, | 1. That Saluation is onely in the Church. | 2. What that Church is. | 3. By what meanes men are added to the | Church. | 4. The Author, or Efficient of this ad- | dition. | 5. The time & continuance of that worke. | 6. The happinesse of those that are added | to the Church. | By Iohn Phillips, Bachelor of Diuinity, and Pastor | of Feuersham in Kent. | . . . (1 line).

London, | Printed by Felix Kingston. | 1625. | Line border. 17.6x13.7 cm. (12), 66p. Mispaged: 53–54 omitted.

PRIDEAUX, John. Lectiones | Novem | De Totidem Religionis | Capitibus præcipuè hoc tempore con- | troversis prout publicè habebantur | Oxoniæ in Vesperijs. | Per | Iohannem Prideavx Exoniensis

Collegii | Rectorem, & S.Th. Professorem Regium. | . . . (5 lines: device).

Oxoniæ, | Excudebant Iohannes Lichfield & | Gvlielmvs Tvrner pro | Henrico Crypps | An.Dom.1625. | 18.5x14.3cm. (10),222p.

PRIDEAUX, John. Perez-Vzzah: | Or | The Breach of Vzzah: | As it was deliuered in a Sermon before His | Maiesty at Woodstocke, August | the 24. Anno 1624. | By | Iohn Prideavx, Rector of Exceter Colledge, | His Maiestie's Professor in Divinity, | and at that time Vice-Chancelor of | the Vniversity of Oxford. | . . . (3 lines: Oxford arms)

Oxford, | Printed by Iohn Lichfield and | William Tvrner. 1625. | 21.3x16.4cm. (4),23,(6)p.

PROCTER, William. The | Watchman | Warning. | A Sermon preached at Pavls | Crosse the 26. of September, | 1624. | By William Procter, Master of | Arts, and Minister of | Gods Word. | . . . (4 lines).

London, | Printed by Avgvstine Mathevves, | and are to bee sold at the New | Exchange. 1625. | Line border. 18.1x13.9 cm. (6),55p.

RAWLINSON, John. Qvadriga | Salvtis. | Fovre | Qvadragesimal, | Or Lent-Sermons, preached | at White-Hall: | By | Io. Rawlinson Doctor of Diuinity, | Principal of Edmund-Hall in Oxford, | and one of his Maiesties | Chaplaines in Ordinary. | (device)

Oxford, | Printed by Iohn Lichfield and William | Tvrner, Printers to the famous Vniuersity, | for Elias Peerse. 1625. | Line border. 18.4 x 14.3 cm. (5,1), 26;(1),29; (1),29; (1),28.(1) p.

Four half-titles; with continuous register, but separate pagination.

ROBINSON, John. A | Ivst And Necessarie | Apologie | Of Certain Christians, | no lesse contumeliously then commonly called | Brownists or Barrowists. | By Mr. Iohn Robinson, Pastor of the Eng- | lish Church at Leyden, first published in Latin in his and the | Churches name over which he was set, after translated into | English by himself, and now republished for the | speciall and common good of our | own Countrimen. | . . . (3 lines; lace ornament).

Printed in the yeere of our Lord | M.DC.XXV. | 18.4x14.8 cm. 72p.

ROBINSON, John. Observati- | ons Divine | And Morall. | For The Fvrthering | of knowledg, and vertue. | By John Robbinson. | . . . (4 lines; lace ornament).

Printed in the year M.DC.XXV. | 19.2x13.7 cm. (4),324,(2)p.

ROGERS, Richard, etc. A | Garden | of Spirituall | Flowers. | Planted By | {Ri. Ro. | Will. Per.} {Ri.Gree. | M.M. | and Geo.Web. |} Corrected and inlarged. | 1(-2) Part. |

London: | Printed by T.S. for T.Pauier, | dwelling in Ivie Lane. | 1625. | Lace border. 14.1x9.4cm. (4, 123; 1, 114)p. 2 Pts. (2d Pt. lacks 3 leaves: C 1-3.)

By Richard Rogers, William Perkins, Richard Greenham, M.M., and George Webbe. Various parts signed.

ROGERS, Thomas. The | Faith, Doctrine, | And Religion, Professed, | And Protected In The | Realme Of England, And | Dominions of the same. | Expressed in thirty nine Articles, concordably | agreed vpon by the reuerend Bishops, and Clergie of this King- | dome, at two seuerall meetings, or Conuocations of theirs, | in the yeeres of our Lord. 1562. and 1604. | The Said Articles Analised Into | Propositions, and the Propositions proued to be agreeable both | to the written word of God, and to the extant Confes- | sions of all the neighbour Churches, | Christianly Reformed. | The Adversaries Also Of Note, And Name | which from the Apostles daies, and Primitiue Church hitherto, haue | crossed, or contradicted the said Articles in generall, or any par- | ticle, or proposition arising from any of them in particular, hereby | are discouered, laid open, and so confuted. | Perused, and by the lawfull authority of the Church of England, allowed to be publike. | . . . (3 lines; ornament).

London, | Printed by Iohn Legatt, and are to be sold at the signe of the Bell in | Paules Church-yard by Andrew Hibb. 1625. | 18.3x13.9 cm. (36),222 p. Preface signed.

SANDYS, George. Sacræ Heptades, | Or | Seaven Problems | concerning | Antichrist. | I. Of his Place. | 2. Of his State. | 3. Of his Names. | 4. Of his Rising. | 5. Of his Raigne. | 6. Of his words and actions. | 7. Of his times. | Necessarie to be read and knowne of all men, who | professe Christ Iesus, and hope to be saved | by no other Name. | By G. S. | . . . (9 lines).

Printed in the yeare M.DC.XXV. | 18.6x14cm. (20),215p.
Ascription doubtful.Cf.Cambr.Univ.Cat.6504.

The | SECOND Part | Of The Protes- | tants Plea, And Pe- | tition For Preists And | Papists. Beeing an historie of the holy | preisthood, and sacrifice of the true | Church of Christ. | Inuincibly prouing them to be, the present sa- | crificing preisthood: prouing also the sacri- | fice of the Masse, vsed in the Catholike Ro- | man church: and that these were promised, | and foretold by the Prophets, instituted by | Christ, and exercised by all his Apostles. | Moreouer that they haue euer from the first plan- | tinge of Christianitie in this our Britanye, in | the dayes of the Apostles, in euery age, | and hundred of yeares, beene conti- | nued and preserued here. | All for the most part, warranted by the writinges, and | testimonies of the best learned Protestant | Doctors, and antiquaries of England, | and others. | . . . (2 lines).

With Licence, Anno 1625. | 15.3x9.3cm. 470, (7); 249, (1)p.

SMITH, Samuel. The | Chiefe Shepheard | Or, | An Exposition Vpon ye | xxiij Psalme. | Wherein is set downe ye | most excellent priuiledges | of those y^t haue ye Lord for | their Shepheard, & that | liue vnder his most gra- | cious protection. | Most needfull for ye time | By Samuell Smith minister | of ye word of God at | Prittlewell in Essex. |

London, | Printed by Nicholas | Okes. 1625. | 14.2x8.2cm.(24),542p. Engr. t.p.

TERRY, John.   Theologicall | Logicke: | Or | The Third Part Of The | Tryall Of Trvth: | Wherein is declared the excellency and æquity of the | Christian Faith, and that it is not withstood and resi- | sted; but assisted and fortified by all the forces of right | reason, and by all the aide that artificiall Logicke can | yeeld. | Against the heathenish Atheist, and the Romish Catholicks, | whereof the one taketh exception against the Faith of | Christ in generall; and the other against the doctrine | thereof, as it is professed in the Reformed Churches, as | being in their opinions absurd, and contrary to the eui- | dent and vndeniable grounds of reason. | By | Iohn Terry Minister of the Word of | God at Stocton. | (woodcuts).

Oxford, | Printed by Iohn Lichfield and | William Tvrner. | Anno. Dom. 1625. | 17.1x13.1cm. 25–229p. T.p. supplied; Lacks 1–24p.

USSHER, James.   An | Answer | To | A Challenge | Made By A Jesvite | In Ireland. | Wherein | The Ivdgement Of | Antiquity in the points questioned is | truly delivered, and the Noveltie of the now | Romish doctrine plainely | discovered | By Iames Vssher bishop of Meath. | . . . (2 lines). Whereunto Is Added A Sermon | Preached before His Majesty at Wansted, | by the same Author. |

London, | Printed for the Society of Stationers. 1625. | Line border. 18.6x14.4 cm.   (22),527,(7,1);(1),42p.

Also another copy, with a Commons sermon, 18 Feb. 1620, substituted. 18.7x 14.6cm   (24),527,(7);(4),50p.

USSHER, James.   A Briefe | Declaration | Of The Vniversali- | tie of the Chvrch | of Christ, and the Vnitie | of the Catholike Faith pro- | fessed therein: | Delivered In A Sermon | before His Majestie the 20th. of Iune, 1624. | at Wansted, | By Iames Vssher, Bishop of Meath. | The second Impression. | (device)

London, | Printed by Robert Young for Thomas Downes and | Ephraim Dawson, and are to be sold at the | Rain-bow neere the Inner Temple | Gate in Fleet-street. | 1625. | Line border. 18.6x14.5cm.   (1),42p.

Appended to An Answer to a Challenge: 1625; with separate register and pagination.

VASE, Robert.   Ionah's | Contesta- | tion Abovt | His Govrd. | In A Sermon | Delivered At | Pauls Crosse, Septemb. 19. | 1624. | By R. V. Preacher of Gods Word. | . . . (4 lines; device).

London, | Printed by I. L. for Robert Bird, and are to be sold | at his shoppe, at the signe of the Bible in | Cheape-side. 1625. | 18x13.8 cm.   (7),63p.

Pollard, Short-Title Catalogue.

WORSHIP, William.   Three | Sermons, | Preached At | Three Severall | Visitations, at Boston, in the | County of Lincolne. | By William Worship, D.D. | . . . (3 lines; device).

At London | Imprinted by Felix Kyngston, for | Iohn Parker, and are to be sold in Pauls | Church-yeard, at the signe of the three | Pigeons. 1625. | Line border. 17.3x13.3 cm.   (5),69p.

1626

AILESBURY, Thomas. The | Passion | Sermon | At | Pavls-Crosse, | vpon Good-Friday last, | Aprill 7. 1626. | By Thomas Ailesbury. | . . . (1 line; device).

London, | Printed by G.M. for Richard Moore, and are to be | sold at his shop in Saint Dunstans Church- | yard, 1626. | Line border. 17.8x13.9cm. (1),32p.

BAYLIE, Thomas. Thomæ Baylæi | Maningfordiensis | Ecclesiæ Pastoris. | De | Merito Mortis Christi, | Et Modo Conversionis. | Diatribæ Dvæ. | Provt Ab Ipso In Schola | Theolgica Apvd Oxonien- | ses publicê ad disputandum | propositæ fuerunt Maij. 8. | An.Dom.1621. | Nec non Concio ejusdem ad | Clerum. | Apvd | Eosdem habita in templo Beatæ Mariæ, | Iulij 5. An.D.1622. |

Oxoniæ, | Excudebant J.L. & W.T. Impensis | Thomæ Huggins, A.D.1626. | 16.9x12.7 cm. (10),63p.

BERNARD, Richard. Rhemes | Against | Rome: | Or, | The Remooving Of | The Gagg Of The New | Gospell, and rightly placing it in the mouthes | of the Romists, by the Rhemists; | in their English Translation of the | Scriptures. | Which Counter-Gagg is heere fitted by the in- | dustrious hand of Richard Bernard, | Rector of Batcomb, in the County | of Sommerset. | (device)

At London, | Imprinted by Felix Kingston, for Ed. Blackmore, and | are to be sold at his shop at the great South doore | of Pauls. 1626. | Line border. 18.6x13.5 cm. (14),326 p.

BRUNÆUS, Richardus. S. Thomæ Cantuariensis, | Et | Henrici II. Illvstris | Anglorvm Regis | Monomachia, | De | Libertate Ecclesiastica | Cvm Svbivncto Eivsdem | argumenti | Dialogo. | Vtrvmqve Pvblicabat | Richardvs Brunæus. | (device)

Coloniæ Agrippinæ, | Apud Cornelivm ab Egmundt. Bibliop. | Anno M.DC. XXVI. | 15.7 x 9.6 cm. (16),387 p.

BURTON, Henry. A Plea | To | An Appeale: | Trauersed Dialogue wise. | By H.B. | . . . (8 lines ; device).

Printed at London, by W.I. | 1626. | 17.8x14.2cm. (23),93p.
Epistle dedicatorie, signed.

BYFIELD, Nicholas. The | Rvle Of | Faith: | Or, | An Exposition Of | the Apostles Creed, so handled as | it affordeth both Milke for Babes, and | strong meat for such as are | at full age. | By that worthy seruant of Gods Church, Master | Nicholas Bifield, late Minister of Gods Word | at Islevvorth, and by him in his life time fully | perfected and transcribed, so much as is now published | for the benefit of Gods Church, by his Sonne, | Adoniram Bifield. | . . . (2 lines: ornament)

London, | Printed by G.M. for Philemon Stephens and Christopher Meredith, | and are to be sold at their shop at the golden Lion in Pauls | Church-yard, 1626. | Line border. 17.6x13.3cm. (8),563,(22)pp. Pp. 65–80, 85–92, misnumbered: 273–300 skipped.

CAMERON, John. An | Examination | Of Those Plavsi- | ble Appearances which seeme | most to commend the Romish | Church, and to preiudice | the Reformed. | Discovering Them | to be but meere shifts, purposely in- | vented, to hinder an exact triall of do- | ctrine by the Scriptures. | By | Mr Iohn Cameron. | Englished out of French. | (ornaments)

Oxford, | Printed by Iohn Lichfield and William Turner, for | Edward Forrest. Ann. Dom. 1626. | 17.5x13.8 cm. (8),173,(1)p.
Also another copy. 17x13.1 cm. (12),173,(1)p.

CARLETON, George. An | Examination | Of those things wherein the Author | of the late Appeale holdeth the Doctrines | of the Pelagians and Arminians, to be the | Doctrines of the Church of England. | Written by George Carleton Dr. | of Divinitie, and Bishop of Chichester. | . . . (5 lines ; ornament)

London, | Printed for William Turner. 1626. | 18.6x14.8 cm. (6),118p.
Suppressed and burned privately by the high commission at the instance of archbishop Laud.

CARLETON, George. An | Examination | Of those things wherein the Author | of the late Appeale holdeth the Doctrines | of the Pelagians and Arminians, to be the | Doctrines of the Church of England. | Written by George Carleton Dr. | of Divinitie, and Bishop of Chichester. | The second Edition, Revised and enlarged by the Author. | Wherevnto also there is annexed a Joynt Atte- | station, avowing that the Discipline of the Church | of England was not impeached by the Synod | of Dort. | . . . (5 lines)

London, | Printed for William Tvrner. | MDCXXVI. | 18.5x14.0 cm. (6),236,(1),26p. 150-189 omitted in numbering
Cambr.Univ.Cat.4918 The Joynte Attestation has separate register and pagination

CULVERWELL, Ezekiel. A Briefe | Ansvvere | To Certaine | Objections against the | Treatise of Faith, made | by Ez.Cvlvervvell. | Clearing him from the | errors of Arminius, | vnjustly layd to | his charge. | (lace ornament).

London, | Printed by I.D. for William | Sheffard, and are to be sold | at his Shop at the entrance in | out of Lumbard streete into | Popes-head Alley. 1626. | Line border. 14.3x8.4cm. (1,22)p.

DONNE, John. A | Sermon, | Preached To | The Kings M^{tie}. At | Whitehall, 24. Febr. | 1625. | By Iohn Donne Deane of | Saint Pauls, London. | And now by his Maiesties com- | mandment Published. |

London, | Printed for Thomas Iones, dwelling | at the Blacke Rauen in the Strand. | 1626. | Line border. 18. x14 cm. (6),50p.

FEATLEY, Daniel. A | Parallel: | Of | Nevv-Old | Pelagiarminian Error. | . . . (2 lines; ornament).

London, | Printed for Robert Milbourne. | 1626. | Line border. 19.3x15.2 cm (7),19p.
Anon. Cambr.Univ.Cat:4335. Against Bishop Montagu.

FEATLEY, Daniel. Parallelismus | nov-antiqui | erroris | Pelagiar-miniani. | . . . (2 lines).
Londini, | Impensis Roberti Mylbovrne. | 1626. | 18.6x13.6 cm. (8,13)p.
Anon. Cambr.Univ.Cat:4336.

FEATLEY, Daniel. Pelagius redivivus. | Or | Pelagivs | Raked Ovt Of | The Ashes By | Arminivs and his | Schollers. | (device).
London, | Printed for Robert Mylbourne. 1626. | Line border. 17.8x13.3 cm. (7),19p.
Anon. Same as his Parallel: Of Nevv-Old Pelagiarminian Error: 1626. Cambr. Univ. Cat: 7592.

FEATLEY, Daniel. A Second | Parallel | Together with | A Writ Of Error | Sved Against The | Appealer. | . . . (1 line; device)
London | Printed for Robert Milbovrne. | M.DC.XXVI. | 17.8x13.3 cm. (15), 95,97p.
Anon.Cambr.Univ.Cat:3529.

FISHER, John. The | Answere | Vnto | The Nine Points of Con-trouersy, | Proposed by our late Soueraygne (of Fa- | mous Memory) vnto M. Fisher | of the Society of Iesvs. | And The | Reioynder | Vnto the Reply of D. Francis | VVhite Minister. | With the Picture of the sayd Minister, or Cen- | sure of his Writings prefixed. | . . . (orna-ment; 3 lines).
Permissu Superiorum, M.DC.XXVI. | 17.8x13.8 cm. (50,4),1–160,400 p.
Gillow.V:263. Second part: Aa1–Ddd4, with sub t.p.

A FORME | Of Prayer, | Necessary to bee vsed in these dange- | rous times, of Warre and Pestilence, | for the safety and preseruation of his | Maiesty and his Realmes. | Set forth by Authoritie. | (royal arms).
London | Printed by Bonham Norton and Iohn Bill, | Printers to the Kings most Excellent | Maiestie. 1626. | 17.6x14.7 cm. (1,82)p.

GATAKER, Thomas. An Anniuersarie | Memoriall | Of | Englands | Delivery From | The Spanish Inuasion: | Delivered In A | Sermon on Psal.48.7,8. | By Thomas Gataker B. of D. | and Pastor of Rotherhith. | (ornament).
London, | Printed by John Haviland for Philemon | Stephens and Christopher Meredith, at the | Golden Lion in Pauls Churchyard. 1626. | 18.5x14.3cm. (8), 24p.

GODWIN, Thomas. Moses and Aaron. | Civil And | Ecclesiasticall | Rites, Vsed By The | ancient Hebrewes; obserued, and | at large opened, for the clearing of many ob- | scure Texts thorowout the whole | Scriptvre. | Herein Likevvise Is | Shewed What Cvstomes The | Hebrewes borrowed from Heathen people: | And that many Heathen-ish customes, originally | haue beene vnwarrantable imitations | of the Hebrewes. | The Second edition. | By Thomas Godwin, B.D. |
London, | Printed by Iohn Haviland, and are to be sold by | Philemon Stephens and Christopher Meredith at | their shop, at the signe of the Golden Lion | in Pauls Church-yard. 1626. | 18.x13.7cm. (8),332,(4)p.

GOUGE, William. A | Gvide | To Goe To | God: | Or, | An Explanation | of the Perfect Patterne of Prayer, | The Lords Prayer. | By William Govge, B. in D. and | Minister of Gods Word in Black-Friers | London. | . . . (2 lines; ornament)

At London, | Printed by G.M. and R.B. for Edward Brewster, and are | to be sold at his shop neere the great North dore of St. | Pauls Church, at the signe of the Bible . | 1626. | Line border. 19x14.5 cm. (14),340,8pp.

GUILD, William. Moses Vnuailed: | Or, | Those Figvres | Which Served Vnto | the patterne and shaddow of heauenly | things, pointing out the Messiah | Christ Iesvs, briefly | explained. | Whereunto is added the Harmonie of | all the Prophets, breathing with one | mouth, the Mystery of his Comming, | and of that Redemption which by his | Death he was to accomplish. | To confirme the Christian, and con- | uince the Ievv: very profitable and | full of Comfort. | By William Gvild Minister of Gods | Word at King Edward in Scotland. | . . . (3 lines).

London, | Printed by G.M. for Robert Allott, and are to | be sold at his shop in Pauls Church-yard, at the signe of the Grey-hound, 1626. | Line border. 14.5x 9.5cm. (14),183; (16),56p. Sep. t.p.
From the library of Walter W. Law.

HARRIS, Robert. Peters | Enlargement | Upon | The Prayers Of | The Chvrch. | By Master Harris. | The fourth Edition. | . . . (3 lines; device).

London, | Printed by Robert Young for John Bartlet, and | are to be sold at the Golden Cup, in the Gold- | Smiths Row in Cheape-side. 1626. | 17.2x13.5 cm. (8),46p. Impf. at end.

HOLYDAY, Barten. A | Sermon | Preached | At Pauls Crosse, | August the 5. | 1623. | By | Barten Holyday, | Now Archdeacon of | Oxford. |

London. | Printed by William Stansby for Nathaniell | Butter, and are to be sold at his Shop at | Saint Austines Gate in Pauls | Church-yard. 1626. | 17.5x14.1 cm. (8),38p.

HOLYDAY, Barten. A | Sermon | Preached | At Pauls Crosse, | March the 24. | 1624. | By | Barten Holyday, | Archdeacon of | Oxford. |

London, | Printed by William Stansby for Nathaniell | Butter, and are to be sold at his Shop at | Saint Austines Gate in Pauls | Church-yard. 1626. | 17.5x14.1 cm. (4),42p.

HOLYDAY, Barten. Three | Sermons | Vpon The Pas- | sion, Resvrrec- | tion And Ascension | Of Ovr Saviovr, | Preached | At Oxford, | By | Barten Holyday, | Now Archdeacon of | Oxford. |

London, | Printed by William Stansby for Nathaniell | Butter, and are to be sold at his Shop at | Saint Austines Gate in Pauls | Church-yard. 1626. | 17.5x14.1 cm. (8),108p.

HUISH, Alexander. Lectures | Upon | The Lords | Prayer. | By Alexander Huish, Master | of Arts, and Fellow of Wadham | College in the Universitie of | Oxford. | Divided into three Parts. | . . . (3 lines).

Imprinted at London, and are to be sold by | William Turner in Oxford. M.DC.XXVI. | 18.8x14.3cm. (5), 148; 351; (8), 196p.
Three parts, with separate registers and pagination.

INSTRVCTIONS | directed from the Kings most | Excellent Maiestie, | Vnto all the Bishops of this Kingdome, | and fit to be put in execution, agreeable to | the necessitie of the Time. | (royal arms.)

London, | Printed by Bonham Norton and Iohn Bill, | Printers to the Kings most | Excellent Maiestie. 1626. | 18.x13.8cm. (1,13)p.

JEWEL, John. Apologia | Ecclesiæ | Anglicanæ. | Authore Ioanne Iuello, | olim Episcopo Saris- | buriensi. | . . . (4 lines; ornament)

Londini, | Impensis Iacobi Boler. | Anno Dom. 1626. | 12x7 cm. (5),197p.

A | IOYNT | Attestation, | Avowing that the Discipline of the | Church of England was not impea- | ched by the Synode of Dort. | (ornament)

London, | Printed by M.Flesher for R.Mylbourne, and are | to be sold at his shop at the great South-doore | of Pauls. 1626. | 18.5x14.0 cm. (1),26p.
Appended to Carleton, Geo. An Examination, etc. 2d ed. 1626; with separate register and pagination.

KING, Henry. A | Sermon | Of | Deliverance. | Preached at the Spittle | on Easter Monday, 1626. | Vpon Entreatie of the Lord Maior | and Aldermen. | Published by Authoritie. | And | Dedicated to the Citie of London. | By Henry King D.D. | One of his Majesties Chaplaines | in Ordinarie. |

London, | Printed by Iohn Haviland, for Iohn | Marriot. 1626. | Line border. 18x13.7cm. (1),80p.

LAUD, William. A | Sermon | Preached | Before His Maiestie, | On Wednesday the fift of Iuly, | At White-Hall. | At the solemne Fast then held. | By the Bishop of S. Davids. | (device).

London, | Printed for Richard Badger. | M.DC.XXVI. | 18. x14 cm. (1),53p.

MASON, Henry. The | Epicvres | Fast: | Or: | A Short Discovrse, | Discovering the Licenciovs- | nesse of the Romane Church in her | religious Fasts. | By | Henrie Mason, Parson of St. | Andrews Vndershaft, London. | (ornament).

London: | Printed by G.P. for Iohn Clarke, and are to be | sold at his Shop, vnder St.Peters Church in | Cornhill. 1626. | 18.x13.7cm. (8),58p.

MORE, Cresacre. D.O.M.S. | The Life And Death Of | Sir Thomas | Moore | Lord high Chancellour of | England. | Written By | M.T.M. and dedicated to the Queens | most gracious Maiestie. | (ornament)

Without imprint. [1626] 19.3x15.5cm. (8),432p. Epistle dedicatory signed M.C.M.E.
Gillow: V:95.

MOULIN, Pierre du. The | Anatomy | Of | Arminianisme: | Or, | The Opening Of The | Controuersies of these times (formerly | handled in the Low-Countries) concer- | ning the doctrine of Prouidence, of Prede- | stination, of the death of Christ, of | Nature and Grace, &c. | By Peter Du Moulin, Minister of the | Church at Paris | . . . (2 lines; ornament).

London, | Printed for Nathanael Newbery. | Anno Dom. 1626. | Line border. 18. x 13.4cm. (18),504p. Pp 166–175, 279 misnumbered; 369–398 skipped; 443–444 repeated.

OWEN, Lewis. The | Rvnning | Register: | Recording | A Trve Relation | Of The State Of The | English Colledges, Seminaries and | Cloysters in all forraine parts. | Together with a briefe and compendious | discourse of the Liues, Practices, Coozenage, | Impostures and Deceits of all our English | Monks, Friers, Iesuites, and Seminarie | Priests in generall. | By Lewis Owen. | . . . (2 lines; ornament).

London, | Printed for Robert Milbourne, and are to be sold at the great | South doore of Pauls. 1626. | 18.8x14.1cm. (7),118p.

PAOLO, Servita. The | History | Of The | Qvarrels | Of Pope Pavl. V. | With | The State of Venice. | In Seven Books. | Faithfully translated out of the Italian, and | compared with the French Copie. | (ornament).

London, | Printed by John Bill, Printer to the | Kings most Excellent Maiesty. | M.DC.XXVI. | Line border. 17.8x14.1cm. (19), 435,(1)p.

Cambr. Univ. Cat. 3531.

PRYNNE, William. The | Perpetvitie | Of A Regen- | rate Mans | Estate. | Wherein it is manifestly proued by sundry | arguments, reasons and authorities. | That such as are | once truly regenerated and ingrafted into Christ by a liuely | faith, can neither finally nor totally fall from grace. | It is also proued, that this hath beene the receiued and | resolued Doctrine, of all the ancient Fathers, of all the Prote- | stant Churches and writers beyond the seas, and of the Church | of England. All the principall arguments that are, or may | be obiected against it, either from Scripture, or from reason, are | here likewise cleared and answered. | By William Prynne Gent: Lincolniensis. | . . . (6 lines).

London, | Printed by William Iones dwelling in Redcrosse- | streete. 1626. | 17.8x13.5cm. (40),410,(1)p. Lacks pp. 177–186.

Suppressed and burned privately by the high commission at the instance of archbishop Laud.

RANDALL, John. Saint Pavls | Triumph, | Or, | Cygnea illa & dulcissima Cantio, | That Swan-like and most sweet Song, of | that learned and faithfull Servant of God, | Mast. Iohn Randall, Bachelor | of Divinitie. | Vttered by him (in an eleven Sermons upon | the eight Chapter of S. Paul his Epistle to the | Romanes, vers.38.39.) lately before his death, in the | time of his great and heavie Affliction, and | upon the Communion dayes, eyther alto- | gether, or for the most part. | The second time published, revised, corrected, and enlar- | ged

with two Tables at the end of the Booke (the first shewing | and
directing to the maine and choice things handled in | this Treatise;
the second, directing to the chiefe | places of Scripture quoted and
expoun- | ded in this Treatise.) By William Holbrooke, Preacher of
the word of God. |

<small>London, | Printed for R.Redmer and N.Newbery, and are to be sould | at the
signe of the Starre in Popes-head-Alley. | Anno Dom. 1626. | Line border. 18x13.6
cm.(8),243,(8)p.</small>

REYNER, Clement. (Editor). Apostolatvs Benedictinorvm | In
Anglia, | Siue | Disceptatio Historica, | De Antiqvitate | Ordinis Con-
gregationisqve | Monachorvm Nigrorvm | S.Benedicti | In Regno An-
gliæ: | Jn qua demonstratur S.Gregorium, eius nationis Apostolum, |
fuisse Benedictinum; ostenditur etiam obiter quanto | numero, qui-
busque temporibus, alij Ordines Re- | ligiosorum in eodem Regno
cœperint agnosci. | Cum appendice copiosa instrumentorum venerandæ
vetustatis, é | quibus fides Antiquitatum Benedictinarum demonstra-
tur: in ijs | præcipuè inueniet Lector Religiosus, Concordiam Regvla- |
rem S.Dvnstani; & Statvta Monastica D.Lan- | franci; & aliquot Acta
Priscorvm Capitvlorvm | Generalivm Congregationis Ordinis- | qve
Eivsdem in Anglia: ante- | hac nunquam typis excusa. | Jussu Patrum
eiusdem congregationis, in Capitulo Generali | anni 1525. congrega-
torum, edita | Opera Et Indvstria | R.P.Clementis Reyneri S.Theol.
Professoris, | & eiusdem Congregationis Secretarij. | . . . (6 lines ;
Maltese cross).

<small>Dvaci, | Ex Officinâ Lavrentii Kellami Typographi iurati, | sub signo Agni Pas-
chalis. 1626. | 29.6x19.5cm. (1),22,(2),248,222; (14),254p. Engr. fore-title, simi-
larly worded.
DNB. 3:4b; 30:125a;48:38a.</small>

ROUS, Francis. Testis Veritatis. | The | Doctrine | {Of King |
Iames | our late Soueraigne of | famous Memory. | Of The Chvrch | Of
England. | Of The Catho- | licke Chvrch.} | Plainely | shewed | to bee |
One | in the | points | of | Prædestination, | Free-will, | Certaintie of |
saluation. | With a discouery | of the Grounds}Naturall | Politicke}of
Arminianisme. | By F. Rovs. |

<small>Printed at London, by W.I. | 1626. | 18.6x13.5cm. (4),92p.
Also an enlarged edition, with identical title, except the insertion of the word
" both " after " Grounds " near the end. 20x15cm. (4),107p.</small>

SHUTE, Nathaniel. Corona Charitatis, | The Crowne | Of Chari-
tie: | A Sermon Preacht in Mer- | cers Chappell, May 10. 1625. at |
the solemne Funerals of his euer-renow- | med Friend, of precious
memory, the | Mirroir of Charitie, Mr. Richard | Fishbvrne, Merchant,
And now | consecrated as an Anniuersary | to his Fame; | By Nat:
Shvte, Rector of the Parish of Saint | Mildred in the Poultry, London. |
. . . (6 lines).

<small>London, | Printed by W. Stansby for Samvel Man, | dwelling at the Swanne in
Pauls Church- | yard, 1626. | Line border. 17.3x13.7 cm. (10),45p.</small>

SUTCLIFF, Matthew. The | Vnmasking | of a Masse-monger. |
Who | In The Covnterfeit | Habit of S.Avgvstine hath | cunningly crept

into the Closets of | many English Ladies. | Or, | The Vindication | of Saint Avgvstines Confessions, | from the false and malicious Calum- | niations of a late noted | Apostate. | By M.S. D. of Exeter. | . . . (8 lines).

London. | Printed by B.A. and T.Favvcet, for Nich:Bovrne, | and are to bee sold at his Shop neere to the Royall- | Exchange. 1626. | Line border. 18.6x14.6cm. (12),84p.
Epistle Dedicatorie, signed.

SYDENHAM, Humphry. Five | Sermons, | Vpon Severall | Occasions Preach'd | At Pavls Crosse, | And | At Saint Maries, | In Oxford. | By | Humphry Sydenham, Mr. of Arts, and | Fellow of Wadham Colledge in | Oxford. | (ornament)

London, | Printed for Iohn Parker. | 1626. | Line border. 17.3x13.cm. (1,4), 156p.
Photostat t.p. For contents, see his Athenian Babler: 1627.

WOTTON, Anthony. A | Dangerovs | Plot Discovered. | By A Discovrse, | Wherein is proved, That, Mr: Ri- | chard Movntagve, in his two | Bookes; the one, called A new Gagg; the | other, A iust Appeale: Laboureth to bring in | the faith of Rome, and Arminius: vnder the | name and pretence of the doctrine and | faith of the Church of England. | A Worke very necessary for all them which haue re- | ceived the truth of God in loue, and desire to escape errour. | The Reader shall finde: | 1. A Catalogue of his erroneous poynts annexed to the | Epistle to the Reader. | 2. A demonstration of the danger of them. cap. 21. | num. 7. &c. pag. 178. | 3. A list of the heads of all the Chapters contained in | this Booke. | . . . (5 lines).

London, | Printed for Nicholas Bourne, at the Exchange. 1626. | Line border. 18.5x14.8 cm. (15),84,190p.
Cambr. Univ. Cat: 3871.

YATES, John. Ibis ad Cæsarem. | Or | A Svbmissive | Appearance | Before Cæsar; | In Answer to Mr. Mountagues Appeale, | in the points of Arminianisme and Popery, main- | tained and defended by him, against the Do- | ctrine of the Church of England. | . . . (8 lines).

London, | Printed for R. Mylbourne. 1626. | Line border. 17.6x13.6cm. (20), 95,168,46p.
Cambr.Univ.Cat:7588. Watt.

1627

ADAMSON, John. Στοιχειωσις | Eloqviorvm Dei, | sive | Methodus Religionis | Christianæ catechetica. | In usum Academiæ | Iacobi Regis, & Scho- | larum Edinburgensium | Conscripta | Ab | Ioanne Adamsono, | Academiæ Moderatore | Primario. | (three devices)

Edinbvrgi, | Excudebant Hæredes Andreæ Hart. | Cum gratiâ & Priviligio. 1627. | 14.2x8.6cm. (6,102)p. T.p. supplied.

BERNARD, Richard. The | Isle Of Man: | Or, | The Legall Proceeding | in Man-Shire against | Sinne. | Wherein, by way of a continued | Allegorie, the chiefe Malefactors di- | sturbing both Church

and Common- | wealth are detected, and attached; | with their Ar-
raignment, and Iu- | diciall tryall, according to the | Laws of England. |
A necessary Direction for waifaring | Christians, not acquainted with
those perilous | ways they must passe, before they happily | arrive at
their wished Hauen. | By R.B. Rector of Batcomb. | Somers. |

    Iondon | Printed by G.M. for Edward | Blackemoore, 1627. | 11.7x6.8cm. (24), 287p.
    Cf.Cambr.Univ.Cat:4409.

BURTON, Henry. The Baiting Of The Popes Bvll. | Or | An vn-
masking of the Mystery of iniquity, folded | vp in a most pernitious
Breeue or Bull, sent from the | Pope lately into England, to cawse a
Rent therein, | for his Reentry. With an advertisement | to the Kings
seduced subiects. | (cut). By H. B. | . . . (4 lines).

    Imprinted at London by W. I. for Michaell Sparke. | 1627. | 18x13.2 cm. (10), 95p.
    Camb.Univ.Cat.No.5032.
    Suppressed and burned privately by the high commission at the instance of archbishop Laud.

BYFIELD, Nicholas. The | Principles | Or, | The Patterne of |
wholesome Words. | Containing a Collection of such | Truths as are of
necessitie to be be- | lieued vnto Saluation, seperated | out of the
bodie of all | Theologie. | Made euident by infallible and | plaine
proofes of Scriptures. | And withall, | The seuerall vses such Principles
should | be put to, are abundantly shewed. | A proiect much desired,
and of singu- | lar vse for all sorts of Christians. | By, | N.Byfeild,
Preacher of Gods | Word at Isleworth in | Middlesex. | The third Edi-
tion, corrected | and amended. |

    London, | Printed by W.Stansby, for Phile.Ste- | phens and Christ.Meredith, dwelling at | the Golden Lyon in Pauls | Church-yard. 1627. | Line border. 13.6x 7.9cm.(19),479, (2)p. Colophon.

CARLETON, George. A | Thankfvll | Remembrance | Of Gods
Mercy. | In an Historicall Collection of the | great and mercifull De-
liverances of the | Church and State of England, since the | Gospel
beganne here to florish, from | the beginning of Queene | Elizabeth. |
Collected by Geo: Carleton, | Doctor of Divinity and Bishop of |
Chichester. | The third Edition revised, and enlarged. | . . . (3 lines).

    London, | Printed by M.Flesher for Robert Mylbourne | and Humphrey Robin-
son at the signe of the three | Pigeons in Pauls Church-yard. | 1627. | Line border.
18.2x13.5cm.(8),291p. Portr. frontisp. and Engr. fore t.p.

DEMPSTER, Thomas. Historia Ecclesiastica | Gentis Scotorvm
Lib.XIX. | Qua Viri Sanctitate, literis, dignitatib[us]. | toto Orbe Il-
lustres, & familiæ, et Scoticæ | in varias Vrbes transmissæ, & precipuè |
Placentiã Recensentur. | Illustrissimo Viro | Fabio Scoto Plac:º | Mice-
ni Com.Dicata. | Auctore Thoma Dempstero Scoto I.C.Baron. | de Mu-
resck, Eq.Aur.Bonon.Prof. | eminente, et in Academia Noctis | Euantio |

    Superior[um]. p[er]missu. Bononiæ Typis Nicolai Thebaldini 1627. | Engr. t.p.
21x15cm (24),690p.

DENISON, Stephen. The | VVhite VVolfe | Or, | A Sermon Preached at Pavls | Crosse, Feb. 11. being the last Sonday in Hillarie | Tearme, Anno 1627. and printed somewhat | more largely then the time would permit | at that present to deliuer. | Wherein Faction is vnmasked, and iustly taxed | without malice, for the safetie of weake | Christians. | Especially, the Hetheringtonian Faction growne | very impudent in this Citie of late | yeeres, is here confuted. | By Stephen Denison, Minister of Katherine | Cree-Church, London. | . . . (6 lines; ornament).

At London, | Printed by George Miller, dwelling in | Blacke-Fryers. 1627. | Border. 17.3x13.4 cm. (12),76p. Two cuts in text.

DENT, Arthur. A | Sermon | Of | Repentance. | A very godly and profita- | ble Sermon, Preached at | Lee in Essex. | By | Arthvr Dent, Minister of Gods Word: | Published at the request of sundry godly, and | well disposed persons. | . . . (3 lines)

London, | Printed by Iohn Dawson, for William Sheffard, | and are to be sold at his Shop in the entrance | in of Popes-head Alley, out of Lumbard-streete. | 1627. | 13.7x9.cm. (4),50p.
From the library of Walter W. Law.

DOWNAME, George. An | Abstract | Of The Dvties Com- | manded, And Sinnes | forbidden in the Law | of God. | By The Right Reverend | Father In God, George Dovvname, | Doctor of Diuinity, and Lord Bishop | of Derry. | . . . (3 lines; device)

At London, | Imprinted by Felix Kyngston. | 1627. | 15.6x11.1cm. (12,274)p.

GAMON, Hannibal. The Praise Of A | Godly VVoman. | A Sermon preached at the Solemne Fu- | nerall of the Right Honourable Ladie, the Ladie | Frances Roberts, at Lanhide-rock- | Church in Cornwall, the tenth of | August, 1626. | By | Hanniball Gamon, Minister of the word | of God, at St.Maugan in the same Countie. | . . . (13 lines)

London, | Printed by I.H. for Iohn Grismond, and are to be sold at his shop in | Ivie-Lane at the signe of the Gunne. 1627. | 19.6x15.2cm. (7),37p.

GATAKER, Thomas. Abrahams | Decease. | A | Meditation | On | Genesis 25.8. | Delivered At The Fv- | nerall Of That Worthy Ser- | uant of Christ, Mr. Richard Stock, | Late Pastor of All-Hallowes | Bread-street: | Together With The Testimo- | nie then giuen vnto him. | By | Thomas Gataker B. of D. and | Pastor of Rotherhith. |

London, | Printed by Iohn Haviland for Fulke Clifton, and are to | be sold at his shop on New-fishstreet hill, vnder | St.Margarets Church, at the signe of the | holy Lambe. 1627. | 18.5x14.3cm.(5),62,(1)p.

GOFFE, Thomas. Deliverance | From | The Grave. | A | Sermon preached at Saint Maries | Spittle in London, on Wednesday in Easter | vveeke last, March 28. 1627. | By | Tho. Goffe, Batchelor of Diuinitie, | lately Student of Christ-Church in Oxford. | (device).

London: | Printed for Ralph Mab. 1627. | 18.3x14.1 cm. (4),42p.

HAKEWILL, George. An | Apologie | Of The Povver And | Providence Of God | In The Government | Of The World. | Or | An Examination | And Censvre Of The | Common Errovr Tovching | Natvres Perpetvall And | Vniversall Decay, Divi- | ded Into Fovre Bookes: | Whereof | The first treates of this pretended decay in generall, together with some prepa- | ratiues thereunto. | The second of the pretended decay of the Heauens and Elements, together with | that of the Elementary bodies, man only excepted. | The third of the pretended decay of mankinde in regard of age and duration, of | strength and stature, of arts and wits. | The fourth of this pretended decay in matter of manners, together with a large | proofe of the future consummation of the World from the testimony of the | Gentiles, and the vses which we are to draw from the consideration thereof. | By G.H. DD. | . . . (3 lines: device).

Oxford, | Printed by Iohn Lichfield and William Tvrner, | Printers to the famous Vniversity. Anno Dom. 1627. | 28.5x17.8cm (36),473,(4)p.
Camb.Univ.Cat.No.5366.

HAMPTON, William. A | Proclamation | Of | VVarre | From The Lord | Of Hosts. | Or | Englands warning by | Israels ruine: Shewing the | miseries like to ensue vpon vs by reason | of Sinne and Securitie. | Deliuered in a Sermon at Pauls Crosse | Iuly the 23. 1626. | By William Hampton Master of | Arts, and Preacher of Gods Word. | . . . (6 lines)

London, | Printed by Iohn Norton for Mathew Lawe and are to be | sold at the signe of the Fox in Saint Paules Church- | yeard, neere Saint Austens Gate. 1627. | Line border. 18.1x14 cm. (6),43p.

JACKSON, Thomas. A | Treatise | Of The Holy | Catholike Faith | and Chvrch. | Diuided into three Bookes. | By | Thomas Iackson Dr. in Di- | uinitie, Chaplaine to his Maiestie | in Ordinarie, and Vicar of Saint Ni- | colas Church in the Towne of | Newcastle vpon Tyne. | The first Booke. |

London, | Printed by M. F. for Iohn Clarke, and are to | be sold at his Shop vnder St. Peters Church | in Cornehill. 1627. | Line border. 19.4x14.1 cm. (8), 206p.

LEVER, Christopher. The | History Of The De | fendors of the Catholique Faith. | Whearevnto are added | Observations{Divine, | Politique, | Morrall. | By Christopher Lever. | . . . (1 line).

London Printed for Nicholas Fussell | and Humphrey Moseley, at the signe | of the Ball in Pauls Church yard. 1627. | 18x13.7cm. (6),371pp. Engraved titlepage and border containing six panels.

MANWARING, Roger. Religion | And | Alegiance: | In Tvvo Sermons | Preached before the Kings | Maiestie: | The one on the fourth of Iuly, Anno 1627. | At Oatlands. | The other on the 29. of Iuly the same yeere, | At Alderton. | By Roger Maynvvaring Doctor | in Diuinitie, one of his Majesties Chaplaines | in Ordinarie: and then, in his Month | of Attendance. | By His Maiesties Speciall Command. | (ornament).

London, | Printed by I. H. for Richard Badger. | 1627. | 18.4x14.3cm. (1),33, 56p.
Ordered to be burned June 24, 1628

MASON, Henry. The | Cvre Of | Cares. | Or | A Short Discovrse, | declaring the condition of worldly | Cares; with some Remedies appro- | priated unto them. | Penned for the use of all, but is most proper | for such as be distressed. | By | Henry Mason Parson of S. Andrews | Vndershaft London. | (device).

London, | Printed by M.F. for Iohn Clarke, and | are to be solde at his shop under S.Peters | Church in Cornhill. 1627. | Line border. 18x13.8cm. (1),51p.

MAYER, John. Ecclesiastica Interpretatio: | Or The | Expositions | Vpon | The Difficvlt | And Dovbtfvll Passages | of the seuen Epistles called Catholike, | and the Revelation. | Collected out of the best esteemed, both old and new | Writers, together with the Authors examinations, | determinations, and short Annotations. | The Texts in the seuen Epistles of Iames, Peter, Iohn and | Iude are six and forty. | The Expositions vpon the Reuelation are set forth by | way of Question and Answer. | Here is also a briefe Commentary vpon euery verse of each | Chapter, setting forth the coherence and sense, and the Authors, | and time of writing euery of these Bookes. | Hereunto is also annexed an Antidot against Popery. | By Iohn Mayer, B. of D. and Pastor of the Church of | Little Wratting in Suffolke. |

London, | Printed by Iohn Haviland, for Iohn Grismand, and are to be | sold at his shop in Iuy-lane at the signe of the Gunne. | 1627. | 18.4x14.2cm. (30), 542p.

Also another copy from the library of Walter W. Law. 17.5x13.8cm.

Also re-issued in 1631 as the third volume of his Commentarie Vpon The New Testament, with new t.p. prefixed.

PRYNNE, William. The | Perpetvitie | Of A Regene- | rate Mans | Estate. | Wherein it is manifestly proued: That | such as are once truely Regenerated and Ingrafted | into Christ by a true and liuely Faith, can neither | finally nor totally fall from Grace. As also, That this hath been | the receiued and resolued Doctrine, of the ancient Fa- | thers; of the Protestant Churches beyond the Seas; | of the Church of England, and of all orthodox and | solid Writers both forraine and domestique. | All the principall arguments that are, or may | bee objected against it, eyther from Scripture, | or from reason, are heere likewise | cleared and answered. | The second Edition perused and inlarged. | By William Prynne Gent: Hositij Lincolniensis. | . . . (6 lines).

London, | Printed by William Iones dwelling in Redcrosse-street. | 1627. | 19.1x 14.2cm. (46), 656p.

RESSOLD, William. Fovre | Sermons, | {I. Sinnes contagion, or the sicknesse of | the soule. | II. The description of a Christian. | III. The blindnesse of a wilfull sinner. | IV. A Race to Heaven. } Published by William Ressold, Master | of Arts and Minister of Gods Word at | Debach in Suffolke. | . . . (3 lines; device).

London, | Printed by H.L. for George Lathvm, at | the Bishops head in Pauls Church-yard. | Anno 1627. | 19.1x14.2cm. (6),138p. Impf. at end: T2 and after.

ROGERS, Richard. Seaven | Treatises | Containing Svch Di- | rection As Is Gathered Ovt | Of The Holie Scriptvres, | leading and guiding to true happinesse, both in | this life, and in the life to come: and may be | called the practice of Christianitie. | Profitable for all such as heartily desire the same: in | the which, more particularly true Christians may learne | how to lead a godly and comfortable life euery day, | notwithstanding their tribulations. | First penned, and now set forth the fourth time, corrected and | enlarged by Richard Rogers, Preacher of the | word of God at Wethersfield in Essex. | . . . (5 lines)

London. | Imprinted by Iohn Dawson, for Richard Meighen by the | assignement of Paul Man, and Ionas Man: 1627. | Line border. 20.2x15.0cm. (36),540, 303,(50)p .
Two parts, with independent register and pagination.

ROUS, Francis. The | Onely | Remedy, | That Can | Cvre A People, | When all other Re- | medies faile. | By F. Rovs. | . . . (3 lines)

London, | Printed for Iames Boler | at the signe of the Mari- | gold in Pauls Church- | yard. 1627. | Line border. 13.4x8.1cm. (8),247p.

SALTER, Robert. Wonderfvll | Prophecies | From The Beginning | of the Monarchy of this Land, hid- | den vnder the Parables of: | Three young Noble-men in a fiary Fornace. | A chast wife, and two old Fornicators. | The Idol Belvs and his Dragon. | Daniel in a Den amid Lyons. | Their agreement with Canonical Prophecies: Also | a Temperate Defence of the Apocryphals annexed to | the Canon of the Scriptures. | Together with an Essay touching the late Prodigious | Comete; how farre forth the Præsages thereof | doe accord with such Prophecies, as are found to | pertaine to these our times. | By all which, the discrete and wise in heart may ga- | ther touching things to come, what is forewarned | vnto Men; as for the General and Publique, so | also for their Priuate and Particular. | By Robert Salter. | . . . (2 lines).

London, | Printed by William Iones dwelling in Red-crosse | streete. 1627. | 18.1x13.5cm. (8),48p.

SCLATER, William. An | Exposition | with Notes vpon | the first and second | Epistles to the Thes- | salonians. | By William Sclater | D.D. and Minister of the | Word of God at Pit- | mister in Som- | merset. |

London, | Printed for I.Parker, and are to | be sold by George Vincent at his shop in | Pauls Church-yard at the signe | of the crosse keyes. | 1627. | Wood cut border. 18.9x14.2cm (8),598;(6),307,(1)p.
Separate title page for second part: A Briefe | Exposition | With Notes, | Vpon | The Second | Epistle To The | Thessalonians. | . . .
London, | Printed by George Miller, for George Vincent, and are to be | sold at the Crosse Keyes at Pauls gate. | 1627. |
Also another copy from the library of Walter W. Law. 17.9x13.7cm.

SCOTUS, Romoaldus. Svmmarivm | Rationvm, Qvi- | bus Cancellarivs An- | gliæ Et Prolocvtor Pvcke- | ringius Elizabethæ Angliæ Reginæ persua- | serunt occidendam esse serenissimam Princi- | pem Mariam Stuartam Scotiæ Regi- | nam & Iacobi sexti Scotorum | Regis matrem: | Vna Cvm Respon- | sionibvs Reginæ An- | gliæ Et Sententia | mortis. | Qvæ Omnia Anglice | Primvm Edita Svnt, Et Lon- | dini

A Typographo Regio Im- | pressa; ac deinde varias in linguas | translata: | His Additvm Est Svpplicivm | & mors Reginæ Scotiæ, vna cum succinctis quibusdam | animaduersionibus, & confutationibus eorum, | quæ ei obiecta sunt. | Opera Romoaldi Scoti. |

Coloniæ | Sumptibus Petri Henningii, | Bibliopolæ Coloniensis. | Anno M.DC. XXVII. | 15x9.2cm (1),109p.

SCUDDER, Henry. The | Christians | Daily VValke | in holy Securitie | and Peace. | Being an Answer to these Questions, | I. How a man may doe each present dayes worke, | with Christian Chearefulnesse? | 2. How to beare each present dayes crosse with | Christian Patience? | Containing familiar directions shevving. | I. How to walke with God in the whole course | of a manslife. | 2. How to be vpright in the said walking. | 3. How to liue without taking care or thought | in any thing. | 4. How to get and keepe true peace with God; | wherein are manifold helpes to prevent and | remove damnable presumption: | also to quiet | and to ease distressed Consciences. | The first three intended onely, for private vse; | but novv (through importunity) vvith the | fourth, published for the common good. | By Henry Scudder Preacher of the Word. | . . . (3 lines).

London, | Printed by I.D. for William Sheffard, and are to | be sould at his shop in the entrance in of Popes | head Alley, out of Lumbard streete. 1627. | Line border. 14.2x8.2cm. (10),372; 294,(22)p. Preface impf. at beginning.

SENHOUSE, Richard. Fovre | Sermons | Preached At | The Covrt Vpon | seuerall occasions, | By | The Late Re- | verend And Lear- | ned Divine, Doctor | Senhovse, L. Bishop of | Carlile. (device).

London, | Printed for R.Dawlman, at the Signe of the | Bible neere the great Conduit in Fleet- | streete. 1627. | 18.1x13.4cm. (1),141p.

SIBTHORPE, Robert. Apostolike | Obedience. | Shewing the Duty of Subjects to pay | Tribute and Taxes to their Princes, accor- | ding to the Word of God, in the Law and | the Gospell, and the Rules of Religion, | and Cases of Conscience; | Determined by the Ancient Fathers, and the | best Moderne Divines; yea even by those | Neoterickes, who in some other things, put too | strict Limits to Regalitie. | A Sermon preached at Northampton, at the | Assises, for the Countie, Feb.22.1626. | By | Robert Sybthorpe, Doctor in | Divinity, Vicar of Brackley. | . . . (3 lines)

London, | Printed by M.F. for Richard Mynne, and are to be | sold at the shop in Little Britaine, at the signe of | Saint Paul, 1627. | Line border. 18.2x13.4cm. (4),36p.

SUFFRAGIUM Collegiale | Theologorvm | Magnæ Britanniæ | De | Qvinqve Contro- | versis Remonstrantium | Articulis, | Judicio Syndico prævium. | Cui adjuncta est | Concio De Gratia | Discriminante, | Habita Cantabrig. ad Clerum: per Sam. | Wardum, S. Theol. D. & Profess. D^{næ}. Margar. | Collegij. Sidneiani Præfectum. | Ab Authore jam recognita. |

Londini, | Excudebat Milo Flesher, impensis | Roberti Milbourn. 1627. | Line border. 17.4x14.1 cm. (3),105,(6),45p. (Two sub-titles).

Two parts, with separate register and pagination.

SYDENHAM, Humphrey. The | Athenian Babler. | A | Sermon | Preached At | St.Maries In Oxford, | the 9. of July, 1626. being | Act-Sunday. | By | Humphry Sydenham, Mr. of Arts, and | Fellow of Wadham College in | Oxford. |

London, | Printed for Iohn Parker. | 1627. | Line border. 17.3x13.cm. (4),156p. Photostat general t.p.

Three sub t.p.: Iacob and Esav: | Election. Reprobation. | Opened And Dis- | cvssed By Way Of | Sermon At Pavls Crosse, | March 4. 1622. | ; The | Arraignment | Of | The Arrian. | His { Beginning. | Height. | Fall. | In a Sermon preached at Pauls Crosse, | Iune 4. 1624. | Being the first Sunday in Trinitie Terme | ; Moses and Aaron | Or | The Affinitie Of | Ciuill and Ecclesiasticke power. | A Sermon Intended | for the Parliament held at Oxon, | August.7.1625. | But by reason of the sudden and vnhap- | py dissolution, then, not preach't, but since vpon | occasion, was; at St.Maries in Oxford, | the 26. of February. 1625. |

In each case the authorship and imprint are identical. Final sermon lacking. Brit. Mus. Cat. Title supplied by Mr. Edward G. Friehold, of London.

TURNER, Robert?. Maria | Stvarta, | Regina Sco- | tiæ, Dotaria | Franciæ, Hæres, An- | gliæ Et Hyberniæ, Mar- | tyr Ecclesiæ, Innocens à cæde | Darleana: | Vindice | Oberto Barnestapolio. | Continet Hæc Episto- | la historiam penè totam vitæ, quam Regina | Scotiæ egit miserè, sed exegit gloriosè.rationem | tituli præfert frons sequentis | pagellæ. | (ornament)

Coloniæ | Sumptibus Petri Henningii, | Bibliopolæ Coloniensis. | Anno M.DC. XXVII. | 15x9.2cm. (6),68,(1)p.

Appended to Romoaldus Scotus, Svmmarivm Rationvm: 1627; with double-letter register, and separate pagination.

VALENTINE, Henry. Noahs Doue: | Or | A Prayer | For The Peace | Of Iervsalem. | Delivered In A Ser- | mon at Pauls Crosse, | Decemb. 31. 1626. | By | H. Valentine, Master in Arts, | and Lecturer at Saint Donstans in the | West. London. | (device).

London, | Printed by I.H. for Iohn Marriot, and are to be sold at his shop | in Saint Donstans Church-yard. 1627. | 18x14. cm. (4),46p. Lacks pp. 41–42.

WAKE, Isaac. Rex Platonicvs: | Sive, | De Potentis- | simi Principis Ia- | cobi Britanniarum | Regis, ad illustrissimam Aca- | demiam Oxoniensem, | adventu, Aug.27. | An.1605. | Narratio | Ab Isaaco Wake Pvbli- | co Academiæ ejusdem Oratore, | tunc temporis conscripta, nunc i- | terum in lucem edita, multis | in locis auctior & e- | mendatior. | Editio Quarta. | (ornament).

Oxoniæ, | Excudebat Iohannes Lichfield | Academiæ Typographus, | 1627. | 12.4x 7.1cm. (7),238, (1, 15)p.

WARD, Samuel. A | Coale From | The Altar To | Kindle The Ho- | ly fire of Zeale. | In a Sermon preached at a generall | Visitation at Ipswich. | By Sam:Ward Preacher of Ipswich. | The fift Edition, corrected and amended. | . . . (1 line; ornament)

London, | Printed by Miles Flesher, for Iohn | Grismand in Ivie Lane at the | signe of the Gun. 1627. | Line border. 15.2x10cm. (9),66p.

Part of his Collection Of Svch Sermons: 1627; with separate register and pagination.

From the library of Walter W. Law.

WARD, Samuel. A | Collection | Of Svch Sermons | and Treatises as haue | beene written and | published | By | Mr. Samvel Ward, Prea- | cher of Ipswich, | Are here gathered into | one Volume. | The Titles whereof are in the next | page following. |

London, | Printed by M.F. for Iohn | Grismand, and are to | bee sold at his shop in Ivie | Lane, at the Signe of the | Gun. 1627. | Line border. 15.2x10cm. (9),45;(12),110;(7),126;(9),86;(8),85;(6),72;(7),54; . . . .? (6),47,(2)p.

Contains eight pieces, each with separate register and pagination. "Woe to Drunkards", missing.

From the library of Walter W. Law.

WARD, Samuel. Gratia | Discriminans. | Concio ad Clerum. | Habita Cantabrigiæ in Ec- | clesia B. Mariæ, Ian. 12. 1625. | Per | Sa: Wardum S^æ Theologiæ Docto- | rem, Professorem Theologicum D^{næ} | Margaretæ, Collegiiq̇; Sidneiani in ea- | dem Academia Præfectum. | Emendatior et auctior. | (ornaments)

Londini, | Excudebat Milo Flesher: impensis Roberti | Mylbourne. 1627. | Line border. 17.3x14.1cm. (6),45p.

Part of Suffragium Collegiale: 1627, with separate register and pagination.

WARD, Samuel. The | Happiness | Of | Practice. | By Samvel Ward, Ba- | chelor in Diuinitie, and Prea- | cher of Ipswich. | (ornament).

London, | Printed by Miles Flesher, for Iohn | Grismand in Ivie Lane at the | signe of the Gun. 1627. | Line border. 15.6x9.6cm.(6), 47, (2)p. Pages misarranged.

Also another copy from the library of Walter W. Law. 15.2x10cm.

WARD, Samuel. Iethro's | Ivstice Of | Peace. | A | Sermon Prea- | ched at a generall Assises held | at Bvry St. Edmvnds, | for the County of | Suffolke. | By Samvel VVard | Bachelour of Diuinity. | (ornament)

London, | Printed by Miles Flesher, for Iohn | Grismand in Ivie Lane at the | signe of the Gun. | 1627. | Line border. 15.2x10cm. (6),72p.

Part of his Collection Of Svch Sermons: 1627; with separate register and pagination.

From the Library of Walter W. Law.

WARD, Samuel. The | Life | Of | Faith. | By Samvel VVard | Preacher of Ipswich. | (ornament)

London, | Printed by Miles Flesher, for Iohn | Grismand in Ivie Lane at the | signe of the Gun. | 1627. | Line border. 15.2x10.cm. (12),110p.

Part of his Collection Of Svch Sermons: 1627: with separate register and pagination.

From the library of Walter W. Law.

WARD, Samuel. The | Life | Of | Faith In | Death. | Exemplified in the liuing | Speeches of Dying | Christians. | By Samvel VVard | Preacher of Ipswich. |

London, | Printed by Miles Flesher, for Iohn | Grismand, in Ivie Lane at the | signe of the Gun. | 1627. | Line border. 15.2x10cm. (7),126p.

Part of his Collection Of Svch Sermons: 1627: with separate register and pagination.

From the library of Walter W. Law.

WARD, Samuel. A | Peace-Offring | To | God | For the blessings we enjoy vnder | his Maiesties reigne, with a Thanks- | giuing for the

Princes safe returne | on Sunday the 5. of October. | 1623. | In a Sermon preached at Manitree in | Essex, on Thursday the 9. of Octo- | ber, next after his Highnesse | happy arriuall. | By Samvel Ward of Ipswich. | (ornament)

London, | Printed for Iohn Grismond. | [1627]. Line border. 15.2x10cm. (7), 54p.

Part of his Collection Of Svch Sermons: 1627; with separate register and pagination.

From the library of Walter W. Law.

WEEMSE, John. The | Povrtraitvre | Of The Image Of | God In Man. | In his three estates, of {Creation. | Restauration. | Glorification. | Digested into two parts. | The first containing, the Image of God both | in the Body and Soule of Man, and Immortalitie | of both: with a description of the seuerall | members of the Body: and the two principall | faculties of the soule, the Vnderstanding | and the Will; in which consisteth his know- | ledge, and libertie of his will. | The second containing, the passions of man in the | concupiscible and irascible part of the soule: his do- | minion ouer the creatures; also a description of | his actiue and contemplatiue life; with | his coniunct or marryed estate. | All set downe by way of collation, and cleered by sundry | distinctions, both out of the Schoolemen and | Moderne Writers. | By Iohn Weemse of Lathoquar in Scot- | land, Preacher of Christs Gospell. |

London, | Printed for Iohn Bellamie, and are to be sold at his shop, | at the signe of the three Golden Lions, in Cornhill, | neere the Royall Exchange. 1627. | Line border. 17.9x13.9 cm. (27),333p.

WHITE, Christopher. Of | Oathes: | Their | Obiect, Forme, | And Bond: | The | Pvnishment Of | Perivrie, | And | The Impietie Of Papall | Dispensations. | Deliuered in three Sermons in Oxenford, to the Vni- | uersitie; by Christopher White, B. of Diuinitie, | and Student of Christs-Church. | . . . (3 lines ; device)

Imprinted at London for Ralph Mab. 1627. | 17. x13.6 cm. (4),55p.

WILLIAMS, Griffith. Seven | Golden | Candlestickes | Holding the seauen grea- | test lights of Christian Religion. | Shewing vnto all men what | they should beleeue, and how | they ought to walke in this | life, that they may at- | taine vnto eternall | Life | By Gr: Williams Doctor of Divinity | 1627 |

Printed for Nathaniell Butter. | 19.4x14.8 cm. (34),744,(29)p.

WILSON, Thomas. A | Commentary | On The Most Divine | Epistle Of S. Pavl To | The Romanes: | Containing | For Matter, the degeneration of our Nature by | Adams Fall; and the restauration thereof, by the Grace of | Christ. Together with the perfection of Faith, | and the imbecility of Workes, in the cause of Justifi- | cation of elect sinners, before | Almighty God. | {For Forme and manner of | handling, it hath}{The Coherence and Method. | The Svmme and Scope. | The Interpretations and the Doctrines. | The Reasons and Vses of euery Text. | All which, are set downe very Familiarly and Compendiously, in | forme of a Dialogue betweene Timotheus and Silas. By | Thomas Wilson late Minister of Gods | Word, at Saint Georges Church in | Canterbvrie. | The Second Edition. | . . . (11 lines, double col; ornament).

London, | Printed by Isaac Iaggard dwelling in Aldersgate-street, and are there | to be sold, M.DC.XXVII. | Line border.   28.4x18.6cm.   (6),651,(7)p.

1628

The | APOLOGIE | Of | The Reformed | Chvrches Of | France. | VVherein are expressed the | Reasons, why they haue Ioyned | their Armies; to those of the King | of Great Brittaine. | Translated according to the French | Coppie. |

London, | Printed for Nathaniell Butter. | 1628. | 18.6x13.8 cm.   (7),55p. Preface signed John Reynolds.

ARTICLES | Agreed Vpon | By the Archbishops and Bishops | of both Prouinces, and the | whole Cleargie: | In the Conuocation holden at London, | in the yeere 1562. | For the auoiding of diuersities of opini- | ons, and for the stablishing of consent | touching true Religion. | Reprinted by His Maiesties Commandement: with | His Royall Declaration prefixed | thereunto. | (royal arms).

London, | Printed by Bonham Norton, and Iohn Bill, | Printers to the Kings most Excellent Maiestie. | M.DC.XXVIII. | 18.5x14.2cm.   (1),6,(21)p.

ARTICLES | Of | Religion, | Agreed Vpon By | The Archbishops, and Bishops, and | the rest of the Clergie of Ireland, | in the Conuocation | Holden At Dvblin In | The yeare of our Lord God 1615. for the | auoyding of Diuersities of Opinions: And | the establishing of Concent touch- | ing true Religion. | (device)

London, | Printed by R.Y. for T.Downes, and are to be sold | at the great North doore of Paules. | 1628. | Line border.   18.3x13.8cm   (2,34)p.

BARCLAY, John.   Iohn | Barclay | His | Argenis, | Translated Ovt | Of Latine Into | English: | The Prose Vpon His | Maiesties Command: | By Sir Robert Le Grys, Knight: | And the Verses by Thomas May, Esquire. | With a Clauis annexed to it for the satisfaction of the | Reader, and helping him to vnderstand, what persons were by | the Author intended, vnder the fained Names imposed | by him vpon them: | And published by his Maiesties Command. | (ornament).

London, | Printed by Felix Kyngston for Richard Meighen and | Henry Seile. 1628. | Line border.   19.2x14.2cm.(8),489p.

BERNARD, Richard.   Ruths Recompence: | Or | A Commen- | tarie Vpon | The Booke Of | Rvth: | Wherein Is Shewed Her | Happy Calling Ovt Of Her Owne | Country and People, into the fellowship and | society of the Lords Inheritance: | Her Vertvovs Life And | holy Carriage amongst them: | And Then, Her Reward In Gods | mercy, being by an honourable Marriage made | a Mother in Israel: | Deliuered in seuerall Sermons, the briefe summe | whereof is now published for the benefit of the | Church of God. | By Richard Bernard, Preacher of Gods Word at Bat- | combe in Sommerset-shire. | (ornament).

London | Printed by Felix Kyngston, and are to be sold by | Simon Waterson. 1628. | Line border. 18.2x13.6cm. (7),479p.

BURTON, Henry. Israels Fast. | Or, | A Meditation | Vpon the Seuenth Chapter | of Joshuah; A faire Prece- | dent for these | Times. | By H.B. Rector of S.Mathews | Fryday-Street. | . . . (7 lines ; lace ornament)

Printed at London. | 1628. | 18.5 x 14.2 cm. (16),38p. Epistle, signed.

BURTON, Henry. The Se- | ven Vials | Or | A briefe and plaine Exposition vp- | on the 15: and 16: Chapters of the Re- | velation, very pertinent and profitable for | the Church of God in these last times. | By H.B. Rector of Saint Matthews | Friday-street. | . . . (9 lines).

London, | Printed by William Jones, dwelling in | Red-crosse-street. 1628. | 17.8x13cm. (12),1–16,19–146p.
Cambr.Univ.Cat:5036.

BURTON, Henry. A | Tryall | Of | Private Devotions. | Or, | A Diall For The | Houres of Prayer. | By H.B. Rector of St.Mathevves | Friday-street. | . . . (7 lines)

London. | Printed for M.S. 1628. | 18.4x14.3cm. (12,87)p. Epistle &c. signed.

BYFIELD, Nicholas. The | Marrovv | Of The Oracles | Of God. | Or | Diuers Treatises, contai- | ning Directions about six of | the waightiest things can | concerne a Christian | in this life. | By N. Bifield late Preacher of | Gods Word at Isleworth in Middlesex. | The sixth Edition.

London, | Printed by T.C. for R.R. and are to be | sold by Philemon Stephens, and Christo- | pher Meredith, dwelling at the | Golden Lyon in Pauls | Churchyard, 1628. | Line border. 14.2x7.6 cm. (5),(16),748p. Six Sub-titles. Lacks pp. 485–504 and incomplete at end.

CALDERWOOD, David. The | Pastor and the Prelate, | Or | Reformation and Conformitie | shortly compared | By the Word of God, By Antiquity and | the proceedings of the Ancient Kirk, By the nature | and use of things indifferent, By the proceedings of our | ovvne Kirk, By the vveill of the Kirk and of the | peoples soules, And by the good of the com- | monvvealth and of our outvvard estate: | with | The Answer of the common & chiefest | objections against everie part: | shewing | Whether of the tvvo is to be follovved | by the true Christian and | Countrieman. | . . . (5 lines).

Anno M.DC.XXVIII. | 18.8x14.5 cm. 72p.
H&L.

CAMERON, John. A | Tract Of The | Soveraigne Iudge | Of Controversies | In Matters Of | Religion. | By Iohn Cameron Minister of the | Word of God, and Divinity Professour | in the Academie of Montauban. | Translated into English by Iohn | Vernevil. M. A. | . . . (6 lines).

Oxford. | Printed by VVilliam Turner Printer to the | famous Vniversity, and are to be sold | by Henry Curteine. 1628. | 18.3x13.8 cm. 48p.

CARLETON, George. Vita | Bernardi | Gilpini, Viri | Sanctissimi, Fa- | maqve Apvd An- | glos Aqvolinares | Celeberrimi. | A Reverendo in Christo Patre | Georgio Carletono Episcopo | Cicistrensi fideliter conscripta, et in gratiam Popu- | larium suorum, à quibus iamdiu vehementer desi- | derata est, in publicum edita. | . . . (3 lines; device)

Londini, | Excusum per Gulielmum Iones: 1628. | 18.2x14.cm. (4),58p.

CHARLES I. Instrvctions | directed from the Kings most | Excellent Maiestie, | Vnto all the Bishops of this Kingdome, | and fit to be put in execution, agreeable to | the necessitie of the Time. | (royal arms).

London, | Printed by Bonham Norton and Iohn Bill, | Printers to the Kings most | Excellent Maiestie. 1626. | 17.7x13.8cm. (1,13)p. Colophon

CHARLES I. His | Maiesties | Declaration | To All His | louing Subiects, | Of the causes which moued him to dissolue | the last Parliament. | Published by his Maiesties speciall command. | (coat of arms).

Imprinted at London by Bonham Norton and Iohn Bill, | Printers to the Kings most Excellent Maiestie. 1628. | 17.5x13.5 cm. (1),45,(1)p. Colophon.

CONN, George. Georgii Conæi | De Dvplici Statv | Religionis | Apvd Scotos | Libri Duo. | Ad Illvstriss.^{mvm} Principem | Franciscvm S.R.E. | Card.Barberinvm | Magnæ Britanniæ Protectorem. | (device).

Romæ, Typis Vaticanis. M.DC.XXVIII. | Svperiorvm Permissv. | 20.8x14.6cm. (12),176,(8)p.

COTTON, Robert Bruce. The | Danger | wherein the Kingdome | now standeth, | & | the Remedie. |

Printed. 1628. | 17.2x12.8cm. (1),21p.
Cambr.Univ.Cat:6978.

DYKE, Daniel. The Mystery | Of | Selfe-Deceiuing. | Or | A Discovrse | And Discouerie of the Deceitfulnesse | of Mans Heart. | Written by the late faithful Minister | of Gods Word, Danyel Dyke, | Batchelour in Diuinitie. | Published since his Death, by his Brother J.D. | Minister of Gods Word. | And now by him augmented and inlarged, with | two exquisite Tables, much enlightning this | whole Treatise. | . . . (5 lines).

London. | Printed by William Stansby, and are to be sold by Michaell | Sparke, in little Old-bayley in Greene-Arbour, at the | Signe of the Blew Bible, 1628. | Line border. 19.1x14.5cm. (18),364,(30)p.

FELLTHAM, Owen. Resolves | Or, | Excogitations. | A | Second Centvrie. | . . . (1 line; device).
London: | Printed for Henry Seile, at the Tygers head, | in St.Pauls Churchyard. 1628. | Line border. 19.1x13.8cm. (10),294,(2)p.
The first part is defective, 3–93p. lacking t.p., dedication and preface, if any. Apparently the third edition.
Dedication: Second Centurie, signed.

FIELD, Richard. Of | The Church, | Five Bookes. | By | Richard Field Doctor | Of Divinity And Some- | times Deane Of | Glocester. | The Second Edition Very Mvch Avg- | mented, in the third booke, and the Appendix to the same. | (device)
At Oxford | Imprinted by William Tvrner, | Printer to the famous Vniuersity. 1628. | 27.9x19.cm. (15),906p.

A | FORME Of | Prayer, | Necessary to bee vsed in these | dangerous times of Warre: | Wherein we are appointed to Fast, ac- | cording to His Maiesties Proclamation; | For the preseruation of His Maiestie, | and His Realmes, and all refor- | med Chvrches. | (royal coat of arms)
London, | Printed by Bonham Norton, and Iohn Bill, | Printers to the Kings most Excellent Maiestie. | M.DC.XXVIII. | 18.2x14.0 cm. (3,89)p.

HODSON, Phineas. The | King's | Reqvest: | Or, | David's Desire. | A Sermon preached at the last ge- | nerall Fast holden at Yorke, the | 21. of Aprill last. | By Phinees Hodson Doctour of | Diuinity, and Chancellour of the Metropo- | liticall Church of St. Peter-Yorke. | (device)
London, | Printed by Tho.Harper, for Edward | Blount, and are to be sold at his shop | in Pauls Church-yard. 1628. | 17.5x13.9cm. (1),34p.

JACKSON, Thomas. A | Treatise | Of The Divine | Essence And | Attributes. | By | Thomas Iackson Doctor in | Diuinitie, Chaplaine to his Majestie in or- | dinary, and Vicar of S.Nicolas Church in | the Towne of Newcastle | upon Tyne. | The first Part. | (ornament).
London, | Printed by M.F. for Iohn Clarke, and are to be | sold at his shop under St.Peters Church in | Cornhill. 1628. | Line border. 18.1 x 13.4 cm. (12), 236p.

KING, Henry. An | Exposition | Vpon | The Lords Prayer. | Deliuered in certaine Sermons, in the | Cathedrall Church of S.Pavl. | By Henry King Archdeacon of Colchester, | and Residentiary of the same Church. | . . . (3 lines; device).
London, | Printed by Iohn Hauiland, and are to be sold by Iohn | Partridge in Pauls Church-yard, at the signe of | the Sunne. 1628. | Line border. 18.8x14cm. (6),365p.

LEIGHTON, Alexander. An | Appeal | To the | Parliament; | Or, | Sions Plea against the Prelacie. | The summe whereoff is delivered in a Decade | of Positions . | Jn the handling whereoff, the Lord Bishops, and | their appurtenances are manifestlie proved, both by di- | vine and humane lawes, to be intruders vpon the Privi- | ledges of Christ, of the King, and of the Common-weal: | And therefore vpon good evidence given, she hartelie | desireth a Iudgement and execution. | . . . (10lines: ornament)

Printed the year & moneth wherein Rochell was lost | [Sept. 1628.] 18.7x13.5 cm. (16),344pp.
Cf.Cambr.Univ.Cat.6980.
Also a reprint, Edinburgh, 1842.

LYNDE, Humphrey. Via tuta: | The | Safe VVay. | Leading all Christi- | ans, by the testimonies, and | confessions of our best learned | Aduersaries, to the true, anci- | ent, and Catholique faith, | now professed in the | Church of England. | By | Hvmfrey Lynde Knight. | . . . (6 lines).

London, | Printed by G.M. for Robert Milbourne, and are | to be sold at his shop in Pauls Churchyard, | at the signe of the Gray-hound. 1628. | Line border. 13.2x7.5cm.(24),323,(1)p.

MATTHIEU, Pierre. The | Povverfvll | Favorite, | Or | The life of | Ælius Seianus. | By P. M. . . . (2 lines; ornament).

Printed at Paris. | 1628. 16.8x12.2cm. (1),62p.
Cambr.Univ.Cat:6222.

MORTON, Thomas. The | Grand | Impostvre | Of | The (now) Chvrch Of | Rome: | Manifested in this one Article of the New | Romane Creede, viz. | " The Holy, Catholike, and Apostolike Romane Church, | " Mother and Mistresse of all other Churches, with- | " out which there is no Saluation. | Proued to be a New, False, Sacrilegious, Scandalous, Schisma- | ticall, Hereticall, and Blasphemous Article (respectiuely) | and euery way Damnable. | The Last Chapter containeth a Determination of the whole | Question, concerning the Separation of Protestants from the | present Church of Rome: whereby may be discerned, whether Side | is to be accounted Schismaticall, or may more iustly pleade | Soules Salvation. | By the B. of Couentrie & Lichfield. | The second Edition, Reuised and Supplyed with necessary Additions (for | Corroboration of sundry Points) which in the Context are thus | marked at the beginning ☞ ; and ending ¶. But the meere | Marginall Additions are thus inserted ¶ betweene ¶. |

London, | Printed by George Miller for Robert Milbovrne, and are | to be sold at his shop in Pauls Church-yard at the signe | of the Gray-hound. 1628. | 19.x 14.3cm. (26),419,(1)p. col. Pp. 98-111, 298-299 mispaged. Title in red and black.
Cambr. Univ. Libr. 4425.

OWEN, Lewis. The | Vnmasking | Of | All popish Monks, Friers, and Iesuits. | Or, | A Treatise of their Genealogie, beginnings, | proceedings, and present state. | Together with some briefe obseruations of their | Treasons, Murders, Fornications, Impostures, Blasphemies, | and sundry other abominable impieties. | Written as a Caueat or forewarning for Great Britaine | to take heed in time of these Romish Locusts. | By Lewis Owen. | . . . (2 lines)

London, | Printed by J.H. for George Gibs, and are | to be sold at his Shop at the signe of the Flower- | de-Luce in Popes head Alley. | 1628. | 18.8x14.4cm. (8),1-160,159-164p.

PAOLO, Servita. A | Discovrse | Vpon the Reasons | Of The Reso-
lvtion | taken in the Valteline against the ty- | ranny of the Grisons
and | Heretiqves. | To the most Mighty Catholique King | of Spaine,
D. Phillip the Third. | VVritten in Italian by the Author of | The
Councell of Trent. | And | Faithfully translated into English. | With
the Translators Epistle to the Commons House | of Parliament. |
(ornament).
London, | Printed for William Lee, at the Turkes head in Fleetstreet, | next to
the Miter and Phœnix. 1628. | 18.8x14.cm.   (1),101p.
Cambr.Univ.Cat:4689.

PARR, Richard. The | End Of The | Perfect Man. | A | Sermon
Preached At | the Buriall of the right Honourable Sir | Robert Spencer
Knight | Baron Spencer of Wormeleighton, | Novemb.6.1627. in Brayn-
ton | Church in Nor- | thamptonshire. | By | Richard Parre Bachelour
in | Divinity, and late Fellow of Brasen-nose Col- | ledge in Oxford,
now Rector of | Ladbrook in Warwickshire. | (device)
Oxford, | Printed by William Tvrner, Printer to the | famous Vniversitie. An.
Dom. 1628. | 18x13.4cm.   (8),29,(5)p.

PRYNNE, William.   A | Briefe Svrvay | And Censvre Of | Mr
Cozens His Couze- | ning Deuotions. | Prouing both the forme and
matter of | Mr Cozens his Booke of Priuate Deuotions, or the | Houres
of Prayer, lately published, to be meerely Po- | pish: to differ from
the priuate Prayers Authorized | by Queene Elizabeth 1560. to be
transcribed out | of Popish Authors, with which they are | here para-
lelled: and to be scandalous | and preiudiciall to our Church, and |
aduantagious onely to the | Church of Rome. | By William Prynne
Gent. Hospitij Lincolniensis. | . . . (7 lines; ornament).
Printed at London. 1628. | 18.1 x 13.4 cm   (24), 104p.
Suppressed and burned privately by the high commission at the instance of
archbishop Laud.

PRYNNE, William.   Healthes: | Sicknesse. | Or | A Compendiovs
And | briefe Discourse; prouing, the Drinking, and | Pledging of
Healthes, to be Sinfull, and vtterly Vnlawfull | vnto Christians; by
Arguments, Scriptures, Fathers, Moderne | Diuines, Christian Authors,
Historians, Councels; Imperiall | Lawes and Constitutions; and by the
voyce, and verdict of prophane, | and Heathen Writers: Wherein all
those ordinary Obiections, | Excuses, or Pretences, which are made to
Iustifie, Extenuate, or | excuse the Drinking, or Pledging of Healthes,
are | likewise cleared and answered. | By William Prynne Gent. Hos-
pitii Lincolniensis. | . . . (16 lines).
Printed in London. 1628. | 17.2x13.cm.   (32),95p. Mispagings.

PRZYPKOWSKI, Samuel.   Anonymi | Dissertatio | De | Pace Et
Concordia | Ecclesiæ. | Edita per | Irænevm Philalethen. | (ornament).
Elevtheropoli. | Typis Godfridi Philadelphi. | Anno | M.DC.XXVIII. | 12.x7.
cm.   (8),94,(6)p.
DNB.24:32b.

R., J. The Spy | Discovering the Danger of | Arminian Heresie | and | Spanish Trecherie: | Written by I. R. | . . . (2 lines; device).

Printed at Strasburgh 1628. | 17.8x13.4 cm. (4,50)p.
B.M.Cat, ascribes to J:R[hodes].

RAINOLDS, John. V. Cl. | D. Ioannis Rainoldi, | Olim Græcæ | Lingvæ Prælec- | toris In Collegio | Corporis Christi | apud Oxonienses. | Orationes Duodecem; cum alijs | quibusdam opusculis. | Adiecta Est Oratio | Funebris in obitu eiusdem, habita | à M. Isaaco Wake, | Oratore Publico. | (ornament).

Londini, | Excudebat Gulielmus Stansbeius, & | vœnum dantur à Roberto Allot, | sub signo Vrsi in Cœmiterio | Paulino. 1628. | 12.4x7 cm. (6),548p. Three sub-title pages.

RALEIGH, Walter. The | Prerogative | Of | Parliaments | in England: | Proued in a Dialogue (pro & | contra) betweene a Councellour | of State and a Iustice | of Peace. | Written by the worthy (much lacked and | lamented) Sir Walter Raleigh Knight, | deceased. | Dedicated to the Kings Maiestie, and to the | House of Parlament now assembled. | Preserued to be now happily | (in these distracted Times) | Published, and |

Printed at Midelburge. | 1628. | 18.7x13.6 cm. (7),65,(1)p.

ROBINSON, John. Nevv | Essayes | Or | Observations | Divine and Morall. | Collected out of the holy Scriptures, Anci- | ent and Moderne Writers, both Diuine | and Humane. | As also out of the great volume of Mens manners. | Tending to the furtherance of Knowledge and Vertue. | By Iohn Robinson. | . . . (4 lines; ornament).

Printed, Anno M DC XXVIII. | 18.2x13.9cm. (4),324,(2)p.

RUDYERD, Benjamin. Sir | Beniamin Rvdierd | His Speech In Behalfe | Of The Clergie, And Of | Parishes miserably destitute of In- | struction, through want of | Maintenance. | Confirmed By The | Testimonies of Bishop Iewel, | Master Perkins, and Sir | Henry Spelman. | . . . (5 lines).

Printed at Oxford, 1628. | And are to be sold by Ph. Stephens and Ch. Meredith at the | Golden Lyon in Pauls Church-yard. | 18x13.6 cm. (1),14p.

SANDERS, Nicholas. Vera Et Sincera | Historia | Schismatis | Anglicani, | De eius Origine ac Progressu: | Tribus libris fideliter conscripta, ab | R.D.Nicolao Sandero | Anglo, Doct: Theologo; | aucta per | Edvardvm Rishtonvm. | Nunc postremùm Appendice ex R.P. Petri Ribadeneiræ | libris, aucta & castigatius edita. |

Coloniæ Agrippinæ | Apud Petrvm Henningivm | Sub signo Cuniculi. | Anno | M.DC XX.VIII. | 15x9.2cm. (16),348,(22),142p.

SMART, Peter. A | Sermon | Preached In | The Cathedrall | Chvrch Of Dvrham. | Ivly 7. 1628. | By Peter Smart. | . . . (3 lines; ornament).

Imprinted, 1628. | 18.7x14.5 cm. (1),38 p.
Burned by order of the bishops in 1628, and the author imprisoned for twelve years.

SMART, Peter. The | Vanitie & Downe-fall | Of | Svperstitiovs Popish | Ceremonies: | Or, | A Sermon Preached In The | Cathedrall Church of Durham by | one Mr. Peter Smart, a Præ- | bend there, July 27. | 1628. | Contayning Not Onely An | Historicall relation of all those severall Popish | Ceremonies and practises which Mr. Iohn | Cosens hath lately brought into | the said Cathedrall Church: | But likewise a punctuall confutation of | them; especially of erecting Altars, | and cringing to them, (a practise | much in vse of late) and of | praying towards the | East. | . . . (9 lines).

Printed at Edenborough in Scotland. 1628. | By the Heyres of Robert Charteris. | 17.5x13.3cm. (1),24p.

SMITH, Samuel. Davids | Blessed | Man: | Or, | A Short Expositi- | on Vpon The First | Psalme, directing a man to | true Happinesse. | Wherein the Estate and Condition | of all Man-kind is layd downe both | for this life, and that which is | to come. | The sixt Edition profitably amplified | by the Author | Samvel Smith, Preacher of the | Word of God at Prittlewell in Essex. | . . . (2 lines).

London: | Printed by Nicholas Okes and Iohn | Norton, and are to be sold by Francis | Falkner at his shop neare S.Mar- | garets Hill in Southwark. 1628. | Line border. 13.8x8.4cm.(20),315,(1)p.

SPARKE, William. The | Mystery | Of | Godlinesse: | A | Generall Discovrse | Of The Reason That Is | In Christian Religion. | By William Sparke Divinity Rea- | der at Magd:Coll: in Oxford, and Par- | son of Blechly in Buckingham-shire. | . . . (8 lines).

Oxford | Printed for William Webb. | 1628. | 18.1x14.2cm. (15),78,78p. Colophon.

VERSTEGAN, Richard. A | Restitvtion | of | Decayed Intelligence: | In antiquities. | Concerning the most noble and renow- | ned English Nation. | By the studie and trauell of R.V. | Dedicated vnto the Kings most excellent Maiestie. | . . . (cut: tower of Babel; Nationum Origo. |

London, | Printed by Iohn Bill, Printer to the Kings | most Excellent Maiestie. 1628. | 17.9x13.5cm.(24),338,(12)p. Title in black and red.

Dedication to James I, signed.

WARD, Samuel. Balme from Gilead | To | Recouer Conscience. | In a Sermon Preached at Pauls-Crosse, | Octob.20.1616. | By Samvel Ward, Bach. of Diuinitie, | and Preacher of Ipswich. | (device)

London, | Printed by G.M. for Edward Brewster. | 1628. | Line border. 15.2x10 cm. (8),85p.

Part of his Collection of Svch Sermons: 1627: with separate register and pagination.

From the library of Walter W. Law.

WHITE, Anthony. Trvth | And Error | Discovered | In Two Sermons In St Ma- | ries in Oxford. | By Antony White Master of Arts | of Corpus Christi Colledge in Oxford. | (device).

Oxford | Printed by Iohn Lichfield, Printer | to the Famous Vniversity for | Henry Curteine. | 1628. | Line border. 17.3x13.2cm. (4),1–32p. Impf.

WILLIAMS, John. Perseuerantia Sanctorum. | A | Sermon | Of Persevering In | Patience, Repentance, and Hu- | miliation, in time of Afflictions, | Preached before the Lords of the Parlia- | ment, at the last Generall Fast, vpon Ash- | wednesday, the 18. day of February 1628. At | the Collegiat Church of S.Peter in | Westminster. | By the Right Honorable, and Right | Reuerend Father in God, Iohn, Lord Bi- | shop of Lincolne, Deane of the sayd | Church. | And now published, by their Lordships order, | and direction. |

London, | Printed by Iohn Bill, Printer to the Kings most | Excellent Maiestie. 1628. | 18. x14.1 cm. (1),58p. (Pp. 51-54 missing.)

1629

AMES, William. Medvlla | S.S. Theologiæ, | Ex Sacris literis, earumque, inter- | pretibus, extracta, & metho- | dicè disposita per | Gvilielmvm Amesivm | S.S. Theologiæ Doctorem ac Professorem, | in illustri Frisiorum Academia | quæ est Franekeræ, | In fine adjuncta est disputatio de fidei | Divinæ veritate. | Editio Tertia priori longè correctior. | (ornament).

Londini, | Apud Robertvm Allottvm. | M DC XXIX. | 13.5x7.8cm.(10), 469p.

ANDREWES, Lancelot. Reverendi | In Christo | Patris, | Lanceloti, | Episcopi VVin- | toniensis, | Opvscvla Qvædam | Posthvma. | device).

Londini, | Excudebat Felix Kyngston pro R.B. | & Andræa Hebb. 1629. | Line border. 21.1x15.6cm. (11),200;(3),87p.

Two parts, with separate registers and pagination. Nine sub. t.p.

ANDREWES, Lancelot. Strictvræ: | Or, | A Briefe | Ansvver To The | XVIII. Chapter of the first Booke of | Cardinall Perron's Reply written | in French, to King Iames — his Answer | written by Mr. Casavbon in | Latine. | (device).

London, | Imprinted by Felix Kyngston for R.B. and | Andrew Hebb. 1629. | Line border. 21.1x15.6cm. (1),87p.

Part of his Two Ansvvers: 1629; with separate register and pagination. One sub. t.p.

ANDREWES, Lancelot. Two | Ansvvers | To Cardinall | Perron, | And Tvvo | Speeches In The | Starr-Chamber: | By | The Right Reverend Father | In God, Lancelot, Late | Bishop of VVinchester. | (device).

London, | Printed by Felix Kyngston for Richard Badger | and Andrew Hebb. 1629. | Line border. 21.1x15.6cm. (3),87p.

Second part of his Opvscvla Qvædam Posthvma: 1629. with separate register and pagination.

ARTICLES | Of | Religion, | Agreed Vpon By | The Archbishops, and Bishops, and | the rest of the Clergie of Ireland, | in the Conuocation | Holden At Dvblin In | The yeare of our Lord God 1615.

for the | auoyding of Diuersities of Opinions, And | the establishing of Concent tou- | ching true Religion. | (device)

London, | Printed for Thomas Downes. | 1629. | Line border. 17.8x13.9cm. (2,34)p.

BENEFIELD, Sebastian. A Commentary | Or | Exposition | Vpon The First | Chapter of the Prophecie of | Amos. | Deliuered | In XXI. Sermons in the Parish Church | of Meysey-Hampton in the | Diocesse of Glocester. | By | Sebastian Benefield Doctor of Diui- | nity, and fellow of Corpus Christi College | in Oxford. | . . . (2 lines: ornament).

London, | Printed by John Hauiland, and are to be | sold by Hugh Perry at the Harrow in | Britaines Burse. 1629. | 18x13.8cm. (1),264p.

BENEFIELD, Sebastian. A Commentary | Or | Exposition | Vpon The Third | Chapter of the Prophecie of | Amos. | Deliuered | In XVII. Sermons in the Parish Church | of Meysey-Hampton in the | Diocesse of Glocester. | By | Sebastian Benefield | Doctor of Diuinitie. | . . . (2 lines; ornament).

London, | Printed by John Hauiland, and are to be | sold by Hugh Perry at the Harrow in | Britaines Burse. 1629. | 18.3x14.1cm. (7),314p.

BOLTON, Edmund. The | Cities | Advocate, | In This Case Or Qve- | stion of Honor and Armes; | Whether Apprentiship extinguisheth Gentry? | Containing a cleare Refutation of the perni- | cious common errour affirming it, swal- | lowed by Erasmus of Roterdam, Sir Thomas | Smith in his Common-weale, Sir John | Fern in his Blazon, Raphe Broke | Yorke Herald, and others. | With the Copies or Transcripts of three Letters which | gaue occasion of this worke. | . . . (2 lines).

London, | Printed for William Lee, at the Signe of the Turkes Head | next to the Miter and Phœnix in Fleet-street. | 1629. | 17.8x13.9cm. (18),61,(1)p. Plate on p. 6.
H&L, new ed. DNB. 5:327a. Gift of Clarence S. Brigham

BOYS, John. The | Workes Of | Iohn Boys | Doctor in Diuinitie | and Deane of | Canterburie |

Imprinted for William Aspley | Anno 1629 | Engr. t.p. 28.8x18.8cm.(1),1–562, (4), 563–988,(10)p. 2 Sub t.p.

A | BREEVE | Of Ovr | Holy Father | The Pope | To The King. | Vpon the taking of Rochell. | (ornament).

Printed at Paris in St.James street by Ed- | mond Martin, lying at the Golden Sunne. | 1629. | With allowance from authority. | 17.9x12.9cm. (1),4;(3),9;(1), 3; 6p.

BURGESS, Cornelius. Baptismall | Regeneration | of Elect Infants, | Professed by the Church of | England, according to the Scriptures, | the Primitiue Church, the pre- | sent Reformed Churches, and | many particular Di- | vines apart. | By Cor: Bvrges, Dr of Divinity, and | one of his Maiesties Chaplaines | in Ordinary. | . . . (6 lines).

At Oxford, | Printed by I. L. for Henry Curteyn. | Ann. Dom. 1629. | Arch. border. 16.8x13 cm. (16),347p.

BURRELL, Percival. Sutton's | Synagogve | Or, | The English | Centvrjon: | Shewing the vnparrallelled bounty | of Protestant piety. | By | Perci. Bvrrell, Preacher at King Iames his | Hospitall in the Charterhouse. | . . . (4 lines: device).

Printed at London, by T.C. for Ralph Mabb. 1629. | Line border. 17.3x13.2cm. (4),25p.

BURTON, Henry. Babel no Bethel. | That is, | The Church of Rome no true visible | Church of Christ. | In answer to Hugh Cholmley's Challenge, and | Rob:Butterfields Maschil, two masculine | Champions for the Synagogue | of Rome. | By H.B. Rector of St. Mathews Friday-street. | . . . (15 lines)

Printed for M.S. 1629. | 18x13.6 cm. (24),131p.
Epistle Dedicatorie, and dedication, signed.
Suppressed and burned privately by the high commission at the instance of archbishop Laud.

BURTON, Henry. Trvth's | Triumph | Over Trent: | Or, | The Great Gvlfe | Betweene | Sion and Babylon. | That Is, | The vnreconcileable opposition betweene the | Apostolicke Church of Christ, and the Apostate | Synagogue of Antichrist, in the maine and fun- | damentall Doctrine of Ivstification, for which | the Church of England Christs Spouse, hath iust- | ly, through Gods mercie, for these manie yeares, ac- | cording to Christs voyce, separated her selfe from | Babylon, with whom from henceforth she must hold | no Communion. | By H.B. Rector of S.Mathews Friday-Street. | . . . (5 lines).

London, | Printed for Mich. Sparke. 1629. | 18.1x13.5cm. (15),373p. Lacks pp. 117-124.

CARPENTER, Nathaniel. Achitophel, | Or, | The Pictvre Of A | Wicked Politician. | Diuided into three Parts. | . . . (6 lines; devices).

Printed for M.S. 1629. | 18.3x14.cm. (5),64p.
Cambr.Univ.Cat:7411. Epistle Dedicatorie, signed N.C.

CHALONER, Edward. Six | Sermons | Now First | Pvblished, | Preached by that learned and | worthy Divine Edward | Chaloner lately deceas'd, Dr in | Divinity, sometimes Cha- | plaine in Ordinary to our | Soveraigne K. Iames, | and to his Maiesty | that novv is; and late | Principall of Al- | ban Hall in | Oxford. | Printed according to the Author's | coppies, written with his owne hand. | (device)

At Oxford, | Printed by W. Turner, for Henry | Curteyn. Ann. Dom. | 1629. | Arch border. 18x13.4 cm. (8),150,(1)p.

CHARLES I. (His Majesties Determi- | nation vpon the first generall Submissions. |)

Colophon: At Edinburgh, Printed by the Heires of Thomas Finlason, his M. Printer. | [1629]. 25.8x16.3cm. 22p.

The | COLLEGIAT | Svffrage | Of The Divines | Of Great | Britaine, | Concerning The | Five Articles | Controverted In | the Low Countries. | VVhich Suffrage was by them delivered | in the Synod of Dort, March 6. Anno 1619. | Being their vote or voice foregoing | the joint and publique judgment | of that Synod. |

London, | Printed for Robert Milbourne, and are to be sold at | his Shop in Pauls Churchyard at the signe of the | Greyhound. 1629. | Line border. 18.4x13.8 cm. (3),178p.

CONN, George. Georgii Conæi | Assertionvm | Catholicarvm | Libri Tres. | In quibus ex solo scripto Dei verbo præcipua hæ- | resum ætatis nostræ dogmata refelluntur. | Ad Sanctissimvm D.N. | Vrbanvm VIII. | Veræ, & Catholicæ Ecclesiæ Pon- | tificem Maximum. | . . . (1 line; device).

Romæ, Apud Hæredem Bartholomæi Zannetti. 1629. | Svperiorvm Permissv. | 21.2x15.5cm. (16),157,(2)p. Colophon.

COOKE, Richard. A | White Sheete, | Or | A Warning for Whoremongers. | A | Sermon preached in the Parish | Church of St.Swithins by London-stone, the | 19. of Iuly, Anno Domi: 1629. the day | appointed by | Honorable authoritie, for penance | to be done, by an Inhabitant there, for | fornication, continued more then two yeares, | with his Maide-servant. | By | Richard Cooke B: of D: and Parson there. | . . . (4 lines).

London, | Printed by Iohn Dawson, for Henry Overton, | and are to be sold at the entrance into Popes-head- | Alley, out of Lumbard-streete. | 1629. | Line border. 20.3x15.5cm. (7),40p.

COWPER, William. The | Workes Of | Mr Williā Cowper | Late Bishop of Galloway | Now newly collected into one | Volume. | Whereunto is added a comentary | on the Reuelation neuer before | published. | Also | An Alphabeticall Table for the | finding out the principall heads | contained in euery Booke. | The second Edition. |

London | Imprinted for Robert Allott, and are | to be sold at his shop in Paules Church- | yard, at the signe of ye blacke Beare. | 1629. | 32x21cm.(6),1122,(20)p

CULVERWELL, Ezekiel. A | Treatise | Of Faith. | Wherein is declared, how | a man may liue by Faith, and | finde reliefe in all his necessities. | Applyed especially vnto the vse of the | weakest Christians. | By Ezekiel Cvlverwell. | The iust shall liue by faith. | The sixth Edition, corrected and | amended by the author. | . . . (6 lines).

London, | printed by E.A. for Henry Ouerton, and | are to be sold at his Shop, at the entring | in of Popes-head Alley, out of | Lumbard streete. 1629. | Line border. 14.2x8.3cm (35),527,17,(21)p.

Incorporated is another tract: The | VVay To | A Blessed E- | state In | This Life. | Same imprint 1630. with separate register and pagination

DENT, Arthur. The | Plaine-Mans | Path-Way | To Heaven. | Wherein euery man may cleerly | see whether he shall be saued | or damned. | Set forth Dialogue-wise, for the | better vnderstanding of | the simple. | By Arth. Dent, Preacher of the Word | of God at South

Shoobery in Essex. | The twentieth Edition. | Corrected and amended: with a Table of all the | principall matters; and three prayers necessary | to be vsed in priuate families hereunto added. | . . . (4 lines).

London, | Printed by H.L. for George Lathum, in Pauls | Church-yard, at the signe of the Bi- | shops head. 1629. | Lace border. 14.6x9.3cm. (7),393,(6 , 24)p.
Also another copy from the library of Walter W. Law. 13.7x9.cm.

DOUGHTY, John. Two | New Sermons, | Preached In | Oxford, | fitted for these times. | The one of Diuine Mysteries: | The other of Church-Schismes, | but the Vnity of Orthodox | Professors. | By J. D. | With speciall Licence. |

London, | Printed for, M. S. 1629. | Line border. 17.9x13.7 cm. (1),26,26p.
DNB.15:258a.

FARMER, Richard. A | Sermon | Preached At | Pavls Crosse | On Sunday, the eight and | twentieth day of Iune. | 1629. | By Richard Farmer, sometimes | of Pembroke-Hall in Cambridge, now Parson | of Charwelton in the County | of Northampton. | (ornament)

London: | Printed for Iames Bovvler, dwel- | ling at the signe of the Marigold in Pauls | Churchyard. 1629. | 16.9x12.8 cm. (4),40p.

FEATLEY, Daniel. Cygnea Cantio: | Or, | Learned | Decisions, | And Most | Prvdent And Poivs | Directions | For Stvdents | In Divinitie; | Delivered by our late Soveraigne of | Happie Memorie, | King Iames, | At White Hall a few weekes before | his Death. | . . . (2 lines).

London, | Printed for Robert Mylbourne at the Signe of the | Greyhound in Pauls Churchyard. 1629. | 17.6x13.9 cm. (7),41p.
Epistle Dedicatory, signed.

FEATLEY, John. A | Sermon | Preached To | The Nobely-De- | serving Gentleman, | Sir Thomas Warner: | And the rest of his Companie: | Bound to the West-Indies. | For their Farevvell: | At St. Buttolphs, Aldersgate, London. | Septemb.6.1629. | By | Iohn Featly, Preacher of | the Word of God. |

London: | Printed for Nicholas Bourne, at the South entrance | of the Royall Exchange. 1629. | Line border. 18.7 x 13.7 cm. (4),34p.

FONSECA, Christoval de. Devovt | Contemplations | Expressed | In two and Fortie Sermons | Vpon all ye Quadragesimall | Gospells | Written in Spanish | by | Fr. Ch. de Fonseca | (ornament). Englished by J.M. of | Magdalen Colledge | in Oxford. |

London | Printed by Adam Islip | Anno Domini 1629. | Engr. t.p. with vignettes. 29.3x19cm. (6), 648, (12)p.

FORBES, John. Irenicum | Amatoribvs | Veritatis Et | Pacis In Eccle- | sia Scoticana. | Prece & studio | Ioannis Forbesii, SS. Theologiæ | Doctoris, & ejusdem Professoris | in Academia Aberdoniensi. | . . . (9 lines; ornament).

Aberdoniæ, | Excvdebat Edvardvs Rabanvs. | Cum Privilegio. 1629. | 17.6x13.7 cm. (4),467p.

The | FORM and Manner | Of | Making & Consecrating | Bishops, | Priests, | And | Deacons: | According to the | Appointment | Of The | Church of England. |

    London, | Printed by Bonham Norton and John Bill, | Printers to the Kings most Excellent | Majesty. 1629. | Border. Colophon: Imprynted at London in Fletestrete. at the | sygne of the Sonne, by me John Byddell. | Cum priuilegio. Anno 1536. | 19.5x15.2cm. Pp. 95–99, 200–226, of Sparrow's Collection: 1661. Also reprinted in the editions of 1675 and 1684.

    GAULE, John. Distractions, | Or | The Holy Madnesse. | Feruently (not Furiously) | inraged against Euill Men; or | against their Euills. | Wherein the Naughty are disco- | uered to Themselues, and Others: and | may here see at once, Who they Are; | What they Doe; And How | they Ought. | Somewhat Delightfull, but Fruitfull | altogether: as Ordered to please | a little; but Aymed to | profit much. | By Iohn Gavle, | Vtriusque olim Academiæ. | (ornament).

    London, | Printed by Iohn Haviland, | for Robert Allot. 1629. | Line border. 14.1x8. cm. (27),490(1)p.

    GAULE, John. Practiqve | Theories: | Or, | Votiue Speculations, vpon | Iesvs | Christs { Prediction. | Jncarnation. | Passion. | Resurrection. | Or, The | Same{Yesterday,sc. | from the | Beginning, {Foretold. | To day.sc. | in Time, {Borne. | Dead. | For euer.sc. | to Eternity, {Risen againe. | Vnder which Foure Heads (as the Foure Riuers | inclosing Paradice) are contained all, and here cou- | ched most of the Mysteries of Mans Redemption. | By Iohn Gavle. |

    London, | Printed for Iames Bowler. | (1629) Line border. 13.9x7.6cm.(21), 425,(1)p. Engr. fore t.p. with date. Eight vignettes.

    HALL, Joseph. An | Ansvver | To Pope Vr- | ban His Invr- | banity, Expressed | In A Breve Sent To Lo- | wis the French King, exasperating | him against the Protestants in France. | VVritten in Latine by the Right | Reverend Father in God, Ioseph | Lord Bishop of Exeter. | Translated into English by B. S. | . . . (2 lines).

    Printed at London by William Jones for Ni- | colas Bourne, at the South Entrance of the | Royall Exchange. 1629. | 19.2x14.4 cm. (4),12,(1),4,(3),9,(1),3,6p. Two sub-title-pages.

    HALL, Joseph. The | Reconciler: | Or | An Epistle Pacificatorie of | the seeming differences of opi- | nion concerning the true | being and visibilitie of the | Roman Church. | Enlarged | With the addition of Letters of | Resolution, for that purpose, | from some famous Divines | of our Chvrch. | By Jos: Exon. |

    London, | Printed for Nath: Bvtter. | 1629. | Line border. 16.9x11. cm. (1), 148p. Pages 45–60 omitted in numbering.

    HILDERSAM, Arthur. Lectvres | Vpon | The Fovrth Of | Iohn. | Preached | At Ashby-Delazovch | In Leicester-shire, | By Arthvr Hildersam. | . . . (5 lines).

    Printed at London by G.M. for Edward | Brewster, & are to be sold in Pauls Church- | yard, at the signe of the Bible, 1629. | 26x17.8cm. (20),457p. T.p. supplied

JACKSON, Thomas. A | Treatise | Of The Divine | Essence And | Attribvtes. | The Second Part. | Containing | The Attribute of Omnipotency, of | Creation and Providence, &c. | By Thomas Iackson Doctor in | Divinitie, Chaplaine to his Majestie in or- | dinary, and Vicar of S.Nicolas Church in | the Towne of Newcastle | vpon Tyne. |

London, | Printed for Iohn Clarke, and are to be | sold at his shop under St. Peters Church in | Cornehill. 1629. | Line border. 18.1x13.4cm. (8),405p.

KELLISON, Matthew. A | Treatise | Of The | Hierarchie | And Divers Orders | Of The Chvrch | Against The Anar- | chie Of Calvin. | Composed by Matthevv Kellison, | Doctour of Diuinitie, &c. | . . . (6 lines; ornament).

Printed at Doway by Gerard Pinchon, | at the signe of Coleyn, 1629. | 16.8x11.1 cm. (44),420 p.

LYNDE, Humphrey. Via Tvta: | The | Safe Way: | Leading all Christians, by the | testimonies, and confessions of our best | learned Aduersaries, to the true, anci- | ent, and Catholike faith, now pro- | fessed in the Church of | England. | By Hvmfrey Lynde, | Knight. | . . . (3 lines). The third Edition reuised by the Author. |

London, | Printed by F.K. for Robert Milbourne, | and are to be sold at his shop, in Pavls | Church-yard, at the signe of the | Gray-Hound. 1629. | 13.7x7.7 cm. (44),332,(7)p.

MAYER, John. Praxis Theologica: | Or, | The Epistle Of | the Apostle St Iames | Resolved, Expovnded, And | Preached vpon by way of Doc- | trine and Vse. | For the benefit and instruction of all Christian | people, and for the helpe and direction of | yong practisers in Theology. | To which is added an Alphabeticall Table of the | distinct Doctrines heere handled, beeing a great part of | the whole body of Doctrines arising out of | the holy Scriptures. | By Iohn Mayer, Doctor of Diuinity. | (ornament).

At London | Printed by I.B. for Robert Bostocke, and | are to be sold at his shop in Pauls Churchyard at the | signe of the Kings head. 1629. | 17.7x13.4cm. (24),331;267;182p

Chapters iv and v have continuous register, but separate paginations.

Also another copy from the library of Walter W. Law. 17.5x13.2cm.

MORTON, Thomas. A | Treatise Of | The Three- | Fold State | Of Man, | Or, | An Anatomie of the Soule. | Wherein | is handled, {1 His Created Holinesse | in his Innocencie. | 2. His Sinfulnesse since | the Fall of Adam. | 3. His Renewed holinesse | in his Regeneration. | By Tho: Morton. | . . . (8 lines)

London. | Printed by B.A. and T.F. for Rob: | Davvlman, at the Brazen Serpent in | Pauls Church-yard 1629. | Line border. 13.6x7.6cm. (28),639p.

OWEN, Lewis. Specvlvm Jesviticvm. | Or, | The Iesvites | Looking- | Glasse. | VVherein they may behold Jgnatius | (their Patron) his Progresse, their owne | Pilgrimage: His life, their beginning, | proceedings, propagation, and | present state, or greatnesse. | Together with a true Catalogue of all their | Colledges, profess'd Houses, Houses of Approbation, | Seminaries, and Houses of Residence in all parts of the | world. And lastly, the true number of the Fellowes of | their Societie, taken out of their owne | Bookes and Catalogues. | Which may serue as a fore-warning for England, to chase | away in time, this trayterous and insociable Societie, | or disordered Iesuiticall Order. | By L.O. that hath beene an occular witnesse of their | Impostures and Hipocrisie. | . . . (1 line)

London, | Printed by T.C. for Michael Sparke, dwelling in Greene- | Arbor, at the signe of the Blue-Bible. | 1629. | 17.2x13.4 cm. (8),70p.

Camb Univ. Cat. 4606

PAOLO, Servita. The | Historie Of | The Covncel | Of Trent. | Conteining Eight Bookes. | In which (besides the ordinarie Actes of the Councell) | are declared many notable Occurrences, which happened in | Christendome, during the space of fourtie | yeeres and more. | And, particularly, the practises of the Court of Rome, to | hinder the reformation of their errors, and to main- | taine their greatnesse. | Written in Italian by Pietro Soaue Polano, and faithfully translated | into English by Nathanael Brent. | Vnto this Second Edition are added diuers obsuerable Passages, | and Epistles, concerning the trueth of this Historie, speci- | fied in the next Page. | (royal arms).

London | Printed by Bonham Norton and Iohn Bill, | Printers to the Kings most Excellent Maiestie. | M.DC.XXIX. | 33.5 x 21.5 cm. (10),881,(16) p.

Cambr. Univ. Cat. 2838, under Sarpi.

PAYBODY, Thomas. A | Iust Apologie | For The Gestvre | Of Kneeling In The Act | Of Receiving The Lords | Svpper. | Against the manifold exceptions of | all opposers in the Churches of Eng- | land, and Scotland. | Wherein this Controversie is handled, | {Fully. | Soundly. | }{Plainly. | Methodically. } By T.P. | . . . (2 lines)

London, | Printed by William Iones, dwel- | ling in Red-crosse-streete. 1629. | 18.1x13.6cm (12),496pp.

Epistle Dedicatory, signed.

PEMBLE, William. Five | Godly, And Pro- | fitable Sermons concerning. | 1 The slaverie of sinne. | 2 The mischeife of ignorance. | 3 The roote of Apostasie. | 4 The benefit of Gods service. | 5 The Christians loue. | Preached in his life time in sundry places. | By that late faithfull Minister of Christ | Mr William Pemble | of Magdalen Hall in the | Vniversitie of | Oxford. | The second Edition. |

At Oxford, | Printed by Iohn Lichfield, | Printer to the famous Vniversity | for Edward Forrest | Ann.Dom.1629. | Arch. border. 18.2x13.6cm.(4),24; 25; 17; 22; 15p. Continuous register

PEMBLE, William. A | Frvitfvll | Sermon, | On I Cor.15.18,19. | VVritten | By VVilliam Pemble | of Magdalen Hall | in Oxford. | (device).

London, | Printed by R.Y. for Iohn Bartlet at the signe | of the gilt-Cup in Cheapeside. | 1629. | 18.2x13.6cm. (6),23p.

PEMBLE, William. An | Introdvction | To The Worthy | Receiving The Sa- | crament of the Lords | Svpper. | By that late learned Minister of Gods ho- | ly Word, William Pemble, of Mag- | dalen Hall in Oxford. | Published since his death by his Friend. | . . . (6 lines; device)

London, | Printed by H.L. for Iames Boler, and are to be sold at the | signe of the Mary-gold in Pauls Church-yard. | Anno Dom. 1629. | Line border. 18.8x14.7 cm. (7),88p.

PEMBLE, William. A Short | And Sweete | Exposition | Vpon The First | Nine Chapters | Of Zachary. | By William Pemble. | . . . (8 lines).

London, | Printed by R.Young for John Bartlet, at the | Signe of the gilt Cup in Cheape-side. | Anno Domini 1629. | Line border. 18.3x13.7cm.(7),165p.

PEMBLE, William. Vindiciæ | Fidei, | Or | A Treatise | of Iustification by Faith, | wherein the truth of that point | is fully cleared, and vindicated | from the cauills of it's | Adversaries | Deliuered at Magdalen Hall | in Oxford; By William | Pemble, Mr of Arts. | The second Edition. | . . . (4 lines).

At Oxford, | Printed by Iohn Lichfield, | Printer to the Vniversitie, for | Edward Forrest. 1629. | Arch. border. 18.2x13.6cm.(8),248p.

PEMBLE, William. Vindiciæ Gratiæ. | A | Plea For | Grace. | More Especially | The Grace | Of Faith. | Or, | Certain Lectvres as touching the | Nature and Properties of Grace and | Faith: Wherein, amongst other | matters of great vse, the maine | sinewes of Arminivs doctrine | are cut asunder. | Delivered By That | late learned and godly man William | Pemble, in Magdalen Hall | in Oxford. | The second Edition. | . . . (3 lines).

London, | Printed by H.L. for I.Bartlet, at the gilt | Cup in Cheape-side. 1629. | Line border. 18.2x13.6cm.(16),27,262p.

PRESTON, John. The | Nevv Covenant, | Or | The Saints | Portion. | A Treatise | Vnfolding the All-sufficiencie of | God, and Mans vprightnes, | and the Covenant of grace. | delivered | in fourteene Sermons vpon Gen.17.1.2. | Wherevnto are adioyned | Foure Sermons vpon Eccles.9.1.2.11.12. | By the late faithfull and worthie | Minister of Iesus Christ, | Iohn Preston. | Dr. in Divinitie, Chaplaine in ordinary to his | Maiestie, Maister of Emmanuel Colledge in Cam- | bridge, and sometimes Preacher of Lincolnes Inne. | . . . (3 lines).

London. | Printed by I.D. for Nicolas Bourne, | and are to be sold at the South entrance | of the Royall Exchange. 1629. | Arch. border. 17.5x13.5 cm. (9),244, 240,128p.

Sermon 8 begins new register and pagination.

PRESTON, John. The | Saints | Daily | Exercise. | A | Treatise concerning the whole dutie of prayer. | Delivered | In fiue Sermons vpon I Thess.5.17. | By the late faithfull and worthy | Minister of Iesus Christ, | Iohn Preston, | Dr. in Divinity, Chaplaine in ordinary to his Ma- | iesty, Master of Emmanuel Colledge in Cambridge, | and sometimes Preacher of Lincolnes Inne. | . . . (6 lines).

London, | Printed by W.I. and are to bee sold by Nicholas | Bourne, at the South Entrance of the Royall Ex- | change. 1629. | 17.4x13.4cm. (4),148p. Last p. supplied.
Appended to the 1632 edition of his New Covenant.
From the library of Walter W. Law.

PRESTON, John. The | Saints | Daily | Exercise. | A Treatise | Vnfolding the whole dutie | of Prayer. | Delivered | In fiue Sermons vpon I Thess.5.17. | By the late faithfull and worthy | Minister of Iesus Christ, | Iohn Preston, | Dr. in Divinity, Chaplaine in ordinary to | his Maiesty. Master of Emmanuel Colledge in Cam- | bridge, and sometimes Preacher of Lincolnes Inne. | The third Edition, corrected. | . . . (4 lines).
London, | Printed by W.I. for Nicholas Bourne, | and are to be solde at the South En- | trance of the Royall Exchange 1629. | Arch. border. 18.8x14.3cm. (4),147,(9)p.

PRYNNE, William. The | Chvrch | Of Englands | Old Antithesis | To New Armi- | nianisme. | Where in 7.Anti-Arminian Orthodox | Tenents, are euidently proued; their 7.opposite | Arminian(once Popish and Pelagian)Errors are manifestly | disproued, to be the ancient, established, and vndoubted | Doctrine of the Church of England; by the concurrent te- | stimony of the seuerall Records and Writers of our | Church, from the beginning of her reformation, | to this present. | By William Prynne Gent.Hospitij Lincolniensis. | . . . (10 lines)
London. 1629. | 18.6x14.2 cm. (56),140p.
Doubtless one of the books against Arminianism referred to by Prynne (History of the trial of Laud), as suppressed and burned privately at the instance of archbishop Laud.

PRYNNE, William. God; | No Impostor, | Nor | Delvder. |
Without t.p. [1629?] 17.7x13.3cm. 27p.

PRYNNE, William. God, | No Impostor | Nor Delvder: | Or, | An Ansvver To A | Popish and Arminian Cauill, in the | defence of Free-Will, and vniuersall Grace; | wherein God's tender of Grace by the outward | Ministry of the Gospel, to Reprobates who neither doe, | nor can receiue it; is vindicated from those aspersions | of equiuocation, falsitie, and collusion, which | some by way of Obiection, cast vpon it. | By William Prynne, an vtter Barrester of Lincolnes Inne. | . . . (8 lines)
Printed, M.DC.XXIX. | 18.6x14.2 cm. (1),34p.

RAINOLDS, John. The Overthrow | Of Stage-Playes, | By the way of controversie betwixt | D. Gager and D. Rainoldes, wherein all the | reasons that can be made for them are notably refu- | ted; the obiections answered, and the case so cleared | and resolved, as that the iudgement of any man, | that is not froward and perverse, may | easilie bee satisfied. | Wherein Is Manifestly Pro- | ved, that it is not onely vnlawfull to be an Actor, | but a beholder of those vanities. | Wherevnto Are Added Also | and annexed in the end certaine Latine Letters betwixt | the said Maister Rainoldes, and Doct, Gentiles, |

Reader of the Civill Law in Oxford, con- | cerning the same matter. | The second edition. | (device).

At Oxford, | Printed by Iohn Lichfield, Printer to the fa- | mous Vniversitie, for E.Forrest, and W.Webbe, | Anno Dom. 1629. | 18.3x13.8cm.   (7),190pp. P. 164 repeated in numbering as 264.

SANDYS, Edwin.   Evropæ Specvlvm | Or, | A View Or Svrvey | Of The State Of Religion | in the VVesterne | parts of the World. | VVherein the Romane | Religion, and the pregnant policies of the | Church of Rome to support the same, | are notably displayed: with some | other memorable discoueries and | memorations, | Never before till now published | according to the Authours | Originall Copie. | . . . (1 line; ornament).

Hagæ-Comitis. | 1629. | 18x13.2 cm.   (11),248p.
Cambr.Univ.Cat:6640.
The unauthorized edition of 1605 was burned at the request of the author.

SCLATER, William.   A | Sermon | Preached at St. Maries in the | Vniuersity of Cambridge. | By William Sclater Do- | ctor of Diuinity, sometimes Fellow of | Kings Colledge, and Minister of the word | of God at Pitmister in Som- | mersetshire. | Now published by his Sonne of the | same Kings Colledge in Cambridge. | (device).

London, | Printed by Thomas Harper for | Robert Allot, and are to be sold at his shop in Pauls | Churchyard at the signe of the blacke | Beare. 1629. | 18.3x14. cm   (6),16p.

SCLATER, William.   A | Sermon | Preached at Tanton in | Sommerset, | By William Sclater, Do- | ctour of Diuinity, and Minister of the word of | God at Pitmister. | Now published by his Sonne of Kings | Colledge in Cambridge. | (device).

London, | Printed by Thomas Harper for | Robert Allot, and are to be sold at his shop in Pauls | Churchyard at the signe of the blacke | Beare. 1629. | 17x13.2 cm.   (7),17–39p.

A | SEMINARY | Priest Pvt To | a Non-plus. | Or, | A Christian and modest Answere, | to certaine Motiues sent by a Popish | Priest to a worthy Gentleman, to | Induce him to turne | Papist. | (ornament).

London. | Printed for William Sheeres. | 1629. | 18.7x14.7cm.   (1),44p.

SMITH, John.   Essex Dove, | Presenting | The VVorld VVith | A Fevv Of Her Olive | Branches: | Or, | A taste of the Workes of that Reuerend, | Faithfull, Iudicious, Learned, and holy Mi- | nister of the Word, Mr. Iohn Smith, late | Preacher of the Word at Clauering in Essex. | Deliuered in three seuerall Treatises, viz. | {1. His Grounds of Religion. | 2. An Exposition on the Lords Prayer. | 3. A Treatise of Repentance. } . . . (5 lines; device)

London, | Printed by A.I. for George Edwardes, and are to be sold at his house in the Old Baily | in Greene Arbor, at the signe of the Angell. 1629. | 18.6x14.1 cm.(20),146; (1),142; (8),198 p.

Parts 2 and 3 have double & triple letter register and separate pagination; sub t.p. with same imprint

SPENCER, Thomas. Maschil Vnmasked. | Jn | A Treatise Defending | this sentence of our Church: | Vidz. | The present Romish Church hath not the na- | ture of the true Church. | Against the publick opposition of Mr.Cholmley, | and Mr. Butterfield, tvvo children revolted in | opinion from their owne subscription, | and the faith of their Mother the | Church of England. | By Thomas Spencer. | . . . (5 lines).

London, | Printed by William Iones, dwel- | ling in Red-crosse-streete. | [1629] 18.1x13.5cm. (27),95p

The | SVFFRAGE | Of The Divines | Of Greate Britaine | Concerning The | Five Articles | Controverted In | the Low Countries. | Which Suffrage was by them delivered | in the Synod of Dort, March 6. Anno 1619. | Being their vote or voice foregoing | the joint and publique judgment | of that Synod. |

London, | Printed for Robert Milbourne, and are to be sold at | his Shop in Pauls Churchyard at the signe of the | Greyhound. 1629. | Line border. 17.7x13.6 cm. (3),178p.

SUTTON, Christopher. Disce Mori: | Learne | To Dye. | A Religious Discourse, | mouing euery Christian | man to enter into a seri- | ous remembrance of | his end. | Wherein also is contained the | meane and manner of disposing him- | selfe to God, before and at the time, | of his departure. | In the whole, somewhat hap- | pily may be obserued, necessary to be | thought vpon while wee are aliue, | and vvhen vve are dying to aduise | our selues and others. | . . . (3 lines).

London: | Printed by Iohn Beal and Tho.Brude- | nell, for Nicholas Bourne, and are | to be sold at his shop at the | Royall Exchange. 1629. | Panelled border. 13.7x7.7cm. (38),400p.

Part 2 of the following. Epistle Dedicatory, signed.

SUTTON, Christopher. Disce viuere: | Learne | To Live. | Disce Mori: | Learne to Dye. | Two briefe Treatises | joyned together: the | one, of learning to liue; | the other, of learning | to Dye. | Wherein is shewed, | in what manner euery well | disposed Christian may | learne, first how to liue the | life of the righteous, | and then how to dye the | death of the righ- | teous. |

London: | Printed by I.B. and T.B. for Nicholas | Bourne, dwelling at the Royall | Exchange. 1629. | Panelled border 13.7x7.7cm. (46),487,(14) ;(38),400p.

Two parts, with separate register and pagination
Epistle dedicatory, signed

SUTTON, Christopher. Disce Viuere: | Learne | To Live. | The first Treatise of | Learning to Liue. | Wherein is shewed, that the | life of Christ is, and ought to be | an expresse patterne for imitation | vnto the life of a Christian, | so far as in him lieth. | . . . (6 lines).

London: | Printed for Nicholas Bourne, and | are to be sold at his shop at the | Royall Exchange. 1629. | Line border. 13.7x7.7cm.(46),487,(14)p.

Pt. 1. of the preceding.

SYMMER, Archibald. A | Spiritvall | Posie For Zion. | Or | Two Decades of Observations, | Theologicall and Philosophicall. | By |

Archibald Symmer, Preacher of | Gods word at Great-Oakley in North- | hampton-shire. | . . . (device; 2 lines).
London, | Printed for W.Sheares. 1629. | Line border. 18.1x13.7cm. (6),42p.

USSHER, James. A Briefe | Declaration | Of The Vniversa- | litie Of The Chvrch | of Christ, and the Vnitie | of the Catholike Faith pro- | fessed therein: | Delivered In A Sermon | before His Maiestie the 20th. of Iune 1624. | at Wansted. | By Iames Vssher, Bishop of Meath. | The third Impression. | (ornament).
London, | Printed by Iohn Dawson, for Ephraim Dawson, | and are to be sold at the Rain-bow neere the | Inner Temple Gate in Fleet-street. | 1629. | Line border. 18.7x15.cm. (1),42p.

WILKINSON, Henry. A | Catechisme, | Contayning | A short Exposition of the | points in the ordinary Cate- | chisme, with proofes of the same | out of the Scripture. | Set forth for the vse of such as | desire to be catechised in the Con- | gregation of Wadsdon in Bucking- | hamshire, or else-where. | By Henry Wilkinson, | Bachelour in Diuinity. | The third Edition. | . . . (3 lines; ornament).
London, | Printed by T. C. for Robert Birde, and | are to bee sold at the signe of the | Bible in Cheap-side, 1629. | 14x9 cm. (1,41)p.

WILLIAMS, Griffith. The | True Church: | Shewed to all men, | that desire to be mem- | bers of the same. | In Six Bookes. | Containing the whole bodie | of Diuinitie. | The Contents whereof are set downe | after the Epistles. | By | Gr. Williams | Dr. of Diuinitie. |
London, | Printed by Iohn Haviland | for Nathaniel Bvtter, and | are to be sold at his shop at the signe of the | pide Bull neere Saint | Austens Gate. | 1629. | Column and vine border. 28.6x18.1cm. (10),933,(23)p.

1630

AMES, William. Coronis | Ad | Collationem | Hagiensem, | Qva Argvmenta Pa- | storvm Hollandiæ | Adversus Remonstrantium | Quinque Articulos | De Divinâ Prædestinatione, & capitibus | ei adnexis, producta, ab horum exceptio- | nibus vindicantur. | Auctore Gvilielmo Amesio. | Editio quarta. | (ornament).
Londini | Excudebat Felix Kingstonus sumptibus | Roberti Allotti. 1630. | 14.2x8.1cm. (24),502p.

ANDREWES, Lancelot. A | Patterne | Of | Catechisticall | Doctrine. | Wherein many profitable | Questions touching Christi- | an Religion are handled. | And | The whole Decalogve | succinctly and judiciously | expounded. | (ornament)
London, | Printed for William Garrett. | 1630. | Line border. 14.2x8.2 cm. (1), 495p.
DNB. I: 404b.

ARTICLES | Agreed Upon | By the Arch-Bishops and | Bishops of both Provinces, and | the whole Clergie; | In the Convocation holden at London, | in the year, 1562. | For the avoiding of diversities of opinions, and for | the establishing of consent touching true | Religion. | Reprinted by His Majesties Commandment: | with His Royal Declaration prefixed | thereunto. | (device)

London, | Printed by Bonham Norton and Iohn Bill, Printers to the Kings | most Excellent Majesty, 1630. | Border. 17.6x13.5cm. (3),6,(21)p.

Repr. also in Sparrow's Collection: 1661, 1675, and 1684, and in Collection of Articles: 1699.

BAYLY, John. Two | Sermons | The Angell | Gvardian. | The Light | Enlightning. | Preached | By Iohn Bayly One Of | His Maiesties Chap- | laines, Gvardian | of Chrrists Hospitall in | Ruthyn, and sometimes | Fellow of Exeter | Coll.Oxon. | (device).

At Oxford, | Printed by Iohn Lichfield Printer to the | Famous Vniversity, A.D. 1630. | 17.6x14.cm. (4),17;(1),14p.

With separate registers and pagination.

BRADSHAW, William. A | Preparation | to the receiuing of | Christs Body | and Blood: | Directing weake Chri- | stians how they may wor- | thily receiue the same. | By W. Bradshavv. | With a profitable Treatise of | the same argument, writ- | ten by another. | The 8. Edition corrected | and inlarged. |

London, | Printed by Iohn Hauiland, | and are to be sold by Robert | Dawlman, at the signe of | the Brazen Serpent in Pauls | Church-yard. | 1630. | Border. 13.7x 7.9 cm. (5),108fol., (10),146p.

Sub-title at fol. 52. Second part by Arthur Hildersam: The Doctrine of | Communicating . . . 1630, which see.

BREREWOOD, Edward. A | Learned Treatise | Of The | Sabaoth, | Written | By Mr Edward Brerewood, | Professor in Gresham Colledge, | London. | To Mr.Nicolas Byfield, | Preacher in Chester. | With Mr Byfields answere and | Mr BrereWoods | Reply. |

At Oxford, | Printed by Iohn Lichfield Printer to the Famous | Vniversity, for Thomas Huggins. | An. Dom. 1630. | 17.8 x 14.1 cm (4),101p. Sub-title at p. 57.

CADE, Anthony. A | Ivstification | Of The Chvrch | Of England. | Demonstrating it to be a true Church | of God, affording all sufficient | meanes to Salvation. | Or, | A Counctercharme against the Romish enchant- | ments, that labour to bewitch the people, with | opinion of necessity to be subiect to | the Pope of Rome. | Wherein is briefly shewed the Pith and Marrow of | the principall bookes written by both sides, touching | this matter: with Marginall reference to the Chapters | and Sections, where the points are handled more at | large to the great ease and satisfaction | of the Reader. | By Anthony Cade, Bachelour | of Divinity. | . . . (3 lines; ornament).

London, | Printed for George Lathvm, dwelling at the Bishops | head in Pauls Church-yard, Anno 1630. | 18.7x14.1 cm. (40),315,112,(27) p.

CLARKE, John. Holy Oyle | For | The Lampes | Of | The Sanctvarie: | Or, | Scriptvre-Phrases | Alphabetically Disposed: | For the vse and benefit of such as de- | sire to speake the Language of Canaan, | more especially the sonnes of the Pro- | phets, who would attaine Elegancie | and Sublimity of expressions. | By Iohn Clarke Master of Arts. | . . . (4 lines).

London, | Printed by Aug. Mathewes for Rob.Milbovrne, | and are to be sold at his Shop at the Grayhound | in Pauls Churchyard. 1630. | Line border. 18.1x 13.8cm. (30),535,(10)p. Engr. fore t.p,

CROMPTON, Richard. Star-Chamber | Cases. | Shewing | What Cavses Pro- | perly Belong To The | Cognizance Of That | Covrt. | Collected for the most part out of Mr. | Crompton, his Booke, entituled | The Iurisdiction of divers Courts. | (device).

London, | Printed for Iohn Grove at Furniuals | Inne Gate. 1630. | 17.1x13.5 cm. (1),57p.

CULVERWELL, Ezekiel. The | VVay To | A Blessed E- | state In | This Life. | By | Ezekiel Cvlvervvell. (ornament).

London, | Printed by E.A. for Henry Ouerton | and are to be sold at his Shop, | at the entring in of Popes- | head Alley, out of | Lumbard-streete. | 1630. | Line border. 14.2x8.2 cm 17p.

Appended to his Treatise of Faith. 6th edit. 1629; with separate register and pagination.

A | DEFENCE | Of | Catholikes | Persecvted | In | England, | Inuincibly prouing their holy Religion to be | that which is the only true Religion of | Christ; and that they in professing it, | are become most faithfull, dutifull, and | loyall Subiects, to God, their King and | Country. And therefore are rather to be | honoured and respected, then persecuted | or molested. Composed by an ould student | in Diuinitie. | . . . (4 lines; ornament).

Printed at Doway by Gerard Pinchon, | at the signe of Coleyn, 1630. | 16.x10.2 cm. (8),175,(1)p.

DENT, Arthur. A | Sermon | Of | Repentance. | A very godly and profitable | Sermon Preached at | Lee in Essex. | By | Arthvr Dent, Minister of Gods Word: | Published at the request of sundry godly, | and well disposed persons. | . . . (3 lines).

London, | Printed by T.C. for Michael Sparke, dwelling | at the Signe of the Blue-Bible in Greene Arbor. | and are to be sold by R.Reystone in Iue-Lane. 1630. | 14.6x9.3cm. (4),50p.

DOD, John, and CLEAVER, Robert. A plaine and familiar | Exposition | Of The | Ten Commandements. | With A Methodicall | Short Catechisme, | Containing briefly the principall grounds of | Christian Religion. | The eighteenth Edition. | Newly corrected and amended by the Author. | . . . (3 lines; device).

London, | Printed by the Assignes of Thomas Man, &c. | and are sold by Iohn Wright at the signe of the Bible | without Newgate. 1630. | 18.8x13.9cm. (6), 338,(24)p.

The appended Catechism is Thomas Cartwright's.
Epistle Dedicatorie, signed.

DODDRIDGE, John. A | Compleat | Parson: | Or, | A Description | Of Advowsons, | or Church-liuing. | Wherein | Is set forth, the intrests of the Parson, | Patron, and Ordinarie, &c. | With | Many other things concerning the same | matter, as they were deliuered at severall | Readings at New - Jnne, | By I. Doderidge, | Anno, 1602, 1603. | And now Published for a Common good, | by W. J. |

London. | Printed by B. A. and T. F. for Iohn Groue, and are to | bee sold at his Shop at Furniuals Jnne gate. | 1630. | 18.1x13.8 cm. (8), 95p. A1 has "A", with row of ornaments above and below.

DOWNAME, John. A Briefe | Concordance | To | The Bible Of The Last | Translation. | Seruing for the more easie finding out of the most | vsefull places therein contained. | Alphabetically Digested, | And | Allowed to be printed, and bound with | the Bible in all Volumes. | . . . (3 lines: device)

London, | Printed by the Assignes of Clement Cotton. 1630. | Cum Priuilegio. | 21.1 x 15.3 cm; (4,115) p.
Prefixed to edition of Bible. To the Reader, signed.

DOWNAME, John. The | Summe | of | Sacred Diunitie | Briefly and Methodically | Propounded: | More largly & cleerely | handled and explaned. | Published | by John Downhame | Batchelor in Diuini- | tie. |

London | Printed by Willi: | Stansby. | [1630]. Engr. t.p. 17.5x13.0cm. (36), 551,(1)pp. Pp. 257-266 skipped.

DYKE, Daniel. The | Mystery | Of Selfe-Deceiuing: | Or, | A Discovrse | and discouery of the Deceitfulnesse | of Mans Heart. | Written by the late faithfull Minister of | Gods Word Daniel Dyke, Batchelor | in Diuinitie. | Published since his death, by his Brother I[eremiah] D[yke] Minister of Gods Word. | And now by him augmented and inlarged, and there- | vnto two exquisite Tables added, enlightening | much the whole Treatise. | . . . (5 lines).

London, | Printed by William Stansby, and are to bee sold by | Richard Higgenbotham, in Pauls Church-yard, at the signe | of the white Lyon. 1630. | Line border. 17.8x13.8cm. (12),438,(24)p.

FEATLEY, Daniel. The | Grand | Sacrilege | Of | The Chvrch | Of Rome, | In taking away the sacred Cup from | the Laiety at the Lords Table: | Detected, and conuinced by the euidence | of holy Scripture, and Testimonies of all | Ages successiuely from the first propaga- | tion of the Catholike Christian Faith | to this present: | Together with two Conferences; the former at Pa- | ris with D. Smith, now stiled by the Romanists B of Calce- | don; the later at London with M Euerard, Priest: | By Dan. Featly, Doctor in Diuinity. | . . . (3 lines).

London, | Printed by Felix Kyngston for Robert Milbourne, and are to be | sold in Pauls Churchyard at the signe of the Greyhound. 1630. | Line border. 18.1x13.7cm. (36),306p. 1-2 blank; 295-296 twice.

FISHER, Ambrose. A | Defence | Of The | Litvrgie | Of | The Church of England, | Or, | Booke of Common Prayer. | In a Dialogue betweene{Novatvs, | And | Irenævs. | By | Ambrose Fisher, sometimes of | Trinitie Colledge in | Cambridge. | . . . (4 lines)

London; | Printed by W. S. for Robert Milbourne in | Pauls Church-yard at the signe of | the Greyhound. 1630. | Arch. border 18.8x14. cm. (22),309,(1)p. Title in red and black.

The | FORM and Manner | Of | Making & Consecrating | Bishops, | Priests, | And | Deacons: | According to the | Appointment | Of The | Church of England. |

London, | Printed by Robert Barker and John | Bill, Printers to the Kings most | Excellent Majesty. | [1630]. 18. x 14.1 cm (2),29p.

See Sayles' Cambridge Catalogue.

GILPIN, Bernard. A | Sermon | Preached In | The Covrt At | Greenwitch, Before | King Edvvard the sixth, the | first Sonday after the Epiphany, | Anno Domini 1552. | By | Bernard Gilpin, | Sometimes Minister of Houghton in the Bi- | shopricke of Durham. | . . . (10 lines).

London, | Printed by William Iones, dwelling in Red- | Crosse-streete. 1630. | 17.9x13.8cm. (4),49p.

GOUGE, William. An | Exposition | Of Part Of The | Fift And Sixt Chap- | ters Of S.Pavles Epistle | to the Ephesians, wherein is handled | all such duties as belong to house- | hold Gouernment: | Also | The Spiritvall | Armovr, Ovt Of | Which A Christian May | Fetch Svfficient | furniture against all his spirituall | Enemies. | (ornament).

London, | Imprinted for Iohn Bartlett, and are to be sold at the signe of | the Gilt Cup in the Goldsmiths Row in Cheapeside. | 1630. | 18.5x13.7cm.(1),164p.

Appended to his An Exposition on the whole of the Fifth Chapter of S.Iohns Gospell: 1630; with separate register and pagination.

Cf.Cambr.Univ.Cat:7412.

GOUGE, William. An | Exposition | On The Whole | Fifth Chapter Of | S.Iohns Gospel: | Also | Notes On Other | Choice Places Of | Scriptvre, Taken By A | Reuerend Diuine, now with God, and | found in his Study after his death, writ- | ten with his owne hand, viz. | An Exposition on the fifth of Iohn. | Notes on Ioh.3.vers.29. to 36. | Notes on certaine verses of the first and | second of Marke. | Notes on Luk.3.ver.19,20. | Notes on Iam.4.vers.7. | Notes on Gen.2.vers.9.& 7.&23. | Notes on Exod.12.vers.8,11,14,15,16. | Notes on Psal.30.2. | An Exposition on part of the fifth and | sixth Chapters of the Ephesians. |

London, | Imprinted for Iohn Bartlett, and are to be sold at the signe of | the gilt Cup in the Goldsmiths Row in Cheapeside. | 1630. | 18.5x13.7cm. (1),192; (1),164p.

Two parts, with separate register and pagination.

Cambr.Univ.Cat:7412

HAKEWILL, George. An | Apologie | Or | Declaration | Of The Povver And | Providence Of God In The | Government Of The World. | Consisting In | An Examination And | Censvre Of The Common | Errovr Tovching Natvres Per- | petuall And Vniversall Decay, | Divided Into Fovre Bookes. | Whereof | The first treates of this pretended decay in generall, together with some preparatiues there- | vnto. | The second of the pretended decay of the Heavens and Elements, together with that of the | Elementary bodies, man onely excepted. | The third of the pretended decay of mankinde in regard of age and duration, of strength and | stature, of arts and wits. | The fourth of this pretended decay in matter of manners, together with a large proofe of the | future consummation of the World from the testimony of the Gentiles,

and the vse which | we are to draw from the consideration thereof. |
By George Hakewill Doctor of | Divinity and Archdeacon of Surrey. |
The second Edition revised, and in sundry passages augmented by the
Authour; | with advertisements and tables newly annexed in the end
of the booke, | an Index whereof is presented in the next page. | . . .
(3 lines).

Oxford, | Printed by William Tvrner Printer to the | famous Vniversity. Anno Dom. 1630. | 28.9x18.3cm. (35),523,(67)p.

HARRIS, Robert. Absaloms | Fvnerall: | Preached At Banbv- | rie,
By A Neighbovr | Minister. | Or, | The Lamentation Of A | Loving
Father For A | rebellious Childe. | . . . (3 lines ; device).

London, | Printed by Iohn Haviland for Iohn Bartlet, and are to | be sold in the Gold-smiths Row in Cheap-side, | at the Signe of the Golden Cup. | 1630. | 18.6x14.2cm. (6),34p.
To the Reader, signed.

HARRIS, Robert. Hezekiah's | Recovery. | Or | A Sermon, Shewing | what use Hezekiah did, and | all should make of their delive- | rance from sicknesse. | First preached, and now published | by Robert Harris Pastor | of Hanwell. | (device).

London, | Printed by Iohn Haviland for Iohn Bartlet, at the golden | Cup in the Goldsmiths Row in Cheape-side. | 1630. | 18.8x14.2cm. (7),48p.

HAYWARD, John. The Life, And Raigne | of King Edward The Sixt. | Written by Sr. Iohn Hayward Kt. | Dr. of Lawe. |

London | Printed for Iohn Partridge, and are to be | sold at the signe of the Sunne in | Paules Churchyard. | 1630. | 18.2x14.2cm. (6),179,(1)p. Engr. t.p. with Portr. K.Edw.VI. Portr. of Author. Colophon.

HILDERSAM, Arthur. The Doctrine of | Communicating wor- | thily in the Lords | Svpper: | Deliuered by way of | Question and Answer, for | the more familiar instru- | ction of the simple. | By A.H. | The 8. Edition reuiued, and | corrected by the Author. | (ornament).

London, | Printed by Iohn Hauiland. | 1630. | Border. 13.7x7.9cm. (10),146p.
Incorporated with Wm.Bradshaw: A Preparation, etc. 1630 ;with continuous register, but separate pagination. DNB. 26:383b(2).

HOMMIUS, Festus. (Præs). LXX. | Dispvtatio- | nes Theologi-cæ; | adversus | Pontificios: | Quibus omnes inter Evangelicos & | Pontificios Controversiæ continentur, & | excutiuntur: In gratiam SS. Theologiæ Stu- | diosorum in Academiâ Leydensi pri- | vatim institutæ, in | Collegio Anti-Bellarminiano, | Præside | Festo Hommio, | Eccl. Lugdun. Pastore. | Editio secunda; adjectionibus in | margine locupletior. | (ornament).

Oxoniæ, | Impensis Gvlielmi Tvrner | Celeberrimæ Academiæ Typographi. | Anno M. DC. XXX. | Line border. 14.4x9.2cm. (16),428,(4)p.

JEROME, St. Certaine | Selected Epistles | Of | S.Hierome | As Also | The Lives Of | Saint Pavl | The First Hermite, | Of Saint Hilarion the first Monke of Syria, | and of S.Malchvs: | VVritten by the same Saint. | Translated into English. | (ornament).

Permissu Superiorum, M.DC.XXX. | 17.8x13cm. 149; (1),55p.

LORD, Henry. A | Discoverie | Of The Sect Of The | Banians. | Containing their History, Law, | Liturgie, Casts Customes, and | Ceremonies. | Gathered from their Bramanes, | Teachers of that Sect: As the particulars | were comprized in the Booke of their Law, | called the Shaster: | Together with a display of their Manners, both | in times past, and at this present. | . . . (3 lines).

   London, | Printed by T. and R. Cotes, for Fra. Constable, | and are to be sold at the signe of the Crane | in Pauls Churchyard. 1630. | Line border. 18.3 x 13.3 cm. (18),95 p.

   Sub t.p. of his Display of two forraigne sects: 1630

LORD, Henry. A Display | of two forraigne sects | in the East Indies | Vizt: | The sect of the Banians the | Ancient Natiues of India | And the sect of the Persees the | Ancient Inhabitants of Persia | together | With the Religion and Maners of each sect | Collected | Into two Bookes by Henry Lord | Sometimes resident in East India | and Preacher to the Hoble.Company | of Merchants trading thether. | . . . (8 lines).

   Imprinted at | London | for Francis | Constable | and are to be | Sold at his | Shoppe in Paules | Church yard | at the signe of | the Crane. | 1630. | Engraved title page. Will:Marshall | sculpsit. | 18.3x13.3cm. (18),95;(12),53p. Two sub-title pages.

LORD, Henry. The | Religion | Of The | Persees. | As it was Compiled from a Booke | of theirs, contayning the Forme of | their Worshippe, written in the | Persian Character, and by them | called their Zundavastaw. | Wherein is shewed the Superstitious | Ceremonies vsed amongst them. | More especially their Idolatrous worshippe | of Fire | . . . (8 lines).

   Printed for Fra.Constable. 1630. | Line border. 18.3x13.3cm. (12),53p.

   Sub t.p. of his Display of two forraigne sects: 1630, with continuous register, but separate pagination.

LYNDE, Humphrey. Via Devia: | The | By-Way | Mis-leading the weake and vn- | stable into dangerous paths of Error, | by colourable shewes of Apo- | cryphall Scriptures, vnwritten | Traditions, doubtfull Fathers, | ambiguous Councells, and | pretended Catholike | Church. | Discouered | by Hvmfrey Lynde, Knight. | . . . (2 lines).

   London, | Printed by Aug.M. for Rob.Mil- | bovrne, and are to be sold at his | Shop at the Grayhound in Pauls | Churchyard. 1630. | Line border. 13.8x7.8 cm. (70),684p.

MOULIN, Pierre du. The | Antibarbarian: | Or, | A Treatise concerning | an vnknowne tongue. | As well in the prayers of | particulars in private as in | the publique Liturgie. | Wherein also are exhibited the prin- | cipall clauses of the Masse, which | would offend the people, if they un- | derstood them. | By Peter Dv Movlin, Mini- | ster of the Word of God in the | Church of Sedan and Professor | of Divinitie. |

   London, | Printed by George Miller, for George Ed- | wards, and are to be sold in the Old Baily, in | Greene Arbour, at the signe of the An- | gell. 1630. | Line border. 14x8.1cm. (22),281,(1)p.

NARNE, William. The | Pearle Of | Prayer | Most Pretiovs, | And Powerfvll, | Or, | A Christian Treatise | Most Necessarie For | all these

that desire to eschew that | wrath to come, the Lords curse, | and everlasting damnation, and | who doe long for Gods favour, | his blessing, and to attaine | to endlesse salvation. | . . . (4 lines) By Mr. William Narne, | P. of Dysert. |
  Edinbvrgh. | Printed by Iohn Wreittoun. 1630. | Line border. 13.6x8.9cm. (16), 453,(1)p.

PISCATOR, Johann. Aphorismi | Doctrinæ | Christianæ | maximam partem ex In- | stitutione Calvini | excerpti. | Sive | Loci Commvnes Theolo- | gici, brevibus sententijs expositi. | Johan; Piscatorem. | Editio Vndecima. | Superioribus tum limatior | locupletior. | (ornament).
  Oxoniæ | Typis Ioh.Lichfield, | Impensis Hen.Cvrteine | M.D.C.XXX. | 12.5x7.5 cm. (9),203,(2)p.

PRESTON, John. The | Breast-Plate | Of | Faith And Love. | A Treatise, | Wherein the ground and exer- | cise of Faith and Love, | as they are set upon Christ their | Object, and as they are expres- | sed in Good Workes, is explained. | Delivered | In 18 Sermons upon three severall Texts, | By the late faithfull and worthy | Minister of Iesus Christ, | Iohn Preston, | Dr. in Divinity, Chaplaine in ordinary to | his Maiesty, Master of Emmanuel Colledge in Cam- | bridge, and sometimes Preacher of Lincolnes Inne. | The second Edition, corrected. | . . . (5 lines).
  London, | Printed by W.I. for Nicolas Bourne, | and are to be solde at the South En- | trance of the Royall Exchange. 1630. | Arch. border. 18.3x14.cm (12), 134;(1),200;216p. 19x14cm. (10),134;(1),200;216,(18)p.
  Continuous register throughout.

PRESTON, John. The | Saints | Daily | Exercise. | A Treatise | Vnfolding the whole dutie | of Prayer. | Delivered | In fiue Sermons vpon I Thess.5.17. | By the late faithfull and worthy | Minister of Iesus Christ, | Iohn Preston, | Dr. in Divinity, Chaplaine in ordinary to | his Maicsty, Master of Emmanuel Colledge in Cam- | bridge, and sometimes Preacher of Lincolnes Inne. | The fourth Edition, corrected. | . . . (4 lines).
  London | Printed by W.I. for Nicolas Bourne, | and are to be solde at the South En- | trance of the Royall Exchange. 1630. | Arch. border. 17.3x12.8cm. (7),147,(7)p.

PRESTON, John. Sermons | Preached Before | his Maiestie; and vpon | other speciall occasions: | Viz. | 1 The Pillar and ground of Truth, in I Tim.3.15. | page 1. | 2 The New life, I John 5.12. page 27. | 3 A sensible demonstration of the Deitie, Isay 64.4. | page 61. | 4 Exact Walking, Ephes.5.15. page 73. | 5 Samuels support of sorrowfull Sinners, in I Sam.12. | V.20,21,22. page 109. | By the late faithfull and worthy Minister of Iesus | Christ, Iohn Preston Dr. in Diuinity, Chaplaine | in ordinary to his Maiestie, Master of Emanuel | College in Cambridge, and sometimes | Preacher of Lincolnes Inne. |
  London, | Printed for Leonard Greene of Cambridge, and are | to bee sold by Iames Boler, at the signe of the | Marigold in Pauls Churchyard. 1630. | Line border. 18.1x13.5cm.(10),154p.
  1st edit?

PRESTON, John. Sermons | Preached Before | his Maiestie; and vpon | other speciall occasions: | Viz. | 1 The Pillar and ground of Truth. | 2 The New Life. | 3 A sensible demonstration of the Deity. | 4 Exact Walking. | 5 Samuels support of sorrowfull Sinners. | By the late faithfull and worthy Minister of Iesus | Christ, Iohn Preston Dr. in Diuinity, Chaplaine | in ordinary to his Maiesty, Master of Emmanuel | College in Cambridge, and sometimes | Preacher of Lincolnes Inne. |

London, | Printed for Leonard Greene of Cam- | bridge, and are to be sold by Iames Boler, at | the Signe of the Marigold in Pauls | Churchyard. 1630. | Line border. 18.8x14.3cm.(6),134p.

PRESTON, John. A | Treatise | Of | Effectvall | Faith: | Deliuered in sixe Sermons vpon I Thes. 1.3. | By the late faithfull and worthy Minister | of Iesus Christ. | Iohn Preston, | Dr. in Diuinity, Chaplaine in ordinary to His | Maiestie; Master of Emanuel Colledge in | Cambridge; and sometime Preacher | of Lincolnes-Inne. | . . . (4 lines; ornament).

London: | Printed for Nicholas Bourne. 1630. | Line border. 18.1x13.5cm.(6), 138: 219; 216, (18)p.

Appended are seven sermons Of Love, without t.p. Continuous double letter register, independent pagination. Also another edition, part of his Breast-Plate: 1630, 2d ed. with continuous register.

PRYNNE, William. Anti- | Arminianisme. | Or | The Church Of Eng- | lands Old Antithesis To | New Arminianisme. | Wherein seven Anti-Arminian Ortho- | dox Tenets, are evidently proved; their seven oppo- | site Arminian (once Popish and Pelagian) Errours, are ma- | nifestly disproved, to be the ancient, established, vndoubted | Doctrine of the primitive and moderne Church of England; (as | also of the primitive and present Churches of Scotland, and | Ireland:) By the concurrent testimony of sundry ancient | Brittish, English, Scottish, Irish Authours and Records, | from the yeare of our Lord 430. till about the yeare 1440: | and by the severall Records and Writers of these | Churches, from the beginning of reforma- | tion to this present. | By William Prynne, an utter-Barrester | of Lincolnes Inne. | The second Edition much enlarged. | . . . (8 lines).

Imprinted, 1630. | 18.x13.8cm (56),280;(3),36;(40)p.
T.p. supplied. Printed twice in 1630.

PRYNNE, William. God, No Impostor, | Nor Delvder. | Or, | An Answer to a Popish and Arminian Cavill, | in the defence of Free-Will, and vniversall Grace; | wherein Gods tender of Grace by the outward | Ministry of the Gospell, to Reprobates who neither | doe, nor can receive it; is vindicated from those | aspersions of equivocation, falsitie, and collu- | sion, which some by way of Obiecti- | on, cast upon it. | By William Prynne, an utter Barrester | of Lincolnes Inne. | . . . (14 lines).

Printed, M.DC.XXX. | 18.1x13.7 cm. (3),36p.
Incorporated in the 2d edition of his Anti-Arminisme: 1630 .

PRYNNE, William. Lame | Giles | His | Havltings, | Or, | A Briefe Svrvey | Of Giles VViddovves His | Confutation of an Appendix, concerning | Bowing at the name of Jesus. | Together With a short Relation of the Po- | pish Originall and Progresse of this groundlesse | novell Ceremony:Wherein Mr.Widdovves | his manifold Forgeries, Oversights, and Absurdities | are in part detected; and the point, Of bowing | at the name of Iesus, together with that, | Of cringing to Altars and Com- | munion-tables, is now | more largely discussed. | By VVilliam Prynne, an Vtter- | Barrester of Lincolnes Inne. | . . . (7 lines)

    Imprinted for Giles Widdowes, MDCXXX. | 18.5x13.6 cm. (1),47,(1),18p.

PRZYPKOWSKI, Samuel. Anonymi | Dissertatio | De | Pace Et Concor- | dia Ecclesiæ. | Edita per | Irenævm Philalethen. | Editio secunda ad ipsius Auctoris | manuscriptum recognita, | multisque locis aucta. | (ornament).

    Elevtheropoli | Typis Godfridi Philadelphi. | Anno | M DC XXX. | 13.5x8.5 cm. (10),89,(7)p.

    Anon. DNB, 24b. Erroneously attributed to John Hales.

RANDALL, John. Three | And Tvventie | Sermons, | Or, | Catechisticall Lectures upon the Sa- | crament of the Lords Supper: | Preached monthly before the Communion. | By that late able, and painfull Preacher, Master | Iohn Randall Bachelour of Divinitie, Pastor of | Saint Andrewes Hubbart in little Eastcheape | London, sometimes Fellow of Lincolne Col- | ledge in Oxford. | Published by his Executor Iosh.Randall, as he found | it corrected by the Authors one hand, | in his Study, since his death. | . . . (3 lines).

    London, | Printed for Fulke Clifton, and are to be sold at his | Shop on new Fishstreet-hill. | 1630. | Line border. 18.3x13.9cm. (4),235,317p.

    Two parts.

    Also another identical edition, but with different imprint:

    London, | Printed for Iohn Bellamie, and are to be sold at his | Shop at the three Golden Lyons in Cornhill | neere the Royall Exchange. | 1630. | Line border. 18.3x14.1cm. (4),235,317p.

A REPLY | To | M. Nicholas | Smith, | His | Discvssion, | of some pointes of | M.Doctovr Kellison | his Treatise of the Hie- | rarchie. | By A Divine. | . . . (5. lines).

    Printet At Doway, | By the Widovve of Marke Wyon. 1630. | 15.7x9.7cm. 22,(15),301,(3)p.

    Gillow:III:684.

RODRIGUEZ, Alfonsus. The | Christian | Mans Gvide. | Wherein | Are contayned two Treatises. | The One | Shewing vs the perfection of our ordi- | nary Workes. | The Other | The purity of Intention we ought to | haue in all our Actions. | Both composed in Spanish by the R.F. | Alfonsvs Rodrigvez | of the Society of Iesvs. | Translated into English. | (ornament).

    Permissu Superiorum, M.DC.XXX. | 13.5x8.8cm. (8),80: (1),75–182p.

ROGERS, Richard. Seven Treatises: | Containing Svch | Direction As Is Gathe- | red Ovt Of The Holy Scriptvres, | leading and guiding to true happinesse, both in this life, | and in the life to come: and may be called the | Practice of Christianity. | Profitable for all such as heartily desire the | same: in the which, more particularly true Christians may | learne how to lead a godly and comfortable life every day, | notwithstanding their tribulations. | First penned, and novv set forth the fifth time, corrected and | enlarged by Richard Rogers, Preacher of the Word | of God at Wethersfield in Essex. | . . . (5 lines; device)

London, | Printed by the Assignes of Thomas Man for Richard Thrale, | and are to be sold at the Crosse-Keys at Pauls gate. | 1630. | 21.2x16.3 cm. (38), 834,(52)p.

RUTHERFORD, Samuel. Christ | And The | Doves | Heavenly Salutations, | With their Pleasant Conference together: | Or A | Sermon | Before The | Communion | In Anwoth.Anno 1630. | By that Flour of the Chvrch, | Mr.Samuel Rutherfurd. |

No imprint. 18.8x14.6cm 29p.
Probably printed after 1700. BMCat: [1630?]

SPENCER, John. The | Triall Of The | Protestant | Private Spirit. | VVherein | Their Doctrine, making the sayd Spirit the sole | ground & meanes of their Beliefe, is confuted. | By { Authority of Holy Scripture. | Testimonies of auncient Fathers. | Euidence of Reason, drawne from the Grounds of | Faith. | Absurdity of consequences following vpon it, against | all Faith, Religion, and Reason. | The Second Part, which is Doctrinall. | Written | By I.S. of the Society of Iesus. | (ornament) . . . (5 lines).

Permissu Superiorum. M.DC.XXX. | 18.4x13.1cm. (15),392,(8)p.
Anon. DNB:53:357b. Ascribed also to James Sharpe, by Gillow.

SQUIRE, John. A | Plaine | Exposition | Vpon The First | part of the second Chapter | of Saint Paul his second Epistle | to the Thessalonians. | Wherein it is plainly proved, that | The Pope is The Antichrist. | Being Lectures, in Saint Pauls, by Iohn | Sqvire Priest, and Vicar of Saint | Leonards Shoredich: | Sometime Fellow of Iesvs Colledge | in Cambridge. | . . . (5 lines).

London, | Printed for Philip Waterhouse, and are to be sold | at his Shop at the signe of St.Pauls Head in Canon | street neare London Stone. 1630. | Line border. 18.2x13.4cm. (17),768p.
From the library of Walter W. Law.

SYDENHAM, Humphrey. Sermons | By | Humph. Sydenham | late Fellow | Of | Wadham Colledge | in | Oxford. | . . . (1 line).

London, | Printed by William Stansby, for | Nathaniel Butter, at Saint | Austens Gate. | 1630. | Border. 18x13.9 cm. (6),44p. One sub-title page.
Contains only VVaters Of | Marah, And | Meribah: | 1630.

TAYLOR, John. All | The Workes | Of Iohn Taylor | The Water-Poet. | Beeing Sixty and three in Number. | Collected into one Volume by | the Avthor: VVith sundry new Additions, corrected, | reuised, and newly Jmprinted, 1630. | (ornament)

At London, | Printed by J. B. for James Boler; at the signe of the | Marigold in Pauls Churchyard. 1630. | 28.5x18.9 cm. (10),148,(2),343,148 p. 13, 14, repeated.

THORNBOROUGH, John. The | Last Will And | Testament Of Iesvs | Christ, touching the blessed Sacrament | of his body, and bloud, Signed, Sealed and | Delivered to the vse of all faithfull Christ- | ans, in the presence of many Witnesses, and | proved in the Prerogatiue of the Church of | Christ, by Reverend Bishops, Learned Doctors, | and Ancient Fathers of the same Church. | Exemplified, copied out, and explaned by the | Reverend Father in God, Iohn Thornbvrgh, | Bishop of Worcester. | (2 lines ; device).

Oxford, | Printed by William Tvrner, Printer | to the Famous Vniversitie. 1630. | 18x13.8cm. (5),118p.

TRAVERS, Walter. Vindiciæ | Ecclesiæ Anglicanæ: | Or | A Ivstification | Of The Religion Now | Professed In | England. | Wherein it it prooued to be the same | which was taught by our Sauiour Iesus | Christ, and by his holy Apostles; writ- | ten for their vse that haue desi- | red such proofe. | By W. T. | . . . (10 lines).

Printed at London by T. C. & R. C. for Michael Sparke, | dwelling at the blue Bible in Greene Arbor. 1630. | 17.9x13.4 cm. (6),80p.
Pollard, Short-Title Catalogue.

WADSWORTH, James. The English | Spanish Pilgrime. | Or, | A Nevv Discoverie | Of Spanish Popery, | And Iesviticall | Stratagems. | VVith the estate of the English Penti- | oners and Fugitiues vnder the King of | Spaines Dominions, and else where | at this present. | Also laying open the new Order of the Iesui- | trices and preaching Nunnes. | Composed by James Wadsworth Gentleman, | newly conuerted into his true mothers bosome, the | Church of England, with the motiues why he left the Sea of | Rome; a late Pentioner to his Maiesty of Spaine, and no- | minated his Captaine in Flanders: Sonne to Mr. | Iames Wadsworth, Bachelor of Diuinity, some- | time of Emanuell Colledge in the Vniuersity of | Cambridge, who was peruerted in the yeere | 1604. and late Tutor to Donia Maria | Infanta of Spaine. | Published by Authority. |

Printed at London by T.C. for Michael Sparke, dwelling at | the blue Bible in Greene-Arbor, 1630. | 18.1x13.5cm. (5),95p.

WADSWORTH, James. The | Present | Estate Of Spayne, | Or | A true relation of some remarkable | things touching the Court, and Gouern- | ment of Spayne, with a Catalogue of all | the Nobility, with their Reuenues. | Composed by Iames Wadsworth, | Gent. Late Pensioner to his Maiesty | of Spayne, and nominated his Cap- | taine in Flanders. | (ornament).

Imprinted at London by A.M. for Richard | Thrale, and Ambrose Ritherdon, and are to be sold | at their Shops in Pauls-Church-Yard. 1630. | 17x13.2cm. (6), 84p.

WIDDOWES, Giles. The Schysmatical | Pvritan. | A | Sermon Preached At Wit- | ney concerning the lawfulnesse of Church- | Authority, for ordaining, and comman- | ding of Rites, and Ceremonies, to | beautifie the Church. | By Giles Widdowes Rector of St | Martins Church in Oxford. | . . . (4 lines; ornament).

Printed at Oxford for the Author. 1630. | 17.8x13.8cm (22,24) p.

1631

ACONTIUS, Jacobus. Stratagematvm | Satanæ | Libri Octo | Quos | Jacobus Acontius | Vir Summi iudicij nec mino- | ris pietatis, annis abhinc penè 70 | primum edidit & Sereniss. | Reginæ Elizabethæ | inscripsit | Editio iterata & emendata | . . . (2 lines).

Oxonii. | Sumptibs Gulliemi Webb | Bibliopolæ Anno M.DC.XXXI | Engraved t.p. 14.5x9.3cm. (16), 426, (32)p.
"70" in 1.7 is interlined.

AILWARD, John. An | Historicall | Narration | Of | The Ivdgement Of | some most Learned and Godly English | Bishops, Holy Martyrs, and | Others: | (Whereof III; viz. Archbishop Cranmer, | B. Latimer, and Bishop Hooper, Suffred | Martyrdome, in the Dayes of Q.Mary, | for the Truth and Gospell of | Christ Iesvs) | Concerning Gods Election, and the | Merit of Christ his | Death, &c. | (devices)

London, | Printed by B.A. and T.F. for Samuel Nealand, and are to be | sold at his shop at the Signe of the Crowne in | Duck-Lane. 1631. | 17.2x13.5cm. (8), 108p.
See Divine And Politike Observations: 1638. p. 52 Prynne, W: Qvench-Coale: 1637. p. 23.

ARTICLES | To Be Inqvired | Of VVithin The | Diocesse of VVinchester. | In the Trienniall Visitation of the Reue- | rend Father in God, Richard, by the | Prouidence of God, Lord Bishop of | Winton, in the yeere of our | lord God, 1631. | (device).

London, | Printed by John Norton, 1631. | 18.5x14.8 cm. (2,14)p.

AUGUSTINE, Saint. Saint Augustines | Confessions translated: | And | With some marginall notes | illustrated. | Wherein, | Diuers Antiquities are | explayned; And the mar | ginall notes of a former Po- | pish Translation, an- | swered. | By | William Watts, Rector | of St. Albanes, | Woodstreete. |

London, | Printed by Iohn Norton, for | Iohn Partridge: and are | to be sold at the signe of the | Sunne in Pauls Church- | yard. 1631. | 13.5x7.7cm.(14),1012, (7)p. Engr. fore t.p.

AVILA, Juan de. Certain | Selected | Spiritvall | Epistles | Written by that most Reuerend holy man | Doctor I. de Auila a most renowned | Preacher of Spaine | Most profitable for all sortes of People, | whoe seeke their saluation. | . . . (3 lines; ornament).

At Roüen by the widdow of | Nicolas Courant. | Permissu Superiorum. | 1631. | Line border. 15.9x10cm.(5),441p.

BALL, John. A | Short | Treatise | Contayning all the Principall | Grounds of Christian | Religion. | By way of Questions and Answers, | very profitable for all men, but es- | pecially for Housholders. | The eight Impression: | (ornament).

London, | Printed by William Stansby and are to | be sold by Edward Brewster and | Robert Bird. | 1631. | 14.1x9cm. (12), 242p.
Anon. Cf.Cambr.Univ.Cat:3190.

BARCLAY, John. The | Mirrovr | Of Mindes, | Or, | Barclay's | Jcon animorum, | Englished by | T.M. |

London, | Printed by Iohn Norton | for Thomas Walkley | and are to be sold at his | shop, at the signe of the | Eagle and Child in Bri- | taines-Burse. 1631. | 12x6.8cm.(9),322; 224p.
Second part: The tenth Chapter, double letter register.

BEARD, Thomas. The | Theatre Of | Gods Iudge- | ments: | Re- uised, and augmented. | Wherein is represented the admirable | justice of God against all notorious sinners, both | great and small; but espe- cially against the most eminent | persons of the world, whose tran- scendent power | breaketh thorow the barres of humane Iustice; | deduced by the order of the Com | mandements. | Collected out of Sacred, Ecclesiasticall, and prophane | Histories. Now thirdly printed, and encreased with | many more Examples. | By the first Author thereof, Tho. Beard; Doctor | of Diuinitie, and Preacher of the Word of God in | the Towne of Huntington. | (ornament)
London, | Printed by Adam Islip, for Michael Sparke, | and are to be sould at the Blew Bible in Greene | Arbour. 1631. | 17.3x13.8cm.   (14),592,(12)pp.

BERNARD, Richard. Christian | See To Thy | Conscience, | Or | A Treatise of the nature, | the kinds and manifold differen- | ces of Conscience, all very briefly, | and yet more fully laid open | then hitherto, | By Richard Bernard, Pastor of Bat- | combe in Somerset- Shire. | Anno 1630. | (ornament).
London, | Imprinted by Felix Kyngston for Ro- | bert Milbourne, and are to be sold at his | shop in Pauls Churchyard at the signe | of the Grayhound. 1631. | Line border.   13.5x7.7cm.   (36),408p.

BOLTON, Robert. A | Discovrse | Abovt The | State Of Trve | Happinesse. | Delivered In Certaine | Sermons in Oxford, and at Pauls Crosse. | By Robert Bolton, Bachelour in Diuinity, and | Minister of Gods Word at Broughton in North- | hampton Shire. | The sixth Edi- tion, corrected and amended, | with a Table thereunto annexed. | . . . (4 lines; ornament).
At London, | Imprinted by Iohn Dawson, for Thomas Weauer, and | are to be sold at his shop at the great North | doore of Pauls Church. | 1631. | Line border. 19x14.5cm.(21), 215, (6)   Portr. frontisp.

BOLTON, Robert. Instrvc- | tions For A | Right Comforting | Af- flicted Consciences, | with speciall Antidotes against some | grievous temptations: | Delivered For | The Most Part In | The Lectvre At | Kettering in North-hampton- | shire: | By Robert Bolton, Batchelor in Divi- | nity, and Preacher of Gods Word at | Broughton in the same Coun- | tie. | (device)
London, | Imprinted by Felix Kyngston for Thomas Weaver, and | are to be sold at his shop at the great North-dore of Saint | Pauls Church. 1631. | Line border.   18.7x13.9cm.   (26),560pp.

BREREWOOD, Edward. A | Learned Treatise | Of The | Sabbath. | Written | By Mr Edward Brerewood | Professor in Gresham Colledge, | London. | To Mr Nicholas Byfield | Preacher in Chester. | With Mr Byfields answere and | Mr Brerewoods Reply. | The second Edition diligently corrected. | (device).
At Oxford, | Printed by Iohn Lichfield Printer to the Famous | Vniversity, for Thomas Huggins. | Anno Dom. 1631. | 17.8x13.8cm.   (3),101p.

BRINSLEY, John. The | Preachers | Charge. | And | Peoples Dvty. | About Preaching and Hearing | of the Word. | Opened | In a Sermon, being the first fruits of a publike | Exercise, begun in the Parish Church of Lownd, | for the benefit of the Island of Louingland | in Suffolke. | By Iohn Brinsley Minister of the Word | in great Yarmovth. | (device)

London, | Printed for Robert Bird, and are to be sold at his shop | at the signe of the Bible in Saint Laurence-lane. 1631. | 18.5x13.8cm. (4),32p. Folded plate.

BURGESS, John. An | Ansvver | Reioyned | To That Mvch Ap- | plauded Pamphlet of a Namelesse | Author, bearing this Title: | Viz. | A Reply To Dr.Mortons | Generall Defence of three Nocent | Ceremonies, &c. | The Innocency And Law- | fvlnesse whereof is againe in this | Reioynder vindicated. | By Dr.Iohn Bvrges, Pastor of | Sutton Coldfield in Warwickeshire. | Published by his Majesties speciall Command. | . . . (1 line).

London, | Printed by Augustine Matthewes for Robert Milbourne, | and are to bee sold at his Shop in Pauls Church- | yard at the Signe of the Grayhound. | 1631. | Line border. 18.8x14.4cm (29),75,654;(10),120p.

Cambr.Univ.Cat:4547. Two parts, with separate register and pagination.

BURGESS, John. The | Lavvfvlnes | Of | Kneeling | In The Act Of | Receiving The | Lords Svpper. | Wherein (by the way) also, some- | what of the Crosse in Baptisme. | First Written for satisfaction of a | Friend, and now published for | Common Benefit. | By Dr.Iohn Bvrges, Pastor of | Sutton Coldfield. |

London, | Printed by Augustine Matthewes for Robert Milbourne, | and are to bee sold at his Shop in Pauls Church- | yard at the Signe of the Grayhound. | 1631. | Line border. 18.8x14.4cm (10),120p.

Appended to his Answer Reioyned: 1631; with separate register and pagination.

BYFIELD, Richard. The | Doctrine | Of The | Sabbath | Vindicated, | In a confutation of a treatise of the Sab- | bath, written by M.Edward Breerwood against | M.Nic.Byfield, wherein these five things | are maintained: | First, that the fourth Commandement is given to the servant and | not to the master onely. | Secondly, that the fourth Commandement is morall. | Thirdly, that our owne light workes as well as gainefull and toile- | some are forbidden on the Sabbath. | Fourthly, that the Lords day is of divine Institution. | Fifthly, that the Sabbath was instituted from the beginning. | By the industrie of an unworthy labourer in Gods Vine- | yard, Richard Byfield, Pastor in Long | Ditton in Surrey. | . . . (2 lines)

London, | Imprinted by Felix Kyngston for Philemon Stephens and Christopher | Meredith at the golden Lyon in Pauls Church-yard. 1631. | Line border. 18.3x14.4cm. (20),227p.

CHAMBERS, David. Davidis | Camerarii | Scoti. | De Scotorvm Fortitvdine, | Doctrina, & Pietate, ac de ortu & progressu hæresis | in Regnis Scotiæ & Angliæ. | Libri Qvatvor. | Nunc Primvm In Lvcem Editi. | (device).

Parisiis. | Sumptibus Petri Baillet, viâ Iacobæâ, | sub Gallo & Leone repente. | M.DC.XXXI. | Cvm Privilegio Regis. | 22.2x16.6cm. (12),288,(9)p.

COTTON, Clement. A | Complete | Concordance | To The | Bible Of The | Last Translation. | By helpe whereof any passage of | holy Scripture may bee | readily turned unto. | The whole reviewed, corrected, | and much enlarged | By | Clement Cotton. | The further use & benefit of this Work is | more fully declared in the Pre- | faces to the Reader. | . . . (4 lines).

London, | Printed for T.Downs | and R. Young. 1631. | Column and vine border. 28.2x18.8cm.(12,885)p.

CRAKANTHORP, Richard. Vigilius Dormitans. | Romes Seer | Overseene. | Or | A Treatise Of The Fift | Generall Councell held at Constantinople, | Anno 553. under Iustinian the Emperour, in the | time of Pope Vigilivs: | The Occasion being those Tria Capitula, which for | many yeares troubled the whole Church. | Wherein Is Proved That The Popes | Apostolicall Constitution and definitive sentence in matter | of Faith, was condemned as hereticall by the Synod. | And the exceeding frauds of Cardinall Baronius and Binius | are clearly discovered. | By | Rich:Crakanthorp Dr. in Divinitie, | And Chapleine in ordinary to his late Majestie | King Iames. | Opus Posthumum. | Pvblished And Set Forth | By | His Brother Geo:Crakanthorp, | According to a perfect copy found written under the Authors owne hand. |

London, | Printed by M.F. for Robert Mylbovrne in Pauls | Churchyard at the signe of the Grey-hound. M DC XXXI. | Line border. 27.2x18.6 cm. (22),506,(9)p.

DAVENANT, John. Prælectiones | De Duobus | In Theologia | Controversis | Capitibus: | De | Judice Contro- | versiarum, | Primo; | De | Justitia Habituali | Et Actuali, | Altero: | Per | Reverendissimum Virum | Joan.Davenantium, | S. Theol.Doctorem (nunc Episcupum Sarisburiensem) | ante aliquot annos in celeberrima Academia Cantabrigiensi | Theologiæ professorem pro Domina Margareta, | in scholis Theologicis auditoribus suis dictatæ. | . . . (6 lines).

Cantabrigiæ, | Ex Academiæ celeberrimæ typographeo. | Anno MDCXXXI. | Border. 28.4x18.9cm (14),201,(6),205-641,(22)p. 589-590 omitted. Engr. portr. dated 1844 laid in.

DENISON, John. The | Heavenly | Banqvet: | Or The Doctrine | of the Lords Supper, set forth | in seuen Sermons. | With two Prayers before and after | the receiuing. | And a Iustification of Kneeling in the | act of Receiuing. | By Iohn Denison, Doctor of Divinity. | The Second Impression. | . . . (3 lines).

London, | Printed by E.A. for Robert Allot, and are | to bee sold within the Turning-Stile | in Holborne. 1631. | Line border. 14.1x9.2cm.(14),364p.

DOWNAME, George. The | Convenant | Of | Grace | Or | An Exposition | Vpon Lvke 1.73.74.75. | By George Downame Doctour | of Divinity, and Bishop of Dery. | (3 lines ; ornament)

Imprinted at Dublin by the Society of Stationers, | Printers to the Kings most Excellent | Maiestie. Anno Dom. 1631. | Line border. 17.6x13.7 cm. (5),414,(3)p. Contains also: A | Treatise Of | The Certainty | Of Perseverance: | Maintaining

The Trveth | Of The 38th Article Of The | Nationall Synode holden at Dublin | in the yeare 1615. | (6 lines; ornament)
  Dvblin, | Printed by the Society of Stationers. An. Dom. 1631. | Pp. 233–414.

DYKE, Daniel. Tvvo | Treatises. | The one, | Of Repentance, | The other, | Of Christs Temptations. | Penned, | By the late faithfull Minister of Gods VVord, | Daniel Dyke, Batchelour | in Diuinitie. | Published since his death by his Brother | I.D. Minister of Gods Word. | . . . (2 lines). The fift impression. |
  London, | Printed by Iohn Beale, and are to be | sold by Phillip Waterhouse at the signe of St. | Pauls head in Canon street, neare | London stone. 1631. | Line border. 19.2x14cm. (6),358p. Sub t.p. at p 199: Michael | And The | Dragon, | . . . with continuous register and pagination.

FLOYD, John. A | Paire Of | Spectacles | For Sir | Hvmfrey Linde | To See His Way Withall. | Or | An Answeare To His | booke called, Via Tvta, A safe way: | wherein the booke is shewed to be a laby- | rinthe of error and the author a blind | guide. By I.R. | . . . (10 lines; ornament).
  [Rouen.] Permissv Svperiorvm. | 1631. | 16.4x10.6cm. (39),530,(2)p. (Pp. 207–8, 333–4 repeated)
  Anon. DNB.34:339b. Gillow,II:303. Ascribed also to Robert Jenison

GARDINER, Richard. Concio | Ad | Clervm | Habita | In Templo Beatæ | Mariæ Oxon: Feb: 14. | Per | Richardvm Gardyner Sa: | Theol: Doct: & Eccles. Cath: | Christi Canonicum. | (device).
  Oxoniæ, | Excudebat Io: Lichfield Impensis | Gvil: Davis, & Ed. Forrest. | Anno Dom. 1631. | Line border. 18.x14.cm. (6),24p.

GODWIN, Thomas. Romanæ | Historiae | Anthologia | Recognita Et Avcta. | An | English Exposition | Of The Roman Anti- | quities, wherein many Roman | & English offices are paralleld | and divers obscure phra- | ses explained | For the vse of Abingdon Schoole. | Newly revised and inlarged by the | Author |
  At Oxford, | Printed by Iohn Lichfield, | Printer to the famous Vniversity | for Henry Cripps. | Ann. Dom. 1631. | Arch. border. 18.x13.6cm. (7),277,(23)p.
  Dedication, signed.

GOUGE, William. The | Chvrches | Conqvest | over the Sword: | Set out on Exod.Chap.XVII.Verse | VIII, &c. to the end. | Hereunto is added, | The Extent of Gods | Providence: On Mat.Chap.X,Vers. | XXIX,XXX,XXXI, Occasioned by a | Downe-fall of Papists. | And | The Dignitie of Chivalry: | Raised out of II.Chron.VIII.IX. | By William Govge. | (ornament).
  London, | Printed by George Miller for Edward Brewster, and are to be sold | at his Shop at the Signe of the Bible, at the great North | doore of Pauls. 1631. | Line border. 18.2x13.5cm. (16),177–436,(6)p.
  Incorporated with his Gods Three Arrowes: 1631 .

GOUGE, William. Dearths | Death: | Or, | A Removall | of Famine: Gathered out of | II Sam. XXI.1. | By William Govge. | . . . (7 lines; ornament)

London, | Printed by George Miller for Edward Brewster, and are to be sold | at his Shop at the Signe of the Bible, at the great North | doore of Pauls. 1631 | Line border. 19.1x14.6cm. (8),129–176p.
Incorporated with his: Gods | Three | Arrovves: | . . . 1631.

GOUGE, William. The | Dignitie | Of | Chivalry, | Set forth in | A Sermon, Preached | before the Artillery Company of | London, Iune xiij. 1626. | The second Edition. | By William Govge. | . . . (6 lines; ornament)

London, | Printed by George Miller for Edward Brewster, and are to be sold | at his Shop at the Signe of the Bible, at the great North | doore of Pauls. 1631. | Line border. 19.1x14.6cm. 403–436p.
Incorporated with the second part of his Gods Three Arrowes: 1631.

GOUGE, William. The | Extent | Of Gods | Providence, | Set out in | A Sermon, Preached | in Black-Fryers Church, V.Nov.1623. | On occasion of the Downe-fall of Papists in a | Chamber at the said Black-Fryers, 1623.Oct.27. | stilo vet.Nov.5.stilo novo. | By William Govge. | . . . (1 line; ornaments).

London, | Printed by George Miller for Edward Brewster, and are to be sold | at his Shop at the Signe of the Bible, at the great North | doore of Pauls 1631. | Line border. 19.1x14.6cm. 371–436,(10)p.
Incorporated with his: Gods | Three | Arrovves: | . . . 1631.

GOUGE, William. Gods | Three | Arrovves: | Plagve, Famine, | Svvord, | In three Treatises. | I. A Plaister for the Plague. | II. Dearths Death. | III. The Churches Conquest over the Sword. | By William Govge Doctor in Divinity, and Preacher | of Gods Word in Black-Friers, London. | . . . (5 lines)

London, | Printed by George Miller for Edward Brewster, and are to be sold | at his Shop at the Signe of the Bible, at the great North | doore of Pauls. 1631. | Line border. 18.2x13.5cm (14),128;(8),129–176,(16),177–436,(6)p.
Continuous register and pagination: Appended are two sermons: The | Extent | Of Gods | Providence, | and, The | Dignitie | Of | Chivalry. |

HARRIS, Robert. The | Arraignement | Of The VVhole | Creatvre, | At the Barre of Religion, Reason, | and Experience. | Occasioned vpon an Inditement preferred | by the Soule of Man against the Prodigals vanity | and Vaine Prodigality. | Explained, | Applyed, and Tryed in the Historie and Misterie | of that Parable. | From whence is drawne this Doome Or- | thodoxall, and Ivdgement Divine. | That no Earthly Vanity can satisfie Mans heavenly Soule. | And by reason of the variety of Instances and Demonstra- | tions, it may serve in some sort as a Common- | Place, for almost all manner of | Readings. | (ornament)

London. | Printed by B. Alsop and Tho: Favvcet, | 1631. | Line border. 18.7x 13.5 cm. (25),335,(1)p.
Epistle dedicatory, signed R.H. BMCat. H&L, new ed.

HARRIS, Robert. Peters | Enlargement | Vpon | The Prayers Of | The Chvrch. | The seuenth Edition. | VVhereunto is added certaine Queres and | Cases touching the Theorie and Practice of Prayer: | also Inducements and Incouragements to Perseuerance in that Dutie. | By Master Harris. | . . . (3 lines; device)

London, | Printed by I.B. for Iohn Bartlet, at the Golden Cup, in the | Gold-Smiths Row in Cheap-side. 1631. | 18.8x14.2 cm. (7),47p.

A1, blank; reverse, "Vpon the Copper-piece". A2: frontispiece, containing title.
Epistle Dedicatory, signed R.H. H&L. Bodl.

HERLE, Charles. Contemplations | And Devotions On | The seuerall passages of our | blessed Saviours Death | and Passion. | Written by Charles Herle, | Master in Arts, and sometimes of | Excester Colledge in Oxford. | Pauls am- | bition of {1 Knowledge. | I Cor.2.2. | . . . (3 lines) 2.Wealth. | Phil.3.8. | . . . (3 lines) 3 Ioy. | Gal 6.14. | . . . (3 lines).
London: | Printed by Aug. Mat. for Humphrey Robinson, | dwelling in Pauls-Churchyard at the signe | of the three Pidgeons. 1631. | Line border. 13.9x8.2cm (9),546,7p.

HOOKER, Richard. Of The | Lawes | of | Ecclesiastical | Politie, | Eight Bookes | By Richard Hooker. |
London | Printed by Will:Stansby, and are | to be sold by Mat:Lownes. | Año D 1617. | Engr. t.p. 28. x19. cm. (58),583,(15)p.
Fifth book has separate t.p. at p. 169, with "grape and column" compartment, dated 1616. Certayne | Divine | Tractates, | with sep. t.p. before p. 453 dated 1622; The | Answere | Of | Mr. Richard Hooker | at p. 467; A | Learned | Discovrse Of | Justification, at p. 485; Five | Learned | Sermons, | at p. 523; and Two | Sermons | Vpon Part | Of S. Ivdes. | Epistle. |, p. 551, all dated 1631, with "grape and column" compartment. Pagination continuous throughout

HUNT, Nicholas. The | Nevv-Borne | Christian: | Or, | A Lively Patterne, | And Perfect Representa- | tion Of The Saint-Militant | Child of God; layd open and described to the | life, by his holy antipathie, and contrariety | to sinne and impiety: his establishment | in grace, and finall perseverance. | . . . (7 lines).
London: Printed by Avg: Matthewes for Richard Col- | lins, and are to be solde at the three Kings in Paules | Church-yard. 1631. | Line border. 18.4 x 13.5 cm. (21),310 p.
Epistle Dedicatorie, signed.

JACKSON, Thomas. Ivstifying | Faith: | Or | The Faith by which the just do live. | A Treatise, containing a De- | scription of the Nature, Properties, and | Conditions of Christian Faith. | With a discovery of misperswasions, breeding pre- | sumption or hypocrisie, and meanes how Faith | may be planted in Vnbeleevers. | The second Edition revised and corrected. | By | Thomas Iackson Dr. of Divinitie, | Chaplaine to his Majesty in Ordinary, and Pre- | sident of Corpus Christi Colledge in Oxford. | . . . (5 lines).
London, | Printed by M.F. for Iohn Clarke, and are to be sold at | his shop under S. Peters Church in Cornhill. 1631. | Line border. 19.5x14.8 cm. (41), 499 p.

KNOTT, Edward. Modesta Ac Brevis | Discvssio | Aliqvarvm | Assertionvm | D. Doctoris | Kellisoni | Quas in suo de Ecclesia- | stica Hierarchia | Tractatu probare conatur: | Auctore Nicolao Smitheo. | . . . (4 lines; device).
Antverpiæ, | Ex Officina Plantiniana | Balthasaris Moreti. | M.DC.XXXI. | 13.8x 8. cm. 262p.
Anon. DNB. 31: 291 b.

MAYER, John. A | Commentarie | Vpon | The New Testament. | Representing the Diuers Expositions ther- | of, out of the Workes of the most learned, both ancient | Fathers and moderne Writers, and hereby sifting out the | true sense of euery passage, for the benefit of | all that desire to read with | vnderstanding. | The third Volume. | Containing the seuen smaller Epistles, called Catholike, | and the Booke of the Reuelation. | By Iohn Mayer, Doctor of Diuinitie. | . . . (3 lines; ornament).

London, | Printed by Iohn Hauiland, for Iohn Grismond, and are to be sold | at his shop in Iuie Lane, at the signe of the Gun. | 1631. | 18.4x14.2cm.(2),(30), 542p.

MAYER, John. A | Commentarie | Vpon The | New Testament. | Representing the divers expositions thereof, | out of the workes of the most learned, both ancient Fa- | thers, and moderne Writers: and hereby sifting out the true | sense of every passage, for the benefit of all that desire | to reade with understanding. | The First Volumne upon the foure Evangelists | and the Acts of the Apostles. | Wherein the places more difficult going under the name of Texts, | are more largely; the lesse difficult, more briefly expounded. | By Iohn Mayer, Dr. in Divinity, and Pastour of the | Church of Reydon in Suffolke. | . . . (5 lines; ornament).

London, | Printed by Thomas Cotes, for John Bellamie, and are to be sold at his shoppe | in Cornehill, at the signe of the three Golden Lyons, neere the | Royall Exchange. 1631. | Line border. 28.7x18.6cm. (10),621,(5)p.

MORTON, Thomas. Of The | Institvtion | Of The Sacrament | Of The Blessed Bodie | And Blood Of Christ, | (by some called) | The Masse of Christ, | Eight Bookes; | Discovering the Superstitious, Sacri- | legious, and Idolatrous Abominations | Of The Romish | Masse. | Together With | The Consequent Obstinacies, Overtures of | Perjuries, and the Heresies discernable | in the Defenders | thereof. | By the R. Father in God | Thomas L. Bishop of Coventry and | Lichfield. |

London, | Printed by W.Stansby, for Robert Mylbovrne | in Pauls Church-yard at the signe of the | Grey-hound. MDCXXXI. | Line border. 28.4x18.7cm. (20), 255,143,(16)p.

PAGE, Samuel. A | Godly | Learned Expo- | sition, Together | with apt and profitable Notes on the | Lords Prayer: | Written by the late Reuerend Ortho- | doxe Diuine, and faithfull Seruant of Iesus | Christ, Samvel Page, Doctor in Diui- | nity, and Preacher of Gods Word at Deptford | Stronde, in the County of Kent. | Published since his death, | By Nathaniel Snape, of Grayes Inne, | Esquire. | (ornament).

London: | Printed by Thomas Harper, | 1631. | 18.7x14.2cm. (5),350p.

PAGE, William. A | Fvrther | Ivstification | Of Bowing At | The Name Of | Iesvs. | Or | An Examination | Of Svch Considera- | ble Reasons As Are | made by Mr Prinne in a reply to | Mr.Widdowes concerning | the same Argument. | By William Page Bac. of Divinity | and Fellow of Alsoules Colledge | in Oxford. | . . . (5 lines).

Oxford | Printed by Iohn Lichfield Printer | to the Famous Vniversity. | Ann. Dom. 1631. | 17.3x12.4cm. (1),140–142,133–206p.

Sub. t.p. of his Treatise or Ivstification: 1631.

PAGE, William. A Treatise | Or | Ivstification | Of Bowing At | The Name Of | Jesvs. | By way of Answere to an Appendix | against it. | Together With An Examinati- | on of such considerable reasons as are made | by Mr Prinne in a reply to Mr | Widdowes concerning the | same argument. | By William Page Bac: of Divinity | and Fellow of All-Soulne Colledge | in Oxford. | Published by Command | . . . (5 lines).

Oxford | Printed by Iohn Lichfield Printer | to the Famous Vniversity. | Ann. Dom. 1631. | 18.5x14.5 cm   (18),1–126,(1),140–2,133–206 p Two sub-title pages, Sig R3–4 omitted.

PEMBLE, William. The | Period | Of | The Persian | Monarchie. | VVherein sundry places of Ezra, | Nehemiah and Daniel are cleered: | Extracted, contracted, and englished, much | of it out of Doctor Raynolds, by the late | learned and godly Man William | Pemble, of Magdalen-Hall | in Oxford. | Published and enlarged since his death by his friend, | Richard Capel. | . . . (3 lines).

London | Printed by R.Y. for Iohn Bartlet at the signe of the | guilt Cup in Cheape-side in the Gold- | smiths Row. 1631. | Line border. 18.2x13.6cm. (3),84p.

Also another impression, identical excepting a hyphen in " Magdalen Hall " and the omission of " his friend ", before the name of Richard Capel. 18.2x13.6 cm. (3),84p.

PERKINS, William. An | Exposition | Of The Symbole | Or Creede Of The | Apostles, According To The | Tenovr Of The Scriptvres, And | The Consent Of The Orthodoxe | Fathers Of The Chvrch. | Reuiewed and corrected, | By | William Perkins. | . . . (2 lines; device).

Printed at London by Iohn Legatt, and are to be sold by | Simon Waterson, at the Signe of the Crowne in | Pauls-Church yard. 1631. | 18.5x14.4cm. (8), 477pp.

PINKE, William. The | Tryall | of a Christians syncere | loue vnto Christ: | By Mr William Pinke, Master | of Arts late Fellow of Mag. | dalen Colledge in | Oxford. | . . . (motto; device).

At Oxford, | Printed by Iohn Lichfield, | Printer to the famous University, | for Edward Forrest. | Ann. Dom. 1631. | Border. 17.5x14.cm. (10),25;28;29,(1)p. Lacks third sermon.

PRESTON, John. The Lavv | Ovt Lavved. | Or, | The Charter of the Gospell shewing the priviledge and pre- | rogative of the Saints by vertue of the Covenant. | Wherein these foure points of doctrine are properly observed, | Plainely proved, both by Scripture and reason: and | pithily applyed. Viz: | Doctrine { 1 That he that is in the state of grace lyeth in no knowne | sinne, no sinne hath dominion over him. | 2 That sinne though it doth not raigne in the Saints, yet | { it doth remaine and dwell in them. | 3 That the way to overcome sinne, is to get assurance of | the Love, and grace, and favour of God, whereby it is | { forgiven them. | 4 That whosoever is under the Law, sinne hath dominion | over him. | By that late faithfull and worthy Minister of Iesus | Christ. Iohn Preston. | Doctor in divinity, Chap- laine in ordinary to his Majestie, Master of | Emmanuel Colledge in Cambridge, and sometimes preacher of | Lincolnes Inne. | . . . (2 lines).

Edinbvrgh Printed by Iohn Wreittoun. 1631. | 17.6x13.6cm. (1,17)p.

PRESTON, John. Three | Sermons | Vpon The Sa- | crament Of The | Lords Svpper. | By the late Faithfull and VVorthy | Minister of Jesus Christ, | Iohn Preston, | Dr. in Divinity, Chaplaine in Ordinary to his | Majestie, Master of Emanuel Colledge in Cam- | bridge, and sometimes Preacher of | Lincolnes Inne. | (ornament).

London, | Printed by Thomas Cotes, for Michael Sparke, and are to | be sold at the blue Bible in Greene Arbor. 1631. | Line border. 18.4x13.9cm. (1),88p.

PRESTON, John. A | Treatise | Of | Effectuall | Faith: | Deliuered in six Sermons vpon I Thes.1.3. | By the late faithfull and worthy Minister | of Iesvs Christ, | Iohn Preston, | Dr. in Diuinity, Chaplaine in ordinary to His | Maiesty; Master of Emanuel Colledge in | Cambridge; and sometime Preacher | of Lincolnes-Inne. | . . . (4 lines; ornament).

London: | Printed for Nicholas Bourne. 1631. | Line border. 18.3x14.0 cm. (1),200p.

Part of his " Breast-Plate of Faith and Love " 1630; with continuous register.

RANDALL, John. Tvventy | Nine Lectvres | Of The Chvrch; | Very necessary for the consolation and | support of Gods Church, especially | in these times: | Wherein is handled, first, in generall concer- | ning first, the Name; secondly, the Titles; thirdly, the Nature, | fourthly, the diuision of the true Church: | Secondly, of the visible Church; first, the Definition secondly, | the Causes; thirdly, the Members; fourthly, the Markes and | Notes; fifthly, the Gouernment; sixthly, the Priuiledges; se- | uenthly, the Aduersaries; eightly, the Authority: | And lastly, the application of it to all Churches in the World so | farre as they are knowne to vs. | By that Learned and Faithfull Preacher, Master Iohn | Randall, Batchelor of Diuinity, Pastor of Saint Andrewes | Hubbart in little Eastcheape, London, and sometimes Fellow of | Lincolne Colledge in Oxford. | Published by the Coppie perfected and giuen by the Author in his life | time; carefully preserued and adorned with Notes in the Margent, by | the late faithfull Minister of Christ, Master | William Holbrooke. | . . . (1 line).

London, Imprinted by Felix Kyngston for Nathanael Newbery, at | the Starre in Popes-head Alley. 1631. | Line border. 18.x13.4cm. (6),311; 230p.

Second part (from nineteenth lecture), with double-letter register, and separate pagination.

REEVE, Edmund. The | Christian | Divinitie, | Contained in the Divine Service of | The Church of England: | Summarily, and for the most part in order, ac- | cording as point on point dependeth, composed; | and with the holy Scriptures plainly and | plentifully confirmed: | Written for the furtherance of the Peoples under- | standing in the true Religion established | by publike Authoritie, | And for the increase of Vnitie in that godly truth eternall. | By | Edmvnd Reeve Bachelour in Diuinitie, | and Vicar of the Parish of Hayes in Middlesex. | . . . (6 lines).

London, | Printed for Nicolas Fussell and Humphrey Mosley, at the signe | of the Ball in Pauls Church-yard. 1631. | Line border. 18.3x14.3 cm. (24),392 p. Title page in red and black.

SELDEN, John. Titles | of | Honor, | By Iohn Selden. | The Second Edition. | . . . (6 lines).

London, | Printed by William Stansby for Richard Whitakers, | and are to be sold at the Kings Armes | in Pauls Churchyard. | MDCXXXI. | 27.9x18.4cm. (36), 941, (1)p.

SMITH, Henry. The | Sermons | Of | Mr. Henry Smith: | Gathered into one volume. | Printed According To His | corrected Copies in his life time. | Wherevnto Is Added, | Gods Arrow against Atheists. | (device)

London, | Printed by the Assignes of Thomas Man, Paul Man, | and Ionah Man. 1631. | 19.8 x 14.3 cm, 600 p.

SMITH, Richard. A Conference | Of The Catholike | And Protestante | Doctrine With The Expresse | Words Of Holie Scriptvre. | Which Is The Second Parte Of The | Prudentiall Balance of Religion. | VVherein | Is Clearely Shewed, That In More | then 260 points of controuersie, Catholiks agree with the holie | Scripture, both in words and sense: and Protestants disagree in | both, and depraue both the sayings, words, and sense of Scripture. | Written First In Latin, Bvt Now Avg- | mented and translated into English. | . . . (6 lines; ornament).

At Doway, | By the widdowe of Marke Wyon, at the signe of the Phenix. | M.DC.XXXI. | 21.4x16cm.(31),798,(10)p.
Anon. Gillow.V:513.

SNAWSELL, Robert. A | Looking-Glasse | For | Married Folkes, | Wherein they may plainly see their | Deformities; and also how to behaue | themselues one to another, and both of | them towards God. | Set forth Dialogue-wise for the more | tastable and plainnesse sake, | By R.S. | . . . (6 lines).

London, | Printed by Iohn Haviland for | Henry Bell, and are to be sold at his | house in Eliots Court, inthe little | Old-Bayley. 1631. | 12.8x9.2cm. (10), 128p.
Preface to the Reader, signed.

STERNHOLD, Thomas, and HOPKINS, John. The Whole | Booke Of | Psalmes: | Collected into English | Meeter by Thomas Sternhold, | Iohn Hopkins, and others. | Set foorth and allowed to be sung in all | Churches, of all the people together, be- | fore and after Morning and Euening | Prayer; and also before & after Sermons, | and moreouer in priuate houses for their | godly solace and comfort: laying apart | all vngodly songs and ballades, which | tend onely to the nourishing of vice, | and corrupting of youth. | . . . (9 lines)

London, | Printed for the Companie | of Stationers. 1631. | Cum Priuilegio Regis Regali. | Lace border. 14.8x8.6cm. (10),99,(9)p.

STOW, John and HOWES, Edmund. Annales, | Or, | A Generall | Chronicle | Of | England. | Begun by Iohn Stow: | Continved And | Augmented with matters For- | raigne and Domestique, Anci- | ent and Moderne, vnto the end of | this present yeere, 1631. | By Edmvnd Howes, Gent. |

Londini, | Impensis Richardi | Meighen, | 1631. | 31.3x21cm. (1), 1–1050, (2), 1057–1062, (4) 1063–1087,(27)p. Pp 819, 891 1003–1014 repeated; 902–990 omitted in numbering. Colophon. Engr. t.p., with vignettes and royal arms

TAYLOR, Thomas. The | Progresse | Of Sants To | Fvll Holinesse. | Described | In sundry Apostolicall Aphorismes, | or short precepts tending to | sanctification. | With a sweete and divine Apostolicall prayer | to attaine the practise of those holy precepts, | which is also expounded. | By Thomas Taylor, Doctor in Di- | vinity, and Pastor of St.Mary Alder- | manbury, London. | . . . (3 lines).

London, | Printed by W.I. for Iohn Bartlet, at the signe of | the Guilded Cuppe in Cheapeside, in Gold- | smiths Rowe. 1631. | Line border. 18x13.3cm.(20),409,(13)p.

TAYLOR, Thomas. Regula Vitæ, | The | Rvle Of | The Law | Vnder The | Gospel. | Containing | A Discovery of the pesti- | ferous sect of Libertines, | Antinomians, and sonnes of | Belial, lately sprung up both to | destroy the Law, and disturbe | the faith of the Gospell: | Wherein is manifestly proved, that | God seeth sinne in iustified persons. | By Thomas Taylor Dr. of | Divinity, and Pastour of S. Mary | Aldermanbury, London. | . . . (3 lines).

Imprinted at London by W. I. for | Robert Dawlman at the Brazen Serpent | in Paules Churchyard: 1631. | Line border. 14x8 cm. (21),234p.
Sig. A1 blank.
Also another copy from the Library of Walter W. Law. 13.6x8.cm.

TWISSE, William. A | Discovery | Of | D. Iacksons | Vanitie. | Or | A perspective Glasse, wherby the admirers of D. Iack- | sons profound discourses, may see the vanitie and | weaknesse of them, in sundry passages, and especially so | farre as they tende to the undermining of the doctrine hi- | therto received. | Written by William Twisse, Doctor of Divinitie, as | they say, from whom the Copie came to the Presse. | . . . (2 lines ; ornament)

Imprinted Anno M.DC.XXXI. | 18.2x13.7 cm. (10),710pp.

USSHER, James. Gotteschalci, | Et | Prædestinatianæ | Controversiæ Ab | Eo Motæ, Historia: | Vnà cum duplice ejusdem Confessione, | nunc primùm in lucem editâ, | â | Iacobo Vsserio Archi- | episcopo Armachano, & | totius Hiberniæ Primate. | (ornament).

Dvblinii, | Ex Typographiâ Societatis Bibliopolarum. | Anno MDCXXXI. | Line border. 17.5x13.5cm. (5),237,(1)p.

WIDDOWES, Giles. The | Lawlesse | Kneelesse | Schismaticall | Pvritan. | Or | A Confvtation | Of The Avthor | Of An Appendix, | concerning bowing at the | name of Iesus. | Written | By Giles Widdowes Rector of St | Martins Church in Oxford, | and late fellow of | Oriell Colledge. | . . . (4 lines).

Printed at Oxford for the Author. 1631. | 17.7x13.7 cm. (6),91,(1)cm. 1-2 blank; 87 repeated.
Cambr.Univ.Cat.5393.

WIDDOWES, Giles. The | Schismatical | Pvritan. | A | Sermon Preached At Wit- | ney concerning the lawfulnesse of Church- | Authority, for ordaining, and comman- | ding of Rites, and Ceremonies, to | beautifie the Church. | By Giles Widdowes Rector of St | Martins Church in Oxford. | The second edition, Augmented. | . . . (4 lines; device).

Printed at Oxford for the Author. 1631. | 17.7x13.7 cm. (23,24)p.

WILLETT, Andrew. Hexapla | In Leviticum | That Is, | A Six-Fold Commen- | tarie Vpon The Third | Booke Of Moses, Called | Leviticus. | Wherein sixe severall things are observed | vpon every Chapter. | 1. The Argument, Parts, and | Contents. | 2.The divers Readings, with | approbation of the best. | || 3. The discussing of doubtfull questions. | 4. Collection of Places of Doctrine. | 5. Confutation of Errors. | 6. Morall observations. | With a large Explication of the naturall properties | of Beasts, Fowles, Fishes, and creeping things, applied | vnto manners out of the II. Chapter. | Wherein more then a thousand Theologicall Questions are | handled, and halfe as many speciall poynts of Doctrine | noted, and Errours confuted. | And wherein is collected and abridged whatsoever worthy | of note, either Christians, or Iewes, the best Writers, | Greekes, or Latines, Old or New, Protestants | or Papists haue written vpon | this Booke: | By the same Author of Hexapla, vpon | the two former Books of the Pentetevch, | Genesis, and Exodvs. | Perused and finished by P.S. Dr. of Divinitie. . . . (1 line)

London, | Printed by Aug. Matthewes, for Robert Milbovrne, at the | signe of the Greyhound in Pauls Church-yard. 1631. | Line border. 28.5 x 18.2 cm. (39), 778 p.

Author named, A3, verso.

WILSON, John. Zachevs | Converted: | Or, | The Rich | Publicans { Repentance. | Restitution. | In which, the Mysteries of | the Doctrine of Conversion, | are sweetly laid open and ap- | plyed for the establishing | of the weakest. | Also | Of Riches in their getting, keeping, | expending; with divers things about almes | and restitution, and many other mate- | riall points and cases insisted upon. | By Iohn Wilson, late Preacher | of Gods Word in Guilford. | (ornament).

Printed at London by T.Cotes, for Fulke | Clifton, and are to be sold at his shop upon | new Fishstreete hill, 1631. | Line border. 14x7.7cm.(37), 584p.

1632

ATTERSOLL, William. Gods Trvmpet, | Sovnding The | Alarme, | Sommoning all persons speedily | to repent, and turne unto God, | teaching the doctrine, removing the hindrances, | and urging the practise of true repentance, | before the evill dayes come which | are at hand. | . . . (9 lines; device).

London. | Printed by T. C. for Michael Sparkes. 1632. | 17.x13.2 cm. (1),134, (2)p. 124–5 repeated.

Anon. DNB.2:240a

BALL, John. A Treatise | Of Faith, | Diuided into two Parts. | The first shewing the | Natvre, | The second, The Life of | Faith. | Both tending to direct the weake | Christian how he may possesse the | whole Word of God as his owne, ouer- | come temptations, better his obedi- | ence, and liue comfortably | in all estates. | By Iohn Ball. | . . . (2 lines). The second Edition corrected and enlarged. |

London, | Printed by George Miller for Edward | Brewster, and are to be sold at the signe of | the Bible, at the great North doore of Pavls. 1632 | Arch. border. 19.1x14.3cm.(32), 428,(50)p. 18.5x14cm. (36), 428,(50)p.

Also another copy from the library of Walter W. Law. 18.2x13.7cm.(36),428,(50)p.

BARLOW, John. An | Exposition | Of The | First And Second | Chapters | Of The Latter Episte | Of The Apostle Paul to Timothie. | Wherein | The Text is logically resolved: The words also plain- | ly explicated; with an easie Metaphrase an- | nexed. Thence doctrines arising are dedu- | ced: And by Scripture, Examples, | and Reason confirmed. | All which, for the better vnderstanding, affecting, and retaining | of the truth, be with familiar similitudes accompanied. | Finally, as the matter would afford definitions, distributions, | sub-divisions, trials, motives, and directions, which be of | speciall use, in their proper order are added. | By Iohn Barlow, sometime Minister of the word at Plimmouth: | but lately one of the Preachers in that ancient | Citie of Chester. | (ornament).

London, | Printed by R. Y. and are to be sold in Pauls Church-yard | by George Lathum and Iames Boler, 1632. | Line border. 28.2x18.3cm. (16),247;(7),215p. T.p. mounted. Sub t.p.

Also another copy from the liprary of Walter W. Law. 27,3x18.5cm.

Second chapter has separate t.p., with 3-letter register and separate pagination.

Contains also his: A seasonable | Discourse | Of Spiritvall | Stedfastnes. | . . . 1632. And The | True Guide | To | Glory. | . . . 1632. wh. see.

BARLOW, John. A seasonable | Discourse | Of Spiritvall | Stedfastnes. | Wherein | {I. It, and a Relapse, with the heads, members, and | degrees of both, are exactly defined. | 2. The Subiects, Causes, and Symptomes of the fear- | full sinne of Apostasie clearly expressed.} As also Directions, Incentives, to recover, re-inkindle the | old-cold-declining Zelot. | Together with Arguments, Motives, that the young or | strong standing Convert may be in Grace | firmely established. | . . . (2 lines) By I. B. Preacher of the Word. | (ornament).

London, | Printed by R.Y. and are to be sold in Pauls Church-yard | by Iames Boler and George Lathum, 1632. | Line border. 28.2x18.3cm. (7),60p.

Appended to his: An | Exposition | Of The | First And Second | Chapters | Of The Latter Episte | Of The Apostle Paul to Timothie. | . . . 1632. | With continuous register, but separate pagination.

BARLOW, John. The | True Guide | To | Glory. | A Sermon Preached | At Plympton-Mary In Devon, | at the Funerals of the Right Worshipfull, and truly | Religious Lady, The Lady Strode | of Newingham. | By Io. Barlow. | . . . (5 lines ; device).

London, | Printed by Iohn Haviland, for Nathaniel Newberrie, and are to besold at | his shop under Saint Peters Church in Cornehill. | 1632. | 28.2x18.3cm. (6),102p.

Appended to his: An | Exposition | Of The | First And Second | Chapters | Of The Latter Episte | Of The Apostle Paul to Timothie. | . . . 1632.

Contains also, each with separate t.p.: The | Good Mans | Refuge in affliction. | ; The | Ioy Of The | Vpright Man. | ; Hierons last Fare-vvell. | ; and A | Christians | last Day, is his best Day. | 1632

BREREWOOD, Edward. A | Second Treatise | Of The | Sabbath, | Or | An Explication Of | the Fourth Commandement. | Written, | By Mr Edward Brerewood | professor in Gresham Colledge | in London. | (ornament)

At Oxford, | Printed by Iohn Lichfield, and are to be sold by | Thomas Huggins, Ann. Dom. 1632. | 17.8x13.8cm. 50p.

BYFIELD, Nicholas. The | Signes, | Or | An Essay Con- | cerning the assurance of | Gods loue, and mans saluation; | gathered out of the holy | Scriptures. | By Nicholas Byfield | one of the Preachers for | the Citie of Chester. | Newly corrected and amended. | . . . (5 lines).

London, | Printed by John Davvson, | for Iohn Bellamy. | 1632. | Line border. 11.8x7.1cm.(16),123p.

CAMERON, John. Ioh.Cameronis | Myrothecivm | Evangelicvm. | Hoc est, | Novi Testamenti Loca | quamplurima ab eo, post aliorum labores, | aptè & commodè vel illustrata, vel | explicata, vel vindicata. | Quibus ad calcem adiectum est, Lvd.Cappelli | Spicilegivm, eiusdem argumenti. | & Diatribæ duæ | I.De Interpretatione Loci Matth.xv.5. | II.De Voto Iephtæ. | (device)

Genevæ, | Apud Petrvm Avbertvm, Reipublicæ | & Academiæ Typographum. | M.DC.XXXII. | 21.6x16.1cm. (14),360; 184,(14)p.
Two parts; continuous register.

CAMUS, John Peter. A | Dravght | Of | Eternitie. | Written in French by Iohn | Peter Camvs Bishope | of Belley. | Translated into English by Miles | Car Preist of the English | Colledge of Doway. | (ornament)

At Doway, | By the Widowe of Marke Wyon, | at the signe of the Phœnix. | M.DC.XXXII. | 14.1x8.4 cm. (22),479p.

CARTWRIGHT, Thomas. Metaphrasis Et | Homiliæ | In Librvm | Salomonis, | qui inscribitur | Ecclesiastes: | Authore | Thoma Cartwright. | Anglo. | (device)

Amstelodami. | Sumptibus Henrici Laurentii. | M.DC.XXXII. | 19x14.3cm. (6),460p. Colophon: Amstelredami, | Typis Cornelii Breugelii, Anno 1632. |

COWPER, William. Heauen | Opened: | Wherein | The counsaile of God, concerning | Mans saluation is so manifested, that | all men may see the Ancient of dayes; the | Iudge of the World, in his generall Iustice | Court, absoluing the Christian | from sinne and death. | Which is the first benefit we haue by our | Lord Iesvs Christ. | . . . | The sixth Edition. | Newly amended and enlarged by | Mr. William Cowper, | Minister of Gods Word. |

London, | Printed by William Stansby. | 1632. | Line border. 18.5x14.5cm. (14), 398,(6),399–457,(12).p. 2 sub-title pages.

DALECHAMP, Caleb. Christian | Hospitalitie | Handled Commonplace-wise in the | Chappel of Trinity Colledge in | Cambridge: | Whereunto is added, A short but honourable | Narration of the life and death of Mr | Harrison, the late hospital Vice- | master of that Royal and Ma- | gnificent Societie: | By | Caleb Dalechamp Minister | of Gods Word, and Master of | Arts in the said Colledge. | . . . (6 lines).

Printed by Th. Buck, printer to the | Universitie of Cambridge. 1632. | Lace border. 19x14.6 cm. (13),127;(3),11 p.

DOD, John, and CLEAVER, Robert. A plaine and familiar | Exposition | Of The | Ten Commandements. | With A Methodicall | Short Catechisme, | Containing briefly the principall | grounds of Christian |

Religion. | The eighteenth Edition. | Newly corrected and amended by the Author. | . . . (3 lines; ornament)

London, | Printed by the Assignes of Thomas Man, Pavl | Man, and Ionah Man. | 1632. 18.7x14.4cm (6),338,(24)pp.
Epistle Dedicatorie, signed.

DYKE, Jeremiah. The | Mischiefe | And Miserie of | Scandals Both Taken, | and Giuen. | By Ier.Dyke, Minister of | Epping in Essex. | . . . (9 lines).

London, | Printed by W.S. for | R.Milbourne, in Pauls | Church-yard at | the Greyhound | 1632. | Arch. border. 17.2x10.6cm. (26),242p.
Two blank fly-leaves.

FEATLEY, Iohn. The | Honor | Of | Chastity. | A Sermon, made and preached | by | Iohn Featly. | . . . (2 lines; device)

London: | Printed by G.P. for Nicholas Bourne, and are | to be sold at his shop, at the South en- | trance of the Royal Exchange, 1632. | Line border. 18.7 x 13.7 cm. (5),33p.

FLETCHER, Giles. Christs | Victorie And | Triumph In Heaven | And Earth, Over | And After Death. | . . . (3 lines). The second Edition. | (device).

Cambridge: | Printed for Francis Green. 1632. | Line border. 17.5x13cm. (14), 84p.
Dedication, signed.

GERHARD, John. A | Golden Chaine | Of | Divine Aphorismes | Written | By John Gerhard | Doctor of Divinitie and | Superintendent of | Heldburg. | Translated By | Ralph Winterton | Fellow of Kings | Colledge in | Cambridge. | (ornament)

Printed by the printers to | the Vniversitie | 1632. | Lace border. 13.9x7.7cm. (30),389p.

GOUGE, William. The Saints | Sacrifice: | Or, | A Commentarie | On The | CXVI.Psalme. | Which is, | A Gratulatory Psalme, for | Deliverance from deadly | Distresse. | By William Govge, D.D. | . . . (5 lines)

London, | Printed by George Miller for Edward | Brewster, and are to be sold at the signe | of the Bible, at the great North doore | of Pauls. 1632. | Arch. border. 19.1x14.6cm. (16),290,(1)p. Imperfect at end.

GROSSE, Alexander. Svveet And | Soule-Perswading | Indvcements | Leading unto Christ. | Dedvced, | 1. From the Consideration of Mans Misery, Emptinesse, | Basenesse, and Dishonour without Christ. | 2. From the Meditation of the Comforts attending the | Soules receiving of Christ. | 3. From the Apprehension of the Joy and Excellency of | Christs living in Man: The whole singularly sweet- | ning the Meditation of Christ to the Soule of Man. | . . . (11 lines). By Alexander Grosse, Minister of Christ. |

London, | Printed by G.M. for Iohn Bartlet at the Signe of the Gilt-Cup neare | Saint Austins-Gate. MDCXXXII. | Border. 18.7x14.1cm. (15), 116, (1), 117–440, (20)p. 2 sub. t.p.

HAKEWILL, George. A | Sermon | Preached At | Barstaple; | Vpon occasion of the late happy success | of Gods church in forraine parts. | By G.H.D.D. | (device).

London, | Printed for R.Allot, and are to be sold at the signe of the | Beare in Pauls Church-yard, 1632. | 17.8x13.5cm. (1),36p.
Anon. Camb.Univ.Cat. No.7594.

HARRIS, Robert. A | Treatise | Of The | Nevv Couenant: | Delivered Ser- | mon-VVise Upon, | Ezechiel 11.Vers.19,20. | By Robert Harris, Pastour | of Hanwell, Batchelor of Diuinity. | . . . (5 lines; ornament)

London, | Printed by I.B. for Iohn Bartlet, and are to be sold | at his shop, at the Signe of the gilt Cup, in Goldsmith- | Row in Cheapside, 1632. | 19.6x14. cm. (6),68,196 pp.

HARRIS, Robert. The | Way To True | Happinesse. | Deliuered in XXIV. Sermons | upon the Beatitvdes. | By Robert Harris, B. in Diuinity, | and Pastor of Hanwell. | Also, | A Treatise Of The | Nevv Covenant; | Set forth Sermon-wise, on Ezechiel the XI. | By the same Author. | . . . (5 lines; ornament).

London, | Printed for Iohn Bartlet, and are to be sold at his shop | in Cheapeside at the Gilded Cup. | 1632. | 19.5x14.2cm. 322,186;(6),68,196p. Pp. 30-39, omitted in numbering, and 49-58 numbered twice.
Title supplied by E.H.F.Mills, Secretary, University Library, Cambridge, England.

HOOKER, Richard. Of The | Lawes | of | Ecclesiastical | Politie, | Eight Bookes | By Richard Hooker. |

London | Printed by William Stansbye | and are to be sold by | George Lathum. | [1632] Engr. t. p. 27.6x18.8cm. (53),583,(15)p. First six pages of preface gone.
6th edition: Five books only. Book V. has separate t.p. " Certayne divine Tractates ", (p.455f.) has no separate t.p., but the seven tracts have, all dated 1631. Continuous register and pagination

JAMES, Richard. An | Apologe- | ticall Essay | For The Righ- | teovsnes Of Mise- | rable Vnhappy | People. | Delivered In A Ser- | mon at S. Maries in Oxford. | By Richard Iames Bachelour of Divi- | nitie, and Fellow of C. C. C. | . . . (3 lines; ornament).

London, | Printed by I. B. for Nathaniel Bvtter. | 1632. | 18.4x13.8cm. (3,28)p.
Appended to his Sermon Concerning The Times of Receiving The Sacrament: 1632, with continuous register; no pagination.

JAMES, Richard. A | Sermon | Concerning | The Times of Re- | ceiving The Sa- | crament; | And Of | Mutuall Forgivenesse. | Delivered In C, C. C. At | the Election of a President; | By Richard Iames B. of Divinitie. | . . . (2 lines; ornament).

London, | Printed by I. B. for Nathaniel Bvtter. | 1632. | 18.4x13.8cm. (4,14)p.

JUAN de Santa Maria, Franciscus. Christian | Policie: | Or, | The Christian | Common-Wealth. | Published for the good of Kings, and | Princes, and such as are in authori- | tie vnder them, and trusted with State | Affaires: | as also for all true hear- | ted Subiects. | Written in Spanish, and translated into English. | (device).

London, | Printed by Thomas Harper, for Richard | Collins, and are to be sold at his shop in Pauls Church- | yard at the signe of the three Kings, |

M.DC.XXXII. | 21.6x16.7cm.(18), 481, (1)p. Author's Epistle Dedicatorie, signed.

L., W. The | Incomparable | Jewell. | Shewed | In a Sermon, which was preached in the | Church of B. in S. at the solemnization | of a Marriage, had betweene W.B. and | E.S. the daughter of I.S. of | London, Merchant. | Wherein, | Is recommended to every good and well dispo- | sed minde the matchless worth of a vertuous | Wife; and wherein also is discovered the | hatefull company and hellish con- | dition of a vitious --- | . . . (3 lines; device).

London, | Printed by Robert Young, and are sold by | G.Lathum. 1632. | Border. 18.2x13.8cm. (8),43p.
Epistle Dedicatorie, signed W.L.

LECHMERE, Edmund. The | Conference Men | tioned By Doctovr | Featly in the end of | his Sacrilege. | With some notes, added vpon occasion of | Ministers Relation; by S.E. | . . . (5 lines; ornament).

At Doway, | By the widdow of Mark Wyon | at the signe of the Phœnix. | M.DC.XXXII. | Line border. 12.4x7.cm. 92p.
H&L, new edition.

LECHMERE, Edmund. A | Dispvtation | Of The | Chvrch, | VVherein the old Reli- | gion is maintained. | V. M. C. F. E. | . . . (5 lines: device).

At Doway, | By the widdow of Mark Wyon, at the signe | of the golden Phœnix. 1632. | With Permission. | 17.8x10.9 cm. (15),649,(4)p.
Anon. Gillow:IV,175.

PAYNTER, Henry. Saint | Pavls Rvle | For Religiovs | Performances. | A Sermon preached May 15. An- | no Domini 1631. | By Henry Paynter B. D. Preacher of Gods Word | in the City of Exeter. | . . . (18 lines; device).

London, | Printed by I. B. for Nathaniel Butter. 1632. | 17.8x14. cm. (5),47p.

PEMBLE, William. Salomons | Recantation | And | Repentance: | Or, | The Booke of Ecclesiastes | briefly and fully explained, | By that late learned and godly man, | William Pemble. | . . . (4 lines; ornament).

London, | Printed by R.B. for Iohn Bartlet, at the gilt | Cup in Cheap-side, 1632. | 18.2x13.6cm.(7),175p.

PRESTON, John. The Deformed | Forme Of A | Formall Profession. | Or, | The description of a true and false christian, either excu- | sing, or accusing him, for his pious, or pretended | conversation. | Shewing that there is a powerfull godlynes necessary to sal- | vation, and that many have but the forme, but not the | power thereof. | In handling whereof | These things are plainely | and powerfully explained and | applyed { what godlines is. | what the power of it. | what the reasons why | some have but the forme thereof. together with the meanes, | and marks, both how to attaine, and to try our selves | whether we have the power thereof or not. | By that late faithfull and worthy Minister of Iesus | Christ. Iohn Preston. | Doctor in divinity, Chaplaine in ordinary to his Majestie, Master of | Emmanuel Colledge in Cambridge, and sometimes preacher of | Lincolnes Inne. | . . . (6 lines).

Edinbvrgh Printed by Iohn Wreittoun. 1632. | 17.7x13.6cm. (1),12p.

PRESTON, John. Life | Eternall | Or, | A Treatise | Of the knowledge of the Di- | vine Essence and | Attribvtes. | Delivered in XVIII. Sermons. | By the late faithfull and worthy Minister | of Iesvs Christ, | Iohn Preston, | D. in Divinity, Chaplaine in ordinary to | his Majestie, Master of Emmanuel Colledge in | Cambridge, and sometimes Preacher | of Lincolns Inne. | The Third Edition, Corrected. | . . . (2 lines).

Imprinted at London by R.B. and are to be sold by | Nicholas Bourne at the Royall Exchange, and by | Rapha Harford, in Pater-noster Rovv | in Queeneshead alley, at the signe | of the guilt Bible. 1632. | Arch. border. 18.5x14cm. (29), 1-180, 5-204, (21)p.

Complete; continuous register, interrupted pagination.

PRESTON, John. The | Nevv Covenant, | Or | The Saints | Portion. | A Treatise | Vnfolding the All-sufficiencie of | God, Mans vprightnes, and | the Covenant of grace. | Delivered | In fourteen Sermons vpon Gen.17.1,2 | Wherevnto are adioyned | Foure Sermons vpon Eccles.9.1.2.11.12. | By the late faithfull and worthy Minister | of Iesus Christ, | Iohn Preston. | Dr. in Divinitie, Chaplaine in ordinary to his | Maiestie, Master of Emmanuel Colledge in Cam- | bridge, and sometimes Preacher of Lincolnes Inne. | The seventh Edition, corrected. | . . . (2 lines).

London | Printed by I.D. for Nicholas Bourne, and | are to be sold at the South entrance | of the Royall Exchange 1632. | Arch. border. 18x13.5cm. (16),612, (18)p.

Also another copy from the library of Walter W. Law. 17.4x13.4cm.(12),612, (18)p. Title supplied.

REYNOLDS, Edward. An | Explication | Of The | Hvndreth And | Tenth Psalme: | Wherein | The severall Heads of Christian | Religion therein contained; touching the | Exaltation of Christ, the Scepter of his Kingdome, | the Character of his Subjects, His Priesthood, Victories, | Sufferings, and Resurrection, are largely | explained and applied. | Being the Substance of severall Sermons | preached at Lincolns | Inne; | By Edward Reynoldes sometimes | Fellow of Merton Colledge in Oxford, late | Preacher to the foresaid Honorable Society, and | Rector of the Church of Braunston in | Northhampton-shire. | (ornament).

London, | Imprinted by Felix Kyngston for Robert Bostocke, and | are to be sold at his shop in Pauls Church- | yard at the signe of the Kings | Head. 1632. | Line border. 19.1x13.9cm. (16), 525, (4)p.

REYNOLDS, Edward. Three | Treatises | Of | The Vanity of the Creature. | The Sinfulnesse of Sinne. | The Life of Christ. | Being The Svb- | stance Of Severall | Sermons Preached At | Lincolns Inne: | By Edward Reynolds Preacher | to that Honourable Society, and late

Fellow | of Merton Colledge in Oxford. | The second Edition, Revised and Corrected | by the Author. | . . . (2 lines; ornament).

London, | Imprinted by Felix Kyngston for Robert Bostocke, and | are to be sold at his shop in Pauls Church- | yard at the signe of the Kings | Head. 1632. | Line border. 17.6x13.6cm. (16), 535p.

Two sub t.p.; continuous register.

ROGERS, John. The | Doctrine | Of | Faith; | Wherein are practi- | cally handled twelve | principall points, which | explaine the Nature | and Vse of it. | By Iohn Rogers, | Preacher of Gods Word | at Dedham in Essex. | The fourth Edition, newly corrected, and | inlarged by the Author. | . . . (3 lines)

London, | Printed for Nathanael Newbery and | Henry Overton, and are to be | sold at their shops in Popes- | head Alley. 1632. | Line border. 14x7.7 cm. (22), 521p.

ROGERS, John. A | Treatise | Of | Love. | Written by Io. Rogers, | Minister of Gods Word | at Dedham in Essex. | The second Edition. | . . . (9 lines).

London, | Printed by Iohn Dawson, for Na- | thanael Newbery, at the signe of | the Starre in Popes-head Alley. | 1632. | Line border. 13.9x8.3 cm. (9),240p.

ROGERS, Nehemiah. The Good | Hovsvvife | With | Her Broome | And Candle: | Or An | Exposition On The | Parable Of The Lost | Groat. | By Nehemiah Rogers, Pastor of | Messing in Essex. | . . . (2 lines; ornament).

London, | Printed by George Miller for Edward Brewster, and are to be sold | at his Shop at the Signe of the Bible, at the great North | doore of Pauls. 1632. | Line border. 18.8x14.2cm. (12),196,(8)p.

Second part of his Trve Convert: 1632. with separate t.p., register and pagination.

ROGERS, Nehemiah. The Indvlgent | Father, | His Graciovs | Entertainment | of his riotous yet repenting | Childe: | Or An | Exposition On The | Parable Of The Prodigall | Or Lost Sonne. Lvk.15.11.12. &c. | By Nehemiah Rogers, Pastor of | Messing in Essex. | . . . (2 lines; ornament).

London, | Printed by George Miller for Edward Brewster, and are to be sold | at his Shop at the Signe of the Bible, at the great North | doore of Pauls. 1632. | Line border. 18.8x14.2cm. (2),406,(10)p.

Part three of his Trve Convert: 1632. with separate register and pagination.

ROGERS, Nehemiah. A | Sermon | Preached At | The Second Trien- | niall Visitation of the Right | Honovrable and Right | Reverend Father In | God, William Lord Bishop | of London, holden at Keluedon in | Essex: September 3. | 1631. | By Nehemiah Rogers, Pastor of | Messing in Essex: | . . . (2 lines; ornament).

Printed by George Miller for Edward Brewster, and are to be sold | at his Shop at the Signe of the Bible, at the great North | doore of Pauls. 1632. | Line border. 18.4x14.2cm. (4), 30p.

ROGERS, Nehemiah. The Trve | Convert: | Or, | An Exposition | Vpon The | XV. Chapter Of | St.Lvkes Gospell, | Containing three

Parables. | The Lost Sheepe. | The Lost Groat. | The Lost Sonne. | By Nehemiah Rogers, Pastor | of the Congregation at Messing in Essex. | . . . (5 lines).

London, | Printed by George Miller for Edward | Brewster, and are to be sold at the signe | of the Bible, at the great North doore | of Pavls. 1632. | Arch. border. 18.8x14.2cm.(13), (16), 264, (9); (12), 196,(8);(20),406, (10)p. 3 Sub. t.p.

Three parts: with separate t.p., register and pagination.

ROGERS, Nehemiah. The | VVatchfvll | Shepheard | His Care Over His Whole | Flock, That None Be Lost | Nor Wanting; | In An | Exposition On The | Parable Of The Lost | Sheep: Lvk.15.1.--8. | By Nehemiah Rogers, Pastor of | Messing in Essex. | . . . (4 lines; ornament)

London, Printed by George Miller for Edward Brewster, and are to be sold | at his Shop at the Signe of the Bible, at the great North | doore of Pauls. 1632. | Line border. 18.8x14.2cm. (16),264,(9)p.

First part of his Trve Convert: 1632. with separate t.p., register and pagination. Also another copy from the library of Walter W. Law. 19.2x13.5cm.

ROGERS, Nehemiah. The | VVild Vine: | Or, | An Exposition On | Isaiah's Parabolicall | Song of the Beloued: | Isa.5.1,2,3,&c. | By Nehemiah Rogers, Pastor of | Messing in Essex. | . . . (3 lines; device).

London, | Printed for Edward Brewster, and are to be sold at his Shop at the | Signe of the Bible, at the great North doore of | Pauls, 1632. | Line border. 18.4x 14.2cm. (14), 319, (7)p. Folded leaf.

SANDERSON, Robert. Tvvelve | Sermons | Preached | I. Ad Clerum. III. | 2. Ad Magistratum. III. | 3. Ad Populum. VI. | By | Robert Savnderson | Batchellor in Divinity, sometimes | Fellow of Lincolne Colledge | in Oxford. | . . . (2 lines).

London, | Printed by Avg.Math. for Robert Davvlman, | and are to be sold by Robert Allet, at the | signe of the Blacke-Beare, in Pauls- | Church-yard. 1632. | Line border. 18.5x13.9cm. (8),564p. 3 sub title pages.

Three parts, with separate t.p., continuous register and pagination.

SMITH, Henry. Gods | Arrow | Against | Atheists. | By Henry Smith. | (device)

London, | Printed by I.H. for Edward Brewster, and | Robert Bird. 1632. | 19.8 x 14.3 cm. (3),96 p.

With his, The | Sermons | Of | Mr.Henry Smith: | Gathered into one volume . . . 1631. With separate register and pagination.

SMITH, Henry. Three | Sermons | Made By Mr. | Henry Smith. | I. The Benefit of Contentation. | II. The Affinity of the Faithfull. | III. The lost sheepe found. | (device)

London, | Printed by W.S. for Iohn Smethwicke, and are to be sold at | his shop in S.Dunstanes Church-yard. | 1632. | 19.8 x 14.3 cm. 56 p.

SMITH, Henry. Tvvelve | Sermons, | Preached | By | Mr Henry Smith. | With | Prayers, both for the Morning and | Euening thereunto adioyned. | And published by a more perfect | Copy than heretofore. | . . . (3 lines; ornaments)

London, | Printed by Iohn Hauiland for George Edwards. | 1632. | 19.8 x 14.3 cm. (4,132; 1, 44,1,76) p. 2 sub-title-pages.

With his, The | Sermons | Of | Mr. Henry Smith: | Gathered into one volume
. . . 1631; with separate register; unpaged. Included also in his Sermons: 1657,
pp. 597-778.

SMITH, Miles. Sermons | Of The Right | Reverend Father | In God
Miles Smith, | Late Lord Bishop | Of Glocester. | Transcribed | Ovt Of
His Originall | Manvscripts, And Now | Pvblished For The | Common
Good. | . . . (4 lines; device).
London, | Printed by Elizabeth Allde for Robert Allot, | dwelling at the Blacke
Beare in Pauls Church- | yard. 1632. | Line border. 27x16.3cm. (16),305p.

STRUTHER, William. A Looking-Glasse | For Princes and
People. | Delivered in a Sermon of Thankes- | giving for the Birth of
the hope- | full Prince Charles. | And since augmented with Allega-
tions | and Historicall Remarkes. | Together with a Vindication of |
Princes, &c. | By M.William Strvther | Preacher at Edinburgh. | . . .
(2 lines).
Printed at Edinburgh, by the Heires | of Andro Hart. 1632. | Ornam. t.p. 18x14
cm. (8),111;(16),180p.
Two parts, with separate t.p., registers and pagination.

STRUTHER, William. A | Looking Glasse | For Princes and
Popes. | Or | A Vindication of the sacred Au- | thoritie of Princes, from
the An- | tichristian vsurpation of the Popes. | By t he same Authour
M.William Struther. | . . . (7 lines; ornament).
Edinbvrgh, | Printeed by the Heires of Andro Hart. 1632. | Line border. 18x14
cm. (16),180p.
Sub. t.p. of second portion of his Looking-Glasse for Princes and People: 1632.
With separate register and pagination. Ornamental head-piece.

SUTTON, Thomas. Lectures | Vpon | The Eleventh Chapter | To |
The Romans. | Preached by that learned and | Godly Divine of fa-
mous memorie, | Dr. Sutton, in St. Marie | Overies in Southwarke. |
Published for the good of all Gods | Church generally, and especially |
of those that were then | his Hearers. | . . . (5 lines)
London, | Printed by I. H. for Nicolas Bourne, | and are to be sold at his shop,
at | the South Entrance of the Royall | Exchange. 1632. | Arch. border. 18.7x14.4
cm. (28),478,(14) p.

The | SVVEDISH | Discipline, | {Religiovs, | Civile, | And Military. |
The First Part, In The | Formes of Prayer daily used by those of the
Swe- | dish Nation, in the Armie. Together with two se- | verall
Prayers, uttered upon severall occasions | by that pious King; which
God immedi- | ately heard and granted him. | The second Part, in the
excellent Orders | observed in the Armie; whereof we here present |
you the Articles, by which the Souldiery is governed. | The third Part,
in the Kings Commission for levy- | ing of a Regiment: his Order for
drawing vp of a | private Company; of a Squadron; and of a Brigade:
with his | manner of Enquartering a private Regiment; and of an |
Army Royall: vnto which is added the best manner of buil- | ding and
fortifying of a Towne of Warre. All, in | fiue severall Figures expressed
and explained. | Last of all, Is the famous Battell of Leip- | sich, in

two fayre Figures also set forth: and | now this second time more fully and | particularly described. |

London, | Printed by Iohn Dawson for Nath: Butter and Nich: Bourne. | 1632. | 20.8x15.5cm. (8),39-90,43p. 4 tab. Lacks Part I.

SYMSON, Andrew. An | Exposition | Vpon | The Second Epistle | Generall of Saint Peter. | Plainely and pithily handled, | By A.Symson Minister of | Gods Word. | With two necessarie Tables, the one prefixed, shewing | the Resolution or Analysis of the Text, with the Doctrines | arising out of every verse. The other annexed, containing the | principall matters, alphabetically set dovvne. | . . . (5 lines; ornament).

London, | Printed by T.Cotes for I.B. and are to be sold by Benjamin Allen | dwelling in Popes-head Alley, 1632. | Line border. 18.8x14.2cm. (48), 514, (6)p.

TWISSE, William. Vindiciæ | Gratiæ, Potestatis, | Ac Providentiæ Dei | Hoc est, | Ad Examen Libelli Perkinsiani | de Prædestinationis modo et ordine, | institutum a Iacobo Arminio, Respon- | sio scholastica, tribus libris absoluta. | Vnà cum Digressionibus ad singulas partes | accommodatis: in quibus illustriores in hoc | Negotio quæstiones fusiùs pertractantur et | accuratè discutiuntur, Vertiasque adversus | Bellarminum, Didacum Alvarez, Gabrielem | Vasques aliosque tum Papistas tum Pelagianos, | asseritur; Nec non opiniones nonnullæ quorun- | dam modernorum Theologorum modestè | examinantur. | Autore Guilielmo Twisso | S. Theologiæ Doctore et Ecclesiæ Christi | Pastore. | Præfixa est operi Tabula Digressionum. |

Amstelodami, | Apud Ioannem Ianssonium. | M DC XXXII. | Engr t.p. 34.4x 21.5cm. (32),21,(2),253,209,224p. Continuous register

TWISSE, William. Vindiciæ | Gratiæ, | Potestatis, | Ac Providentiæ Dei: | hoc est, | Ad Examen Libelli Perkinsiani, | De Prædestinationis modo & ordine, | Institutum à Iacobo Arminio, | Responsio Scholastica, | III Libris absoluta. | Vna cum Digressionibus ad singulas partes accomodatis; in quibus illustriores in hoc Negotio | quæstiones fusius pertractantur & accurate discutiuntur, Veritasque adversus Bellarminum, Didacum Alvarez, | Gabrielem Vasques aliosque tum Papistas tum Pelagianos, asseritur; Nec non opiniones nonnullæ | quorumdam modernorum Theologorum modeste examinantur. | Auctore Gvilielmo Twisso SS.T.D. | Et Ecclesiæ Christi Pastore. | Præfixa est operi Tabula Digressionum. | Editio Secvnda | In qua verus ordo, qui non servatus in editione à Ioanne Iansonio facta, | juxta Autoris mentem restitutus est; errata quamplurima sublata; | & Index locupletissimus adjectus. | (device)

Amsterdami, | Prostant apud Gvilielmvm Blaev. | M DC XXXII. | 20.4x15.8 cm. (8),341,478,122,(10)p. Double column.

1633

The | ACTS Made | In The First | Parliament | Of Our | Most High And | Dread Soveraigne | Charles, | By The Grace Of God, | King of Great Britaine, France, and Ireland, Defender | of the Faith, &c. | Holden by Himselfe, present in Person, With his Three Estates, at |

Edinburgh, upon the twentie eight day of Iune, | Anno Domini 1633. | (royal arms).

<small>Edinbvrgh, | Printed by Robert Young, Printer to the Kings most | excellent Maiestie, Anno 1633. | Cvm Privilegio. | Line border. 26.8x16.8cm. 66,(8)p. Contains table of unprinted acts.</small>

AMES, William. A Fresh Svit | Against | Human | Ceremonies | In Gods VVorship. | Or | A Triplication unto. | D.Bvrgesse His Rejoinder | For | D.Morton. | The First Part. | . . . (3 lines; ornament).

<small>Printed Anno 1633. | 18.1x14.cm. (93,11);(16),156;(10),531;64p. (Another copy has parts differently disposed). 17.9x13.3cm. (95);(16),156;64;531,(10,8)p. Imperfect at end. Portrait laid in, p. (3). The proper order of the parts is: (93 or 95), (16), 156; 531, (10,11); 64p.
Camb.Univ.Cat.No.7015. Author named in the Advertisement.</small>

AMES, William. Gvilielmi Amesii | Anti-Synodalia | Scripta, | Vel | Animadversiones | in dogmatica illa, quæ Remonstrantes in | Synodo Dordracena exhibuerunt, & | postea divulgarunt. | (device).

<small>Amsterdami | Apud Gvilielmvm Blaev. | An. M DC XXXIII. | 12.6x7.cm. 344p.</small>

ANDERTON, Laurence. The Progenie | Of | Catholicks | And | Protestants. | Whereby | On the one side is proued the lineal Descent of Catholicks, | for the Roman Faith and Religion, from the | holie Fathers of the Primitiue Church, | euen from Christ's verie time vntil | these our dayes: | And | On the other, the neuer-Being of Protestants or their | nouel Sect during al the foresayd time, otherwise | then in confessed and condemned | Hereticks. | And al this is conuinced by the manifold and clearest | acknowledgements of Protestant Writers, both | forrain and domesticks. | . . . (2 lines; ornament).

<small>At Roven, | By the Widow of Nicolas Covrant. | M.DC.XXXIII. | 23.4x16.9 cm. (20),32,90(96),59,40,26,(10) p. Book II, pp 85-90, repeated.
DNB. I: 397 a. Epistle Dedicatorie, signed N.N.</small>

ANDERTON, Roger. The | Non-Entity | Of | Protestancy. | Or | A Discourse, wherein is demon- | strated, that Protestancy is not | any Reall thing, but in it selfe | a Platonicall Idæa; a wast of all | Positiue Fayth; and a meere | Nothing. | VVritten by a Catholike Priest of the | Society of Iesvs. | . . . (ornament; 5 lines).

<small>Permissu Superiorum 1633. | 16.9x10.5 cm. (16),263p.
Gillow.I:41. Epistle Dedicatory, signed W.B.</small>

ARISTEAS. The | Aunciect History | Of the | Septuagint. | VVritten in Greeke; by | Aristevs 1900. Yeares | since. Of his Voyage to Hierusalem, | as Ambassador from Ptolomevs | Philadelphvs, vnto | Eleazer then Pontiffe of | the Iewes. | Concerning the First Translation | of the Holy Bible, by | the 72. Interpreters. | With many other remarkable Cir- | cumstances. Newly done | into English. | By I. Done. | . . . (1 line).

<small>London: | Printed by N.Okes. 1633. | Line border. 14.7x8.8cm. (13), 219p.</small>

ATTERSOLL, William. A | Commentarie | Vpon The Epistle Of | Saint Pavle To | Philemon. | Wherein, the Apostle handling a meane |

and low subject, intreating for a Fraudulent and Fugitive Ser- | vant, mounteth aloft unto God, and de- | livereth sundry high Mysteries of true | Religion, and the practise of Duties}{ œconomicall. | Politicall. | Ecclesiasticall. | As { Of Persecution for Righteousnesse sake. | Of Christian Equity, and Moderation. | Of Gods free Grace forgiving offences. | Of Houshold Government, and private possessions. | Of the Conversion of Sinners, and Communion of Saints. | Of Faith, and good workes. | Of Friendship, and Suretiship. | Of Prayer, and Hospitality. | Of the Gospell, and Almes-deedes. | Of Gods Providence. | And of the force and fruit of the Ministery. | Moving all the Ministers of the Gospell, to a diligent labouring in the spirituall Harvest; | and the people, to a conscionable attending to the word of Salvation, as to Gods high and | holy ordinance for our conversion, with assured hope of his wonderfull blessing | upon the sound Preaching of the one, and the saving hearing | of the other. | Written by William Attersoll, Minister of the word | of God, at Isfield in Sussex. | The second Edition, corrected and enlarged. | . . . (2 lines).

Printed at London by Tho.Cotes, and are to be sold by Michael Sparke, dwelling | at the signe of the blue Bible in Greene-Arbor. 1633. | Line border. 28.4x19.1 cm.(22), 506,(6)p.

BALCANQUHALL, Walter. The | Honour | Of Christian | Chvrches; | And | The Necessitie Of | frequenting of Divine Service and | Publike Prayers in them. | Delivered in a Sermon at White-Hall | before the Kings most excellent Majestie on the | eight day of December last being Sunday, | By Walter Balcanqvall Doctor of | Divinity and Deane of Rochester being then in | his ordinarie attendance. | And now published by his Majesties | speciall commandement. | (device).

London, | Printed by George Miller for Robert Allot at the blacke | Beare in Pauls Church-yard. 1633. | 17.6x13.5 cm. (1),29p.

BARKER, Peter. A Learned and Familiar | Exposition | vpon the | Ten Commandements. | Wherein the Text is opened, Questions and | Doubts are resolved, Errours confuted, and sun- | dry Instructions effectually applyed. | First delivered in severall Sermons, and now pub- | lished to the glory of God, and for the fur- | ther benefit of his Church. | By Peter Barker, Preacher of Gods word at | Stowre Paine in Dorsetshire. | . . . (3 lines) The second Edition much enlarged by the Author. | (device).

London, | Printed by Thomas Harper for Iohn Harison, and are to be | sold at his shop in Pater-noster Row at the signe of | the Vnicorne. 1633. | 19x14.4cm. (13),423pp.

BOLTON, Robert. Mr.Boltons | Last And Lear- | ned Worke | of the | Foure last Things, | Death, Ivdgement, | Hell, and Heaven. | With An | Assise-Sermon, | and Notes on Iustice | Nicolls his Funerall. | Together with the Life and | Death of the Authour. | Published by E.B. And re-viewed, with | Marginall Notes, and an Alphabeticall | Table added thereunto. |

London, | Printed by George Miller, | dwelling in the Black-Friers. 1633. | Arch. border. 18.7x13.9cm. (55),264,(8)pp. Frontispiece: Portrait of author.

BROUGHTON, Richard. The | Ecclesiasticall | Historie | Of | Great Britaine | Dedvced | By Ages, Or Centenaries | From The Nativitie Of Ovr Saviovr, Vnto | the happie Conuersion of the Saxons, in the seuenth hundred yeare; where- | by is manifestly declared a continuall Succession of the true Catholike | Religion, which at this day is professed & taught in, and | by the Roman Church. | Written. | By Richard Brovghton. | The First Tome. | Containing The Fower Hundred First Yeares | To Which Are Annected For The Greater Bene- | fite of the Reader ample Indexes after the Preface, both of the Authors out of which | this Historie hath bene collected, and of the Chapters; and at the end of this | Tome a copious Index of the Speciall, and particular matters | contained in these fower hundred of yeares. | . . . (2 lines: device).

At Doway, | By the Widowe of Marke Wyon, at the signe of the Phœnix. | M.DC.XXXIII. | Line border. 28.3x18.8cm. (26), 611, (42)p. Title mounted.

CATLIN, Zachary. The | Hidden | Treasvre: | Opened In | Two Sermons | Preached by Zachary Catlin | Minister of Gods word at Thurstone | in Svffolke: | Upon Matthew 13. 44. | . . . (2 lines; device).

London, | Printed by M. Flesher for Robert Davvlman | at the signe of the Brazen-Serpent in Pauls | Churchyard. 1633. | Line border. 19.3x14.8 cm. (1),43p. Sub-title at p. 21.

CHARLES I. The Kings | Maiesties | Declaration to | His Subiects, | Concerning | lawfull Sports to | bee vsed. | (ornament).

Imprinted at London by | Robert Barker, Printer to the Kings | most Excellent Maiestie: And by | the Assignes of Iohn Bill. | M.DC.XXXIII. | 17.5x13cm. (2), 17 p .

Burned by order of the Commons, passed May 10 and Nov. 12, 1643, and Apl. 6, 1644.

COLE, Nathanael. The | Godly | Mans Assurance: | Or | A Christians Cer- | taine Resolution of his owne | Salvation. | VVherein are set downe the infallible | Markes of Gods Children, Together with | the principall Graces, required of all such as | looke to be saued: and the especiall | meanes to attaine them. | Newly published, to the glory of God, and the | benefit of his Chvrch. | By Nathanael Cole, Preacher of Gods | Word, at Much-Parringdon in Essex, neere Harlowe. | The Fourth Edition. | . . . (4 lines)

London, | Printed by Iohn Beale, and are to be sold by Francis Cowles, at his shop at | the vpper end of the Old-Bayly neere Newgate 1633. | Border. 17.9x13.8 cm. (16),444,(20)p. 1-2 blank.

CONSTITVTIONS | And Canons | Ecclesiasticall, | Treated vpon by the Bishop of Lon- | don, President of the Conuocation for the | Prouince of Canterbury, and the rest of the | Bishops and Clergy of the | sayd Prouince: | And agreed vpon with the Kings Maiesties licence in their | Synod begun at London, Anno Dom. 1603. And in the | yeere of the Raigne of our Soueraigne Lord Iames | by the grace of God, King of England, France, | and Ireland the first, and of | Scotland, the 37. | And now Published for the due obseruation of them, by his Maie- | sties Authority vnder the Great Seale of England. | (ornament)

London, | Printed by Iohn Norton, for Ioyce Norton, and | Richard Whitaker, and are to bee sold at their | shop, at the Kings Armes, in Pauls | Church-yard. 1633. | 18.5x14.2cm (16,104)p.

CONSTITVTIONS, | And Canons | Ecclesiasticall. | Treated upon by the Bishop of | London, President of the Convocation for | the Province of Canterbury, and the rest of | the Bishops, and Cleargy of | the sayd Province: | And agreed upon with the Kings Majesties Licence in | their Synod begun at London, Anno Dom. 1603. And | in the yeere of the raigne of our Soveraigne Lord, | Iames by the grace of God, King of England, | France, and Ireland, the first, and of | Scotland, the 37. | And now published for the due observation of them, by his Ma- | jesties authority under the Great Seale of England. |

London, | Printed by Iohn Norton, for Ioyce Nor- | ton, and Richard Whitaker, and are to | be sold at their shop, at the Kings Armes, in | S.Pauls Church-yard. 1633. | 17.4x13.3cm.(16,104)p

CRASHAW, William. Milke for Babes. | Or, | A Countrey Catechisme. | Made plaine and easie, to the Capacity | of the simpliest. With houshold | Prayers for Families and Gra- | ces for Children. | The sixth Impression corrected and reuised | by the Author William Crashavv, | Batchellor in Diuinity. | (ornament).

Printed by Nicholas Okes, 1633. | 13.2x8.8 cm. (2),45p.

DOWNE, John. Certaine | Treatises | Of | The Late Reverend | and Learned Divine, Mr Iohn | Downe, Rector of the Church of Instow | in Devonshire, Bachelour of Divi- | nity, and sometimes Fellow of Ema- | nuell Colledge in Cambridge. | Published at the instance of his friends. | . . . (1 line; ornament).

Oxford, | Printed by Iohn Lichfield for | Edward Forrest. | A.D. 1633. | Arch. border. 18.4x13.9cm. (5), 57; (1), 185; (1), 34; (1), 26; (1),34; (1),24; (1),27; (1), 51; (1), 125;(1), 68p. Continuous register throughout.

DOWNING, Calybute. A | Discovrse | Of The | State Ecclesia- | sticall Of This | Kingdome, in relation to the Civill. | Considered vnder three Conclusions. | With a Digression, discussing | some ordinary Exceptions against | Ecclesiasticall Officers. | By C.D. | (device)

Oxford, | Printed by William Turner, 1633. | 18.9x14.6 cm. (4),98p. Dedication, signed.

DYKE, Daniel. The | Second | And Last Part | Of The VVorkes | of the late faithfull Ser- | vant of God Daniel | Dyke, Batchelour | in Divinity. | Viz. |Sixe Evangelicall Histories. | A Commentary upon the Epistle | to Philemon. | The School of Affliction. | Published since his death, by his Brother, Ier.Dyke, | Minister of Gods Word in Epping in Essex. | The Second Edition. |

London, | Printed by A.M. for Robert Milbovrne, | and are to bee sold in Pauls Church-yard at the | Signe of the Grey-hound. 1633. | Line border. 18.7x14.2cm. (8), 352; (8), 375p.

DYKE, Daniel. Sixe | Evangelical | Histories, | Of { Water turned into Wine, | The Temples purgation. | Christ and Nicodemvs. | Iohns last Testimonie. | Christ, and the Woman of Samaria. | The Rvlers Sonnes healing.} Contained in the 2. 3. and 4. Chapters | of St. Iohns Gospel. | Opened and handled by the late faithfull servant of | God, Daniel Dyke, Batchelour in Divinity. | Published since his death by his Brother Ier.Dyke, | Minister of Gods Word at Epping in Essex. |

London, | Printed by Aug.Math. for Robert Milbovrne, | and are to bee sold in Pauls Church-yard at the | Signe of the Grey-hound. 1633. | Line border. 18.7x 14.2cm. (6),352p.
Part of The Second And Last Part Of The VVorkes: 1633.

DYKE, Daniel. Tvvo | Treatises: | The One, | A most fruitfull Exposition | upon Philemon: | The Other, | The Schoole of Affliction. | Both penned by the late faithfull Minister of Gods | Word, Daniel Dyke, Batchelour in Divinity | Published since his death by his Brother Ier.Dyke, | Minister of Gods Word at Epping in Essex. | (ornament).

London, | Printed by Aug.Math. for Robert Milbovrne, | and are to bee sold in Pauls Church-yard at the | Signe of the Grey-hound. 1633. | Line border. 18.7x 14.2cm. (8),324p.
Part of The Second And Last Part Of The VVorkes: 1633 ; with separate register and pagination.

ESTWICK, Nicolas. A | Learned | And | Godly Sermon | Preached on the XIX. day of December, | Anno Dom. MDCXXXI. at the Funerall of | Mr.Robert Bolton Batchelour in Di- | vinity and Minister of Broughton in | Northampton-Shire. By Mr.Nicolas Estvvick, | Batchelour in Divinity, and sometimes fellow of | Christs Colledge in Cambridge, and now Mini- | ster of Warkton in Northampton-Shire. | Revised and somewhat enlarged by the Author, and now at | the importunity of some friends published. | (device)

London, | Printed by George Miller dwelling in Black-Friers. 1633. | 18.7x13.9 cm. (1),72,(1)p.

EVANS, William. A | Translation | of the Booke of | Natvre, | into the Vse of | Grace. | Performed and Principally | intended for the benefit of those who | plead ignorance, or that they are not Book- | learned, or that they want teachers and | so thinke to excuse themselues | in their sinnes. | By William, Evans Mr of Arts of | St Mary Hall in Oxford. | . . . (6 lines).

Oxford, | Printed by Iohn Lichfield Printer to the Vniversity, and | are to be sold by Thomas Huggins. 1633. | 17.5x14.cm (14),95,(1)p.

FULKE, William. A | Defense | Of | The Sincere | And Trve Translation | Of The Holy Scriptvres In- | to The English Tongve, | against the manifold cavils, frivolous quarrels, | and impudent slanders of Gregorie Martin, one | of the Readers of Popish Divinitie in the traiterous | Seminarie of Rhemes. | By William Fvlke D. in Divinitie, and | M. of Pembrooke-Hall in Cambridge. | Whereunto is added a briefe Confutation of all such quarrels | and cavils, as haue been of late uttered by divers Papists in | their English Pamphlets, against the Writings of | the said William Fvlke. | (device).

London, | Printed by Aug.Mathewes, one of the Assignes of | Hester Ogden. 1633. | Cum Privilegio. | 33.5x21.5cm.(4), 25; (1), 206,(2), 17p.
Appended to his Text of the New Testament: 1633.

FULKE, William. The | Text Of The | New Testament | Of Iesus Christ, | Translated out of the vulgar Latine by | the Papists of the traiterous Se- | minarie at Rhemes. | With Arguments of Bookes, Chapters & | Annotations, pretending to discouer the | corruptions of divers Translations, & to cleare | the controuersies of these dayes. | Wherevnto Is Added | the Translatation out of the Original | Greeke, commonly vsed in the | Church of England: | With | A confutation of all Such Arguments, | Glosses, and Annotations, as conteine manifest | impietie, or Heresie, Treason, & Slander against | the Catholike Church of God, and the true Teachers | thereof, or the Translations vsed in the Church of | England. | The Whole Worke Pervsed | and enlarged in diuers places by the | Authors owne hand, before his death, | with sundrie Quotations, and Authorities | out of Holy Scriptures, Counsels, Fathers, & | Historie. | By W:Fvlke D. in Diuinitie, Sometimes | Mr. of Pembroock Hall in Cambridge. | The | 4th Edition, wherein are many grosse | absurdities Corrected. |

London | Printed by Augustine Mathewes | on of the assignes of Hester Ogden. | Cum privilegio Regis. 1633. | .33.5x21.5cm. (60), 912,(13); (4),25; (1),206,(2), 17p. Engr. t.p.

HALL, Joseph. The Olde | Religion: | A Treatise | VVherein Is Laid | Dovvne The True State | Of The Difference Betvvixt | The Reformed, and Romane | Church, And The Blame Of This | Schisme is cast upon the true Authours. | Serving | For The Vindication Of | Our Innocence, For The | setling of wavering mindes, for a preserva-tive | against Popish insinuations. | With An Advertisement, For | such Readers as formerly stumbled at some passages in the Booke. | By Ios.Hall, B. of Exon. | (ornament).

Printed Anno M DC XXXIII. | Line border. 31x19.6cm. (8),214p.
Appended to his Contemplations: 1634 : with continuous register, but separate pagination.

HAWKINS, Henry. Partheneia Sacra. | Or | The Mysteriovs And Deliciovs | Garden | Of The | Sacred Parthenes; | Symbolically set forth and enriched | With | Piovs Devises And Emblemes | for the entertainement of | Devovt Sovles; | Contriued | Al To The Honovr | of the Incomparable Virgin | Marie | Mother of | God; | For the pleasure and deuotion especially of the | Parthenian Sodalitie | of her Immaculate | Conception. | By | H.A. | (ornament).

Printed by Iohn Covstvrier. | (M.D.C.XXX.III.) 16.6x11.1cm. (16), 271p. Engr. fore t.p. 50 cuts.
Cambr.Univ.Cat:6259.

HILDERSAM, Arthur. The | Doctrine | Of Fasting | And Praier, And | Humiliation for Sinne. | Delivered | In sundry Sermons at the Fast appointed by | publique authority, in the yeere 1625. | By that

Late Faithfull and Worthy Minister | of Iesus Christ. | Arth.Hildersam. |

London, | Printed by George Miller, for Edward Brewster, and are to | be sold at his shop at the great North-doore of S.Pauls | at the signe of the Bible. 1633. | Lace border. 18.3x13.8cm. (16),143;(1),30p.

Sermon, Oct 4, 1629, appended.

HOARD, Samuel. Gods | Love To | Mankind. | Manifested, | By Dis-prooving his Absolute | Decree for their Dam- | nation. | . . . (8 lines; ornament).

Imprinted, Anno, 1633. | 18.1x14 cm. (5),110 p.

Anon. Camb.Univ.Cat.No.7017.

JONES, William. An Exposi | tion Of The | Whole Catechis- | me Of The Chvrch | Of England. | Collected out of very many | Catechismes and learned ex- | positors. | By W. Jones B. D. sometime one | of the Senior fellowes of Kings | Colledge in Cambridge. Now Vicar | of Arreton and Lecturer to the | Isle of Wight at Newport. | . . . (ornament; 2 lines).

London, | Printed by VVil. Jones for Charles | Greene, 1633. | 14.4x9 cm. (6,144)p.

Top of t.p. trimmed

KELLET, Edward. Miscellanies | Of | Divinitie | Divided into three books, | Wherein is explained at large the estate of the Soul | in her origination, separation, particular judge- | ment, and conduct to eternall | blisse or torment. | By Edvvard Kellet | Doctour in Divinitie, and one of | the Canons of the Cathedrall | Church of Exon. | . . . (5 lines; device).

Printed by the Printers to the Vniversitie of | Cambridge. Ann. Dom. 1633. | Border. 29.9x19.8cm. (22), 197; 237, (9)p.

3 Books.: continuous register.

LEIGH, Edward. A | Treatise | Of the | Divine Promises. | In five Bookes. | In the first, A generall description of their nature, kinds, excellencie, | right use, properties, and the persons to whom they belong. | In the foure last, A declaration of the Covenant it selfe, the Bundle and | Body of all the Promises, and the Speciall Promises likewise, which | concerne a mans selfe, or others, both Temporall, | Spirituall, and Eternall. | By Edvvard Legh, Master of Arts of Magdalen Hall | in Oxford. | . . . (6 lines: ornament)

London, | Printed by George Miller, dwelling in Blacke Friers. | MDCXXXIII. | 19.3x14.2cm (16),120,(6),121 260,(6)p.

Also another copy from the library of Walter W. Law. 18.2x13.7cm.

NASH, Thomas. Qvaternio | Or | A Fovrefold | VVay To A Happie | Life; set forth in a Dialogue be- | tweene a Countryman and a Citizen, | a Divine and a Lawyer. | Per Tho: Nash Philopolitem. | . . . (13 lines).

London, | Printed by Iohn Davvson. | 1633. | 21.8x16.8cm. (16), 280p.

PEMBLE, William. An | Introdvction | To The VVorthy | Receiving The Sa- | crament of the Lords | Svpper. | By that late learned

Minister of Gods | holy Word, William Pemble, of | Magdalen Hall in Oxford. | Published since his death by his friend. | . . . (6 lines; ornament).

   London: | Printed by I.B. for Iames Boler, and are to be sold at the | signe of the Mary-gold in Pauls Church-yard. | Anno Dom. 1633. | Line border. 18.2x13.6 cm. (7),88p.

   PLAYFERE, Thomas. Hearts | Delight. | A | Sermon Preached | at Pauls Crosse in London in | Easter Tearme. 1593. | By | Thomas Playfere Profes- | sor of Diuinity for the Lady Mar- | garet in Cambridge. | (device).

   Printed at London by I.L. and are to bee | sold in Pauls Church-yard at the Signe of the | Marigold, by James Boler. 1633. | Line border. 15.9x10.2cm. (6),49p.

   Part of his VVhole Sermons: 1633, with separate register and paging.

   PLAYFERE, Thomas. Nine | Sermons. | Preached | By that eloquent Divine | of famous memory, Tho. | Playfere, Doctor | in Divinitie. | . . . (3 lines; ornament)

   London: | Printed by I.B. for Iames Boler, and are to | be sold at the signe of the Marigold in | Pauls-Churchyard. 1633. | Line border. 15.9x10.2cm. (8),253p.

   Part of his VVhole Sermons: 1633, with separate register and paging.

   PLAYFERE, Thomas. The | Povver Of | Prayer. | A | Sermon Preached | in the Cathedrall Church of | Exeter in August, 1596. | By | Thomas Playfere Profes- | sor of Diuinity for the Lady Mar- | garet in Cambridge. | (device)

   Printed at London by I.L. 1633. | 15.9x10.2cm. (4),36p.

   Part of his VVhole Sermons: 1633, with continuous register, but separate paging.

   PLAYFERE, Thomas. The | Sicke Mans | Covch. | A | Sermon Preached | before the most noble Prince | Henry at Greenewich, | Mar. 12. Ann. 1604. | By | Thomas Playfere Profes- | sor of Diuinity for the Lady Mar- | garet in Cambridge. | (device).

   Printed at London by I.L. 1633. | Line border. 15.9x10.2cm. (6),84p.

   Part of his VVhole Sermons: 1633, with continuous register, but separate paging.

   PLAYFERE, Thomas. The | VVhole | Sermons Of | That Eloquent Diuine Tho- | mas Playfere, Doctor in Diuinity. | Gathered into one volume, the | Titles thereof are in the next page. | The sixt Edition. |

   London, | Printed by Iohn Norton, and are | to be sold by Iames Bowler, at | the signe of the Marigold in Pauls Church-yard. | 1633. | 15.9x10.2cm. (7),121, (7),123-232; (6),49; (4),36; (6),84; (8),253p.

   POTTER, Christopher. Want Of | Charitie | Iustly charged, | On All Svch Roma- | nists, as dare (without truth or | modesty) affirme, that Prote- | stancie destroyeth Salvation. | In Answer to a late Po- | pish Pamphlet intituled | Charity Mistaken &c. | By | Christopher Potter D.D. | Chaplaine to his Ma[ty] in Ordina- | rie, and Provost of Queenes | Colledge in Oxford. |

Oxford, | Printed by the Printers to the | University: for William | Webb. 1633. | Line border. 17.2x11cm. (24),128,120p.

PRESTON, John. The | Cvppe | Of | Blessing: | Delivered In | three Sermons, upon | I Cor. 10. 16. | By the late faithfull and worthy | Minister of Iesus Christ, | Iohn Preston, | D. in Divinity, Chaplaine in ordinary to | his Majestie, Master of Emmanuel Colledge in | Cambridge, and sometimes Preacher | of Lincolns Inne. |

London, | Printed by R.B. for Nicholas | Bourne, and are to be sold at | his shop at the Royall | Exchange. 1633. | Arch. border. 17.4x13.4cm. (1),99p.

Third part of his Saints Qualification: 1633, with separate pagination and double letter register.

From the library of Walter W. Law.

PRESTON, John. The | Nevv Creatvre: | Or | A Tratise Of | Sanctification. | Delivered in Nine Sermons, upon | 2 Cor. 5. 17. | By the late faithfull and worthy Minister of | Iesus Christ, | Iohn Preston, | Doctor in Divinitie, Chaplaine in Ordinary to his Majestie, | Master of Emmanuel Colledge in Cambridge, and | sometime Preacher of Lincolns Inne. | . . . (6 lines).

London, | Printed by R.B. for Nicolas Bourne, and are to be sold | at his shop at the Royall Exchange. 1633. | Border. 17.4x13.4cm. (1),224:p.

Second part of his Saints Qualification, with separate pagination and register.

From the library of Walter W. Law.

PRESTON, John. The | Saints | Daily | Exercise. | A Treatise | Vnfolding the whole Duty | of Prayer. | Delivered in five Sermons, | upon I.Thess.5.17. | By that late Faithfull and Worthy | Minister of Iesvs Christ, | Iohn Preston, | Doctor in Divinity, Chaplaine in ordinary to his | Majesty, Master of Emanuel College in Cambridge, | and sometimes Preacher of Lincolnes Inne. | The Eighth Edition, Corrected. | . . . (4 lines).

London, | Printed by Elizabeth Purslow, for Nicholas | Bourne, and are to be sold at his shop | at the South Entrance of the | Royall Exchange. 1633. | Arch. border. 18x13.5cm. (8),147,(8)p.

PRESTON, John. The Saints Qvalification: . . . By the late faithfull and worthy Minister of | Iesus Christ, | John Preston, | Doctor in Divinitie, Chaplain in Ordinarie to his Majestie, | Master of Emmanuel Colledge in Cambridge, and | sometime Preacher of Lincolns Inne. | . . . (5 lines)

London, | Printed by R.B. for Nicolas Bourne, and are to be sold | at his shop at the Royall Exchange. 1633. | Border. 17.4x13.4cm. (14),305;(1),224;(1),99,(20)p.

Upper part of t.p. torn away: cf. under 1634. Includes The New Creatvre: and The Cvppe Of Blessing: each with separate pagination.

From the library of Walter W. Law.

PRESTON, John. Sins Overthrow: | Or, A | Godly And Lear- | ned Treatise | Of | Mortification. | Wherein is excellently handled; | First, the generall Doctrine of Morti- | fication: | And then particularly, | how to Mortifie } Fornication. | Vncleannes. | Evill Concvpiscence. | Inordinate Affection. | And Covetovsnes. | All being the substance of severall Sermons upon | Colos.III.V. | Mortifie therefore your Members,&c. | Delivered by that late faithful Preacher, | and worthy Instrument of Gods glory, | Iohn Preston, | Dr. in Divinity, Chaplaine in Ordinary to his Maiesty, Master | of Emanuel Colledge in Cambridge, and sometimes Preacher | of Lincolns-Inne. | The second Edition, corrected and enlarged. |

London: | Printed by I.Beale, for Andrew Crooke, at the Black Beare | in Pauls Church-yard. 1633. | 18.8x13.2cm. (22),256p.

PRYNNE, William. Histrio-Mastix. | The | Players Scovrge, | Or, | Actors Tragædie, | Divided into Two Parts. | Wherein it is largely evidenced, by divers | Arguments, by the concurring Authorities and Reso- | lutions of Sundry texts of Scripture; of the whole Primi- | tive Church, both under the Law and Gospell; of 55 Synodes and | Councels; of 71 Fathers and Christian Writers, before the yeare | of our Lord 1200; of above 150 foraigne and domestique Protestant | and Popish Authors, since; of 40 Heathen Philosophers, Hi- | storians, Poets; of many Heathen, many Christian Nations, Repub- | liques, Emporors, Princes Magistrates; of sundry Aposto- | licall, Canonicall Imperiall Constitutions; and of our owne | English Statutes, Magistrates, Vniversities, | Writers, Preachers. | That popular Stage-playes (the very Pompes of the Divell | which we renounce in Baptisme, if we beleeve the Fathers)are sin- | full, heathenish, lewde, ungodly Spectacles, and most pernicious Cor- | ruptions; condemned in all ages, as intolerable Mischiefes to Churches, | to Republickes, to the manners, mindes and soules of men. And that the | Profession of Play-poets, of Stage players; together with the penning, acting, and | frequenting of Stage-playes, are unlawfull, infamous and misbeseeming Chri- | stians. All pretences to the contrary are here likewise fully answered; and | the unlawfulnes of acting, of beholding Academicall Enterludes, | briefly discussed; besides sundry other particulars con- | cerning Dancing, Dicing, Health-drinking,&c. of | which the Table will informe you. | By William Prynne, an Vtter-Barrester of Lincolnes Inne. | . . . (12 lines)

London, | Printed by E.A. and W.I. for Michael Sparke, and are to be sold | at the Blue Bible, in Greene Arbour, in little Old Bayly. 1633. | 18.6x14. cm. (34), 1–514p. 515–568fol, 545–1006, (40)p.

For publishing this book the author was sentenced to pay a fine of £5000, to lose both ears, one at Westminster and the other in Cheapside, to be deprived of his university degrees, to be excluded from Lincoln's Inn, and to be imprisoned for life. The book was condemned to be burned before his face by the hangman.

RANDOL, John. Noble Blastus: | The | Honor | Of A Lord | Chamberlaine: | And | Of A Good Bed- | Chamber-Man: | Or | The Covrtier justified in | Conditions of Peace. | Being | A Sermon preacht the 27. of March, 1631. | before Sir Lvcivs Cary, and the Congrega- | tion at Burford Church in Oxfordshire; | With | Speciall Relation to the Coronation-day, and the | Plague and Dearth among the People. | By | Iohn Randol Bachelor in Divinitie, of | Brasen-nose Colledge in Oxford. |

London, | Printed for Tho:Lambert neare the Hospitall-gate | in Smithfield. 1633. | Line border. 17.7x13.7cm. (1),1–32p. Impf. at end .

ROGERS, Daniel. A | Practicall | Catechisme: | Or, | A vievv of those principall truths of | the word, which most directly tend to life | and godlinesse. | Divided into three Parts. | The first, shewing the misery of all men by nature, in respect of sinne | and punishment; with the true use of the morrall Law in that behalfe. | The second, manifesting the remedy ordained by God to deliver | them from this misery, together with the meane of receiving it, | viz. Faith, and how it may be attained. | The third, declaring how those who are delivered, ought to order | their whole Conversation; with the meanes to procure it, the lets | resisting, and the priviledges encouraging to it. | Serving for the use of those who first heard them taught, as also for | all others who shall carefully peruse them. | The second Edition, corrected, enlarged, and restored to order. | By D.R.B. in Divin. and Minister of the Gospell. | . . . (5 lines)

Printed at London by T.Cotes, for Iohn Bellamie, at the three golden | Lyons in Cornehill, neere the Royall Exchange. 1633. | 18.9x14.3 cm. (39,115;244; 192p.

Camb.Univ.Cat. No. 4628.

RUTHERFORD, Samuel. Christs Napkin: | Or, A | Sermon | Preached In | Kirkcvbright | At The | Communion, | May 12. 1633. | By that Flower of the Church; Famous, famous, | Mr. Samuel Rutherfurd. | Never before Printed. | . . . (7 lines).

No imprint. 18.1x13.9cm. 23p.
Probably printed after 1700.

SALVIANUS. Sancti | Salviani | Massiliensis | Presbyteri, | De | Gvbernatione | Dei, & de justo præsentiq; | ejus judicio ad S.Salonium | Episcopum, Lib.VIII. | Eiusdem Epistolarum Lib.I. | Timothei Nomine Ad | Ecclesiam Catholic. Lib.IV. | Cum duplici indice. |

Oxoniæ, | Excudebat Iohannes Lichfield | Academiæ Typographus, Impensis | Henrici Cvrteyn. | M DC XXXIII. | Line border. 14.6x8.3cm. (13), 512p.

SCHLOER, Frederike. The | Death | Of The | Tvvo | Rcnowncd Kings | Of Sweden And | Bohemia, | Happening both in one and the | same yeare and moneth; viz: in | November 1632. | Publikely lamented in a Sermon, held be- | fore a Princely, Noble, and frequent Assem- | bly, in the High-Dutch Congregation | at the Hagve | By Mr. Frederike Schloer, | Minister of Gods Word. | Translated out of the High-Dutch | Printed Coppie. |

London, | Printed by I. D. for Nicolas Bourne and are to | be sold at his Shop, at the South entrance of | the Royall Exchange. | 1633. | Line border. 18.1x13.6 cm. (7),47,(1)p.

SMITH, Samuel. The | Great Assize | Or, | Day Of Ivbilee: | Deliuered in foure Sermons, vp- | on the 20. Chap. of the Revel. | Ver. 12, 13, 14, 15. | Whereunto are annexed two Ser- | mons vpon the 1. Chapter of the | Canticles, Verse 6. 7. | The seuenth Impression, Corrected | and amended by the Author Samvel | Smith, Minister of the Word. | . . . (4 lines).

London: | Printed by N.Okes, and are to | be sold by Henry Taunton | in St. Dunstons Church- | yard Fleetstreet 1633. | Line border. 15.2x9.7cm. (16),350p. Engraved fore-title-page. Sub-title at p. 227.

STERNHOLD, Thomas, and HOPKINS, John. The | Whole Book | Of Psalmes: | Collected into English Meeter | by Thomas Sternhold, Iohn Hopkins, | and others, conferred with the Hebrew, | with apt notes to sing them withall. | Set forth and allowed to be sung in all Chur- | ches, of all the people together, before and after | Morning and Euening Prayer, and also before | and after Sermons: & moreouer in priuate hou- | ses for their godly solace and comfort, laying a- | part all vngodly songs and ballades: which | tend onely to the nourishing of vice, | and corrupting of youth. | . . . (8 lines).

London, | Printed by G.M. for the Companie | of Stationers. | Cum Priuilegio Regis Regali. | 1633. | Lace border. 16.2x10.5cm. (10), 91, (3)p.

TAYLOR, Francis. Selfe- | Satisfaction | Occasionally taught the Citizens | in the Lecture | At St.Magnes neere London-bridge. | By Francis Tayler, | M. of A. | and Pastour of Clapham. |

London, | Printed by Iohn Norton, for Ro- | bert Bird, and are to be sold at his shop | at the signe of the Bible, in St.Lau- | rence-Lane. 1633. | 17.7x14.3 cm. (4,56)p.

TAYLOR, Thomas. Christs | Victorie | Over The Dragon: | Or | Satans Downfall: | Shewing | The glorious Conquests of our Saviovr | for his poore Chvrch, against the | greatest Persecutors. | In a plaine and pithy Exposition of the twelfth | Chapter of S.Iohns Revelation. | Delivered in sundry Lectures | By | That late faithfull Servant of God, Thomas Taylor | Doctor in Divinitie, and Pastor of Aldermanbury London. | Perfected and finished a little before his death. | . . . (2 lines)

London, | Printed by M.F. for R.Dawlman, at the signe of the Brazen | Serpent in Pauls Churchyard. 1633. | Line border. 19.2x14.2 cm. (14),855,(10)p. Pp. 209–218 omitted in numbering. Also another copy from the library of Walter W. Law. 17.5x13.cm.

TAYLOR, Thomas. Three Treatises: | The Pearle Of | the Gospel, | The Pilgrims | Profession: | And | A Glasse for Gentle- | women to dresse them- | selues by. | To which is added | A short Introduction to | the worthy receiuing of | the Lords Supper. | By Thomas Taylor, Doctor in Di- | uinity, and late Preacher of | Aldermanbury Church in | London. |

London: | Printed by I.B. for Iohn Bartlet, at | the gilt Cup in Cheaq-side. 1633. | Line border. 13.7x7.8cm. (12),238p. Mispaged after p. 228.
From the library of Walter W. Law.

TORSHELL, Samuel. The | Saints | Hvmiliation. | Being the Substance of nine pro- | fitable Sermons upon severall Texts. | Viz: {1 The nature of a Fast; on Iudges 20.26. | 2 The Christians Watchfulnesse; on Mark.13.37. | 3 Gods Controversie for sinne; on Hosea 4.12. | 4 The Remedy of Distresse; on Gen.32.9.11. | 5 The use of the Covenant & Promises; on Gen.32.10. | 6 The Broken Sacrifice; on Psalme 51.17. | 7 Good wishes for Sion; on Psalme 51. 17. | 8 Motives to Repentance; | 9 An exhortation to Repentance; { on Math.3.7.8. | First Preached and applied by Samvel Torshel, | Minister of Gods Word at Bunbury, and now | published for the common good. | . . . (2 lines).

London, | Printed by Iohn Dawson for Henry Overton, and | are to be sold at his Shop at the entering into | Popes-head-alley out of Lumbard-streete. | 1633. | Line border. 18.1x13.6cm. (38), 116; 79p.

WEEMSE, John. The | Christian | Synagogue. | Wherein is contained the diverse Reading, | The right Pointing, Translation, and Collation of | Scripture with Scripture. | With the Customes of the Hebrewes and Proselytes, and of all those | Nations, with whom they were conversant. | Digested into three Bookes. | The First, shewing the meanes both inward and outward, to attaine to the | knowledge of the Sense of the whole Scripture. | The second, unfoulding the true sense of the Scripture it selfe, as also teaching | the right way of gathering Doctrines from any text of Scripture. | The third, teaching the true manner of Confirmation, Illustration, and Appli | cation of Doctrines, rightly gathered from the true Sense of Scripture. | Serving generally for a helpe to the understanding of all, that desire to know and obey | the will of God in holy Writ; But more especially for all young Students in Divi- | nitie, that they may more easily understand the Languages of Canaan and Greeke, and | make a profitable use of them in Preaching. | The fourth Edition, corrected and amended. | With foure Tables nevvly added, the first of the Scripture, the second of the Hebrevv | vvords, the third of the Greeke vvords explained, and the fourth an Al- | phabeticall Table of the cheefe things contained in the Booke. | By Iohn Weemse, of Lathoquar, in Scotland, Preacher of | Christs Gospel. | . . . (5 lines).

London, | Printed by Tho.Cotes, for Iohn Bellamy, and are to be sold at his Shop, at the | three Golden Lyons in Cornehill, neare the Royall Exchange. 1633. | Line border. 20.9x16.3cm. (24),312p

Also incorporated in his Workes: 1637. 20.9x16.2cm.(24),312p.

1634

ANDERTON, Laurence. The | Triple Cord | Or | A Treatise | Proving The | Truth of the Roman Religion, | By Sacred Scriptures {Taken in the Literall Sense. | Expounded by Ancient Fathers. | Interpreted by Protestant Writers. | With | A Discouery of sundry subtile Sleights vsed by Protestants, for | euading the force of strongest Arguments, taken from | cleerest Texts of the foresaid Scriptures. | . . . (ornament; 4 lines).

Permissu Superiorum, M DC XXXIIII. | 19x13 cm. (72),801,(11) p.
Anon. Gillow:I:38.

BALCANQUHALL, Walter. The | Honour | Of Christian | Chvrches; | And | The Necessitie Of | frequenting of Divine Service and | Publike Prayers in them. | Delivered in a Sermon at White-Hall be- | fore the Kings most excellent Maiesty on the | eight day of December last being Sunday, | By Walter Balcanqvall Doctour of | Divinity and Deane of Rochester being then in | his ordinarie attendance. | And now published by his Majesties speciall command. | (device).

London, | Printed by Iohn Legatt for Robert Allott, and are to sold at | the signe of the Beare in Pauls Church-yard. | 1634. | 18.8x13.9 cm. (1),29p.

BALCANQUHALL, Walter. A | Sermon | Preached At | St. Maries Spittle On | Mvnday In Easter | Weeke, the fourteenth day | of Aprill, Anno Dom. | 1623. | By Walter Balcanqual, Doctor of | Divinitie, and Master of the | Savoy. | (device).

London, | Printed by Iohn Legatt for Robert Allott, and are to sold at | the signe of the Beare in Pauls Church-yard. | 1634. | 18x13.8 cm. (1),61p.

BASTWICK, John. Elenchvs | Papisticæ | Religionis, | In quo probatur | Neque Apostolicam, neque Ca- | tholicam, imo neque Romanam | esse. | Editio Tertia, | Noviter non tantum à scioli cujusdam calumniis, sed | & à Doctorum aliquot argumentis vindicata. | Authore Iohanne Bastvvick | Anglo M.D. | Accedit ad calcem, ejusdem Authoris exercitatio quædam Theo- | logica, adversus Episcoporum Papalium usurpationem. Item Epistola | ad quendam, qui à Reformata Relig. ad Papismum defecerat. | (device).

Amstelodami, | Apud Ioannem Ianssonium, 1634. | 15.6x9.6cm. (42),284p.

BAYNES, Paul. A Commentarie | Vpon The First | And Second Chapters | Of Saint Paul To The | Colossians. | Wherein, | The Text Is Cleerely | opened, Observations thence perspicuous- | ly deducted, Vses and Applications succinctly and | briefely inferred, sundry holy and spirituall Medi- | tations out of his more ample Dis- | course extracted. | Together With Divers Places | of Scripture briefely explained. | By Mr. Paul Bayne. B.D. | (device).

London, | Printed by Richard Badger, for Nicholas Bourne, | and are to be sold at his Shop at the Royall | Exchange. 1634. | 19.4x14.6cm. (18), 378; (3), 315p.

BERNARD, Richard. The | Isle Of Man | Or, | The Legall Proceeding | in Man-shire against | Sinne. | Wherein, by way of a continued | Allegorie, the chiefe Malefactours di- | sturbing both Church and Common- | Wealth, are Detected and Attached; | with their Arraignement and Iu- | diciall triall, according to the | Lawes of England. | The spirituall vse thereof, with an Apo- | logie for the manner of handling, most | necessarie to be first read, for direction in | the right vse of the Allegory through- | out, is added in the end. | By R.B. Rector of Batcomb. in Somers. | The ninth edition. |

London. | Printed by G.M. for Edward Blackmore, and are | to be sold in Pauls Church-yard at the | signe of the Angell. 1634. | Line border. 13.7x8.1cm. (23), 262,(16)p.
Epistle dedicatorie, signed.

BOLTON, Robert. The | Saints | Selfe-enriching | Examination. | Or | A Treatise concerning the Sacra- | ment of the Lords Svpper. | Which, as a Glasse or Touch-stone, clearly | discovers the triall and truth of grace; requi- | site to be looked into daily; chiefly before we | come to the Lords Table. | By the late Reverend, Learned, and Godly Minister of | Christ Jesus, Robert Bolton, Bachelour of Divinity, | and sometimes Preacher of Gods Word | at Broughton in Northampton-shire. | . . . (4 lines). .

London, | Printed by Anne Griffin, for Rapha Harford, in | Queenes-head-alley in Pater Noster Row, | at the signe of the Gilt Bible. 1634. | Border. 18.x13.5cm. (1),328,(7)p.

Second part of his Three-Fold Treatise: 1634, with separate register and pagination.
Also another copy from the library of Walter W. Law. 18.3x13.7cm.

BOLTON, Robert. The | Saints | Soule-exalting | Hvmiliation; | Or | Soule-fatting fasting: | VVhich (Iacob-like) prevailes with | God, diverts judgements felt or feared, | and procures mercies nationall and per- | sonall, either wanting or withdrawne. | By the late Reverend, Learned, and Godly Minister of Christ | Jesus, Robert Bolton, Bachelour of Divinity, and some- | times Preacher of Gods Word at Broughton in | Northampton-shire. | . . . (7 lines).

London, | Printed by Iohn Haviland, for Rapha Harford, in | Queenes-head-alley in Pater Noster Row, | at the signe of the Gilt Bible. 1634. | Border. 18.6x 14.1cm.(8), 179p.
Third sub. t.p. of his Three-Fold Treatise: 1634; with double letter register, and separate pagination.
Also another copy from the library of Walter W. Law. 18.3x13.7cm.

BOLTON, Robert. The | Saints Svre | And Perpetvall | Gvide. | Or, | A Treatise concerning the | Word. | Which, as the Israelites Cloud, conducts | us from Ægypt to Canaan; whereunto wee | must take heed, as unto a Light that shineth in | a darke place, till the Day dawne, and the Day- | starre arise in our hearts. | By | That Reverend, Learned, and Godly Minister | of Christ Iesus, Robert Bolton, Bache- | lour of Divinitie, and late Preacher of | Gods Word at Broughton in | Northampton-shire. | . . . (5 lines).

London, | Printed by E.Purslow, for Rapha Harford, in | Queenes-head-Alley in Pater-Noster-Row, at | the Signe of the Gilt Bible. 1634. | Border. 19x14cm. (1),252,(6)p
First sub-t.p. of his Three-Fold Treatise: 1634.
Also another copy from the library of Walter W. Law. 18.3x13.7cm.

BOLTON, Robert. Some | Generall | Directions | For A Comfor- | table Walking | With God: | Delivered In The Lectvre | At Kettering In North- | Hamptonshire, With | enlargement: | By Robert Bolton, Batchelor In | Divinitie, and Preacher of Gods Word at Broughton | in the same County. | The fourth Edition: corrected and amended; | with a Table thereunto annexed. | (ornament).

London, | Imprinted by Iohn Legatt, for Edmund Weaver, and are | to be sold at his shop at the great North doore | of Pauls Church. 1634. | Line border. 19x 14.5cm.(15), 391,(7)p.

BOLTON, Robert. A | Three-Fold | Treatise: | Containing the | Saints { Sure and perpetuall Gvide. | Selfe-enriching Examination. | Soule-fatting Fasting. | Or, | Meditations, Concerning the | Word, the Sacrament of the Lords | Svpper, and Fasting. | By | The Labours of that late Reverend, and Learned | Divine, Master Robert Bolton, Bache- | lour in Divinitie, and sometimes Preacher | of Gods Word at Broughton in | Northampton-shire. | (ornament).

London, | Printed by E.Purslow, for Rapha Harford, in | Queenes-head-Alley in Pater-Noster-Row, at | the Signe of the Gilt Bible. 1634. | Border. 18x13.5cm. (10),(1),252,(6);(1),328,(7);(8)179p.
Also another copy from the library of Walter W. Law.

BROWNE, Thomas. The | Copie Of The | Sermon preached before the | Vniversitie at S.Maries in | Oxford, on Tuesday the | XXIV. of Decem. 1633. | By Tho. Browne, One of the | Students of Christ-church. | (device)

 Imprinted at Oxford by | John Lichfield. Anno 1634. | 18.1x13.4cm. 53p. Colophon.

CALVIN, John. The | Institvtion | Of | Christian Religion. | Written in Latine by M.Iohn Calvin. | Translated into English accor- | ding to the Authours last Edition. | With sundry Tables to finde the | principall matters intreated | of in this Booke. | And also the declaration of places of | Scripture therein expounded. | By Thomas Norton. | Whereunto there are newly added in | the margine of the Booke, Notes con- | taining in briefe the substance of | the matter handled in each | Section. |

 Imprinted at London by Anne Griffin, for | Ioyce Norton, and R.Whitaker, 1634. | Engraved border. 27.5 x 18.5 cm. (20),749,(159) p.
 Line for line repr. of ed. of 1611.

CANNE, John. A | Necessitie Of | Separation | From the Church of England, prooved by the | Nonconformists Principles. | Specially opposed vnto Dr. Ames, his Fresh Suit | against humane ceremonies, in the point of Separation only. | Also | Dr. Laiton, Mr. Dayrel, and Mr. | Bradshaw, are here answered, where- | in they have written against us. | With a Table in the later end, of the principal occurrents | in this Treatise. | By Iohn Canne, | Pastor of the ancient English church, in Amsterdam. | . . . (6 lines; ornament).

 Printed in the yeare 1634. | 17.2 x 12cm. (8),264,(11)p. Lacks pp. 45-6, 139-142, 179-182.

CERTAINE Argvments | And Motives, | Of speciall moment, propounded to the consideration | of our most noble King and State: | Tending to perswade them to abolish that unhappy and | unhallowed government of our Church by Bishops; and | in stead thereof to set up the government of the Lord | Iesus Christ, and his holy Ordinances, in | their purity and power. | . . . (12 lines).

 Anno M.DC.XXXIV. | 19.7x14. cm. 36p.

CLARKE, John. Holy | Incense | For The | Censers of the Saints. | Or, | A method of Prayer, with matter | and formes in selected Sentences | of sacred Scripture. | Also | A Praxis upon the Holy | Oyle shewing the Vse of | Scripture-Phrases. | And | Choyse Places taken out of the | singing Psalmes, digested into | a Method of Prayer and Praises. | . . . (3 lines).

 London, | Printed for Robert Milbourne, at the signe | of the Greyhound in Pauls Church- | yard. 1634. | Line border. 14x8.2 cm. (25),283,(5),40,(12)p. Sub-title-page.
 Two parts, with separate register and pagination.
 Epistle dedicatorie, signed.

DAVENANT, John. Determinationes | Quæstionum | Quarundam | Theologicarum, | Per | Reverendissimum Virum | Joannem Davenantium, | S. Theologiæ Doctorem (nunc Episcopum Sarisburiensem) |

ante aliquot annos in celeberrima Academia Cantabrigiensi | Theologiæ Professorem pro Domina Margareta, | publicè disputatarum. | . . . (3 lines ; device).

Cantabrigiæ, | Apud Thomam & Joannem Buck, ac Rogerum Daniel, | celeberrimæ Academiæ Typographos. | Anno Dom. MDCXXXIV. | Border. 28.3x18.5 cm. (4),239p.

DAVENPORT, John. A Ivst Com- | plaint Against | An Vnivst Doer. | Wherein | Is declared the miserable slaverie & bondage that | the English Church of Amsterdam is now in, by | reason of the Tirannicall government and | corrupt doctrine, of Mr. Iohn Pagett | their present Minister. | The | Which things are plainly manifested in two certein letters, | the one written by Mr. Iohn Davenport to the | dutch Classis, the other given vp to the English | Consistorie by some of the brethren. With | other briefe passages tending to | the same effect. | Published by one that much pitties them and prayes | dayly for their deliverance. | . . . (8 lines).

Printed Anno 1634. | 17.3x12.2cm. (3),24p.
Also a reprint, Mass.Hist.Soc.: Proceedings, Vol. XLIII, Pp. 47-65. Oct. 1909.
BMCat. Letter to Classis, signed.

DENISON, Stephen. The | Doctrine | Of Both The | Sacraments: | To wit, | Baptisme, and the | Svpper of the Lord. | Delivered in sundry Sermons | by Stephen Denison, Preacher of | Gods Word at Cree-Church, | London. | . . . (7 lines).

London, | Printed by A.M. for Robert Milbourne, | at the Signe of the Greyhound in Pauls | Church-yard. 1634. | Line border. 12.9x7.5cm. (22),383p.
From the library of Walter W. Law.

DOWNAME, John. The | Christian | warfare | Against the Deuill | World and Flesh | Wherein is described their | nature, the maner of | their fight and meanes | to obtaine victorye | By Iohn Downame | Bachelar in Divinity and | preacher of Gods Word. |

London | Printed by William Stansby | (1634.) 36.9x23.3cm. (69),1167,(42)p.
Three parts, with continuous register and pagination. Second and third parts dated 1633.

DOWNING, Calybute. A | Discovrse | Of The | State Ecclesia- | sticall Of This | Kingdome, in relation to the Civill. | Considered under three Conclusions. | With a Digression discussing | some ordinary Exceptions concer- | ning Ecclesiasticall Officers. | By C.D. | The second Edition, revised and enlarged. | (device)

Oxford. | Printed by William Turner, and are to be sold | by Ed.Forrest. 1634. | Line border. 17.6x13.1 cm. (3),112p.
Dedication, signed.

DURY, John. Anonymi | Theoria | De | Consilijs Ecclesiasticæ Pacis | inter Ecclesias Christianas | capessendis. | Cum | Parænesi ad Lectorem. | (ornament)

Anno 1634. | 18.2x14 cm. 49p.
Attribution by Dr. Charles A. Briggs.

DURY, John. De Pacis Ecclesiasticæ Ra- | tionibus inter Evangelicos | usurpandis, | Et de | Theologorum fundamentali consensu | in Colloquio Lipsiensi inito, | Trium in Ecclesia Anglicana venerabi- | lium Episcoporum, | Dn.Johannis Davenantii, Episcopi Sarisburiensis, | Dn.Thomæ Mortoni, Episcopi Dunelmensis, | Dn. Josephi Halli, Episcopi Exoniensis, | Sententiæ Iohanni Dvræo ab ipsis ad Ecclesiarum | Evangelicarum ædificationem & reconciliationem promoven- | dam traditæ. | (ornament)

Anno M.DC.XXXIV. | 18.3x14 cm. 43p.

DURY, John. A Summarie Relation | of that which John Durie hath prosecuted | in the worke of Ecclesiasticall Pacifica- | con in Germanie since ye latter end of | Julie 1631 till 26 September | 1633. |

(Manuscript) [1634] 20.5x15.3 cm. (26)p.

FELLTHAM, Owen. Resolves | A Duple Century | ye 5th Edition | By Owen Felltham wth | a large Alphabeticall | Table therevnto. | . . . (2 lines).

London | Imprinted for Henry | Seile and are to be sould at | the Tygers head in St Paules | Church yard. 1634. | 17.8x14.5cm. (4),448,(17)pp. Engraved title-page

GARTHWAIT, Henry. Μονοτέσσαρον. | The | Evangelicall | Harmonie, | Reducing the foure Evangelists into one | continued context; and in it the entire | historie of the acts and sayings, | life and death of our | Lord and Saviour | Jesus Christ: | duely ordered according to the | distinction of times. | By | Henry Garthwait. |

Printed by Thomas Buck and | Roger Daniel, Printers to the | Vniversitie of Cambridge. | MDCXXXIIII. | Border. 17.7x14cm. (23), 262, (2)p.Engr. fore t.p.

GOUGE, William. Of | Domesticall | Dvties, | Eight Treatises. | I. An Exposition of that part of Scripture out of which Do- | mesticall Duties are raised. | II. { 1. A right Conjunction of Man and Wife. | 2 Common mutuall Duties betwixt Man and Wife. | III. Particular Duties of Wives. | IV. Particular Duties of Husbands. | V. Duties of Children. | VI. Duties of Parents. | VII. Duties of Servants. | VIII. Duties of Masters. | The third Edition. | Whereunto are added Patterns of Prayers for the severall members | of a Family, gathered out of the severall Treatises of Domesticall | Duties. And an Alphabeticall Index. | By William Govge. |

London, | Printed by George Miller, for Edward Brewster, and are to be | sold at the signe of the Bible, neere the North doore | of Saint Pauls Church. 1634. | Line border. 19.2x14.3 cm. (24),704,31pp.

GREENWOOD, Henry. Greenwoods | Workes | Contained in | Seven Severall | Tractates. | 1}Of | the{Day of Judgement. | 2 Lord's Prayer. | 3 Race to Saluation. | 4 Torment of Tophet. | 5 Birth of Christ. | 6 Baptisme of Christ. | 7 Jaylers Jayle-deliuerie. | Newly corrected and amended | by the Author. | The twelfth Impression. | (ornament)

London, | Printed by E.P. for H.B. and M.B. | and are to be sold by Iohn Grismond, at | his Shop in Ivie Lane, at the | Signe of the Gunne. | 1634. | Border. 13.5x7.9 cm. (8),509p. Seven sub-title pages.

GRIFFITH, Matthew. Bethel: | Or, | A Forme For | Families: | In which all sorts, of both Sexes, are so | squared, and framed by the Word of | God, as they may best serve in their | severall places, for usefull pieces | in God's Building. | By Matthew Griffith. | . . . (2 lines; ornament).

London, | Printed by Richard Badger, for Henry Tanton, | and are to bee sold at his shop in St.Dunstans | Church-yard in Fleetstreet. | MDCXXXIII. | Border. 18.x13.4cm. (23),528p. Engraved t.p. preceding .

H., I. The Life Of | Ovr Lord | And Saviovr | Iesvs-Christ. | Gathered out of the famous Doctor | S.Bonauenture, & other deuout | Catholike Writers. | Augmented, and enriched, with many | most Excellent, and Goodly | Docvments. | By I. H. | The Third Edition. | (device).

Permissu Superiorum, 1634. | Line border. 12.3x6.5cm. 815, (13)p.

HALL, Joseph. Contemplations. | The First | Booke. | Containing | The Angell and Zachary. | The Annuntiation. | The Birth of Christ. | The Sages and the Starre. | The Purification. | Herod and the Infants. | By Jos. Hall, D. of Divinitie, and Deane | of VVorcester. | (ornament).

Imprinted at London in the yeare 1634. | Line border. 31x19.6cm.(5),452; (8), 214p.

HALL, Joseph. The | Works | Of | Joseph Hall | B.of | Exceter. | VVith a Table now | added to the same. |

London, | Printed for Ph.Stephens | and Ch.Meredith, at the | Golden Lion in | Pauls Church-yard. 1634. | Column and vine border. 32.8x21.5cm. (10),1353, (22)p. 57 sub t.p.

HARRIS, Robert. Peters | Enlargement | Vpon | The Prayers Of | The Chvrch. | The eighth Edition. | VVhereunto is added certaine Queres and | Cases touching the Theory and Practice of Prayer: | also Induccments and Incouragements to Per- | severance in that Dutie. | By Master Harris. | . . . (3 lines; device).

London, | Printed by T.P. for Iohn Bartlet, at the Golden Cup, in the | Gold-Smiths Row in Cheap-side. 1634. | 17.8x13.7cm. (8),46,(1)p.

HIERON, Samuel. The | Workes | Of | Mr.Sam.Hieron. | late Pastor of Mod- | bvry in De- | von. | The Second Uolume. | . . . (3 lines)

London, | Printed by William Stansby, | 1634. | " Grape and column " border. 27.7x18.2cm. (16),(6),500,(11)p.

Contents: Doctrines Triall; Christians Liue-Loode; Penance For Sinne; Fovre Learned And Godly Sermons; Present For Cæsar; Bargaine Of Salt; all dated 1634 .

HOWARD, William. A | Patterne | Of | Christian | Loyaltie: | VVhereby any prudent man may clearely | perceive, in what manner the New Oath of Allegiance, | and every Clause thereof, may in a true, and Catholike | sense, without danger of Perjury, be taken by | Roman Catholikes. | And | All the chiefe Objections, which are usually made | against the said Oath, either in particular, or in generall, | may according to the grounds of Catholike Religion | bee easily answered. |

Collected out of Authours, who have handled the whole | matter more largely. | By William Hovvard | an English Catholike. | . . . (1 line; device).

London, | Printed by R. Badger, 1634. | 18x13.6 cm. (18),61p.

JACKSON, Thomas. The | Knowledg | Of Christ Jesus. | Or | The Seventh | Book Of Commen- | taries Vpon The | Apostles Creed: | Containing | The first and generall Principles of | Christian Theologie: | With the more immediate Principles concerning | the true Knowledge of Christ. | Divided into foure Sections. | Continved | By | Thomas Jackson Dr. in Divinitie, | Chaplaine to his Majestie in ordinarie, and | President of Corpus Christi Colledge in | Oxford. |

London, | Printed by M.F. for John Clarke under S.Peters Church | in Cornhill. M DC XXXIV. | Line border. 18.1x13.8cm. (12), 441, (2)p.

KNOTT, Edward. Mercy & Trvth. | Or | Charity | Maintayned | by Catholiques. | By way of Reply vpon an Answere lately framed by | D. Potter to a Treatise which had former- | ly proued, That Charity was Mistaken | by Protestants: With the want whereof Catholi- | ques are vniustly charged for affirming, That Pro- | testancy vnrepented destroyes Salvation. | Deuided into tvvo Parts. | (ornament).

Permissu Superiorum, M.DC.XXXIIII. | 18.8x13.7 cm. (8),299,(1);206,(5)p. Anon. DNB. 31: 291b.

MASON, Francis. The | Avthority | Of The Chvrch | in making Canons and | Constitutions concerning | things indifferent. | And | The Obedience | Thereto Reqvired; | with particular application | to the present estate of the | Church of England. | By Fran.Mason,Batchelor of Diuinity, | and sometime fellow of Merton | Colledge in Oxford. | The second edition Revised. | . . . (3 lines).

Oxford | Printed by Iohn Lichfield Printer to the | Famous Vniuersity. | 1634. | Cum Privilegio. | 19.3x14.8cm. (6),72p.

MASON, Henry. The | Nevv Art | Of Lying, | Covered | By Iesvits | Under The | Vaile of Equivocation; | Discovered | And Disproved | By | Henry Mason Parson of | S. Andrews Vndershaft London. | (ornament).

London, | Printed for John Clark, | and are to be sold at his shop | under S. Peters Church in | Cornhill. 1634. | Line border. 14x7.9cm. (54),347p.

MATTHEW, Roger. Peters | Net Let Dovvne: | Or, | The Fisher And | The Fish | Both | Prepared towards a blessed haven. | Delivered at a Synod at Chipping-Nor- | ton in Oxford-shire; By R.Matthevv | a neighbour Minister. | Reviewed by the Author and Published. | . . . (5 lines; ornament).

London, | Printed by George Miller for George Edwards, and are to be sold at | his house in Greene-Arbour at the signe of | the Angell. 1634. | 17.2x12.4cm. (6),31p.

PEACHAM, Henry. The | Compleat | Gentleman. | Fashioning him absolut, in the most necessa- | ry and commendable Qualities concerning | Minde or Body, that may be required | in a Noble Gentleman. | Wherevnto Is Annexed A De- | scription of the order of a Maine Battaile or | Pitched Field, eight severall wayes: with the | Art of Limming and other Additions | newly Enlarged. | By | Henry Peacham Master of Arts:Sometime | of Trinitie Colledge in Cambridge. | . . . (2 lines).

London, | Printed for Francis Constable, and are to bee sold at his | shoppe in Pauls Church yard, at the signe of the | the Crane. 1634. | 17.7x13.cm. (13), 1–153,(6),154–255,(7) ;163p. Engr.fore t.p.

Second part has separate t.p. register, and pagination.

PERKINS, William. A | Reformed | Catholike: | Or, | A Declaration Shewing | how neere wee may come to the present | Church of Rome in sundry points of | Religion: and wherein we must for | euer depart from them: | With an | Aduertisement to all fauourers of the | Romane Religion, shewing how the said | Religion is against the Catholike | principles and grounds of the | Catechisme. | (device)

London, | Printed by Iohn Legatt. | 1634. | 14x8.8cm. (8),330p. Epistle Dedicatorie, signed.

POTTER, Christopher. Want Of | Charitie | Justly charged, | On All Such Ro- | manists, as dare (without truth or | modesty) affirme, that Protestan- | cie destroyeth Salvation. | Or | An Answer To A Late | Popish Pamphlet intituled | Charity mistaken &c. | By | Christopher Potter D.D. | Chaplaine to his Ma^{ty} in Ordina- | rie, and Provost of Queenes | Colledge in Oxford. | The second Edition, revised and enlarged. |

London, | Printed by M.F. for Iohn Clarke and are to | be sold at his shop under S. Peters Church | in Corne-hill. 1634. | Line border. 15.7x10.5cm. (24), 261, (1)p.

PRESTON, John. The | Breast-Plate | Of | Faith And Love. | A Treatise, | Wherein the ground and exercise | of Faith and Love, as they are set upon | Christ their Object, and as they are ex- | pressed in Good Works, is explained. | Delivered | In 18. Sermons upon three severall Texts, | By the late faithfull and worthy Mini- | ster of Jesus Christ, | John Preston, | Dr. in Divinity, Chaplaine in ordinary to his | Majestie, | Master of Emmanuel Colledge in Cam- | bridge, and sometime Preacher | of Lincolnes Inne. | The fifth Edition. | . . . (4 lines).

Imprinted at London by R.Y. for Nicholas Bourne, | and are to be sold at the South entrance of | the Royall Exchange. 1634. | Lace border. 19x14cm. (8), 296; 241, (18)p.

Also another copy from the library of Walter W. Law. 17.5x13.5cm.

PRESTON, John. Life | Eternall | Or, | A Treatise | Of the knowledge of the Di- | vine Essence and | Attribvtes. | Delivered in XVIII. Sermons, | By the late Faithfull and Worthy | Minister of Iesvs Christ, | Iohn Preston, | Doctor in Divinity,Chaplaine in ordinary to his | Majesty,Master of Emanuel College in Cambridge, | and sometimes Preacher of Lincolnes Inne. | The fourth edition, Corrected. | . . . (3 lines).

London, | Printed by E.P. and are to be sold by Nicholas Bourne | at the Royall Exchange, and by Rapha Harford | in Pater-noster Row in Queenes- |

head Alley, at the signe of the | Gilt Bible. 1634. | Arch. border. 19x14cm. (24), 175,204,(18)pp.

Also another copy from the library of Walter W. Law. 17.4x13.4cm.

PRESTON, John. Remaines | Of That | Reverend | And Learned | Divine, | John Preston, | Dr. in Divinity,Chaplaine in Ordinary to his | Majesty, Master of Emanuel Colledge in | Cambridge, and sometimes Preacher | of Lincolnes-Inne. | Containing three excellent Treatises, | Namely,{Ivdas's Repentance. | The Saints Spirituall Strength. | Pavls Conversion. | . . . (2 lines; ornament)

London: | Printed for Andrew Crooke. 1634. | 17.6x12.9 cm. (12),1–178,(10), 179–299p. (Three sub-title-pages).

PRESTON, John. The | Saints | Qvalification: | Or | A Treatise | I. Of Humiliation, in Tenne Sermons. | II. Of Sanctification, in nine Sermons: | Wherevnto Is Added A | Treatise of Communion with Christ in the | Sacrament, in three Sermons. | Preached, | By the late faithfull and worthy Minister of | Iesvs Christ, | Iohn Preston, | Doctor in Divinitie, Chaplaine in Ordinary to his Majestie, | Master of Emmanuel Colledge in Cambridge, and | sometime Preacher of Lincolns Inne. | The second Edition, Corrected. | . . . (5 lines)

London, | Printed by R.B. for Nicolas Bourne, and are to be sold | at his shop at the Royall Exchange. 1634. | Border. 18.5x14.cm. (14),594,555–591,(20)p.

PRESTON, John. Sermons | Preached Be | fore His Maiestie, | and upon other speciall | occasions. | Viz. | 1 The Pillar and ground of Truth,in I Tim.3.15.page 1. | 2 The New Life,I John 5.12.page 27. | 3 A sensible Demonstration of the Deity,Isa.64.4.page 59. | 4 Exact Walking, Ephes.5.15. page 91. | 5 Samuels support of sorrowfull Sinners, in I Sam.12.ver. | 20,21,22. page 125. | By the late faithfull and worthy Minister of Ie- | sus Christ, Iohn Preston,Dr.in Divinity, Chaplaine | in Ordinary to his Majesty,Master of Emanuel, | College in Cambridge,and sometimes | Preacher of Lincolnes Inne. | The fourth Impression,Corrected and amended. |

London: | Printed for Iames Boler and Ioanne Greene, and are | to be sold at the Marigold in Pauls Church- | yard. 1634. | Line border. 18x13.5cm. (10),150p.

PRIDEAUX, John. The | Doctrine | Of The | Sabbath. | Delivered in the Act at Oxon. | Anno, 1622. | By Dr. Prideavx his Majesties Profes- | sour for Divinity in that Vniversity. | And now translated into English for the | benefit of the common People. | . . . (3 lines; device).

London, | Printed by E.P. for Henry Seile, and are to be sold at | his shop at the signe of the Tygers-head, | in St. Pauls Church-yard, 1634. | Line border. 17.7x14. cm. (18),41p.

QUARLES, Francis. Divine | Poems: | Containing | The History of } Jonah. | Ester. | Job. | Sampson. | Sions } Sonets. | Elegies. | Written and newly augmented, | By | Fra:Quarles. |

London, | Printed by M.F. for I.Marriot, and | are to be sold at his shop in St. Dunstans | Church-yard in Fleet-street. | 1634. | 13.6x8.8cm. (14),526p. Lacks frontisp .

RIDLEY, Thomas. A | View Of | The | Civile And | Ecclesiasti- | call Law: | And wherein the Practice of them | is streitened, and may be releeved | within this Land. | VVritten by Sr Thomas Ridley Knight, | and Doctor of the Civile Law. | The second Edition, by I.G.Mr.of Arts. | (device).

Oxford, | Printed by William Turner, Printer to the University: 1634 | Cum Privilegio. | Line border. 18.8x13.8cm. (12), 277, (24)p. Title in red and black.

ROGERS, John. The | Doctrine | Of | Faith, | Wherein are practically hand- | led twelve principall points, | which explaine the Na- | ture and Vse of it. | By Iohn Rogers, Preacher of | Gods Word at Dedham in Essex. | The sixth Edition newly corrected, and | inlarged by the Author. | . . . (3 lines).

London, | Printed by G.M. for Nathanael New- | bery and Henry Overton, and are to | be sold at their Shops in Popes- | Head Alley. 1634. Line border. 13.9x 7.8cm. (22),521p.
From the library of Walter W. Law.

A SHORT Discovrse, | Evincing | Necessarily By | Ten Severall Solid | And Svbstantiall Argvments. | That the Churchwardens & Sidemen of England | can not execute their places (according to that | Oath which they take at their admittance into | their Office) without sining against God | and that in a very high nature. | . . . (12 lines; ornament).

Printed Anno 1634. | 19.7x14. cm. (1),9p. Mispaged.

SKINNER, Robert. A | Sermon | Preached Be- | fore The King | at White-Hall, the third | of December. | By Robert Skinner Chaplaine in Ordi- | nary to His Maiestie. | Published by His Maiesties | command. | (device)

London, | Imprinted by I.L. for Andrew Hebb. | 1634. | 17.6x12.9cm. (1),43p.

STERNHOLD, Thomas, and HOPKINS, John. The Whole | Booke Of | Psalmes: | Collected into English | Meteer by Thomas Sternhold, | Iohn Hopkins, and others. | Set foorth and allowed to be sung in all | Churches, of all the people together,be- | fore and after Morning and Euening | Prayer, and also before & after Sermons, | and moreouer in priuate houses for their | godly solace and comfort: laying apart | all vngodly songs and ballades,which | tend onely to the nourishing of vice, | and corrupting of youth. | . . . (9 lines).

London, | Printed by G.M. for the | Companie of Stationers. | 1634. | Cum Priuilegio Regis Regali. | Lace border. 14.8x8.5cm. (1),99,(9)p.

STUDLEY, Peter. The | Looking-Glasse | of Schisme: | Wherein by a briefe and true Nar- | ration of the execrable Murders, done | by Enoch ap Evan, a downe-right | Separatist, on the bodies of his Mother | and Brother, with the cause moo- | ving him thereunto, | The disobedience of that Sect, against | Royall Majesty, and the Lawes of our | Church is plainly set forth. | By Peter Studley, Master of Arts, and Minister of Gods Word, in | Shrevvsbvry. | . . . (6 lines).

London, | Printed by R. B. for Thomas Alchorne, | and are to be sold at the signe of the greene | Dragon in Pauls Church-yard. 1634. | 13.6x8 cm. (9),299p.

WEEMSE, John.   Exercitations | Divine: | Containing diverse Questions and | Solutions for the right understanding of | the Scriptures: | Proving the necessitie, majestie, integritie, perspi- | cuitie, and sense thereof. | As also shewing the singular prerogatives wherewith the | Lord indued those whom he appointed to bee the | Pen-men of them. | Together with the excellencie and use of Divinitie above | all humane Sciences. | All which are cleared out of the Hebrew, and Greeke, the two origi | nall languages in which the Scriptures were first written, by comparing | them with the Samaritane, Chaldie, and Syriack copies, and with the | Greeke Interpretors, and vulgar Latine translation. | . . . (2 lines) By Iohn Weemse, of Lathocker in Scotland, Preacher of | Christs Gospell. |

London. | Printed by T.Cotes for Iohn Bellamie, and are to be sold at his shoppe | at the signe of the three Golden Lyons in Cornehill, neere the | Royal Exchange. 1634. | Line border. 21.1x16. cm.   (30),188,(3)p.

Part of vol. III of his Works: 1636, with continuous register, but separate pagination.

WILLET, Andrew.   Synopsis | Papismi, | That Is, | A Generall View Of Pa- | pistrie: VVherein The VVhole Mysterie of Iniquitie, and Summe of Antichristian Doctrine | is set downe, which is maintained this day by the Synagogue of | Rome, against the Church of Christ. | Together With An Antithesis | Of the true Christian Faith, and an Antidotum or Counter- | poyson out of Scripture, against the Whore of Babylons | filthy cup of abominations. | Confuted by Scriptures, Fathers, Councels, Imperiall Constitu- | tions, Pontificiall Decrees, their owne Writers, and our Martyrs, | and the consent of all Christian Churches in the world. | Divided into five Books or Centuries, that is, so many | hundreds of Popish heresies and errours. | Now the fifth time published by the Authoritie of his Majesties Royall Letters | Patens, with addition of a Preface truly relating the life and death of the | learned and laborious Doctor Andrew Willet, the Author of | this, and many other works. | By Peter Smith, Dr. in Divinitie. | There are also annexed in the end three Tables, 1 Of the Controversies and | Questions, 2 Of the Scriptures, 3 Of the Matters. | . . . (11 lines; ornament)

London, | Printed by John Haviland, and are to be sold by | Robert Milbourne. 1634. | 32.5 x 22.2 cm.   (46),1243; (10),1233–1352,(36) p.

WOOD, William.   Nevv | Englands | Prospect. | A true,lively,and experimen- | tall description of that part of America, | commonly called Nevv England: | discovering the state of that Coun- | trie, both as it stands to our new-come | English Planters; and to the old | Native Inhabitants. | Laying downe that which may both enrich the | knowledge of the mind-travelling Reader, | or benefit the future Voyager. | By William Wood. | (ornament).

Printed at London by Tho.Cotes, for Iohn Bellamie, and are to be sold | at his shop, at the three Golden Lyons in Corne-hill, neere the | Royall Exchange. | 1634. | 18.4x12.6cm.   (8),98,(5)p. Folded map.

Laid in: a photostat copy of the title-page of an edition, identical, except for the date: 1635. Also a re-print, by E.M.Boynton, Boston, Mass., Dec.22,1897

1635

AURELIUS Antoninus, Marcus. Marcvs Avrelivs | Antoninus | The Roman Emperovr, | His Meditations | concerning Himselfe: | Treating Of A Natvrall | Mans happinesse; Wherein it consisteth, and of | the meanes to attaine unto it. | Translated Ovt Of The | Originall Greeke; with Notes: | By | Meric Casavbon, B. of D. and Prebendarie | of Christ Church, Canterbury. | The second Edition; with a Table containing | the Principall matters in the Booke. | . . . (3 lines).

London, | Printed by M.Flesher, for Richard Mynne, in | Little Britaine at the Signe of S.Paul. | M DC XXXV. | Line border. 18.2x13.6cm. (14),27,209,52,(8)p. 1 pl.

BALL, John. A | Short | Treatise | Contayning all the Principall | Grounds of Christian | Religion. | By way of Questions and Answers, very | profitable for all men, but especi- | ally for the Housholders. | The tenth Impression. | (device).

London, | Printed by William Stansby, and are to | be sold by Edward Brewster and | Robert Bard. | 1635. | 14.1x9.cm. (12),242p.
Anon. Cf. Cambr.Univ.Cat:3190.

BENTHAM, Joseph. The | Christian | Conflict: | A Treatise, | Shewing the Difficulties and Duties of this | Conflict,with the Armour, and speciall Graces | to be exercised by Christian Souldiers. | Particularly applied to | Magistrates, Minister,} {Husbands, Wives,} {Parents, Children,} {Masters, Servants. || The Case of Vsury and Depopulation, and the errours of | Antinomists occasionally also discussed. | Preached in the Lecture of Kettering in the County of Northampton,and | with some enlargement published by Ioseph Bentham, Rector | of the Church of Broughton in the same County. | (ornament)

London, | Printed by G.M. for Philemon Stephens and Christopher Meredith at the | golden Lion in Pauls Church-yard. 1635. | 17.6x13.4cm. (20),364,(4),p.

BERNARD, Richard. The Ready Way | To | Good Works, | Or, | A Treatise of Charitie, | wherein, besides many other things, | is shewed how wee may bee alwayes | readie and prepared both in affection | and action to give cheerefully to | the poor and to pious uses never | heretofore published | By | Richard Bernard, | Rector of the Parish of Batcombe | in Sommerset-shire. | . . . (8 lines).

London, | Printed by Felyx Kyngston, and are to | be sold by Edward Blackmore, at | the signe of the Angell in Pauls | Church-yard. 1635. | Line border. 13.8 x7.9 cm (21) 486,(1)p.

BEST, William. The | Chvrches | Plea for her Right. | Or | A Reply to an Answer, | Made Of | Mr. Iohn Paget, | Against William Best and others. | Wherein | The maine points of our present differences | are handled: And the principall causes of | our troubles declared. | Published by William Best. | . . . (5 lines; ornament).

At Amsterdam, | Printed in the Yeare M.DC.XXXV. | 18.4x13.4 cm. (8), 100p.

BIRCKBEK, Simon. The | Protestants | Evidence, | Taken Ovt of Good | Records; Shewing that for Fifteene | hundred yeares next after

Christ, divers | worthy Guides of Gods Church, have in sundry | weightie poynts of Religion, taught as the | Church of England now doth: | Distribvted Into Severall | Centvries, and opened, | By Simon Birckbek, Bachelor in Divinitie, | sometime Fellow of Queenes Colledge in Oxford, | and now Minister of Gods Word at Gilling | in Richmondshire. | (ornament).

London, | Printed for Robert Milbourne, and are to bee | sold at the Signe of the Grayhound in Pauls | Church-yard. 1635. | Line border. 20.3x15.3cm. (38),248;206,(1)p. Title in red and black.

BOLTON, Robert. Instrvctions | For a Right comforting | Afflicted Consciences: | With speciall Antidotes against some | grievous Temptations. | Delivered for the most part in the | Lecture at Kettering in Northamp- | tonshire. | By Robert Bolton, Batchelor in | Divinitie, and Preacher of Gods Word at Brough- | ton in the same Countie. | The second Edition, divided into Chapters, with a Table | of the Contents annexed. | (ornament).

London, | Printed by T.H. for Thomas Weaver. | 1635. | Line border. 19x14.5 cm.(26), 595, (4)p.

BOUGHEN, Edward. A | Sermon | Preached At | Saint Paul's Crosse, | The eighteenth of Aprill, | 1630. | By Edward Boughen, Par- | son of Woodchurch in Kent. | (device)

London, | Printed by R.B. 1635. | 17.8x14.cm. (1),52p.
Second of his Tvvo Sermons: 1635; with separate register and pagination.

BOUGHEN, Edward. Tvvo | Sermons: | The First, | Preached At | Canterbvry, At The | Visitation Of The Lord | Archbishops Peculiars, in Saint Margarets | Church, April 14. 1635. | The Second, | Preached At | Saint Paul's Crosse, | The eighteenth of April, | 1630. | By Edward Boughen Parson of | Wood-Church in Kent. |

London, | Printed by R.B. 1635. | 17.8x14.cm. (1),28;(1),52p.

CERTAINE Ar- | gvments And | Motives Of Speciall Mo- | ment, Propovnded To The | consideration of our most | noble King and State, | Tending to perswade them to abolish that unhap- | pie and unhallowed government of our Church | by Bishops; and in stead thereof to set | up the government of the Lord | Iesus Christ, snd his holy Or- | dinances in their pnritie and power | ... (9 lines). The second Edition.|

Printed Anno M.DC.XXXV. | 13.7x8.5 cm. 47 p.

CLARKE, Thomas. The | Popes | deadly VVound: | Tending to resolue all | men, in the chiefe and principall | points now in controversie | betweene the Papists | and Vs. | Written by T.C. and published by | Doctor Burges, pastor of Sutton | Coldfield in Warwickshire. | (ornaments).

Printed at London by A.G. for N.Newbery, | and are to be sold at the signe of the Star | in Popes head Alley. 1635. | 13.9x7.9cm. (14),518p.
Author named in introductory letter.

CONSTITVTIONS, | And Canons | Ecclesiasticall, | Treated vpon by the Archbishops, and | Bishops, and the rest of the | Cleargie of

Ireland. | And agreed upon with the Kings Majesties licence in | their Synod begun at Dublin, Anno Dom.1634. | And in the yeare of the Raigne of our Soveraigne | Lord Charles by the grace of God, | King of Great Britaine, France, | and Ireland, the tenth. | And now published for the due observation of them, | by his Majesties Authoritie under the | Great Seale of Ireland. |

Dvblin, | Printed by the Societie of Stationers, Printers to the | Kings Most Excellent Majesty, An. Dom. 1635. | 17.7x12.8cm. (11),113p. 1 folded plate.

CRASHAW, William. Decimarvm Et Oblationvm | Tabvla. | A Tithing Table. | Or | Tables of Tithes and Oblations, according | to the Kings Ecclesiasticall Lawes and Ordi- | nances established in the Church of England: | Now newly reduced into a Booke. | Contayning as well the very letter of the | Law under which these rights be seuerally comprised, together | with such Questions of Tything, and their Resolution by | the Lawes Canon, Ciuill, and approued Doctors opinions | of the same, as be ordinarily moued, and which doe of- | ten proue to controuersies heerin: | As also a briefe and summarie declaration of | Composition, Transaction, Custome, Prescription, Priuilege; | And how they preuaile in Tything. | Compiled by W.C.Bach. of the Civill Lavv. |

London, | Printed by Thomas Purfoot. | An. Dom. 1635. | 18.3x13.8cm. (8, 48)p. Royal arms on Sig A1 reverse.
BMCat. Gerould.

DICKSON, David. A Short | Explanation, | Of the Epistle of Pavl | To The Hebrewes. | By David Dickson, | Preacher of Gods Word, | At Irwin. | (ornament)

Aberdene, | Imprinted by Edw.Raban. | Anno 1635. | Lace border. 14.2x9.2cm. (13),333p.

DOD, John. A | Plaine | And Familiar | Exposition | On The Lords | Prayer. | First preached in divers Sermons; | The Substance whereof, is now publi- | shed for the benefit of the Chvrch. | Newly corrected and amended by Iohn Dod | Minister of the Word. | The second Edition. | . . . (5 lines: ornament).

London, | Printed by M.D. for Daniel Pakeman, and are to | be sold at the signe of the Raine-bow, neere the | Inner-Temple Gate in Fleet-street. | 1635. | 17.7x14cm.(5), 234p.

DOD, John, and CLEAVER, Robert. A plain and familiar | Exposition | Of The | Ten Commandements. | With A Methodicall | Short Catechisme, | Containing briefly the principall | grounds of Christian | Religion. | The ninthteenth Edition. | Newly corrected and amended by the Author. | . . . (3 lines:ornament).

London, | Printed by the Assignes of Ioane Man, | and Benjamin Fisher. | 1635. | 18.5x13.8cm. (6),338,(24)p.
From the library of Walter W. Law.

DOWNAME, George. The | Christians | Freedome, | Wherein is fully expressed the | Doctrine of Christian | Libertie. | By the Rt.Reuerend Father in God, | George Downeham, | Doctor of Diuinity and | Ld.Bp. of Derry. | The Second Edition. | (ornament).

Oxford, | Printed by Leonard Lichfield | for William Webb. | An.Dom. M.DC.XXXV. | Line border. 16.2x10.4cm. (7), 156; 80p. Title in red and black

Has subtitle: A Briefe Summe Of Diuinitie: 1652. Lacks table. Cf. Madan's Oxford Press, p.184.

DOWNE, John. A | Treatise | Of The Trve | Natvre And Definition | of justifying faith; | Together With A Defence | of the same, against the Answere of | N.Baxter. | By Iohn Downe B.in Divinity, and some- | time Fellow of Emanvel C.in Cambridge. | . . . (15 lines).

Oxford, | Printed by Iohn Lichfield for | Edward Forrest. 1635. | 18.4x13.7cm. (16),404p.

DYKE, Daniel. Comfortable | Sermons Vpon | The CXXIIII Psalme. | Being thankefull Remebrances for Gods | wonderfull deliuerance of vs from the | late Gvnpovvder-Treason. | Preached before the Lady Elizabeth | Her Grace, At Combe. | By Daniel Dike, Batchelor in Diuinity. | . . . (7 lines; ornament).

London: | Printed by Iohn Beale. 1635. | Line border. 18.2x13.3cm. (14), 98,(4)p.

DYKE, Daniel. Two | Treatises. | The one | Of Repentance, | The other | Of Christs Temptations. | Penned | By the late faithfull Minister of Gods Word, | Daniel Dyke, Batchelour | in Diuinitie: | Published since his death by his brother | I.D.Minister of Gods Word. | . . . (2 lines). The sixt impression. | (ornament).

London: | Printed by Iohn Beale. 1635. | Line border. 18.2x13.3cm (6),358, (17)p. Sub-t.p.at p.199: Michael | and the | Dragon, | . . . 1635.

FIELD, Richard. Of The | Church, | Five Bookes. | By | Richard Field, Doctor Of | Divinity, And Sometimes | Deane of Glocester. | The Third Edition. | (device).

Oxford, | Printed by William Turner, Printer | to the famous Vniversitie: M.DC.XXXV. | 28.5x18cm.(15),906p.

GILL, Alexander, Sr. The | Sacred | Philosophie | Of the | Holy Scripture, | Laid downe as Conclusions | on the Articles of our Faith, com- | monly called the Apostles creed. | Proved by the Principles or | rules taught and received in the | light of understanding. | Written by Alexander Gil, | Master of Pauls Schole. | . . . (2 lines).

Imprinted at London by Anne Griffin for | Ioyce Norton and Rich.Whitaker. 1635. | Grape & column border. 28x18.4cm. (32),196,207,(1),211–232p.
Longer form of title on p.3.

The GRIEVANCES | given in by the Mini- | sters before the Parliament hol- | den in June 1633. | Propositions concerning kneeling | before the bread in the Sacrament. | Master William Coupers Letter to | the Bishop of Dumblane. | The Bishops instruction to Master Gawin | Hammiltoun, Bishop of Galloway. | Mr. George Gladstones letter to the King. | Master William Struthers letter to the | Earle of Airth. | (ornament)

Printed Anno 1635. | 13.7x8.5 cm. 31 p.

HAKEWILL, George. An | Apologie | Or | Declaration | Of The Povver And | Providence Of God In The | Government Of The World. | Consisting In | An Examination And | Censvre Of The Common | Errovr Tovching Natvres Per- | petuall And Universall Decay, | Divided Into Six Bookes. | Whereof | The first treates of this pretended decay in generall, together with some preservatives thereunto. | The second of the pretended decay of the Heavens and Elements, together with that of the | Elementary bodies, man onely excepted. | The third of the pretended decay of mankinde in regard of age and duration, of strength and | stature, of arts and wits. | The fourth of this pretended decay in matter of manners, together with a large proofe of the | future consummation of the World from the testimonie of the Gentiles, and the use which we | are to draw from the consideration thereof. | The fifth and sixth are spent in answering Objections made since the second impression. | By George Hakewill Doctour of | Divinitie and Archdeacon of Surrey. | The third Edition, revised, and in sundry passages and whole Sections augmented by | the Authour; besides the addition of two entire bookes not formerly published. | . . . (3 lines)

Oxford, | Printed by William Turner Printer to the | famous Vniversitie. Anno Dom. 1635. | Engraved half-title. 28.7x18.5cm. (49),606,(6),378,(42) p.

HARRIS, Robert. The VVorks | Of | Robert Harris; | B.D. And Pastor Of Han- | well in Oxfordshire. | Revised, | And In Sundrie Places | Corrected, and now collected | into one Volume. | Whereunto | Are added two other Sermons, as | they were taken from the Authors mouth in | publike, and published by a lover of the | Common Good. | As Also, | Two Tables; the one of the Texts and Doctrines, | the other Alphabeticall, of the principall matters | contained in this Booke. | . . . (2 lines;device).

London, | Printed by R.Y. for J.Bartlet in Cheape-side in the | Gold-smiths-row at the signe of the Gilt-Cup. 1635. | Line border. 27.2x18cm. (14), (1), 55, (1), 61–79, (1), 81–151, (1), 155–275, (3), 241–613, (6)p. 16 Sub t.p. dated 1634 & 1635.

HARSNET, Adam. A | Tovch-Stone | Of | Grace. | Discovering the differences | betweene true and coun- | terfeit grace: | Laying downe infallible Evi- | dences and markes of true | Grace. | Serving for the tryall of a mans | spiritualle estate. | By A.Harsnet. | Bachelor in Divinity, and Minister | of Gods Word at Cranham | in Essex. | . . . (5 lines).

London, | Printed by A.G. for P.Stephens and C.Me | redith, dwelling at the Golden Lyon in | Pauls Church yard. 1635. | Line border. 14. x 8.1cm. (17), 390 p.

HEYWOOD, Thomas. The | Hierarchie | of the blessed | Angells. | Their Names, orders | and Offices | The fall of Lucifer | with his Angells | Written by Tho. Heywood. | . . . (1 line).

London | Printed by | Adam Islip | 1635 | Engr. t.p. 27.7x19.0 cm. (10),3–622, (4)p.
Lacks all after Gggl.

HIERON, Samuel. [Works.]

Contains pieces dated 1613 to 1634, but with continuous paging: The Christians Iovrnall:1632; Trvths Pvrchase:1613; The Dignitie of the Scriptvre:1613; The Abridgement of the Gospell:1634; The Back-Parts of Iehovah:1634; The Worth of the VVater of Life:1634; The Discouerie of Hypocrisie:1613; The Baptizing of the Evnvch:1634; The Triall of Adoption:1613; The Spiritvall Sonne-Ship:1633; The Life and Death of Dorcas:1613; The Spiritvall Tillage: n.d.[1634]; The Remedy of Secvrity:1634; The VVorld-lings Dovvne-Fall:1634; The Bride-Groome:1634; The Preachers Plea:1634; An Answer to a Popish Rime:1634; The Dignitie of Preaching:1634; The spirituall Mans Taske:1634; A Caveat and a Comfort to Beleeuers:1634; The Spiritvall Fishing:1634; Certaine Vsefull Meditations Touching Death:1634; The Doctrine of the Beginning of Christ:1634; A Helpe vnto Devotion, 14th edition:1634.

JACKSON, Thomas. The | Hvmiliation | of the Sonne of God, | By His Becomming | the Son of man, by taking the forme | of a Servant, and by his sufferings | under Pontius Pilat, &c. | Or | The Eighth Book Of | Commentaries Vpon | the Apostles Creed: | Continved | By | Thomas Jackson Dr. in Divinitie, | Chaplaine to his Majestie in ordinarie, and | President of Corpus Christi Colledge in | Oxford. | Divided into foure Sections. |

London, | Printed by M.Flesher for John Clark, | and are to be sold at his shop under S.Peters Church | in Cornhill. MDCXXXV. | Line border. 19.9x15.2 cm.(8),398p.

JEWEL, John. The | Apology | Of The | Church of England. | With a briefe and plaine | declaration of the true Reli- | gion professed and vsed | in the same. | Published by the most Reve- | rend Father in God | Iohn Ivell, | Bishop of Salisbvry. | . . . (4 lines).

London, | Printed by Iohn Beale. | 1635. | Border. 12.3x7cm.(16), 366p.

LATIMER, Hugh. Frvitfvll | Sermons: | Preached By | the right Reverend Father, and con- | stant Martyr of Iesus Christ, Master Hvgh | Latimer, newly imprinted with others not | heretofore set forth in print, to the edify- | ing of all which will dispose themselves | to the reading of the same. | Seene and allowed according to the | order appointed in the Kings Maje- | sties Injunctions. | (device).

Printed at London by Thomas Cotes, for the | Companie of Stationers. | 1635. | Cum Privilegio. | Line border. 18.6x13.1cm. (9), 328 fol. Fol. 67 and 175 repeated; 226-7 omitted. Portr. frontisp.

LAWRENCE, Thomas. Two | Sermons. | The First | Preached At St Maries | in Oxford Iuly 13. 1634. | being Act-Sunday. | The Second, | In The Cathedrall | Chvrch Of Sarvm, At The | Visitation of the most Reverend | Father in God William | Arch-Bishop of Canterbury, | May 23, 1634. | By Thomas Lavrence Dr of Divinity, | and late Fellow of Allsoules Colledge, | and Chaplaine to his Maiesty | in Ordinary.|

Oxford, | Printed by Iohn Lichfield | Anno Dom. 1635. | Line border. 18x 13.9 cm. (1), 40, 34p. First sermon defective: lacks pp.35-36.

LECHMERE, Edmund. A | Relection | Of Certaine | Avthors | That are pretended to disauow | The Chvrches | Infallibilitie | In Her General Decrees | of Faith. | By F.E. | . . . (3 lines; ornament).

At Doway | By the widdow of Mark Wyon at | the golden Phœnix. 1635. | 14.9x9.8cm. (36), 200p.
Gillow, IV, 176.

LUTHER, Martin. A | Commentarie | Of Master Doctor | Martin Luther Upon The | Epistle of S. Paul To | The Galathians. | First collected and gathered word by word out of his | preaching, and now out of Latine faithfully translated | into English for the unlearned. | Wherein is set forth most excellently the glorious riches of Gods grace, | and the povver of the Gospell, vvith the difference betvveene the Lavv and the | Gospell, and the strength of Faith declared: to the joyfull comfort and confir- | mation of all true Christian beleevers, especially such as invvardly being afflicted | and grieved in conscience, do hunger and thirst for justification in Christ Iesu. | For vvhose cause most chiefly this Booke is translated and printed, and dedicated | to the same. | . . . (1 line; device)
London, | Printed by George Miller, dwelling in | the Black-Fryers. 1635. | 18.3x13.5cm. (4),296p.

MOLINIER, Etienne. A | Mirrovr | For | Christian | States: | Or, | A Table of Politick Vertues considerable | amongst Christians. | Divided, into Three Bookes. | Reviewed, and augmented, by E. Molinier, | of Tolose Priest, and Doctor of Divinitie. | And by him Dedicated, to the most Illustrious | Lord, the Lord Cardinall of Valette, Archbishop of | Tolose. | Translated into English, by VVilliam | Tyrvvhit, Sen. Esquire. | . . . (2 lines).
London, | Printed by Thom. Harper. 1635. | Line border. 18.2x14.5cm. (23), 361p.

MONTAGUE, Richard. Apparatvs | Ad Origines | Ecclesiasticas. | Collectore | R.Montacvtio. | (device)
Oxoniæ, | Excudebat Leonardvs Lichfield, Academiæ | Typographus An. Dom. M.DC.XXXV. | Border of printer's ornaments. 28.2x18.7cm. (29),393,(11)p.

PAGIT, Ephraim. Christia- | nographie, | Or | The Description of the multi- | tude and sundry sorts of Christians | in the VVorld not subiect to | the Pope. | VVith their Vnitie, and hovv | they agree with us in the principall | points of Difference betweene | us and the Church of | Rome. | . . . 8 lines)
London, | Printed by T.P. and W.J. for Matthew | Costerden, Stationer. 1635. | 20.7x16.3 cm. (24),156;57;(13,1)p. 4 maps. Lacks pp. 15-16, 23-24.
Epistle dedicatorie, signed.

PEMBLE, William. A Briefe | Introdvction | To Geography, | Containing | A Description Of The | Grounds, And Generall | Part Thereof. | Very necessary for young students in that science. | Written By That Learned Man, | Mr William Pemble, Master of Arts, of | Magdalen Hall in Oxford. | (device)
London, | Printed by M.Flesher, for Edward Forrest, and are sold by R. Royston, | in Ivy lane, at the signe of the Angell. | M DC XXXV. | Line border. 28x18.2cm.28p.
Appended to his VVorkes: 1635; with separate register and pagination.

PEMBLE, William. De | Formarum | Origine. | Gvilielmi Pembeli, | Angli, Oxoniensis, Trac- | tatvs. | Editio Posthuma. | (device).

Londini, | Excudebat T.Cotes sumptibus I.Bartlet, sub | signo deaurati Calicis in Cheap- | side. 1635. | Line border. 28x18.2cm. 48p.
Appended to his VVorkes: 1635; with separate register and pagination.

PEMBLE, William. A | Summe Of | Moral | Philosophy: | Succinctly Gathered, | Elegantly Composed, | And Methodically | handled, | By | That Learned Scholler | And VVorthy Divine | William Pemble, | Master of Arts, and late Com- | moner of Mag.Hall. | . . . (3 lines; ornament).

London, | Printed by M.Flesher, for Edward Forrest, and are sold by R. Royston | in Ivy lane at the signe of the Angell. | (1635). Line border. 28x 18.3cm. (4),50p.
Appended to his VVorkes: 1635; with separate register and pagination.

PEMBLE, William. The | VVorkes | Of That Lear- | ned Minister | Of Gods Holy | VVord, Mr. VVilliam | Pemble, Master of Art, and | late of Magdalen Hall | in Oxford. | Containing sundry Treatises and Ex- | positions, before extant in severall Tracts, and | now collected into one intire | Volume. | The third Edition. | (device)

Printed at London by Tho.Cotes, for E.F. and are to be sold by | Richard Royston at the signe of the Angell in | Jvie Lane. 1635. | Line border. 28x 18.2cm (27),590;48;28;(4),50p. T.p. mounted. 11 sub-t.p.

PERKINS, William. The | VVorkes Of | That Famovs And | Worthy Minister Of Christ | in the Vniversitie of Cambridge, | Mr. William Perkins. | The First Volume: | (-3rd) Newly Corrected | According To His | Owne Copies. | With Distinct Characters, And | Contents of every Booke, and two Tables of the whole: one of | the matter and questions, the other of choice places of Scripture. | . . . (6 lines; device)

London, | Printed by Iohn Legatt. | 1635. | Line border. 31.8 x 21.cm. I (12),116,(6),121–322,(3),328,(1),327–554,(3),556–779,(16); II: 1613. (14),727,(24) (index incomp, after Rrr6 III: 1618. (8),264,(19);(4),206;(12),207–370;(10),371–409; (5),411–427; (5),429–439; (4),441–463; (4),465–477; (8),479–605; (9),607–667; (7),669–700;(10)(index incompl. aften Vuuu 1.

PLESSIS, Armand John de. The | Principall | Points | Of The Faith Of The | Catholike Chvrch. | Defended against a writing sent to the King | by the 4. Ministers of Charenton. | By The Most Eminent | Armand Ihon De Plessis | Cardinal Dvke | De Richeliev. | Englished by M.C.Confessor to the English | Nuns at Paris. | (device).

At Paris. | By Sebastien Cramoisy. | Printer to the King. | M.DC.XXXV. | 17x11cm. (22), 335, (4)p.

PRESTON, John. The | Saints | Daily | Exercise. | A Treatise, | Vnfolding the whole Duty | of Prayer. | Delivered in five Sermons, | upon I Thess.5.17. | By the late Faithfull and Worthy | Minister of Iesus Christ, | Iohn Preston, | . . . (3 lines) The Ninth Edition, Corrected. | . . . (4 lines).

London, | Printed by Elizabeth Purslow for Nicholas | Bourne, and are to be sold at his shop | at the South Entrance of the | Royall Exchange. 1635. | Border. 18.5x14.cm (8),147,(8)pp.

PRIDEAUX, John. The | Doctrine | Of The | Sabbath. | Delivered in the Act at Oxon. | Anno, 1622. | By Dr. Prideavx his Majesties Profes- | sour for Divinity in that Vniversity. | And now translated into English for the | benefit of the common People. | The third Edition. | . . . (3 lines; device).

London, | Printed by E.P. for Henry Seile, and are to be sold at | his shop at the signe of the Tygers-head, | in St. Pauls Church-yard, 1635. | Line border. 19x 15cm. (18),41p.

ROGERS, Daniel. A | Treatise | Of The Two | Sacraments Of | The Gospell: | Baptisme And The | Svpper Of The Lord. | Divided into two Parts. | The first treating of the Doctrine and Nature of the | Sacraments in generall, and of these two in speciall; together | with the Circumstances attending them. | The second containing the manner of their due pre- | paration to the Receiving of the Supper of the Lord; As | also, of our behavior in and after the same. | Whereunto is Annexed an Appendix, shewing; First, how a | Christian may finde his Preparation to the Supper sweete and easie: | Secondly, the causes why the Sacrament is so unworthily Re- | ceived by the worst; and so fruitlesly by the better | sort: with the Remedies to avoyd them both. | The second Edition. | By D.R.B. of Divin. Minister of the Gospell. | . . . (4 lines).

London Printed by Tho.Cotes, for Iohn Bellamie. 1635. | 18.9x14. 2cm. (16), 360,(15) p.
DNB. 49:118a.

SANDERSON, Robert. Two | Sermons: | The Former, | Concerning The | right use of Christian Liberty, | Preached | At S.Pauls Crosse Lond. | 6. May 1632. | The Later, Concerning | the perswasion of Conscience, | Preached | At a Metropoliticall visitation at Grantham | Lincoln:22. Aug. 1634. | By Robert Saunderson Chaplaine | to his Maiestie. |

London, | Printed by M.F. for R. Dawlman and L. Fawne at the signe | of the Brazen serpent in Pauls Churchyard. | M DC XXXV. | Line border. 18x14.2cm. (8),98p.

SELDEN, John. Ioannis Seldeni | Mare Clausum | Seu | De Dominio Maris | Libri Duo. | Primo, Mare, ex Jure Naturæ seu Gentium, omni- | um hominum non esse Commune, sed Dominii | privati seu Proprietatis capax, pariter ac Tellurem, | esse demonstratur. | Secundo, Serenissimum Magnæ Britanniæ Regem | Maris circumflui, ut individuæ atque perpetuæ | Imperii Britannici appendicis, Dominum esse. | asseritur. | . . . (1 line:ornament).

Londini, | Excudebat Will. Stanesbeius, pro Richardo Meighen. | MDCXXXV. | 28.8x18.7cm. (26),304,(14) p.

SHELFORD, Robert. Five Piovs | And Learned | Discourses, | 1. A Sermon shewing how we ought to be- | have our selves in Gods house. | 2. A Sermon preferring holy Charity before | Faith, Hope, and Knowledge. | 3. A Treatise shewing that Gods Law, now | qualified by the Gospel of Christ, is possi- | ble, and ought to be fulfilled of us in this | life. | 4. A Treatise of the Divine attributes. | 5. A Treatise shewing the Antichrist not to | be yet to come. | By Robert Shelford | of Ringsfield in Suffolk, | Priest. | . . . (5 lines)

Printed by the printers to the Univer- | sitie of Cambridge. 1635. | Border. 18x13.6 cm. (11),326p.

SPRINT, John. Propositions, | Tending | To Proove | the necessary Vse of the | Christian Sabbath, or Lords | Day: And that it is commanded by the Word. | Whereunto is added the Pra- | ctice of that sacred Day, framed | after the same Word. | By Iohn Sprint, an unworthy | Minister of the Gospell of Iesus | Christ, at Thornebery in | Gloucester-shire, sometimes | Students of Christ Church | in Oxon. |

London, | Printed for Iohn Crismond, in | Ivie-Lane, at the Signe of | the Gun. 1635. | Line border. (11), 213p. 213 is misnumbered 177; lacks pp. 107–110.

STERNHOLD, Thomas, and HOPKINS, John. The | Whole Book | Of Psalmes: | Collected into English Meteer | by Thomas Sternhold, Iohn Hopkins, | and others, conferred with the Hebrew, | with apt notes to sing them withall. | Set forth and allowed to be sung in all Chur- | ches, of all the people together, before and after | Morning and Euening Prayer, and also before | and after Sermons: & moreouer in priuate hou- | ses for their godly solace and comfort, laying a- | part all vngodly songs and ballades: which | tend onely to the nourishing of vice, | and corrupting of youth. | . . . (8 lines).

London, | Printed by G.M. for the Companie | of Stationers. | Cum Priuilegio Regis Regali. | 1635. | Lace border. 16.4x10.8cm. (10),91,(3)p.

SUTTON, William. The | Falshood | Of The Cheife | grounds of the Ro- | mish Religion. | Descried and convinced | in a briefe Answere to | certaine Motiues sent by | a Priest to a Gentleman | to induce him to | turne Papist. | By W. S. | (ornament)

Printed for the Author | Anno Dom. 1635. | 12.3x6.8 cm. (7),122p.
Epistle Dedicatory, signed.

SWAN, John. Specvlvm | Mundi. | Or | A Glasse Re- | presenting The Face | Of The World; Shewing | both that it did begin, and must also end: | The manner How, and time When, | being largely examined. | Whereunto Is Joyned | an Hexameron, or a serious discourse of the | causes, continuance, and quality of things | in Nature; occasioned as matter pertinent | to the work done in the six dayes of | the Worlds creation. | . . . (3 lines).

Printed by the Printers to the | Vniversitie of Cambridge. 1635. | Border. 18.8x14.2cm. (16),504,(26)p.

Engraved fore t.p.: Speculum | Mundi, | or | A Glasse representing the Face of the | World. | Whereunto is added a Discourse of the Creation, | together wth a Consideration of such things as are pertinent | to each dayes Worke. | Written | by John Swan Mr of Arts | late Student of Trinitie Colledge Camb. | Pri. in Cambridge. | By T:Buck and R:Daniel. | 1635. |

TAYLOR, Thomas. Christ | Revealed, | Or, | The Old Testament | Explained. | A Treatise of the Types and Shadowes | of our Saviovr contained throughout | the whole Scriptvre: | All opened and made lively description of | Spirituall Death and Life. | 3. The Doctrine of Selfe-deniall. | 4. Vpon the Sacrament of the Lords | Supper. | Delivered | In sundry Sermons, by that late famous Preacher, | and worthy instrument of Gods glory, Iohn Preston, | Doctor of Divinity, Chaplaine in Ordinary to his | Majesty, Master of Emanuel Colledge, | and sometime Preacher of Lin- | colnes Inne. | The fourth Edition. |

Printed at London by A.G. for Michael Sparke, and are to be sold | at the blue Bible in the Greene Arbor. 1636. | Line border. 18.7x14.4cm. (23), 333p.

Also another volume, from the library of Walter W. Law, with identical title, but different contents in part: Contains A | Sermon | Preached | At | Lincolnes Inne | On | Gen. xxij, xiv: 1635; with separate pagination, but continuous register. 17.4x13.4cm. (39),1–102;(1),26;(1),49–333p.

PRIDEAUX, John. Gowries Conspiracie. | A | Sermon | Preached At | St Maries In Oxford, | the fifth of August. | By Iohn Prideavx, Doctor of | Divinity, Regius Professor, and Rector | of Exeter Colledge. | (device).

Oxford, | Imprinted by Leonard Lichfield | Anno Salutis, 1636. | Line border. 18.5x12.8cm. (1),26p.

PRIDEAUX, John. Higgaion & Selah: | For The Dis- | covery Of The | Powder-Plot. | A Sermon Preached | At StMaries In Oxford, | the fift of November. | By Iohn Prideavx, Doctor of | Divinity, Regius Professor, and Rector | of Exeter Colledge. | (device)

Oxford, | Imprinted by Leonard Lichfield | Anno Salutis, 1636. | Line border. 18.x13.5cm. (1),27p.

PRIMROSE, David. A | Treatise | Of The | Sabbath | And The | Lords-Day. | Distinguished into foure parts. | Wherein Is Declared Both The | Nature, Originall, and Observation, as well of the one | under the Old, as of the other under the New Testament. | Written In French By David Primerose | Batchelour in Divinitie in the Vniversity of Oxford, | and Minister of the Gospell in the Protestant | Church of Roven. | Englished out of his French Manuscript by his Father G.P. D.D. | (ornament).

London, | Printed by Richard Badger for William Hope, and are | to be sold at his Shop at the signe of the Glove in | Corne-Hill. 1636. | 19.2x14.3 cm. (14), 338,(1)p.

PRYNNE, William. A Looking-Glasse | for all | Lordly Prelates. | Wherein They May | Cleerely behold the true divine Originall and laudable | Pedigree, whence they are descended; together with | their holy lives and actions laid open in a double | Parallel, The first, betweene the Divell; | The Second betweene the Iewish High- | Priests, and Lordly Prelates; and by | their double dissimilitude | from Christ, and his | Apostles. | . . . (12 lines).

Printed Anno M.DC.XXXVI. | 19.5x14.2cm. (19),104p.
Anon.Cambr.Univ.Cat:7027.

PRYNNE, William. Newes from Ipswich. | Discovering certaine late detestable practises of some | domineering Lordly Prelates, to undermine the established | doctrine and discipline of our Church, extripate all Orthodox sin- | cere Preachers and preaching of Gods Word, usher in Popery, Su- | perstition and Idolatry; with their late notorious Purgations of the new Fast- | booke, contrary to his Maiesties Proclamation, and their intoelrable affront | therein offered to the most Illustrious Lady Elizabeth, the Kings onely | Sister, and her Children (even whiles they are now royally en- | tertained at Court) in leauing them out of the Collect; | and to his Maiestie, his Queene, and their Royall | Progeny, in blotting them out of the | number of Gods Elect. | . . . (9 lines; ornament).

Printed at Ipswich, An. 1636. | 19. x15.5 cm. (8)p.
Signed Matthew White. DNB. 46:433 a
Burned by order of Star Chamber, June 30 and July 2, 1637.

PRYNNE, William. The Vnbishoping Of | Timothy And Titvs. | Or | A briefe elaborate Discourse, prooving Timothy to be | no Bishop (much lesse any sole, or Diocæsan Bishop) of Ephesus, | nor Titus of Crete; and that the power of ordination, or imposition | of hands, belongs Iure Divino to Presbyters, as well | as to Bishops, and not to Bishops | onely. | Wherein all Objections and Pretences to the contrary | are fully answered; and the pretended superiority of Bishops | over other Ministers and Presbyters Iure Divino, (now much | contended for) utterly subverted in a most perspicuous | maner. | By a Wellwisher to Gods truth and people. | . . . (7 lines)

In the Yeare M.DC. XXXVI. | 19.5x14.2cm. (1),3–173,(5)p.
Also another edition, with identical t.p., but without errata,etc. 18x13cm. 165p. Anon. H & L.

QUELCH, William. Chvrch- | Cvstomes | Vindicated: | In | Two Sermons | Preached At | Kingstone upon Thames: | The One | At the Primary Visitation of the Right | Reverend Father in God Richard by the | grace of God late L.B. of Winton, Anno 1628. | The Other | At the first Metropoliticall Visitation of | the Most Reverend Father in God William | by the grace of God Lord Arch-Bishop of Canterbury | his Grace,&c. July 9. 1635. | By William Quelch B.D. and R. of | East-horsly Surrey. | . . . 3 lines).

London, | Printed by M.F. for Nathaniel Butter neare S.Austins | Gate at the Signe of the Pyde Bull. 1636. | Line border. 18.2x14.3cm. (5),56p.

REEVE, Edmund. The | Commvnion | Book Catechisme | Expovnded, | According to Gods holy Word, and the established | Doctrine of the Church. | VVritten for the furtherance of Youth | and ignorant persons, in the understanding of | the grounds and principles of the Christian | Religion. | Wherein, besides the continued Explanation of the | points expressed in the Catechisme, there are delivered | sundry matters very profitable to be considered: | Whereof some are mentioned in the Index | afore the Worke. | . . . (6 lines; ornament).

London, | printed by M.F. for Humphrey Mosley in S.Pauls Church- | yard at the signe of the three Kings. 1636. | Border. 18.6x14.4cm. (24),216p. Title in black and red.
Epistle Dedicatorie, signed.

REYNOLDS, Edward. The | Shields | Of | The Earth. | A | Sermon Preached | Before the Reverend | Judges, Sir Richard Hutten, | and

Sir George Crooke, at | the Assizes holden at North-hampton: | February 25. 1634. | By Edward Reynolds, Rector of | the Church at Braunston in North- | hampton Shire. | (device)

London, | Imprinted by Felix Kyngston, for Robert Bostock, and | are to be sold at his shop in Pauls Churchyard | at the signe of the Kings-head, 1636. | Line border. 18x13.2cm. (1),50,(1)p.
From the library of Walter W. Law.

RUTHERFORD, Samuel. Exercitationes | Apologeticæ | Pro Divina Gratia, | In quibus vindicatur doctrina orthodoxa de divinis decre- | tis, & Dei tum æterni decreti, tum gratiæ efficacis | operationis, cum hominis libertate consocia- | tione & subordinatione amicâ: | Adversus Jacobum Arminium ejusque asseclas, & Jesuitas, | inprimis vero Fran.Suarezium, Gabri.Vasquezium, | Lodiv.Molinam, Leonard. Lessium, Pet.Fon- | secam & Robertum Bellarminum. | Studio & industria | Samuelis Rhætorfortis, | Ecclesiæ Anwetensis, in Gallovidia Scotiæ Provincia, | Pastoris. | . . . (3 lines ; device).

Amstelredami, | Apud Henricum Laurentii Bibliopolam. | Anno M.DC. XXXVI. | 17.4x10.6cm. (14),544p. Pp. 161-180, 229-298 skipped in numbering.

SELDEN, John. Ioannis Seldeni | De | Successionibus | In | Bona Defuncti, | Ad Leges Ebræorum, | Liber Singularis. | Editio altera, correctior & multùm auctior. | Accedunt ejusdem | De | Successione | In | Pontificatum | Ebræorum, | Libri Duo. | Prior Historicus est; Pontificum ab Aharone usque ad Tem- | pli Secundi Excidium Successionem continens. | Posterior est Juridicus; Legitima, seu quæ in Successione | Pontificali adeoque in admissione ad munus Sacerdotale | apud Ebræos Juris fuere complexus. | (ornament).

Londini. | Excudebat Richardus Bishop. | MDCXXXVI. | 27.9x18cm.(6), XXIV,(4),266p. Title in red and black

SELDEN, John. Iohannis Seldeni | Mare Clavsvm, | Sev | De Dominio Maris | Libri Duo. | Primo, | Mare, ex Iure Naturæ, seu Gentium, omnium hominum | non esse Commune, sed Dominii privati, seu | Proprietatis capax, pariter ac Tellurem, | esse demonstratur. | Secundo, | Serenissimum Magnæ Britanniæ Regem Maris cir- | cumflui, ut individuæ atque perpetuæ Im- | perii Britannici appendicis, Dominum | esse, asseritur. | . . . (1 line: device)

Lvgdvni Batavorvm, | Apud Joannem, & Theodorvm Maire. | M DCXXXVI. | 20.1x15. cm (12),244p. 2 maps, 3 cuts. Title page in red and black.

SIBBES, Richard. The | Sovles | Conflict | with it selfe, | And Victory | over it selfe by Faith. | A Treatise of the inward disquiet- | ments of distressed spirits, with | comfortable remedies to establish | them. | . . . (2 lines). By R.Sibbs D.D.Master of | Katherine Hall in Cambridge, and | Preacher of Grayes-Inne London. | The Third Edition. |

London | Printed by M.F. for R.Dawlman | at the Brazen Serpent in Pauls- | Churchyard. 1636. | Arch. border. 16.4x10.6cm. (20), 572,(14)p.

A SOVERAIGNE Antidote | Against | Sabbatarian | Errovrs. | Or, | A Decision of the chiefe Doubts and | Difficulties touching the Sabbath. | Wherein these three Questions (beside others | coincident) are clearly and succinctly | determined, viz. | I. Which is the fittest Name whereby to call the Day of | Christian Weekly Rest, whether Sabbath day, | Lords-day, or Sunday. | II. What is the meaning of that Prayer, appointed to | be used by our Church: Lord have mercy upon us, | and encline, &c. as it is repeated and applyed to the | words of the Fourth Commandment. | III. Whether it be lawfull to use any Bodily Recreation | on the Lords-day? and if so, what kind of Recreation? | By a Reverend, Religious, and judicious Divine. |

London: | Printed by Thomas Harper for Benjamin Fisher, and are | to be sold at his Shop in Aldersgate-street at the | signe of the Talbot. 1636. | 18.x 13.5cm (6),27,(3)p. Colophon.

Attributed to Robert Sanderson: H&L.

SPENSER, Benjamin. Vox Civitatis, | Or, | Londons Complaint | against her Children in the | Covntrie. | Shewing to them her {Infirmitie. | Povertie. | Desolate misery. | Upbraiding them with{Unkindnesse. | Uncharitablenesse. | Distrustfulnesse. | Informing them of her {Comfort in God. | Counsell to them. | Chiding the Coun- | trie for their{Ignorance of{God. | And his Hand. | {Hard-heartednesse in}Entertaining. | Burying. | Taken from her own mouth, and written by | Benjamin Spencer, Master in Arts. | . . . (3 lines).

London, | Printed by E. P. for William Hope, and are to be sold | at his Shop at the signe of the Glove in Cornehill | neere the Royall Exchange. 1636. | 18.3x13.6 cm. (4),31,(1)p.

Spelling of name from BMCat.

WARD, Samuel. A | Collection | Of Svch Sermons | And Treatises | as have beene written | and Published | By Samvel Ward, Bachelor in Divinitie, and Preacher | of Ipswich, | Are here gathered into one | Volume | The Titles whereof are in the | next Page following. |

London, | Printed for Iohn Grismond, and are to bee | sold in Ivie Lane at the Signe of the | Gunne. 1636. | 16.3x10.4cm. (6),602p.

Contains nine pieces, with same imprint, dated 1635: Christ is all in All; Life of Faith; Life of Faith in Death; Coale from the Altar; Balme from Gilead . . . Sermon preached at Pauls-Crosse, Oct. 20, 1616; Iethro's Ivstice of Peace; Peace-Offering to God; Woe to Drvnkards; and Happinesse of Practice .

WEEMSE, John. An | Exposition | Of The | Ceremoniall Lavves | Of Moses, As They Are | Annexed To The Tenne | Commandements. | Wherein are cleared divers customes of the | Iewes, and also the customes of the Gentiles, as | they have relation to the Iewish, out of the Originall | Tongues, the Hebrew and Greeke. | Together with directions how to make the | right use of them in Preaching. | All serving to let us see how they leade us as types to Ie- | svs Christ, whom we see more clearely when | the vayle is taken away. | . . . (2 lines) By Iohn Weemse, of Lathocker in Scotland, Preacher of | Christs Gospell. |

London: | Printed by M.Dawson for Iohn Bellamie, and are to be sold at his Shop at the | signe of the three golden Lyons in Cornehill, neere the Royall Exchange. 1636. | Line border. 21.1x16. cm. (30),261,(1)p.

Incorporated in his workes. vol. III, 1636. 20.9x16.2cm.(30),261,(1)p. Separate pagination but continuous register.

WEEMES, John. An | Exposition | Of The | Ivdiciall Lavves | of Moses, | Plainely discovering divers of their ancient | Rites and Customes. | As in their Governours, Government, Synedrion, Punishments, | Civill Accompts, Contracts, Marriages, Warres, and Burials. | Also their Oeconomicks, (Vizt.) their dwellings, Feasting, Clo- | thing, and Husbandrie. | Together with two Treatises, the one shewing the different estate of | the godly and the wicked in this life, and in the life to come. | The other, declaring how the wicked may bee inlightned by the | Preaching of the Gospell, and yet become worse after they be | illuminated. | All which are cleered out of the Originall Languages and doe serve | as a speciall helpe for the true understanding of divers difficult | Texts of Scripture. | . . . (2 lines) By Iohn Weemes, of Lathocker in Scotland, | Preacher of Gods Word. |

London, | Printed by M.Dawson for Iohn Bellamie, and are to be sold at his Shop at the | signe of the three golden Lyons in Cornehill, neere the Royall Excharge. 1636. | Line border. 21.1x16. cm. (27),223,(1)p.

Incorporated in his workes; 1636. Vol. III. 20.9x16.2cm. (27),223,(1)p. Separate pagination but continuous register.

WEEMSE, John. Observations, | Natvrall | And | Morall. | With A Short Treatise | of the Numbers, Weights, and Measures, | used by the Hebrewes; with the valuation of | them according to the Measures of the | Greekes and Romans. | For the clearing of sundry places of Scripture, in which | these weights and measures are set downe | by way of Allusion. | By Iohn Weemes, of Lathocker in Scotland, | Preacher of Christs Gospell. | (ornament).

London, | Printed by M.Dawson for Iohn Bellamie, and are to be sold at his Shop at the | signe of the three golden Lyons in Cornehill, neere the Royall Exchange. 1636. | Line border. 20.9x16.5cm. (4),144p.

Incorporated in his Workes: 1637, with continuous register.

WEEMSE, John. The | Portraitvre | Of The Image Of | God In Man. | In his three estates, of Creation. | Restauration. | Glorification. | Digested into two parts. | The first containing, the Image of God both in the Bo- | dy and Soule of Man, and Immortality of both: with a descripti- | on of the severall members of the Body, and the two principall fa- | culties of the soule, the understanding and the Will; in | which consisteth his knowledge, and liberty | of his will. | The second containing, the passions of man in the con- | cupiscible and irascible part of the soule: his dominion over the | creatures; also a description of his active and contemplative | life; with his conjunct or married estate. | Whereunto is annexed an explication of sundry naturall and morall | Observations for the clearing of divers Scriptures. | All set downe by way of collation, and cleared by sundry distinctions, both | out of the Schoolemen, and moderne Writers. | The Third Edition, corrected and enlarged. | By I.Weemse, of Lathocker in Scotland, Preacher of Christs Gospel. |

London, | Printed by T.C. for Iohn Bellamie, and are to be sold at the signe | of the three Golden Lyons in Cornehill, neere the Royall Exchange. 1636. | Line border. 20.9x16.5cm. (28),283;(4),144p. Second part has separate t.p.; continuous register, separate pagination

Incorporated in his Workes: 1637. 20.9x16.2cm. (28),283;(4),144p. With continuous register.

WEEMSE, John. A | Treatise | Of | The Fovre Dege- | nerate Sonnes, | Viz. | {the Atheist | the Magician} {the Idolater | and the Jew.} Wherein are handled many profitable que- | stions concerning Atheisme, Witchcraft, Idolatry, | and Iudaisme: and sundry places of Scrip- | ture, cleared out of the | Originall Tongues. | . . . (11 lines). Being the fourth Volume, of the Workes of Mr.Ioh. Weemse | of Lathocker in Scotland, and Prebend of Dunelm. |

London Printed by Thomas Cotes and are to be sold by Iohn Bellamie, | dwelling at the three golden Lyons in Corne-hill, neere the Royall Exchange. 1636. | Line border. 20.9x16.2cm. (23), 382, (3)p.

WEEMSE, John. The | VVorkes Of | Mr.Iohn VVeemse of Lathocker in | Scotland. | The second Volumne. | Containing An | Exposition | Of The | Morall Law, | Or Ten | Commandements | Of Almightie God; | VVherein is contained an explanation of diverse | Questions and Positions for the right under- | standing thereof. | Together with an explication of these Scriptures which depend | upon, or belong unto every one of the Commandements. | All which are cleared out of the originall languages, the custome of the | Iews, and the distinctions of the Schoolemen. | . . . (2 lines).

Printed at London by Tho. Cotes, for John Bellamie, and are to be sold at his shop | at the three golden Lyons in Cornehill, neere the Royall Exchange, 1636. | Line border. 20.9x16.2cm. (27), 254; (28), 348p. 2 pts.

WEEMES, John. The | VVorkes Of | M.Iohn Weemes of Lathocker in | Scotland. | The third Volumne. | Containing An | Exposition | Of The Lavves | Of Moses, | Viz.{Ceremoniall | and | Iudiciall. | Wherein is contained an explanation of di- | vers Questions and Positions for the right | understanding of them. | Together with | Exercitations Divine. | Proving the Necessitie, Majestie, integritie and perspicuitie and | sence of the Scriptures. | All which are cleared out of the originall Languages, and Customes of the | Iewes, and the distinctions of the Schoole-men. | . . . (2 lines).

London. | Printed by M.Dawson for Iohn Bellamie, and are to be sold at his Shop at the | signe of the three golden Lyons in Cornehill, neere the Royall Exchange. 1636. | Line border. 20.9x16.2cm. (1), (30), 261, (1); (27), 223, (1); (30), 188, (3)p.

WHITE, Francis. A | Treatise | Of The | Sabbath-Day. | Containing, | A Defence Of The | Orthodoxall Doctrine of the Church | of England, against Sabbatarian- | Novelty. | By Dr. Fr. White, L. Bishop of Ely. | . . . (5 lines). The Third Edition. | (ornament).

London, | Printed by R. B. and are to be sold at St. | Dunstans Church-yard in Fleetstreet. | 1636. | 18.1x14 cm. (30),311,(6) p.

WILLIAMS, Griffith. The Best | Religion; | Wherein is largely explaned | the Summe and principall Heads | of the Gospell. | In certaine Sermons and Treatises, the | Particulars and Dependance whereof are | set downe immediately after | the Epistle. | With a large Alphabeticall Table. | By Gr.Williams Doctor in Divinity, | and Deane of Bangor. | . . . (3 lines).

London, | Printed by George Miller, for Philemon | Stephens and Christopher Meredith at the | golden Lion in Pauls Church-yard. | MDCXXXVI. | Arch. border. 27.6x18.3cm.(4),1–350, (6), 351–419,(8),421–563,(14) 565–1106,(34)p. 3 Sub t.p. Continuous register.

WILLIAMS, Griffith. The | Right VVay | To The Best | Religion, | Wherein is largely explained the summe and | principall heads of the Gospell. | In certaine Sermons and Treatises; The particulars | and dependance whereof are set downe | immediately after the Epistle, with a large | Alphabeticall Table. | By Gr. Williams Doctor in Divinity | and Deane of Bangor. | . . . (2 lines; device).

London, | Printed by George Miller, for Philemon Stephens and Christopher | Meredith, at the golden Lyon in Pauls Church-yard. | MDCXXXVI. | Line border. 27.8x18 cm. (6), 1–350,(6), 351–419, (18), 421–563,(14), 565–1105, (1)p.

T.p. mounted. Three sub. t.p., with continuous register and pagination Same as preceding, but lacks index.

1637

AMBROSE, St. Christian | Offices | Crystall | Glasse. | In three Bookes. | First Written In Latine, | By That Famovs | and renowned Father, Saint | Ambrose Bishop of | Millane. | Whereunto is added | His Conviction Of | Symmachvs the Gentile. | A worke tending to the advancement of Vertue, | and of Holinesse: and to shew how much the | morality of the Gentiles, is exceeded by | the doctrine of Christianity. | Translated into English by Richard Hvmfrey | Minister of old Windsore. | . . . (2 lines).

Printed at London for Iohn Dawson, and are to bee | sold at the signe of the White-Lyon in Paules- | Church-yard. 1637. | Line border. 18.4x14.1cm. (65), 142; (9),75; (8), 64; (38); (20), 41p. folded leaf. 3 Sub. t.p. 3 Books.
The final part: Trvths Trivmph: has separate register and pagination.

AUSTIN, William. Devotionis | Avgvstinia- | næ Flamma, | Or, | Certaine Devovt, | Godly, And Learned | Meditations. | Written, by the excellently-Accomplisht Gentleman, | William Austin, of Lincolnes-Inne, Esquire. | The Particulars whereof, The Reader may finde | in the Page following; | Set forth, after his Decease, by his deare Wife and Executrix, | M^ris Anne Austin, as a Surviving Monument of some | part of the great worth of her ever-honoured Husband, who | changed His life, Ian.16.1633. | (device).

London, | Printed for Richard Meighen, and Iohn Legatt, and | are to be sold at the Middle-Temple-Gate. 1637. | 29x18.8cm.(7),30,(1), 31–54,(1),55–95,(1),97–292. 12 Sub. t.p. Engr. fore t.p.

BABINGTON, Gervase. A | Sermon | Preached at Pavls | Crosse, The Second | Svnday in Michael- | mas Terme. | 1590. | By Gervase Babington Doctor | of Divinity. | (device).

London, | Printed by M.Flesher. | 1637. | Line border. 32.1x20.5cm. Pp. 269–286 of his Works: 1637.

BABINGTON, Gervase. A | Very Fruit- | fvll Exposition Of | The Commandements, | By Way Of Qvestions And | Answers For Greater | Plainnesse. | Together with an Application of every one to the | Soule and Conscience of Man, profitable for all, and especially | for them that (being not otherwise furnished) are yet desirous | both to see themselves, and to deliver to others some | larger speech of every point, that is but | briefly named in the shorter | Catechismes. | By the Right Reverend Father in God, Gervase Babington, | late Bishop of Worcester. | Whereunto is newly annexed a Table, containing the | principall Matters in this Booke. | . . . (3 lines; device).

London, | Printed by M.Flesher. | 1637. | Line border. 32.1x20.5cm. (12),311p. Part of his Works: 1637; with separate register and pagination.

BABINGTON, Gervase. The | Works | Of The | Right Reverend | Father In God, | Gervase Babington, | Late Bishop of Worcester. | Containing | Comfortable Notes Upon | The Five Bookes of Moses, viz. | {Genesis. | Exodus. | Leviticus. | Numbers. | Deuteronomie. | As Also | An Exposition Upon { The Creed. | The Commandements. | The Lords Prayer. | With | A conference betwixt mans Frailtie and Faith. | And | Three Sermons. | With Alphabeticall Tables of the principall matters | to each severall Worke. | . . . (4 lines).

London, | Printed by Miles Flesher. | 1637. | Line border. 32.1x20.5cm.(14),427; (3),163,(1),165–263; (12),311p. 9 sub t.p. Portr. frontisp.

BAKER, Richard. Meditations | And | Disqvisitions | Upon The | Lords Prayer. | By Sr. Richard Baker, Knight. | . . . (2 lines). The second Edition, Corrected and amended. | (device).

London, | Printed by Anne Griffin, for Anne Bouler, and are | to be sold at the signe of the Marigold, in | the Goldsmith-row, in Cheapside. 1637. | Line border. 18.2x14.3cm. (8), 213p.

BALL, John. A | Short | Catechisme. | Containing the Principles | of Religion. | Very profitable for all sorts of | People. | The eighteenth Impression. | (ornament)

London, | Printed by R. Bishop for Robert Bird, | at the signe of the Bible in Saint | Laurence-lane. 1637. | 14.1x9.cm. (1),43p.
Attribution by Dr.Charles A. Briggs. Expanded in the Short Treatise by Ball.

BALL, John. A | Short | Treatise, | Contayning all the Principall | Grounds of Christian | Religion. | By way of Questions and Answers, very | profitable for all men, but especi- | ally for Housholders. | The eleventh Impression. | . . . (ornament).

London. | Printed by R.Bishop, for Robert Bird, | at the Signe of the Bible in | Saint Laurence Lane | 1637. | 13.9x9.4cm. (12),1–116p. impf. after H8.
Anon. Cambr.Univ.Cat:5107.

BALL, John. A | Treatise | Of Faith. | Divided into two Parts: | The first shewing the | Nature, | The second, the Life | of Faith: | Both tending to direct the weake Christian how he | may possesse the whole Word of God as his | owne, overcome temptations, better | his obedience, and live comfor- | tably in all estates. | By John Ball. | . . . (2 lines). The third Edition corrected and enlarged. |

London, | Printed by Robert Young for Edward Brewster, and are | to be sold at his Shop at the signe of the Bible | upon Fleet bridge, 1637. | Border. 18.2x 14cm.(36), 428,(50)p.

BANCROFT, Richard. A | Sermon | Preached At | Pavls Crosse | the 9. of February, being the | first Sunday in the Parliament, Anno Dom. 1588. | by Richard Bancroft D. of Divinity, | and Chaplaine to the right Honourable | Sir Christopher Hatton Knight, Lord Chan- | cellour of England. | Wherein some things are | added, which then were omitted, | either through want of time or de- | fault in memory. | . . . (3 lines).

London | Printed by John Norton, and are to be | sold by Godfrey Emerson. 1637. | Line border. 18.5x14.3cm. (1),87p. T.p. supplied.

BASTWICK, John. The Ansvver | Of | Iohn Bastwick, | Doctor of Phisicke, | To the exceptions made against his | Letany by A learned Gentleman, | Which Is | Annexed to the Letany it selfe, as Articles superaddi- | tionall against the | Prelats. | In the vvhich there is, A full, demonstration and proof of the | Reall Absence of Christ in the Sacrament of the Lords Supper, with the vanity | and impiety of the Consecration of Temples Churches and Chapples, | Also | The necessity of the perpetuall motion and circulation of worship | if men be found to bow the knees at the name of Jesus. | This is to follow the Letany as A second part thereof. | (ornament).

Printed | In the yeare of Remembrance, Anno 1637. | 18.3x14.3 cm. (1).29p. Running head: The Second Part, Of The Letany.

BASTWICK, John. The Answer | Of | John Bastwick, | Doctor of Phisicke, | To the Information of Sir Iohn Bancks | Knight, Atturney universall. | Jn Which | There is a sufficient Demonstration, | That the Prelats are Jnvaders of the Kings Prerogative | Royall, Contemners and Despisers of holy Scrip- | ture, Advancers of Poperie, Superstition, | Idolatry and Prophanesse: | Also | That they abuse the Kings Authoritie, to the oppression of his loyallest | Subjects, and therein exercise great crueltie, tyrannie and in- | justice; and in the execution of these impious performances | they shew neither wit, honestie, nor temperance. | Nor | That they are either Servants of God or of the King (as they are | not indeed) but of the Devill: being enemies of God and the | King: and of every living thing that is good. | All which the sayd Doctor Bastwick is ready to maintaine before King and Counsell, against them all, with the hazard of otherwise | being exposed to extremest miserie. | (ornament).

Printed in the yeare 1637. | 17.3x13.5cm. 29p.

BASTWICK, John. The Letany | Of | John Bastvvick, | Doctor of Phisicke, | Being now full of Devotion, as well in respect of the | common calamities of plague and pestilence; as also | of his owne patticular miserie: lying at this instant in Limbo | Patrum. Set downe in two Letters to Mr. Aquila Wykes, | keeper of the Gatehouse, his good Angell. | Jn Which | There is an universall challenge to the vvhole World, | to prove the parity of Ministers, to be jure divino. | Also | A full demonstration, that the Bishops are neither Christs, nor the Apostles | Successors, but enemies of Christ and his Kingdome, and of the Kings | most excellent Majesties prerogative Royall. | All which hee undertaketh to make good before King and Counsell, with the | hazard of otherwise being made a prey to their insatiable indignation. | A Booke very usefull, and profitable for all good Christians to read, for the | stirring up of devotion in them likewise. | . . . (3 lines).

Printed | By the speciall procurement, and for the especiall use of our English Prelats | in the Yeare of Remembrance, Anno 1637. | 17.3x13.6 cm. (1),21;(1), 29;(1),25;(1),7;29p. Pagination includes four parts.
Burned by order of Star Chamber, June 30 and July 2, 1637.

BASTWICK, John. A | More Fvll Answer | Of | John Bastwick, | Dr. Of Phisick, | Made to the former exceptions newly propounded by an- | other wellwiller to him, against some expressions in | his Letany, with his reasons for the | printing of it. | All set downe as more Articles superadditionall vpon super- | additionall, against the Prelats. | This is to follow the Letany as a Fovrth Part of it. | (ornament).

Printed in the Yeare of the English Prelats malice, | and crualty, against and upon Gods faith- | full people, 1637. | 17.3x13.5cm. (1),7p.

BASTWICK, John. The Vanity And Mischeife | Of The Old | Letany. | Or | A further answer of John Bastwick , Doctor of Physick, to some other exceptions made against his Letany by a learned | Gentlemen: annexed unto the Letany as more su- | peradditionall articles against the Prelats. | In Which | There is a full demonstration of the fruitlessenes and impiety of the Ser- | vice-booke, with the hurt and mischeif that hath done, and dayly doth | through the Kingdome, to the infinit dishonor of God and the King, and | endangering of this florishing Kingdome and State. | Also | Certaine sufficient reasons to prove the unprofitablenes and need- | lesnes both of the study and citation of Fathers in Theolo- | gicall writings, and the reason of the corruption | of the youth and Scholars in both | Universities. | This is to follow the Letany as a third Part of it. | (ornament)

Printed in the Yeare of Remebrance, 1637. | 17.3x13.5cm. (1),25p.

BAYNE, Paul. Christian Letters | Of | Mr.Paul Bayne. | Replenished with di- | vers Consolations, Exhortati- | ons, and Directions, tending | to promote the Honour | of Godlinesse. | Hereunto is added a fruitfull | Sermon for the Triall of a | Christians Estate. | . . . (4 lines)

London, | Printed by E.G. for I.N. and are | to be sold by Samuel Enderby at his shop | in Popes-head-Alley, at the signe | of the Starre, 1637. | Line border. 14x8 cm. (7),421; (6),42p.

BAYNE, Paul. The | Triall | Of A | Christians Estate: | Or, | A Discoverie of the Causes, | degrees, signes and differences | of the Apostasie both of | true Christians and false: | In a Sermon preached in London, | by Master Paul Bayne, and | afterward sent in writing to | his friend W.F. | (ornament).

London, | Printed by A.G. for I.N. and are | to be sold by Sam.Enderby, at his | shop, at the Starre in Popes | head Alley. 1637. | Line border. 14x8cm. (6), 42p.
Appended to his Christian Letters: 1637; with separate register and pagination.

BOLTON, Robert. Helps To | Hvmiliation. | By | Robert Bolton. | And | Published before his Death. | The fourth Edition. | . . . (2 lines; cut, with printed line on each side)
    Study me in thy prime
    Bury Death and weary Time.
    The Glasse doth run, and Time doth Goe,
    Death hath his End, I have not so.
 London: | Printed by Iohn Okes, for Michael Spark, dwelling | at the blew Bible in Greene-arbor. 1637. | Border. 18.3x14.cm. (6),56p.

A BRIEFE | Relation | Of certain speciall and most ma- | teriall passages, and speeches in the Starre- | Chamber, occasioned and delivered Iune the 14th. | 1637. at the censure of those three worthy Gentle- | men, Dr. Bastwicke, Mr. Bvrton and | Mr. Prynne, as it hath beene truely and | faithfully gathered from their owne | mouthes by one present at | the sayd Censure. | (device).
 Printed in the Yeere 1637. | 17.4x13.5 cm. 30,(1)p.

BYFIELD, Nicholas. A | Commentary | Vpon | The Three First Chap- | ters Of The First Epistle | generall of St.Peter. | VVherin Are Most Judici- | ously and profitably handled such points of Do- | ctrine as naturally flow from the Text. | Together with very usefull Application thereof: | and many good Rules for a godly life. | By Nicholas Byfield Preacher of Gods Word | at Isleworth in Middlesex. | To which is now newly added an Alphabeticall Table, | not formerly published. | . . . (3 lines; ornament).
 London, | Printed by Miles Flesher and Robert Young. | M DC XXXVII. | Line border. 28.5x18.5cm (14),1–196p.197–200fol.(4),201–707,(19)p.
 Three sub t.p., dated 1636 and 1637.

BYFIELD, Nicholas. The | Principles, | Or, | The Patterne of | wholsome words. | Containing a Collection | of such Truths as are of neces- | sitie to be beleeved unto sal- | vation, separated out of the | body of all Theologie: | Made evident by infallible and | plaine proofes of Scriptures. | And withall, | The severall Uses such Principles | should be put to are abundantly shewed. | A project much desired, & of singular | use for all sorts of Christians. | By N. Byfield, Preacher of | Gods Word at Isleworth in Middlesex. | The sixth Edition, corrected & amended. |
 London, | Printed by Jo. Dawson, for Philemon | Stephens and Christopher Meredith, | dwelling at the golden Lyon in Pauls | Church-yard. 1637. | Line border. 13.7x7.8cm. (20),479p.

BYFIELD, Nicholas. The | Spiritvall | Tovch-Stone, | Or, | The Signes Of | A Godly Man. | Drawne in so plaine and profi- | table manner, as all sorts of | Christians may trie them- | selves thereby. | Together with Directions, how the | weak Christian, by the use of these signes, | may establish his assurance. | By Nicolas Byfield, late | Preacher of Gods Word at Isleworth | in Middlesex. | . . . (5 lines).
 London, | Printed by J. Norton, for Iohn | Bellamy. 1637. | Line border. 11.8x7. cm. (17),130p.

CHURCH, Henry. Miscellanea | Philo-Theologica, | Or, | God, & Man. | A Treatise compendiously describing | the Nature of God in his Attributes, with a lively pourtraiture | of his Wisedome in ordering, and disposing of the | Celestiall, and terrestriall | Bodies. | Containing much variety of Matter | Theologicall, and Philosophicall; wherein many secrets in Scripture, | and in Nature, are unbowelled, with solid Proofes, and apt | Applications singular for brevity, and perspicuity. | By Henry Church. . . . (8 lines)

London, | Printed for John Rothwell, and are to be sold at | the Sunne, in Pauls Church-yard. | M.DC.XXXVII. | Line border. 17.9x13.6 cm. (11), 280, 83p.
Two portions: with separate register and pagination.

CLERKE, Richard. Sermons | Preached | By That | Reverend And | Learned Divine | Richard Clerke, | Dr. in Divinitie; | Sometimes Fellovv | of Christ Colledge in Cambridge. One of the | most Learned Translators of our English | Bible; Preacher in the Famous Metropo- | litan Church of Christ, | Canterbury. | Since his death, published for the Common good, | By Charles White, | Mr. in Arts, and one of the Six Preachers of | Christ Church, Canterbury. | . . . (4 lines; ornament).

London, | Printed by T.Cotes, for Thomas Alchorn, and are to be sold at his shoppe at the | signe of the Greene Dragon in S.Pauls Church yard. 1637. | Border of printer's ornaments. 27.4x18.3cm.(10), 1–72,(8),73–248,(16),249–577p.

COMENIUS, Joannes Amos. Porta Sapientiæ | Reserata: | Sive | Pansophiæ Christianæ | Seminarivm. | Hoc est, | Nova, compendiosa, & solida omnes Sci- | entias & Artes, & quicquid manifesti vel occulti | est, quod ingenio humano penetrare, solertiæ imitari, | linguæ eloqui datur, breviùs, veriùs, meliùs, quàm | hactenus, addiscendi Methodus. | Auctore | Reverendo Clarissimóque Viro | Domino Iohanne Amoso Comenio. | . . . (4 lines; ornament)

Oxoniæ, | Ex Officina Guilielmi Turneri | Academiæ Typographi. M.DC. XXXVII. | 17.8x13.6 cm. (2),52,(6)p.

COWELL, John. The | Interpreter: | Or | Booke, Containing | the Signification of Words. | Wherein is set forth the true meaning of all, | or the most part of such words and Termes, | as are mentioned in the Law Writers, or | Statutes of this victorious and renowned | Kingdome, requiring any Exposition | or Interpretation. | A Worke not onely profitable, but necessary for | such as desire throughly to be instructed in the | knowledge of our Lawes, Statutes, or | other Antiquities. | Collected by John Cowell, Doctor, sometime | the Kings Majesties Professour of the Civill Law | in the Universitie of Cambridge. | . . . (1 line).

London, Printed for William Sheares. 1637. | Line border. 18.6x14.5cm.(7), A–Cccc4.
The original edition of 1607 was burned by the hangman in June 1608 by order of James I, and on March 26, 1610 by order of parliament.

A | DECLARATION | Of The | Pfaltzgraves: | Concerning | The Faith | And | Ceremonies | Professed | In His | Churches. | According to the Originall printed | in the High Dutch, translated | by I. R. |

London, | Printed for Thomas Iones, and are to bee sold at his | Shop in the Strand neere Yorke-House. | 1637. | 17.3x12.5 cm. (1,45)p.

DOW, Christopher. Innovations | Unjustly charged upon the Present | Chvrch and State. | Or | An Ansvver | To The Most | Materiall Passages | of a Libellous Pamphlet | Made By | Mr. Henry Burton, | And Intitvled | An Apologie of an Appeale, &c. | By Christopher Dow B. D. |

London, | Printed by M. F. for John Clark, and are to be | sold at his Shop under S. Peters Church in Cornhill. | M DC XXXVII. | 18.9x14.7 cm. (12), 104p.,105–120fol.,121-214,(1)p.

GATAKER, Thomas. Certaine | Sermons, | First Preached, | And After Published | at severall times, | By M.Thomas Gataker B. of D. | and Pastor at Rotherhith. | And Now Gathered | together into one Volume: | . . . (2 lines; ornament).

London, | Printed by John Haviland for Phylemon Stephens | and Christopher Meredith. | 1637. | Line border. 27.6x18.3cm. (8),347;(6),320p.
19 sub-t.p., all dated 1637, but with varying imprints.

GATAKER, Thomas. . . . . | Davids Instructer. | A | Sermon Preached At | The Visitation Of | the Free-Schoole at Tunbridge in | Kent by the Wardens of the Worshipfull | Company of Skinners: | (ornaments). By | Thomas Gataker | B. of D. and Pastor of Rotherhith. | (ornaments)

London, | Printed by Anne Griffin. | 1637. | 27.8x18.8cm. (4),347p.
Also another edition, with different imprint: London, Printed by Iohn Haviland. 1637, being the first sub-title in his Certaine Sermons: 1637.

GATAKER, Thomas. Noah | His | Obedience, | With | The Grovnd Of It: | Or, | His Faith, Feare, and Care. | A Meditation | On | Hebrevves 11. 7. | Delivered in a Sermon at Lincolnes-Inne: | By | Thomas Gataker, Batcheler of Divinity; | sometime Preacher there: | And now Pastor of Rotherhith. | (device).

London, | Printed by Anne Griffin for | Edvvard Brevvster. | 1637. | 27.8x 18.8cm. (6),320p.
Second part of his Certaine Sermons: 1637, with continuous register.

GILLESPIE, George. A Dispvte | Against | The English-Popish | Ceremonies, | Obtrvded | Vpon The Chvrch Of | Scotland. | Wherein | Not only our ovvne Argvmemts against the | same are strongly confirmed, but likewise the An- | svvers and Defences of our Opposites, | Svch As | Hooker, Mortovne, Bvrges, Sprint, | Paybody, Andrewes, Saravia, Tilen, | Spotswood, Lindsey, Forbesse, &c. | particularly confuted. | . . . (7 lines; device).

Printed in the yeare of our Lord 1637. | 18.5x13.8cm. (22),36;54; 202,(1)p.
Four parts, with doubled letter registers, but separate pagination.
Anon. H&L.Cambr.Univ.Cat.7036.
Burned by virtue of a proclamation dated Oct. 17, 1637.

GOODWIN, Thomas. Aggravation | Of | {Sinne: | And | Sinning | Against { Knowledge. | Mercie. | Delivered in severall | Sermons | upon divers occasions. | By | Tho: Goodvvin B.D. | (ornament).

London, | Printed by M.Flesher, for R.Dawlman and I.Rothwell, | and are to be sold at the signe of the Brazen | Serpent, and Sun in Pauls Churchyard. | M DC XXXVII. | Line border. 18.5x14.5cm. (8), 91; (4), 42, (1)p.
Second part has separate register and pagination.

GOUGE, William. A | Briefe Method | Of Catechizing. | VVherein are briefely handled the funda- | mentall Principles of Christian Religion. | Needfull to be knowne by all Christians before they | be admitted to the Lords Table. | Whereunto are added sundry Prayers, with Thanksgivings before | and after Meate. | The eighth Edition, corrected and inlarged by | William Govge. | . . . (3 lines ; device)
London: | Printed by John Beale. 1637. | Line border. 18x14.4 cm. (2,15)p.
A reprint, appended to his Whole Armour of God: 1647, with continuous register.
Also another copy from the library of Walter W. Law: 18.5x14.6cm.

HALL, Joseph. The | Remedy | Of | Prophanenesse. | Or, | Of | The true sight and feare of | the Almighty. | A needfull Tractate. | In two Bookes. | By | Ios.Exon. |
London, | Printed by Thomas Harper, for Na- | thanael Butter, and are to be sold at his | shop at the signe of the pyde-Bull, | at S.Austins Gate, 1637. | Line border. 16x10.5cm. (11), 252; (11), 83p.
Appended is A Sermon Preach't in the City of Excester . . . Aug.24.1637.

HALL, Joseph. A | Sermon | Preach't in the City of | Excester, | At the Consecration of a new | Buriall-place, there, | On | Saint Bartholomews day, Aug.24. | 1637. | By | Ios.B.of Exon. |
London, | Printed by Thomas Harper, for Na- | thanael Butter, and are to be sold at his | shop at the signe of the pyde-Bull, | at S.Austins Gate, 1637. | Line border. 16x10.5cm. (11),83p.
Appended to his Remedy of Prophanenesse: 1637.

HAYWARD, John. The | Strong | Helper, | Offering to beare every | Mans Burthen. | Or, | A Treatise | teaching in all Troubles | how to cast our Burthen upon | God: but chiefly delivering in- | fallible Grounds of comfort | for quieting of troubled | Consciences. | By Iohn Haiward. | The third Edition, corrected and enlarged. | . . . (4 lines).
London, | Printed by R.Bishop. 1637. | Line border. 16.5x10.5cm, (24), 613p.

HEYLYN, Peter. Antidotvm | Lincolniense. | Or | An Answer | To A Book Entitvled, | The | Holy Table, | Name, & Thing, &c. | Said to be written long agoe by a Minister in Lincolnshire, | And Printed for the Diocese of Lincolne, A°. 1637. | VVritten and inscribed to the grave, learned, | and religious Clergie of the Diocese of Lincoln. | By | Pet: Heylyn Chapleine in Ordinary to his M^{atie}. | . . . (2 lines ; device).
London, | Printed for John Clark, and are to be sold at his shop under | St. Peters Church in Cornhill. 1637. | 18.6x14.3cm. (32),132,132,78,(1)p.
Three sections, separately paged.

HEYLYN, Peter. A Briefe and | Moderate | Answer, | To | The seditious and scandalous Chal- | lenges of Henry Burton, late of | Friday-Streete; | In the two Sermons, by him preached on the | Fifth of November. 1636. And in the | Apologie prefixt before them. | By | Peter Heylyn. | . . . (5 lines).

London: | Printed by Ric.Hodgkinsonne; and are to be sold by Daniel | Frere, dwelling in Little-Brittan, at the signe of the | red-Bull. Anno Domini 1637. | Border. 18.5x14.5cm. (32), 194p.

HOARD, Samuel. The | Chvrches | Avthority | Asserted: | In | A Sermon | Preached at Chelmsford, at the Metro- | politicall Visitation of the most Reverend | Father in God, VVilliam, | Lord Arch-bishop of Canterbury his | Grace, &c. March 1. 1636. | By Samuel Hoard B. D. and | Parson of Morton in Essex. | . . . (5 lines).

London, | Printed by M. F. for John Clark, and are to be | sold at his Shop under S. Peters Church in Cornhill. | M DC XXXVII. | Line border. 18.1x13.1 cm. (4),72p.

HOOKER, Thomas. The | Sovles | Effectvall | Calling To | Christ. | By T.H. | (device).

London, | Printed by J.H. for Andrew Crooke, at the | signe of the Beare in Pauls Church-yard. | 1637. | Line border. 18.3x13.7cm. (24),33–668p.
Cf DNB.27:296a.(6).

HOOKER, Thomas. The Soules | Implantation. | A Treatise | Containing, | The broken Heart, on | Esay 57.15. | The Preparation of the Heart, | on Luk.1.17. | The Soules ingraffing into Christ, | on Mal.3.1. | Spirituall Love and Joy, | on Gal.5.22. | . . . (3 lines; ornament)

London, | Printed by J.H. for Andrew Crooke, at the | signe of the Beare in street-hill. | 1637. | Border. 17.9 x 13.5 cm. (1),266 p. 141–152 misnumbered.
Anon. DNB.27:296a(2).

HOOKER, Thomas. The | Sovles | Ingrafting | into Christ. | By T.H. | (device).

London, | Printed by J.H. for Andrew Crooke, at the | signe of the Beare in Pauls Church-yard. | 1637. | Line border. 19.x14.3cm. (1),30p.
DNB.27:296a(3).

HURST, Thomas. The | Descent | Of | Avthoritie: | Or, | The Magistrates | Patent From Heaven. | Manifested in a Sermon preached | at Lincolnes Assizes, March 13. | 1636. | By Thomas Hvrste Dr. of Divinity, and | one of his Majesties Chaplains. | . . . (2 lines; device).

London, | Printed for Iohn Clark, and are to bee sold at his Shop | under Saint Peters Church in Cornhill. 1637. | Line border. 18.6x13.6 cm. (6),33p. 1–2 blank.

IRONSIDE, Gilbert. Seven | Qvestions | Of The | Sabbath | Briefly Dispvted, | after the manner of the | Schooles. | Wherein such cases, and scruples, as are | incident to this subject, are cleared, and resolved, | By Gilbert Ironside B.D. | . . . (6 lines ; ornaments).

Oxford, | Printed by Leonard Lichfield Printer to the | Famous Vniversity, and are to be sold by | Edward Forrest. | Anno Sallutis M.DC.XXXVII. | Line border. 18x13.7cm. (23),297,(1)p.

JACKSON, Thomas. Diverse | Sermons, | With A Short | Treatise | Befitting These | Present Times, | Now first published | By | Thomas

Iackson, Dr. in Divinity, | Chaplaine in ordinary to his Majestie, | and President of Corpus Christi Col- | ledge in Oxford. | . . . (3 lines; ornament).

Oxford. | Printed by Leonard Lichfield | An.Dom. 1637. | Line border 17.7x 13.7cm. (4),51; (1),70;(1),28;(1),1-6,35-70,71-96p (3 sub-titles).

Continuous register, but separate pagination. Contains, Three | Sermons | Preached | Before The | King, | *and,* A | Treatise | Concerning | The Signes Of | The Time. . . .

JACKSON, Thomas. Three | Sermons | Preached | Before The | King, | Vpon Ier.26.19. | By Thomas Iackson Dr | in Divinity, and Chaplaine | in ordinary to his | Maiesty. | (device)

Oxford, | Printed by Leonard Lichfield | An.Dom.1637. | 17.7x13.7cm. (1),70p.

Part of his Diverse Sermons: 1637, with continuous register, but separate pagination.

JACKSON, Thomas. A | Treatise | Concerning | The Signes Of | The Time, Or Gods | Forewarnings. | Containing | The summe of some few Sermons delive- | red partly before the Kings Majesty partly | in the Towne of New-Castle | upon Tine. | (ornament)

Oxford, | Printed by Leonard Lichfield, | An.Dom.1637. | Line border. 17.7x 13.7cm. (1),28;(1),1-6,35-70,71-96p.

Part of his Diverse Sermons: 1637. with continuous register but separate pagination.

LAUD, William. A Speech | Delivered In The | Starr-Chamber, | On Wednesday, The | XIV of Iune, MDCXXXVII. | At The Censvre, | Of{Iohn Bastwick, | Henry Burton, & | William Prinn; | Concerning pretended Innovations | In the Church. | By the most Reverend Father in God, | William, | L. Archbishop of Canterbury his Grace. | (device).

London, | Printed by Richard Badger. | MDCXXXVII. | 18.2x14 cm. (13),77p.

LAWRENCE, Thomas. A | Sermon | Preached Be- | fore The Kings | Maiesty, at White-Hall, the Seventh | of February, 1636. | By Thomas Lawrence Dr. of Divinity, | and Chaplaine to his Maiestie | in Ordinarie. | Published by the Kings speciall Command. | . . . (5 lines ; device).

London, | Printed by Richard Badger. | 1637. | 19.2x13.9cm. (1),32p.

LUPTON, Donald. Transl. The | History | of the Moderne Pro- | testant Divines, | Containing their Pa- | rents, Countries, Education, | Studies, Lives, and the | yeare of our Lord in | which they dyed. | With a true register of all | their severall Treatises, and Wri- | tings that are extant. | Faithfully translated out of | Latine by D.L. | . . . (2 lines).

London: | Printed by N. and John Okes, 1637. | Border. 14x9.3cm. (22), (8), 364p. Engr. fore t.p. Cont. 44 portr.

A translation from Jacob Verheiden and Henry Holland. DNB.34:286a. Epistle dedicatory, signed.

LUTHER, Martin. A | Commentarie | Vpon The XV. Psalmes, | called Psalmi Graduum, that is, | Psalmes of Degrees: | Faithfully copied out of the Lectures of | D.Martin Luther, very fruitfull and com- | fortable for all Christian afflicted | consciences to read. | Translated out of Latine into English, | By Henry Bull. | (device).

London, Printed by George Miller, dwelling in the | Black-Friers. MDCXXXVII. | Border. 17.8x13.5cm. (10), 318p.

LYNCH, John. Pascha | Christianum; | The | Christian | Passeover. | A Sermon appointed for the Spittle, | but preached at St.Pauls on Wednesday in | Easter Weeke, 1637. | By | John Lynch, Parson of Herietsham in | Kent, and Chaplain unto the R.Reverend | Father in God the Lord Bishop | of Sarum. | . . . (5 lines).

London, | Printed by Robert Young, for | Humfrey Blunden, 1637. | 18.1x 13.5cm. Pp. 45–88 of Squier,J: and Lynch,J: Three Sermons: 1637.

MEDE, Joseph. The Name | Altar, | Or | Θυσιαστήριον, | anciently given to the | Holy Table. | A Common-place, or Theologicall | Discourse, in a Colledge Chappell, | more than two yeares since. | By | Joseph Mede B. D. and Fellow | of Christs Colledge in Cambridge. | (ornament).

London, | Printed by M. F. for John Clark, and are to | be sold at his Shop under St Peters Church in Cornhill. | M DC XXXVII. | Line border. 18.8x14.4 cm. (6),39p.

Also re-issued as part of his Diatribae: 1642; with separate register and pagination

MORTON, Thomas. Antidotum | Adversus | Ecclesiæ Romanæ | De | Merito | propriè dicto | Ex Condigno | Venenum: | Ex antiquæ Ecclesiæ Catholicæ Testi- | moniis locupletissimis confectum: | Juxta Ecclesiæ Anglicanæ, & | Protestantium omnium unanimem | sententiam: | In Gloriam Gratiæ Divinæ, | Meritorum Christi, & ad veræ | pietatis profectum salutarem. | Autore R.P.Thoma Mortono | Episcopo Dunelmensi. |

Cantabrigiæ, | Ex Academiæ celeberrimæ Typographeo. | Anno Dom. M DC XXXVII. | 17.8x13.9 cm. (32),236p.

The OATHS of Allegiance, Supremacy, and | Canonical Obedience. |

22.6x16.5cm. Pp. 129–134 of Sparrow's Collections: 1675. Colophon: Imprinted at London by Robert Barker, Printer to the Kings | Most Excellent Majesty, and by the Assigns of | John Bill. MDCXXXVII. |

POCKLINGTON, John. Altare Christianum: | Or, | The dead Vicars Plea. | Wherein the Vicar of Gr. being dead, yet | speaketh, and pleadeth out of Antiquity, against | him that hath broken down his Altar. | Presented and humbly submitted to | the consideration of his Superiours, the | Governours of our Church. | By Iohn Pocklington, Dr.D. | . . . (4 lines; ornaments).

London, | Printed by Richard Badger. | 1637. | 19.2x14.6 cm. (8),163p. Order to burn passed Mar. 10, 1641.

PRESTON, John. The | Doctrine | Of | The Saints | Infirmities. | Delivered in severall Ser- | mons by John Preston | Doctor in Divinity, Mr. of | Emanuel Colledge in | Cambridge. | And late preacher of Lincolnes-Inne. |

London, | Printed by Nich. and Iohn Okes | for Henry Taunton, and are to be | sold at his shop in St. Dunstans | Church-yard in Fleet- | street. 1637. | Border. 14.1x8.5cm. (12),216p. Engraved fore-title page.

PRESTON, John. Remaines | Of That | Reverend | And Learned | Divine, | John Preston, | Dr. in Divinity, Chaplaine in Ordinary to his | Majesty, Master of Emanuel Colledge in | Cambridge, and sometimes Preacher | of Lincolnes-Inne. | Containing three excellent Treatises, | Namely, { Iudas's Repentance, | The Saints Spirituall Strength. | Pauls Conversion. | . . . (2 lines). The Second Edition. | (ornaments).

London, | Printed by R.B. for Andrew Crooke. 1637. | Border. 17.6x13cm. (12),5–52;(9),65–177; (10),179–299p. Three sub-t.p.

Also another copy from the library of Walter W. Law. 17.5x13.4cm. (12),1–52;(9),65–177;(10),179–299p.

PRESTON, John. The | Saints | Qvalification: | Or, | A Treatise | I.Of Humiliation, in Tenne Sermons. | II. Of Sanctification, in nine Sermons. | Wherevnto Is Added A | Treatise of Communion with Christ in the | Sacrament, in three Sermons. | Preached, | By the late faithful and worthy Minister of | Iesvs Christ, | Iohn Preston, | Doctor in Divinity, Chaplaine in Ordinary to his Majestie, | Master of Emanuel Colledge in Cambridge, and sometime | Preacher of Lincolnes Inne. | The third Edition corrected. | . . . (5 lines).

London, | Printed by R.B. for N.Bourne, and are to be sold by VV.Hope at the Vnicorne | neere to the Royall Exchange. 1637. | Border. 18.7x14.4cm. (16), 558, (20)p. 4 sub t.p.

PRESTON, John. A | Sermon | Preached At | A Generall Fast | Before The Com- | mons-House of Parlia- | ment: the second of | Iuly, 1625. | In the time of the Plague. | By the late faithfull and worthy | Minister of Iesus Christ, | Iohn Preston, | D. in Divinity, Chaplaine in ordinary to | his Majestie, Master of Emmanuel Colledge in | Cambridge, and sometimes Preacher | of Lincolns Inne. |

London, | Printed by R.B. for Nicholas | Bourne, and are to be sold at | his shop at the Royall | Exchange. 1637. | Arch border. 18.7x14.4cm. pp. 227–281 of his Saints Qualification : 1637.

PRYNNE, William. A Breviate of the Prelates intol- | lerable usurpations, both upon the Kings | Prerogative Royall, and the Subjects | Liberties. | . . . (25 lines). Published by W. Hvntley, Esquier. | Edition 3. much enlarged. |

In the Yeare 1637. | 17.7x13.6 cm. 325,(4)p.
Cambr.Univ.Cat:6362. First edition, 1635.

PRYNNE, William. A Catalogve | Of Svch Testi- | monies In All | Ages As Plainly Evidence | Bishops And Presbyters To Be Both | One, Equall And The Same In Iurisdiction, | Office, Dignity, Order, and degree, by divine Law and instituti- | on, and their disparity to be a meere humane ordinance long | after the Apostles times; And that the name of a Bishop is | onely a Title of Ministration, not Dominion, of La- | bour not of Honour, of Humility, not of Prelacy, | of painfullnesse not of Lordlinesse, with a | Briefe Answer to the Objections out | of Antiquity, that seeme to | the contrary. | (ornament)

Printed in the Yeere. 1637. | 20x15 cm. (1),23p.
Attribution by Dr. Charles A. Briggs.

PRYNNE, William. A Qvench-Coale. | Or | A briefe Disquisition and Inquirie, in vvhat place | of the Church or Chancell the Lords-

Table | ought to be situated, especially vvhen | the Sacrament is administred? | VVherein is evidently proved, that the Lords-Table ought to | be placed in the Midst of the Church, Chancell, or | Quire North and South, not Altar-wise, with one side against | the wall: That it neither is or ought to be stiled an Altar; | That Christians have no other Altar but Christ alone, who | hath abolished all other Altars, which are either Heathenish, | Jewish, or Popish, and not tollerable among Christians. | All the Pretences, Authorities, Arguments of Mr. Richard | Shelford, Edmond Reeve, Dr. John Pocklington, and | A late Coale from the Altar, to the contrary in | defence of Altars, calling the Lords- | Table an Altar, or placing it Altar- | wise, are here likewise fully | answered and proved to | be vaine or forged. | By a wellwisher to the truth of God, and the Church of England. | . . . (8 lines)

Printed in the yeare 1637. | Line border. 18x13.9 cm. 78,358p. Pp. 321-328 mispaged.
Anon.Cambr.Univ.Cat:6365.

PRYNNE, William. XVI. New | Qværes | Proposed to our Lord | Prælates. | (device).
Printed in the Yeare M.D.CXXXVII. | 17.6x14.2 cm. (4),17p.
Signed M.E. . Cambr.Univ.Cat.7038

ROGERS, John. A | Treatise | Of | Love. | Written by Io.Rogers, | Minister of Gods Word | at Dedham in Essex. | The third Edition. | . . . (9 lines).
London, | Printed by Mary Dawson, for | Ione Newbery, at the signe of | the Starre in Popes-head Alley. | 1637. | Line border. 14x8cm. (9),240p.

SANDERSON, Robert. Tvvelve | Sermons, | Preached | I. Ad Clerum. III. | 2. Ad Magistratum. III. | 3. Ad Populum. VI. | Whereunto | Are now added two Sermons more, | the one Preached at St. Pauls Crosse, the | other at a Visitation, Concerning the Perswasion | of Conscience. | By | Robert Saunderson, Dr. in Divinity, and | Chaplaine in Ordinary to his Maiesty. | The third Edition. | . . . (2 lines).
London, | Printed by R.B. for R. Dawlman and are to be sold at the signe | of the Brazen Serpent in Pauls Church-yard. | 1637. | Line border. 18.8x14.7cm. (8),1-544,(9),557-655p.

SIBBES, Richard. The | Christians | Portion. | Wherein is unfolded the | unsearchable Riches he hath by | his interest in Christ. Whom in- | joying hee possesseth all | things else. | By R.Sibbs D.D. and Preacher | to the Honorable Society of Grayes- | Inne, and Master of Catherine | Hall in Cambridge. | Published by | T.G. and P.N. |
London. | Printed by John Norton | for John Rothvvell, and | are to be sold at the Sunne in Pauls | Church-yard, 1637. | Line border. 13.5x8cm. (1),67,(1)p.

SIBBES, Richard. A | Fountain Sealed: | Or, | The duty of the sealed to the | Spirit, and the worke of the Spirit | in Sealing. | Wherein | Many things are handled about the | Holy Spirit, and grieving of it: | As also | Of assurance and sealing what it is, the |

priviledges and degrees of it, with the | signes to discerne, and meanes to preserve it. | Being | The substance of divers Sermons prea- | ched at Grayes Inne. | By that Reverend Divine, | Richard Sibbes, | D.D. and sometimes Preacher to that | Honourable Society. |

London, | Printed by Thomas Harper, for Law- | rence Chapman, and are to be sold at | his shop at Chancery lane end, in | Holborne, 1637. | Line border. 14.1x8.2cm (22), 251; (11), 103p. Portr. on engr. t.p.

SIBBES, Richard. The | Saints | Cordialls; | Delivered In | Svndry Sermons | At Graies-Inne, And In | The Citie Of London. | Whereunto is now added, | The Saints Safety | In Evill Times, | Preached In Cambridge | upon speciall Occasions. | By Richard Sibbs D.D. Late Master of Katherine-Hall | in Cambridge, and Preacher at Grayes-Inne. | . . . (device; 2 lines).

London, | Printed by M.F. for Henry Overton, and are to be sold at the | entring in of Popes Head Alley out of Lumbard street. 1637. | Line border. 25.1x 17.5cm.(10), 395p.9 Sub t.p. with different imprint: Printed for R.Davvlman, at the brazen Serpent in Pauls Churchyard: 1637. Portr. mounted.

SIBBES, Richard. The | Spirituall-Mans | Aime. | Guiding A Christian in his | Affections & Actions, through the | sundry passages of this Life. So that | Gods glory and his Salvation may be | the maine end of all. | By the faithfull and Reverend | Divine, R.Sibbes, D.D. and some- | time Preacher to the Honourable | Society of Graies Inne. | Published by T.G. and P.N. |

London, | Printed by E.G. for Iohn Rothwell, | and are to be sold at the Sunne in | Pauls Church-yard. 1637. | Line border. 13.5x8cm. (1),92,(7)p.

SIBBES, Richard. Tvvo | Sermons | Vpon the first words of | Christs last Sermon, | Iohn 14.1. | Being also the last Sermons of | Richard Sibbs D.D. | Preached to the honourable socie- | ty of Grayes Inne, Iune 21. | and 28. 1635. | Who the next Lords day follow- | ing, dyed, and rested from all | his labours. | . . . (2 lines). The third Edition. |

London, | Printed by Thomas Harper, for Law- | rence Chapman, and are to be sold at | his shop in Holborne, at Chancery | lane end. 1637. | Line border. 14.1x 8.2cm. (11), 103p.

SPARROW, Anthony. A Sermon | Concerning | Confession | Of | Sinnes, | And | The Povver | Of | Absolvtion. | Preached by Mr. Sp. of Queenes | Colledge in Cambridge. | (ornament).

London, | Printed by R. Bishop for Iohn Clark, and are to | bee sold at his shop under Saint Peters | Church in Corn-hill, 1637. | Line border. 17x13. cm. (1),20p.
Cambr.Univ.Cat:5108.

SQUIER, John. A | Thankes- | Giving, | For The Decreasing, | and hope of the removing of the | Plagve. | Being a Sermon Preached at St. Pauls | in London, vpon the 1. of Ianuary, 1636. | By Iohn Sqvier Priest, | Vicar of St. Leonards Shordich, sometime Fellow | of Iesus Colledge in Cambride. | The Contents of this Sermon. | I. {Prayer to God alone, not to Saints. | II. The Power of Prayer, rightly qualified. |

III. Prayer and Fasting with, or without a Sermon. | IV. The Newes-Carryer of Ipswich confuted. | V. A Tribute of Thankfulnesse due to God, for his | mercy in Decreasing the Plague. | . . . (2 lines.)

London, | Printed by B. A. and T. F. for Iohn Clark, and are to be | sold at his Shop vnder St. Peters Church in Cornhill. | 1637. | Border. 18.3x14.2cm. (6), 42p. P.1, double device: A ; p 2, blank .

SQUIER, John, and LYNCH, John. Three | Sermons: | Two Of Them | Appointed For | The Spittle, preached in | St.Pauls Church, | By John Squier, Vicar of St.Leonards | Shoredich in Middlesex: | And | John Lynch, Parson of Herietsham | in Kent. | (device)

London, | Printed by Robert Young for Humfrey Blunden, | neere the Castle Taverne in Corne- | Hill. 1637. | Border. 18.1x13.5cm. (3),108p. Two sub-title pages.

STERNHOLD, Thomas, and HOPKINS, John. The | VVhole Book | Of Psalmes: | Collected into English metre, by Thomas | Sternhold, John Hopkins, and others, | conferred with the Hebrew, with apt | notes to sing them withall. | Set forth and allowed to be sung in all churches, of all the people | together, before and after morning and evening prayer, and also be- | fore and after sermons: and moreover in private houses, for their | godly solace and comfort, laying apart all ungodly songs | and ballads, which tend onely to the nourishing | of vice, and corrupting of youth. | . . . (7 lines; device).

Printed by Thomas Buck, and Roger Daniel, printers | to the Universitie of Cambridge. 1637. | Border. 20.9x14.6 cm. (10),94p.

SYDENHAM, Humphrey. The Christian Duell. | In Two | Sermons, | Ad Magistratum. | Preached at two severall Assizes, | held at Taunton in Sommerset. | Anno Domini, 1634. 1635. | By Humphrey Sydenham. | . . . (6 lines; ornament).

London, | Printed by Iohn Beale, for Humprey | Robinson, at the Signe of the Three Pigeons | in Pauls Church-yard. 1637. | Line border. 18.1x14.cm. (1),39–316,(1)p.

Lacks general t.p., and first sermon. Contains six sub t.p.: Jehovah-Jireh; Osculum Charitatis; The Blinde Ethiopian; The foolish Prophet; The Good Pastor.

SYDENHAM, Humphrey. Five | Sermons | Preached Upon | Severall Occasions; | Viz. | 1.The Athenian Babbler, at S. Maries in Oxford. | 2.Iacob and Esau, Election and Reprobation, at | Pauls Crosse. | 3.The Arraignment of the Arrian, at Pauls Crosse. | 4.Moses and Aaron, at S.Maries in Oxford. | 5.Natures Overthrow and Deaths Triumph, at the | Funerall of Sir Iohn Sydenham at Brimpton. | By | H.Sydenham M. of Arts, and Fellow | of Wadham College in Oxford. | The third Edition. | (ornaments).

London, | Printed by I.Haviland, and are sold by N.Fussell | at the White Lion and Ball in Pauls Church-yard. | 1637. | Line border. 18.4x14.3cm. (6),39;(4),49–86;(1),89–125; (4),131–156;(4),161–186p. 4 sub. t.p.

A false title, used both independently and also prefixed to his Sermons | Vpon | Solemne Occasions: | 1637.

SYDENHAM, Humphrey. Sermons | Vpon | Solemne Occasions: | Preached In | Severall Auditories. | By | Hvmphrey Sydenham, Rector of | Pokington in Somerset. | . . . (3 lines; ornament).

London, | Printed by Iohn Beale, for Humphrey | Robinson, and are to be sold at the Signe of the | Three Pigeons in Pauls Church-yard. | M.DC.XXXVII. | Line border. 18.1x14.cm. (10),37–316,(1)p.

SYM, John. Lifes | Preservative | Against | Self-killing. | Or, | An Vsefvl Treatise | Concerning Life and Self-murder; Shewing | {The Kindes, and Meanes of them both: | The Excellency and preservation of the former: | The Evill, and prevention of the latter. } Containing | The Resolution of manifold Cases, and | Questions concerning that Subject; with plen- | tifull variety of necessary and usefull Observa- | tions, and practicall Directions, needfull | for all Christians. | . . . (3 lines). By John Sym Minister of Leigh in Essex. |

London, | Printed by M.Flesher, for R.Dawlman, and L.Fawne, | at the Brazen Serpent in Pauls-Churchyard. 1637. | Line border. 17.7x14.3cm. (36), 326, (16)p.

UDALL, John. A | Commentarie | Vpon The | Lamentations | Of | Jeremy. | Wherin are contained; First, the method and | order of every Chapter laid open in several Tables; then, | a literall interpretation of the Text out of the Hebrew, with a Pa- | raphrasticall exposition of the sence thereof: Afterward, a colle- | ction of divers Doctrines, gathered sometimes out of a whole | Verse in generall, or from the coherence of the Text; and some- | times out of the particular words of the same; with examples, | now and then, shewing how the same Doctrines have been | verified in experience; Moreover, the reason and | proof of every Doctrine; and lastly, the particular uses | that are to be made of them for the edification | of the Church of God. | By Iohn Vdall. | . . . (4 lines).

London, | Printed by the Assignes of Ioane Man, and Beniamin Fisher, | for Phil. Stephens, and Christ. Meredith, 1637. | 17.4x13.1cm. (7),195p. 3 folded pages.

VERTUE, Henry. A Plea for Peace: | Or | A Sermon | Preached | in St.Pavls Church | in London. | Iuly 9.1637. | By Henry Vertue, Parson of the | Parish Church of Alhollowes Honey-Lane | in London. | (device).

London, | Printed by M.F. for Iohn Clark neare | S.Peters Church in Cornhill. 1637. | Line border. 18.2x14.1cm. (4),62p.

WATTS, William. Mortification | Apostolicall. | Delivered In A Sermon | in Saint Pauls Church, upon Sum- | mons received for the Crosse: | On the last Sunday in Easter Terme, | May 21.1637. | By VVilliam VVats, Rector of | St.Albans Woodstreet London. | (device).

London, | Printed by I.L. for Iohn Cowper, and are to be | sold at the Holy Lambe neere the East end | of Saint Pauls Church. | 1637. | 17.2x13.8cm. (6), 48p.

WEEMES, John. The | VVorkes Of | Mr.Iohn VVeemse Of | Lath-ocker In Scotland, | In Fovre Volvmnes. | Containing these nine

Bookes. | Viz. { Vol.1. { 1.The Christian Synagogue. | 2.The Portraiture of the Image of God in Man. | 3.Observations Naturall and Morall. | Vol.2. { 4.An exposition of the first Table of the Morall Law. | 5.An exposition of the second Table of the Morall Law. | Vol.3. { 6.An exposition of the Ceremoniall Law. | 7.An exposition of the Iudiciall Law. | 8.Exercitations Divine. | Vol.4. { 9.A Treatise of Atheisme, Witchcraft, Idolatry, and | Iudaisme. | Serving generally for a helpe to the understanding of all, that desire | to know and obey the will of God in holy writt; But more especially | for all young Students in Divinitie, that they may more easily under- | stand the languages of Canaan, and Greece, and make profitable use of | them in Preaching. | With five Tables prefixed. | Viz. {1.Of the Contents of each Chapter. | 2.Of the Texts of Scriptures. | 3.Of the Hebrew words. | 4. Of the Greeke words.} Expounded. | 5. An Alphabeticall Table of the principall distinctions, and chiefest | matters in every Booke contained. | . . . (1 line).

London, | Printed by T.Cotes, for Iohn Bellamie, and are to be sold at his shop at | the signe of the three Golden-Lyons in Cornhill, neere the Royall Exchange. 1637. | Line border. 20.9x16.2cm. 4 vols: I (1637): (1),(24),312;(28),283;(4), 144p. II (1636): (27),254;(28),348p. III (1636):(1),(30),261;(1);(27),223,(1);(30), 188,(3)p. IV (1636);(23),382,(3)p.

WHATELY, William. The | Oyle | Of | Gladnesse. | Or, | Comfort for dejected | sinners. | First preached in the Parish Church | of Banbury in certaine Sermons, | And now published in this pre- | sent Treatise. | By William Whately | Minister there. |

London, | Printed by G M for George Edwards, and are to | be sold at his house in Greene-Arbour, at the | signe of the Angell 1637. | Line border. 12x7.2 cm. (14),199p.

WHITBIE, Oliver. Londons | Returne, | After the decrease of the | Sicknes: | In a Sermon (appointed for the Crosse) | but preached in St. Pauls Chvrch. | January 8. 1637. | By O. W. P. | . . . (2 lines).

London, | Printed by N. and I. Okes; and are to bee | sold by Richard Whitaker, at the signe of the Kings | Armes in Saint Pauls Church-yard. 1637. | Border. 18x14 cm. (4),31p.

Epistle dedicatory, signed.

WHITE, Francis. An | Examination | And | Confvtation | of a Lawlesse Pamphlet, | Intitvled, | A briefe Answer to a late Treatise of the | Sabbath-Day: | Digested Dialogue-wise betweene two Divines, | A and B. | By Dr. Fr. White, L. Bishop of Ely. | . . . (4 lines; ornament).

London, | Printed by R. B. and are to be sold in S. Dunstans Church- | yard in Fleetstreet, at the little Shop turning up to Cliffords-Inne. | 1637. | 17.9x13.9 cm. (7),162p.

WILLIAMS, John. The | Holy Table, | Name & Thing, | More Anciently, | properly, and literally used | under the New Testament, | then that of an | Altar: | Written long ago by a Minister in Lincoln- | shire, in answer to D. Coal, a judicious | Divine of Q. Maries dayes. | . . . (3 lines; ornaments).

Printed for the Diocese of Lincoln. | 1637. | 18.3x14.1 cm. (3),234 p. Cambr.Univ.Cat:7040; cf.7577.

YATES, John. A | Treatise | Of The Honor | Of Gods Hovse: | Or, | The Trve Paterne | Of the Church, shewed in the parts | And pietie of it; | With a Discovery of the true Cause and Cure | Of our present Contentions, | And an answer of such Objections as may | Offend the weake. | . . . (4 lines).

London, | Printed by T. C. for William Cooke, and are to be | sold at his Shop neere Furnivalls Inne | Gate in Holbourne. 1637. | 18x13.4 cm. (26),1-28,33-70p. Complete.
Epistle Dedicatory, signed.

1638

ABERNETHIE, Thomas. Abjuration Of Pope- | rie, By Thomas Abernethie: | Sometime Jesuite, but now penitent | Sinner, and an unworthie Member | of the true reformed Church of God in | Scotland, at Edinburgh, in the Gray- | frier Church, the 24. of August, 1638. | . . . (8 lines; device).

Printed at Edinburgh, in King James his | College, by George Anderson. 1638. | 17.3x13.8cm. 48p.

An | ABRIDGEMENT | Of that Booke | which the Ministers | Of | Lincolne Diocesse | delivered to his Majestie, upon the | first of December 1605. | Being | The first part of an | Apologie | for themselves and their Brethren, | that refuse the Subscription and Con- | formitie which is required. | Whereunto is annexed, | A Table of sundry Points not handled in | this Abridgement, which are other ex- | ceptions they take to the Subscrip- | tion required, and shall be the | Argument of the se- | cond part of their | Apologie. |

Reprinted, Anno Dom. 1638. | Border. 13.4x8.5 cm. (12),107p.

AMES, William. Bellarminus | Enervatus | a | Gvil. Amesio | S.S. Theologiæ | Doctore. | In quatuor Tomos | divisus. | Editio | Ab Auctore novissimè ante | obitum recognita & aucta. |

Amstelodami | Apud Ioannem Ianssonium | A°. M.DC.XXXVIII. | Cum Privilegio. | Engraved t.p. 12.3 x 6.9 cm. (24),259,(4),787 p. 3 sub title pages.

The | ANSVVERES | Of Some Brethren | Of The Ministerie, | To | The Replyes | Of The Ministers | and Professours of Divinitie | in Aberdeene. | Concerning | The Late Covenant. | . . . (4 lines; device).

Printed in the yeare of God, 1638. | 18x13.8cm. (10,34)p.

ARTICLES | To Be | Inqvired Of | In The Trienniall | Visitation Of The Most | Reverend Father, | VVilliam, | By Gods providence, Lord Arch-Bishop of | Canterburie, Primate of all England; and | Metropolitan: | In and for the Diocesse of Lincolne, during the Suspension of | the L. Bishop there; and in the yeere of our Lord God 1638. | And in the 5th. yeere of his Graces Translation. | (device).

Printed at London, by Richard Badger. | 1638. | 20.2x14.3 cm. (2,11)p.

ARTICLES | To Be | Inqvired Of | VVithin The Dioces | Of Ely: | In the first Visitation of the R. Reverend Father in God, | Matthevv, | Lord Bishop Of Ely. | (device).

Printed at London, by Richard Badger. | 1638. | 19.4x15.1 cm. (2,21)p.

BACON, Nathaniel. A | Relation | Of The Feare- | Fvll Estate Of | Francis Spira, in the | yeare, 1548. | . . . (2 lines; ornament)

London, | Printed by I.L. for Phil.Stephens, and | Christoph.Meredith, at the golden | Lyon in Pauls Church-yard. | 1638. | 13.8x7.8cm. (6),134,(1)p.
Preface signed N.B. Cut of Franciscus Spira laid in.
B.M.Cat.

BACON, Thomas. Regvla Viva | Sev | Analysis Fidei | In Dei | Per Ecclesiam Nos Docentis | Avctoritatem: | In qua perspicuè solidéque ostenditur, veram fidem infallibili | præsentis Ecclesiæ testimonio niti, idque sine vllo | circularis regressus vitio. | Avctore | Thoma Bacono, aliàs Sovthvvello, Norfolciensi, | Societatis Iesv, in Collegio Anglicano eiusdem Societatis Leodij | sacræ Theologiæ Professore. | . . . (3 lines; device).

Antverpiæ, | Apud Ioannem Mevrsivm | M.DC.XXXVIII. | 19.9x14cm. (12), 263, (15)p.

BAKER, Richard. Meditations | And | Disqvisitions | Upon | The first Psalme of | David. | Blessed is the Man. | By Sr. Richard Baker, Knight. | (device).

London, | Printed by Edward Griffin, for Anne Bowler, and are | to be sold at the Marigold, in Pauls Church- | yard. 1638. | Line border. 17.2x13.2cm. (6), 128p.

BARLOW, William. The | Svmme | And | Svbstance | Of | The Conference, | Which it pleased his excellent | Majestie to have with the Lords Bishops, and | others of his Clergie (at which the most of the | Lords of the Councell were present) in his | Majesties Privie-Chamber, at | Hampton Court, Ianu.14. 1603. | Contracted by William Barlovv, | Doctor of Divinity, and Deane of Chester. | Whereunto are added some Copies (scattered | abroad) unsavory and untrue. (royal arms).

London, | Printed by John Norton, and are to bee sold by | Ioshua Kirton, and Thomas Warren. 1638. | 18.3 x 13.8 cm. (8),106,(6) p.

The | BEAST Is Wovnded. | Or | Information from Scotland, concerning | their Reformation. | Wherein | Is breifly declared, the true cause and ground of all the late | Troubles there; and the reasons why they have re- | jected the Bishops, with their Courts, Canons, | Ceremonies and Service-booke. | Hereto | Is added some fruitfull obvervations, upon the former declarati- | on: by Io: Bastwicks younger Brother. | . . . (2 lines) The first part. | (arms)

Printed in the yeare that the Bishops had their downefall | in Scotland. | [1638]. 18.9x13.7 cm. 24p.

The | BEAST Is Wovnded. | Or | Information | from Scotland, concerning | their Reformation. | Wherein | Is breifly declared, the true cause and ground of all the late | Troubles there; and the reasons why they have re- | jected the Bishops, with their Courts, Canons, | Ceremonies and Service-booke. | Hereto | Is added some fruitfull Observations, upon the former declaration: | By: Jo: Bastwicks younger brother. | . . . (2 lines). The first part. | (arms)

[Edinburgh] Printed in the yeare that the Bishops had their downefall | in Scotland. | [1638.] 18.4x13.6cm. 24p.
[2d edition].

BOLTON, Robert. A | Discovrse | Abovt The | State Of Trve | Happinesse. | Delivered In Certaine | Sermons in Oxford, and at St. Pauls Crosse. | By Robert Bolton, Batchelour in Divinitie, | and Minister of Gods Word at Broughton in | Northampton Shire. | The seventh Edition, corrected and amended, | with a Table thereunto annexed. | . . . (4 lines ; ornament)

At London, | Imprinted by Iohn Legatt, for Edmund Weaver, and are to be sold | at the Greyhound in Pauls Church-yard. 1638. | Line border. 18.3x14.3 cm. (21),214,(4)p.
Incorporated in his Workes | . . . 1641 ; with separate register and pagination.

BOLTON, Robert. Some | Generall | Directions | For A Comfor- | table Walking | With God: | Delivered In The Lectvre | At Kettering In North- | Hamptonshire, With | enlargement: | By Robert Bolton, Bachelor In | Divinitie, and Preacher of Gods Word at Broughton | in the same County. | The fifth Edition: corrected and amended; | with a Table thereunto annexed. | (ornament).

At London, | Imprinted by Iohn Legatt, for Edmund Weaver, and are to be sold | at the Greyhound in Pauls Church-yard. 1638. | Line border. 18.4x13.8cm. (15),390,(8)pp.
Also another copy: 17.2x13.5cm. with portrait.

BOUGHEN, Edward. A | Sermon | Concerning | Decencie and Order | in the Church. | Preached at VVood-Church, | in the Diocesse of Canterburie, | April. 30. 1637. | By Edward Boughen | Parson of Wood-Church. | . . . (4 lines).

London, | Printed by I. Raworth for I. Cowper, and are to be | sold at his shop, at the East end of Saint | Pavls Church. 1638. | 17.9x13.8 cm. 26p.

A BRIEFE | Relation | Of | Certaine speciall, and most materiall passages, | and speeches in the Starre-Chamber, | Occasioned | And delivered Iune the 14th. 1637. at the Censure of those | three worthy Gentlemen, | Dr.Bastvvicke, Mr.Burton, aud | Mr.Prynne, | As it hath beene truely and faithfully gathered from their | owne mouthes by one present at the said Censure. | (device)

Printed in the yeare 1638. | 17.8x13.8 cm. 30,(1)p.

BURROUGHS, Jeremiah. The | Excellency | Of | A Gracious Spirit. | Delivered | In A Treatise | vpon the 14. of Numbers, | Verse 24. | By Ier. Burroughes | Minister of Gods Word. | . . . (2 lines; ornament).

London, | Printed by M.F. for R.Davvlman, | and L.Fawne, at the Brazen Serpent in Pauls | Church-yard. 1638. | Line border. 16x10.3cm. (28), 431, (5)p.

BYTHNER, Victorinus. לשון למודים. | Lingua Eruditorum. | Hoc est, | Nova Et Methodica | Institvtio | Linguæ Sanctæ, | Usui eorum | Quibus Fontes Israëlis plenè | intelligere, & ex illis limpidissimas |

aquas haurire, curæ cordique est, | accommodata. | Studio & Operâ | Victorini Bythner. |

Oxoniæ, | Typis Guil: Turner. | Impensis Authoris. | 1638. | 16.1x10cm. (8), 224,(1)p.

CALDERWOOD, David. An | Ansvvere | to M. I. Forbes of Corse, | His peaceable Warning. | . . . (7 lines; ornament).

Printed. Anno Dom. 1638. | Head-piece ornament. 16.2x13.6cm. (35)p.
Anon. H&L, new edition.

CALDERWOOD, David. Quæres | Concerning | The state of the Church | Of | Scotland. | . . . (4 lines; ornament).

Re printed in the yeare 1638. | Border. 16x11.6 cm. 16p.
Anon. H&L. Advoc.Libr.

CASAUBON, Meric. A | Treatise | Of Vse And | Cvstome. | . . . (1 line; ornament).

London | Printed by I.L. Anno. Dom. | M.D.C.XXXVIII. | 20 x 15 cm. (4), 188,(6)p. Title in red and black.
Anon.Cambr.Univ.Cat:4738.

CHILLINGWORTH, William. The | Religion Of | Protestants | A Safe VVay | To Salvation. | Or | An Ansvver To A | Booke Entitled | Mercy And Trvth, | Or, Charity maintain'd by | Catholiques, Which pre- | tends to prove the | Contrary. | By William Chillingworth Master | of Arts of the Vniversity of Oxford. | . . . (12 lines; ornaments).

Oxford | Printed by Leonard Lichfield, and are to be | sold by Iohn Clarke under St Peters Church in Corn-hill. | Anno Salutis M.DC.XXXVIII. | Line border. 27.9x18.1cm.(31),413,(1)p.

CHILLINGWORTH, William. The | Religion | Of | Protestants | A Safe way to Salvation. | Or | An Ansvver To A Booke | Entitvled | Mercy And Trvth, | Or | Charitie maintain'd by Catholiques: | Which Pretends To Prove | The Contrary. | By William Chillingworth Master of Arts | of the Universitie of Oxford. | . . . (12 lines). The second Edition. |

London, | Printed for Iohn Clark, and are to be sold at his shop | under S. Peters Church in Cornhill. | Anno Salutis MDCXXXVIII. | Line border. 27.8x 18.4cm.(30), 393p.

The | CONFESSION of Faith | Of the | Kirk of Scotland. | Subscribed | By the Kings Maiestie and his Housholde, in the | yeare of God 1580. | With a Designation of such Acts of Parliament, as are expedient, | for justifying the Vnion, after mentioned. | And subscribed by the Nobles, Barrons, Gentlemen, | Burgesses, Ministers, and Commons, in the yeare of God 1638. | . . . (12 lines)

Printed in the yeare of God 1638. | 17.2x13.4 cm. 16p.

The | CONFESSION of Faith | Of the Kirk of | Scotland. | Svbscribed | By the Kings Majestie and his Hous- | holde, in the yeare of God 1580. | With a Designation of such Acts of Parlament, as are ex- | pedient, for justefying the Vnion, after mentioned. | And Subscribed by the Nobles, Barrons, Gentle- | men, Burgesses, Ministers and Commons, in | the yeare of God 1638. | . . . (ornament; 10 lines; ornament).

No Imprint. 16.6x12.4cm. 15,(4)p. Colophon: Printed in the yeare of God 1638. |

The | CONFESSION | Of The Faith, And | Doctrine Believ- | ed and professed by the Pro- | testants of Scotland, exhibi- | ted to the Estates of the first Parlia- | ment of King James the sixt: Holden | at Edinburgh, the 25 day of December. | 1568. and authorized there. | (cut)

Edinburgh, Printed by George Anderson, 1638. | Border. 17.9x13.8cm. (1), 28p.

Page 1 contains another t.p.: The Confession | of the Faith and Doctrine, believed | and professed by the Protestants of Scot- | land, exhibited to the Estates of the first Parlia- | ment of King James the sixth: Holden at | Edinburgh, the 25. of December, in the | year of God 1567. where this Confessi- | on was authorized. | . . . (17 lines; device)
Printed at Edinburgh by George Anderson, 1638. |

COOPER, John. The | Foolish | Prophets | Dispaied, | By John Cooper, Priest. | . . . (4 lines; ornament).

London, | Printed by Thomas Harper, for Nicholas Vavasour, | and are to be sold at his Shoppe, in the Inner | Temple, neere the Church-dore, 1638. | Border. 17.3x13.1cm. (6),30p.

DIVINE And Politike | Observations | Nevvly translated out of the Dutch language, vvhere- | in they vvere lately divulged. | Upon | Some Lines in the speech of the Arch. B. of Canterbury, pronoun- | ced in the Starre-Chamber upon 14. June, 1637. | Very | Expedient for preventing all prejudice, which as well through igno- | rance, as through malice and flattery, may be incident to the | judgement which men make thereby, either of his Graces | power over the Church, and with the King, or of | the Equity, Justice, and Wisdome of his end | in his said speech, and of the reasons used | by him for attaining to his | said end. | . . . (device; 4 lines).

Printed in the yeare of our Lord | MDC.XXXVIII. | 18.4x13.6 cm. (6),62, (1)p.

DURY, John. De Pace | Inter Evangelicos procuranda | Sententiæ | Qvatvor: | Quarum tres | a Reverendis | Dominis | Episcopis { Tho. Dvnelmensi. | Io.Sarisbvriensi. | Ios.Exoniensi. | Vltima ab eximijs quibusdam in | Gallia Theologis conscripta est. | Traditæ pridem fuerunt Johanni | Dvræo Scoto viro docto ac prudenti | qui in opere hoc pijssimo jam per | aliquot annos non infeliciter | desudavit. | Prodeunt vero Hæ (præsertim tres | priores) istis Amstelodami anteà editis | non paulo pulchriores, utpote quæ ab | Autoribus revisæ sunt, nec non proprijs | ipsorum manibus tum auctæ tum | emendatæ. | Accessit Syllabus brevis Eorum qui de hoc | Argumento antehâc scripserunt. |

Londini, | Per G.M. pro Gualtero Hammond & pro- | stant venales per Bernardum Langford juxta pon- | tem Holborne sub signo Biblij. MDCXXXVIII. | Line border. 12.6x7.2cm. (2),233,(1)p.

DYKE, Jeremiah. A | VVorthy | Communicant: | Or, | A Treatise, | Shewing the Due Order of | Receiving the Sacrament of the | Lords Supper. | By Ier. Dyke, | Minister of Epping, in Essex. | . . . (7 lines)

London, | Printed by R.Bishop for R.Dawlman, and L.Fawne, at | the Brazen Serpent in S.Pauls Church-yard. | 1638. | Border. 15.8 x 10.4 cm. (16),573 p.

FEATLEY, Daniel. Transubstantiation | exploded: | Or An | En-covnter | With Richard | the Titularie Bishop of Chalcedon | concerning Christ his presence at | his holy Table. | Faithfully related in a Letter sent to D. Smith | the Sorbonist, stiled by the Pope | Ordinarie of England and Scotland. | By Daniel Featley D.D. | Whereunto is annexed a publique and so- | lemne disputation held at Paris with Christo- | pher Bagshaw D. in Theologie, and Rector | of Ave Marie Colledge. | . . . (8 lines).

London, | Printed by G.M. for Nicolas Bourne, at the South entrance | of the Royall Exchange. 1638. | 14.7x8.7 cm. (12),276p.

Also another copy, 14.8x8.5cm, with folding plate before p. 229.

FEATLEY, Daniel. Strictvræ | In | Lyndomastigem: | Or, | An Answere by way of Supplement | to the Chapters remaining in the Booke | Intituled, A Case For The | Spectacles. | Together | With a Funerall Sermon preached | at Cobham, June 14th. 1636. | By Daniel Featley, D.D. | (ornaments).

London, | Printed by M.P. for Robert Milbourne, at the signe | of the Vnicorne in Fleet-street, neere Fleet- | Bridge. 1638. | Line border. 18.2x 14.2 cm. (8),220;167p.

FOLIOT, Gilbert. Gilberti Foliot | Episcopi Londinensis, | Expositio | In | Canticum Canticorum, | Una Cum Compendio | Alcuini. | Nunc primùm è Bibliotheca | Regia in lucem prodiit, | Opera & Studio | Patricii Junii | Bibliothecarii Regii. | . . . (1 line; royal arms).

Londoni | Ex Typographio Regio. | MDCXXXVIII. | 17.6x13.8cm. (8),344, (2)p.

GARDINER, Richard. A | Sermon | Preach'd In | The Cathedrall | Chvrch Of Christ | In Oxford, | On Christmas Day: | Wherein is defended the Catholique | Doctrine that Christ is True | God Truely Incarnate. | Against The Olde De- | cay'd heresies newely Reviu'd in | these later Dayes. | By | Richard Gardyner, D. D. And | Canon of the same Church. |

Oxford, | Printed by Leonard Lichfield, Printer | to the Vniversity for William Davis, | Anno Dom. 1638. | Line border. 17.4x13.1 cm. (6),31p.

GARDINER, Richard. A Sermon | Preach'd | On Easter-Day | At Oxford, In Saint | Peters Chvrch In The | East, the Accustomed place for the | Rehearsall Sermon on | That Day: | Wherein is prov'd the Sonne's | Equality with the Father, the | Deity ofthe Holy Ghost, | And | The Resurrection of the same Numericall Body, | Against the old, and Recent Oppugners of | these Sacred Verities. | By | Richard Gardyner, D. D. and Canon of | the Cathedrall Church of Christ in Oxford. |

Oxford, | Printed by Leonard Lichfield, Printer to the | Vniversity, for Francis Bowman, Anno Dom. 1638. | Line border. 17.4x13. cm. (7),31p.

GATAKER, Thomas. Saint | Stevens | Last Will | And | Testament. | A | Fvnerall Sermon | On | Acts 7. Ver. 59. | Preached at the

Enterrement of the Remaines | of M^ris Joice Featly. | Together with the Testimonie then given unto her | By Tho.Gataker, B. of D. and Rector of | Rotherhith. | (device)

London, | Printed by E.P. for Nicholas Bourne, and are to be sold at | his Shop at the South Entrance of the Royall | Exchange. 1638. | 27.6x18.3cm. (4),16p.
Included in his Certaine Sermons: 1637; with separate register and pagination.

GENERALL | Demands | Concerning | The Late | Covenant: | Propounded by the Mini- | sters and Professors of Divinity in Aber- |dene, to some Reverend Brethren, who | came thither to recommend the late Covenant | to them, and to those who are com- | mitted to their charge. | Together With | The Answers of those Reverend Brethren | to the said Demands. | As Also | The Replyes of the foresaid Ministers and | Professors to their Answers. | . . . (7 lines).

Printed by Robert Young, His Majesties Printer | for Scotland. Anno 1638. | 17.8x14.3cm. (1),37p.
Preceded by James Hamilton's Vindication.

GERHARD, John. Gerards | Prayers: | Or, | A daily practise | of Pietie. | Divided into foure Parts. | 1 Of Confession of sinnes. | 2 Of Thanksgiving for benefits. | 3 Of Petitions for our selves. | 4 Of Supplications for our neigh- | bours. | Written originally in the Latine tongue | by John Gerard Doctour in | Divinitie, and Superintendant | of Heidelberg. | Translated and revised | By Ralph Winterton | Fellow of Kings Colledge. | The sixth Edition. | Whereunto is added a morning | and evening prayer for a | familie. |

Printed by the Printers | to the Universitie of | Cambridge. 1638. | Border. 13.7x 8.3cm. (6), 323; (10), 155p.

GILLESPIE, George. Reasons | For which the Service Booke, urged upon | Scotland | ought to bee refused. |

Colophon: Printed in the year of God, 1638. | [at Edinburgh]. 18.6 x 13.8 cm. (4) p.
Anon. Letter from Robert Baillie to William Spang.

GOODWIN, Thomas. The | Vanity | Of | Thovghts | Discovered: | With | Their Danger | And Cvre. | By | Tho: Goodvvin, B.D. | (ornament).

London, | Printed by M.F. for R.Dawlman, and L.Fawne, | at the signe of the brazen Serpent in | Pauls Church-yard. 1638. | Line border. | 18.5x14.5cm.(5), 54, (1)p.

HAMILTON, James. [Episcopacy not abolished.] (Statement as to the "Act of Councell, which explaineth the Confession of Faith lately commanded to be sworn by his Majestie").

Without t.p. Imprinted at Edinburgh by | Robert Young, Printer to | the Kings most excel- | lent Majestie. | Cvm Privilegio. | Anno 1638. | 18.1x13.2cm. (1),19p.
Prefatory statement signed.

HAMILTON, James. (Vindication: introductory to Generall | Demands | Concerning | The Late | Covenant: |)

Imprinted by [His Majesties] | Printer f[or Scotland] | [1638]. | 18.7x14.3cm. (15)p.
Royal arms on Sig. A1; Hamilton arms on reverse . Imprint torn.
Cambr.Univ.Cat.No.4997.

HOOKER, Thomas. The | Sovles | Exaltation. | A | Treatise | containing | The Soules Vnion with Christ, | on I Cor.6.17. | The Soules Benefit from Vnion | with Christ, on I Cor.I.30. | The Soules Justification, on | 2 Cor.5.21. | By T.H. | . . . (3 lines).
London, | Printed by Iohn Haviland, for Andrew Crooke, | and are to bee sold at the black Beare in S.Pauls | Church-yard, 1638. | Line border. 19.x14.3cm. (16),311p.
Contains also: The Sovles Ingrafting into Christ. 1637; and The Vnbeleevers Preparing For Christ. 1638 .
DNB. 27: 296 a (4).

HOOKER, Thomas. The | Vnbeleevers | Preparing For | Christ. | . . . (3 lines). By T.H. | (ornament).
London, | Printed by Tho Cotes for Andrew Crooke, and are to be | sold at the Black Beare in Saint Pauls Church- | yard. 1638. | Line border. 19.x14.3cm. (4), 204,(4);119,(4)p. 2 pts.
B.M.Cat.

JACKSON, Thomas. A | Treatise | Of The Consecration | Of The Sonne Of | God to his everlasting | Priesthood. | And | The Accomplishment | of it by his glorious Resurrection | and Ascension. | Being The Ninth Book | of Commentaries upon the | Apostles Creed. | Continved By | Thomas Iackson Doctor in | Divinity, Chaplaine in ordinary to | his Maiesty, and President of | C.C.C. in Oxford. |
Oxford, | Printed by Leonard Lichfield | printer to the Famous Vniversity. | An.Dom. 1638. | Line border. 18x13.5cm. (23),355p.

JERMIN, Michael. Paraphrasticall | Meditations, | By Way Of | Commentarie, | Upon The | VVhole Booke Of The | Proverbs Of Solomon. | Written by Michael Iermin, D. in Divinity. | . . . (5 lines; device).
London, | Printed by R.Badger, for Philemon Stephens and Christopher Meredith, at | the golden Lyon in St. Pauls Church-yard. 1638. | 27.6x18.5cm.(6), 729, (27)p.

A | LICHT For The Ignorant | Or | A Treatise shevving, that in the nevv Testament, is | set forth three Kingly States or Governments, | that is, the Civill State, the true Ecclesi- | asticall-State, and the false Ecclesi- | asticall State. | (3 lines; device; 1 line). Seene and allowed.
Printed in the Yeare, 1638. | 17.6x14.3 cm. 20p.

LILBURN, John. A Worke Of The Beast, | Or | A Relation of a most vnchristian Censure, Execu- | ted vpon Iohn Lilbvrne, (Novv | prisoner in the fleet) the 18 of Aprill 1638. | With the heavenly speech vttered by | him at the time of his | suffering. | Very vsefull for these times both for the encouragement of | the Godly to suffer, And for the terrour and shame | of the Lords Adversaries. | . . . (6 lines; device).
Printed in the yeare the Beast was | Wounded 1638. | 17.8x13.8cm. 30,(2)p.
Signed at end.

LISLE, William. A | Testimony | Of | Antiqvity: | Shewing | The Ancient Faith | in the Church of England, touching | the Sacrament of the body and bloud of the | Lord here publickly preached, and also received | in the Saxons time about 600 yeares agoe. | . . . (5 lines; ornament).

London, | Printed by E.G. for Francis Eglesfield, and are to be sold | at the signe of the Marigold in S . Pauls | Church-yard. 1638. | 17.3x13.5cm. (23),(1–11),12–43;(8),14,(6,2)fol.
To the Readers, signed.

LYNDE, Humphrey. A Case for the Spectacles, | Or, | A Defence of Via Tuta, | The Safe Way, | By Sir Hvmphrey Lynde Knight, | In Answer to a Book written by J.R. called, | A Paire Of Spectacles, | Together with a Treatise Intituled, | Stricturæ In Lyndomastygem, | by way of Supplement to the Knights | Answer, where he left off, pre- | vented by Death. | And | A Sermon preached at his Funerall, at | Cobham, Iune 14th 1636. | By Daniel Featley, D.D. | . . . (4 lines)

London, | Printed by M.P. for Robert Milbourne, at the signe | of the Vnicorne in Fleete-street, neere Fleet- | Bridge. 1638. | Line border. T.p. in red and black. 18.2x14.2cm. (1),(14),279;(8),220;167pp. (Separate title-page for the Stricturæ.)

MEDE, Joseph. Chvrches, | That Is, | Appropriate Places | For | Christian VVorship; | Both In, And Ever Since | The Apostles Times. | A Discourse at first more briefly deli- | vered in a Colledge Chappell, and | since enlarged. | By | Joseph Mede B.D. and Fellow of Christs | Colledge in Cambridge. | (ornament).

London, | Printed by M.F. for John Clark, and are to | be sold at his Shop under S.Peters Church in Cornhill. | MDCXXXVIII. | Line border. 17.4x13.8cm. (3),31–78p.
Also another edition: 18.5x14.2cm. (4),74p.
Included also in his Diatribæ: 1642; with separate register and pagination.

MEDE, Joseph. The | Reverence | Of | Gods House. | A Sermon preached at | St. Maries in Cambridge, | Before | The Universitie On St. | Matthies day, Anno 1635/6. | By | Joseph Mede B.D. and late Fellow of | Christs Colledge in Cambridge. | . . . (7 lines)

London, | Printed by M.F. for Iohn Clark, and are to be | sold at his Shop under St. Peters Church | in Cornhill. 1638. | Line border. 18.5 x 14.2 cm. (2), 71 p.
Re-issued as part of his Diatribæ: 1642 ; with separate register and pagination.

MEENE, Joshua. A | Liberall | Maintenance | Is Manifestly Dve | To The Ministers | of the Gospell. | By | Ioshua Meene Vicar of | Wymondham in Norfolke. | (ornament).

London, | Printed by Thomas Harper, for Lawrence Chapman, and | William Certain, and are to be sold at Chan- | cery lane end in Holborne , 1638. | Line border. 18.3x14.3cm. (8),74,(1)p.

MORTON, Thomas. Replica. | Sev, | Adversus Nu- | perriman Confu- | tationem Aliqvotæ | particulæ Partis prioris Apologiæ | Tho.Mortoni, | (Authore C.R. Theologo) | Brevis Velitatio. | (device).

Londini, | Typis R.B. Impensis R.Whitaker, & R.Badger. | MDCXXXVIII. | 18.3x14.7cm. (16),112, (1) p.

MOTIVES | Maintained. | Or | A Reply vnto M. Chillingvvorthes | Ansvvere to his ovvne Motiues | of his Conuersion to Ca- | tholike Religion: | . . . (device; 2 lines).

Permissu Superiorum. 1638. | 17.5x12.9 cm. 24p.
Pollard, Short-Title Catalogue. Attrib. to Ed: Knott.

NORRIS, Edward. The | Nevv Gospel , | Not The | Trve Gospel. | Or, | A discovery of the Life and Death, Do- | ctrin, and Doings of Mr. Iohn Traske, and | the effects of all, in his Followers. | Wherein a mysterie of iniquity is briefly | disclosed, a Seducer unmasked, and all war- | ned to beware of Impostors. | As also a Confutation of the uncomfortable error, | of Mr. Boye, concerning the Plague, | out of Psal. 91. | . . . (3 lines) By Edvv. Norice. |

London, | Printed by R. Bishop, for Henry Hood, and are to be sold | at his Shop in St. Dunstans Church-yard in | Fleetstreet. 1638. | 17.1x14.2 cm. (3),55p. P (1) blank.

PRESTON, John. The | Churches | Marriage; | Or, | Dignitie: | Delivered In Svndry | Sermons at Lincolnes Inne. | By the late learned and reverend Divine, | Iohn Preston, | Dr. in Divinity, Chaplaine in Ordinary to His Majesty, | Mr. of Emanuel Colledge in Cambridge, and | sometime Preacher at Lincolnes Inne. | . . . (6 lines).

London, | Printed by R.B. for N.Bourne, and are to be sold by Rapha Harford | at the gilt Bible in Queenes-head Alley in Pater-noster Row, | and by Francis Eglesfield at the Marigold in | Pauls Church-yard. 1638. | Border. 17.6x 13.cm. (1),142,(11)p.
Part of his Golden Scepter: 1638; with double letter register, and separate pagination.
Also a single sermon, with identical t.p., 17.8x13.2cm. (1),23p., with independent register and pagination.

PRESTON, John. The | Doctrine | Of | The Saints | Infirmities. | Delivered in severall Sermons by | John Preston | Doctor in Divinity, Maister of | Emanuell Colledge in Cam- | bridge. | And late Preacher of Lincolnes | Inne, &c. | (ornament).

Imprinted at London by I.Okes, for H.Taunton, | and are to be sold at his shop in S.Dunstons | Church-yard in Fleet-street. 1638. | Border. 18.7x14.4cm. (4), 91p.

PRESTON, John. The Golden Scepter | held forth to the humble. | VVith The | Chvrches Dignitie | by her Marriage. | And The | Chvrches Dvtie | in her Carriage. | In three Treatises. | The former delivered in sundry Sermons in Cambridge, | for the weekely Fasts, 1625. | The two latter in Lincolnes Inne. | By the late learned and reverend Divine, | Iohn Preston, | Dr. in Divinity, Chaplaine in Ordinary to His Majesty, | Mr. of Emanuel Colledge in Cambridge, and | sometime Preacher at Lincolnes Inne. | . . . (6 lines).

London, | Printed by R.Badger for N.Bourne at the Royall Exchange, and R. | Harford at the gilt Bible in Queenes-head Alley in Pater-noster- | Row, and by F.Eglesfield at the Marigold in | Pauls Church-yard. 1638. | Border. 17.6x13cm. (14),292;(1),142,(11)p. Engr. fore t.p. dated 1639.
Also another copy with identical t.p., 17.8x13.2cm. (13),292;(1),23p. . See his Churches Marriage: 1638.

PRESTON, John. Movnt Ebal, | Or | A Heavenly Treatise | Of Divine Love. | Shewing the {Equity | and | Necessity}of his being accursed that | loves not the Lord Iesus | Christ. | Together with the Motives | Meanes | Markes} of our love towards him. | By that late Faithfull and worthy Divine, | John Preston, Doctor in Divinitie, Chap- | laine in Ordinary to his Majestie, Master of Em- | manuel Colledge in Cambridge, and some- | times Preacher of Lincolnes Inne. | . . . (5 lines)

London, | Printed by M.P. for Iohn Safford, and are to be | sold at his house in Black horse Alley in | Fleet-street. 1638. | Line border. 20.2x14.4cm. (1),51p. Colophon: November, 30. 1637. | Imprimatur Tho: | VVykes. |

The | PROTESTATION | Of The Noblemen, | Barrons, Gentle- | men, Borrowes, Mini- | sters, And Commons, | Subscribers of the Confession of | Faith and Covenant, lately renewed within the | Kingdome of Scotland, made at the Mer- | cate Crosse of Edinburgh, the 4. of Iulij im- | mediately after the reading of the procla- | mation, dated 28. Iune | 1638. | (ornament).

Printed in the year of God, 1638. | 18.2x13.5cm. (1,12)p.

RAMSAY, Andrew. A | Warning To Come | Ovt Of Babylon, | In a Sermon preached by Master | Andrew Ramsay, Minister at | Edinburgh; | At the receiving of Mr.Thomas Abernethie, | sometime Jesuite, into the societie of the true- | ly reformed Church of Scotland. | . . . (3 lines; device).

Printed at Edinburgh, in King James his | College, by George Anderson. 1638. | 17.6x13.8cm (1),46p. Lacks pp. 41–42 .

RANCHIN, Guillaume du. A | Review | Of The | Covncell | Of | Trent. | VVherein are contained the severall | nullities of it: With the many grievan- | ces and prejudices done by it to Christian | Kings and Princes: | As also to all Catholique Churches in the | World; and more particularly to the | Gallicane Church. | First writ in French by a learned Roman-Catholique. | Now | Translated into English by G.L. | . . . (2 lines; ornament)

Oxford, | Printed by William Turner, Printer to the famous | Vniversitie, for VV.T.Edw:Forrest, and VVil: VVeb. | Anno Domini M D CXXXVIII. | Line border. 26.7 x 17.2 cm. (27),388,(4) p. Table of contents impf.

REASONS | For | A Generall | Assemblie. | . . . (3 lines motto and device with date,) June 29. 1638. ornament.

Printed in the year of God, 1638. | 19.3x14.cm. (1,9)p.

REYNOLDS, Edward. Meditations | On The Holy | Sacrament | Of The | Lords last Supper. | Written many yeares since | By Edvvard Reynolds then Fellow | of Merton College in Oxford. | (device)

London, | Imprinted by Felix Kyngston for Iohn Maynard, and | are to be sould at his shop in Fleetstreet at the signe of | the George neare S.Dunstans Church. 1638. | Line border. 17.8x13.5 cm. (8),1–94,81–240,(4)p

Also another impression, from the library of Walter W. Law. London, | Imprinted by Felix Kyngston for Robert Bostock, and | are to be sould at his shop in S.Pauls Church-yard at | the signe of the Kings Head. 1638. | Line border. 18x13.2cm. (9),1–94;81–240,(4)p.

REYNOLDS, Edward. A | Sermon | Touching The | Peace & Edification | Of The | Church. | Preached at the Second Trienniall | Visitation of the Right Reverend Father | in God Francis Lord Bishop of Peter- | borough, at Daventrie in Northampton- | shire, Iuly xij. 1637. | By | Edvvard Reynolds Rector of | the Church of Braunston. | . . . (2 lines ; device).

London, | Imprinted by Felix Kyngston for Robert Bostock, and | are to be sould at his shop in S. Pauls Church-yard at | the signe of the Kings Head. 1638. | Line border. 18.2x14.3cm. (3),46p. Lacks pp. 41–2 .
Also another copy from the library of Walter W. Law. 18x13.2cm.(2),46p.
Also reprinted in 1659, and included in his Twenty Sermons: 1660 .

ROBINSON, John. Essayes; | Or, | Observations | Divine And | Morall. | Collected Ovt Of | holy Scriptures, Ancient and | Moderne Writers, both di- | vine and humane. | As also, out of the great volume | of mens manners: Tending to the | furtherance of knowledge | and vertue. | By Iohn Robinson. | The second Edition, with two Tables, the one of | the Authours quoted; The other of the mat- | ters contained in the Observations. | . . . (4 lines).

London, | Printed by I. D. for I. Bellamie, at the | three golden Lyons in Cornhill neere | the Royall Exchange. 1638. | 14.3x8.4 cm. (31),566p.

ROSS, Alexander. Virgilii | Evangelisantis | Christiados | Libri XIII. | In quibus omnia quæ de Domino no- | stro Iesu Christo in utroque Testa- | mento, vel dicta vel prædicta sunt, altiso- | na Divina Maronis tuba suavissime | decantantur. | Instante Alexandro Rosæo Aberdonense. | . . . (2 lines).

Londini, | Typis Iohannis Legate, sumpti- | bus Richardi Thrale, in Cœmiterio Paulina, | Anno Domini, 1638. | 13.1x9.3cm. (20),(1),311p.

ROUS, Francis. The | Heavenly | Academie. | . . . (7 lines; ornament)

London, | printed by Robert Young for | John Bartlet, and are to be sold | at his shop in Pauls Church-yard | neere St.Austins gate. | 1638. | Line border. 10.7x 6.9cm. (21),189,(1)p.
Epistle Dedicatorie, signed.

SANDYS, George. A | Paraphrase | Vpon The | Divine Poems. | By | George Sandys. | (device).

London, | At the Bell in St.Pauls Church-yard. | M. D C. XXXVIII. | 27.7x 17.8cm. (22),55,(12),171,15,(1),33,(1)p. Colophon.

A SHORT | Relation | Of the State of the Kirk of Scotland | since the Reformation of Religion, to the | present time for information, and ad- | vertisement of our Brethren in the | Kirk of England, By an hearty | Well-wisher to both | Kingdomes. | (device)

[Edinburgh] Printed in the yeare of God, 1638. | 18x13.7cm. (1 , 20)p.
By James Melvill? Cambr.Univ.Cat:7042.

SIBBES, Richard. The | Chvrches | Riches | By | Christs Poverty | By | The late Learned and Reverend Divine, | Richard Sibbs, | Dr. in Divinity, Master of Katharine-Hall in | Cambridge, and sometimes Preacher at | Graies-Inne. | . . . (5 lines; ornament).

London, | Printed by R.Badger for N.Bourne at the Royall | Exchange, and R.Harford at the gilt Bible in | Queenes-head Alley in Pater-Noster Row. | 1638. | Line border. 18.4x13.4cm. 157,(13)p.

Part of his Light from Heaven: 1638 ; with continuous register, double letter

SIBBES, Richard. Light | From | Heaven, | Discovering | The { Fountaine Opened. | Angels Acclamations. | Churches Riches. | Rich Povertie. | In foure Treatises. | By | The late Learned and Reverend Divine, | Rich. Sibs, | Doctor in Divinitie, Master of Katherine Hall | in Cambridge, and sometimes Preacher | at Grayes-Inne. | Published according to the Authors owne | appointment, subscribed with his hand; | to prevent imperfect Copies. | . . . (3 lines).

London, | Printed by E.Purslow for N.Bourne, at the Royall | Exchange, and R.Harford, at the gilt Bible in | Queenes-head Alley in Pater-Noster-Row. | 1638. | Border. 18.4x13.4cm. (15), 199; (1), 201–297; 157, (13)p. 3 Sub. t.p.

SIBBES, Richard. A | Miracle Of Miracles | Or | Christ in our nature. | Wherein is contained | The Wonderfull Conception, | Birth, and Life of Christ, who | in the fulnesse of time became man | to satisfie divine Iustice, and to | make reconciliation be- | tweene God and man. | Preached | To the honourable Society of Grayes | Inne, by that godly and faithfull minister | of Iesus Christ, Richard Sibbes, D.D. | . . . (4 lines).

London | Printed by E.G. for Iohn Rothwell at the signe | of the Sunne in Pauls Church yard, 1638. | Line border. 17.5x13.2cm. (1), 25; 27, (1)p.

SIMSON, Archibald. A | Sacred | Septenarie, | Or, | A Godly And | Frvitfvll Expositi- | on On The Seven | Psalmes Of | Repentance. | viz. the|VI. | XXV. | XXXII. | XXXVIII. | LI. | CXX. | CXLIII.}the {1. | 2. | 3. | 4. | 5. | 6. | 7.} of the Pe- | nitentials. | Serving especially for the direction and com- | fort of all such, who are either troubled in minde, | diseased in body, or persecuted by | the wicked. | By Mr. Archibald Symson, late Pastor | of the Church at Dalkeeth in Scotland. |

London, | Printed by Thomas Paine for Iohn Bellamie, and are | to be sold at his shop, at the three Golden Lyons in | Cornehill, neare the Royall-Exchange. | 1638. | Border of ornaments. 19.2x14.5cm. (20),298p. 153–182 omitted in numbering.

TAYLOR, Jeremy. A | Sermon | Preached In | Saint Maries | Church in Oxford. | Vpon the Anniversary of the | Gunpowder-Treason. | By Ieremy Taylor, Fellow of | Allsoules Colledge in Oxford. | . . . (1 line; device).

Oxford, | Printed by Leonard Lichfield | Printer to the Vniversity. | M.DC. XXXVIII. | Line border. 16.8x13cm. (10),1–34,37–52,45–64p. Mispaged.

The TRIALL | Of | The English Liturgie, | Or | A Copie of a Letter, wherein seve- | rall Exceptions and Argvments | against the imposition and use of the | Service Book in the English Churches, | are set forth and discussed. | Written | By a Reverend Divine, to his Christian | Friend, for his private satisfaction in | this particular. | And now published for publicke good. | (device).

Printed in the yeare 1638. | 19.1x14.8cm. (1),32p.

TYMME, Thomas. A | Silver Watch-Bell: | The Sovnd | whereof is able (by the grace of | God) to win the most profane worldling, | and carelesse liver (if there be but the least | spark of Grace remaining in him) to | become a true Christian indeed, that | in the end hee may obtaine ever- | lasting Salvation. | Whereunto is adjoyned | A Treatise of the holy Sacrament | of the Lords Svpper, | in part augmented. | By Thomas Tymme. | The eighteenth Impression. |

London, | Printed by Iohn Haviland, for | Thomas Alchorn. | 1638. | Line border. 14.3x8.9cm. (12),288p.

USSHER, James. Immanuel, | Or | The Mystery | Of The | Incarnation | Of The | Son of God; | unfolded by | Iames, Archbishop of Armagh. | . . . (2 lines; device).

London, | Printed by I.H. for John Parker, &c. 1638. | Line border. 19x14.4cm. (2),66p. (T.p. has Sig. A 2).

WILKINS, John. The | Discovery | Of A | World | In The | Moone. | Or, | A Discovrse | Tending | To Prove | that 'tis probable there | may be another habitable | World in that Planet. | . . . (4 lines; ornament).

London, | Printed by E.G. for Michael Sparke | and Edward Forrest. 1638. | Line Border. 13.9x8.8cm. (7),209,(4)p. Frontisp.
Camb.Univ.Cat.No.5199.

YOUNGE, Richard. The Drunkard's | Character, | Or, | A True Drunkard | with such sinnes as | raigne in him, | viz. {Pride | Ignorance | Enmity | Atheisme} {Idlenesse. | Adultery | Murther} with many the like. | Lively set forth in their colours. | Together With | Compleat Armovr | Against Evill Society. | The which may serve also for a Common- | place-booke of the most usuall sinnes | By R. Junius. |

London, | Printed by R.Badger, for George Latham, at the | Bishops-head in S. Pauls Churchyard. 1638. | 16.7x10.2cm. (17),692,(1),689–863,(18)p.
Sub t.p., of his Sinne Stigmatized: 1639. Compleat Armovr, has separate t.p., dated 1638.
Cambr.Univ.Cat:4392.

1639

ABBOT, Robert. A | Triall Of Ovr | Chvrch-Forsakers. | Or | A Meditation Ten- | ding To Still The | passions of unquiet Brownists, | upon Heb. 10. 25. | Wherein is Iustified, against them, | that the blessed Church of | England | {1 Is a true Church. | 2 Hath a true Ministry. | 3 Hath a true Worship. | By Robert Abbot, Vicar of | Cranbrooke in Kent. | . . . (3 lines).

London, | Printed by Thomas Payne for Philemon | Stephens and Christopher Meredith, and are | to be sould at their shoppe at the signe | of the Golden Lyon in Saint Pauls | Church-yard. 1639. | Border. 15.8x10.2 cm. (30),249,(2)p.

AINSWORTH, Henry. Annotations | Vpon | The Five Bookes Of | Moses, | The Booke Of The | Psalmes, | And The | Song Of Songs, | Or, | Canticles. | VVherein The Hebrevv VVords | and Sentences, are compared with, and explained by the ancient | Greeke and Chaldee Versions, and other Records and Monuments of | the Hebrews: But chiefly by conference with the Holy Scriptures, | Moses his words, lawes, and ordinances, the Sacrifices, and other | legall Ceremonies heretofore commanded by God to the | Church of Israel, are explained. | With | An Advertisement touching some Objections made against | the sinceritie of the Hebrew Text, and allegation of the | Rabbines in these Annotations. | As Also, | Tables directing unto such principall things as are observed in the | Annotations upon each severall Booke. | By Henry Ainsworth. | . . . (2 lines).

London, | Printed by M.Parsons for John Bellamie, and are to be sold | at his Shop in Cornehill, at the Signe of the three Golden Lyons, | neere the Royall Exchange. 1639. | Line border. 32.5x21.4cm. (10),172; 156;184;206,(1);168,(23); (4),189,(6);59p. 7 sub. t.p.

The parts have separate pagination, and doubled letter registers.

An | ANSWER To The | Profession And | Declaration. | Made by Iames Marques Of | Hammilton, His Maiesties | High Commissioner, | Imprinted at Edinburgh Anno 1638, | in December. |

Edinburgh | Printed by Iames Bryson, 1639. | 18.2x14.cm. 52p.

ARTICLES | To Be Enqvired | Of By The Minister | And Chvrch-Wardens | of every Parish within the Arch- | Deaconrie of Northumberland; | Which are given in Charge in the Annuall | Visitation of E.Gower, B. in Divinitie, | late Fellow of Jesvs Colledge in Cam- | bridge, and Arch-Deacon of that | Jurisdiction. | . . . (2 lines; ornament).

London, | Printed for Robert Milbourne. | 1639. | 17.x13.2cm. (2,6)p.

B., A. The Life | Or The | Ecclesiasticall | Historie | Of S.Thomas | Archbishope | Of Canterbury. | . . . (ornament).

Colloniæ. | M.DC.XXXIX. | 17.6x11.5cm. (6), 50; 396p.
Camb.Univ.Cat. No.6337. Dedication signed A.B.

BAKER, Richard. Meditations | And | Disqvisitions | Upon | The Seven Psalmes of David, | commonly called the Peniten- | tiall Psalmes. | By Sr.Richard Baker, Knight. | (ornament).

London, | Printed by Iohn Dawson, for Francis Eglesfield, and | are to bee sold at the Marigold, in Pauls | Church-yard. 1639. | Line border. 18.8x14.2cm. (6), 245,(1)p.

BALBANI, Nicholas. The | Italian | Convert, | Newes from Italy, of a | second Moses: | Or, | The Life of Galeacius | Caracciolus the noble | Marquesse of Vico. | Containing the story of his | admirable conversion from Popery, | and forsaking of a rich Marquesdome | for the Gospels sake. | Written first in Italian, thence | translated into Latin by reverend Beza, | and for the benefit of our people put | into English: and now published | By W.C. | . . . (3 lines).

London, | Printed by R.Bishop, for M.S. and are to | be sold at his house in Green Arbour at the | signe of the Bible, 1639. | Line border. 12.9x7.3cm. (24), 227p.
Cambr.Univ.Cat.3953.

BOLTON, Robert. Mr. Boltons | Last And Lear- | ned Worke | of the | Foure last Things, | Death, Iudgement, | Hell, and Heaven. | With his | Assise-Sermons | and Notes on Iustice | Nicolls his Funerall. | Together with the Life and Death | of the Authour. | Published by E.B. and re-viewed, with | Marginall Notes, and an Alphabeticall | Table added thereunto. | Hereunto is added the Sermon at M. Boltons | Funerall, by M. Nic. Estvvick. | The fourth Edition. |
London, | Printed by George Miller, | dwelling in the Black-Friers. 1639. | Arch. border. 17.2x13.5cm. (12),41,(1) ;264,(7) ;(6),97;(1),70;23p.
Also another copy from the library of Walter W. Law. 17.2x13.6cm.

BOLTON, Robert. Two | Sermons | Preached At | Northampton | At Two Severall | Assises There. | The one in the time of the Shrevalty | of Sir Erasmus Dryden Baronet. | Anno Domini, 1621. | The other in the time of the Shrevalty | of Sir Henery Robinson Knight, | Anno Domini, 1629. | By Robert Bolton Batchelour in Divinity, late Minister of | Broughton in Northampton-shire, and sometimes | Fellow of Brasen-nose Colledge in Oxford. | Published by E.B. |
London, | Printed by George Miller dwelling in the Black- | Fryers. MDCXXXIX. | 17.2x13.5cm. (6),97p.
Part of the 4th ed. of his . . . Foure last Things: 1639; with separate register and pagination

BURROUGHS, Jeremiah. The | Excellency | Of | A Gracious Spirit. | Delivered | In A Treatise | upon the 14. of Numbers, | Verse 24. | By Ier. Burroughes | Minister of Gods Word. | . . . (2 lines: ornament).
London, | Printed by M.F. for R.Dawlman, and | L.Fawne, at the Brazen Serpent in Pauls | Church-yard. 1639. | Line border. 16.4x10.5cm, (24),431p.

CADE, Anthony. A | Sermon | Necessarie | For These | Times, | Shewing the nature of Consci- | ence, with the corruptions thereof, and the | repairs or means to inform it with right knowledge, | and stirre it up to upright practise, and how | to get and keep a good Con- | science. | To which is adjoyned a necessarie, brief, and | pithy treatise of the Ceremonies of the | Church of England. | By Anthony Cade Batch. | of Divinitie. | . . . (4 lines)
Printed by the Printers to the Vniversitie of | Cambridge.And are to be sold by John Sweeting | near Popes head alley in Corn-hill. | 1639. | Line border. 18. x14 cm. (7),62; (6),44p. Appendix has sub-title page .

CAMUS, John Peter. Admirable | Events: | Selected | Ovt Of Fovre | Bookes, | VVritten in French by the Right | Reverend, John Peter Camus, | Bishop of Belley, | Together with morall Relations, written | by the same Author. | And translated into English by | S. Du Verger. | (ornament).
London, | Printed by Thomas Harper for William Brooks, | and are to be sold at his shop in Holborn | in Turnstile Lane. | 1639. | Border. 18.4x13.cm. (30), 357,(1)p. Subt.p at p.139.

CHARLES I. His Majesties | Proclamation | In | Scotland: | With | An Explanation | Of The Meaning Of | The Oath And | Covenant. | By the Lord Marquesse, his Majesties | high Commissioner. | Set forth by the Kings speciall licence. | (ornament).

London, | Printed by Robert Young, His Majesties Printer | for Scotland. 1639. | Are sold at the Starre on Bread-street hill. | 19.2x14.5cm. (1),14;(2),17p.

CHARLES I. A Large | Declaration | Concerning | The Late Tumults | In Scotland, From | Their first originalls: | Together With | A Particular Deduction | Of the seditious Practices of the prime | Leaders of the Covenanters: | Collected Out of their Owne | foule Acts and Writings: | By which it doth plainly appeare, that Religion was | onely pretended by those Leaders, but | nothing lesse intended | by them. | By the King. |

London, | Printed by Robert Young, His Majesties | Printer for Scotland, Anno Dom. | M.DC.XXXIX. | Line border. 27.4x18.1cm. (1),430,(1)p. Portrait of the King.

CLAPHAM, Henoch. A | Briefe | Of The | Bibles | History. | Drawne first into English | Poesie, and then illustrated | by apt Annotations: wher- | to is added a Synopsis of the | Bibles Doctrine. | By Henoch Clapham. | The fourth Edition. |

London, | Printed by Thom.Harper for Na- | thaniel Butter, and are to be sold | at his shop at Saint Austens | Gate, 1639. | Border. 13.5x8.cm. (13),222,(1)p. Sub t.p. at p.111.

CORBET, John. The | Vngirding | Of The | Scottish Armour: | Or, | An Ansvver To The | Informations for Defensive Armes against | the Kings Majestie, which were drawn up at Edenburgh, | by the common help and industrie of the three Tables of the | rigid Covenanters of the Nobility, Barons, Ministry, and | Burgesses, and ordained to be read out of Pulpit by each | Minister, and pressed upon the people, to draw them to | take up armes, to resist the Lords Anointed, | throughout the whole Kingdome | of Scotland. | By Iohn Corbet, Minister of Bonyl, one of the Collegiate | Churches of the Provostrie of Dunbartan. | . . . (4 lines)

Dvblin, | Printed by the Society of Stationers, 1639. | 18.1x14.2 cm. (8),56p.

COWPER, William. The | Triumph of a Christian, | Containing three excellent | and Heavenly Treatises: | |1. Iacobs wrestling with God. | 2. The Conduit of Comfort. | 3. A Preparative for the Lords Supper. | Full of sweet consolations for all that | desire the comfortable sweetnesse of Iesus | Christ; and necessary for those who are | troubled in Conscience. | Written by that worthy man, Master | William Covvper, Minister | of Gods Word. | The Tenth Impression. | Corrected & amended: with two Prayers | to be used in private Families hereunto added. |

London, | Printed by R.Badger, and are to be sold | by Iasper Emry, in St. Pauls Church-yard at | the signe of the Eagle and Child. 1639. | Line border. 14.4x9.5cm,(6),149; (1),153–238; (1) 241–368, (6)p. 2 sub t.p. dated 1636.

The | DECLINATOR | And | Protestation | Of The | Archbishops and Bishops, of the Church | of Scotland, and others their | adherents within that Kingdome, | Against the pretended generall Assembly | holden at Glasgow Novemb. 21. | 1638. | (ornaments.)

London, | Printed by John Ravvorth, for George | Thomason and Octavian Pullen, and are to be | sold at their shop, at the Rose in S.Pauls Churchyard. 1639. | 18.9x14.4cm. (2),33p.

DOWNAME, George. An | Apostolicall | Injunction for Unity | and Peace. | Or, a Sermon Preached by George | Downame Master of Arts of Christs Colledge | in Cambridge, to the Parishioners of Saint | Stephens in Walbrooke, at his departure | from them. | . . . (6 lines).

London: | Printed by J. Okes dwelling in little S. | Bartholomews. 1639. | Border. 18.5x14.6 cm. (4),40p.

DOWNAME, George. A | Treatise | Of | Iustification: | Wherein | Is First Set Dovvne The | Trve Doctrine | in the{Causes | Effects | Fruits | Consequents } of it, according to the Word of God. | And then all Obiections and Cavils of the Ad- | versaries to Gods free Iustification by Grace, are | answered and confuted, especially of Robert | Bellarmine, Jesuit and Cardinal. | Wherein also the popish Doctrine of merits is re- | futed and disproved, with many other weighty | points of Christian Religion, occasionally hand- | led and discussed, and difficult places of | holy Scriptures expounded and | vindicated. | By George Downame, Dr of Divinitie, | and Bishop of Dery. | Jeremiah 23. 5, 6. | . . . (6 lines).

London, | Printed by E. Purslow, for Nicholas Bourne, and part of the Impression | made over for the benefit of the children of Master Iohn | Minshew, deceased. | 1639. | Line border 27.3x19.2 cm. (7),660,(22) p. Pp. 212-221, 444-447 omitted; 566-567, repeated.

DYKE, Jeremiah. The | Righteovs Mans | Conversation: | Or, | A life in Heaven, | Handled upon Phil.3.20. | Published | By Ier.Dike, Minister of Epping. | . . . (8 lines).

London, | Printed by E.G. for I.Rothwell, and are to be | sold at his shop, at the signe of the Sunne, in | S.Pauls Church-yard. 1639. | Line border. 16.4x11.1 cm. (1),86p.
Part of his Righteous Mans Tower: 1639 ; with continuous register

DYKE, Jeremiah. The | Righteovs Mans | Honovr. | Or, | Gods Favovrite, | Published | By Ier.Dike, Minister of Epping. | . . . (5 lines; ornament).

London, | Printed by E.G. for I.Rothwell, and are to be sold at his | shop, at the signe of the Sunne, in S.Pauls Church-yard. 1639. | Line border. 16.4x11.1cm. (1),112p.
Part of his Righteous Mans Tower: 1639 ; with continuous register .

DYKE, Jeremiah. The | Righteovs Mans | Tovver. | Or, | The way to be safe in | a case of danger. | Published | By Ier.Dike, Minister of Epping in Essex. | . . . (11 lines).

London, | Printed by E.G. for I.Rothwell, and are to be | sold at his shop, at the signe of the Sunne, in | S.Pauls Church-yard. 1639. | Line border. 16.4x11.1 cm. (29), 115; (1), 112; (1), 86p. 3 Sub. t.p,
Also another copy from the library of Walter W. Law. 16x10.6cm. (25),115; (1),112; (1),86p.

ESTWICK, Nicolas. A | Learned | And | Godly Sermon | Preached on the XIX. day of December, | Anno Dom. MDCXXXI. at the Funerall of | Mr.Robert Bolton Batchelour in Di- | vinity and Minister of Broughton in | Northampton-Shire. | By Mr.Nicolas Estvvick, | Batchelour in Divinity, and sometimes fellow of | Christs Colledge in Cambridge, and now Mini- | ster of Warkton in Northampton-Shire. | Revised and somewhat enlarged by the Author, and now | at the importunity of some friends published. | (device).

London, | Printed by George Miller dwelling in Black-Friers, 1639. | 17.2x13.5 cm. (1),70p.

Part of the 4th ed. of Bolton's . . . Foure last Things: 1639 ;with separate register and pagination.

FOXLEY, George. The | Groanes | Of The | Spirit, | Or | The Triall | of the Truth of | Prayer. | . . . (6 lines).

Oxford, | Printed by Leonard Lich- | field, and are to be sold by | George Hutton, at the | Turne-stile in | Holborne. | 1639. | Border. 13.5x8.3cm. (15),242p.

Camb.Univ.Cat.No.5490. Epistle Dedicatory, signed.

FULLER, Thomas. The Historie | of the | Holy Warre; | By | Thomas Fvller, | B.D.Prebendarie of Sarum, late of Sidney | Colledge in Cambridge. | (device)

Printed by Thomas Buck, one of | the Printers to the Universitie of | Cambridge, 1639. | Border. 28.3x18.7cm. (16),286,(28)p.

Engr. fore-title, with " A declaration of the Frontispice ". Folded leaf.

GOUGE, William. A | Recovery | From | Apostacy. | Set out in | A Sermon Preached in Stepny | Church neere London at the receiving | of a Penitent Renegado into the | Church, Octob. 21. 1638. | By William Govge D.D. and Min. | in Black-Friers London | Herein is the History of the surprizall and admi- | rable escape of the said Penitent. | . . . (3 lines; device)

London, | Printed by George Miller, for Ioshua Kirton, and Thomas | Warren, at their shop in Pauls Church-yard, at | the vvhite Horse, 1639. | Border. 17x13.3 cm. (6),90p.

HALL, Joseph. Certaine | Irrefragable | Propositions | Worthy Of | Serious Consideration. | By J.H. | B. of Exon. | (ornament).

London, | Printed by M.F. for Nath:Butter. | M DC XXXIX. | 18x14cm. (5),7p.

HAMILTON, James. An | Explanation | Of The Meaning | Of The Oath And | Covenant. | Published | By the L.Marques, | his Majesties High Commissioner | in Scotland, | By the Kings speciall command. | (device).

London, | Printed by His Majesties Printer for Scotland, | Anno Dom. 1639. | 19.2x14.5cm. (2),17p.

Appended to Charles I.: His Majesties Proclamation: 1639; with continuous register.

Cambr.Univ.Cat. 5006.

HENDERSON, Alexander. The | Remonstance | Of The Nobility, Bar- | rones, Burgesses, Ministers | And Commons Within The | Kingdome of Scotland, | Vindicating them and their proceed- | ings from the crymes, wherewith | they are charged by the late Proclamation | in England, Feb.27. 1639. | (ornament)

Edinburgh | Imprinted by Iames Bryson Anno | Domini 1639. | 17.4 x 12.8 cm. 32 p.
Anon. DNB. 25: 394 b(4).

An | INFORMATION | Concerning | the meanes of Peace Ecclesiasticall. | . . . (3 lines; device: Licht Right).

Printed in the yeare 1639. | 16.6x12.5cm. (1),15–34p.

An | INFORMATION | to all good Christians vvith- | in the kingdome of England, | from the Noblemen, Barrons, | Borrows, Ministers, and Commons of the | kingdome of Scotland, for vindica- | ting their intentions and actions from the | unjust callumnies of their enemies. | (ornament).

Edinburgh, | Printed by Iames Bryson, Anno 1639. | 18.2x13.8cm. 13p.

JACKSON, ———. VVisdome | Crying out to Sinners to re- | turne from their evill wayes. | Contained in Three | pious and learned Treatises, Viz. | I. Of Christs fervent love to | bloudy Jerusalem. | II. Of Gods just hardening of | Pharaoh, when he had filled up | the measure of his iniquity. | III.Of Mans timely remem- | bring of his Creator. | Heretofore communicated to some friends | in written Copies: but now published | for the generall good. | . . . (5 lines).

London, | Printed by M.P. for Iohn Stafford, dwelling in | Black-horse-Alley neere Fleetstreet. 1639. | Line border. 16x10.3cm. (1), 319p.
Pollard, Short-Title Catalogue, attrib. to W: Milbourne.

JERMIN, Michael. A | Commentary, | Upon | The Whole Booke | Of | Ecclesiastes | Or The | Preacher. | Wherein | The originall Hebrew text is carefully examined, | our owne English Translation and others are | duely viewed and compared, in | which also | The literall sense is chiefly considered, other senses | as usefull are not omitted. | The exposition of the ancient Fathers, and other ancient and classicall | Authours being diligently observed: | the whole | Is also illustrated with frequent passages and sentences taken out | of them. | . . . (3 lines). By Michael Jermin, Dr. in Divinitie, and | Rect. of St. Martins Lud-gate. London. |

London: | Printed by Ric. Hodgkinsonne, for John Clark, and are to be sold at | his shop under Saint Peters Church in Corne-hill. 1639. | Line border. 28.5x 18cm. (6),1–247, 265–457,(22)p. 249–264 omitted.

LACEY, William. The | Ivdgment | Of An | Vniversity-Man | Concerning | M.VVilliam Chillingvvorth his | late Pamphlet, in Ansvvere to | Charity Maintayned. | (device).

Imprinted with Licence, Anno | M.DC.XXXIX. | 17.8x13.4 cm. 158p.
Cambr.Univ.Cat:6565.

LAUD, William. A | Relation | Of | The Conference | Betweene | William Lawd, | Then, Lrd. Bishop of St. Davids; | Now, | Lord Arch-Bishop of Canterbvry: | And Mr. Fisher the Jesuite, by the Command of | King James of ever | Blessed Memorie. | VVith an Answer to such Exceptions as | A.C. takes against it. | By the sayd Most Reverend Father in God, | William, | Lord Arch-Bishop of Canterbury. | (device).

London, | Printed by Richard Badger, Printer to the Prince | His Highnes. | MDCXXXIX. | 30.3x19.5cm. (24),388,(15)p.

LEIGH, Edward. Critica | Sacra: | Or, | Philologicall and Theologicall Observati- | ons, upon all the Greek words of the New Testa- | ment, in order alphabeticall: wherein usually the | etymon of the word is given, its force and emphasis | observed, and the severall acceptions of it in | Scripture, and versions by Exposi- | tors are set down. | By Edward Legh, Master of Arts of both | the Universities. | . . . (4 lines; ornament).

London, | Printed by Robert Young, and are sold by George Lathum in | Pauls-Church-yard, and by Ph.Nevill, in Ivie-lane. | Anno Dom. 1639. | 18.6x14.1 cm. (18), 631, 52p.

LESLIE, Henry. A | Speech, | Delivered At | The Visitation Of | Downe and Conner, | Held in Lisnegarvy the 26th. of September, | 1638. | Wherein, for the convincing of the Non- | conformists, there is a full Confutation of the | Covenant | Lately sworne and subscribed by many in | Scotland. | Published by Authority. | . . . (3 lines).

London, | Printed by John Raworth, for George Thomason and Octavian | Pullen, and are to be sold at the Rose in St. Pauls Church-yard. | 1639. | 20.5x 15.5cm. (1),38p. Mispagings.
Anon. Cambr.Univ.Cat.5152.

LESLIE, Henry. A | Treatise Of | The Avthority | Of The Chvrch. | The summe whereof was delivered in a | Sermon preached at Belfast, at the Visitation | of the Diocese of Downe and Conner. | By Henrie Leslie, Bishop of the Diocese. | Intended for the satisfaction of them who in those | places oppose the Orders of our Church, and now | published upon occasion of a Libell sent abroad in wri- | ting, wherin this Sermon, and all his proceedings | are most falsely traduced | Together with an Answer to certain objections | made against the Orders of our Church, especially | kneeling at the Communion. | . . . (7 lines).

Dvblin, | Printed by the Society of Stationers, Printers to the Kings most | Excellent Majesty. Anno Dom. 1639. | 18.1x13.1 cm. (15),190,(1)p.

MORE, Cresacre. A | Myrrhine | Posie | Of The Bitter | Dolovrs Of | Christ | His Passion, | And Of The | Seaven VVords | He Spake On The | Crosse, | Composed By | Ch.M. | . . . (2 lines; ornaments).

Printed at Doway by L.Kellam, | Anno 1639. | 14.7x9.cm. 13,(5),211p.
Gillow:V:95.

MORTON, Thomas. A | Sermon | Preached | Before the Kings most Excellent | Majestie, in the Cathedrall | Church of Durham. | Upon Sunday, being the fifth day | of May. 1639. | By the Right Reverend Father in God, | Thomas Lord Bishop | of Duresme. | Published by his Majesties speciall command. | (ornament).

Imprinted at Newcastle upon Tyne, | by Robert Barker, Printer to the | Kings most Excellent Majestie: And by | the Assignes of John Bill. | 1639. | 17.7x13.7 cm. (1),1–38p. Impf.

PAOLO, Servita. The | History | Of The | Inqvisition: | Composed by the Reverend | Father Paul Servita, who | was also the Compiler of the | Councell of Trent. | A Pious, Learned, and Curious | Worke, necessary for Councellors, | Casuists, and Politicians. | (ornaments). Translated out of the Italian Copy, by Robert | Gentilis. | (ornaments).

London: | Printed by J.Okes, for Humphrey Mosley and are to be | sold at his shop in Pauls Church-yard, at the | signe of the Princes Armes 1639. | Border. 19.9x15.6cm (5),90p.

Title in red and black. Imprimatur . . . Janu.12.1638. A1, verso.

PEACHAM, Henry. The | Dvty Of All | Trve Svbiects To | Their King: | As also to their Native Countrey, | in time of extremity and danger. | With some memorable examples of the miserable | ends of perfidious Traytors. | In two Bookes. | Collected and Written by H.P. | . . . (2 lines ; device)

London, | Printed by E.P. for Henry Seyle, and are to be sold at | his Shop, at the Tygers Head in Fleetstreet, | over against St.Dunstanes Church. | 1639. | Line border. 17.5x13.8 cm. (10),63p. Pp. 47–8 omitted.

Cambr.Univ.Cat:4124.

PONET, John. A | Short Treatise | of politike power, and of the true obedience | which Subjects owe to Kings and other civill | Governours. | Chap.I. | Whereof politike power groweth, wherefore it was ordained, and the right use and | duty of the same. | Chap.II. | Whether Kings, Princes, and other Governours have an absolute power and autho- | rity over their Subjects. | Chap.III. | Whether Kings, Princes, and other politike Governours be subject to Gods Laws, | and the positive laws of their Countries. | Chap.IV. | In what things, and how farre Subjects are bound to obey their Princes and | Governours. | Chap.V. | Whether all the Subjects goods be the Emperours or Kings own, and that they | may lawfully take them as their own. | Chap.VI. | Whether it be lawfull to depose an evill Governour, and kill a Tyrant. | Chap.VII. | What confidence is to be given to Princes and Potentates. | Composed by me D.I.P.B.R.W. | . . . (2 lines; device).

Printed in the year 1556. and now reprinted 1639. | 16.8x13.4cm. 68p. Cambr.Univ.Cat:7044.

The | PRINCIPALL Acts | Of The Solemne Generall | Asscmbly Of The Kirk Of | Scotland: | Indicted By The | Kings Majestie, | And Conveened | At Glasgow the xxi. of | November 1638. | Visied, collected, and extracted | forth of the Register of the acts of | the Assembly, by the Clerk thereof. | (ornament).

Edinbvrgh, | Printed by the Heirs of Andrevv Hart, | Anno Dom. 1639. | 30.x 20.cm.(4),51,(1)p.

The | PROTESTATION | Of The Generall | Assembly Of The Kirke | Of Scotland, And Of | The Noblemen, Barrons, | Gentlemen, Borrowes, | Ministers And Commons; | Subscribers of the Covenant |

lately, made at the Mercate Crosse | of Edinburgh the 18. of December- | ber. 1638. | (device).

Printed at Edinburgh by Iames Bryson, | in the year of God, 1639. | 18.8x13.7 cm. (1,50)p.

REYNOLDS, Edward. Meditations | On The Holy | Sacrament | Of The | Lords last Supper. | By | Edward Reynolds sometimes | Fellow of Merton College in Oxford, and | now Rector of the Church of Braunston | in Northampton-Shire. | The second Edition corrected and revised | by the Author. | (device).

London, | Imprinted by John Norton for Robert Bostock, and | are to be sold at his shop in S.Pauls Church-yard at | the signe of the Kings-Head. 1639. | Line border. 18.5x14.cm (10),223p.

ROBARTES, Fulke. Gods Holy | Hovse | And | Service, | According to the primitive | and most Christian forme thereof, | described by Foulke Robarts, Bachelor | of Divinity, and Prebendary of | Norvvich. | . . . (3 lines; ornaments).

London, | Printed by Tho.Cotes, and are to be sold at the Grey-hound | in Saint Pauls Church yard. 1639. | 17.8x12.2cm. (8), 99, (2)p.

ROBINSON, John. A | Ivstification | Of | Separation | from the Chvrch of England: | Against Mr Richard Bernard his invective, | Intitvled; | The Separatists schisme. | By John Robinson. | . . . (3 lines; device).

Printed in the yeere 1639. | 17.8x12.8 cm. 383,(5)p.

ROGERS, Thomas. A | Treatise | Vpon Svndry | Matters Contained | In The Thirty Nine | Articles of Religion, which are professed in the Church of | England. | Long since written and published | by Thomas Rogers. | . . . (4 lines; ornament).

London, | Printed by John Legatt, and are to be sold by | Richard Thrale, at the signe of the Crosse-keyes | at Pauls Gate. 1639. | 17.6x13.3cm. (36),232p. Mispagings.

SALTMARSH, John. The | Practice | Of | Policie | In A | Christian Life. | Taught from the Scriptures. | Written by I.Saltmarshe, | M. of Arts of Magd.Col. | in Cambridge. | . . . (2 lines; ornaments).

London, | Printed by E.G. for Samuel Endarby | and are to be sold at his Shop at | the Signe of the Starre in | Popes headalley, 1639. | Line border. 14.5x8.5cm. (16),304p. Pp. 255-264 repeated.

SEDGWICK, Obadiah. Military | Discipline | for the Christian | Souldier. | Drawne out in a Sermon | Preached to the Captaines and | Souldiers exercising Armes in the | Artillery Garden, at their Generall | meeting | In Saint Andrew's Vndershaft, in London, | October 18. 1638. | By Obadiah Sedgvvicke, | Batchelor of Divinity, and Preacher | to the Inhabitants of Saint Mildreds | Bredstreete in London. | . . . (5 lines).

London, | Printed by G.M. for Thomas Nicholes, and are to be | sold at the signe of the Bible in Popes-head- | Alley, 1639. | Border. 16x9.7cm. (10),98p.

SERRE, Le Sieur de la. The | Mirrour | Which | Flatters | Not. | Dedicated to their Maiesties | of Great Britaine, | By | Le Sieur de la Serre, Historiographer | of France. | Enriched with faire Figures. | Transcrib'd English from the | French, by T.C. | And devoted to the well-disposed | Readers. | . . . (2 lines).

London, | Printed by E.P. for R.Thrale, and are to be sold | at his shop at the Signe of the Crosse-Keyes, | at Pauls Gate. 1639. | Line border. 15.5x10.1cm, (34), 228, (17)p. Engr. frontisp. 4 full pages illustr. "The Designe of the Frontispiece", on Sig. A1, reverse

SIBBES, Richard. Beames | Of Divine | Light, | Breaking forth from severall places | of holy Scripture, as they were | learnedly opened, | In XXI. Sermons. | The III. first being the fore-going Sermons | to that Treatise called The Bruised-Reed, | Preached on the precedent words. | By the late Reverend and Iudicious Divine, | Richard Sibs, | D.D.Mr. of Katharine Hall in Camb: and sometimes | Preacher at Grayes Inne. | Published according to the Doctor his owne | appointment subscribed with his hand; | to prevent imperfect Coppies. | . . . (7 lines)

London. | Printed by G.M. for N.Bourne, at the Royal Exchange, and R. Harford, | at the guilt Bible in Queenes-head Alley in Pater-Noster-Row. | MDCXXXIX. | Border. 18.2 x 13.1 cm. (11),330;(1),232,(14)p. 9 sub title-pages; continuous register.

SIBBES, Richard. The | Beasts | Dominion | over Earthly Kings. | A Sermon preached upon the 5th of | November, in remembrance of Our | Deliverance from the Papists | Powder-Treason. | By | The late Learned and Reverend Divine, | Rich.Sibbs. | Doctor in Divinity, Mr. of Katherine Hall | in Cambridge, and sometimes Preacher | to the Honourable Society of | Grayes-Inne. | . . . 3 lines).

London, | Printed by T.B. for N.Bourne, at the Royall Exchange, | and R. Harford, at the Bible in Queenes-head Alley | in Pater-noster-Row. 1639. | Border. 18.8x13.1cm. 55p.

First part, incorporated in his Evangelicall Sacrifices: 1640 ; beginning with Sig.B.

SIBBES, Richard. The Excellencie | Of | The Gospell | above the Law. | Wherein the Liberty of the | Sonnes of God is shewed. | With the Image of their Graces | here, and Glory hereafter. | Which affords much Comfort and | great Incouragement, to all such as Be- | gin Timely, and Continue Constant- | ly in the wayes of God. | By R.Sibbs, D.D.Mr. of Katherin | Hall Cambridge, and Preacher | of Grayes-Inne, London. | Begun in his life time, and published | by T.G. and P.N. |

London, | Printed by Tho. Cotes, and are to be sold by | Iohn Bartlet, at his shop, at the Signe of the guilt | Cup, neere S.Austins gate. 1639. | Line border. 14.1x8.2cm. (19), 650p.

SIBBES, Richard. An | Exposition | Of The | Third Chapter | Of The Epistle Of | St.Paul to the Philippians. | Also { Two Sermons of Christian watch- | fulnesse. | The first upon Luke 12.37. | The Second upon Revel.16.15. | An Exposition of part of the second | Chapter of the Epistle to the Philipp. | A Sermon upon Mal.4.2.3. | By the late

Reverend Divine Richard | Sibbes, D.D.Master of Katherine Hall in Cam- | bridge, and sometimes Preacher at Grayes-Inne. | . . . (3 lines).

London, | Printed by T.Cotes for Peter Cole, and are to be sold at the | Glove & Lyon in Corne-hill, neare the Royall Exchange, 1639. | Border. 18.8x13.1cm. (20), 256; 204p.

SIBBES, Richard. The | Hidden | Life. | In two Funerall Sermons upon | Col.3.3,4. | By | The late Learned and Reverend Divine, | Rich. Sibbs: | Doctor in Divinity, Mr of Katherine Hall | in Cambridge, and sometimes Preacher | to the Honourable Society of | Grayes-Inne. | . . . (3 lines).

London, | Printed by E. Purslow, for N.Bourne, at the Roy- | all Exchange, and R. Harford at the gilt | Bible in Queenes head Alley, in Pater- | Noster-Row. 1639. | Border. 18.8x14cm. (1), 238, (8)p.

Part of his Evangelicall Sacrifices: 1640 ; with double letter register. and 5 sub t.p.

SIBBES, Richard. The | Retvrning | Backslider, | Or, | A Commentarie | upon the whole XIIII. Chapter | of the Prophecy of the Prophet Hosea. | Wherein is shewed the large extent of Gods free | Mercy, even unto the most miserable forlorne and | wretched sinners that may be, upon their | Humiliation and Repentance. | Preached by that Learned and Judicious Divine, | Dr. Sibbs, late Preacher to the Honourable Society | of Grayes Inne, and Master of Katherine Hall in | Cambridge. | Published by his owne Permission before | his Death. | . . . (6 lines).

London, | Printed by G.M. for George Edwards in the Old Baily in Greene-Arbour | at the signe of the Angell, MDCXXXIX. | Border. 18.7x14.1cm. (13), 511, (16)p. Portr. frontisp.

SPELMAN, Henry. Concilia, | Decreta, Leges, | Constitvtiones, | In Re Ecclesiarum | Orbis Britannici. | Viz. | Pambritannica, | Panangli-ca, | Scotica, Hibernica, | Cambrica, Mannica, | Provincialia, | Dioece-sana. | Ab initio Christianæ ibidem Religionis, | ad nostram usque ætatem. | Uti reperiuntur in eorundem Actis, Canonibus Ecclesiasticis, | Regnorum Constitutionibus, Senatus Consultis, Principum Rescriptis, | Libris impressis, & antiquè Mss. in Regnum etiam priscorum | Diplomatibus, Chartis, Schedis, & Monumentis | veteribus, studiosè congesta. | Operâ & Scrutinio | Henrici Spelman, Eq.Aur. | Tribus distincta Tomis: | . . . (4 lines).

Londini, | Typis B.Badger, Impensis Ph.Stephani, & Ch.Meredith, sub Aureo Leone in | Cœmeterio Paulino: M.DC.XXXIX. | 30.7x20.3cm. I: (24),637,(25)p. II: (17),747,(27)p.

SYMONDS, Joseph. The | Case And Cure | Of | A deserted Soule. | Or, | A Treatise | Concerning the nature, kindes, | Degrees, Symptomes, Causes, | Cure of, and mistakes about | Spirituall Desertions. | By | Jos: Symonds Minister of St.Martins | Iremonger-Lane London. | . . . (5 lines; ornaments).

London, | Printed by M.Flesher, for Luke Fawne, and S.Gellibrand, at the | Brazen Serpent in Pauls Church yard. 1639. | Line border. 16.4x10.4cm,(47),558p.

TWISSE, William. Dissertatio | De Scientia | Media | Tribus Libris Absoluta, | Quorum | Prior Gabrielem Penottvm ad partes vocat in suo Libertatis humanæ | Propugnaculo: & ad Quindecem Capita posteriora Libri Tertii | Responsionem exhibet: | Posteriores duo Francisco Suaresio oppositi sunt, duosque Libros ejus | De Scientia Dei inscriptos refellendos suscipiunt. | I. Alterum de Scientia futurorum contingentium absoluta. | II. Alterum de Scientia futurorum contingentium conditionata. | Unà cum | Digressionibvs | Quarum Catalogus post Præf. exhibetur. | Autore Gulielmo Tvvisse S.Theologiæ Doctore. | . . . (2 lines; ornament).

Prostant | Arnhemii apud Jacobum à Biesium | M.DC.XXXIX. | 30.7x20.3cm. (25),498,(10)p.

TWISSE, William. Guilielmi Twissi | Anglo-Britanni | S.S.Theologiæ Doctoris, | Ad | Jacobi Arminii Collationem | cum Francisco Junio; & Johan. | Arnoldi Corvini Defensionem | sententiæ Arminianæ, | De Prædestinatione, | Gratia, & Libero Arbitrio, &c. | Quam | Adversus Danielis Tileni Conside- | rationem edidit, | Animadversiones. | Nunc primum in lucem editæ. | Cum Indicibus. | (device).

Amstelodami | Apud Joannem Janssonium. | M DC XLIX. | 30.7x20.3cm. (12),134;474,(23)p.

USSHER, James. Britannicarum | Ecclesiarvm | Antiqvitates. | Quibus inserta est pestiferæ adversùs | Dei gratiam à Pelagio Britanno in | Ecclesiam inductæ Hæreseos | Historia. | Collectore | Jacobo Vsserio | Archiepiscopo Armachano, | totius Hiberniæ Primate. | (device)

Dublinii, | Ex Officinâ Typographicâ Societatis Bibliopolarum. | Anno M DC XXXIX. | 18.9 x 14.3 cm. (24),1196 p.

WELLES, John. The | Sovles Progresse | To the Celestiall Canaan, | or Heavenly Jervsalem. | By way of godly Meditation, and | holy contemplation: accompanied with | divers learned exhortations, and pithy | perswasions, tending to Christianity | and humanity. | Divided into two Parts. | The first Part treateth of the Divine Essence, | Quality and Nature of God, and his holy Attri- | buts: and of the creation, fall, state, death, and misery | of an unregenerated man, both in this life and | in the world to come: Put for the whole | scope of the Old Testament. | The second Part is put for the summe and compen- | dium of the Gospell, and treateth of the Incarna- | tion, Nativity, Words, Works, and sufferings of Christ, | and of the happinesse and blessednesse of a godly | man in his state of Renovation, being | reconciled to God in Christ. | Collected out of the Scriptures, and out of the wri- | tings of the ancient Fathers of the Primitive Church, | and other Orthodoxall Divines: by John Welles, | of Beccles in the County of Suffolk. |

London, | Printed by E.G. and are to be sold by Henry Shep- | hard in Chancery-lane, at the signe of the Bible, | between Serjeants-Inne and Fleetstreet, neere the | Kings-head-Taverne. 1639. | Line border. 17.8x13.8cm. (26),372,(1) p.

YOUNG, Thomas. Dies Dominica, | Sive | Succincta narratio ex S.Scripturarum, & | venerandæ antiquitatis Patrum testimoniis | concinnata, | Et | Duobus Libris distincta: | Quorum | Priori, diei Dominicæ observationem ab ipsis | Apostolis, Ecclesiaque Christiana continua serie solennem | fuisse habitam, ejus institutionem fuisse divinam, & | quæ ejus solennitatem impediant, declaratur: | Posteriori Vero | In quibus ejus sanctificatio consistat ostenditur. | In Qvibvs Etiam | Variæ Ecclesiasticæ antiquitates cognitu non | indignæ explicantur. . . . (10 lines)

Anno 1639. | 19.2x15. cm. (22),132p.
Attribution by Dr. Charles A. Briggs.

YOUNGE, Richard. Sinne | Stigmatized: | Or, | The Art to { Know savingly, | Believe rightly, | Live Religiously, | Taught both by similitude and contrariety | from a serious scrutiny or survey of | The { Profound Humanist, | Cunning Polititian, | Cauterized Drunkard, | Experimentall Christian: | Wherein the beauties of all Christian graces are illu- | strated by the blacknesse of their opposite vices. | Also, | That enmity which God proclaimed in Para- | dise betweene the seed of the Serpent and the seed | of the Woman, unvailed and anatomized. | Whereunto is annexed, | Compleat Armor against evill society: toge- | ther with the skill, will, and industry of leud ones | in tempting to sinne, and drawing to perdition. | The which may serve also for a common place booke | of the most usuall vertues and vices: or as a repository | of rhetoricall figures and formes of speech. | By R.Junius. |

London, | Printed for G.Latham at the signe of the Bishops head | in St.Pauls Church-yard. [1639] | 16.7x10.2cm. (17),692,(1),689–863,(18)p.
General t.p., preceding his The Drunkard's Character: 1638. Date mutilated. Cambr.Univ.Cat:4392.

1640

The | ACCVSATION | And | Impeachment | Of | Iohn | Lord | Finch, | Baron Of Fordwich, | Lord | Keeper Of The Great | Seale Of England, | By The | House of Commons. | (device).

Printed Anno Dom. 1640. | 17.8x12.6 cm. 10p.
Also in Speeches and Passages: 1641, and Regni argumenta Consilii: 1659.

ARTICLES | Exhibited | In Parliament | Against | William | Archbishop | Of Canterbury, | 1640. | (lace ornament).

Printed in the yeare 1640 | 18x13.2cm. (1),5p.

ARTICLES | To Be | Enquired Of | VVithin the Diocesse of | London. | In the third Trienniall Visitation | Of the Right Honourable, and | Right Reverend Father in God, | William, | Lord Bishop of London, | Lord High Treasurer of England. | Holden in the Yeare of our Lord God, 1640. | (device).

London, | Printed by Richard Badger. | M.DC.XL | 18x13.8cm. (2,25)p.

BACON, Francis. Certaine | Considerations | touching the better pacification, | and Edification of the Church | of England: | Dedicated to his most Excellent | Majestie. | (ornament)

Printed, M.DC.XXXX. | 18x13.7 cm. (1, 42)p. A1, blank. Orn. head-piece. Anon Cambr.Univ.Cat:7578. First 1640 edition.

BACON, Francis. Certaine | Considerations | Tovching The | better Pacification, and | Edification of the Church of | England. | Dedicated to His most Excellent | Majesty. | (ornaments).

Printed, MDC.XXXX. | 20.3x15.cm. (3,42)p. A1, blank. Head-piece of printers' ornaments. Second edition
Anon. Cambr.Univ.Cat: 7618.

BAILLIE, Robert. Ladensivm | 'Αυτοκατακρισις, | The Canterbvrians | Self-Conviction. | Or | An evident demonstration of the avowed | Arminianisme, Poperie, and tyrannie of that | Faction, by their owne confessions. | With a Post-script to the Personate Jesuite Lysimachus | Nicanor, a prime Canterburian. | (lace ornament).

Written in March, and printed in April, 1640. | 17.4x13.8cm. (22),128,28p.
Anon. H&L. Advoc.Libr.

BAKER, Richard. Meditations | And | Disqvisitions | Vpon The | Lords Prayer. | By Sr.Richard Baker, Knight. | . . . (2 lines). The fourth Edition, Corrected and amended. | (device).

London, | Printed by Thomas Paine, for Francis Eglesfield, | and are to be sold at the Marigold, in Pauls | Church-yard. 1640. | Line border. 18.6x14.2cm. (8), 213p.

BAKER, Richard. Meditations | And | Disqvisitions, | Upon | The Seven psalmes of David, | commonly called the Penitentiall | Psalmes. | Namely, | The 6. | The 32. | The 38.} {The 51. | The 102. | The 130. | The 143. | By Sir Richard Baker Knight. | (ornament).

London, | Printed by I.D. for Francis Eglesfield, and are to be | sold at the signe of the Mary-gold in Pauls | Church-yard. 1640. | Line border. 18.6x14.2cm. (6), 1–170, 169–183; (5), 139–180, (1), 181–245, (1)p.

BAKER, Richard. Meditations | And | Disqvisitions, | Upon | Seven Consolatorie | Psalmes Of David: | Namely, | The 23. | The 27. | The 30.} {The 34. | The 84. | The 103. | The 116. | By Sir Richard Baker Knight | (ornament).

London | Printed by John Dawson, for Francis Eglesfield, and are | to be sold at the signe of the Marigold in | Pauls Church-yard. 1640. | Line border. 18.6x 14.2cm. (8),206p. T.p. supplied by Mr. Edward G. Friehold, of London.

BALL, John. A | Friendly Triall | Of The Grounds | Tending To | Separation; | In a plain and modest Dispute touching the | Lawfulnesse of a stinted Liturgie and set | form of Prayer, Communion in | mixed assemblies, and the Primi- | tive subject and first recepta- | cle of the power of | the Keyes: | Tending to satisfie the doubtfull, recall the wan- | dring, and to strengthen the weak: | By | John Ball. | . . . (5 lines).

Printed by Roger Daniel printer to the | Universitie of Cambridge; | For Edward Brewster, and are to be sold at his shop | at the Bible on Fleet-bridge. 1640. | Border. 18.8x14.3cm (16), 314, (5)p.

BANCROFT, Richard. Dangerous | Positions | And | Proceedings, | Published | And Practised | VVithin This Iland | of Britaine, under pretence of | Reformation, and for the | Presbyteriall Discipline. | Collected, and set forth by Richard Bancroft, Doctor in Divinity, | then Lord Bishop of London, and afterwards Lord | Archbishop of Canterbury. | . . . (4 lines).

London, | Printed by R. Young and R. Badger. Anno 1640. | 18.8x14. cm. (8), 1–64,41–48,73–183p.

BLENKOW, John. Michaels | Combat | With The | Divel: | Or, | Moses his Funerall. | Delivered in a Sermon Preached in St | Pauls Church, on Sunday Morning, | being the Feast of St Michael, 1639. | By Iohn Blenkovv LL.B. sometime Fellow | of S.Iohn Bap.Coll. in Oxford. | . . . (3 lines).

London, | Printed by Thomas Harper. 1640. | 17.9x13.4cm. (3),26p.

BOLTON, Robert. A | Cordiall | For Christians | In The Time | Of Affliction. | Or, | A Sermon Preached | At Kethering Lecture by Master | Robert Bolton, Bache- | lour of Divinity, and sometimes | Fellow of Brasen-nose Colledge | in Oxford. | Published by I.S. | (device)

London. | Printed by George Miller dwelling | in the Blacke-Fryers, MDCXL. | 17.2x13.5cm. (8),27pp.
Also another copy from the library of Walter W. Law. 17.2x13.6cm.

BOLTON, Robert. Instrvctions | For a Right comforting | Afflicted | Conciences: | VVith speciall Antidotes against | some grievous Temptations. | Delivered for the most part in the Lecture | at Kettering in Northamptonshire. | By Robert Bolton, Batchelor in Divinitie, | and Preacher of Gods Word at Broughton in | the same Countie. | The third Edition, divided into Chapters, with a Table | of the Contents annexed. | (ornaments)

London, | Printed by Tho.Badger, for Tho.Weaver, | 1640. | Border. 18.3x14.3 cm. (29),595,(4)p.
Part of his: The Workes | Of: 1641.

BRADSHAW, William. Unreasonablnes | Of The | Separation; | Made apparent, in an Examination of, and An- | swere to, certaine Reasons of | Maister Francis Johnson; | Whereby he laboureth to justifie his Schisme from the Church-Assemblies | Of England; | By Maister VVilliam Bradshaw deceased. | Together with a Rejoinder, in defence of the said Answere, against the | late Reply of Maister Iohn Canne (a Leader to a Company of | Brownists in Amsterdam) thereunto, by a Freind | of the deceased. | (device).

Prnited in the Yeare of our Lord, 1640. | 16.4x12.3 cm. (8),149p.

BURROUGHS, Jeremiah. The | Excellency | Of | A Gracious Spirit. | Delivered | In A Treatise | Vpon the 14. of Numbers, | Verse 24. | By Jer.Burroughes, | Minister of Gods Word. | . . . (2 lines; ornament)

London, | Printed by M.F. for R.Dawlman, and | L.Fawne, at the Brazen Serpent in Pauls | Church-yard. 1640. | Line border. 16.2x10.2 cm. (24),431p.

BURROUGHS, Jeremiah. The | Sea-Mans | Direction In | Time Of Storme. | Delivered in a Sermon up- | on occasion of a strong stormie | Wind lately happening. | By Ier.Burroughs | . . . (2 lines).

London: | Printed by T.Paine and M.Sim- | mons. 1640. | Border. 15.4x10.4cm. (7),87p.
From the library of Walter W. Law.

BURTON, Henry. Iesv-Worship | Confvted | Or | Certaine Arguments A- | gainst Bowing At The | Name Iesvs. | With | Objections to the contrary, Fully Answered. | By H. B. | . . . (3 lines; device).
Printed Anno 1640. | 12.8x8.6 cm. (1),12p.
Attribution by Dr. Charles A. Briggs.

BURTON, Henry. A | Replie | To A | Relation | Of The | Conference | Between William Laude | and Mr. Fisher the Jesuite. | By a Witnesse of Jesus Christ. | . . . (8 lines)
Imprinted, Anno MDCXL. | 17.7x13.6 cm. (48),405 p. T.p. mounted in strips.
Attribution by Dr. Charles A. Briggs.

BYFIELD, Nicholas. The | Marrovv Of | The Oracles | Of God. | Or, | Divers Treatises, | containing Directions about six | of the waightiest things can | concerne a Christian in | this life. | By N.Bifield, late Preacher | of Gods Word at Isleworth in | Middlesex. | The eleventh Edition. | (ornaments).
London, | Printed by Iohn Legatt. | 1640. | Line border. 13.6x8.1 cm. (14), 767p. 5 sub-t.p.

CARTER, John. Vindiciæ | Decimarvm. | Of Tithes, | a Plea for the | Ivs Divinvm. | Drawne from the Text, | By Iohn Carter Diacon. | . . . (9 lines).
Printed at London by T. Cotes. 1640. | Border. 17.7x13.9 cm. 56p. Title in red and black.

CERTAINE | Sermons | Or | Homilies, | appointed to be read | in Churches. | In the time of the late Queene | Elizabeth of famous | memory. | And now thought fit to be reprinted | by authority from the Kings most | Excellent Majesty. |
London, | Printed by R.H. and J.N. for | Richard Whitaker, and are to be sold | at his Shop at the Kings Armes | in St.Pauls Church- | yard. | 1640. | Grape & column border. 26.8x18.2cm. (7), 98; (4), 320, (3)p.

CHARLES I. His | Majesties | Declaration, | Concerning | His Proceedings with His | Subjects of Scotland, | Since the Pacification in the | Camp neere Berwick. | (device)
London, | Printed by R.Young, His Majesties Printer for Scotland, | and R. Badger, Printer to the Prince his Highnesse. | M.DC.XL. | 20x15. cm. (1),63p.

CHARLES I. His | Majesties | Declaration: | To All His Loving | Subjects, | Of the causes which moved him to | dissolve the last Parliament. | Published by His Majesties speciall command. | (royal arms).
London: | Printed by Robert Barker, Printer to | the Kings most Excellent Majestie: And | by the Assignes of John Bill. | M D C X L. | 18x13.7cm. (2), 55p. Colophon

CHRIST | On His | Throne. | Or, | Christs Church-government brief- | ly laid downe; and how it ought to | bee set up in all Christian Con- | gregations. | Resolved in sundry Cases of Conscience. | . . . (7 lines).
Printed in the yeare 1640. | Border. 17.4x13.5 cm (11),78p.

CONSTITUTIONS | And | Canons | Ecclesiasticall; | Treated upon by the Archbishops of | Canterbury and York, Presidents of the Convoca- | tions for the respective Provinces of Canter- | bury and York, and the rest of the Bishops | and Clergie of those Provinces; | And agreed upon with the Kings Majesties | Licence in their severall Synods begun | at London and York. 1640. | In the yeer of the Reign of our Soveraign Lord Charles, | by the grace of God, King of England, Scotland, | France, and Ireland, the Sixteenth. | And now Published for the due observation of them, by His Majesties | Authority under the Great Seal of England. | (royal arms).

London: | Printed by Robert Barker, Printer to the | Kings most Excellent Majestie: And by the | Assignes of John Bill. 1640. | 19.4x15.2 cm. (1),10,(41)p. Repr. also in Sparrow's Collection of Articles: 1661, 1675 & 1684;

CORBET, John. The | Epistle | Congratulatorie | Of | Lysimachus Nicanor | Of the Societie of Jesu, | To The | Covenanters | In Scotland. | VVherin is paralleled our sweet Harmony | and correspondency in divers materiall points | of Doctrine and Practice. | . . . (8 lines).

Anno Domini M.DC.XL. | 17.5x13.8 cm. (1),78p. Title in red and black. Anon. Cf.Cambr.Univ.Cat. 7637 and 7638. Page 3, last line, end " com-mand ".

DAVENANT, John. Ad | Fraternam | Communionem | inter Evangelicas Ecclesias | restaurandam Adhortatio; | In eo fundata, Quòd non dissentiant in | ullo Fundamentali Catholicæ | Fidei articulo. | Per | Reverendum in Christo Patrem, | Johann.Davenantium | Episcopum Sarisburiensem. | Cui præfixa est Ejusdem De | Pace itidem Ecclesiastica | Commentatio Johanni Duræo | non ità pridem missa. |

Cantabrigiæ, | Ex officina Rogeri Danielis | almæ Academiæ Typographi. | M DC XL. | Border 13.5x8.cm. (4),164p.

DENNE, Henry. Grace, | Mercy, | And | Peace. | Conteining | 1. Gods Reconciliation to Man. | 2. Mans Reconciliation to God. | By Henry Denne, | An unworthy servant of the Church, | . . . (3 lines: ornament)

London, | Printed for the Benefit of the | Citie of Rochester. | [1640?] (Border). 13.9x8.5 cm (2),78p.

DEPOSITIONS | And | Articles | Against | Thomas | Earle Of | Strafford, | Febr.16.1640. | (device).

Printed in the yeare, 1640. | 18.5x14.1cm. (1),45p.

a | DIALOGVE. | Wherin | Is Plainly Layd | Open The Tyran- | nicall Dealings Of Lord Bishops | Against Gods Children. | With | Certaine Points Of Doctrine | Wherein They Approve Them- | selves (according to Dr.Bridges his judgement) | to be truely the Bishops of the Divell. | Published, by the worthy gentleman Dr.Martin Mar-Prelat, | Doctor in all the Faculties, Primate and Metropolitan. | . . . (6 lines)

Reprinted in the time of Parliament, Anno Dom. 1640. | 17.5x13cm. (3,24)p.

DIGBY, George. The | Third | Speech | Of | The Lord | George Digby, | To the House of Commons, | Concerning Bishops, and the | Citie Petition, the 9th. of | Febr: 1640. | (device)

Printed for Tho:Walkley. | 1640. | 18.7 x12.3 cm. 3–19p.
Also incorporated in Speeches and Passages: 1641, and Regni argumenta Consilii: 1659 .

DONNE, John. LXXX | Sermons | Preached | By That Learned And | Reverend Divine, | Iohn Donne, | Dr In Divinity, | Late Deane of the Cathedrall | Church of S.Pauls London. | (device).

London, | Printed for Richard Royston, in Ivie-lane, and Richard | Marriot in S.Dunstans Church-yard in Fleetstreet. | M DC XL. | Line border. 32.7x21.5cm. (31), 1–75, (1), 77–826,(22)p.

DORISLAUS, Isaac. Prælium | Nuportanum | Rerum fide tradebat. | Is:Dorislaus.I.C. | (device).

Londini: | 1640. | 18.4x14.3cm. (1),37p.

DOVE, John. A | Confvtation | Of | Atheisme. | By Iohn Dove Doctor | of Divinitie. | The Contents are to be seene in | the Page following. | . . . (4 lines).

London, | Printed by E.P. for Nicholas Bourne, and | are to be sold at his shop at the South | entrance of the Royall Exchange, | 1640. | 13.8 x 8. cm. (8), 227 p.

DURY, John. Informatio | Ecclesiis Re- | formatis | Oblata, | De conciliis, quæ agitata | fuerunt in | Pace Religiosa | Cum ecclesiis Augustanis | quærenda, | à | Johanne Duræo | ecclesiaste Britanno. | (device)

Bremæ, Typis Bertholdi Villeriani scholæ | typogr. Anno M DC XL. | 20.5x 16. cm. 11p.

DYKE, Jeremiah. Divers Select | Sermons | On | Severall Texts. | Viz. { 1. Of Quenching the Spirit. I. Thessalon. | 5.16. | 2. Of the Sinner's suite for Pardon. 2 Sam. | 24.10. | 3. Of Eating and Digesting the Word. | Ier.15.16. | 4. Of buying and keeping the Truth. Prov. | 23.23. | Preached by that Reverend and Faithfull | Minister of the Word, Ier. Dyke, | late Preacher of Epping in Essex. | Finished by his owne pen in his life time, And | now published by his Sonne Dan. Dyke | Master of Arts. |

London, | Printed by Tho.Paine for Iohn Rothwell, at the | signe of the Sun in Pauls Church-yard. 1640. | Line border. 15.8x10.2cm. (15), (1), 393, (3)p. 4 Sub t.p.

DYKE, Jeremiah. A | VVorthy | Communicant: | Or, | A Treatise, | Shewing the Due Order of | Receiving the Sacrament of the | Lords Supper. | By Ier.Dyke, Minister of Epping, | in Essex. | . . . (7 lines)

London, | Printed by T.B. for L.Fawne, and S. | Gellibrand, at the brasen Serpent in | S:Pauls Church Yard 1640. | Line border. 16.5x10.8 cm. (16),573p.

ENGLANDS | Complaint | To | Iesvs Christ, | Against | The Bishops | Canons. | Of The Late Sinfull Synod, A Sedi- | tious Conventicle, A Packe Of Hy- | pocriets, a Sworne Confederacy, a Traiterous Conspiracy against | the true Religion of Christ, and the Weale Publicke | of the Land, and consequently against the | Kingdome and Crowne. |

In this Complaint are Specified those impieties and insolencies, which are | most notorious, Scattered through the Canons and Constitutions of the | said Sinfull Synod. And confuted by Arguments annexed hereunto. | . . . (12 lines).

Printed Anno Dom. 1640. | 18.5x14.5cm. (1,50)p.

F., L. A | Speedy Remedie | Against | Spiritvall | Incontinencie. | Shewing It To Be Sinfull In Any, | To Heare A False Ministrie. | With a briefe description of a True Church of Christ. | . . . (7 lines ; ornament).

Printed in the time of Parliament, Anno Dom. 1640. | 17.8x14. cm. (8) 69p On page 51 is a sub. t.p.: An Index | To The | Chvrches Codex | With Its Vindex And Ivdex. | Or, | A Speedy Remedy And Speciall | Spirituall Receipt For A Soul-Sick | Saint and Sonne, who would be a worshipper and servant | of Christ his Redeemer. | . . . (16 lines)., By me L.F. | Printed in the first yeare of the Parliament, | and of the Beasts downfall in England. | An Dom. 1640. | Colophon, dated 1641.

Signed L.F. at end and on sub t.p.

FEATLEY, Daniel, and others. Θρηνοικος. | The House | Of Movrning; | Fvrnished | With } Directions for | Preparations to | Meditations of | Consolations at { the houre of Death. | Delivered In | XLVII. Sermons, | Preached At The | Funeralls of divers faithfull | servants of Christ. | By { Daniel Featly | Martin Day }{ Richard Sibbs | Thomas Taylor } Doctors in Divinitie. | And other Reverend Divines. | . . . (8 lines).

London, | Printed by John Dawson, for R.M. and are to be sold by Philip Nevill, | at the signe of the Gunne in Ivie-lane. | 1640. | Border. 27.8x18.6cm. (15),916p.

FENNER, William. The Souls | Looking-glasse, | lively representing its | Estate before God: | with | A Treatise Of Conscience; | wherein the definitions and di- | stinctions thereof are un- | folded, and severall | Cases resolved: | By that reverend and faithfull Minister of the Word, | William Fenner, B.D. sometimes | Fellow of Pembroke-hall in Cambridge, | and late Parson of Rochford | in Essex. | . . . (3 lines).

Cambridge: | Printed by Roger Daniel, Printer to the | Universitie; for John Rothwell at the | Sunne in Pauls church-yard. 1640. | Border. 16x9.6cm. (19), 323p.

FOX, John. Reformatio | Legum | Ecclesiasticarum, | Ex Authoritate Primum | Regis Henrici 8. inchoata: | Deinde per Regem Edovardum 6. pro- | vecta, adauctáque in hunc modum, atq; | nunc ad pleniorem ipsarum reformati- | onem in lucem edita. | (ornament).

Londini, | Typis T. H. & R. H. impensis Laurentii Sadler habi- | tantis in parva Britannia, ad insigne aurei | Leonis. An. Dom. M. DC. XL. | Line border. 19.1x14.0 cm. (16),303p.

DNB.20:146b. Attributed to Thomas Cranmer. DNB.13:31a. Cambr.Univ. Cat.No.825.

FULLER, Thomas. The Historie | of the | Holy VVarre; | By | Thomas Fvller, | B.D.Prebendarie of Sarum, late of Sidney | Colledge in Cambridge. | The second edition. | (device)

Cambridge, | Printed by R.Daniel, for Thomas Buck, | and are to be sold by John VVilliams | at the signe of the Greyhound in Pauls | Church-Yard. 1640. | Lace border. 26.8x18.2cm. (14),286,(28)p.
Lacks frontisp, but has " declaration ".

GATAKER, Thomas. The Decease | Of | Lazarus | Christ's Friend. | A Funerall Sermon | On | Iohn Chap.11. Vers. 11. | Preached at the Buriall of | Mr.John Parker Merchant | and Citizen of London. | By Tho.Gataker B. of D. and Rector | of Rotherhith. | (ornament).

London. | Printed by E.G. for Edward Brewster, and Fulke Clyfton, and | are to be sold at the Bible on Fleet-bridge, and on | New-Fishstreet-Hill. 1640. | 17.9x12.3cm. (8),48p.

GERHARD, John. The Summe | Of | Christian | Doctrine, | Written originally | in Latine | By | John Gerhard | Doctour in | Divinitie; | And translated by | Ralph Winterton | Fellow of Kings Colledge | in Cambridge. |

Cambridge, | Printed by Roger Daniel, | 1640. | And are to be sold by William | Hope, near the Exchange | in Cornhill. | Border. 12.5x6.9cm. (34),302p. Engr fore-t.p. Imperfect after N 11.

GOODWIN, John. The | Saints | Interest | In God: | Opened | In Severall | Sermons, Preached Anni- | versarily upon the fifth of | November. | By | John Goodwin | Pastor of S.Stephens Coleman-street. | . . . (4 lines).

London, | Printed by M.F. for Henry Overton, | and are to be sold at his Shop at the entring | into Popes Head Alley, out of | Lumbard Street. 1640. | Line border. 14x8.3cm. (60), 341p.

A | GRANT | Of The | Benevolence | Or | Contribution | To His most Excellent Majestie, by | the Clergie of the Province of | Canterburie. | In the Convocation or Sacred Synode holden | at London. Anno Domini 1640. | (device).

London: | Printed by Robert Barker, Printer to the | Kings most Excellent Majestie: And by the | Assignes of John Bill. 1640. | 17.6x12.8cm. (1),26p.

GREENWOOD, John. More vvorke for Priests: | Or | An Answere to George | Giffords pretended defence of Read | Prayers and devised Leitourgies, comprised | in the first part of his booke; Intituled | A short Treatise against the Do- | natists of England: | Wherein | Is proved that the serving of God in such | away and manner is a supersti- | tious and vaine worship. | Written | By John Greenwood | Christs faythfull Martyr: | Here-unto | Is added by another man, many other | arguments against stinted service | and booke prayer. | . . . (3 lines)

Printed in the yeere 1640. | 15.3x8.4cm. 112p.

GROSSE, Alexander. Deaths | Deliverance, | And Eliahes Fiery Charet, | Or | The Holy mans Triumph after Death. | Delivered in two Sermons prea- | ched at Plymovth, the one the 16. | the other the 19. of August: the former | at the Funerall of Thomas Sherwill, | an Eminent and pious Magistrate | of that place. 1631. | By Alexander Grosse | now Pastor of Bridford. | . . . (3 lines).

London, | Printed by Thomas Paine, for Francis | Eaglesfield, and are to be sold at the Mary- | gold in Saint Pauls Church-yard. | 1640. | Border. 15.8x10.6 cm. (16),40; 63p.

Eliahs Fiery Chariot has separate t.p. and pagination; continuous register

GROSSE, Alexander. The | Happines Of | Enjoying, | And Making A True | And Speedie Use | Of Christ. | Setting Forth, | First, | The Fulnesse Of Christ. | Secondly, | The danger of neglecting Christ, and the oppor- | tunity of grace. | Thirdly, | The Lord Jesus the soules last Refuge. | Whereunto is added, | St. Pauls Legacies, or Farewell | to the men of Corinth. | By Alexander Grosse B.D. Minister of | the Gospel, and Pastour of Bridford. | . . . (6 lines).

London, | Printed by Robert Young, for John Bartlet, at the signe of the gilt-cup | neere Saint Austens Gate. 1640. | Line border. 15.8x10.6 cm. (25),286,54p. Sub t. p. at p 255

Saint Pauls Legacie begins with sig.B., with separate pagination.

GROSSE, Alexander. A Heavenly | Discourse | Of | Christs Fulnes: | Tending To | The making of Christ most amiable | and glorious in the eyes, and most joyous | and pleasant, sweet and satisfactory, to | the Soules of all beleeving | Christians; | That their hearts may be comforted, being | knit together in love, and unto all riches of the full | assurance of understanding, to the acknowledg- | ment of the mystery of God, and of the Father, | and of Christ; in whom are hid all the | treasures of wisedome and | knowledge, Col.2.2,3. | . . . (3 lines). By A.G. B.D. |

London, | Printed by R.Young, for John Bartlet, at the gilt | Cup neere Saint Austins gate, 1640. | Line border. 15.8x10.6cm. (1),253p.

Sub. t.p. of his Happines: 1640.

HALL, Joseph. Christian | Moderation | In two Books. | By Jos: Exon. | (device).

London, | Printed by Miles Flesher, and are | to be sold by Nathaniel Butter. | M.DCXL. | Line border. 16.2x10.6cm. (13),191,175p.

HALL, Joseph. Episcopacie | By | Divine Right. | Asserted, | By | Jos. Hall, B. of Exon. | (device).

London, | Printed by R. B. for Nathanael Butter, at the Pide-Bull | by S. Augustine's Gate. 1640. | 18.6x14.3 cm. (13),80,135,56p. 3 pts

HALL, Joseph. An Humble | Remonstrance | To The | | High Covrt | Of | Parliament, | By | A dutifull Sonne of the | Chvrch. | (device).

London, | Printed for Nathaniel Butter in Pauls | Church-yard at the pyde-Bull neare | St. Austins gate. 1640. | 18.8x14.6cm. (1),43p. Mispaging . Anon.Cambr.Univ.Cat:7591.

HARSNET, Adam. Gods | Svmmons | Unto A Generall | Repentance. | Wherein Is Disco- | vered The Folly, And | danger of putting off, and de- | laying of Repentance untill | Sicknesse, or Old age. | And also, the necessitie of daily | Repentance. | By Adam Harsnet, B.D. late Minister | of Gods Word, at Cranham in Essex. | . . . (5 lines).

London, |·Printed by Iohn Dawson, 1640. | Border. 14.1x8.2cm. (22), 645p.

HOMES, Nathaniel. Usury | Is | Injury. | Cleared in an examination of | its best Apologie, alleaged by a countrey | Minister, out of Doctor Ames, in his | Cases of Conscience, as a party and Patron | of that Apologie. | Both answered here, | By Nath: Holmes, Dr. in Divinity. | (device).

London, | Printed by Richard Bishop, for Iasper Emery, and are to be | sold at his shop at the signe of the Eagle and Childe | in S. Pauls Church-yard next Watlin street. | 1640. | 18.8 x 14. cm (1),52p.

HOOKER, Thomas. The Soules | Implantation | Into | The Naturall | Olive. | By T.H. | Carefully corrected, and much enlarged, with | a Table of the Contents prefixed. | . . . (3 lines ; device).

London, | Printed by R.Young, and are to be sold by Fulke | Clifton on New-Fish-street-hill. 1640. | Line border. 18.7x14. cm. (6),398p.
DNB.27:296(2).

HOW, Samuel. The | Svfficiencie | Of The Spirits | Teaching, | Without | Hvmane-Learning: | Or | A Treatise, Tending To Proue Hv- | mane-Learning To Be No Help To | the Spirituall understanding of the Word of God. | Written (if it may be) for the Silencing of such false and scanda- | lous reports, as have been rumored about concerning this | Matter; and also for the affording of true information | to all such as desire to know the Truth. | By Samuel How. | . . . (16 lines).

Seen, Allowed, and Printed, by us &c. 1640. | 18.7x14cm. (8,36)p.

HUGHES, Lewis. Certaine | Greevances, | VVell VVorthy | The Serious Considera- | tion Of The Right Ho- | norabe And High Covrt | Of Parliament. | Set forth by way of Dialogue, or | Conference betweene a Countrey Gentle- | man, and a Minister of Gods word; for the satis- | fying of those that doe clamour, and maliciously | revile them that labour to have the | errors of the Booke of Common | Prayer reformed. | By Levves Hevves, Minister | of Gods Word. | (ornament).

Printed in the Yeare 1640. | 17.8x14. cm. (1),40p.

HUGHES, Lewis. Certaine | Grievances | Well Worthy The | Serious Consideration Of The | Right Honourable, And High Court Of | Parliament. | (ornament).

Printed Anno Dom. 1640. | 18x13.5 cm. (1),18p.
Camb.Univ.Cat. No.7050. Signed at end.

The | INTENTIONS | Of The Army Of | The Kingdome Of | Scotland, | Declared To | Their Brethren Of | England, | By the Commissioners of the late | Parliament, and by the Generall, | Noblemen, Barons, and others, | Officers of the Army. | (device).

Printed at Edinburgh by Robert Bryson, | and are to be solde at his Shop at the | signe of Jonah. 1640. | 17.2x13.6cm. 19p.

KEM, Samuel. The | Nevv Fort | Of Trve | Honovr, | Made Im- | pregnable. | Or, | The Martialists dignity and dutie. | Presented in a Sermon, preached to the Cap- | taines, and Souldiers exercising Armes in the | Martiall Garden, at their | generall meeting. | In Saint Mary Overies in Southwarke, | August 11, 1640. | By Samvel Keme Batchelor of Divinity, and Rector | of Little Chart in Kent. | . . . (5 lines).

London, | Printed by Richard Ovlton, 1640. | Line border. 17.6x13.4cm. (8), 27p.

KER, William. A True | Representation | Of | The Proceedings Of | The Kingdome Of | Scotland; | Since the late pacification: | By | The Estates Of The | Kingdome: | Against mistakings in the late | Declaration, 1640. |

Printed in the year of God, 1640. | 18.4x13 cm. 72,102p.
Anon, DNB.31:65a.

KING, Henry. A | Sermon | Preached | At St.Pavls | March 27. 1640. | Being | The Anniversary | Of His Maiesties | Happy Inauguration | To His Crowne. | By Henry King, Deane of Rochester, | and Residentiary of St.Pauls: One of His | Majesties Chaplaines in Ordinary. | (device)

London, | Printed by Edward Griffin. 1640. | Line border. 19.4x14.cm. (1),59p.

LECHMERE, Edmund. A | Dispvtation | Of The | Chvrch, | VVherein the old Reli- | gion is maintained. | By E.S.F. | . . . (5 lines ; device).

At Doway, | By the widdow of Mark Wyon, at the signe | of the golden Phœnix. 1640. | With Permission. 16.6x10.9cm. (24),614;682,(3)p.
Gillow,IV:175.

LUPTON, Donald. The | Glory | Of | Their | Times. | Or | The Liues of ye Primitiue Fathers. | Cōtayning their Chiefest Actions, | workes, Sentences, and | Deaths. | . . . (2 lines).

London. | Printed by I.Okes. and are to be sold | in Pauls Church-yard at the | white Lyon. | 1640. | 17.9x12.7cm. (8), 1-64, 77-300, 309-324, 321-336, 329-440, 451-538p. Lacks pp. 301-8. Engr t.p.
Anon.Cambr.Univ.Cat:3730.

MONTAGU, Richard. Θεανθρωπικον | Seu | De Vita Jesu Christi | Domini Nostri | Originum | Ecclesiasticarum | Pars Posterior. | Accedit Græcorum versio, & Index | utrisque partis. | Collectore | Richardo Mountacutio, | Norwic. Episcopo. | (device)

Londini, | Typis R.Olton & Eliz. Purslow, & prostant | venales apud Jos.Kirton & Tho. Warren sub signo | Equi albi, in Cœmeterio Paulino. | M.DC.XL. | 28.4 x 18.4 cm (1), 508, (8)p.

MOULIN, Peter du, Jr. A | Letter | Of | A French | Protestant | To | A Scotishman Of | The Covenant. | VVherein one of their chiefe pretences | is removed, which is their conformitie with | the French Churches in points of | Discipline and Obedience. | (device).

London, | Printed by R.Young, and R.Badger. 1640. | 18.1x14.2cm. . (3),51p.
P. (1-2) blank

An | ORDER | Made To a | Select | Committee: | Chosen | By the whole house of Commons to re- | ceive Petitions touching Ministers. | (device).

London, | Printed by I.D. for Henry Overton, and | are to be sold at his Shop entring into Popes-head | Alley out of Lumbard streete. 1640. | 18x14.1cm. (1,5)p.

PAGIT, Ephraim. Christianography, | Or | The Description of the multitude and sundry | sorts of Christians in the World, not | subject to the Pope. | With their unity, and how they agree with the Prote- |

stants in the principall poynts of difference | betweene them and the Church of Rome. | To which is added a Treatise of the Religion of the ancient | Christians in Brittanie, and how they also differed | from the now Romish Church. | With certaine Letters and Confessions of the | Easterne Churches | and others. | The third Edition inlarged. | The chiefe Additions are in the Page following the Epistle. | . . . (3 lines).

London, | Printed by J.Okes, for Matthew Costerden, | Stationer. 1640. | 27.8x 18cm. (16), 1–258, (2), 259–280; 64; 33p.
Dedication, signed.

PAOLO, Servita. The | Historie Of | The Councel | Of Trent. | In Eight Bookes. | In which (besides the ordinarie Acts of the Councell) | are declared many notable Occurrences, which happened in | Christendome, during the space of fourtie | yeeres and more. | And particularly, the practices of the Court of Rome, to | hinder the reformation of their errours, and to | maintaine their greatnesse. | Written in Italian by Pietro Soaue Polano, and faithfully translated | into English by Nathanael Brent. | Unto this Third Edition are added divers observable Passages, | and Epistles, concerning the truth of this Historie, | specified in the next Page. | (royal arms)

London, | Printed by Robert Young and John Ravvorth, | for Richard Whittaker, and are to be sold at | the Kings armes in Pauls Church-yard. | 1640. | 32.6 x 22. cm. (10),881,(15) p.

PARKER, Henry. The Case of | Shipmony | briefly discoursed, | According To The | Grounds of Law, Policy, | and Conscience. | And | Most Hvmbly | Presented To The | Censure and Correction of the | High Court of Parliament, | Nov. 3. 1640. | (device).

Printed Anno Dom. 1640. | 18.4x14.1cm. (1),49p.
Anon. H&L.

A | PART of the | Lyturgy | Of | The Reformed Chvrches in the | Netherlands. | Or | The Formes which they use | In{The administration of the Sacraments. | The Exercise of Ecclesiasticall discipline. | The confirmation of Ecclesiasticall Officers, Mini- | sters, Elders and Deacons. | The Celebration of Marriage before the Church. | Translated out of Dutch into English. | (device).

Printed at Leyden. | [1640] 18.3x14.4 cm. 40p.

PRESTON, John. The Fulnesse of | Christ for Us. | A Sermon preached at the Court | before King James of | Blessed Memory. | By John Preston, Dr. in | Divinity, Chaplaine in Ordinary | to his Majesty, Master of Emanuel | Colledge in Cambridge, and | sometimes Preacher of | Lincolnes Inne. | . . . (3 lines).

London: | Printed by J.Okes, for John Stafford, | dwelling in Black-horse Alley neare | Fleetstreet. 1640. | Border. 18.2x13.9cm. (6),26p.
Also another copy from the library of Walter W. Law. 17.3x13.4cm.(6),26,(1)p.

The | PRIVILEDGES | And Practice | Of | Parliaments | In | England. | Collected out of the Common | Lawes of this Land. | Seene and allowed by the Learned in | the Lawes. | Commended | To the High Court of Parliament | now Assembled. | (ornament).

Printed. 1640. | 17.6 x 13.8 cm. (4),46p. A1, blank

PRYNNE, William. Lord Bishops, | None Of The | Lords | Bishops. | Or | A Short Discovrse, | Wherin Is Proved That Prelati- | call Jurisdiction, Is Not Of Divine | Institution, but forbidden by Christ himselfe, as Heathenish, | and branded by his Apostles for Antichristian; wherin | also sundry notable passages of the Arch-Prelate | of Canterbury in his late Booke, Intituled, A | Relation of a Conference, &c. are by the | way met withall. | . . . (9 lines).

Printed in the Moneth of November, 1640. | 19.2x14.2 cm. (4,82)p.
Anon.Cambr.Univ.Cat:7052.

A | REMONSTRANCE | Concerning the present | Troubles, | From the meeting of the Estates | of the Kingdome of Scotland, | Aprill 16. unto the Parlia- | ment of England. | (device)

Printed in the year of God, 1640. | 17.2x13.5 cm. (1),39p.

REYNOLDS, Edward. A | Treatise | Of The | Passions | And | Facvlties | of the Soule of Man. | With the severall Dignities and Cor- | ruptions thereunto belonging. | By Edvvard Reynoldes, late Preacher | to the Honorable Society of Lincoln's Inne: And now | Rector of the Church of Braunston in Northamptonshire. | . . . (3 lines ; ornament)

London, | Printed by R.H. for Robert Bostock, dwelling in Saint | Pauls Church-yard at the Signe of the | Kings Head. 1640. | Line border. 19.7x14.4 cm. (19),553p.

RICHWORTH, William. The Dialogves | Of | William Richworth | Or | The iudgmend of common | sense in the choise of | Religion. | (ornament).

Printed at Paris by | Iohn Mestais, | 1640. | 14.3x8 cm. (6),582 p.

ROGERS, Daniel. A | Practicall | Catechisme | Or, | A view of those principall truths of the | word, which most directly tend to life | and godlinesse. | Divided into three Parts. | The first, shewing the misery of all men by nature, both in respect of | sinne and punishment; with the true use of the morrall Law in that behalfe. | The second, manifesting the remedy ordained by God to deliver | them from this misery, together with the meanes of receiving it, | viz. Faith, and how it may be attained. | The third, declaring how those who are delivered, ought to order | their whole Conversation; with the meanes to procure it, the lets | resisting, and the priviledges encouraging to it. | Serving for the use of those who first heard them taught, as also for | all others who shall carefully peruse them. | The third Edition, corrected and much enlarged. | By D.Rogers B. in Divin. and Minister of the Gospell. | . . . (5 lines)

Printed at London by I.D. for Iohn Ballamie, and Ralph Smith, at the | three golden Lyons in Cornehill, neere the Royall Exchange. 1640. | 18.5x13.8cm. (14), 100;251;195;(23)p.
Sub-tp, of his Tvvo Treatises: 1640.

ROGERS, Daniel. Tvvo | Treatises, | First, | The Practicall | Catechisme. | Wherein, | Those Principall | Truthes, which most directly, tend to life | and godlinesse; are handled. | Secondly | A Treatise Of

The Two Sacraments | Of the Gospell, Baptisme and the | Lords Supper. | Divided into two parts. | The first, shewing the nature of the Sacraments | in Generall. | The second, the manner of due preparation to the | receiving of the Lords Supper, and our behaviour, | in and after the same. | By D.Rogers B. in Divin. and Minister of the Gospell. |

Printed at London by I.D. for Iohn Bellamie, and Ralph Smith, at the | three golden Lyons in Cornehill, neer the Royall Exchange. 1640. | 18.5x13.8cm.(16), 100;251;195;(23)p. Pt. II, pp. 218–251 misnumbered.
Lacks the second treatise.

ROGERS, John. The | Doctrine | Of | Faith, | Wherin are practi- | callie handled twelve prin- | cipall points, which ex- | plaine the Nature and | Use of it. | By Jo.Rogers, Preacher | of Gods Word at Dedham in Essex. | The eighth Edition, newly corrected, and | inlarged by the Author. | . . . (3 lines).

London, | Printed by E.G. for Henry Overton, | and Samuell Enderby, and are to | be sold at their Shops in Popes- | Head-Alley. 1640. | Line border. 14.1x8cm. (22), 500p.

ROGERS, Nehemiah. The Good | Samaritan, | Or | An Exposition | On That Parable | Luke X. Ver. XXX–XXXVIII. | A certaine man went downe from | Ierusalem to Iericho and fell | amongst Theeves, &c. | By Nehemiah Rogers Vicar of Mes- | sing in Essex, and one of the Prebendaries | of the Cathedrall Church of Ely. | . . . (2 lines: ornament).

London, | Printed by G.M. for Edward Brewster, and are to be sold at his | Shop at the signe of the Bible on Fleet-Bridge, 1640. | Border. 18.4x14.2cm. (8), 228,(11)p. folded leaf.

ROSS, Alexander. Gods House | Made A Den Of | Theeves. | Delivered | In A Second Sermon | In Southampton. | By Alexander Rosse, his Majesties Chaplaine | in Ordinarie. | . . . (4 lines; ornament)

London, | Printed in the yeare 1640. | Border 19x14.3cm. (2),14p.
Last figure in date obscured in ink.

ROSS, Alexander. Gods House, | Or | The Hovse Of | Prayer, | Vindicated from prophanenesse | and sacriledge. | Delivered in a Sermon the 24. day | of February, Anno 1640 in | Southampton. | By Alexander Rosse, his Majesties Chaplaine | in Ordinarie. | (ornament)

London, | Printed in the yeare 1640. | 19x14.3cm (4),16p.
Last figure in date obscured in ink.

RUNNE from | Rome. | Or | A Breif Treatise, | Shewing | The necessity to forsake that false | Church, and to cleave onely | unto Christ. | . . . (5 lines).

Printed in the yeare of our Lord, | M.DC.XL. | 15.3x8.4cm. 32p.

SALTMARSH, John. Holy | Discoveries | And Flames. | (Eye and heart devices). By John Saltmarshe, Mr. of | Arts of Magdalen Colledge in | Cambridge, and Rector of West- | Ilesterton in York-shire. | . . . (3 lines)

London, | Printed by R.Y. for P.Nevill in Ivie-lane. 1640. | Line border. 14.3x 8.3 cm. (12),225p. Engraved fore title.

SANDERSON, Thomas. A | Briefe Summe | Of | Christian Religion. | Collected for a preparation | to the Lords Supper. | Published for the benefit of | the simpler sort of people of | the Parish of Saint | Lawrence. | By | Thomas Sanderson | Doctor in Divinitie. | . . . (6 lines).

London, Printed by E. P. for F. Coules, at his | shop in the Old-Bayly, neere the | Sessions-house. 1640. | 14.4x8.9 cm. (15)p.

The | SECOND Tome | Of | Homilies, | Of Such Matters | As Were Promised, And | Entituled in the former part of | Homilies. | Set out by the Authority of the late Queenes Majesty: | and to be read in every Parish Church agreeably. | (arms).

London: Printed by R.H. and I.N. for Richard Whitaker, and are to be sold at his | Shop, at the Kings Armes in St. Pauls Church-yard. | 1640. | 26.8x18.2cm. (4), 320, (3)p,

Appended to Certaine Sermons: 1640; with continuous register.

SEDGWICK, John. The | Bearing | And | Bvrden Of | the Spirit. | Wherein the sicknesse and | soundnesse of the soule is ope- | ned, and eight Cases of conscience | cleared and resolved for the setling | and comforting of perplexed con- | sciences. | By | John Sedgvvick, | Batchelor in Divinity and Prea- | cher of Gods Word in | London. | The second Edition corrected. | (ornament).

London, | Printed by G.M. for Rapha Harford, in | Queens-head-Alley in Paternoster-Row, | at the guilt Bible, 1640. | Border. 13.7x8.3 cm. (8),361,(9)p.

SEDGWICK, Obadiah. Christs | Counsell to his lan- | guishing Church of | Sardis. | Or, | The dying or decaying | Christian, with the meanes and | helpes of his recovery and | strengthening. | By | Obadiah Sedgwicke, | B. of D. late Preacher to the Inhabi- | tants of S. Mildreds Bredstreet, | London | . . . (3 lines).

London, | Printed by T.B. for L.Fawne, and | S.Gellibrand, at the brasen | Serpent in S. Pauls Church-yard, | 1640. | Border. 16.x10.3cm. (14),262, (7).p.

SIBBES, Richard. Evangelicall | Sacrifices. | In xix. Sermons. | 1. Thankfull commemorations for Gods mercy in our | great deliverance from the Papists powder-plot. | 2. The successefull seeker. | 3. Faith Triumphant. | 4. Speciall preparations to fit us for our | latter end in foure Funerall Sermons. | 5. The faithfull Covenanter. | 6. The demand of a good Conscience. | 7. The sword of the wicked. | By | The late Learned and Reverend Divine, | Rich. Sibbs. | Doctor in Divinity, Mr. of Katherine Hall in | Cambridge, and sometimes Preacher to the Honou- | rable Society of Grayes-Inne. | The third Tome. | Published and perused by D.Sibbs owne appointment, subscri- | bed with his hand to prevent imperfect Copies after his decease. | . . . (4 lines).

London, | Printed by T.B. for N.Bourne, at the Royall Exchange, and | R. Harford at the guilt Bible in Queenes-head Alley in | Pater-noster-Row. 1640. | Border. 18.8x14cm. (8), 318; (1), 238, (8)p. 11 Sub t.p. all dated 1639.

Two parts: second, The Hidden Life: 1639; with double letter register, separate pagination.

SMITH, Samuel. Davids | Repentance: | Or, | A plaine and familiar Ex- | position of the 51.Psalme: First | Preached, and now published for | the benefit of Gods Church. | Wherein every Christian may set | before his eyes the patterne of unfeig- | ned Repentance: Likewise exhorting every | man to labour for Repentance before | sicknesse and death seize upon them: | for after Death there is no repen- | tance to be had or expected. | The fourteenth Edition, newly revised | & profitably amplified by the Author Samuel | Smith, late Preacher of the Word at | Pritlewell in Essex. | . . . (2 lines).

London: Printed by John Okes. 1640. | Border. 14.4x9.5cm. (12),1–320,301–540p. Engr. fore t.p.

SPANG, William. Brevis Et Fidelis | Narratio | motuum in regno & Ecclesia | Scotica, | Excerpta ex scriptis utriusque partis | scitu dignissimis. | Per | Irenævm Philalethen. | . . . (9 lines; ornament).

Dantisci, Anno 1640. | 18.9x14.9cm. (4,65)p.
Also another impression with identical t.p., except for capitalization of "Regno" in line 3 .
B.M.Cat, sub Philalethes. Huntington Libr. attributed to Louis du Moulin.

STOUGHTON, John. The | Arraignement | Of | Covetousnesse, | In three Sermons. | By | John Stoughton, | Doctor in Divinitie, sometimes Fellow of | Immanuel Colledge in Cambridge, late of | Aldermanbury, London. | . . . (2 lines).

London, | Printed for Iohn Bellamie, Henry Overton, Iohn Rothwell, | Richard Serger, and Ralph Smith. | 1640. | Border. 18.4x13.9cm. (8),68p.
Part of his Seaven Sermons: 1640; with separate register and pagination.

STOUGHTON, John. Baruch's Sore | Gently Opened: | God's Salve | Skilfvlly Applied: | In two Sermons. | By | John Stoughton, | Doctor in Divinity, sometimes Fellow of | Immanuel Colledge in Cambridge, late of | Aldermanburie, London. | . . . (2 lines).

London, | Printed by R.B. for Iohn Bellamie, Henry Overton, | Iohn Rothwell, and Ralph Smith. 1640. | Line border. 18.4x13.9cm. (7),55p.
Part of his Seaven Sermons: 1640; with separate register and pagination.

STOUGHTON, John. The | Burning Light. | A | Sermon Preached | at a Visitation in Christs | Church, London. |

London, | Printed by Thomas Cotes for | Daniel Frere. 1640. | Line border. 18.2x13.7 cm. 32 p. p. 27–30 missing .
Another impression, with separate register and correct pagination, and ornament, is included in his XV. Choice Sermons: 1640. 18.4x13.9cm. (1),32p.

STOUGHTON, John. Choice | Sermons | Preached Upon | Selected occasions. | Viz. | The Happinesse of Peace: Before K.James at | Trinitie Colledge in Cambridge. | The Love-sick Spouse: At St. Pauls Crosse. | The Burning Light: At a Visitation in Christ | Church, London. | The Magistrates Commission, or, Wisdome justi- | fied: Before the Judges. | By John Stoughton, Doctor in Divinitie, som- | time Fellow of Emanuel Colledge in Cambridge, | late Preacher of Aldermanbury, London. | According to the Originall Copie which was left | perfected by the Author before his death. | . . . (2 lines).

London, | Printed by Richard Hodgkinson for Daniel Frere, and | are to be sold at the Red Bull in Little | Britaine. 1640. | Line border. 18.4x13.9cm.(6,1),156;(1),32;64p. Sub t.p. in his XV. Choice Sermons: 1640.

STOUGHTON, John. The Christians | Prayer | For | The Chvrches | Peace. | Or, | A Sermon Vpon | Psal.122.ver.6. | Preached at Mercers Chappell. | By John Stovghton. | Doctor in Divinity, late of Alderman- | bury, London. | . . . (6 lines).

London, | Printed by John Dawson, for Iohn Bellamie, and | Ralph Smith, and are to be sold at their shop, at the | three golden Lions in Cornehill neere the | Royall Exchange, 1640. | Line border. 18.4x13.9cm. (8),76p.
Part of his Seaven Sermons: 1640 .

STOUGHTON, John. XI. Choice | Sermons, | Preached Upon | Selected Occasions, in | Cambridge. | Viz. | I.The Preachers Dignity, and Duty: In five | Sermons, upon 2.Corinth.5.20. | II. Christ Crucified, the Tree of Life: In six | Sermons, on 1.Corinth.2.2. | By | John Stoughton, | Doctor in Divinity, sometimes Fellow of | Immanuel Colledge in Cambridge, late Preacher | of Aldermanburie, London. | According to the Originall Copie, which was left | perfected by the Authour before his death. |

London, | Printed by R.B. for Iohn Bellamie, Henry Overton, | Iohn Rothwell, and Ralph Smith. 1640. | Line border. 18.4x13.9cm. (6),(7),104;(6),131p.
Part of his XV. Choice Sermons: 1640 .; with separate register and pagination.

STOUGHTON, John. Felicitas Vltimi Sæculi: | Epistola | In Qua, Inter Alia, Cala- | mitosus ævi præsentis status, seriò deplo- | ratur, certa felicioris posthac spes osten- | ditur, & ad provomendum publicum | Ecclesiæ & Rei literariæ bonum | omnes excitantur: | In gratiam Amici cujusdam paulo ante obitum, | Scripta à Reverendo Viro | Johanne Stoughtono, | SS. Theol. Doctore, | Coll. Emanuel. Cantabr. olim socio, postea, | Eccles. Aldermanburiensis Londini, | Pastore dignissimo: | Nunc, post decessum ejus ad fidem | autographi, publici juris facta | à | S.H. |

Londini, | Typis Richardi Hodgkinson impensis | Danielis Frere habitantis in Parva | Britannia, ad insigne Tauri rubri. | Anno MDCXL. | 14.5x8.3cm (8),132, (1)p. Folded leaf at end, with imprimatur, Aug. 24. 1639. Edge of t.p. shaved.

STOUGHTON, John. XV. Choice | Sermons, | Preached | Vpon | Selected Occasions. | Viz. | 1 The Happinesse of Peace: Before K. James at Trinity Col- | ledge in Cambridge. | 2 The Love-sicke Spouse: At S.Paul's Crosse. | 3 The Burning Light: At a Visitation in Christ's Church, | London. | 4 The Magistrates Commission, or, Wisdome justified: Before | the Judges. | 5 The Preachers Dignity, and Duty: In five Sermons, on | 2 Cor.5.20. Preached in Cambridge. | 6 Christ Crucified, the Tree of Life: in sixe Sermons, on | 1 Cor.2.2. Preached in Cambridge. | By John Stoughton, Doctor in Divinity, somtime | Fellow of Immanuel Colledge in Cambridge, late | Preacher of Aldermanburie, London. | According to the Originall Copie, which was left perfected | by the Authour before his death. |

London, | Printed for I.Bellamie, H.Overton, I.Rothwell, R.Royston, | D.Frere, and R.Smith. 1640. | Line border. 18.4x13.9cm. (1,6,1),156;(1),32;64;(6),(7),104; (6),131p.

STOUGHTON, John. Five | Sermons, | On | II Cor.V.XX. | Preached at Cambridge, | By | John Stoughton, Doctor in Divinitie, sometimes Fellow of Immanuel | Colledge in Cambridge, late of Aldermanbury, | London. | Perfected by the Author in his lifetime. | . . . (5 lines).

London, | Printed by R.B. for Iohn Bellamie, and Ralph Smith, | and are to be sold at their Shop, at the three golden Lions | in Cornehill, neere the Royall Exchange. 1640. | Border. 18.4x13.9cm. (7),104p.
Part of his XI. Choice Sermons: 1640 .

STOUGHTON, John. A | Forme | Of Wholsome | Words; | Or, | An Introduction | to the Body of Divinity: | In three Sermons on 2 Timothy,1.13. | Preached | By John Stoughton, | Doctor in Divinity, sometimes Fellow of | Immanuel Colledge in Cambridge, late | Preacher of Aldermanbury, | London. | . . . (2 lines).

London, | Printed by J.R. for J.Bellamy, H.Overton, A.Crook, J.Roth- | well, R.Sergeir, D.Frere, and Ralph Smith. 1640. | Line border. 18.4x13.9cm (24),95p.
First t.p. in his XIII Sermons: 1640.
Also another copy from the library of Walter W. Law.

STOUGHTON, John. The | Heavenly | Conversation | And The | Natvrall | Mans | Condition. | In two Treatises. | By Iohn Stovghton, | Doctor in Divinitie, sometimes | Fellow of Emanuel Colledge | in Cambridge; and late Preacher | of Gods Word in Alder- | man-bury London. |

Printed at London by Tho.Cotes, for | Daniel Frere, and are to be sold at his | Shop, at the Signe of the Bull in | Little Brittaine. 1640. | Border. 14.5x8.3cm. (22),238,(12)p.

STOUGHTON, John. A | Learned | Treatise: | In three parts, | 1 The Definition | 2 The Distribution } of Divinity. | 3 The Happinesse of Man: | As it was Scholastically handled by | John Stoughton D.D. | in Immanuel Colledge | Chappell in Cambridge, | while he was fel- | low there: | And now published according to the Copy left | under his own hand. | (ornaments)

London, | Printed by Ric.Hodgkinson for John Bel- | lamy, Daniel Frere and Ralph | Smith. 1640. | Line border. 18.4 x 13.9 cm. (4),100p.
Part of his XIII Sermons: 1640, with separate register and pagination.
Also another copy from the library of Walter W. Law.: 17.5x13.3cm.

STOUGHTON, John. The | Magistrates | Commission, | Or | Wisedome | Ivstified. | In | A Sermon Prea- | ched Before The | Judges. | (ornament).

London | Printed by T.Cotes for Daniel Frere. 1640. | Line border. 18.4x13.9 cm. 64 p.
Part of his XV. Choice Sermons: 1640 , with double letter register.

STOUGHTON, John. The | Righteovs | Mans Plea To | Trve Happinesse. | In | Ten Sermons, on Psal. | 4.ver.6. | Preached by John Stoughton Doctor | in Divinity, sometimes Fellow of | Emanuell Colledge in Cam- | bridge, late Preacher of Alder- | manbury, London. | . . . (3 lines).

Printed at London by Tho.Cotes, for Iohn Bellamie, | H.Overton, A Crooke, I.Rothwell, I.Crooke, R.Sergier, | D.Freere, and R.Smith. 1640. | Line border. 18.4x13.9cm. (17),135,1–99,105–149,(1)p.
Part of his XIII Sermons: 1640, with doubled letter register.
Also another copy from the library of Walter W. Law. 17.5x13.3cm

STOUGHTON, John. Seaven | Sermons, | Preached | Vpon | Severall Occasions. | Viz. | 1 The Christians Prayer for the Churches Peace. One Sermon | on Psal.122.6. | 2 One Sermon on 1 Sam.2.30 | 3 Baruchs Sore gently opened; Gods Salve skilfully | applyed. In two Sermons on Jeremy 45.5. | 4 The Araignement of Coveteousnesse. In three Sermons on | Luke 12.15. | By John Stoughton, Doctor in Divinitie, | late of Aldermanburie, London. | (ornament).

London, | Printed by J.D. for John Bellamie, and Ralph Smith, and | are to be sold at their Shop, at the three Golden-Lyons | in Cornhill neere the Royall-Exchange. 1640. | 18.4x13.9cm. (1,8),76;(7),55;(8),68p. 4 sub t.p.

STOUGHTON, John. Sixe | Sermons, | On | I Cor.II.II. | Preached at Cambridge, | By | John Stoughton, | Doctor in Divinitie, sometimes Fellow of | Immanuel Colledge in Cambridge, late of | Aldermanbury, London. | Perfected by the Author in his life time. | . . . (2 lines).

London, | Printed by R.B. for Iohn Belllamie, Henry Overton, | Iohn Rothwell, and Ralph Smith. | 1640. | Border. 18.4x13.9cm. (6),131p.
Part of his XI. Choice Sermons: 1640.

STOUGHTON, John. XIII. | Sermons, | Preached | In the Church of Aldermanbury, | London: | Viz. | 1. The form of wholsome words, or An Introduction to | the Body of Divinity. In 3 Sermons on 2 Tim. 1.13. | 2. The Righteous mans Plea to true Happinesse. In | 10 Sermons on Psal.4.6. | To which is added, | An exact and learned Discourse, | perfected by the Author, | Concerning { The Definition | and | Distribution of} Divinity: | And | The Happinesse of Man. | By John Stoughton, | Doctor in Divinity, sometimes Fellow of Immanuel Colledge in | Cambridge, and late Preacher of Aldermanbury, London. |

London, | Printed by J.Raworth, for J.Bellamy, H.Overton, A.Crook, J.Rothwell, | R.Sergeir, J.Crook, D.Frere, and R.Smith. 1640. | Line border. 18.4x13.9cm. (1,24),95;(17),135,1–99,105–149,(1);(4),100p. Edited by Anthony Burgess.

SWAN, John. Redde Debitvm. | Or, | A Discovrse In | defence of three chiefe Fatherhoods, | grounded upon a Text dilated to the Lati- | tude of the Fift Commandement; and is ther- | fore grounded thereupon, because t'was | first intended for the Pulpit, and should | have beene concluded in one or | two Sermons, | Bvt Is Extended Since | to a larger Tract; | And Written Chiefely | in confutation of all disobedient and | factious kinde of People, who are ene- | mies both to the Church, | and State. | By John Svvan. | . . . (2 lines).

London, | Printed by I.D. for Iohn Williams, at the Signe of | the Crane, in St. Pauls Church-yard. 1640. | Border. 18.9x14.2cm. (11),240p.

TORSHELL, Samuel. An | Exercitation | Vpon The | Prophecie | Of | Malachy | Wherein, { The Context is illustrate by a cleare Analyse, | The originall Text is examined, | Most translations extant are conferred, | The expositions of the ancients and others are | weighed, | Together with some occasionall observations. | By | Samuel Torshell, | Intended by way of Addition to a larger | Commentary upon the same Prophecy, by that | reverend and godly Divine Mr. Richard Stock, | and now since his death at last published with | the consent of his Executors by the same Author. | (device).

London, | Printed by Edward Griffin, for Daniel Frere, and William | Wells, and are to be sold at their shops in little | Brittaine, 1640. | Line border. 27.8x18.6cm. (22), 94p.
Appended to Stock's Commentary: 1641

A | TRVE | Relation | Of The Forme | And Government | of the Kirke of | Scotland; | 1640. |
No title page. 18.3x13.5 cm Pp.11. Fragment: F1–4, G1–2.
Part of The Humble Address both of Church and Poore: 1641.

TWITTEE, Thomas. Ad | Clervm | Pro | Forma Concio | Habita In Templo | Beatæ Mariæ Oxon: | Martij 13. 1634. | Per Tho: Twittee Sanctæ | Theologiæ Bac. è Coll. Oriell. | . . . (3 lines).
Oxoniæ, | Excudebat Leonard. Lichfield, | An. Dom. 1640. | Line border. 17.8x 13.9 cm. (3),24p.

TYMME, Thomas. A | Silver | VVatch-Bell. | The sound whereof is able | (by the grace of God) to win the | profanest worldling, if there bee | the least sparke of Grace remaining | in him, to become a true Christian, | that in the end be may obtain | everlasting Salvation. | VVhereunto is adjoyned a Treatise of | the holy Sacrament of the Lords Supper, | as also certaine Godly Rules concerning chri- | stian Practice, fit to be observed of all | those that would bee | saved. The Eighteenth Impression. | By Thomas Tymme. |
London: | Printed by E.P. for Thomas Knight. 1640. | Border. 14. x 9.3 cm. (14),296p.

A VERY | Lively Portraytvre, | Of The | Most Reverend | Arch-Bishops, | The Right Reverend B^s. | Of The Chvrch Of | England: | Set forth in XX. irrefragable positions, | concerning their Authority, power, and practise, as | they onely are our Diocesan Lord Bishops, | so grounded upon Scripture, Reason, and Ex- | perience, by evident demonstrative | practises, as their troublesome opposites, | may cleerely see, how greatly | they are deceived in | all these. | A Labour undertaken for the peace of all Gods | people, and for a just condemnation of al those, | that cause division, and offences, contrary to | the Doctrine and Discipline of | Christs Church. |
Printed in the yeare, 1640. | 18.6x14.4 cm. (1),60,(1)p.
Also another copy, differently arranged, 18.6x14.5 cm (4),60p.

WALKER, George. The | Manifold | Wisedome | Of God: | In the divers dispensation | of Grace by Iesus Christ. | In the {Old | Nevv} Testament. | In the Covenant of {Faith. | Workes.} | Their Agreement and Difference. | (ornaments).
London, | Printed by R.H. for Iohn Bartlet, and are to | besold at the Signe of the Gilt Cup, | neere S.Austins Gate in Pauls | Church-yard. 1640. | Line border. 14.7x8.4 cm. (14),173p.
Attribution by Dr. Charles A. Briggs.

WARD, Richard. {Theologicall Qvestions, | Dogmaticall Observations, | And Evangicall Essays,} | Vpon | The Gospel | Of | Jesus Christ, | According To | St. Matthew. | Wherein, | About two thousand six hundred and fifty necessary, | and profitable Questions are discussed; and five hundred and | eighty speciall points of Doctrine noted;

and five hundred and | fifty Errours confuted, or Objections answered: together with | divers Arguments, whereby divers Truths, and | true Tenents are confirmed. | By Richard Ward, | Sometimes Student in the famous Vniversities | Of {Cambridge | St. Andrews} {In {England: | Scotland:} And | Master of Arts of both the Kingdoms; And now a Preacher in the | famous City of London. | . . . (6 lines).

London, | Printed for Peter Cole, and are to be sold at his shop in Cornhill, at the | sign of the Glove and Lyon, neer the Royall Exchange. | M.DC.XL. | Line border. 33x21.6cm. (1),528,(2),411,(1)p.

WARD, Samuel. The | Wonders | Of The | Load-stone. | Or, | The Load-Stone | newly reduc't into a | Divine and Morall | Vse. | By | Samvel Ward, | of Ipswich. B.D. | . . . (2 lines)

London, | Printed by E.P. for Peter | Cole, and are to be sold at | his shop, at the signe of the glove | and Lyon in Cornehill, o- | ver against the Conduit. | 1640. | 14.1x7.4 cm. (22),96,111–142,151–281,(1)p. 1 plate frontisp. Imprimatur: April. 29. 1640.

WHATELY, William. Prototypes, | Or, | The Primarie | Precedent Presidents | Ovt Of The Booke Of | Genesis. | Shewing, | The{Good | and | Bad}things{They did | and | Had}Practically applied to our In- formation | and Reformation. | By that faithfull and painefull Preacher of Gods | Word, William Whately late Pastour of Banbury. | Published by those who were appointed by the Authour to peruse | his manu- scripts, and printed by his owne Coppy. | . . . (9 lines).

London. | Printed by G.M. for George Edwards in the Old-Baily in Greene Arbour, | at the signe of the Angell, MDCXL. | Border. 27.5x18.7cm. (26),267 182,36,(24)p. Portrait.

Also another copy from the library of Walter W. Law: 28.1x18.1cm.

WOODWARD, Hezekiah. A | Childes | Patrimony | Laid Ovt Vp- on | The Good Cvltvre | Or Tilling Over | His Whole Man. | The first Part, | Respecting a Childe in his | first and second Age. | . . . (9 lines).

London, printed by I.Legatt. 1640. | 18.7x13.6cm. (19),47,(7),182p. Reissued as part of his Sons Patrimony: 1643.

WOODWARD, Hezekiah. A | Childes | Patrimony. | Laid out upon the good Nurture, or | Tilling over the whole Man. | In two Parts. | The former, Respecting a Childe in his | first and second Age. | The latter Manuring A Childe grown | up, and at Mans Estate. | The Ap- pendix sheweth the scope of the | Booke; The rule also, and right | Method of Edification. | By Ezekias Woodvvard. | . . . (6 lines).

London, | Printed by I.L. and are to be sold by Henry Overton, at his shop | at the entring in to Popes-head-alley out of | Lumbard-street. 1640. | 18.7x13.6 cm. (11,80)p.

Reissued as part of the 1643 ed. of his Sons Patrimony,

WOODWARD, Hezekiah. A | Child's | Portion. | The Second Part: | Respecting A Childe | Growne Vp. | . . . (14 lines)

London, printed by I.Legatt. | 1640. | 18.7x13.6 cm. (12),14,(6),207,(3)p. Re- issued as part of his Sons Patrimony: 1643 .

Ref
Z
7757
E5 N5
v.1